W9-BUD-918

The Council of State Governments

STATE DIRECTORY

Directory I—
Elective Officials 2015

The Council of State Governments
2760 Research Park Drive
Lexington, KY 40511-8482

Contact the Publication Sales Department at
1-800-800-1910 or sales@csg.org to order:

Directory I—Elective Officials 2015,

Directory II—Legislative Leadership, Committees and Staff 2015,

Directory III—Administrative Officials 2015

or mailing lists of state government officials.

STACKS

CSG

Since 1933, The Council of State Governments has served our nation's state leaders by providing a forum for "sharing capitol ideas." As the only state services organization spanning all three branches of government, CSG offers a unique look into the issues shaping state policy and legislation from the national and regional perspectives. This unique arrangement contributes to a strong national presence for CSG, creating unparalleled opportunities to network, collaborate and form problem-solving partnerships.

The Council of State Governments Officers

President **Gov. Brian Sandoval**, Nev.

Chair **Sen. Carl Marcellino**, N.Y. ▪ *Chair-Elect* **Sen. Beau McCoy**, Neb. ▪ *Vice Chair* **Sen. Kelvin Atkinson**, Nev.

The Council of State Governments

David Adkins, Executive Director CEO

2760 Research Park Drive ▪ Lexington, KY 40511-8482 ▪ (859) 244-8000 ▪ Fax: (859) 244-8001 ▪ www.csg.org

Eastern Office
Wendell M. Hannaford, Director
22 Cortlandt Street, 22nd Floor
New York, NY 10007
(212) 482-2320
Fax: (212) 482-2344
www.csgeast.org

Midwestern Office
Michael H. McCabe, Director
701 East 22nd Street, Suite 110
Lombard, IL 60148
(630) 925-1922
Fax: (630) 925-1930
www.csgmidwest.org

Southern Office
Colleen Cousineau, Director
P.O. Box 98129
Atlanta, GA 30359
(404) 633-1866
Fax: (404) 633-4896
www.slcatlanta.org

Western Office
Edgar E. Ruiz, Director
1107 9th Street, Suite 730
Sacramento, CA 95814
(916) 553-4423
Fax: (916) 446-5760
www.csgwest.org

Washington Office
444 N. Capitol Street, N.W., Suite 401
Washington, DC 20001
(202) 624-5460
Fax: (202) 624-5452
www.csgdc.org

Editorial Staff

Kelley Arnold ▪ Jessica Clay ▪ Eric Lancaster ▪ Heather Perkins

Special thanks to the CSG regional offices and the clerks and secretaries of the legislature for each state.

Copyright 2015
The Council of State Governments
Lexington, Kentucky 40511

Printed in the United States of America
ISBN #978-0-87292-793-3
Price: $65.00

All rights reserved.

Inquiries for use of any material, updates or corrections should be directed to:
Editorial Staff, CSG State Directories
The Council of State Governments
(800) 800-1910

Table of Contents

Table of Contents by Region

Eastern Region

Midwestern Region

Southern Region

Western Region

How to Use This Directory

This volume contains: names of the governor, lieutenant governor, secretary of state, attorney general, auditor, treasurer and other constitutionally elected officials; state court of last resort judges (whether elected or appointed); state legislators who are serving as of January 2015; congressional members and government-related facts about each state.

Elected branch officials are listed with the office title, party affiliation, address, phone number, fax number and email address, if available.

Courts of last resort members, as well as the clerk of the court of last resort, are listed with the name, address, phone number, fax and email address, if available. Since members of these courts are not elected by the public in all states, a two-letter code appears next to the name of the court to indicate the method by which the judges are selected and retained in office.

Legislative rosters for all states and other U.S. jurisdictions are organized by chamber and include the name, party, district, preferred mailing address, phone number, fax number and email address, if available.

Congressional members are listed alphabetically with the party affiliation and district number.

Information current as of press time.

General Abbreviations

N.A.	Not available
*	New legislator

Party Abbreviations

D	Democrat
R	Republican
REFORM	Reform
C	Covenant
CONST	Constitution
I	Independent
L	Libertarian
G	Green
ICM	Independent Citizen Movement
DFL	Democratic-Farmer-Labor
NP	Nonpartisan
P	Progressive
NPP	New Progressive Party
PDP	Popular Democratic Party
PIP	Puerto Rican Independent Party
TRIBAL	Delegate representing a Native American tribe
U	Unenrolled

Courts of Last Resort Abbreviations

(FA)	Appointed by federal official. In the District of Columbia, U.S. president makes appointments from a list of nominees submitted by the nominating commission. In American Samoa, U.S. secretary of the Interior appoints judges.
(GA)	Gubernatorial appointment. In Delaware, gubernatorial appointment is made with consent of Senate.
(LA)	Legislative appointment.
(MC)	Gubernatorial appointment from a list of nominees submitted by a nominating or selection commission. In Hawaii, appointments require consent of Senate and reappointments are made by the nominating selection commission. In Massachusetts, appointments are for life. In Vermont, judges are retained unless the Legislature votes for removal.
(MR)	Gubernatorial appointment from a list of nominees submitted by a nominating or selection commission; judges run in retention election for subsequent terms. In California, judges are initially appointed by the governor and confirmed by judicial appointments commission.
(NE)	Nonpartisan election.
(PE)	Partisan election. In Illinois and Pennsylvania, judges are selected in partisan elections for initial term and run in nonpartisan retention elections for subsequent terms.

2015 Party Control Maps

(as of Feb. 2015)

Gubernatorial

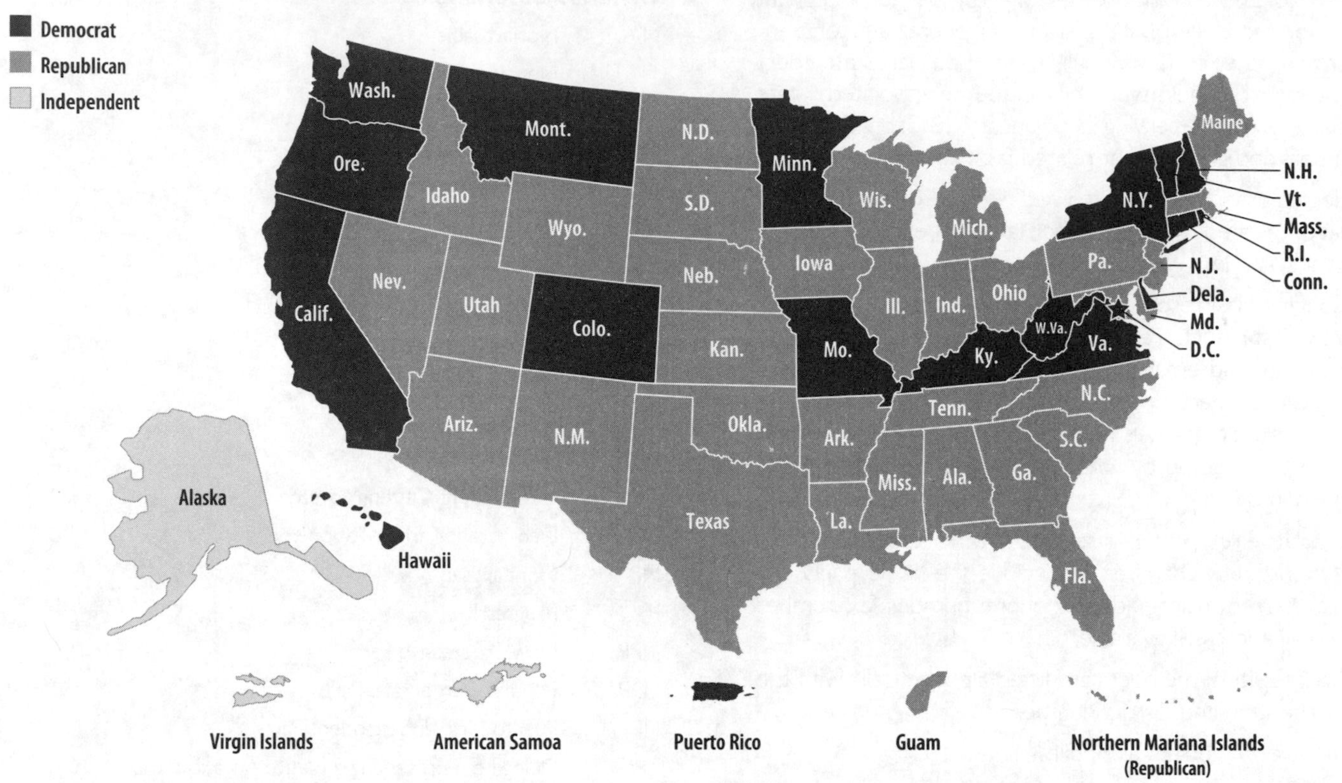

Legislative

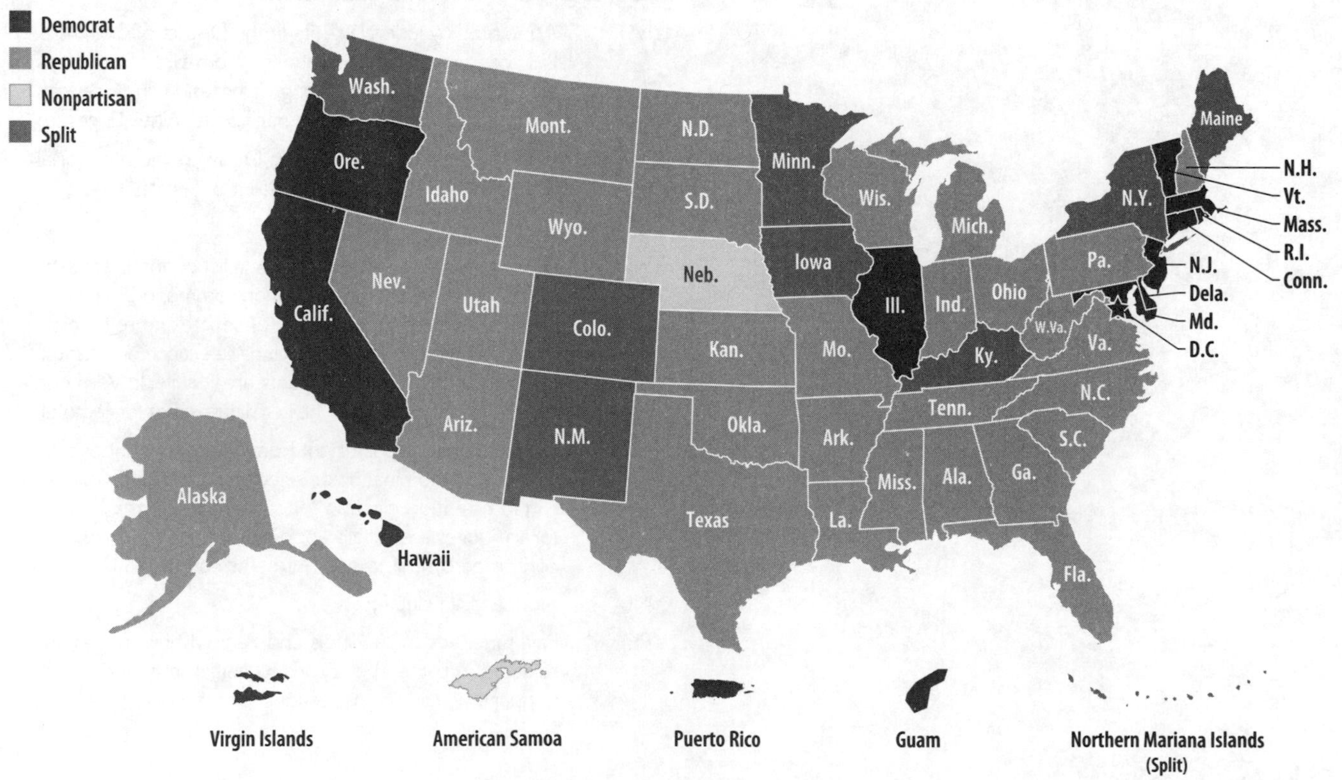

Alabama

Executive

Governor

Hon. Robert J. Bentley (R)
Governor
State Capitol
600 Dexter Avenue
Montgomery, AL 36130
P: (334) 242-7100
F: (334) 353-0004

Lieutenant Governor

Hon. Kay Ivey (R)
Lieutenant Governor
11 South Union Street, Suite 725
Montgomery, AL 36130
P: (334) 242-7900
F: (334) 242-4661
E: kay.ivey@ltgov.alabama.gov

Commissioner of Agriculture & Industries

Hon. John McMillan (R)
Commissioner
1445 Federal Drive
P.O. Box 3336
Montgomery, AL 36107
P: (334) 240-7100
F: (334) 240-7190

Attorney General

Hon. Luther Strange (R)
Attorney General
501 Washington Avenue
P.O. Box 300152
Montgomery, AL 36130
P: (334) 242-7300

Auditor

Hon. Jim Zeigler (R)
State Auditor
State Capitol, Room S-101
600 Dexter Avenue
Montgomery, AL 36130
P: (334) 242-7010
F: (334) 242-7650
E: jim.zeigler@auditor.alabama.gov

Public Service Commission

Mr. Chip Beeker Jr. (R)
Commissioner
100 North Union Street, Suite 818
P.O. Box 304260
Montgomery, AL 36130
P: (334) 242-5191
E: chip.beeker@psc.alabama.gov

Ms. Twinkle Andress Cavanaugh (R)
President
100 North Union Street, Suite 850
P.O. Box 304260
Montgomery, AL 36130
P: (334) 242-5203
F: (334) 242-0509
E: twinkle.cavanaugh@psc.alabama.gov

Mr. Jeremy Oden (R)
Commissioner
100 North Union Street, Suite 818
P.O. Box 304260
Montgomery, AL 36130
P: (334) 242-5203
E: jeremy.oden@psc.alabama.gov

Secretary of State

Hon. John Merrill (R)
Secretary of State
P.O. Box 5616
Montgomery, AL 36103
P: (334) 242-7200
F: (334) 242-4993
E: john.merrill@sos.alabama.gov

Treasurer

Hon. Young Boozer (R)
State Treasurer
600 Dexter Avenue, S-106
Montgomery, AL 36104
P: (334) 242-7501
F: (334) 242-7592
E: young.boozer@treasury.alabama.gov

Judiciary

Supreme Court (PE)

Ms. Julia Jordan Weller
Clerk
300 Dexter Avenue
Montgomery, AL 36104
P: (334) 229-0700

Hon. Roy Moore
Chief Justice
Hon. Michael F. Bolin
Hon. Tommy Bryan
Hon. James Allen Main
Hon. Glenn Murdock
Hon. Tom Parker
Hon. Greg Shaw
Hon. Lyn Stuart
Hon. Alisa Kelli Wise

Legislative Senate

Senate President

Hon. Kay Ivey (R)
Lieutenant Governor
11 South Union Street, Suite 725
Montgomery, AL 36130
P: (334) 242-7900
F: (334) 242-4661
E: kay.ivey@ltgov.alabama.gov

President Pro Tempore of the Senate

Sen. Del Marsh (R)
President Pro Tempore
State House, Room 722
11 South Union Street
Montgomery, AL 36130
P: (334) 242-7877
F: (334) 242-8819
E: del.marsh@alsenate.gov

Senate Majority Leader

Sen. J.T. Waggoner (R)
Majority Leader
State House, Room 726
11 South Union Street
Montgomery, AL 36130
P: (334) 242-7892
F: (334) 242-2278
E: jabo.waggoner@alsenate.gov

Senate Minority Leader

Sen. Vivian Davis Figures (D)
Minority Leader
State House, Room 736
11 South Union Street
Montgomery, AL 36130
P: (334) 242-7871
F: (334) 242-8819
E: vivian.figures@alsenate.gov

Secretary of the Senate

Mr. D. Patrick Harris
Secretary of the Senate
State House, Senate Chamber
11 South Union Street
Montgomery, AL 36130
P: (334) 242-7803
F: (334) 242-8819

Members of the Senate

Albritton, Greg (R, 22)
State House, Room 735
11 South Union Street
Montgomery, AL 36130
P: (334) 242-7800
F: (334) 242-4759
E: galbritton@att.net

Allen, Gerald (R, 21)
State House, Room 729
11 South Union Street
Montgomery, AL 36130
P: (334) 242-7889
F: (334) 242-8819
E: gerald.allen@alsenate.gov

Beasley, Billy (D, 28)
State House, Room 737
11 South Union Street
Montgomery, AL 36130
P: (334) 242-7868
F: (334) 242-8819
E: billy.beasley@alsenate.gov

Blackwell, Slade (R, 15)
State House, Room 729
11 South Union Street
Montgomery, AL 36130
P: (334) 242-7851
F: (334) 242-8819
E: sb@sladeblackwell.com

Brewbaker, Dick (R, 25)
State House, Room 734
11 South Union Street
Montgomery, AL 36130
P: (334) 242-7895
F: (334) 242-8819
E: dick.brewbaker@alsenate.gov

Bussman, Paul (R, 4)
State House, Room 738
11 South Union Street
Montgomery, AL 36130
P: (334) 242-7855
F: (334) 242-8819
E: p_bussman@bellsouth.net

Chambliss Jr., Clyde (R, 30)*
State House, Room 733
11 South Union Street
Montgomery, AL 36130
P: (334) 242-7883
F: (334) 242-8819
E: clyde.chambliss@alsenate.gov

Coleman, Linda (D, 20)
State House, Room 738
11 South Union Street
Montgomery, AL 36130
P: (334) 242-7864
F: (334) 242-8819
E: linda.coleman@birminghamal.gov

Dial, Gerald (R, 13)
State House, Room 732
11 South Union Street
Montgomery, AL 36130
P: (334) 242-7874
F: (334) 242-8819
E: gerald_dial@yahoo.com

Dunn, Priscilla (D, 19)
State House, Room 737
11 South Union Street
Montgomery, AL 36130
P: (334) 242-7793
F: (334) 353-9625

Figures, Vivian Davis (D, 33)
State House, Room 736
11 South Union Street
Montgomery, AL 36130
P: (334) 242-7871
F: (334) 242-8819
E: vivian.figures@alsenate.gov

Glover, Rusty (R, 34)
State House, Room 721
11 South Union Street
Montgomery, AL 36130
P: (334) 242-7886
F: (334) 353-3970
E: kay.dierlam@alsenate.gov

Hightower, Bill (R, 35)
State House, Room 733
11 South Union Street
Montgomery, AL 36130
P: (334) 242-7882
F: (334) 242-8819
E: bill.hightower@alsenate.gov

Holley, Jimmy W. (R, 31)
State House, Room 732
11 South Union Street
Montgomery, AL 36130
P: (334) 242-7845
F: (334) 242-8819

Holtzclaw, Bill (R, 2)
State House, Room 731
11 South Union Street
Montgomery, AL 36130
P: (334) 242-7854
F: (334) 242-8819
E: bill.holtzclaw@alsenate.gov

Livingston, Steve (R, 8)*
State House, Room 731
11 South Union Street
Montgomery, AL 36130
P: (334) 242-7858
F: (334) 242-8819
E: steve.livingston@alsenate.gov

Marsh, Del (R, 12)
State House, Room 722
11 South Union Street
Montgomery, AL 36130
P: (334) 242-7877
F: (334) 242-8819
E: del.marsh@alsenate.gov

McClendon, Jim (R, 11)
State House, Room 729
11 South Union Street
Montgomery, AL 36130
P: (334) 242-7800
F: (334) 242-4759
E: jimmcc@windstream.net

Melson, Tim (R, 1)*
State House, Room 735
11 South Union Street
Montgomery, AL 36130
P: (334) 242-7888
F: (334) 242-8819

Orr, Arthur (R, 3)
State House, Room 730
11 South Union Street
Montgomery, AL 36130
P: (334) 242-7891
F: (334) 242-8819

Pittman, Trip (R, 32)
State House, Room 730
11 South Union Street
Montgomery, AL 36130
P: (334) 242-7897
E: trip.pittman@alsenate.gov

Reed, Greg (R, 5)
State House, Room 726
11 South Union Street
Montgomery, AL 36130
P: (334) 242-7894
F: (334) 242-8819
E: greg.reed@alsenate.gov

Ross Jr., Quinton T. (D, 26)
State House, Room 740
11 South Union Street
Montgomery, AL 36130
P: (334) 242-7880
F: (334) 242-8819
E: Quinton.ross@alsenate.gov

Sanders, Hank (D, 23)
State House, Room 736
11 South Union Street
Montgomery, AL 36130
P: (334) 242-7860
F: (334) 242-8819

Sanford, Paul (R, 7)
State House, Room 731
11 South Union Street
Montgomery, AL 36130
P: (334) 242-7867
F: (334) 242-8819
E: paul.sanford@alsenate.gov

Scofield, Clay (R, 9)
State House, Room 731
11 South Union Street
Montgomery, AL 36130
P: (334) 242-7876
F: (334) 242-8819
E: clay.scofield@alsenate.gov

Shelnutt, Shay (R, 17)*
State House, Room 735
11 South Union Street
Montgomery, AL 36130
P: (334) 242-7794
F: (334) 242-8819
E: shay.sd17@gmail.com

Singleton, Bobby (D, 24)
State House, Room 738
11 South Union Street
Montgomery, AL 36130
P: (334) 242-7935
F: (334) 242-7191
E: bsingle362@gmail.com

Smith, Harri Anne (I, 29)
State House, Room 737
11 South Union Street
Montgomery, AL 36130
P: (334) 242-7879
F: (334) 242-8819
E: harriannesmith@graceba.net

Smitherman, Rodger Mell (D, 18)
State House, Room 737
11 South Union Street
Montgomery, AL 36130
P: (334) 242-7870
F: (334) 242-8819
E: rodger.smitherman@alsenate.gov

Stutts, Larry (R, 6)*
State House, Room 735
11 South Union Street
Montgomery, AL 36130
P: (334) 242-7862
F: (334) 242-8819
E: larrycstutts@aol.com

Waggoner, J.T. (R, 16)
State House, Room 726
11 South Union Street
Montgomery, AL 36130
P: (334) 242-7892
F: (334) 242-2278
E: jabo.waggoner@alsenate.gov

Ward, Cam (R, 14)
State House, Room 719
11 South Union Street
Montgomery, AL 36130
P: (334) 242-7873
F: (334) 242-8819
E: camjulward@aol.com

Whatley, Tom (R, 27)
State House, Room 734
11 South Union Street
Montgomery, AL 36130
P: (334) 242-7865
F: (334) 242-8819
E: tom.whatley@alsenate.gov

Williams, Phil (R, 10)
State House, Room 733
11 South Union Street
Montgomery, AL 36130
P: (334) 242-7857
F: (334) 242-8819
E: Phil@williamsstatesenate.com

House

Speaker of the House

Rep. Mike Hubbard (R)
Speaker of the House
State House, Room 519-A
11 South Union Street
Montgomery, AL 36130
P: (334) 242-7668
F: (334) 242-4759
E: mike.hubbard@alhouse.gov

Speaker Pro Tempore of the House

Rep. Victor Gaston (R)
Speaker Pro Tempore
State House, Room 519-E
11 South Union Street
Montgomery, AL 36130
P: (334) 242-7664
F: (334) 242-4759
E: hvgaston04@yahoo.com

House Majority Leader

Rep. Micky Hammon (R)
Majority Leader
State House, Room 401
11 South Union Street
Montgomery, AL 36130
P: (334) 242-7709
F: (334) 242-4759
E: mickyhammon@gmail.com

House Minority Leader

Rep. Craig Ford (D)
Minority Leader
State House, Room 434
11 South Union Street
Montgomery, AL 36130
P: (334) 242-7690
F: (334) 242-4759
E: Craig.Ford@alhouse.org

Clerk of the House

Mr. Jeff Woodard
Clerk of the House
State House
11 South Union Street
Montgomery, AL 36130
P: (334) 242-7609
F: (334) 242-2488

Members of the House

Ainsworth, Will (R, 27)*
State House, Room 524-B
11 South Union Street
Montgomery, AL 36130
P: (334) 242-7600
F: (334) 242-4759
E: will.ainsworth@alhouse.gov

Alexander, Louise (D, 56)*
State House, Room 537-B
11 South Union Street
Montgomery, AL 36130
P: (334) 242-7600
F: (334) 242-4759
E: louise.alexander@alhouse.gov

Baker, Alan (R, 66)
State House, Room 427-B
11 South Union Street
Montgomery, AL 36130
P: (334) 242-7720
F: (334) 242-4759
E: staterep@co.escambia.al.us

Ball, Mike (R, 10)
State House, Room 401-A
11 South Union Street
Montgomery, AL 36130
P: (334) 242-7683
F: (334) 242-4759
E: mikeball@knology.net

Bandy, George C. (D, 83)
State House, Room 529
11 South Union Street
Montgomery, AL 36130
P: (334) 242-7721
F: (334) 242-4759
E: George.Bandy@alhouse.org

Beckman, Paul (R, 88)
State House, Room 427-D
11 South Union Street
Montgomery, AL 36130
P: (334) 242-7499
F: (334) 242-4759
E: paulbeckmanjr@yahoo.com

Beech, Elaine (D, 65)
State House, Room 427-E
11 South Union Street
Montgomery, AL 36130
P: (334) 242-7702
F: (334) 242-4759
E: elainebeech83@gmail.com

Black, Marcel (D, 3)
State House, Room 435
11 South Union Street
Montgomery, AL 36130
P: (334) 242-7686
F: (334) 242-4759
E: marcel.black42@gmail.com

Boothe, Alan C. (R, 89)
State House, Room 417-H
11 South Union Street
Montgomery, AL 36130
P: (334) 242-7710
F: (334) 242-4759
E: Alan.Boothe@alhouse.org

Boyd, Barbara B. (D, 32)
State House, Room 525-C
11 South Union Street
Montgomery, AL 36130
P: (334) 242-7692
F: (334) 242-4759
E: babs_131@att.net

Bracy Jr., Napoleon (D, 98)
State House, Room 540-A
11 South Union Street
Montgomery, AL 36130
P: (334) 242-7756
F: (334) 242-4759
E: Napoleon.Bracy@alhouse.org

Brown, K.L. (R, 40)
State House, Room 423
11 South Union Street
Montgomery, AL 36130
P: (334) 353-1778
F: (334) 242-4759
E: klbrown@cableone.net

Buskey, James E. (D, 99)
State House, Room 540-C
11 South Union Street
Montgomery, AL 36130
P: (334) 242-7757
F: (334) 242-4759
E: james.buskey@alhouse.org

Butler, Mack (R, 30)
State House, Room 526-A
11 South Union Street
Montgomery, AL 36130
P: (334) 242-7446
F: (334) 242-4759
E: mack.butler@alhouse.gov

Carns, Jim (R, 48)
State House, Room 534-C
11 South Union Street
Montgomery, AL 36130
P: (334) 242-7600
F: (334) 242-4759
E: jwcarns@yahoo.com

Chesteen, Donnie (R, 87)
State House, Room 427-J
11 South Union Street
Montgomery, AL 36130
P: (334) 242-7742
F: (334) 242-4759
E: dchesteen@panhandle.rr.com

Clarke, Adline (D, 97)
State House, Room 540-B
11 South Union Street
Montgomery, AL 36130
P: (334) 242-7449
F: (334) 242-4759
E: adline.clarke@alhouse.gov

Clouse, Steve (R, 93)
State House, Room 410-D
11 South Union Street
Montgomery, AL 36130
P: (334) 242-7717
F: (334) 242-4759
E: Steve.Clouse@alhouse.org

Coleman-Evans, Merika (D, 57)
State House, Room 537-A
11 South Union Street
Montgomery, AL 36130
P: (334) 242-7755
F: (334) 242-4759
E: Merika.Coleman@alhouse.org

Collins, Terri (R, 8)
State House, Room 427-A
11 South Union Street
Montgomery, AL 36130
P: (334) 242-7693
F: (334) 242-4759
E: terri@terricollins.org

Daniels, Anthony (D, 53)*
State House, Room 522-F
11 South Union Street
Montgomery, AL 36130
P: (334) 242-7600
F: (334) 242-4759
E: anthony.daniels@alhouse.gov

Davis, Randy (R, 96)
State House, Room 417-G
11 South Union Street
Montgomery, AL 36130
P: (334) 242-7724
F: (334) 242-4759
E: rmdavis14@aol.com

Drake, E. Richard (R, 45)
State House, Room 528-B
11 South Union Street
Montgomery, AL 36130
P: (334) 242-7727
F: (334) 242-4759
E: ddrake1080@aol.com

Drummond, Barbara (D, 103)*
State House, Room 536-C
11 South Union Street
Montgomery, AL 36130
P: (334) 242-7600
F: (334) 242-4759
E: drummondbarbara@att.net

England, Christopher J. (D, 70)
State House, Room 539-B
11 South Union Street
Montgomery, AL 36130
P: (334) 242-7703
F: (334) 242-4759
E: cengland1@hotmail.com

Farley, Allen (R, 15)
State House, Room 427-L
11 South Union Street
Montgomery, AL 36130
P: (334) 242-7767
F: (334) 242-4759
E: allenfarley@bellsouth.net

Faulkner, David (R, 46)*
State House, Room 522-B
11 South Union Street
Montgomery, AL 36130
P: (334) 242-7600
F: (334) 242-4759
E: david.faulkner@alhouse.gov

Alabama

Faust, Joe (R, 94)
State House, Room 426
11 South Union Street
Montgomery, AL 36130
P: (334) 242-7699
F: (334) 242-4759
E: jfaust@co.baldwin.al.us

Fincher, Bob (R, 37)*
State House, Room 538-A
11 South Union Street
Montgomery, AL 36130
P: (334) 242-7600
F: (334) 242-4759
E: rsfincher77@gmail.com

Ford, Craig (D, 28)
State House, Room 434
11 South Union Street
Montgomery, AL 36130
P: (334) 242-7690
F: (334) 242-4759
E: Craig.Ford@alhouse.org

Forte, Berry (D, 84)
State House, Room 540-D
11 South Union Street
Montgomery, AL 36130
P: (334) 242-7553
F: (334) 242-4759
E: berry.forte@alhouse.gov

Fridy, Matt (R, 73)*
State House, Room 403-E
11 South Union Street
Montgomery, AL 36130
P: (334) 242-7600
E: mdfridy@gmail.com

Garrett, Danny (R, 44)*
State House, Room 538-B
11 South Union Street
Montgomery, AL 36130
P: (334) 242-7600
E: jdaniel.garrett
@yahoo.com

Gaston, Victor (R, 100)
State House, Room 519-E
11 South Union Street
Montgomery, AL 36130
P: (334) 242-7664
F: (334) 242-4759
E: hvgaston04@yahoo.com

Givan, Juandalynn (D, 60)
State House, Room 528-E
11 South Union Street
Montgomery, AL 36130
P: (334) 242-7684
F: (334) 242-4759
E: Juandalynn.givan
@alhouse.gov

Greer, Lynn (R, 2)
State House, Room 403-C
11 South Union Street
Montgomery, AL 36130
P: (334) 242-7576
F: (334) 242-4759
E: Lynn.Greer@alhouse.gov

Grimsley, Dexter (D, 85)
State House, Room 537-F
11 South Union Street
Montgomery, AL 36130
P: (334) 242-7740
F: (334) 242-4759
E: wlmdex@hotmail.com

Hall, Laura (D, 19)
State House, Room 517-D
11 South Union Street
Montgomery, AL 36130
P: (334) 242-7688
F: (334) 242-4759
E: annihall@gmail.com

Hammon, Micky (R, 4)
State House, Room 401
11 South Union Street
Montgomery, AL 36130
P: (334) 242-7709
F: (334) 242-4759
E: mickyhammon@gmail.com

Hanes, Tommy (R, 23)*
State House, Room 527-D
11 South Union Street
Montgomery, AL 36130
P: (334) 242-7600
F: (334) 242-4759
E: jhanes55@gmail.com

Harbison, Corey (R, 12)*
State House, Room 526-F
11 South Union Street
Montgomery, AL 36130
P: (334) 242-7600
F: (334) 242-4759
E: corey.harbison
@alhouse.gov

Harper, Alan (D, 61)
State House, Room 403-B
11 South Union Street
Montgomery, AL 36130
P: (334) 242-7732
F: (334) 242-4759
E: salanharper@gmail.com

Henry, Ed (R, 9)
State House, Room 401-F
11 South Union Street
Montgomery, AL 36130
P: (334) 242-7736
F: (334) 242-4759
E: Ed.Henry@alhouse.gov

Hill, Jim (R, 50)*
State House, Room 526-B
11 South Union Street
Montgomery, AL 36130
P: (334) 242-7600
F: (334) 242-4759
E: jim.hill@alhouse.gov

Hill, Mike (R, 41)
State House, Room 403-A
11 South Union Street
Montgomery, AL 36130
P: (334) 242-7715
F: (334) 242-4759
E: mhillcolum@aol.com

Holmes, Alvin (D, 78)
State House, Room 525-A
11 South Union Street
Montgomery, AL 36130
P: (334) 242-7706
F: (334) 242-4759
E: Alvin.Holmes@alhouse.org

Holmes, Mike (R, 31)*
State House, Room 527-A
11 South Union Street
Montgomery, AL 36130
P: (334) 242-7215
E: mike.holmes@alhouse.gov

Howard, Ralph (D, 72)
State House, Room 525-A
11 South Union Street
Montgomery, AL 36130
P: (334) 242-7759
F: (334) 242-4759
E: Ralph.Howard@alhouse.org

Hubbard, Mike (R, 79)
State House, Room 519-A
11 South Union Street
Montgomery, AL 36130
P: (334) 242-7668
F: (334) 242-4759
E: mike.hubbard@alhouse.gov

Hurst, Steve (R, 35)
State House, Room 427-K
11 South Union Street
Montgomery, AL 36130
P: (334) 353-9215
F: (334) 242-4759
E: Steve.Hurst@alhouse.org

Ingram, Reed (R, 75)*
State House, Room 531
11 South Union Street
Montgomery, AL 36130
P: (334) 242-7600
F: (334) 242-4759
E: reedingram75@gmail.com

Jackson, Thomas E. (D, 68)
State House, Room 437-D
11 South Union Street
Montgomery, AL 36130
P: (334) 242-7738
F: (334) 242-4759
E: Thomas.Jackson
@alhouse.org

Johnson, Ken (R, 7)
State House, Room 417-E
11 South Union Street
Montgomery, AL 36130
P: (334) 242-7754
F: (334) 242-4759
E: kenjohnsonrep@gmail.com

Johnson, Ronald G. (R, 33)
State House, Room 413-B
11 South Union Street
Montgomery, AL 36130
P: (334) 242-7777
F: (334) 242-4759
E: Ronald.Johnson
@alhouse.org

Jones, Mike (R, 92)
State House, Room 421
11 South Union Street
Montgomery, AL 36130
P: (334) 242-7739
F: (334) 242-4759
E: mljatty@andycable.com

Knight Jr., John F. (D, 77)
State House, Room 539-A
11 South Union Street
Montgomery, AL 36130
P: (334) 242-7512
F: (334) 242-4759
E: John.Knight@alhouse.org

Lawrence, Kelvin (D, 69)*
State House, Room 536-A
11 South Union Street
Montgomery, AL 36130
P: (334) 242-7600
F: (334) 242-4759
E: kelvinj73@gmail.com

Ledbetter, Nathaniel (R, 24)*
State House, Room 522-D
11 South Union Street
Montgomery, AL 36130
P: (334) 242-7600
F: (334) 242-4759
E: nathaniel.ledbetter
@alhouse.gov

Lee, Paul (R, 86)
State House, Room 410-F
11 South Union Street
Montgomery, AL 36130
P: (334) 242-7675
F: (334) 242-4759
E: pwlee@graceba.net

Lindsey, Richard J. (D, 39)
State House, Room 432
11 South Union Street
Montgomery, AL 36130
P: (334) 242-7713
F: (334) 242-4759
E: richard.lindsey
@alhouse.gov

Martin, James M. (R, 42)
State House, Room 404
11 South Union Street
Montgomery, AL 36130
P: (334) 242-7772
F: (334) 242-4759
E: jamesmartin
@bellsouth.net

McCampbell, Artis (D, 71)
State House, Room 539-F
11 South Union Street
Montgomery, AL 36130
P: (334) 242-7747
F: (334) 242-4759
E: Artis.McCampbell
@alhouse.org

McClammy, Thad (D, 76)
State House, Room 534-A
11 South Union Street
Montgomery, AL 36130
P: (334) 242-7780
F: (334) 242-4759
E: thad.mcclammy
@alhouse.org

McCutcheon, Mac (R, 25)
State House, Room 519-C
11 South Union Street
Montgomery, AL 36130
P: (334) 242-7673
F: (334) 242-4759
E: c.mac.mccutcheon
@gmail.com

McMillan, Stephen A. (R, 95)
State House, Room 532
11 South Union Street
Montgomery, AL 36130
P: (334) 242-7723
F: (334) 242-4759
E: bcld07@gmail.com

Melton, Darrio (D, 67)
State House, Room 431
11 South Union Street
Montgomery, AL 36130
P: (334) 242-7540
F: (334) 242-4759
E: darriomelton@gmail.com

Millican, Michael J. (R, 17)
State House, Room 427-F
11 South Union Street
Montgomery, AL 36130
P: (334) 242-7354
F: (334) 242-4759
E: mike.millican
@alhouse.gov

Mooney, Arnold (R, 43)*
State House, Room 538-D
11 South Union Street
Montgomery, AL 36130
P: (334) 242-7600
F: (334) 242-4759
E: arnold.mooney
@alhouse.gov

Moore, Barry (R, 91)
State House, Room 422
11 South Union Street
Montgomery, AL 36130
P: (334) 242-7773
F: (334) 242-4759
E: barry
@barrymooreindustries.com

Moore, Mary (D, 59)
State House, Room 539-D
11 South Union Street
Montgomery, AL 36130
P: (334) 242-7608
F: (334) 242-4759
E: mamoor48@bellsouth.net

Morrow, Johnny Mack (D, 18)
State House, Room 517-F
11 South Union Street
Montgomery, AL 36130
P: (334) 242-7698
F: (334) 242-4759
E: Johnny.Morrow
@alhouse.org

Nordgren, Becky (R, 29)
State House, Room 401-D
11 South Union Street
Montgomery, AL 36130
P: (334) 353-9032
F: (334) 242-4759
E: rebeccasnordgren
@gmail.com

Patterson, Jim (R, 21)
State House, Room 427-H
11 South Union Street
Montgomery, AL 36130
P: (334) 242-7531
F: (334) 242-4759
E: jimpattersonhd21
@gmail.com

Pettus, Phillip (R, 1)*
State House, Room 524-C
11 South Union Street
Montgomery, AL 36130
P: (334) 242-7600
F: (334) 242-4759
E: phillip.pettus
@alhouse.gov

Polizos, Dimitri (R, 74)
State House, Room 522-C
11 South Union Street
Montgomery, AL 36130
P: (334) 242-7600
F: (334) 242-4759
E: dimitri.polizos
@alhouse.gov

Poole, Bill (R, 63)
State House, Room 514
11 South Union Street
Montgomery, AL 36130
P: (334) 242-7624
F: (334) 242-4759
E: bill.poole@alhouse.gov

Pringle, Chris (R, 101)
State House, Room 427-M
11 South Union Street
Montgomery, AL 36130
P: (334) 242-7600
F: (334) 242-4759
E: chrispringle
@southerntimberlands.com

Rich, Kerry (R, 26)
State House, Room 427-C
11 South Union Street
Montgomery, AL 36130
P: (334) 242-7538
F: (334) 242-4759
E: kerryrich@mclo.org

Robinson, Oliver (D, 58)
State House, Room 534-B
11 South Union Street
Montgomery, AL 36130
P: (334) 242-7769
F: (334) 242-4759
E: Oliver.Robinson
@alhouse.org

Rogers Jr., John W. (D, 52)
State House, Room523-A
11 South Union Street
Montgomery, AL 36130
P: (334) 242-7761
F: (334) 242-4759
E: yke@cec.conteduc.uab.edu

Rowe, Connie (R, 13)*
State House, Room 538-C
11 South Union Street
Montgomery, AL 36130
P: (334) 242-7600
F: (334) 242-4759
E: connie.rowe@alhouse.gov

Sanderford, Howard (R, 20)
State House, Room 413-C
11 South Union Street
Montgomery, AL 36130
P: (334) 242-4368
F: (334) 242-4759
E: hs1989@aol.com

Scott, Roderick (D, 55)
State House, Room 425
11 South Union Street
Montgomery, AL 36130
P: (334) 242-7752
F: (334) 242-4759
E: rodhscott@gmail.com

Sells, Chris (R, 90)*
State House, Room 526-E
11 South Union Street
Montgomery, AL 36130
P: (334) 242-6600
F: (334) 242-4759
E: csea@centurytel.net

Sessions, David (R, 105)
State House, Room417-I
11 South Union Street
Montgomery, AL 36130
P: (334) 242-0947
F: (334) 242-4759
E: d.r.sessions@att.net

Shedd, Randall (R, 11)
State House, Room 524-A
11 South Union Street
Montgomery, AL 36130
P: (334) 242-7330
F: (334) 242-4759
E: randall.shedd
@alhouse.gov

Shiver, Harry (R, 64)
State House, Room 526-D
11 South Union Street
Montgomery, AL 36130
P: (334) 242-7745
F: (334) 242-4759
E: harryshiver@aol.com

South, Kyle (R, 16)*
State House, Room 427-G
11 South Union Street
Montgomery, AL 36130
P: (334) 242-7600
F: (334) 242-4759
E: ksouth@watvc.com

Standridge, David (R, 34)
State House, Room 524-D
11 South Union Street
Montgomery, AL 36130
P: (334) 242-7475
E: david.standridge
@alhouse.gov

Alabama

Todd, Patricia (D, 54)
State House, Room 539-E
11 South Union Street
Montgomery, AL 36130
P: (334) 242-7718
F: (334) 242-4759
E: reptodd@gmail.com

Treadaway, Allen (R, 51)
State House, Room 528-A
11 South Union Street
Montgomery, AL 36130
P: (334) 242-7685
F: (334) 242-4759
E: bsketa@aol.com

Tuggle, Mark (R, 81)
State House, Room 410-C
11 South Union Street
Montgomery, AL 36130
P: (334) 242-7219
F: (334) 242-4759
E: tughd81@gmail.com

Vance, Lesley (R, 80)
State House, Room 404
11 South Union Street
Montgomery, AL 36130
P: (334) 242-7687
F: (334) 242-4759
E: Lesley.Vance@alhouse.org

Wadsworth, Tim (R, 14)*
State House, Room 428-D
11 South Union Street
Montgomery, AL 36130
P: (334) 242-7600
F: (334) 242-4759
E: wadsworth@centurytel.net

Warren, Pebblin (D, 82)
State House, Room 517-B
11 South Union Street
Montgomery, AL 36130
P: (334) 242-7734
F: (334) 242-4759
E: tiger9127@bellsouth.net

Weaver, April (R, 49)
State House, Room 417-A
11 South Union Street
Montgomery, AL 36130
P: (334) 242-7731
F: (334) 242-4759
E: April.Weaver@alhouse.org

Whorton, Isaac (R, 38)*
State House, Room 427-C
11 South Union Street
Montgomery, AL 36130
P: (334) 242-7600
F: (334) 242-4759
E: isaac.whorton
@alhouse.gov

Whorton, Ritchie (R, 22)*
State House, Room 526-C
11 South Union Street
Montgomery, AL 36130
P: (334) 242-7600
F: (334) 242-4759
E: ritchiewhorton@gmail.com

Wilcox, Margie (R, 104)*
State House, Room 524-F
11 South Union Street
Montgomery, AL 36130
P: (334) 242-7546
F: (334) 242-4759
E: margie.wilcox
@alhouse.gov

Williams, Dan (R, 5)
State House, Room 427-I
11 South Union Street
Montgomery, AL 36130
P: (334) 242-7741
F: (334) 242-4759
E: hizonor92@yahoo.com

Williams, Jack (R, 47)
State House, Room 417-A
11 South Union Street
Montgomery, AL 36130
P: (334) 242-7779
F: (334) 242-4759
E: jack@jackwilliams.org

Williams, Jack W. (R, 102)*
State House, Room 524-F
11 South Union Street
Montgomery, AL 36130
P: (334) 242-7600
F: (334) 242-4759
E: jackwilliams55
@icloud.com

Williams, Phil (R, 6)
State House, Room 401-C
11 South Union Street
Montgomery, AL 36130
P: (334) 242-7704
F: (334) 242-4759
E: philhouse44@gmail.com

Wingo, Rich (R, 62)*
State House, Room 522-D
11 South Union Street
Montgomery, AL 36130
P: (334) 242-7554
F: (334) 242-4759
E: rich
@blackwaterresources.com

Wood, Randy (R, 36)
State House, Room 424
11 South Union Street
Montgomery, AL 36130
P: (334) 242-7700
F: (334) 242-4759
E: Randy.Wood@alhouse.org

Congress

Senate

Sessions, Jeff (R)
Shelby, Richard C. (R)

House

Aderholt, Robert B. (R, 4)
Brooks, Mo (R, 5)
Byrne, Bradley (R, 1)
Palmer, Gary (R, 6)
Roby, Martha (R, 2)
Sewell, Terri A. (D, 7)

Alaska

Executive

Governor

Hon. Bill Walker (I)
Governor
State Capitol Building, 3rd Floor
P.O. Box 10001
Juneau, AK 99811
P: (907) 465-3500
F: (907) 465-3532

Lieutenant Governor

Hon. Byron Mallot (I)
Lieutenant Governor
550 West 7th Street, Suite 1700
Anchorage, AK 99501
P: (907) 269-7460
F: (907) 269-0263

Secretary of State

Alaska does not have the office of secretary of state. Some of the duties of the secretary of state are performed by the office of the lieutenant governor.

Attorney General

Hon. Craig Richards
(appointed)
Attorney General
P.O. Box 110300
Juneau, AK 99811
P: (907) 465-2133
F: (907) 465-2075

Auditor

Hon. Kris Curtis
(appointed by the Legislature)
Legislative Auditor
P.O. Box 113300
Juneau, AK 99811
P: (907) 465-3830
F: (907) 465-2347

Treasurer

Hon. Pamela Leary
(appointed)
State Treasurer
P.O. Box 110405
Juneau, AK 99811
P: (907) 465-3751
E: pam.leary@alaska.gov

Judiciary

Supreme Court (MR)

Ms. Marilyn May
Clerk of the Appellate Courts
303 K Street
Anchorage, AK 99501
P: (907) 264-0612
F: (907) 264-0878
E: mmay
@appellate.courts.state.ak.us

Hon. Dana Fabe
Chief Justice
Hon. Joel H. Bolger
Hon. Peter J. Maassen
Hon. Craig F. Stowers
Hon. Daniel E. Winfree

Legislative Senate

Senate President

Sen. Kevin Meyer (R)
Senate President
State Capitol, Room 111
Juneau, AK 99801
P: (907) 465-4945
F: (907) 465-3476
E: Senator.Kevin.Meyer
@akleg.gov

Senate Majority Leader

Sen. John Coghill Jr. (R)
Majority Leader
State Capitol, Room 119
Juneau, AK 99801
P: (907) 465-3719
F: (907) 465-3258
E: Senator.John.Coghill
@akleg.gov

Senate Minority Leader

Sen. Berta Gardner (D)
Minority Leader
State Capitol, Room 9
Juneau, AK 99801
P: (907) 465-4930
F: (907) 465-3834
E: Senator.Berta.Gardner
@akleg.gov

Secretary of the Senate

Ms. Liz Clark
Secretary of the Senate
State Capitol, Room 211
Juneau, AK 99801
P: (907) 465-3701
F: (807) 465-2832
E: liz.clark@akleg.gov

Members of the Senate

Bishop, Click (R, C)
State Capitol, Room 115
Juneau, AK 99801
P: (907) 465-2327
F: (907) 465-5241
E: Senator.Click.Bishop
@akleg.gov

Coghill Jr., John (R, B)
State Capitol, Room 119
Juneau, AK 99801
P: (907) 465-3719
F: (907) 465-3258
E: Senator.John.Coghill
@akleg.gov

Costello, Mia (R, K)
State Capitol, Room 510
Juneau, AK 99801
P: (907) 465-4968
F: (907) 465-2040
E: Senator.Mia.Costello
@akleg.gov

Dunleavy, Mike (R, E)
State Capitol, Room 11
Juneau, AK 99801
P: (907) 465-6600
F: (907) 465-3805
E: Senator.Mike.Dunleavy
@akleg.gov

Egan, Dennis (D, Q)
State Capitol, Room 417
Juneau, AK 99801
P: (907) 465-4947
F: (907) 465-2108
E: Senator.Dennis.Egan
@akleg.gov

Ellis, Johnny (D, J)
State Capitol, Room 7
Juneau, AK 99801
P: (907) 465-3704
F: (907) 465-2529
E: Senator.Johnny.Ellis
@akleg.gov

Gardner, Berta (D, I)
State Capitol, Room 9
Juneau, AK 99801
P: (907) 465-4930
F: (907) 465-3834
E: Senator.Berta.Gardner
@akleg.gov

Giessel, Cathy (R, N)
State Capitol, Room 427
Juneau, AK 99801
P: (907) 465-4843
F: (907) 465-3871
E: Senator.Cathy.Giessel
@akleg.gov

Hoffman, Lyman (D, S)
State Capitol, Room 508
Juneau, AK 99801
P: (907) 465-4453
F: (907) 465-4523
E: Senator.Lyman.Hoffman
@akleg.gov

Huggins, Charlie (R, D)
State Capitol, Room 103
Juneau, AK 99801
P: (907) 465-3878
F: (907) 465-3265
E: Senator.Charlie.Huggins
@akleg.gov

Kelly, Pete (R, A)
State Capitol, Room 516
Juneau, AK 98801
P: (907) 465-3709
F: (907) 465-4714
E: Senator.Pete.Kelly
@akleg.gov

MacKinnon, Anna (R, G)*
State Capitol, Room 516
Juneau, AK 99801
P: (907) 465-3777
F: (907) 465-2819
E: Senator.Anna.MacKinnon
@akleg.gov

McGuire, Lesil (R, K)
State Capitol, Room 121
Juneau, AK 99801
P: (907) 465-2995
F: (907) 465-6592
E: Senator.Lesil.McGuire
@akleg.gov

Meyer, Kevin (R, M)
State Capitol, Room 111
Juneau, AK 99801
P: (907) 465-4945
F: (907) 465-3476
E: Senator.Kevin.Meyer
@akleg.gov

Micciche, Peter (R, O)
State Capitol, Room 514
Juneau, AK 99801
P: (907) 465-2828
F: (907) 465-4779
E: Senator.Peter.Micciche
@akleg.gov

Alaska

Olson, Donald (D, T)
State Capitol, Room 504
Juneau, AK 99801
P: (907) 465-3707
F: (907) 465-4821
E: Senator.Donny.Olson@akleg.gov

Stedman, Bert (R, R)
State Capitol, Room 30
Juneau, AK 99801
P: (907) 465-3873
F: (907) 465-3922
E: Senator.Bert.Stedman@akleg.gov

Stevens, Gary (R, P)
State Capitol, Room 429
Juneau, AK 99801
P: (907) 465-4925
F: (907) 465-3517
E: Senator.Gary.Stevens@akleg.gov

Stoltze, Bill (R, F)
State Capitol, Room 125
Juneau, AK 99801
P: (907) 465-4958
F: (907) 465-4928
E: Senator.Bill.Stoltze@akleg.gov

Wielechowski, Bill (D, H)
State Capitol, Room 419
Juneau, AK 99801
P: (907) 465-2435
F: (907) 465-6615
E: Senator.Bill.Wielechowski@akleg.gov

House

Speaker of the House

Rep. Mike Chenault (R)
Speaker of the House
State Capitol, Room 208
Juneau, AK 99801
P: (907) 465-3779
F: (907) 465-2833
E: Representative.Mike.Chenault@akleg.gov

House Majority Leader

Rep. Charisse E. Millett (R)
Majority Leader
State Capitol, Room 204
Juneau, AK 99801
P: (907) 465-3879
F: (907) 465-2069
E: Representative.Charisse.Millett@akleg.gov

House Minority Leader

Rep. Chris Tuck (D)
Minority Leader
State Capitol, Room 404
Juneau, AK 99801
P: (907) 465-2095
F: (907) 465-3810
E: Representative.Chris.Tuck@akleg.gov

Clerk of the House

Ms. Suzanne Lowell
Chief Clerk of the House
Thomas B. Stewart Building
Room 202
Juneau, AK 99801
P: (907) 465-3725
F: (907) 465-5334
E: Suzi.Lowell@akleg.gov

Members of the House

Chenault, Mike (R, 29)
State Capitol, Room 208
Juneau, AK 99801
P: (907) 465-3779
F: (907) 465-2833
E: Representative.Mike.Chenault@akleg.gov

Claman, Matt (D, 21)*
State Capitol, Room 405
Juneau, AK 99801
P: (907) 465-4919
F: (907) 465-2137
E: Representative.Matt.Claman@akleg.gov

Colver, Jim (R, 9)*
State Capitol, Room 424
Juneau, AK 99801
P: (907) 465-4859
F: (907) 465-3799
E: Representative.Jim.Colver@akleg.gov

Drummond, Harriet (D, 18)
State Capitol, Room 112
Juneau, AK 99801
P: (907) 465-3875
F: (907) 465-4588
E: Representative.Harriet.Drummond@akleg.gov

Edgmon, Bryce (D, 37)
State Capitol, Room 410
Juneau, AK 99801
P: (907) 465-4451
F: (907) 465-3445
E: Representative.Bryce.Edgmon@akleg.gov

Foster, Neal (D, 39)
State Capitol, Room 434
Juneau, AK 99801
P: (907) 465-3789
F: (907) 465-3242
E: Representative.Neal.Foster@akleg.gov

Gara, Les (D, 20)
State Capitol, Room 400
Juneau, AK 99801
P: (907) 465-2647
F: (907) 465-3518
E: Representative.Les.Gara@akleg.gov

Gattis, Lynn (R, 7)
State Capitol, Room 500
Juneau, AK 99801
P: (907) 465-4833
F: (907) 465-4586
E: Representative.Lynn.Gattis@akleg.gov

Gruenberg, Max (D, 16)
State Capitol, Room 110
Juneau, AK 99801
P: (907) 465-4940
F: (907) 465-3766
E: rep.max.gruenberg@akleg.gov

Guttenberg, David (D, 4)
State Capitol, Room 415
Juneau, AK 99801
P: (907) 465-4457
F: (907) 465-3519
E: Representative.David.Guttenberg@akleg.gov

Hawker, Mike (R, 28)
State Capitol, Room 502
Juneau, AK 99801
P: (907) 465-4949
F: (907) 465-4979
E: Representative.Mike.Hawker@akleg.gov

Herron, Bob (D, 38)
State Capitol, Room 406
Juneau, AK 99801
P: (907) 465-4942
F: (907) 465-4589
E: Representative.Bob.Herron@akleg.gov

Hughes, Shelley S. (R, 11)
State Capitol, Room 13
Juneau, AK 99801
P: (907) 465-3743
E: Representative.Shelley.Hughes@akleg.gov

Johnson, Craig (R, 24)
State Capitol, Room 103
Juneau, AK 99801
P: (907) 465-4993
F: (907) 465-3872
E: Representative.Craig.Johnson@akleg.gov

Josephson, Andy (D, 17)
State Capitol, Room 430
Juneau, AK 99801
P: (907) 465-4939
F: (907) 465-2418
E: Representative.Andy.Josephson@akleg.gov

Kawasaki, Scott (D, 1)
State Capitol, Room 418
Juneau, AK 99801
P: (907) 465-3466
F: (907) 465-2937
E: Representative.Scott.Kawasaki@akleg.gov

Keller, Wes (R, 10)
State Capitol, Room 403
Juneau, AK 99801
P: (907) 465-2186
F: (907) 465-3818
E: Representative.Wes.Keller@akleg.gov

Kito III, Sam (D, 33)
State Capitol, Room 422
Juneau, AK 99801
P: (907) 465-4766
F: (907) 465-4748
E: rep.sam.kito.III@akleg.gov

Kreiss-Tomkins, Jonathan (D, 35)
State Capitol, Room 426
Juneau, AK 99801
P: (907) 465-3732
F: (907) 465-2652
E: Representative.Jonathan.Kreiss-Tomkins@akleg.gov

LeDoux, Gabrielle (R, 15)
State Capitol, Room 118
Juneau, AK 99801
P: (907) 465-4998
F: (907) 465-4419
E: Representative.
Gabrielle.LeDoux
@akleg.gov

Lynn, Bob (R, 26)
State Capitol, Room 108
Juneau, AK 99801
P: (907) 465-4931
F: (907) 465-4316
E: Representative.Bob.Lynn
@akleg.gov

Millett, Charisse E. (R, 25)
State Capitol, Room 204
Juneau, AK 99801
P: (907) 465-3879
F: (907) 465-2069
E: Representative.
Charisse.Millett
@akleg.gov

Munoz, Cathy (R, 34)
State Capitol, Room 501
Juneau, AK 99801
P: (907) 465-3744
F: (907) 465-2273
E: Representative.
Cathy.Munoz@akleg.gov

Nageak, Benjamin (D, 40)
State Capitol, Room 126
Juneau, AK 99801
P: (907) 465-3473
F: (907) 465-2827
E: Representative.
Benjamin.Nageak@akleg.gov

Neuman, Mark (R, 8)
State Capitol, Room 505
Juneau, AK 99801
P: (907) 465-2679
F: (907) 465-4822
E: Representative.
Mark.Neuman@akleg.gov

Olson, Kurt (R, 30)
State Capitol, Room 24
Juneau, AK 99801
P: (907) 465-2693
F: (907) 465-3835
E: Representative.
Kurt.Olson@akleg.gov

Ortiz, Daniel H.*
State Capitol, Room 114
Juneau, AK 99801
P: (907) 465-3824
F: (907) 465-3175
E: Representative.
Dan.Ortiz@akleg.gov

Pruitt, Lance (R, 27)
State Capitol, Room 421
Juneau, AK 99801
P: (907) 465-3438
F: (907) 465-4565
E: Representative.
Lance.Pruitt@akleg.gov

Reinbold, Lora (R, 14)
State Capitol, Room 432
Juneau, AK 99801
P: (907) 465-3822
F: (907) 465-3756
E: Representative.
Lora.Reinbold@akleg.gov

Saddler, Dan (R, 13)
State Capitol, Room 513
Juneau, AK 99801
P: (907) 465-3783
F: (907) 465-2293
E: Representative.
Dan.Saddler@akleg.gov

Seaton, Paul (R, 31)
State Capitol, Room 102
Juneau, AK 99801
P: (907) 465-2689
F: (907) 465-3472
E: Representative.
Paul.Seaton@akleg.gov

Stutes, Louise B. (R, 32)*
State Capitol, Room 416
Juneau, AK 99801
P: (907) 465-2487
F: (907) 465-4956
E: Representative.
Louise.Stutes@akleg.gov

Talerico, David M. (R, 6)*
State Capitol, Room 104
Juneau, AK 99801
P: (907) 465-4527
F: (907) 465-2197
E: Representative.
Dave.Talerico@akleg.gov

Tarr, Geran (D, 19)
State Capitol, Room 409
Juneau, AK 99801
P: (907) 465-3424
F: (907) 465-3793
E: Representative.
Geran.Tarr@akleg.gov

Thompson, Steve (R, 2)
State Capitol, Room 515
Juneau, AK 99801
P: (907) 465-3004
F: (907) 465-2070
E: Representative.
Steve.Thompson@akleg.gov

Tilton, Cathy (R, 12)*
State Capitol, Room 411
Juneau, AK 99801
P: (907) 465-2199
F: (907) 465-4587
E: Representative.
Cathy.Tilton@akleg.gov

Tuck, Chris (D, 23)
State Capitol, Room 404
Juneau, AK 99801
P: (907) 465-2095
F: (907) 465-3810
E: Representative.
Chris.Tuck@akleg.gov

Vazquez, Liz (R, 22)*
State Capitol, Room 428
Juneau, AK 99801
P: (907) 465-3892
F: (907) 465-6595
E: Representative.
Liz.Vazquez@akleg.gov

Wilson, Tammie (R, 3)
State Capitol, Room 412
Juneau, AK 99801
P: (907) 465-4797
F: (907) 465-3884
E: Representative.
Tammie.Wilson@akleg.gov

Wool, Adam (D, 5)*
State Capitol, Room 420
Juneau, AK 99801
P: (907) 465-4976
F: (907) 465-3883
E: Representative.
Adam.Wool@akleg.gov

Congress

Senate
Murkowski, Lisa (R)
Sullivan, Daniel S. (R)

House
Young, Don (R, At-Large)

American Samoa

Executive

Governor

Hon. Lolo Matalasi Moliga (I)
Governor
Executive Office Building, Third Floor
Utulei
Pago Pago, AS 96799
P: (684) 633-4116
F: (684) 633-2269

Lieutenant Governor

Hon. Lemanu Peleti Mauga (I)
Lieutenant Governor
Territory of American Samoa
Pago Pago, AS 96799
P: (684) 633-4116
F: (684) 633-2269

Secretary of State

American Samoa does not have the office of secretary of state. Some of the duties of the secretary of state are performed by the office of the lieutenant governor.

Attorney General

Hon. Talauega Eleasalo V. Ale
(appointed)
Attorney General
American Samoa Government
Exeuctive Office Building, Utulei
Pago Pago, AS 96799
P: (684) 633-4163

Auditor

Mr. Francis Sefo
Territorial Auditor
Executive Office Building
AP Lutali - 2nd Floor
Pago Pago, AS 96799
P: (684) 633-5191
F: (684) 633-1039

Treasurer

Hon. Falema'o M. Pili
Treasurer
American Samoa Government
Pago Pago, AS 96799
P: (684) 633-4155
F: (684) 633-4100

Judiciary

High Court (FA)

Mr. Robert Gorniak
Chief Clerk
American Samoa Government
Pago Pago, AS 96799
P: (684) 633-4131
F: (684) 633-1318

Hon. F. Michael Kruse
Chief Justice
Hon. Lyle Richmond

Legislative Senate

Senate President

Sen. Gaoteote Palaie Tofau (NP)
Senate President
Legislature of American Samoa
P.O. Box 485
Pago Pago, AS 96799
P: (684) 633-5853
F: (684) 633-1638

Secretary of the Senate

Mr. Leo'o V. Ma'o
Secretary of the Senate
American Samoa Senate
P.O. Box 127
Pago Pago, AS 96799
P: (684) 633-5866
F: (684) 633-1638

Members of the Senate

Aigamaua, Avegalio (NP, 11)
Legislature of American Samoa
P.O. Box 485
Pago Pago, AS 96799
P: (684) 633-4568
F: (684) 633-1638

Asuega, Mauga Tasi (NP, 6)
Legislature of American Samoa
P.O. Box 485
Pago Pago, AS 96799
P: (684) 633-5359
F: (684) 633-1638

Aufata, Fonoti Tafa'ifa (NP, 8)
Legislature of American Samoa
P.O. Box 485
Pago Pago, AS 96799
P: (684) 633-5553
F: (684) 633-1638

Eteuati, Amituana'i (NP, 6)
Legislature of American Samoa
P.O. Box 485
Pago Pago, AS 96799
P: (684) 633-4759
F: (684) 633-1638

Faoa, Lualemaga (NP, 9)
Legislature of American Samoa
P.O. Box 485
Pago Pago, AS 96799
P: (684) 633-4654
F: (684) 633-1638

Fuamatu, Fuamatu J.V. (NP, 12)
Legislature of American Samoa
P.O. Box 485
Pago Pago, AS 96799
P: (685) 633-4457
F: (685) 633-1638

I'atala, Fuata T. (NP, 3)
Legislature of American Samoa
P.O. Box 485
Pago Pago, AS 96799
P: (684) 633-5668
F: (684) 633-1638

La'au, Seui (NP, 7)
Legislature of American Samoa
P.O. Box 485
Pago Pago, AS 96799
P: (684) 633-5854
F: (684) 633-1638

Lam Yuen, Tulifua Tini (NP, 10)
Legislature of American Samoa
P.O. Box 485
Pago Pago, AS 96799
P: (684) 633-5757
F: (684) 633-1681

Lauvai, Asuega Fa'amamata (NP, 6)
Legislature of American Samoa
P.O. Box 485
Pago Pago, AS 96799
P: (684) 633-4947
F: (684) 633-1638

Maui, Letalu (NP, 1)
Legislature of American Samoa
P.O. Box 485
Pago Pago, AS 96799
P: (684) 633-4656
F: (684) 633-1638

Savali Jr., Velega (NP, 2)
Legislature of American Samoa
P.O. Box 485
Pago Pago, AS 96799
P: (684) 633-5663
F: (684) 633-1638

Setu, Malepeai (NP, 5)
Legislature of American Samoa
P.O. Box 485
Pago Pago, AS 96799
P: (684) 633-5754
F: (684) 633-1638

Stevenson, Alo P. (NP, 7)
Legislature of American Samoa
P.O. Box 485
Pago Pago, AS 96799
P: (684) 633-4553
F: (684) 633-1638

Tofau, Gaoteote Palaie (NP, 4)
Legislature of American Samoa
P.O. Box 485
Pago Pago, AS 96799
P: (684) 633-5853
F: (684) 633-1638

Tu'ufuli, Galeai (NP, 1)
Legislature of American Samoa
P.O. Box 485
Pago Pago, AS 96799
P: (685) 633-5453
F: (685) 633-1638

House

Speaker of the House

Rep. Savali Talavou Ale (NP)
Speaker
Legislature of American Samoa
P.O. Box 485
Pago Pago, AS 96799
P: (684) 633-5763
F: (684) 633-1681

Clerk of the House

Ms. Fialupe Lutu
Chief Clerk of the House
Legislature of American Samoa
P.O. Box 485
Pago Pago, AS 96799
P: (684) 633-5763
F: (684) 634-1681

Members of the House

Afalava, Atualevao Gafatasi (NP, 17)
Legislature of American Samoa
P.O. Box 485
Pago Pago, AS 96799
P: (684) 633-5763
F: (684) 633-1681

Ale, Savali Talavou (NP, 14)
Legislature of American Samoa
P.O. Box 485
Pago Pago, AS 96799
P: (684) 633-5763
F: (684) 633-1681

Allen, Faimealelei Anthony F. (NP, 11)
Legislature of American Samoa
P.O. Box 485
Pago Pago, AS 96799
P: (684) 633-5458
F: (684) 633-1681

Amituanai, Vailoata Eteuati (NP, 7)
Legislature of American Samoa
P.O. Box 485
Pago Pago, AS 96799
P: (684) 633-4657
F: (684) 633-1681

Anoai, Maugaoali'I Sipa (NP, 8)*
Legislature of American Samoa
P.O. Box 485
Pago Pago, AS 96799
F: (684) 633-1681

Asifoa, Atalina (NP, 17)*
Legislature of American Samoa
P.O. Box 485
Pago Pago, AS 96799
P: (684) 633-1681

Autele, Toeaina F. (NP, 2)
Legislature of American Samoa
P.O. Box 485
Pago Pago, AS 96799
P: (684) 633-4754
F: (684) 633-1681

Fautanu, Vesi Talalelei (NP, 1)*
Legislature of American Samoa
P.O. Box 485
Pago Pago, AS 96799
F: (684) 633-1681

Fetui Jr., Fetu (NP, 1)
Legislature of American Samoa
P.O. Box 485
Pago Pago, AS 96799
P: (684) 633-4822
F: (684) 633-1681

Koko, Puletu D.S. (NP, 13)
Legislature of American Samoa
P.O. Box 485
Pago Pago, AS 96799
P: (684) 633-5669
F: (684) 633-1681

Mageo, Meauta Lauoi (NP, 9)*
Legislature of American Samoa
P.O. Box 485
Pago Pago, AS 96799
F: (684) 633-1681

Malula, Mulinuu Vae'iaitu Fi (NP, 12)*
Legislature of American Samoa
P.O. Box 485
Pago Pago, AS 96799
F: (684) 633-1681

Mauga, Legae'e (NP, 3)*
Legislature of American Samoa
P.O. Box 485
Pago Pago, AS 96799
F: (684) 633-1681

Moliga, Tuumolimoli Saena (NP, 10)
Legislature of American Samoa
P.O. Box 485
Pago Pago, AS 96799
P: (684) 633-4058
F: (684) 633-1681

Sanitoa, Larry S. (NP, 15)
Legislature of American Samoa
P.O. Box 485
Pago Pago, AS 96799
P: (684) 633-5363
F: (684) 633-1681

Saulo, Vui Florence Tuaumu (NP, 15)*
Legislature of American Samoa
P.O. Box 485
Pago Pago, AS 96799
F: (684) 633-1681

Su'a, Talaimatai Elisara (NP, 4)
Legislature of American Samoa
P.O. Box 485
Pago Pago, AS 96799
P: (684) 633-5763
F: (684) 633-1681

Talo, Lemapu Suiaunoa (NP, 6)
Legislature of American Samoa
P.O. Box 485
Pago Pago, AS 96799
P: (684) 633-4059
F: (684) 633-1681

Tufele Jr., Puleleiite Li'amatua (NP, 5)
Legislature of American Samoa
P.O. Box 485
Pago Pago, AS 96799
P: (684) 633-5557
F: (684) 633-1681

Wilson, Manumaua Wayne (NP, 12)*
Legislature of American Samoa
P.O. Box 485
Pago Pago, AS 96799
F: (684) 633-1681

Yeun, Timusa Tini Lam (NP, 16)*
Legislature of American Samoa
P.O. Box 485
Pago Pago, AS 96799
P: (684) 633-1681

Congress

House Delegate

Radewagen, Amata (R, At-Large

Arizona

Executive

Governor
Hon. Doug Ducey (R)
Governor
1700 West Washington Street
Executive Tower
Phoenix, AZ 85007
P: (602) 542-4331
F: (602) 542-1381

Lieutenant Governor
This state does not have the office of lieutenant governor. The secretary of state is next in line of succession to the governorship.

Attorney General
Hon. Mark Brnovich (R)
Attorney General
1275 West Washington Street
Phoenix, AZ 85007
P: (602) 542-4266
F: (602) 542-4085

Auditor
Hon. Debra K. Davenport
(appointed by the Legislature)
Auditor General
2910 North 44th Street, Suite 410
Phoenix, AZ 85018
P: (602) 553-0333
F: (602) 553-0051
E: ddavenport@azauditor.gov

State Mine Inspector
Hon. Joe Hart (R)
State Mine Inspector
1700 West Washington, 4th Floor
Phoenix, AZ 85007
P: (602) 542-5971
F: (602) 542-5335

Corporation Commission
Hon. Robert Burns (R)
Commissioner
Commissioner's Wing
1200 West Washington, 2nd Floor
Phoenix, AZ 85007
P: (602) 542-3682
F: (602) 542-3708
E: rburns-web@azcc.gov

Hon. Tom Forese (R)
Commissioner
Commissioner's Wing
1200 West Washington, 2nd Floor
Phoenix, AZ 85007
P: (602) 542-2237
E: forese-web@azcc.gov

Hon. Doug Little (R)
Commissioner
Commissioner's Wing
1200 West Washington, 2nd Floor
Phoenix, AZ 85007
P: (602) 542-2237
E: little-web@azcc.gov

Hon. Susan Bitter Smith (R)
Commissioner
Commissioner's Wing
1200 West Washington, 2nd Floor
Phoenix, AZ 85007
P: (602) 542-3625
F: (602) 542-3669
E: bittersmith-web@azcc.gov

Hon. Bob Stump (R)
Chair
1200 West Washington
Phoenix, AZ 85007
P: (602) 542-3935
F: (602) 542-0752
E: bstump@azcc.gov

Secretary of State
Hon. Michele Reagan (R)
Secretary of State
Capitol Executive Tower, 7th Floor
1700 West Washington
Phoenix, AZ 85007
P: (602) 542-4285
F: (602) 542-1575
E: sosadmin@azsos.gov

Superintendent of Public Instruction
Hon. Diane Douglas (R)
Superintendent of Public Instruction
1535 West Jefferson Street
Phoenix, AZ 85007
P: (602) 542-5393

Treasurer
Hon. Jeff De Wit (R)
State Treasurer
1700 West Washington Street
Phoenix, AZ 85007
P: (602) 542-7800
F: (602) 542-7176

Judiciary

Supreme Court (MR)
Ms. Janet Johnson
Clerk of the Court
1501 West Washington, Suite 402
Phoenix, AZ 85007
P: (602) 452-3396
E: scclerk@courts.az.gov

Hon. W. Scott Bales
Chief Justice
Hon. Rebecca White Berch
Hon. Robert Brutinel
Hon. John Pelander
Hon. Ann Scott Timmer

Legislative Senate

Senate President
Sen. Andy Biggs (R)
Senate President
1700 West Washington
Room 205
Phoenix, AZ 85007
P: (602) 926-4371
F: (602) 417-3248
E: abiggs@azleg.gov

President Pro Tempore of the Senate
Sen. Sylvia Tenney Allen (R)
President Pro Tempore
1700 West Washington
Room 303
Phoenix, AZ 85007
P: (602) 926-5409
F: (602) 417-3105
E: sallen@azleg.gov

Senate Majority Leader
Sen. Steven B. Yarbrough (R)
Majority Leader
1700 West Washington
Room 212
Phoenix, AZ 85007
P: (602) 926-5863
F: (602) 417-3121
E: syarbrough@azleg.gov

Senate Minority Leader
Sen. Katie Hobbs (D)
Minority Leader
1700 West Washington
Room 213
Phoenix, AZ 85007
P: (602) 926-5325
F: (602) 417-3149
E: khobbs@azleg.gov

Secretary of the Senate
Ms. Charmion Billington
Secretary of the Senate
Capitol Complex, Room 204
1700 West Washington Street
Phoenix, AZ 85007
P: (602) 926-4231

Members of the Senate
Ableser, Ed (D, 26)
1700 West Washington
Room 305
Phoenix, AZ 85007
P: (602) 926-4118
F: (602) 417-3224
E: eableser@azleg.gov

Allen, Sylvia Tenney (R, 6)
1700 West Washington
Room 303
Phoenix, AZ 85007
P: (602) 926-5409
F: (602) 417-3105
E: sallen@azleg.gov

Barto, Nancy K. (R, 15)
1700 West Washington
Room 307
Phoenix, AZ 85007
P: (602) 926-5766
F: (602) 417-3261
E: nbarto@azleg.gov

Begay, Carlyle (D, 7)
1700 West Washington
Room 315
Phoenix, AZ 85007
P: (602) 926-5862
F: (602) 417-3099
E: cbegay@azleg.gov

Biggs, Andy (R, 12)
1700 West Washington
Room 205
Phoenix, AZ 85007
P: (602) 926-4371
F: (602) 417-3248
E: abiggs@azleg.gov

Bradley, David T. (D, 10)
1700 West Washington
Room 315
Phoenix, AZ 85007
P: (602) 926-5262
F: (602) 926-3429
E: dbradley@azleg.gov

Burges, Judy (R, 22)
1700 West Washington
Room 302
Phoenix, AZ 85007
P: (602) 926-5861
F: (602) 417-3104
E: jburges@azleg.gov

Cajero Bedford, Olivia (D, 3)
1700 West Washington
Room 314
Phoenix, AZ 85007
P: (602) 926-5835
F: (602) 417-3262
E: ocajerobedford@azleg.gov

Contreras, Lupe Chavira (D, 19)
1700 West Washington
Room 313
Phoenix, AZ 85007
P: (602) 926-5284
F: (602) 417-3106
E: lcontreras@azleg.gov

Dalessandro, Andrea (D, 2)
1700 West Washington
Room 312
Phoenix, AZ 85007
P: (602) 926-5342
F: (602) 417-3169
E: adalessandro@azleg.gov

Dial, Jeff (R, 18)
1700 West Washington
Room 304
Phoenix, AZ 85007
P: (602) 926-5550
F: (602) 417-3120
E: jdial@azleg.gov

Driggs, Adam (R, 28)
1700 West Washington
Room 309
Phoenix, AZ 85007
P: (602) 926-3016
F: (602) 417-3007
E: adriggs@azleg.gov

Farley, Steve (D, 9)
1700 West Washington
Room 213
Phoenix, AZ 85007
P: (602) 926-3022
F: (602) 417-3128
E: sfarley@azleg.gov

Farnsworth, David C. (R, 16)
1700 West Washington
Room 304
Phoenix, AZ 85007
P: (602) 926-3020
F: (602) 417-3119
E: dfarnsworth@azleg.gov

Griffin, Gail (R, 14)
1700 West Washington
Room 212
Phoenix, AZ 85007
P: (602) 926-5895
F: (602) 417-3025
E: ggriffin@azleg.gov

Hobbs, Katie (D, 24)
1700 West Washington
Room 213
Phoenix, AZ 85007
P: (602) 926-5325
F: (602) 417-3149
E: khobbs@azleg.gov

Kavanagh, John (R, 23)
1700 West Washington
Room 303A
Phoenix, AZ 85007
P: (602) 926-5170
F: (602) 417-3108
E: jkavanagh@azleg.gov

Lesko, Debbie (R, 21)
1700 West Washington
Room 302
Phoenix, AZ 85007
P: (602) 926-5413
F: (602) 417-3109
E: dlesko@azleg.gov

Linkous, Terry
100 North 15th Avenue
Suite 400
Phoenix, AZ 85007
P: (602) 542-2250
F: (602) 542-4272

McGuire, Barbara (D, 8)
1700 West Washington
Room 314
Phoenix, AZ 85007
P: (602) 926-5836
F: (602) 417-3131
E: bmcguire@azleg.gov

Meza, Robert (D, 30)
1700 West Washington
Room 311
Phoenix, AZ 85007
P: (602) 926-3425
F: (602) 417-3114
E: rmeza@azleg.gov

Miranda, Catherine (D, 27)
1700 West Washington
Room 311
Phoenix, AZ 85007
P: (602) 926-4893
F: (602) 417-3116
E: cmiranda@azleg.gov

Pancrazi, Lynne (D, 4)
1700 West Washington
Room 308
Phoenix, AZ 85007
P: (602) 926-3004
F: (602) 417-3179
E: lpancrazi@azleg.gov

Pierce, Steve (R, 1)
1700 West Washington
Room 301
Phoenix, AZ 85007
P: (602) 926-5584
F: (602) 417-3101
E: spierce@azleg.gov

Quezada, Martin J. (D, 29)
1700 West Washington
Room 313
Phoenix, AZ 85007
P: (602) 926-5911
F: (602) 417-3113
E: mquezada@azleg.gov

Shooter, Don (R, 13)
1700 West Washington
Room 200
Phoenix, AZ 85007
P: (602) 926-4139
F: (602) 417-3024
E: dshooter@azleg.gov

Smith, Steve (R, 11)
1700 West Washington
Room 303
Phoenix, AZ 85007
P: (602) 926-5685
F: (602) 417-3167
E: stsmith@azleg.gov

Ward, Kelli (R, 5)
1700 West Washington
Room 306
Phoenix, AZ 85007
P: (602) 926-4138
F: (602) 417-3165
E: kward@azleg.gov

Worsley, Bob (R, 25)
1700 West Washington
Room 310
Phoenix, AZ 85007
P: (602) 926-5760
F: (602) 417-3091
E: bworsley@azleg.gov

Yarbrough, Steven B. (R, 17)
1700 West Washington
Room 212
Phoenix, AZ 85007
P: (602) 926-5863
F: (602) 417-3121
E: syarbrough@azleg.gov

Yee, Kimberly (R, 20)
1700 West Washington
Room 300
Phoenix, AZ 85007
P: (602) 926-3024
F: (602) 417-3110
E: kyee@azleg.gov

House

Speaker of the House

Rep. David Gowan (R)
Speaker of the House
1700 West Washington
Room 223
Phoenix, AZ 85007
P: (602) 926-3312
F: (602) 417-3130
E: dgowan@azleg.gov

Speaker Pro Tempore of the House

Rep. Bob Robson (R)
Speaker Pro Tempore
1700 West Washington
Room 222
Phoenix, AZ 85007
P: (602) 926-5549
F: (602) 417-3157
E: brobson@azleg.gov

House Majority Leader

Rep. Steve Montenegro (R)
Majority Leader
1700 West Washington
Room 208
Phoenix, AZ 85007
P: (602) 926-5955
F: (602) 417-3168
E: smontenegro@azleg.gov

Arizona

House Minority Leader

Rep. Eric Meyer (D)
Minority Leader
1700 West Washington
Room 320
Phoenix, AZ 85007
P: (602) 926-3037
F: (602) 417-3111
E: emeyer@azleg.gov

Clerk of the House

Mr. Jim Drake
Chief Clerk
Capitol Complex, Room 203
1700 West Washington
Phoenix, AZ 85007
P: (602) 926-3032

Members of the House

Ackerley, John Christopher (R, 2)*
1700 West Washington
Room 127
Phoenix, AZ 85007
P: (602) 926-3077
F: (602) 417-3277
E: jackerley@azleg.gov

Allen, John (R, 15)
1700 West Washington
Room 131
Phoenix, AZ 85007
P: (602) 926-4916
F: (602) 417-3150
E: jallen@azleg.gov

Alston, Lela (D, 24)
1700 West Washington
Room 330
Phoenix, AZ 85007
P: (602) 926-5829
F: (602) 417-3115
E: lalston@azleg.gov

Andrade, Richard C. (D, 29)*
1700 West Washington
Room 125
Phoenix, AZ 85007
P: (602) 926-3130
F: (602) 417-3292
E: randrade@azleg.gov

Barton, Brenda (R, 6)
1700 West Washington
Room 114
Phoenix, AZ 85007
P: (602) 926-4129
F: (602) 417-3010
E: bbarton@azleg.gov

Benally, Jennifer D. (D, 7)*
1700 West Washington
Room 121
Phoenix, AZ 85007
P: (602) 926-3079
F: (602) 417-3278
E: jbenally@azleg.gov

Bolding, Reginald (D, 27)*
1700 West Washington
Room 116
Phoenix, AZ 85007
P: (602) 926-3132
F: (602) 417-3274
E: rbolding@azleg.gov

Borrelli, Sonny (R, 5)
1700 West Washington
Room 113
Phoenix, AZ 85007
P: (602) 926-5051
F: (602) 417-3153
E: sborrelli@azleg.gov

Bowers, Russell (R, 25)*
1700 West Washington
Room 309
Phoenix, AZ 85007
P: (602) 926-3128
F: (602) 417-3290
E: rbowers@azleg.gov

Boyer, Paul (R, 20)
1700 West Washington
Room 129
Phoenix, AZ 85007
P: (602) 926-4173
F: (602) 417-3153
E: pboyer@azleg.gov

Brophy McGee, Kate (R, 28)
1700 West Washington
Room 304
Phoenix, AZ 85007
P: (602) 926-4486
F: (602) 417-3170
E: kbrophymcgee@azleg.gov

Campbell, Noel (R, 1)*
1700 West Washington
Room 345
Phoenix, AZ 85007
P: (602) 926-3124
F: (602) 417-3287
E: ncampbell@azleg.gov

Cardenas, Mark (D, 19)
1700 West Washington
Room 334
Phoenix, AZ 85007
P: (602) 926-3014
F: (602) 417-3048
E: mcardenas@azleg.gov

Carter, Heather (R, 15)
1700 West Washington
Room 303
Phoenix, AZ 85007
P: (602) 926-5503
F: (602) 417-3107
E: hcarter@azleg.gov

Clark, Ken (D, 24)
1700 West Washington
Room 115
Phoenix, AZ 85007
P: (602) 926-3108
F: (602) 417-3285
E: kenclark@azleg.gov

Cobb, Regina (R, 5)*
1700 West Washington
Room 335
Phoenix, AZ 85007
P: (602) 926-3126
F: (602) 417-3289
E: rcobb@azleg.gov

Coleman, Doug (R, 16)
1700 West Washington
Room 306
Phoenix, AZ 85007
P: (602) 926-3160
F: (602) 417-3151
E: dcoleman@azleg.gov

Espinoza, Diego (D, 19)*
1700 West Washington
Room 118
Phoenix, AZ 85007
P: (602) 926-3134
F: (602) 417-3273
E: despinoza@azleg.gov

Fann, Karen (R, 1)
1700 West Washington
Room 316
Phoenix, AZ 85007
P: (602) 926-5874
F: (602) 417-3001
E: kfann@azleg.gov

Farnsworth, Eddie (R, 12)
1700 West Washington
Room 224
Phoenix, AZ 85007
P: (602) 926-5735
F: (602) 417-3122
E: efarnsworth@azleg.gov

Fernandez, Charlene R. (D, 4)*
1700 West Washington
Room 126
Phoenix, AZ 85007
P: (602) 926-3098
F: (602) 417-3281
E: cfernandez@azleg.gov

Finchem, Mark (R, 11)*
1700 West Washington
Room 337
Phoenix, AZ 85007
P: (602) 926-3122
F: (602) 417-3286
E: mfinchem@azleg.gov

Friese, Randall (D, 9)*
1700 West Washington
Room 325
Phoenix, AZ 85007
P: (602) 926-3138
F: (602) 417-3272
E: rfriese@azleg.gov

Gabaldon, Rosanna (D, 2)
1700 West Washington
Room 117
Phoenix, AZ 85007
P: (602) 926-3424
F: (602) 417-3129
E: rgabaldon@azleg.gov

Gonzales, Sally Ann (D, 3)
1700 West Washington
Room 331
Phoenix, AZ 85007
P: (602) 926-3278
F: (602) 417-3127
E: sgonzales@azleg.gov

Gowan, David (R, 14)
1700 West Washington
Room 223
Phoenix, AZ 85007
P: (602) 926-3312
F: (602) 417-3130
E: dgowan@azleg.gov

Gray, Rick (R, 21)
1700 West Washington
Room 224
Phoenix, AZ 85007
P: (602) 926-5993
F: (602) 417-3225
E: rgray@azleg.gov

Hale, Albert (D, 7)
1700 West Washington
Room 323
Phoenix, AZ 85007
P: (602) 926-4323
F: (602) 417-3160
E: ahale@azleg.gov

Kern, Anthony (R, 20)*
1700 West Washington
Room 341
Phoenix, AZ 85007
P: (602) 926-3102
F: (602) 417-3282
E: akern@azleg.gov

Larkin, Jonathan (D, 30)
1700 West Washington
Room 318
Phoenix, AZ 85007
P: (602) 926-5058
F: (602) 417-3015
E: jlarkin@azleg.gov

Lawrence, Jay (R, 23)*
1700 West Washington
Room 339
Phoenix, AZ 85007
P: (602) 926-3095
F: (602) 417-3280
E: jlawrence@azleg.gov

Leach, Vince (R, 11)*
1700 West Washington
Room 342
Phoenix, AZ 85007
P: (602) 926-3106
F: (602) 417-3284
E: vleach@azleg.gov

Livingston, David (R, 22)
1700 West Washington
Room 207
Phoenix, AZ 85007
P: (602) 926-4178
F: (602) 417-3154
E: dlivingston@azleg.gov

Lovas, Phil (R, 22)
1700 West Washington
Room 110
Phoenix, AZ 85007
P: (602) 926-3297
F: (602) 417-3004
E: plovas@azleg.gov

Mach, Stefanie (D, 10)
1700 West Washington
Room 329
Phoenix, AZ 85007
P: (602) 926-3398
F: (602) 417-3126
E: smach@azleg.gov

McCune Davis, Debbie (D, 30)
1700 West Washington
Room 333
Phoenix, AZ 85007
P: (602) 926-4485
F: (602) 417-3014
E: ddavis@azleg.gov

Mendez, Juan (D, 26)
1700 West Washington
Room 120
Phoenix, AZ 85007
P: (602) 926-4124
F: (602) 417-3017
E: jmendez@azleg.gov

Mesnard, J. D. (R, 17)
1700 West Washington
Room 308
Phoenix, AZ 85007
P: (602) 926-4481
F: (602) 417-3152
E: jmesnard@azleg.gov

Meyer, Eric (D, 28)
1700 West Washington
Room 320
Phoenix, AZ 85007
P: (602) 926-3037
F: (602) 417-3111
E: emeyer@azleg.gov

Mitchell, Darin (R, 13)
1700 West Washington
Room 313
Phoenix, AZ 85007
P: (602) 926-5894
F: (602) 417-3012
E: dmitchell@azleg.gov

Montenegro, Steve (R, 13)
1700 West Washington
Room 208
Phoenix, AZ 85007
P: (602) 926-5955
F: (602) 417-3168
E: smontenegro@azleg.gov

Norgaard, Jill (R, 18)*
1700 West Washington
Room 128
Phoenix, AZ 85007
P: (602) 926-3140
F: (602) 417-3265
E: jnorgaard@azleg.gov

Olson, Justin (R, 25)
1700 West Washington
Room 204
Phoenix, AZ 85007
P: (602) 926-5288
F: (602) 417-3161
E: jolson@azleg.gov

Otondo, Lisa (D, 4)
1700 West Washington
Room 123
Phoenix, AZ 85007
P: (602) 926-3002
F: (602) 417-3124
E: lotondo@azleg.gov

Petersen, Warren (R, 12)
1700 West Washington
Room 312
Phoenix, AZ 85007
P: (602) 926-4136
F: (602) 417-3222
E: wpetersen@azleg.gov

Pratt, Frank (R, 8)
1700 West Washington
Room 226
Phoenix, AZ 85007
P: (602) 926-5761
F: (602) 417-3023
E: fpratt@azleg.gov

Rios, Rebecca (D, 27)
1700 West Washington
Room 322
Phoenix, AZ 85007
P: (602) 926-3073
F: (602) 417-3288
E: rrios@azleg.gov

Rivero, Tony (R, 21)*
1700 West Washington
Room 344
Phoenix, AZ 85007
P: (602) 926-3104
F: (602) 417-3283
E: trivero@azleg.gov

Robson, Bob (R, 18)
1700 West Washington
Room 222
Phoenix, AZ 85007
P: (602) 926-5549
F: (602) 417-3157
E: brobson@azleg.gov

Saldate IV, Macario (D, 3)
1700 West Washington
Room 332
Phoenix, AZ 85007
P: (602) 926-4171
F: (602) 417-3162
E: msaldate@azleg.gov

Sherwood, Andrew (D, 26)
1700 West Washington
Room 119
Phoenix, AZ 85007
P: (602) 926-3028
F: (602) 417-3038
E: asherwood@azleg.gov

Shope, T.J. (R, 8)
1700 West Washington
Room 112
Phoenix, AZ 85007
P: (602) 926-3012
F: (602) 417-3123
E: tshope@azleg.gov

Steele, Victoria (D, 9)
1700 West Washington
Room 324
Phoenix, AZ 85007
P: (602) 926-5683
F: (602) 417-3147
E: vsteele@azleg.gov

Stevens, David (R, 14)
1700 West Washington
Room 205
Phoenix, AZ 85007
P: (602) 926-4321
F: (602) 417-3146
E: dstevens@azleg.gov

Thorpe, Bob (R, 6)
1700 West Washington
Room 130
Phoenix, AZ 85007
P: (602) 926-5219
F: (602) 417-3118
E: bthorpe@azleg.gov

Townsend, Kelly (R, 16)
1700 West Washington
Room 302
Phoenix, AZ 85007
P: (602) 926-4467
F: (602) 417-3018
E: ktownsend@azleg.gov

Ugenti, Michelle (R, 23)
1700 West Washington
Room 111
Phoenix, AZ 85007
P: (602) 926-4480
F: (602) 417-3155
E: mugenti@azleg.gov

Velasquez, Ceci (D, 29)*
1700 West Washington
Room 124
Phoenix, AZ 85007
P: (602) 926-3144
F: (602) 417-3245
E: cvelasquez@azleg.gov

Weninger, Jeff (R, 17)*
1700 West Washington
Room 338
Phoenix, AZ 85007
P: (602) 926-3092
F: (602) 417-3279
E: jweninger@azleg.gov

Wheeler, Bruce (D, 10)
1700 West Washington
Room 321
Phoenix, AZ 85007
P: (602) 926-3300
F: (602) 417-3028
E: bwheeler@azleg.gov

Arizona

Congress

Senate

Flake, Jeff (R)
McCain, John (R)

House

Franks, Trent (R, 8)
Gallego, Ruben (D, 7)
Gosar, Paul (R, 4)
Grijalva, Raul M. (D, 3)
Kirkpatrick, Ann (D, 1)
McSally, Martha (R, 2)
Salmon, Matt (R, 5)
Schweikert, David (R, 6)
Sinema, Kyrsten (D, 9)

Arkansas

Executive

Governor

Hon. Asa Hutchinson (R)
Governor
State Capitol
500 Woodlane Street, Suite 250
Little Rock, AR 72201
P: (501) 682-2345

Lieutenant Governor

Hon. Tim Griffin (R)
Lieutenant Governor
State Capitol
500 Woodlane Street, Suite 270
Little Rock, AR 72201
P: (501) 682-2144
F: (501) 682-2894

Attorney General

Hon. Leslie Rutledge (R)
Attorney General
323 Center Street, Suite 200
Little Rock, AR 72201
P: (800) 482-8982
F: (501) 682-8084

Auditor

Hon. Andrea Lea (R)
Auditor of State
P.O. Box 251906
Little Rock, AR 72201
P: (501) 371-2124
F: (501) 682-6005

Secretary of State

Hon. Mark Martin (R)
Secretary of State
256 State Capitol Building
Little Rock, AR 72201
P: (501) 682-1010
F: (501) 682-3510
E: info@sos.arkansas.gov

Judiciary

Supreme Court (PE)

Ms. Stacy Pectol
Clerk of the Courts
1320 Justice Building
625 Marshall Street
Little Rock, AR 72201
P: (501) 682-6849

Hon. Jim Hannah
Chief Justice
Hon. Karen Baker
Hon. Paul E. Danielson
Hon. Courtney Hudson Goodson
Hon. Josephine L. Hart
Hon. Rhonda Wood
Hon. Robin F. Wynne

Legislative Senate

Senate President

Hon. Tim Griffin (R)
Lieutenant Governor
State Capitol
500 Woodlane Street, Suite 270
Little Rock, AR 72201
P: (501) 682-2144
F: (501) 682-2894

President Pro Tempore of the Senate

Sen. Jonathan Dismang (R)
President Pro Tempore
State Capitol
500 Woodlane Street, Suite 320
Little Rock, AR 72201
P: (501) 682-2902
E: dismang28@gmail.com

Senate Majority Leader

Sen. Jim Hendren (R)
Majority Leader
State Capitol
500 Woodlane Street, Suite 320
Little Rock, AR 72201
P: (501) 682-2902
E: jim.hendren@senate.ar.gov

Senate Minority Leader

Sen. Keith M. Ingram (D)
Minority Leader
State Capitol
500 Woodlane Street, Suite 320
Little Rock, AR 72201
P: (501) 682-2902
E: friendsforkeith@gmail.com

Secretary of the Senate

Ms. Ann Cornwell
Director & Secretary of the Senate
Room 320, State Capitol
Little Rock, AR 72201
P: (501) 682-5951
F: (501) 682-2917
E: ann.cornwell@senate.ar.gov

Members of the Senate

Bledsoe, Cecile (R, 3)
State Capitol
500 Woodlane Street, Suite 320
Little Rock, AR 72201
P: (501) 682-2902
E: cecile.bledsoe@senate.ar.gov

Burnett, David (D, 22)
State Capitol
500 Woodlane Street, Suite 320
Little Rock, AR 72201
P: (501) 682-2902
E: david.burnett@senate.ar.gov

Caldwell, Ronald (R, 23)
State Capitol
500 Woodlane Street, Suite 320
Little Rock, AR 72201
P: (501) 682-2902
E: ronald.caldwell@Senate.ar.gov

Cheatham, Eddie (D, 26)
State Capitol
500 Woodlane Street, Suite 320
Little Rock, AR 72201
P: (501) 682-2902
E: eddie.cheatham@senate.ar.gov

Chesterfield, Linda (D, 30)
State Capitol
500 Woodlane Street, Suite 320
Little Rock, AR 72201
P: (501) 682-2902
E: lchesterfield@comcast.net

Clark, Alan (R, 13)
State Capitol
500 Woodlane Street, Suite 320
Little Rock, AR 72201
P: (501) 682-2902
E: alan.clark@senate.ar.gov

Collins-Smith, Linda (R, 19)
State Capitol
500 Woodlane Street, Suite 320
Little Rock, AR 72201
P: (501) 682-2902
E: Linda.Collins-Smith@senate.ar.gov

Cooper, John (R, 21)
State Capitol
500 Woodlane Street, Suite 320
Little Rock, AR 77201
P: (501) 682-2902
E: john.cooper@senate.ar.gov

Dismang, Jonathan (R, 28)
State Capitol
500 Woodlane Street, Suite 320
Little Rock, AR 72201
P: (501) 682-2902
E: dismang28@gmail.com

Elliott, Joyce (D, 31)
State Capitol
500 Woodlane Street, Suite 320
Little Rock, AR 72201
P: (501) 682-2902
E: joyce.elliott@senate.ar.gov

English, Jane (R, 34)
State Capitol
500 Woodlane Street, Suite 320
Little Rock, AR 72201
P: (501) 682-2902
E: jane.english@senate.ar.gov

Files, Jake (R, 8)
State Capitol
500 Woodlane Street, Suite 320
Little Rock, AR 72201
P: (501) 682-2902
E: Jake.Files@Senate.ar.gov

Flippo, Scott (R, 17)*
State Capitol
500 Woodlane Street, Suite 320
Little Rock, AR 72201
P: (501) 682-2902
E: scott.flippo@senate.ar.gov

Flowers, Stephanie (D, 25)
State Capitol
500 Woodlane Street, Suite 320
Little Rock, AR 72201
P: (501) 682-2902
E: stephanie.flowers@senate.ar.gov

Hendren, Jim (R, 2)
State Capitol
500 Woodlane Street, Suite 320
Little Rock, AR 72201
P: (501) 682-2902
E: jim.hendren@senate.ar.gov

Arkansas

Hester, Bart (R, 1)
State Capitol
500 Woodlane Street, Suite 320
Little Rock, AR 72201
P: (501) 682-2902
E: bart.hester@senate.ar.gov

Hickey, Jimmy (R, 11)
State Capitol
500 Woodlane Street, Suite 320
Little Rock, AR 72201
P: (501) 682-2902
E: jimmy.hickey@senate.ar.gov

Hutchinson, Jeremy (R, 33)
State Capitol
500 Woodlane Street, Suite 320
Little Rock, AR 72201
P: (501) 682-2902
E: Jeremy.Hutchinson@senate.ar.gov

Ingram, Keith M. (D, 24)
State Capitol
500 Woodlane Street, Suite 320
Little Rock, AR 72201
P: (501) 682-2902
E: friendsforkeith@gmail.com

Irvin, Missy (R, 18)
State Capitol
500 Woodlane Street, Suite 320
Little Rock, AR 72201
P: (501) 682-2902
E: Missy.Irvin@senate.ar.gov

Johnson, Blake (R, 20)*
State Capitol
500 Woodlane Street, Suite 320
Little Rock, AR 72201
P: (501) 682-2902
E: blake.johnson@senate.ar.gov

Johnson, David (D, 32)
State Capitol
500 Woodlane Street, Suite 320
Little Rock, AR 72201
P: (501) 682-2902
E: david.johnson@senate.ar.gov

King, Bryan (R, 5)
State Capitol
500 Woodlane Street, Suite 320
Little Rock, AR 72201
P: (501) 682-2902
E: bryan.king@senate.ar.gov

Lindsey, Uvalde (D, 4)
State Capitol
500 Woodlane Street, Suite 320
Little Rock, AR 72201
P: (501) 682-2902
E: uvalde.lindsey@senate.ar.gov

Maloch, Bruce (D, 12)
State Capitol
500 Woodlane Street, Suite 320
Little Rock, AR 72201
P: (501) 682-2902
E: bruce.maloch@senate.ar.gov

Pierce, Bobby (D, 27)
State Capitol
500 Woodlane Street, Suite 320
Little Rock, AR 72201
P: (501) 682-2902
E: bobby.pierce@senate.ar.gov

Rapert, Jason (R, 35)
State Capitol
500 Woodlane Street, Suite 320
Little Rock, AR 72201
P: (501) 682-2902
E: jason.rapert@senate.ar.gov

Rice, Terry (R, 9)
State Capitol
500 Woodlane Street, Suite 320
Little Rock, AR 72201
P: (501) 682-2902
E: terry.rice@senate.ar.gov

Sample, Bill (R, 14)
State Capitol
500 Woodlane Street, Suite 320
Little Rock, AR 72201
P: (501) 682-2902
E: bill.sample@senate.ar.gov

Sanders, David (R, 15)
State Capitol
500 Woodlane Street, Suite 320
Little Rock, AR 72201
P: (501) 682-2902
E: davidjamessanders@gmail.com

Stubblefield, Gary (R, 6)
State Capitol
500 Woodlane Street, Suite 320
Little Rock, AR 72201
P: (501) 682-2902
E: gary.stubblefield@senate.ar.gov

Teague, Larry R. (D, 10)
State Capitol
500 Woodlane Street, Suite 320
Little Rock, AR 72201
P: (501) 682-2902
E: Larry.Teague@senate.ar.gov

Williams, Eddie Joe (R, 29)
State Capitol
500 Woodlane Street, Suite 320
Little Rock, AR 72201
P: (501) 682-2902
E: eddiejoe.williams@senate.ar.gov

Woods, Jon (R, 7)
State Capitol
500 Woodlane Street, Suite 320
Little Rock, AR 72201
P: (501) 682-2902
E: jon.woods@senate.ar.gov

House

Speaker of the House

Rep. Jeremy Gillam (R)
Speaker
State Capitol
500 Woodlane Street, Suite 350
Little Rock, AR 72201
P: (501) 682-6211
E: jeremy@growing45.com

Speaker Pro Tempore of the House

Rep. Jon Eubanks (R)
Speaker Pro Tempore
State Capitol
500 Woodlane Street, Suite 350
Little Rock, AR 72201
P: (501) 682-6211
E: Jon.Eubanks@arkansashouse.org

House Majority Leader

Rep. Ken Bragg (R)
Majority Leader
State Capitol
500 Woodlane Street, Suite 350
Little Rock, AR 72201
P: (501) 682-6211
E: kenbragg@windstream.net

House Minority Leader

Rep. Eddie L. Armstrong (D)
Minority Leader
State Capitol
500 Woodlane Street, Suite 350
Little Rock, AR 72201
P: (501) 682-6211
E: earmstrong4rep@gmail.com

Clerk of the House

Ms. Sherri Stacks
Chief Clerk of the House/Fiscal Officer
Room 350, State Capitol
Little Rock, AR 72201
P: (501) 682-7771
E: sherri.stacks@arkansashouse.org

Members of the House

Armstrong, Charles L. (D, 30)
State Capitol
500 Woodlane Street, Suite 350
Little Rock, AR 72201
P: (501) 682-6211
E: ffa191@sbcglobal.net

Armstrong, Eddie L. (D, 37)
State Capitol
500 Woodlane Street, Suite 350
Little Rock, AR 72201
P: (501) 682-6211
E: earmstrong4rep@gmail.com

Baine, John (D, 7)
State Capitol
500 Woodlane Street, Suite 350
Little Rock, AR 72201
P: (501) 682-6211
E: john.baine@arkansashouse.org

Ballinger, Bob (R, 97)
State Capitol
500 Woodlane Street, Suite 350
Little Rock, AR 72201
P: (501) 682-6211
E: bob@bobballinger.com

Baltz, Scott (D, 61)
State Capitol
500 Woodlane Street, Suite 350
Little Rock, AR 72201
P: (501) 682-6211
E: scottbaltz@yahoo.com

Beck, Rick (R, 65)*
State Capitol
500 Woodlane Street, Suite 350
Little Rock, AR 72201
P: (501) 682-6211
E: rick.beck
@arkansashouse.org

Bell, Nate (R, 20)
State Capitol
500 Woodlane Street, Suite 350
Little Rock, AR 72201
P: (501) 682-6211
E: nate.bell
@arkansashouse.org

Bennett, Camille (D, 14)*
State Capitol
500 Woodlane Street, Suite 350
Little Rock, AR 72201
P: (501) 682-6211
E: camille.bennett
@arkansashouse.org

Bentley, Mary (R, 73)*
State Capitol
500 Woodlane Street, Suite 350
Little Rock, AR 72201
P: (501) 682-6211
E: mary.bentley
@arkansashouse.org

Blake, Charles (D, 36)*
State Capitol
500 Woodlane Street, Suite 350
Little Rock, AR 72201
P: (501) 682-6211
E: charles.blake
@arkansashouse.org

Boyd, Justin (R, 77)*
State Capitol
500 Woodlane Street, Suite 350
Little Rock, AR 72201
P: (501) 682-6211
E: justin.boyd.pharm.d
@gmail.com

Bragg, Ken (R, 15)
State Capitol
500 Woodlane Street, Suite 350
Little Rock, AR 72201
P: (501) 682-6211
E: kenbragg@windstream.net

Branscum, David (R, 83)
State Capitol
500 Woodlane Street, Suite 350
Little Rock, AR 72201
P: (501) 682-6211
E: davidbranscum
@hotmail.com

Broadaway, Mary (D, 57)
State Capitol
500 Woodlane Street, Suite 350
Little Rock, AR 72201
P: (501) 682-6211
E: mary
@marybroadawayarkansas.co

Brown, Karilyn (R, 41)*
State Capitol
500 Woodlane Street, Suite 350
Little Rock, AR 72201
P: (501) 682-6211
E: karilyn.brown
@arkansashouse.org

Collins, Charlie (R, 84)
State Capitol
500 Woodlane Street, Suite 350
Little Rock, AR 72201
P: (501) 682-6211
E: clcollins6@cox.net

Copeland, Donnie (R, 38)*
State Capitol
500 Woodlane Street, Suite 350
Little Rock, AR 72201
P: (501) 682-6211
E: donnie.copeland
@arkansashouse.org

Cozart, Bruce (R, 24)
State Capitol
500 Woodlane Street, Suite 350
Little Rock, AR 72201
P: (501) 682-6211
E: bruce.cozart
@arkansashouse.org

Davis, Andy (R, 31)
State Capitol
500 Woodlane Street, Suite 350
Little Rock, AR 72201
P: (501) 682-6211
E: andy.davis
@arkansashouse.org

Deffenbaugh, Gary (R, 79)
State Capitol
500 Woodlane Street, Suite 350
Little Rock, AR 72201
P: (501) 682-6211
E: Gary.Deffenbaugh
@arkansashouse.org

Della Rosa, Jana (R, 90)*
State Capitol
500 Woodlane Street, Suite 350
Little Rock, AR 72201
P: (501) 682-6211
E: dellarosa4arkansas
@gmail.com

Dotson, Jim (R, 93)
State Capitol
500 Woodlane Street, Suite 350
Little Rock, AR 72201
P: (501) 682-6211
E: jim.dotson
@arkansashouse.org

Douglas, Charlotte Vining (R, 75)
State Capitol
500 Woodlane Street, Suite 350
Little Rock, AR 72201
P: (501) 682-6211
E: charlotte.douglas
@arkansashouse.org

Douglas, Dan M. (R, 91)
State Capitol
500 Woodlane Street, Suite 350
Little Rock, AR 72201
P: (501) 682-6211
E: dan-douglas
@sbcglobal.net

Drown, Trevor (R, 68)*
State Capitol
500 Woodlane Street, Suite 350
Little Rock, AR 72201
P: (501) 682-6211
E: trevor.drown
@arkansashouse.org

Eads, Lance (R, 88)*
State Capitol
500 Woodlane Street, Suite 350
Little Rock, AR 72201
P: (501) 682-6211
E: lance.eads@gmail.com

Eaves, Les (R, 46)*
State Capitol
500 Woodlane Street, Suite 350
Little Rock, AR 72201
P: (501) 682-6211
E: les.eaves
@arkansashouse.org

Eubanks, Jon (R, 74)
State Capitol
500 Woodlane Street, Suite 350
Little Rock, AR 72201
P: (501) 682-6211
E: Jon.Eubanks
@arkansashouse.org

Farrer, Joe (R, 44)
State Capitol
500 Woodlane Street, Suite 350
Little Rock, AR 72201
P: (501) 682-6211
E: jfarrer@suddenlink.net

Ferguson, Deborah (D, 51)
State Capitol
500 Woodlane Street, Suite 350
Little Rock, AR 72201
P: (501) 682-6211
E: deborah.ferguson
@arkansashouse.org

Ferguson, Ken (D, 16)*
State Capitol
500 Woodlane Street, Suite 350
Little Rock, AR 72201
P: (501) 682-6211
E: kenneth.ferguson
@arkansashouse.org

Fielding, David (D, 5)
State Capitol
500 Woodlane Street, Suite 350
Little Rock, AR 72201
P: (501) 682-6211
E: david.fielding
@arkansashouse.org

Fite, Charlene (R, 80)
State Capitol
500 Woodlane Street, Suite 350
Little Rock, AR 72201
P: (501) 682-6211
E: charlenefiteforstaterep
@yahoo.com

Fite, Lanny (R, 23)*
State Capitol
500 Woodlane Street, Suite 350
Little Rock, AR 72201
P: (501) 682-6211
E: lanny.fite@att.net

Flowers, Vivian (D, 17)*
State Capitol
500 Woodlane Street, Suite 350
Little Rock, AR 72201
P: (501) 682-6211
E: vivian.flowers
@arkansashouse.org

Gates, J.P. Mickey (R, 22)*
State Capitol
500 Woodlane Street, Suite 350
Little Rock, AR 72201
P: (501) 682-6211
E: mickey@mickeygates.com

Gillam, Jeremy (R, 45)
State Capitol
500 Woodlane Street, Suite 350
Little Rock, AR 72201
P: (501) 682-6211
E: jeremy@growing45.com

Gonzales, Justin (R, 19)*
State Capitol
500 Woodlane Street, Suite 350
Little Rock, AR 72201
P: (501) 682-6211
E: justinrory@yahoo.com

Arkansas

Gossage, Bill (R, 82)
State Capitol
500 Woodlane Street, Suite 350
Little Rock, AR 72201
P: (501) 682-6211
E: bill@billgossage.com

Gray, Michael John (D, 47)*
State Capitol
500 Woodlane Street, Suite 350
Little Rock, AR 72201
P: (501) 682-6211
E: michael.gray
@arkansashouse.org

Gray, Michelle (R, 62)*
State Capitol
500 Woodlane Street, Suite 350
Little Rock, AR 72201
P: (501) 682-6211
E: michelle.gray
@arkansashouse.org

Hammer, Kim (R, 28)
State Capitol
500 Woodlane Street, Suite 350
Little Rock, AR 72201
P: (501) 682-6211
E: kimdhammer@yahoo.com

Harris, Justin (R, 81)
State Capitol
500 Woodlane Street, Suite 350
Little Rock, AR 72201
P: (501) 682-6211
E: Justin.Harris
@arkansashouse.org

Henderson, Kenneth (R, 71)*
State Capitol
500 Woodlane Street, Suite 350
Little Rock, AR 72201
P: (501) 682-6211
E: ken4arkansas@gmail.com

Hendren, Kim (R, 92)
State Capitol
500 Woodlane Street, Suite 350
Little Rock, AR 72736
P: (501) 682-2902
E: kim.hendren
@arkansashouse.org

Hickerson, Mary P. (R, 1)
State Capitol
500 Woodlane Street, Suite 350
Little Rock, AR 72201
P: (501) 682-6211
E: prissy.hickerson
@arkansashouse.org

Hillman, David (D, 13)
State Capitol
500 Woodlane Street, Suite 350
Little Rock, AR 72201
P: (501) 682-6211
E: dhillman@futura.net

Hodges, Grant (R, 96)*
State Capitol
500 Woodlane Street, Suite 350
Little Rock, AR 72201
P: (501) 682-6211
E: grant.hodges
@arkansashouse.org

Hodges, Monte (D, 55)
State Capitol
500 Woodlane Street, Suite 350
Little Rock, AR 72201
P: (501) 682-6211
E: monte.hodges
@arkansashouse.org

Holcomb, Mike (D, 10)
State Capitol
500 Woodlane Street, Suite 350
Little Rock, AR 72201
P: (501) 682-6211
E: mike.holcomb
@arkansashouse.org

House, Douglas (R, 40)
State Capitol
500 Woodlane Street, Suite 350
Little Rock, AR 72201
P: (501) 682-6211
E: housedouglas@gmail.com

Jean, Lane (R, 2)
State Capitol
500 Woodlane Street, Suite 350
Little Rock, AR 72201
P: (501) 682-6211
E: l_jean@sbcglobal.net

Jett, Joe (D, 56)
State Capitol
500 Woodlane Street, Suite 350
Little Rock, AR 72201
P: (501) 682-6211
E: joe.jett
@arkansashouse.org

Johnson, J.P. Bob (D, 42)*
State Capitol
500 Woodlane Street, Suite 350
Little Rock, AR 72201
P: (501) 682-6211
E: bobjohnsoncpa@gmail.com

Ladyman, Jack (R, 59)*
State Capitol
500 Woodlane Street, Suite 350
Little Rock, AR 72201
P: (501) 682-6211
E: jackladyman@gmail.com

Lampkin, Sheilla (D, 9)
State Capitol
500 Woodlane Street, Suite 350
Little Rock, AR 72201
P: (501) 682-6211
E: Sheilla.Lampkin
@arkansashouse.org

Leding, Greg (D, 86)
State Capitol
500 Woodlane Street, Suite 350
Little Rock, AR 72201
P: (501) 682-6211
E: greg@gregleding.com

Lemons, Tim (R, 43)*
State Capitol
500 Woodlane Street, Suite 350
Little Rock, AR 72201
P: (501) 682-6211
E: arstrep43@gmail.com

Linck, Kelley (R, 99)
State Capitol
500 Woodlane Street, Suite 350
Little Rock, AR 72201
P: (501) 682-6211
E: kelley@kelleylinck.com

Love, Fredrick J. (D, 29)
State Capitol
500 Woodlane Street, Suite 350
Little Rock, AR 72201
P: (501) 682-6211
E: fjlove@att.net

Lowery, Mark (R, 39)
State Capitol
500 Woodlane Street, Suite 350
Little Rock, AR 72201
P: (501) 682-6211
E: markdlowery@mac.com

Lundstrum, Robin (R, 87)*
State Capitol
500 Woodlane Street, Suite 350
Little Rock, AR 72201
P: (501) 682-6211
E: robin.lundstrum
@arkansashouse.org

Magie, Stephen (D, 72)
State Capitol
500 Woodlane Street, Suite 350
Little Rock, AR 72201
P: (501) 682-6211
E: stephen.magie
@arkansashouse.org

Mayberry, Julie (R, 27)*
State Capitol
500 Woodlane Street, Suite 350
Little Rock, AR 72201
P: (501) 682-6211
E: julie-mayberry@att.net

McElroy, Mark D. (D, 11)
State Capitol
500 Woodlane Street, Suite 350
Little Rock, AR 72201
P: (501) 682-6211
E: mdmcelroy1@yahoo.com

McGill, George B. (D, 78)
State Capitol
500 Woodlane Street, Suite 350
Little Rock, AR 72201
P: (501) 682-6211
E: georgemcgill
@sbcglobal.net

McNair, Ron (R, 98)*
State Capitol
500 Woodlane Street, Suite 350
Little Rock, AR 72201
P: (501) 682-6211
E: rmcnair1950@gmail.com

Meeks, David (R, 70)
State Capitol
500 Woodlane Street, Suite 350
Little Rock, AR 72201
P: (501) 682-6211
E: David.Meeks
@arkansashouse.org

Meeks, Stephen (R, 67)
State Capitol
500 Woodlane Street, Suite 350
Little Rock, AR 72201
P: (501) 682-6211
E: Stephen.Meeks
@arkansashouse.org

Miller, Josh (R, 66)
State Capitol
500 Woodlane Street, Suite 350
Little Rock, AR 72201
P: (501) 682-6211
E: josh.miller
@arkansashouse.org

Murdock, Reginald (D, 48)
State Capitol
500 Woodlane Street, Suite 350
Little Rock, AR 72201
P: (501) 682-6211
E: rkm_72360@yahoo.com

Neal, Micah S. (R, 89)
State Capitol
500 Woodlane Street, Suite 350
Little Rock, AR 72201
P: (501) 682-6211
E: micah.neal
@arkansashouse.org

Nicks Jr., Milton (D, 50)*
State Capitol
500 Woodlane Street, Suite 350
Little Rock, AR 72201
P: (501) 682-6211
E: milton.nicks
@arkansashouse.org

Overbey, Betty (D, 69)
State Capitol
500 Woodlane Street, Suite 350
Little Rock, AR 72201
P: (501) 682-6211
E: Betty.Overbey
@arkansashouse.org

Payton, John (R, 64)
State Capitol
500 Woodlane Street, Suite 350
Little Rock, AR 72201
P: (501) 682-6211
E: paytonforthepeople
@yahoo.com

Petty, Rebecca (R, 94)*
State Capitol
500 Woodlane Street, Suite 350
Little Rock, AR 72201
P: (501) 682-6211
E: pettyforar@yahoo.com

Pitsch, Mathew W. (R, 76)*
State Capitol
500 Woodlane Street, Suite 350
Little Rock, AR 72201
P: (501) 682-6211
E: mathew.pitsch@cox.net

Ratliff, James (D, 60)
State Capitol
500 Woodlane Street, Suite 350
Little Rock, AR 72201
P: (501) 682-6211
E: jamesratliff3468
@gmail.com

Richey, Chris (D, 12)
State Capitol
500 Woodlane Street, Suite 350
Little Rock, AR 72201
P: (501) 682-6211
E: chris.richey
@arkansashouse.org

Richmond, Marcus E. (R, 21)*
State Capitol
500 Woodlane Street, Suite 350
Little Rock, AR 72201
P: (501) 682-6211
E: marcus.richmond
@arkansashouse.org

Rushing, Laurie (R, 26)*
State Capitol
500 Woodlane Street, Suite 350
Little Rock, AR 72201
P: (501) 682-6211
E: laurie.rushing
@arkansashouse.org

Sabin, Warwick (D, 33)
State Capitol
500 Woodlane Street, Suite 350
Little Rock, AR 72201
P: (501) 682-6211
E: wsabin@wsabin.org

Scott, Sue (R, 95)
State Capitol
500 Woodlane Street, Suite 350
Little Rock, AR 72201
P: (501) 682-6211
E: grandmotherscott
@yahoo.com

Shepherd, Matthew (R, 6)
State Capitol
500 Woodlane Street, Suite 350
Little Rock, AR 72201
P: (501) 682-6211
E: matthew.shepherd
@arkansashouse.org

Smith, Brandt (R, 58)*
State Capitol
500 Woodlane Street, Suite 350
Little Rock, AR 72201
P: (501) 682-6211
E: brandt.smith
@arkansashouse.org

Sorvillo, Jim (R, 32)*
State Capitol
500 Woodlane Street, Suite 350
Little Rock, AR 72201
P: (501) 682-6211
E: sorvillo4house@gmail.com

Speaks, Nelda (R, 100)*
State Capitol
500 Woodlane Street, Suite 350
Little Rock, AR 72201
P: (501) 682-6211
E: nelda@neldaspeaks.com

Sturch, James (R, 63)*
State Capitol
500 Woodlane Street, Suite 350
Little Rock, AR 72201
P: (501) 682-6211
E: jmsturch@yahoo.com

Sullivan, Dan (R, 53)*
State Capitol
500 Woodlane Street, Suite 350
Little Rock, AR 72201
P: (501) 682-6211
E: dan.sullivan
@AR53@gmail.com

Talley, Brent (D, 3)
State Capitol
500 Woodlane Street, Suite 350
Little Rock, AR 72201
P: (501) 682-6211
E: brent.talley
@arkansashouse.org

Tosh, Dwight (R, 52)*
State Capitol
500 Woodlane Street, Suite 350
Little Rock, AR 72201
P: (501) 682-6211
E: dwight.tosh
@arkansashouse.org

Tucker, Clarke (D, 35)*
State Capitol
500 Woodlane Street, Suite 350
Little Rock, AR 72201
P: (501) 682-6211
E: clarke.tucker
@arkansashouse.org

Vaught, DeAnn (R, 4)*
State Capitol
500 Woodlane Street, Suite 350
Little Rock, AR 72201
P: (501) 682-6211
E: deann.vaught
@arkansashouse.org

Vines, John (D, 25)
State Capitol
500 Woodlane Street, Suite 350
Little Rock, AR 72201
P: (501) 682-6211
E: jtvines13@sbcglobal.net

Walker, John W. (D, 34)
State Capitol
500 Woodlane Street, Suite 350
Little Rock, AR 72201
P: (501) 682-6211
E: johnwalkeratty@aol.com

Wallace, Dave (R, 54)*
State Capitol
500 Woodlane Street, Suite 350
Little Rock, AR 72201
P: (501) 682-6211
E: dave.wallace
@arkansashouse.org

Wardlaw, Jeff (D, 8)
State Capitol
500 Woodlane Street, Suite 350
Little Rock, AR 72201
P: (501) 682-6211
E: jeff@jeffwardlaw.com

Whitaker, David (D, 85)
State Capitol
500 Woodlane Street, Suite 350
Little Rock, AR 72201
P: (501) 682-6211
E: david.whitaker
@arkansashouse.org

Womack, Richard (R, 18)
State Capitol
500 Woodlane Street, Suite 350
Little Rock, AR 72201
P: (501) 682-6211
E: richard
@richardwomack.com

Wright, Marshall (D, 49)
State Capitol
500 Woodlane Street, Suite 350
Little Rock, AR 72201
P: (501) 682-6211
E: marshall.wright
@arkansashouse.org

Congress

Senate

Boozman, John (R)
Cotton, Tom (R)

House

Crawford, Rick (R, 1)
Hill, French (R, 2)
Westerman, Bruce (R, 4)
Womack, Steve (R, 3)

California

Executive

Governor

Hon. Edmund G. Brown Jr. (D)
Governor
State Capitol
Sacramento, CA 95814
P: (916) 445-2841
F: (916) 558-3160

Lieutenant Governor

Hon. Gavin Newsom (D)
Lieutenant Governor
State Capitol, Room 1114
Sacramento, CA 95814
P: (916) 445-8994
F: (916) 323-4998

Attorney General

Hon. Kamala Harris (D)
Attorney General
1300 I Street, Sutie 1740
Sacramento, CA 95814
P: (916) 445-9555

Auditor

Hon. Elaine M. Howle (appointed)
State Auditor
621 Capitol Mall, Suite 1200
Sacramento, CA 95814
P: (916) 445-0255
F: (916) 323-0913
E: elaineh@bsa.ca.gov

Controller

Hon. Betty T. Yee (D)
State Controller
P.O. Box 942850
Sacramento, CA 94250
P: (916) 445-2636
F: (916) 322-4404

Secretary of State

Hon. Alex Padilla (D)
Secretary of State
1500 11th Street
Sacramento, CA 95814
P: (916) 653-7244
F: (916) 653-4795
E: secretarypadilla@sos.ca.gov

Superintendent of Public Instruction

Hon. Tom Torlakson (D)
State Superintendent of Public Instruction
1430 N Street
Sacramento, CA 95814
P: (916) 319-0800
F: (916) 319-0175
E: superintendent@cde.ca.gov

Board of Equalization

Hon. Diane L. Harkey (R)
Board Member
400 Capitol Mall, Suite 2580
P.O. Box 942849
Sacramento, CA 94249
P: (916) 319-2073
F: (916) 323-0546

Hon. Jerome Horton (D)
Board Member
450 N Street, MIC: 72
Sacramento, CA 95814
P: (916) 445-4154
F: (916) 323-2869

Hon. Fiona Ma (D)
Board Member
1215 K Street, Suite 1700
Sacramento, CA 94249
P: (916) 445-4081
F: (916) 319-2112

Hon. George Runner (R)
Board Member
500 Capitol Mall, Suite 1750
Sacramento, CA 95814
P: (916) 445-2181
F: (916) 327-4003
E: george.runner@boe.ca.gov

Treasurer

Hon. John Chiang (D)
State Treasurer
915 Capitol Mall, C-15
Sacramento, CA 95814
P: (916) 653-2995
F: (916) 653-3125

Judiciary

Supreme Court (MR)

Mr. Frank A. McGuire
Clerk of the Court
350 McAllister Street
San Francisco, CA 94102
P: (415) 865-7000

Hon. Tani Cantil-Sakauye
Chief Justice
Hon. Ming W. Chin
Hon. Carol A. Corrigan
Hon. Mariano-Florentino Cuéllar
Hon. Leondra R. Kruger
Hon. Goodwin Liu
Hon. Kathryn Mickle Werdegar

Legislative Senate

Senate President

Hon. Gavin Newsom (D)
Lieutenant Governor
State Capitol, Room 1114
Sacramento, CA 95814
P: (916) 445-8994
F: (916) 323-4998

President Pro Tempore of the Senate

Sen. Kevin De Leon (D)
President Pro Tem
State Capitol, Room 205
Sacramento, CA 95814
P: (916) 651-4024
F: (916) 651-4924
E: Senator.DeLeon@senate.ca.gov

Senate Majority Leader

Sen. William W. Monning (D)
Majority Floor Leader
State Capitol, Room 313
Sacramento, CA 95814
P: (916) 651-4017
F: (916) 651-4917
E: Senator.Monning@senate.ca.gov

Senate Minority Leader

Sen. Robert Huff (R)
Minority Leader
State Capitol, Room 305
Sacramento, CA 95814
P: (916) 651-4029
F: (916) 651-4929
E: Senator.Huff@senate.ca.gov

Secretary of the Senate

Mr. David Alvarez
Secretary of the Senate
State Capitol, Room 3044
Sacramento, CA 95814
P: (916) 651-4171
F: (916) 651-4181

Members of the Senate

Allen, Ben (D, 26)*
State Capitol, Room 2054
Sacramento, CA 95814
P: (916) 651-4026
F: (916) 651-4926
E: Senator.Allen@senate.ca.gov

Anderson, Joel (R, 38)
State Capitol, Room 5052
Sacramento, CA 95814
P: (916) 651-4038
F: (916) 651-4938
E: Senator.Anderson@senate.ca.gov

Bates, Patricia C. (R, 36)
State Capitol, Room 4048
Sacramento, CA 95814
P: (916) 651-4036
F: (916) 651-4936
E: Senator.Bates@senate.ca.gov

Beall Jr., Jim (D, 15)
State Capitol, Room 5066
Sacramento, CA 95814
P: (916) 651-4015
F: (916) 651-4915
E: Senator.Beall@senate.ca.gov

Berryhill, Tom (R, 8)
State Capitol, Room 3076
Sacramento, CA 95814
P: (916) 651-4008
F: (916) 651-4908
E: Senator.Berryhill@senate.ca.gov

Block, Marty (D, 39)
State Capitol, Room 4072
Sacramento, CA 95814
P: (916) 651-4039
F: (916) 651-4939
E: Senator.Block@senate.ca.gov

Cannella, Anthony (R, 12)
State Capitol, Room 5082
Sacramento, CA 95814
P: (916) 651-4012
F: (916) 651-4912
E: Senator.Cannella@senate.ca.gov

De Leon, Kevin (D, 24)
State Capitol, Room 205
Sacramento, CA 95814
P: (916) 651-4024
F: (916) 651-4924
E: Senator.DeLeon@senate.ca.gov

Fuller, Jean (R, 16)
State Capitol, Room 3063
Sacramento, CA 95814
P: (916) 651-4016
F: (916) 651-4916
E: Senator.Fuller
@senate.ca.gov

Gaines, Ted (R, 1)
State Capitol, Room 3070
Sacramento, CA 95814
P: (916) 651-4001
F: (916) 651-4901
E: senator.gaines
@senate.ca.gov

Galgiani, Cathleen (D, 5)
State Capitol, Room 2059
Sacramento, CA 95814
P: (916) 651-4005
F: (916) 651-4905
E: Senator.Galgiani
@senate.ca.gov

Hall III, Isadore (D, 35)
State Capitol, Room 4085
Sacramento, CA 95814
P: (916) 651-4035
F: (916) 651-4935
E: Senator.Hall
@senate.ca.gov

Hancock, Loni (D, 9)
State Capitol, Room 2082
Sacramento, CA 95814
P: (916) 651-4009
F: (916) 651-4909
E: Senator.Hancock
@senator.ca.gov

Hernandez, Edward P. (D, 22)
State Capitol, Room 2080
Sacramento, CA 95814
P: (916) 651-4022
F: (916) 651-4922
E: Senator.Hernandez
@senate.ca.gov

Hertzberg, Robert M. (D, 18)
State Capitol, Room 5035
Sacramento, CA 95814
P: (916) 651-4018
F: (916) 651-4918
E: Senator.Hertzberg
@senate.ca.gov

Hill, Jerry (D, 13)
State Capitol, Room 5064
Sacramento, CA 95814
P: (916) 651-4013
F: (916) 651-4913
E: Senator.Hill
@senate.ca.gov

Hueso, Ben (D, 40)
State Capitol, Room 4035
Sacramento, CA 95814
P: (916) 651-4040
F: (916) 651-4940
E: Senator.Hueso
@senate.ca.gov

Huff, Robert (R, 29)
State Capitol, Room 305
Sacramento, CA 95814
P: (916) 651-4029
F: (916) 651-4929
E: Senator.Huff
@senate.ca.gov

Jackson, Hannah-Beth (D, 19)
State Capitol, Room 2032
Sacramento, CA 95814
P: (916) 651-4019
F: (916) 651-4919
E: Senator.Jackson
@senate.ca.gov

Lara, Ricardo (D, 33)
State Capitol, Room 5050
Sacramento, CA 95814
P: (916) 651-4033
F: (916) 651-4933
E: Senator.Lara
@senate.ca.gov

Leno, Mark (D, 11)
State Capitol, Room 5100
Sacramento, CA 95814
P: (916) 651-4011
F: (916) 651-4911
E: Senator.Leno
@senate.ca.gov

Leyva, Connie M. (D, 20)*
State Capitol, Room 4061
Sacramento, CA 95814
P: (916) 651-4020
F: (916) 651-4920
E: Senator.Leyva
@senate.ca.gov

Liu, Carol (D, 25)
State Capitol, Room 5097
Sacramento, CA 95814
P: (916) 651-4025
F: (916) 651-4925
E: Senator.Liu
@senate.ca.gov

McGuire, Mike (D, 2)*
State Capitol, Room 5064
Sacramento, CA 95814
P: (916) 651-4002
F: (916) 651-4902

Mendoza, Tony (D, 32)
State Capitol, Room 5061
Sacramento, CA 95814
P: (916) 651-4032
F: (916) 651-4932

Mitchell, Holly J. (D, 30)
State Capitol, Room 5080
Sacramento, CA 95814
P: (916) 651-4030
F: (916) 651-4930
E: Senator.Mitchell
@senate.ca.gov

Monning, William W. (D, 17)
State Capitol, Room 313
Sacramento, CA 95814
P: (916) 651-4017
F: (916) 651-4917
E: Senator.Monning
@senate.ca.gov

Morrell, Mike (R, 23)
State Capitol, Room 3056
Sacramento, CA 95814
P: (916) 651-4023
F: (916) 651-4923
E: Senator.Morrell
@senate.ca.gov

Nguyen, Janet (R, 34)*
State Capitol, Room 3048
Sacramento, CA 95814
P: (916) 651-4034
F: (916) 651-4934

Nielsen, Jim (R, 4)
State Capitol, Room 2068
Sacramento, CA 95814
P: (916) 651-4004
F: (916) 651-4904
E: Senator.Nielsen
@senate.ca.gov

Pan, Richard (D, 6)
State Capitol, Room 4070
Sacramento, CA 95814
P: (916) 651-4006
F: (916) 651-4906
E: Senator.Pan
@senate.ca.gov

Pavley, Fran (D, 27)
State Capitol, Room 5108
Sacramento, CA 95814
P: (916) 651-4027
F: (916) 651-4927
E: Senator.Pavley
@senate.ca.gov

Roth, Richard (D, 31)
State Capitol, Room 4034
Sacramento, CA 95814
P: (916) 651-4031
F: (916) 651-4931
E: Senator.Roth
@senate.ca.gov

Stone, Jeff (R, 28)*
State Capitol, Room 4062
Sacramento, CA 95814
P: (916) 651-4028
F: (916) 651-4928

Vidak, Andy (R, 14)
State Capitol, Room 3082
Sacramento, CA 95814
P: (916) 651-4014
F: (916) 651-4914
E: Senator.Vidak
@senate.ca.gov

Wieckowski, Bob (D, 10)
State Capitol, Room 3086
Sacramento, CA 95814
P: (916) 651-4010
F: (916) 651-4910
E: Senator.Wieckowski
@senate.ca.gov

Wolk, Lois (D, 3)
State Capitol, Room 5114
Sacramento, CA 95814
P: (916) 651-4003
F: (916) 651-4903
E: senator.wolk
@senate.ca.gov

Assembly

Speaker of the Assembly

Asmblywmn. Toni Atkins (D)
House Speaker
State Capitol, Room 219
P.O. Box 942849
Sacramento, CA 94249
P: (916) 319-2078
F: (916) 319-2178
E: Assemblymember.Atkins
@assembly.ca.gov

Speaker Pro Tempore of the Assembly

Asmblymn. Kevin Mullin (D)
Speaker Pro Tempore
State Capitol, Room 3160
P.O. Box 942849
Sacramento, CA 94249
P: (916) 319-2022
F: (916) 319-2122
E: Assemblymember.Mullin
@assembly.ca.gov

Assembly Majority Leader

Asmblymn. Kevin Mullin (D)
Speaker Pro Tempore
State Capitol, Room 3160
P.O. Box 942849
Sacramento, CA 94249
P: (916) 319-2022
F: (916) 319-2122
E: Assemblymember.Mullin
@assembly.ca.gov

California

Assembly Minority Leader

Asmblywmn. Kristin Olsen (R)
Minority Leader
State Capitol, Room 3104
P.O. Box 942849
Sacramento, CA 94249
P: (916) 319-2012
F: (916) 319-2112
E: Assemblymember.Olsen@asm.ca.gov

Clerk of the Assembly

Mr. E. Dotson Wilson
Chief Clerk of the Assembly
State Capitol, Room 3196
Sacramento, CA 95814
P: (916) 319-2856
E: Dotson.Wilson@asm.ca.gov

Members of the Assembly

Achadjian, Katcho (R, 35)
State Capitol, Room 4098
P.O. Box 942849
Sacramento, CA 94249
P: (916) 319-2035
F: (916) 319-2135
E: Assemblymember.Achadjian@assembly.ca.gov

Alejo, Luis A. (D, 30)
State Capitol, Room 2117
P.O. Box 942849
Sacramento, CA 94249
P: (916) 319-2030
F: (916) 319-2130
E: Assemblymember.Alejo@assembly.ca.gov

Allen, Travis (R, 72)
State Capitol, Room 4015
P.O. Box 942849
Sacramento, CA 94249
P: (916) 319-2072
F: (916) 319-2172
E: Assemblymember.Allen@assembly.ca.gov

Atkins, Toni (D, 78)
State Capitol, Room 219
P.O. Box 942849
Sacramento, CA 94249
P: (916) 319-2078
F: (916) 319-2178
E: Assemblymember.Atkins@assembly.ca.gov

Baker, Catharine (R, 16)*
State Capitol, Room 4153
P.O. Box 942849
Sacramento, CA 94249
P: (916) 319-2016
F: (916) 319-2116
E: Assemblymember.Baker@asm.ca.gov

Bigelow, Franklin E. (R, 5)
State Capitol, Room 6027
P.O. Box 942849
Sacramento, CA 94249
P: (916) 319-2005
F: (916) 319-2105
E: Assemblymember.Bigelow@assembly.ca.gov

Bloom, Richard (D, 50)
State Capitol, Room 2003
P.O. Box 942849
Sacramento, CA 94249
P: (916) 319-2050
F: (916) 319-2150
E: Assemblymember.Bloom@assembly.ca.gov

Bonilla, Susan (D, 14)
State Capitol, Room 4140
P.O. Box 942849
Sacramento, CA 94249
P: (916) 319-2014
F: (916) 319-2114
E: Assemblymember.Bonilla@assembly.ca.gov

Bonta, Rob (D, 18)
State Capitol, Room 6005
P.O. Box 942849
Sacramento, CA 94249
P: (916) 319-2018
F: (916) 319-2118
E: Assemblymember.Bonta@assembly.ca.gov

Brough, William (R, 73)*
State Capitol, Room 2174
P.O. Box 942849
Sacramento, CA 94249
P: (916) 319-2073
F: (916) 319-2173
E: Assemblymember.Brough@asm.ca.gov

Brown, Cheryl (D, 47)
State Capitol, Room 2136
P.O. Box 942849
Sacramento, CA 94249
P: (916) 319-2047
F: (916) 319-2147
E: Assemblymember.Brown@assembly.ca.gov

Burke, Autumn (D, 62)*
State Capitol, Room 5144
P.O. Box 942849
Sacramento, CA 94249
P: (916) 319-2062
F: (916) 319-2162
E: Assemblymember.Burke@asm.ca.gov

Calderon, Ian C. (D, 57)
State Capitol, Room 2148
P.O. Box 942849
Sacramento, CA 94249
P: (916) 319-2057
F: (916) 319-2157
E: Assemblymember.Calderon@assembly.ca.gov

Campos, Nora (D, 27)
State Capitol, Room 4016
P.O. Box 942849
Sacramento, CA 94249
P: (916) 319-2027
F: (916) 319-2127
E: Assemblymember.Campos@assembly.ca.gov

Chang, Ling-ling (R, 55)*
State Capitol, Room 2149
P.O. Box 942849
Sacramento, CA 94249
P: (916) 319-2055
F: (916) 319-2155

Chau, Ed (D, 49)
State Capitol, Room 2179
P.O. Box 942849
Sacramento, CA 94249
P: (916) 319-2049
F: (916) 319-2149
E: Assemblymember.Chau@assembly.ca.gov

Chavez, Rocky I. (R, 76)
State Capitol, Room 2170
P.O. Box 942849
Sacramento, CA 94249
P: (916) 319-2076
F: (916) 319-2176
E: Assemblymember.Chavez@assembly.ca.gov

Chiu, David (D, 17)*
State Capitol, Room 2196
Sacramento, CA 94249
P: (916) 319-2017
F: (916) 319-2117
E: Assemblymember.Chiu@asm.ca.gov

Chu, Kansen (D, 25)*
State Capitol, Room 5175
Sacramento, CA 94249
P: (916) 319-2025
F: (916) 319-2125
E: Assemblymember.Chu@asm.ca.gov

Cooley, Ken (D, 8)
State Capitol, Room 3146
P.O. Box 942849
Sacramento, CA 94249
P: (916) 319-2008
F: (916) 319-2108
E: Assemblymember.Cooley@assembly.ca.gov

Cooper, Jim (D, 9)*
State Capitol, Room 5158
P.O. Box 942849
Sacramento, CA 94249
P: (916) 319-2009
F: (916) 319-2109
E: Assemblymember.Cooper@assembly.ca.gov

Dababneh, Matthew (D, 45)
State Capitol, Room 4112
P.O. Box 942849
Sacramento, CA 94249
P: (916) 319-2045
F: (916) 319-2145
E: Assemblymember.Dababneh@assembly.ca.gov

Dahle, Brian (R, 1)
State Capitol, Room 2158
P.O. Box 942849
Sacramento, CA 94249
P: (916) 319-2001
F: (916) 319-2101
E: Assemblymember.Dahle@assembly.ca.gov

Daly, Tom (D, 69)
State Capitol, Room 3126
P.O. Box 942849
Sacramento, CA 94249
P: (916) 319-2069
F: (916) 319-2169
E: Assemblymember.Daly@assembly.ca.gov

Dodd, Bill (D, 4)*
State Capitol, Room 2137
P.O. Box 942849
Sacramento, CA 94249
P: (916) 319-2004
F: (916) 319-2104
E: Assemblymember.Dodd@assembly.ca.gov

Eggman, Susan Talamantes (D, 13)
State Capitol, Room 3173
P.O. Box 942849
Sacramento, CA 94249
P: (916) 319-2013
F: (916) 319-2113
E: Assemblymember.Eggman@assembly.ca.gov

Frazier, Jim (D, 11)
State Capitol, Room 3091
P.O. Box 942849
Sacramento, CA 94249
P: (916) 319-2011
F: (916) 319-2111
E: Assemblymember.Frazier@assembly.ca.gov

Gaines, Beth (R, 6)
State Capitol, Room 2130
P.O. Box 942849
Sacramento, CA 94249
P: (916) 319-2006
F: (916) 319-2106

Gallagher, James (R, 3)*
State Capitol, Room 5128
P.O. Box 942849
Sacramento, CA 94249
P: (916) 319-2003
F: (916) 319-2103
E: Assemblymember.Gallagher@assembly.ca.gov

Garcia, Cristina (D, 58)
State Capitol, Room 2013
P.O. Box 942849
Sacramento, CA 94249
P: (916) 319-2058
F: (916) 319-2158
E: Assemblymember.Garcia@assembly.ca.gov

Garcia, Eduardo (D, 56)*
State Capitol, Room 4162
P.O. Box 942849
Sacramento, CA 94249
P: (916) 319-2056
F: (916) 319-2156

Gatto, Mike (D, 43)
State Capitol, Room 3152
P.O. Box 942849
Sacramento, CA 94249
P: (916) 319-2043
F: (916) 319-2143
E: Assemblymember.Gatto@assembly.ca.gov

Gipson, Mike (D, 64)*
State Capitol, Room 4164
P.O. Box 942849
Sacramento, CA 94249
P: (916) 319-2064
F: (916) 319-2164
E: Assemblymember.Gipson@assembly.ca.gov

Gomez, Jimmy (D, 51)
State Capitol, Room 2114
P.O. Box 942849
Sacramento, CA 94249
P: (916) 319-2051
F: (916) 319-2151
E: Assemblymember.Gomez@assembly.ca.gov

Gonzalez, Lorena (D, 80)
State Capitol, Room 6012
P.O. Box 942849
Sacramento, CA 94249
P: (916) 319-2080
F: (916) 319-2180
E: Assemblymember.Gonzalez@assembly.ca.gov

Gordon, Richard S. (D, 24)
State Capitol, Room 3013
P.O. Box 942849
Sacramento, CA 94249
P: (916) 319-2024
F: (916) 319-2124
E: Assemblymember.Gordon@assembly.ca.gov

Gray, Adam (D, 21)
State Capitol, Room 4117
P.O. Box 942849
Sacramento, CA 94249
P: (916) 319-2021
F: (916) 319-2121
E: Assemblymember.Gray@assembly.ca.gov

Grove, Shannon L. (R, 34)
State Capitol, Room 4208
P.O. Box 942849
Sacramento, CA 94249
P: (916) 319-2034
F: (916) 319-2134
E: Assemblymember.Grove@assembly.ca.gov

Hadley, David (R, 66)*
State Capitol, Room 4102
P.O. Box 942849
Sacramento, CA 94249
P: (916) 319-2066
F: (916) 319-2166
E: Assemblymember.Hadley@assembly.ca.gov

Harper, Matthew (R, 74)*
State Capitol, Room 2002
P.O. Box 942849
Sacramento, CA 94249
P: (916) 319-2074
F: (916) 319-2174
E: Assemblymember.Harper@assembly.ca.gov

Hernandez, Roger (D, 48)
State Capitol, Room 5016
P.O. Box 942849
Sacramento, CA 94249
P: (916) 319-2048
F: (916) 319-2148
E: Assemblymember.Hernandez@assembly.ca.gov

Holden, Chris (D, 41)
State Capitol, Room 319
P.O. Box 242849
Sacramento, CA 94249
P: (916) 319-2041
F: (916) 319-2141
E: Assemblymember.Holden@assembly.ca.gov

Irwin, Jacqui (D, 44)*
State Capitol, Room 6011
P.O. Box 942849
Sacramento, CA 94249
P: (916) 319-2044
F: (916) 319-2144
E: Assemblymember.Irwin@assembly.ca.gov

Jones, Brian W. (R, 71)
State Capitol, Room 3141
P.O. Box 942849
Sacramento, CA 94249
P: (916) 319-2071
F: (916) 319-2171
E: Assemblymember.Jones@assembly.ca.gov

Jones-Sawyer Sr., Reginald B. (D, 59)
State Capitol, Room 4126
P.O. Box 942849
Sacramento, CA 94249
P: (916) 319-2059
F: (916) 319-2159
E: Assemblymember.Jones-Sawyer@assembly.ca.gov

Kim, Young O. (R, 65)*
State Capitol, Room 4177
P.O. Box 942849
Sacramento, CA 94249
P: (916) 319-2065
F: (916) 319-2165
E: Assemblymember.Kim@assembly.ca.gov

Lackey, Tom (R, 36)*
State Capitol, Room 4009
P.O. Box 942849
Sacramento, CA 94249
P: (916) 319-2036
F: (916) 319-2136
E: Assemblymember.Lackey@assembly.ca.gov

Levine, Marc (D, 10)
State Capitol, Room 2141
P.O. Box 942849
Sacramento, CA 94249
P: (916) 319-2010
F: (916) 319-2110
E: Assemblymember.Levine@assembly.ca.gov

Linder, Eric (R, 60)
State Capitol, Room 2016
P.O. Box 942849
Sacramento, CA 94249
P: (916) 319-2060
F: (916) 319-2160
E: Assemblymember.Linder@assembly.ca.gov

Lopez, Patty (D, 39)*
State Capitol, Room 5160
P.O. Box 942849
Sacramento, CA 94249
P: (916) 319-2039
F: (916) 319-2139
E: Assemblymember.Lopez@assembly.ca.gov

Low, Evan (D, 28)*
State Capitol, Room 2175
P.O. Box 942849
Sacramento, CA 94249
P: (916) 319-2028
F: (916) 319-2128
E: Assemblymember.Low@assembly.ca.gov

Maienschein, Brian (R, 77)
State Capitol, Room 4139
P.O. Box 942849
Sacramento, CA 94249
P: (916) 317-2077
F: (916) 317-2177
E: Assemblymember.Maienschein@assembly.ca.gov

Mathis, Devon (R, 26)*
State Capitol, Room 5126
Sacramento, CA 94249
P: (916) 319-2026
F: (916) 319-2126
E: Assemblymember.Mathis@assembly.ca.gov

Mayes, Chad (R, 42)*
State Capitol, Room 4144
P.O. Box 942849
Sacramento, CA 94249
P: (916) 319-2042
F: (916) 319-2142
E: Assemblymember.Mayes@assembly.ca.gov

McCarty, Kevin (D, 7)*
State Capitol, Room 2160
P.O. Box 942849
Sacramento, CA 94249
P: (916) 319-2007
F: (916) 319-2107
E: Assemblymember.McCarty@assembly.ca.gov

California

Medina, Jose (D, 61)
State Capitol, Room 5135
P.O. Box 942849
Sacramento, CA 94249
P: (916) 319-2061
F: (916) 319-2161
E: Assemblymember.Medina@assembly.ca.gov

Melendez, Melissa A. (R, 67)
State Capitol, Room 6031
P.O. Box 942849
Sacramento, CA 94249
P: (916) 319-2067
F: (916) 319-2167
E: Assemblymember.Melendez@assembly.ca.gov

Mullin, Kevin (D, 22)
State Capitol, Room 3160
P.O. Box 942849
Sacramento, CA 94249
P: (916) 319-2022
F: (916) 319-2122
E: Assemblymember.Mullin@assembly.ca.gov

Nazarian, Adrin (D, 46)
State Capitol, Room 4146
P.O. Box 942849
Sacramento, CA 94249
P: (916) 319-2046
F: (916) 319-2146
E: Assemblymember.Nazarian@assembly.ca.gov

Obernolte, Jay (R, 33)*
State Capitol, Room 4116
P.O. Box 942849
Sacramento, CA 94249
P: (916) 319-2033
F: (916) 319-2133
E: Assemblymember.Obernolte@assembly.ca.gov

O'Donnell, Patrick (D, 70)*
State Capitol, Room 4166
P.O. Box 942849
Sacramento, CA 94249
P: (916) 319-2070
F: (916) 319-2170
E: Assemblymember.O'Donnell@assembly.ca.gov

Olsen, Kristin (R, 12)
State Capitol, Room 3104
P.O. Box 942849
Sacramento, CA 94249
P: (916) 319-2012
F: (916) 319-2112
E: Assemblymember.Olsen@asm.ca.gov

Patterson, Jim (R, 23)
State Capitol, Room 3132
P.O. Box 942849
Sacramento, CA 94249
P: (916) 319-2023
F: (916) 319-2123
E: Assemblyman.Patterson@assembly.ca.gov

Perea, Henry T. (D, 31)
State Capitol, Room 3120
P.O. Box 942849
Sacramento, CA 94249
P: (916) 319-2031
F: (916) 319-2131
E: Assemblymember.Perea@assembly.ca.gov

Quirk, Bill (D, 20)
State Capitol, Room 2163
P.O. Box 942849
Sacramento, CA 94249
P: (916) 319-2020
F: (916) 319-2120
E: Assemblymember.Quirk@assembly.ca.gov

Rendon, Anthony (D, 63)
State Capitol, Room 5136
P.O. Box 942849
Sacramento, CA 94249
P: (916) 319-2063
F: (916) 319-2163
E: Assemblymember.Rendon@assembly.ca.gov

Ridley-Thomas, Sebastian (D, 54)
State Capitol, Room 2176
P.O. Box 942849
Sacramento, CA 94249
P: (916) 319-2054
F: (916) 319-2154
E: Assemblymember.Ridley-Thomas@assembly.ca.gov

Rodriguez, Freddie (D, 52)
State Capitol, Room 6025
P.O. Box 942849
Sacramento, CA 94249
P: (916) 319-2052
F: (916) 319-2152
E: Assemblymember.Rodriguez@assembly.ca.gov

Salas Jr., Rudy (D, 32)
State Capitol, Room 2188
P.O. Box 942849
Sacramento, CA 94249
P: (916) 319-2032
F: (916) 319-2132
E: Assemblymember.Salas@assembly.ca.gov

Santiago, Miguel (D, 53)*
State Capitol, Room 5119
P.O. Box 942849
Sacramento, CA 94249
P: (916) 319-2053
F: (916) 319-2153
E: Assemblymember.Santiago@assembly.ca.gov

Steinorth, Marc (R, 40)*
State Capitol, Room 2111
P.O. Box 942849
Sacramento, CA 94249
P: (916) 319-2040
F: (916) 319-2140
E: Assemblymember.Steinorth@assembly.ca.gov

Stone, Mark (D, 29)
State Capitol, Room 5155
P.O. Box 942849
Sacramento, CA 94249
P: (916) 319-2029
F: (916) 319-2129
E: Assemblymember.Stone@assembly.ca.gov

Thurmond, Tony (D, 15)*
State Capitol, Room 5150
P.O. Box 942849
Sacramento, CA 94249
P: (916) 319-2015
F: (916) 319-2115
E: Assemblymember.Thurmond@assembly.ca.gov

Ting, Philip Y. (D, 19)
State Capitol, Room 3123
P.O. Box 942849
Sacramento, CA 94249
P: (916) 319-2019
F: (916) 319-2119
E: Assemblymember.Ting@assembly.ca.gov

Wagner, Donald P. (R, 68)
State Capitol, Room 3098
P.O. Box 942849
Sacramento, CA 94249
P: (916) 319-2068
F: (916) 319-2168
E: Assemblymember.Wagner@assembly.ca.gov

Waldron, Marie (R, 75)
State Capitol, Room 5128
P.O. Box 942849
Sacramento, CA 94249
P: (916) 319-2075
F: (916) 319-2175
E: Assemblymember.Waldron@assembly.ca.gov

Weber, Shirley N. (D, 79)
State Capitol, Room 6026
P.O. Box 942849
Sacramento, CA 94249
P: (916) 319-2079
F: (916) 319-2179
E: Assemblymember.Weber@assembly.ca.gov

Wilk, Scott (R, 38)
State Capitol, Room 4158
P.O. Box 942849
Sacramento, CA 94249
P: (916) 319-2038
F: (916) 319-2138
E: Assemblymember.Wilk@assembly.ca.gov

Williams, Das (D, 37)
State Capitol, Room 4005
P.O. Box 942849
Sacramento, CA 94249
P: (916) 319-2037
F: (916) 319-2137
E: Assemblymember.Williams@assembly.ca.gov

Wood, Jim (D, 2)*
State Capitol, Room 5164
P.O. Box 942849
Sacramento, CA 94249
P: (916) 319-2002
F: (916) 319-2102
E: Assemblymember.Wood@assembly.ca.gov

Congress

Senate

Boxer, Barbara (D)
Feinstein, Dianne (D)

House

Aguilar, Pete (D, 31)
Bass, Karen (D, 37)
Becerra, Xavier (D, 34)
Bera, Ami (D, 7)
Brownley, Julia (D, 26)
Calvert, Ken (R, 42)
Capps, Lois (D, 24)
Cardenas, Tony (D, 29)
Chu, Judy (D, 27)
Cook, Paul (R, 8)
Costa, Jim (D, 16)
Davis, Susan A. (D, 53)
Denham, Jeff (R, 10)
DeSaulnier, Mark (D, 11)
Eshoo, Anna G. (D, 18)
Farr, Sam (D, 20)
Garamendi, John (D, 3)
Hahn, Janice (D, 44)
Honda, Michael M. (D, 17)
Huffman, Jared (D, 2)
Hunter, Duncan (R, 50)
Issa, Darrell E. (R, 49)
Knight, Steve (R, 25)
LaMalfa, Doug (R, 1)
Lee, Barbara (D, 13)
Lieu, Ted W. (D, 33)
Lofgren, Zoe (D, 19)
Lowenthal, Alan (D, 47)
Matsui, Doris O. (D, 6)
McCarthy, Kevin (R, 23)
McClintock, Tom (R, 4)
McNerney, Jerry (D, 9)
Napolitano, Grace F. (D, 32)
Nunes, Devin (R, 22)
Pelosi, Nancy (D, 12)
Peters, Scott (D, 52)
Rohrabacher, Dana (R, 48)
Roybal-Allard, Lucille (D, 40)
Royce, Edward R. (R, 39)
Ruiz, Raul (D, 36)
Sanchez, Linda (D, 38)
Sanchez, Loretta (D, 46)
Schiff, Adam B. (D, 28)
Sherman, Brad (D, 30)
Speier, Jackie (D, 14)
Swalwell, Eric (D, 15)
Takano, Mark (D, 41)
Thompson, Mike (D, 5)
Torres, Norma J. (D, 35)
Valadao, David G. (R, 21)
Vargas, Juan (D, 51)
Walters, Mimi (R, 45)
Waters, Maxine (D, 43)

Colorado

Executive

Governor

Hon. John Hickenlooper (D)
Governor
136 State Capitol
Denver, CO 80203
P: (303) 866-2471
F: (303) 866-2003

Lieutenant Governor

Hon. Joe Garcia (D)
Lieutenant Governor & Executive Director
130 State Capitol
Denver, CO 80203
P: (303) 866-2087
F: (303) 866-5469
E: josephagarcia@state.co.us

Attorney General

Hon. Cynthia Coffman (R)
Attorney General
Ralph L. Carr Colorado Judicial Center
1300 Broadway, 10th Floor
Denver, CO 80203
P: (720) 508-6000
F: (720) 508-6030
E: attorney.general@state.co.us

Auditor

Hon. Diane E. Ray
(appointed by the Legislature)
State Auditor
State Services Building
1525 Sherman Street, 7th Floor
Denver, CO 80203
P: (303) 869-2800
F: (303) 869-3060
E: diane.ray@state.co.us

Secretary of State

Hon. Wayne Williams (R)
Secretary of State
1700 Broadway, Suite 200
Denver, CO 80290
P: (303) 894-2200
F: (303) 869-4860
E: secretary@sos.staet.co.us

Treasurer

Hon. Walker Stapleton (R)
State Treasurer
200 East Colfax Avenue
State Capitol, Suite 140
Denver, CO 80203
P: (303) 866-2441
F: (303) 866-2123
E: treasurer.stapleton@state.co.us

Judiciary

Supreme Court (MR)

Mr. Christopher T. Ryan
Clerk of the Supreme Court
2 East 14th Avenue
Denver, CO 80203
P: (720) 625-5150
E: Christopher.Ryan@judicial.state.co.us

Hon. Nancy E. Rice
Chief Justice
Hon. Brian D. Boatright
Hon. Nathan B. Coats
Hon. Allison Eid
Hon. Gregory J. Hobbs Jr.
Hon. William W. Hood III
Hon. Monica M. Marquez

Legislative Senate

Senate President

Sen. Bill L. Cadman (R)
Senate President
200 East Colfax Avenue
Denver, CO 80203
P: (303) 866-4880
E: bill.cadman.senate@state.co.us

President Pro Tempore of the Senate

Sen. Ellen S. Roberts (R)
President Pro Tem
200 East Colfax Avenue
Denver, CO 80203
P: (303) 866-4884
E: ellen.roberts.senate@state.co.us

Senate Majority Leader

Sen. Mark Scheffel (R)
Majority Leader
200 East Colfax Avenue
Denver, CO 80203
P: (303) 866-4869
E: mark.scheffel.senate@state.co.us

Senate Minority Leader

Sen. Morgan Carroll (D)
Minority Leader
200 East Colfax Avenue
Denver, CO 80203
P: (303) 866-4879
E: morgan.carroll.senate@state.co.us

Secretary of the Senate

Ms. Cindi Markwell
Secretary of the Senate
State Capitol, Room 250
200 East Colfax Avenue
Denver, CO 80203
P: (303) 866-4838
F: (303) 866-4543
E: cindi.markwell@state.co.us

Members of the Senate

Aguilar M.D., Irene (D, 32)
200 East Colfax Avenue
Denver, CO 80203
P: (303) 866-4852
E: irene.aguilar.senate@state.co.us

Balmer, David G. (R, 27)
200 East Colfax Avenue
Denver, CO 80203
P: (303) 866-4883
E: david.balmer.senate@state.co.us

Baumgardner, Randy L. (R, 8)
200 East Colfax Avenue
Denver, CO 80203
P: (303) 866-5292
E: randy.baumgardner.senate@state.co.us

Cadman, Bill L. (R, 12)
200 East Colfax Avenue
Denver, CO 80203
P: (303) 866-4880
E: bill.cadman.senate@state.co.us

Carroll, Morgan (D, 29)
200 East Colfax Avenue
Denver, CO 80203
P: (303) 866-4879
E: morgan.carroll.senate@state.co.us

Cooke, John (R, 13)*
200 East Colfax Avenue
Denver, CO 80203
P: (303) 866-4451
E: john.cooke.senate@state.co.us

Crowder, Larry (R, 35)
200 East Colfax Avenue
Denver, CO 80203
P: (303) 866-4875
E: larry.crowder.senate@state.co.us

Donovan, Kerry (D, 5)*
200 East Colfax Avenue
Denver, CO 80203
P: (303) 866-4871
E: kerry.donovan.senate@state.co.us

Garcia, Leroy M. (D, 3)
200 East Colfax Avenue
Denver, CO 80203
P: (303) 866-4878
E: leroy.garcia.senate@state.co.us

Grantham, Kevin (R, 2)
200 East Colfax Avenue
Denver, CO 80203
P: (303) 866-4877
E: kevin.grantham.senate@state.co.us

Guzman, Lucia (D, 34)
200 East Colfax Avenue
Denver, CO 80203
P: (303) 866-4862
E: lucia.guzman.senate@state.co.us

Heath, Rollie (D, 18)
200 East Colfax Avenue
Denver, CO 80203
P: (303) 866-4872
E: rollie.heath.senate@state.co.us

Hill, Owen (R, 10)
200 East Colfax Avenue
Denver, CO 80203
P: (303) 866-2737
E: owen.hill.senate@state.co.us

Hodge, Mary (D, 25)
200 East Colfax Avenue
Denver, CO 80203
P: (303) 866-4855
E: mary.hodge.senate@state.co.us

Holbert, Chris (R, 30)
200 East Colfax Avenue
Denver, CO 80203
P: (303) 866-4881
E: chris.holbert.senate@state.co.us

Jahn, Cheri (D, 20)
200 East Colfax Avenue
Denver, CO 80203
P: (303) 866-4856
E: cheri.jahn.senate@state.co.us

Johnston, Michael (D, 33)
200 East Colfax Avenue
Denver, CO 80203
P: (303) 866-4864
E: mike.johnston.senate@state.co.us

Jones, Matt (D, 17)
200 East Colfax Avenue
Denver, CO 80203
P: (303) 866-5291
E: senatormattjones@gmail.com

Kefalas, John (D, 14)
200 East Colfax Avenue
Denver, CO 80203
P: (303) 866-4841
E: john.kefalas.senate@state.co.us

Kerr, Andy (D, 22)
200 East Colfax Avenue
Denver, CO 80203
P: (303) 866-4859
E: senatorandykerr@gmail.com

Lambert, Kent D. (R, 9)
200 East Colfax Avenue
Denver, CO 80203
P: (303) 866-4835
E: senatorlambert@comcast.net

Lundberg, Kevin (R, 15)
200 East Colfax Avenue
Denver, CO 80203
P: (303) 866-4853
E: kevin@kevinlundberg.com

Marble, Vicki (R, 23)
200 East Colfax Avenue
Denver, CO 80203
P: (303) 866-4876
E: vicki.marble.senate@state.co.us

Martinez Humenik, Beth (R, 24)*
200 East Colfax Avenue
Denver, CO 80203
P: (303) 866-4863
E: beth.martinezhumenik.senate@state.co.us

Merrifield, Michael (D, 11)
200 East Colfax Avenue
Denver, CO 80203
P: (303) 866-6364
E: michael.merrifield.senate@state.co.us

Neville, Tim (R, 16)
200 East Colfax Avenue
Denver, CO 80203
P: (303) 866-4873
E: tim.neville.senate@state.co.us

Newell, Linda (D, 26)
200 East Colfax Avenue
Denver, CO 80203
P: (303) 866-4846
E: linda.newell.senate@gmail.com

Roberts, Ellen S. (R, 6)
200 East Colfax Avenue
Denver, CO 80203
P: (303) 866-4884
E: ellen.roberts.senate@state.co.us

Scheffel, Mark (R, 4)
200 East Colfax Avenue
Denver, CO 80203
P: (303) 866-4869
E: mark.scheffel.senate@state.co.us

Scott, Ray (R, 7)
200 East Colfax Avenue
Denver, CO 80203
P: (303) 866-3077
E: ray.scott.senate@state.co.us

Sonnenberg, Jerry (R, 1)
200 East Colfax Avenue
Denver, CO 80203
P: (303) 866-6360
E: senatorsonnenberg@gmail.com

Steadman, Pat (D, 31)
200 East Colfax Avenue
Denver, CO 80203
P: (303) 866-4861
E: pat.steadman.senate@state.co.us

Todd, Nancy (D, 28)
200 East Colfax Avenue
Denver, CO 80203
P: (303) 866-3432
E: nancy.todd.senate@state.co.us

Ulibarri, Jessie (D, 21)
200 East Colfax Avenue
Denver, CO 80203
P: (303) 866-4857
E: jessie.ulibarri.senate@state.co.us

Woods, Laura J. (R, 19)*
200 East Colfax Avenue
Denver, CO 80203
P: (303) 866-4840
E: laura.woods.senate@state.co.us

House

Speaker of the House

Rep. Dickey Lee Hullinghorst (D)
Speaker of the House
200 East Colfax Avenue
Denver, CO 80203
P: (303) 866-2348
E: dl.hullinghorst.house@state.co.us

Speaker Pro Tempore of the House

Rep. Dan Pabon (D)
Speaker Pro Tem
200 East Colfax Avenue
Denver, CO 80203
P: (303) 866-2954
E: dan.pabon.house@state.co.us

House Majority Leader

Rep. Crisanta Duran (D)
Majority Leader
200 East Colfax Avenue
Denver, CO 80203
P: (303) 866-2925
E: crisanta.duran.house@state.co.us

House Minority Leader

Rep. Brian DelGrosso (R)
Minority Leader
200 East Colfax Avenue
Denver, CO 80203
P: (303) 866-5523
E: brian@briandelgrosso.com

Clerk of the House

Ms. Marilyn Eddins
Chief Clerk of the House
200 East Colfax Avenue, Room 246
Denver, CO 80203
P: (303) 866-2345
E: marilyn.eddins@state.co.us

Members of the House

Arndt, Jeni (D, 53)*
200 East Colfax Avenue
Denver, CO 80203
P: (303) 866-2917
E: jeni.arndt.house@state.co.us

Becker, Jon (R, 65)
200 East Colfax Avenue
Denver, CO 80203
P: (303) 866-3706
E: jon.becker.house@state.co.us

Becker, K.C. (D, 13)
200 East Colfax Avenue
Denver, CO 80203
P: (303) 866-2578
E: kcbecker.house@state.co.us

Brown, J. Paul (R, 59)
200 East Colfax Avenue
Denver, CO 80203
P: (303) 866-2914
E: jpaul.brown.house@state.co.us

Buck, Perry (R, 49)
200 East Colfax Avenue
Denver, CO 80203
P: (303) 866-2907
E: perrybuck49@gmail.com

Buckner, John W. (D, 40)
200 East Colfax Avenue
Denver, CO 80203
P: (303) 866-2944
E: john.buckner.house@state.co.us

Colorado

Carver, Terri (R, 20)*
200 East Colfax Avenue
Denver, CO 80203
P: (303) 866-2191
E: terri.carver.house@state.co.us

Conti, Kathleen (R, 38)
200 East Colfax Avenue
Denver, CO 80203
P: (303) 866-2953
E: kathleen.conti.house@state.co.us

Coram, Don (R, 58)
200 East Colfax Avenue
Denver, CO 80203
P: (303) 866-2955
E: don.coram.house@state.co.us

Court, Lois (D, 6)
200 East Colfax Avenue
Denver, CO 80203
P: (303) 866-2967
E: lois.court.house@state.co.us

Danielson, Jessie (D, 24)*
200 East Colfax Avenue
Denver, CO 80203
P: (303) 866-5522
E: jessie.danielson.house@state.co.us

DelGrosso, Brian (R, 51)
200 East Colfax Avenue
Denver, CO 80203
P: (303) 866-5523
E: brian@briandelgrosso.com

Dore, Timothy (R, 64)
200 East Colfax Avenue
Denver, CO 80203
P: (303) 866-2398
E: tim.dore.house@state.co.us

Duran, Crisanta (D, 5)
200 East Colfax Avenue
Denver, CO 80203
P: (303) 866-2925
E: crisanta.duran.house@state.co.us

Esgar, Daneya (D, 46)*
200 East Colfax Avenue
Denver, CO 80203
P: (303) 866-2968
E: daneya.esgar.house@state.co.us

Everett, Justin (R, 22)
200 East Colfax Avenue
Denver, CO 80203
P: (303) 866-2927
E: justin.everett.house@state.co.us

Fields, Rhonda (D, 42)
200 East Colfax Avenue
Denver, CO 80203
P: (303) 866-3911
E: rhonda.fields.house@state.co.us

Foote, Mike (D, 12)
200 East Colfax Avenue
Denver, CO 80203
P: (303) 866-2920
E: mike.foote.house@state.co.us

Garnett, Alec (D, 2)*
200 East Colfax Avenue
Denver, CO 80203
P: (303) 866-2911
E: alec.garnett.house@state.co.us

Ginal, Joann (D, 52)
200 East Colfax Avenue
Denver, CO 80203
P: (303) 866-4569
E: joann.ginal.house@state.co.us

Hamner, Millie (D, 61)
200 East Colfax Avenue
Denver, CO 80203
P: (303) 866-2952
E: rephammer@gmail.com

Hullinghorst, Dickey Lee (D, 10)
200 East Colfax Avenue
Denver, CO 80203
P: (303) 866-2348
E: dl.hullinghorst.house@state.co.us

Humphrey, Stephen (R, 48)
200 East Colfax Avenue
Denver, CO 80203
P: (303) 866-2943
E: rephumphrey48@yahoo.com

Joshi, Janak (R, 16)
200 East Colfax Avenue
Denver, CO 80203
P: (303) 866-2937
E: janak.joshi.house@state.co.us

Kagan, Daniel (D, 3)
200 East Colfax Avenue
Denver, CO 80203
P: (303) 866-2921
E: repkagan@gmail.com

Keyser, Jon (R, 25)*
200 East Colfax Avenue
Denver, CO 80203
P: (303) 866-2582
E: jon.keyser.house@state.co.us

Klingenschmitt, Gordon (R, 15)*
200 East Colfax Avenue
Denver, CO 80203
P: (303) 866-5525
E: klingenschmitt.house@state.co.us

Kraft-Tharp, Tracy (D, 29)
200 East Colfax Avenue
Denver, CO 80203
P: (303) 866-2950
E: reptracy29@gmail.com

Landgraf, Lois (R, 21)
200 East Colfax Avenue
Denver, CO 80203
P: (303) 866-2946
E: lois.landgraf.house@state.co.us

Lawrence, Polly (R, 39)
200 East Colfax Avenue
Denver, CO 80203
P: (303) 866-2935
E: polly.lawrence.house@state.co.us

Lebsock, Steve (D, 34)
200 East Colfax Avenue
Denver, CO 80203
P: (303) 866-2931
E: steve.lebsock.house@state.co.us

Lee, Pete (D, 18)
200 East Colfax Avenue
Denver, CO 80203
P: (303) 866-2932
E: pete.lee.house@state.co.us

Lontine, Susan (D, 1)*
200 East Colfax Avenue
Denver, CO 80203
P: (303) 866-2966
E: susan.lontine.house@state.co.us

Lundeen, Paul (R, 19)*
200 East Colfax Avenue
Denver, CO 80203
P: (303) 866-2924
E: paul.lundeen.house@state.co.us

McCann, Beth (D, 8)
200 East Colfax Avenue
Denver, CO 80203
P: (303) 866-2959
E: beth.mccann.house@state.co.us

Melton, Jovan (D, 41)
200 East Colfax Avenue
Denver, CO 80203
P: (303) 866-2919
E: jovan.melton.house@state.co.us

Mitsch Bush, Diane (D, 26)
200 East Colfax Avenue
Denver, CO 80203
P: (303) 866-2923
E: diane.mitschbush.house@state.co.us

Moreno, Dominick (D, 32)
200 East Colfax Avenue
Denver, CO 80203
P: (303) 866-2964
E: dominick.moreno.house@state.co.us

Navarro, Clarice (R, 47)
200 East Colfax Avenue
Denver, CO 80203
P: (303) 866-2905
E: clarice.navarro.house@state.co.us

Neville, Patrick (R, 45)*
200 East Colfax Avenue
Denver, CO 80203
P: (303) 866-2948
E: patrick.neville.house@state.co.us

Nordberg, Dan (R, 14)
200 East Colfax Avenue
Denver, CO 80203
P: (303) 866-2965
E: dan.nordberg.house@state.co.us

Pabon, Dan (D, 4)
200 East Colfax Avenue
Denver, CO 80203
P: (303) 866-2954
E: dan.pabon.house@state.co.us

Pettersen, Brittany (D, 28)
200 East Colfax Avenue
Denver, CO 80203
P: (303) 866-2939
E: brittany.pettersen.house@state.co.us

Primavera, Dianne (D, 33)
200 East Colfax Avenue
Denver, CO 80203
P: (303) 866-4667
E: dianne.primavera.house@state.co.us

Priola, Kevin (R, 56)
200 East Colfax Avenue
Denver, CO 80203
P: (303) 866-2912
E: kpriola@gmail.com

Rankin, Bob (R, 57)
200 East Colfax Avenue
Denver, CO 80203
P: (303) 866-2949
E: bob.rankin.house@state.co.us

Ransom, Kim (R, 44)*
200 East Colfax Avenue
Denver, CO 80203
P: (303) 866-2933
E: kim.ransom.house
@state.co.us

Rosenthal, Paul (D, 9)
200 East Colfax Avenue
Denver, CO 80203
P: (303) 866-2910
E: paulrosenthal5280
@gmail.com

Roupe, Kit (R, 17)*
200 East Colfax Avenue
Denver, CO 80203
P: (303) 866-3069
E: kit.roupe.house
@state.co.us

Ryden, Su (D, 36)
200 East Colfax Avenue
Denver, CO 80203
P: (303) 866-2942
E: su.ryden.house
@state.co.us

Saine, Lori (R, 63)
200 East Colfax Avenue
Denver, CO 80203
P: (303) 866-2906
E: lori.saine.house
@state.co.us

Salazar, Joseph A. (D, 31)
200 East Colfax Avenue
Denver, CO 80203
P: (303) 866-2918
E: joseph.salazar.house
@state.co.us

Sias, Lang (R, 27)*
200 East Colfax Avenue
Denver, CO 80203
P: (303) 866-2962
E: lang.sias.house
@state.co.us

Singer, Jonathan (D, 11)
200 East Colfax Avenue
Denver, CO 80203
P: (303) 866-2780
E: jonathan.singer.house
@state.co.us

Tate, Jack (R, 37)*
200 East Colfax Avenue
Denver, CO 80203
P: (303) 866-5510
E: jack.tate.house
@state.co.us

Thurlow, Dan (R, 55)*
200 East Colfax Avenue
Denver, CO 80203
P: (303) 866-3068
E: danthurlow55@gmail.com

Tyler, Max (D, 23)
200 East Colfax Avenue
Denver, CO 80203
P: (303) 866-2951
E: max@maxtyler.us

Van Winkle, Kevin (R, 43)*
200 East Colfax Avenue
Denver, CO 80203
P: (303) 866-2936
E: kevin.vanwinkle.house
@state.co.us

Vigil, Edward (D, 62)
200 East Colfax Avenue
Denver, CO 80203
P: (303) 866-2916
E: edvigil1@gmail.com

Willett, Yeulin (R, 54)*
200 East Colfax Avenue
Denver, CO 80203
P: (303) 866-2583
E: yeulin.willett.house
@state.co.us

Williams, Angela (D, 7)
200 East Colfax Avenue
Denver, CO 80203
P: (303) 866-2909
E: angela.williams.house
@state.co.us

Wilson, James D. (R, 60)
200 East Colfax Avenue
Denver, CO 80203
P: (303) 866-2747
E: james.wilson.house
@state.co.us

Windholz, JoAnn (R, 30)*
200 East Colfax Avenue
Denver, CO 80203
P: (303) 866-2945
E: joann.windholz.house
@state.co.us

Winter, Faith (D, 35)*
200 East Colfax Avenue
Denver, CO 80203
P: (303) 866-2843
E: faith.winter.house
@state.co.us

Young, Dave (D, 50)
200 East Colfax Avenue
Denver, CO 80203
P: (303) 866-2929
E: dave.young.house
@state.co.us

Congress

Senate

Bennet, Michael F. (D)
Gardner, Cory (R)

House

Buck, Ken (R, 4)
Coffman, Mike (R, 6)
DeGette, Diana (D, 1)
Lamborn, Doug (R, 5)
Perlmutter, Ed (D, 7)
Polis, Jared (D, 2)
Tipton, Scott R. (R, 3)

Connecticut

Executive

Governor

Hon. Dan Malloy (D)
Governor
210 Capitol Avenue
Hartford, CT 06106
P: (800) 406-1527
F: (860) 524-7395

Lieutenant Governor

Hon. Nancy Wyman (D)
Lieutenant Governor
State Capitol, Room 304
210 Capitol Avenue
Hartford, CT 06106
P: (860) 524-7384
F: (860) 524-7304

Attorney General

Hon. George C. Jepsen (D)
Attorney General
55 Elm Street
Hartford, CT 06106
P: (860) 808-5318

Auditor

Hon. John C. Geragosian
(appointed by the Legislature)
State Auditor
State Capitol
210 Capitol Avenue
Hartford, CT 06106
P: (860) 240-8651
F: (860) 240-8655
E: john.geragosian@cga.ct.gov

Hon. Robert M. Ward
(appointed by the Legislature)
State Auditor
State Capitol
210 Capitol Avenue
Hartford, CT 06106
P: (860) 240-8653
F: (860) 240-8655
E: robert.ward@cga.ct.gov

Secretary of State

Hon. Denise W. Merrill (D)
Secretary of State
30 Trinity Street
Hartford, CT 06106
P: (860) 509-6200
F: (860) 509-6209
E: denise.merrill@ct.gov

Treasurer

Hon. Denise L. Nappier (D)
State Treasurer
55 Elm Street
Hartford, CT 06106
P: (860) 702-3010
F: (860) 702-3043
E: denise.nappier@ct.gov

Judiciary

Supreme Court (LA)

Ms. Michele T. Angers
Chief Clerk
231 Capitol Avenue
Hartford, CT 06106
P: (860) 757-2200
F: (860) 757-2217

Hon. Chase T. Rogers
Chief Justice
Hon. Carmen E. Espinosa
Hon. Dennis G. Eveleigh
Hon. Andrew J. McDonald
Hon. Richard N. Palmer
Hon. Richard A. Robinson
Hon. Christine S. Vertefeuille
Hon. Peter T. Zarella

Legislative Senate

Senate President

Hon. Nancy Wyman (D)
Lieutenant Governor
State Capitol, Room 304
210 Capitol Avenue
Hartford, CT 06106
P: (860) 524-7384
F: (860) 524-7304

President Pro Tempore of the Senate

Sen. Martin M. Looney (D)
President Pro Tempore
Legislative Office Building
Room 3300
Hartford, CT 06106
P: (860) 240-8600
F: (860) 240-0208
E: Looney@senatedems.ct.gov

Senate Majority Leader

Sen. Bob Duff (D)
Majority Leader
Legislative Office Building
Room 3300
Hartford, CT 06106
P: (860) 240-8600
F: (860) 240-0208
E: Bob.Duff@cga.ct.gov

Senate Minority Leader

Sen. Leonard A. Fasano (R)
Minority Leader
Legislative Office Building,
Room 3400
300 Capitol Avenue
Hartford, CT 06106
P: (860) 240-8800
F: (860) 240-8306
E: Len.Fasano@cga.ct.gov

Secretary of the Senate

Mr. Garey E. Coleman
Clerk of the Senate
State Capitol, Room 305
Hartford, CT 06106
P: (860) 240-0500
E: Garey.Coleman@cga.ct.gov

Members of the Senate

Bartolomeo, Dante (D, 13)
State Capitol
Room 011
Hartford, CT 06106
P: (860) 240-8600
F: (860) 240-0208

Boucher, Toni (R, 26)
Legislative Office Building,
Room 3400
300 Capitol Avenue
Hartford, CT 06106
P: (860) 240-8800
F: (860) 240-8306
E: Toni.Boucher@cga.ct.gov

Bye, Beth (D, 5)
Legislative Office Building
Room 2700
Hartford, CT 06106
P: (860) 240-8600
F: (860) 240-0208
E: Bye@senatedems.ct.gov

Cassano, Steve (D, 4)
Legislative Office Building
Room 2200
Hartford, CT 06106
P: (860) 240-8600
F: (860) 240-0208

Chapin, Clark J. (R, 30)
Legislative Office Building,
Room 3400
300 Capitol Avenue
Hartford, CT 06106
P: (860) 240-8800
F: (860) 240-8306
E: Clark.Chapin@cga.ct.gov

Coleman, Eric D. (D, 2)
Legislative Office Building
Room 2500
Hartford, CT 06106
P: (860) 240-8600
F: (860) 240-0208
E: Eric.Coleman@cga.ct.gov

Crisco Jr., Joseph J. (D, 17)
Legislative Office Building
Room 2800
Hartford, CT 06106
P: (860) 240-8600
F: (860) 240-0208
E: Crisco@senatedems.ct.gov

Doyle, Paul R. (D, 9)
Legislative Office Building
Room 3900
Hartford, CT 06106
P: (860) 240-8600
F: (860) 240-0208
E: Doyle@senatedems.ct.gov

Duff, Bob (D, 25)
Legislative Office Building
Room 3300
Hartford, CT 06106
P: (860) 240-8600
F: (860) 240-0208
E: Bob.Duff@cga.ct.gov

Fasano, Leonard A. (R, 34)
Legislative Office Building,
Room 3400
300 Capitol Avenue
Hartford, CT 06106
P: (860) 240-8800
F: (860) 240-8306
E: Len.Fasano@cga.ct.gov

Flexer, Mae (D, 29)
Legislative Office Building
Room 1800
Hartford, CT 06106
P: (860) 240-8600
F: (860) 240-0208
E: Mae.Flexer@cga.ct.gov

Fonfara, John W. (D, 1)
Legislative Office Building
Room 3700
Hartford, CT 06106
P: (860) 240-8600
F: (860) 240-0208
E: Fonfara@senatedems.ct.gov

Formica, Paul (R, 20)*
Legislative Office Building,
Room 3400
300 Capitol Avenue
Hartford, CT 06106
P: (860) 240-8800
F: (860) 240-8306
E: paul.formica@cga.ct.gov

Frantz, L. Scott (R, 36)
Legislative Office Building,
Room 3400
300 Capitol Avenue
Hartford, CT 06106
P: (860) 240-8800
F: (860) 240-8306
E: Scott.Frantz@cga.ct.gov

Gerratana, Terry B. (D, 6)
Legislative Office Building
Room 3000
Hartford, CT 06106
P: (860) 240-8600
F: (860) 240-0208

Gomes, Edwin A. (D, 23)
Legislative Office Building
Room 3200
Hartford, CT 06106
P: (860) 240-8600
F: (860) 240-0208
E: gomes@senatedems.ct.gov

Guglielmo, Anthony (R, 35)
Legislative Office Building,
Room 3400
300 Capitol Avenue
Hartford, CT 06106
P: (860) 240-8800
F: (860) 240-8306
E: Anthony.Guglielmo@cga.ct.gov

Hartley, Joan V. (D, 15)
Legislative Office Building
Room 3100
Hartford, CT 06106
P: (860) 240-8600
F: (860) 240-0208
E: Hartley@senatedems.ct.gov

Hwang, Tony (R, 28)
Legislative Office Building,
Room 3400
300 Capitol Avenue
Hartford, CT 06106
P: (860) 240-8800
F: (860) 240-8306
E: Tony.Hwang@cga.ct.gov

Kane, Robert J. (R, 32)
Legislative Office Building,
Room 3400
300 Capitol Avenue
Hartford, CT 06106
P: (860) 240-8800
F: (860) 240-8306
E: Rob.Kane@cga.ct.gov

Kelly, Kevin C. (R, 21)
Legislative Office Building,
Room 3400
300 Capitol Avenue
Hartford, CT 06106
P: (860) 240-8800
F: (860) 240-8306
E: Kevin.Kelly@cga.ct.gov

Kennedy Jr., Ted (D, 12)*
Legislative Office Building
Room 3200
Hartford, CT 06106
P: (860) 240-8600
F: (860) 240-0208

Kissel, John A. (R, 7)
Legislative Office Building,
Room 3400
300 Capitol Avenue
Hartford, CT 06106
P: (860) 240-8800
F: (860) 240-8306
E: John.A.Kissel@cga.ct.gov

Larson, Timothy D. (D, 3)
Legislative Office Building
Room 3600
Hartford, CT 06106
P: (860) 240-8600
F: (860) 240-0208
E: Timothy.Larson@cga.ct.gov

Leone, Carlo (D, 27)
Legislative Office Building
Room 2400
Hartford, CT 06106
P: (860) 240-8600
F: (860) 240-0208
E: Carlo.Leone@cga.ct.gov

Linares, Art (R, 33)
Legislative Office Building,
Room 3400
300 Capitol Avenue
Hartford, CT 06106
P: (860) 240-8800
F: (860) 240-8306
E: Art.Linares@cga.ct.gov

Looney, Martin M. (D, 11)
Legislative Office Building
Room 3300
Hartford, CT 06106
P: (860) 240-8600
F: (860) 240-0208
E: Looney@senatedems.ct.gov

Markley, Joe (R, 16)
Legislative Office Building,
Room 3400
300 Capitol Avenue
Hartford, CT 06106
P: (860) 240-8800
F: (860) 240-8306
E: Joe.Markley@cga.ct.gov

Martin, Henri (R, 31)*
Legislative Office Building,
Room 3400
300 Capitol Avenue
Hartford, CT 06106
P: (860) 240-8800
F: (860) 240-8306
E: Henri.Martin@cga.ct.gov

Maynard, Andrew M. (D, 18)
Legislative Office Building
Room 2300
Hartford, CT 06106
P: (860) 240-8600
F: (860) 240-0208
E: Maynard@senatedems.ct.gov

McLachlan, Michael A. (R, 24)
Legislative Office Building,
Room 3400
300 Capitol Avenue
Hartford, CT 06106
P: (860) 240-8800
F: (860) 240-8306
E: Michael.McLachlan@cga.ct.gov

Moore, Marilyn (D, 22)*
Legislative Office Building
Room 2000
Hartford, CT 06106
P: (860) 240-8600
F: (860) 240-0208

Osten, Cathy (D, 19)
Legislative Office Building
Room 2100
Hartford, CT 06106
P: (860) 240-8600
F: (860) 240-0208

Slossberg, Gayle S. (D, 14)
Legislative Office Building
Room 3100
Hartford, CT 06106
P: (860) 240-8600
F: (860) 240-0208
E: Slossberg@senatedems.ct.gov

Winfield, Gary (D, 10)*
Legislative Office Building
Room 3800
Hartford, CT 06106
P: (860) 240-8600
F: (860) 240-0208
E: Winfield@senatedems.ct.gov

Witkos, Kevin (R, 8)
Legislative Office Building,
Room 3400
300 Capitol Avenue
Hartford, CT 06106
P: (860) 240-8800
F: (860) 240-8306
E: Kevin.Witkos@cga.ct.gov

House

Speaker of the House

Rep. J. Brendan Sharkey (D)
Speaker
Legislative Office Building
Room 4100
Hartford, CT 06106
P: (860) 240-8500
E: Brendan.Sharkey@cga.ct.gov

Speaker Pro Tempore of the House

Rep. Linda M. Gentile (D)
Deputy Speaker
Legislative Office Building
Room 2100
Hartford, CT 06106
P: (860) 240-8585
E: Linda.Gentile@cga.ct.gov

Rep. Bob Godfrey (D)
Deputy Speaker
Legislative Office Building
Room 4107
Hartford, CT 06106
P: (860) 240-8500
E: Bob.Godfrey@cga.ct.gov

Rep. Patricia Billie Miller (D)
Deputy Speaker
Legislative Office Building
Room 4046
Hartford, CT 06106
P: (860) 240-8585
E: Patricia.Miller@cga.ct.gov

Connecticut

Rep. Bruce V. Morris (D)
Deputy Speaker
Legislative Office Building
Room 4030
Hartford, CT 06106
P: (860) 240-8585
E: Bruce.Morris@cga.ct.gov

Rep. Linda A. Orange (D)
Deputy Speaker
Legislative Office Building
Room 4109
Hartford, CT 06106
P: (860) 240-8585
E: Linda.Orange@cga.ct.gov

Rep. Kevin Ryan (D)
Deputy Speaker
Legislative Office Building
Room 4012
Hartford, CT 06106
P: (860) 240-8585
E: Kevin.Ryan@cga.ct.gov

Rep. Peggy Sayers (D)
Deputy Speaker
Legislative Office Building
Room 4049
Hartford, CT 06106
P: (860) 240-8585
E: Peggy.Sayers@cga.ct.gov

House Majority Leader

Rep. Joe Aresimowicz (D)
Majority Leader
Legislative Office Building
Room 4110
Hartford, CT 06106
P: (860) 240-8489
E: Joe.Aresimowicz @cga.ct.gov

House Minority Leader

Rep. Themis Klarides (R)
Minority Leader
Legislative Office Building
Room 4200
Hartford, CT 06106
P: (860) 240-8700
F: (860) 240-0207
E: Themis.Klarides @housegop.ct.gov

Clerk of the House

Maj. Martin J. Dunleavy
Clerk of the House
State Capitol, Room 109
Hartford, CT 06106
P: (860) 240-0400

Members of the House

Abercrombie, Catherine F. (D, 83)
Legislative Office Building
Room 2002
Hartford, CT 06106
P: (860) 240-8500
E: Catherine.Abercrombie @cga.ct.gov

Ackert, Timothy (R, 8)
Legislative Office Building
Room 4200
Hartford, CT 06106
P: (860) 240-8700
F: (860) 240-0207
E: Tim.Ackert @housegop.ct.gov

Adams, Terry (D, 146)*
Legislative Office Building
Hartford, CT 06106
P: (860) 240-8585
E: Terry.B.Adams@cga.ct.gov

Adinolfi, Alfred (R, 103)
Legislative Office Building
Room 4200
Hartford, CT 06106
P: (860) 240-8700
F: (860) 240-0207
E: Al.Adinolfi @housegop.ct.gov

Alberts, Mike (R, 50)
Legislative Office Building
Room 4200
Hartford, CT 06106
P: (860) 240-8700
F: (860) 240-0207
E: Mike.Alberts @housegop.ct.gov

Albis, James M. (D, 99)
Legislative Office Building
Room 3201
Hartford, CT 06106
P: (860) 240-8585
E: James.Albis@cga.ct.gov

Alexander, David (D, 58)
Legislative Office Building
Room 4000
Hartford, CT 06106
P: (860) 240-8585
E: David.Alexander @cga.ct.gov

Altobello, Emil (D, 82)
Legislative Office Building
Room 4015
Hartford, CT 06106
P: (860) 240-8585
E: Emil.Altobello @cga.ct.gov

Aman, Bill (R, 14)
Legislative Office Building
Room 4200
Hartford, CT 06106
P: (860) 240-8700
F: (860) 240-0207
E: Bill.Aman@cga.ct.gov

Arce, Angel (D, 4)
Legislative Office Building
Room 4000
Hartford, CT 06106
P: (860) 240-8585
E: Angel.Arce@cga.ct.gov

Arconti, David (D, 109)
Legislative Office Building
Room 4000
Hartford, CT 06106
P: (860) 240-8466
E: David.Arconti@cga.ct.gov

Aresimowicz, Joe (D, 30)
Legislative Office Building
Room 4110
Hartford, CT 06106
P: (860) 240-8489
E: Joe.Aresimowicz @cga.ct.gov

Backer, Terry (D, 121)
Legislative Office Building
Room 2102
Hartford, CT 06106
P: (860) 240-8585
E: Terry.Backer@cga.ct.gov

Baker Jr., Andre (D, 124)*
Legislative Office Building
Room 5008
Hartford, CT 06106
P: (860) 240-8585
E: Andre.Baker@cga.ct.gov

Baram, David A. (D, 15)
Legislative Office Building
Room 5006
Hartford, CT 06106
P: (860) 240-8500
E: David.Baram@cga.ct.gov

Becker, Brian (D, 19)
Legislative Office Building
Room 4009
Hartford, CT 06106
P: (860) 240-8585
E: Brian.Becker@cga.ct.gov

Belsito, Sam (R, 53)
Legislative Office Building
Room 4200
Hartford, CT 06106
P: (860) 240-8700
F: (860) 240-0207
E: sam.belsito @housegop.ct.gov

Berger, Jeffrey J. (D, 73)
Legislative Office Building
Room 4109
Hartford, CT 06106
P: (860) 240-8500
E: Jeffrey.Berger @cga.ct.gov

Berthel, Eric (R, 68)*
Legislative Office Building
Room 4200
Hartford, CT 06106
P: (860) 240-8700
F: (860) 240-0207
E: Eric.Berthel @housegop.ct.gov

Betts, Whit (R, 78)
Legislative Office Building
Room 4200
Hartford, CT 06106
P: (860) 240-8700
F: (860) 240-0207
E: Whit.Betts @housegop.ct.gov

Bocchino, Mike (R, 150)*
Legislative Office Building
Room 4200
Hartford, CT 06106
P: (860) 240-8700
F: (860) 240-0207
E: Mike.Bocchino @housegop.ct.gov

Bolinsky, Mitch (R, 106)
Legislative Office Building
Room 4200
Hartford, CT 06106
P: (860) 240-8700
F: (860) 240-0207
E: Mitch.Bolinsky @housegop.ct.gov

Boukus, Elizabeth A. (D, 22)
Legislative Office Building
Room 4017
Hartford, CT 06106
P: (860) 240-8585
E: Betty.Boukus@cga.ct.gov

Brycki, Paul (D, 45)*
Legislative Office Building
Room 5008
Hartford, CT 06106
P: (860) 240-8585
E: Paul.Brycki@cga.ct.gov

Buck-Taylor, Cecilia (R, 67)
Legislative Office Building
Room 4200
Hartford, CT 06106
P: (860) 240-8700
F: (860) 240-0207
E: Cecilia.Buck-Taylor @housegop.ct.gov

Bumgardner, Andrè (R, 41)*
Legislative Office Building
Room 4200
Hartford, CT 06106
P: (860) 240-8700
F: (860) 240-0207
E: Aundre.Bumgardner@housegop.ct.gov

Butler, Larry B. (D, 72)
Legislative Office Building
Room 5001
Hartford, CT 06106
P: (860) 240-8585
E: Larry.Butler@cga.ct.gov

Byron, Gary (R, 27)*
Legislative Office Building
Room 4200
Hartford, CT 06106
P: (860) 240-8700
F: (860) 240-0207
E: Gary.Byron@housegop.ct.gov

Camillo, Fred (R, 151)
Legislative Office Building
Room 4200
Hartford, CT 06106
P: (860) 240-8700
F: (860) 240-0207
E: Fred.Camillo@housegop.ct.gov

Candelaria, Juan R. (D, 95)
Legislative Office Building
Room 1804
Hartford, CT 06106
P: (860) 240-8585
E: Juan.Candelaria@cga.ct.gov

Candelora, Vincent J. (R, 86)
Legislative Office Building
Room 4200
Hartford, CT 06106
P: (860) 240-8700
F: (860) 240-0207
E: Vincent.Candelora@housegop.ct.gov

Carney, Devin (R, 23)*
Legislative Office Building
Room 4200
Hartford, CT 06106
P: (860) 240-8700
F: (860) 240-0207
E: Devin.Carney@housegop.ct.gov

Carpino, Christie (R, 32)
Legislative Office Building
Room 4200
Hartford, CT 06106
P: (860) 240-8700
F: (860) 240-0207
E: Christie.Carpino@housegop.ct.gov

Carter, Dan (R, 2)
Legislative Office Building
Room 4200
Hartford, CT 06106
P: (860) 240-8700
F: (860) 240-0207
E: Dan.Carter@housegop.ct.gov

Case, Jay (R, 63)
Legislative Office Building
Room 4200
Hartford, CT 06106
P: (860) 240-8700
F: (860) 240-0207
E: Jay.Case@housegop.ct.gov

Conroy, Theresa W. (D, 105)
Legislative Office Building
Room 4000
Hartford, CT 06106
P: (860) 240-8585
E: Theresa.Conroy@cga.ct.gov

Cook, Michelle (D, 65)
Legislative Office Building
Room 4044
Hartford, CT 06106
P: (860) 240-8585
E: Michelle.Cook@cga.ct.gov

Cuevas, Victor (D, 75)
Legislative Office Building
Room 4000
Hartford, CT 06106
P: (860) 240-8585
E: Victor.Cuevas@cga.ct.gov

Currey, Jeffrey (D, 11)*
Legislative Office Building
Room 4010
Hartford, CT 06106
P: (860) 240-8585
E: Jeff.Currey@cga.ct.gov

D'Agostino, Mike (D, 91)
Legislative Office Building
Room 4000
Hartford, CT 06106
P: (860) 240-8585
E: Michael.DAgostino@cga.ct.gov

D'Amelio, Anthony J. (R, 71)
Legislative Office Building
Room 4200
Hartford, CT 06106
P: (860) 240-8700
F: (860) 240-0207
E: Anthony.DAmelio@housegop.ct.gov

Dargan, Stephen D. (D, 115)
Legislative Office Building
Room 3603
Hartford, CT 06106
P: (860) 240-8585
E: Stephen.Dargan@cga.ct.gov

Davis, Christopher (R, 57)
Legislative Office Building
Room 4200
Hartford, CT 06106
P: (860) 240-8700
F: (860) 240-0207
E: Christopher.Davis@housegop.ct.gov

Demicco, Mike (D, 21)
Legislative Office Building
Room 4000
Hartford, CT 06106
P: (860) 240-8585
E: Mike.Demicco@cga.ct.gov

Devlin, Laura (R, 134)*
Legislative Office Building
Room 4200
Hartford, CT 06106
P: (860) 240-8700
F: (860) 240-0207
E: Laura.Devlin@housegop.ct.gov

Dillon, Patricia A. (D, 92)
Legislative Office Building
Room 4019
Hartford, CT 06106
P: (860) 240-8585
E: Patricia.Dillon@cga.ct.gov

Dubitsky, Doug (R, 47)*
Legislative Office Building
Room 4200
Hartford, CT 06106
P: (860) 240-8700
F: (860) 240-0207
E: Doug.Dubitsky@housegop.ct.gov

Esposito Jr., Louis P. (D, 116)
Legislative Office Building
Room 4112
Hartford, CT 06106
P: (860) 240-8500
E: Lou.Esposito@cga.ct.gov

Ferraro, Charles (R, 117)*
Legislative Office Building
Room 4200
Hartford, CT 06106
P: (860) 240-8700
F: (860) 240-0207
E: Charles.Ferraro@housegop.ct.gov

Fleischmann, Andrew M. (D, 18)
Legislative Office Building
Room 3101
Hartford, CT 06106
P: (860) 240-0429
F: (860) 240-0206
E: Andrew.Fleischmann@cga.ct.gov

Floren, Livvy R. (R, 149)
Legislative Office Building
Room 4200
Hartford, CT 06106
P: (860) 240-8700
F: (860) 240-0207
E: Livvy.Floren@housegop.ct.gov

Fox, Daniel J. (D, 148)
Legislative Office Building
Room 5009
Hartford, CT 06106
P: (860) 240-8585
E: Dan.Fox@cga.ct.gov

France, Mike (R, 42)*
Legislative Office Building
Room 4200
Hartford, CT 06106
P: (860) 240-8700
F: (860) 240-0207
E: Mike.France@housegop.ct.gov

Frey, John H. (R, 111)
Legislative Office Building
Room 4200
Hartford, CT 06106
P: (860) 240-8700
F: (860) 240-0207
E: John.Frey@housegop.ct.gov

Fritz, Mary G. (D, 90)
Legislative Office Building
Room 4013
Hartford, CT 06106
P: (860) 240-8500
E: Mary.Fritz@cga.ct.gov

Genga, Henry (D, 10)
Legislative Office Building
Room 4030
Hartford, CT 06106
P: (860) 240-8585
E: Henry.Genga@cga.ct.gov

Connecticut

Gentile, Linda M. (D, 104)
Legislative Office Building
Room 2100
Hartford, CT 06106
P: (860) 240-8585
E: Linda.Gentile@cga.ct.gov

Giegler, Janice R. (R, 138)
Legislative Office Building
Room 4200
Hartford, CT 06106
P: (860) 240-8700
F: (860) 240-0207
E: Janice.Giegler@housegop.ct.gov

Godfrey, Bob (D, 110)
Legislative Office Building
Room 4107
Hartford, CT 06106
P: (860) 240-8500
E: Bob.Godfrey@cga.ct.gov

Gonzalez, Minnie (D, 3)
Legislative Office Building
Room 4031
Hartford, CT 06106
P: (860) 240-8585
E: Minnie.Gonzalez@cga.ct.gov

Guerrera, Antonio (D, 29)
Legislative Office Building
Room 2301
Hartford, CT 06106
P: (860) 240-8585
E: Tony.Guerrera@cga.ct.gov

Haddad, Gregg (D, 54)
Legislative Office Building
Room 4115
Hartford, CT 06106
P: (860) 240-8585
E: Gregory.Haddad@cga.ct.gov

Hampton, John (D, 16)
Legislative Office Building
Room 4000
Hartford, CT 06106
P: (860) 240-8585
E: John.Hampton@cga.ct.gov

Hennessy, Jack F. (D, 127)
Legislative Office Building
Room 5002
Hartford, CT 06106
P: (860) 240-8585
E: Jack.Hennessy@cga.ct.gov

Hewett, Ernest (D, 39)
Legislative Office Building
Room 4040
Hartford, CT 06106
P: (860) 240-8585
E: Ernest.Hewett@cga.ct.gov

Hoydick, Laura (R, 120)
Legislative Office Building
Room 4200
Hartford, CT 06106
P: (860) 240-8700
F: (860) 240-0207
E: Laura.Hoydick@housegop.ct.gov

Janowski, Claire L. (D, 56)
Legislative Office Building
Room 1003
Hartford, CT 06106
P: (860) 240-8585
E: Claire.Janowski@cga.ct.gov

Johnson, Susan (D, 49)
Legislative Office Building
Room 5007
Hartford, CT 06106
P: (860) 240-8585
E: Susan.Johnson@cga.ct.gov

Jutila, Ed (D, 37)
Legislative Office Building
Room 4046
Hartford, CT 06106
P: (860) 240-8585
E: Ed.Jutila@cga.ct.gov

Kiner, David W. (D, 59)
Legislative Office Building
Room 4006
Hartford, CT 06106
P: (860) 240-8585
E: David.Kiner@cga.ct.gov

Klarides, Themis (R, 114)
Legislative Office Building
Room 4200
Hartford, CT 06106
P: (860) 240-8700
F: (860) 240-0207
E: Themis.Klarides@housegop.ct.gov

Kokoruda, Noreen (R, 101)
Legislative Office Building
Room 4200
Hartford, CT 06106
P: (860) 240-8700
F: (860) 240-0207
E: Noreen.Kokoruda@housegop.ct.gov

Kupchick, Brenda (R, 132)
Legislative Office Building
Room 4200
Hartford, CT 06106
P: (860) 240-8700
F: (860) 240-0207
E: Brenda.Kupchick@housegop.ct.gov

Labriola, David K. (R, 131)
Legislative Office Building
Room 4200
Hartford, CT 06106
P: (860) 240-8700
F: (860) 240-0207
E: David.Labriola@housegop.ct.gov

Lavielle, Gail (R, 143)
Legislative Office Building
Room 4200
Hartford, CT 06106
P: (860) 240-8700
F: (860) 240-0207
E: Gail.Lavielle@housegop.ct.gov

LeGeyt, Timothy (R, 17)
Legislative Office Building
Room 4200
Hartford, CT 06106
P: (860) 240-8700
F: (860) 240-0207
E: Tim.LeGeyt@housegop.ct.gov

Lemar, Roland (D, 96)
Legislative Office Building
Room 4041
Hartford, CT 06106
P: (860) 240-8585
E: Roland.Lemar@cga.ct.gov

Lesser, Matthew (D, 100)
Legislative Office Building
Room 4032
Hartford, CT 06106
P: (860) 240-8585
E: Matthew.Lesser@cga.ct.gov

Lopes, Rick (D, 24)
Legislative Office Building
Room 4014
Hartford, CT 06106
P: (860) 240-8585
E: Rick.Lopes@cga.ct.gov

Luxenberg, Kelly (D, 12)*
Legislative Office Building
Room 4028
Hartford, CT 06106
P: (860) 240-8585
E: Kelly.Luxenberg@cga.ct.gov

MacLachlan, Jesse (R, 35)*
Legislative Office Building
Room 4200
Hartford, CT 06106
P: (860) 240-8700
F: (860) 240-0207
E: Jesse.MacLachlan@housegop.ct.gov

McCarty, Kathleen (R, 38)*
Legislative Office Building
Room 4200
Hartford, CT 06106
P: (860) 240-8700
F: (860) 240-0207
E: Kathleen.McCarty@housegop.ct.gov

McCrory, Douglas (D, 7)
Legislative Office Building
Room 4053
Hartford, CT 06106
P: (860) 240-8585
E: Douglas.McCrory@cga.ct.gov

McGee, Brandon L. (D, 5)
Legislative Office Building
Room 4000
Hartford, CT 06106
P: (860) 240-8585
E: Brandon.McGee@cga.ct.gov

McGorty, Ben (R, 122)*
Legislative Office Building
Room 4200
Hartford, CT 06106
P: (860) 240-8700
F: (860) 240-0207
E: Ben.McGorty@housegop.ct.gov

Megna, Robert W. (D, 97)
Legislative Office Building
Room 2802
Hartford, CT 06106
P: (860) 240-8585
E: Robert.Megna@cga.ct.gov

Miller, Patricia Billie (D, 145)
Legislative Office Building
Room 4046
Hartford, CT 06106
P: (860) 240-8585
E: Patricia.Miller@cga.ct.gov

Miller, Philip J. (D, 36)
Legislative Office Building
Room 4011
Hartford, CT 06106
P: (860) 240-8585
E: Philip.Miller@cga.ct.gov

Miner, Craig A. (R, 66)
Legislative Office Building
Room 4200
Hartford, CT 06106
P: (860) 240-8700
F: (860) 240-0207
E: Craig.Miner@housegop.ct.gov

Morin, Russell A. (D, 28)
Legislative Office Building
Room 4110
Hartford, CT 06106
P: (860) 240-8585
E: Russell.Morin@cga.ct.gov

Morris, Bruce V. (D, 140)
Legislative Office Building
Room 4030
Hartford, CT 06106
P: (860) 240-8585
E: Bruce.Morris@cga.ct.gov

Mulligan, Gayle (R, 55)*
Legislative Office Building
Room 4200
Hartford, CT 06106
P: (860) 240-8700
F: (860) 240-0207
E: Gayle.Mulligan@housegop.ct.gov

Mushinsky, Mary M. (D, 85)
Legislative Office Building
Room 4038
Hartford, CT 06106
P: (860) 240-8585
E: Mary.Mushinsky@cga.ct.gov

Nicastro, Frank N. (D, 79)
Legislative Office Building
Room 4034
Hartford, CT 06106
P: (860) 240-8585
E: Frank.Nicastro@cga.ct.gov

Noujaim, Selim G. (R, 74)
Legislative Office Building
Room 4200
Hartford, CT 06106
P: (860) 240-8700
F: (860) 240-0207
E: Selim.Noujaim@housegop.ct.gov

O'Dea, Thomas (R, 125)
Legislative Office Building
Room 4200
Hartford, CT 06106
P: (860) 240-8700
F: (860) 240-0207
E: Tom.ODea@housegop.ct.gov

O'Neill, Arthur J. (R, 69)
Legislative Office Building
Room 4200
Hartford, CT 06106
P: (860) 240-8700
F: (860) 240-0207
E: Arthur.ONeill@housegop.ct.gov

Orange, Linda A. (D, 48)
Legislative Office Building
Room 4109
Hartford, CT 06106
P: (860) 240-8585
E: Linda.Orange@cga.ct.gov

Pavalock, Cara Christine (R, 77)*
Legislative Office Building
Room 4200
Hartford, CT 06106
P: (860) 240-8700
F: (860) 240-0207
E: Cara.Pavalock@housegop.ct.gov

Perillo, Jason (R, 113)
Legislative Office Building
Room 4200
Hartford, CT 06106
P: (860) 240-8700
F: (860) 240-0207
E: Jason.Perillo@housegop.ct.gov

Perone, Chris (D, 137)
State Capitol, Room 110
Hartford, CT 06106
P: (860) 240-8585
E: Chris.Perone@cga.ct.gov

Piscopo, John E. (R, 76)
Legislative Office Building
Room 4200
Hartford, CT 06106
P: (860) 240-8700
F: (860) 240-0207
E: John.Piscopo@housegop.ct.gov

Porter, Robyn (D, 94)*
Legislative Office Building
Room 4006
Hartford, CT 06106
P: (860) 240-8585
E: Robyn.Porter@cga.ct.gov

Rebimbas, Rosa C. (R, 70)
Legislative Office Building
Room 4200
Hartford, CT 06106
P: (860) 240-8700
F: (860) 240-0207
E: Rosa.Rebimbas@housegop.ct.gov

Reed, Lonnie (D, 102)
Legislative Office Building
Room 4026
Hartford, CT 06106
P: (860) 240-8585
E: Lonnie.Reed@cga.ct.gov

Riley, Emmett D. (D, 46)
Legislative Office Building
Room 4037
Hartford, CT 06106
P: (860) 240-8585
E: Emmett.Riley@cga.ct.gov

Ritter, Matt (D, 1)
Legislative Office Building
Room 4003
Hartford, CT 06106
P: (860) 240-8585
E: Matthew.Ritter@cga.ct.gov

Rojas, Jason (D, 9)
Legislative Office Building
Room 4001
Hartford, CT 06106
P: (860) 240-8585
E: Jason.Rojas@cga.ct.gov

Rosario, Christopher (D, 128)*
Legislative Office Building
Room 5006
Hartford, CT 06106
P: (860) 240-8585
E: Christopher.Rosario@cga.ct.gov

Rosati, Christine (D, 44)*
Legislative Office Building
Room 4014
Hartford, CT 06106
P: (860) 240-8585
E: Christine.Rosati@cga.ct.gov

Rose, Kim (D, 118)
Legislative Office Building
Room 4002
Hartford, CT 06106
P: (860) 240-8585
E: Kim.Rose@cga.ct.gov

Rovero, Daniel S. (D, 51)
Legislative Office Building
Room 4004
Hartford, CT 06106
P: (860) 240-8585
E: Danny.Rovero@cga.ct.gov

Rutigliano, David (R, 123)
Legislative Office Building
Room 4200
Hartford, CT 06106
P: (860) 240-8700
F: (860) 240-0207
E: David.Rutigliano@housegop.ct.gov

Ryan, Kevin (D, 139)
Legislative Office Building
Room 4012
Hartford, CT 06106
P: (860) 240-8585
E: Kevin.Ryan@cga.ct.gov

Sampson, Rob (R, 80)
Legislative Office Building
Room 4200
Hartford, CT 06106
P: (860) 240-8700
F: (860) 240-0207
E: Rob.Sampson@housegop.ct.gov

Sanchez, Robert (D, 25)
Legislative Office Building
Room 4018
Hartford, CT 06106
P: (860) 240-8585
E: Bobby.Sanchez@cga.ct.gov

Santiago, Ezequiel (D, 130)
Legislative Office Building
Room 3802
Hartford, CT 06106
P: (860) 240-8585
E: Ezequiel.Santiago@cga.ct.gov

Santiago, Hilda E. (D, 84)
Legislative Office Building
Room 4000
Hartford, CT 06106
P: (860) 240-8585
E: Hilda.Santiago@cga.ct.gov

Sayers, Peggy (D, 60)
Legislative Office Building
Room 4049
Hartford, CT 06106
P: (860) 240-8585
E: Peggy.Sayers@cga.ct.gov

Scanlon, Sean (D, 98)*
Legislative Office Building
Room 4024
Hartford, CT 06106
P: (860) 240-8585
E: Sean.Scanlon@cga.ct.gov

Scott, John (R, 40)*
Legislative Office Building
Room 4200
Hartford, CT 06106
P: (860) 240-8700
F: (860) 240-0207
E: John.Scott@housegop.ct.gov

Serra, Joseph C. (D, 33)
Legislative Office Building
Room 4021
Hartford, CT 06106
P: (860) 240-8585
E: Joseph.Serra@cga.ct.gov

Connecticut

Shaban, John (R, 135)
Legislative Office Building
Room 4200
Hartford, CT 06106
P: (860) 240-8700
F: (860) 240-0207
E: John.Shaban
@housegop.ct.gov

Sharkey, J. Brendan (D, 88)
Legislative Office Building
Room 4100
Hartford, CT 06106
P: (860) 240-8500
E: Brendan.Sharkey
@cga.ct.gov

Simanski, Bill (R, 62)
Legislative Office Building
Room 4200
Hartford, CT 06106
P: (860) 240-8700
F: (860) 240-0207
E: Bill.Simanski
@housegop.ct.gov

Simmons, Caroline (D, 144)*
Legislative Office Building
Room 4016
Hartford, CT 06106
P: (860) 240-8585
E: Caroline.Simmons
@cga.ct.gov

Smith, Richard (R, 108)
Legislative Office Building
Room 4200
Hartford, CT 06106
P: (860) 240-8700
F: (860) 240-0207
E: Richard.Smith
@housegop.ct.gov

Sredzinski, JP (R, 112)*
Legislative Office Building
Room 4200
Hartford, CT 06106
P: (860) 240-8700
F: (860) 240-0207
E: JP.Sredzinski
@housegop.ct.gov

Srinivasan, Prasad (R, 31)
Legislative Office Building
Room 4200
Hartford, CT 06106
P: (860) 240-8700
F: (860) 240-0207
E: Prasad.Srinivasan
@housegop.ct.gov

Stallworth, Charlie L. (D, 126)
Legislative Office Building
Room 4050
Hartford, CT 06106
P: (860) 240-8585
E: Charlie.Stallworth
@cga.ct.gov

Staneski, Pam (R, 119)*
Legislative Office Building
Room 4200
Hartford, CT 06106
P: (860) 240-8700
F: (860) 240-0207
E: Pam.Staneski
@housegop.ct.gov

Steinberg, Jonathan (D, 136)
Legislative Office Building
Room 4020
Hartford, CT 06106
P: (860) 240-8585
E: Jonathan.Steinberg
@cga.ct.gov

Tercyak, Peter A. (D, 26)
Legislative Office Building
Room 3804
Hartford, CT 06106
P: (860) 240-8585
E: Peter.Tercyak@cga.ct.gov

Tong, William (D, 147)
Legislative Office Building
Room 2405
Hartford, CT 06106
P: (860) 240-8585
E: William.Tong@cga.ct.gov

Tweedie, Mark (R, 13)*
Legislative Office Building
Room 4200
Hartford, CT 06106
P: (860) 240-8700
F: (860) 240-0207
E: Mark.Tweedie
@housegop.ct.gov

Urban, Diana S. (D, 43)
Legislative Office Building
Room 4042
Hartford, CT 06106
P: (860) 240-8585
E: Diana.Urban@cga.ct.gov

Vahey, Cristin McCarthy (D, 133)*
Legislative Office Building
Room 4001
Hartford, CT 06106
P: (860) 240-8585
E: Cristin.McCarthyVahey
@cga.ct.gov

Vail, Kurt (R, 52)*
Legislative Office Building
Room 4200
Hartford, CT 06106
P: (860) 240-8700
F: (860) 240-0207
E: Kurt.Vail
@housegop.ct.gov

Vargas, Edwin (D, 6)
Legislative Office Building
Room 4000
Hartford, CT 06106
P: (860) 240-8585
E: Edwin.Vargas@cga.ct.gov

Verrengia, Joe (D, 20)
Legislative Office Building
Room 4048
Hartford, CT 06106
P: (860) 240-8585
E: Joe.Verrengia@cga.ct.gov

Walker, Toni E. (D, 93)
Legislative Office Building
Room 2702
Hartford, CT 06106
P: (860) 240-8585
E: Toni.Walker@cga.ct.gov

Willis, Roberta B. (D, 64)
Legislative Office Building
Room 1802
Hartford, CT 06106
P: (860) 240-8585
E: Roberta.Willis
@cga.ct.gov

Wilms, Fred (R, 142)*
Legislative Office Building
Room 4200
Hartford, CT 06106
P: (860) 240-8700
F: (860) 240-0207
E: Fred.Wilms
@housegop.ct.gov

Wood, Terrie E. (R, 141)
Legislative Office Building
Room 4200
Hartford, CT 06106
P: (860) 240-8700
F: (860) 240-0207
E: Terrie.Wood
@housegop.ct.gov

Yaccarino, David (R, 87)
Legislative Office Building
Room 4200
Hartford, CT 06106
P: (860) 240-8700
F: (860) 240-0207
E: dave.yaccarino
@housegop.ct.gov

Zawistowski, Tami (R, 61)*
Legislative Office Building
Room 4200
Hartford, CT 06106
P: (860) 240-8700
F: (860) 240-0207
E: Tami.Zawistowski
@housegop.ct.gov

Ziobron, Melissa (R, 34)
Legislative Office Building
Room 4200
Hartford, CT 06106
P: (860) 240-8700
F: (860) 240-0207
E: Melissa.Ziobron
@housegop.ct.gov

Zoni, David (D, 81)
Legislative Office Building
Room 4000
Hartford, CT 06106
P: (860) 240-8585
E: David.Zoni@cga.ct.gov

Zupkus, Lezlye (R, 89)
Legislative Office Building
Room 4200
Hartford, CT 06106
P: (860) 240-8700
F: (860) 240-0207
E: Lezlye.Zupkus
@housegop.ct.gov

Congress

Senate

Blumenthal, Richard (D)
Murphy, Christopher S. (D)

House

Courtney, Joe (D, 2)
DeLauro, Rosa L. (D, 3)
Esty, Elizabeth (D, 5)
Himes, Jim (D, 4)
Larson, John B. (D, 1)

Delaware

Executive

Governor

Hon. Jack Markell (D)
Governor
Legislative Hall
Dover, DE 19901
P: (302) 744-4101
F: (302) 739-2775

Lieutenant Governor

Vacant
Carvel State Office Building
820 North French Street
Wilmington, DE 19801
P: (302) 577-8787

Attorney General

Hon. Matthew Denn (D)
Attorney General
Carvel State Office Building
820 North French Street
Wilmington, DE 19801
P: (302) 577-8338
E: matthew.denn@state.de.us

Auditor

Hon. R. Thomas Wagner Jr. (R)
Auditor of Accounts
401 Federal Street
Townsend Building, Suite 1
Dover, DE 19901
P: (302) 739-5055
F: (302) 739-6707
E: r.thomas.wagner@state.de.us

Commissioner of Insurance

Hon. Karen Weldin Stewart (D)
Commissioner
841 Silver Lake Boulevard
Dover, DE 19904
P: (302) 674-7300
F: (302) 739-5280
E: karen.stewart@state.de.us

Secretary of State

Hon. Jeffrey Bullock (D) (appointed)
Secretary of State
Townsend Building
401 Federal Street, Suite 3
Dover, DE 19901
P: (302) 739-4111
F: (302) 739-3811
E: kathy.bradford@state.de.us

Treasurer

Hon. Ken Simpler (R)
State Treasurer
820 Silver Lake Boulevard, Suite 100
Dover, DE 19904
P: (302) 672-6700
F: (302) 739-5635

Judiciary

Supreme Court (GA)

Ms. Cathy L. Howard
Clerk of the Court
Carvel State Office Building
820 North French Street, 11th Floor
Wilmington, DE 19801
P: (302) 739-4187
F: (302) 577-3702

Hon. Leo E. Strine Jr.
Chief Justice
Hon. Randy J. Holland
Hon. Henry DuPont Ridgeley
Hon. Karen Valihura
Hon. James T. Vaughn Jr.

Legislative Senate

Senate President

Vacant
Carvel State Office Building
820 North French Street
Wilmington, DE 19801
P: (302) 577-8787

President Pro Tempore of the Senate

Sen. Patricia M. Blevins (D)
President Pro Tempore
411 Legislative Avenue
Dover, DE 19901
P: (302) 744-4133
E: Patricia.Blevins@state.de.us

Senate Majority Leader

Sen. David B. McBride (D)
Majority Leader
411 Legislative Avenue
Dover, DE 19901
P: (302) 744-4167
E: David.McBride@state.de.us

Senate Minority Leader

Sen. F. Gary Simpson (R)
Minority Leader
411 Legislative Avenue
Dover, DE 19901
P: (302) 744-4134
F: (302) 739-5049
E: gsimpson@udel.edu

Secretary of the Senate

Mr. Bernard J. Brady
Secretary of the Senate
Legislative Hall
411 Legislative Avenue
Dover, DE 19901
P: (302) 744-4129
F: (302) 739-7718
E: Bernard.Brady@state.de.us

Members of the Senate

Blevins, Patricia M. (D, 7)
411 Legislative Avenue
Dover, DE 19901
P: (302) 744-4133
E: Patricia.Blevins@state.de.us

Bonini, Colin R.J. (R, 16)
411 Legislative Avenue
Dover, DE 19901
P: (302) 744-4169
F: (302) 739-5049
E: senator-colin@prodigy.net

Bushweller, Brian J. (D, 17)
411 Legislative Avenue
Dover, DE 19901
P: (302) 744-4162
F: (302) 739-6890
E: Brian.Bushweller@state.de.us

Cloutier, Catherine L. (R, 5)
411 Legislative Avenue
Dover, DE 19901
P: (302) 744-4197
F: (302) 739-5049
E: catherine.cloutier@state.de.us

Ennis, Bruce C. (D, 14)
411 Legislative Avenue
Dover, DE 19901
P: (302) 744-4310
F: (302) 739-6890
E: bruce.ennis@state.de.us

Hall-Long, Bethany A. (D, 10)
411 Legislative Avenue
Dover, DE 19901
P: (302) 744-4286
E: bethany.hall-long@state.de.us

Henry, Margaret Rose (D, 2)
411 Legislative Avenue
Dover, DE 19901
P: (302) 744-4191
E: MargaretRose.Henry@state.de.us

Hocker, Gerald W. (R, 20)
411 Legislative Avenue
Dover, DE 19901
P: (302) 744-4144
E: Gerald.Hocker@state.de.us

LaVelle, Gregory F. (R, 4)
411 Legislative Avenue
Dover, DE 19901
P: (302) 744-4048
F: (302) 739-5049
E: Greg.Lavelle@state.de.us

Lawson, David G. (R, 15)
411 Legislative Avenue
Dover, DE 19901
P: (302) 744-4237
E: Dave.Lawson@state.de.us

Lopez, Ernesto B. (R, 6)
411 Legislative Avenue
Dover, DE 19901
P: (302) 744-4136
F: (302) 739-5049
E: Ernesto.Lopez@state.de.us

Marshall, Robert I. (D, 3)
411 Legislative Avenue
Dover, DE 19901
P: (302) 744-4168
E: robert.marshall@state.de.us

Delaware

McBride, David B. (D, 13)
411 Legislative Avenue
Dover, DE 19901
P: (302) 744-4167
E: David.McBride
@state.de.us

McDowell III, Harris B. (D, 1)
411 Legislative Avenue
Dover, DE 19901
P: (302) 744-4147
E: Harris.McDowell
@state.de.us

Peterson, Karen E. (D, 9)
411 Legislative Avenue
Dover, DE 19901
P: (302) 744-4163
E: Karen.Peterson
@state.de.us

Pettyjohn, Brian (R, 19)
411 Legislative Avenue
Dover, DE 19901
P: (302) 744-4048
E: Brian.Pettyjohn
@state.de.us

Poore, Nicole (D, 12)
411 Legislative Avenue
Dover, DE 19901
P: (302) 744-4164
F: (302) 739-6890
E: Nicole.Poore@state.de.us

Richardson, Bryant L. (R, 21)*
411 Legislative Avenue
Dover, DE 19901
P: (302) 744-4298
E: Bryant.Richardson
@state.de.us

Simpson, F. Gary (R, 18)
411 Legislative Avenue
Dover, DE 19901
P: (302) 744-4134
F: (302) 739-5049
E: gsimpson@udel.edu

Sokola, David P. (D, 8)
411 Legislative Avenue
Dover, DE 19901
P: (302) 744-4139
E: David.Sokola@state.de.us

Townsend, Bryan (D, 11)
411 Legislative Avenue
Dover, DE 19901
P: (302) 744-4165
E: Bryan.Townsend
@state.de.us

House

Speaker of the House

Rep. Peter C. Schwartzkopf (D)
Speaker
411 Legislative Avenue
Dover, DE 19901
P: (302) 744-4351
E: Peter.Schwartzkopf
@state.de.us

Speaker Pro Tempore of the House

Rep. Helene M. Keeley (D)
House Speaker Pro Tem
411 Legislative Avenue
Dover, DE 19901
P: (302) 744-4351
E: helene.keeley
@state.de.us

House Majority Leader

Rep. Valerie Longhurst (D)
Majority Leader
411 Legislative Avenue
Dover, DE 19901
P: (302) 744-4047
E: Valerie.Longhurst
@state.de.us

House Minority Leader

Rep. Daniel B. Short (R)
Minority Leader
411 Legislative Avenue
Dover, DE 19901
P: (302) 744-4172
F: (302) 739-2773
E: Daniel.Short@state.de.us

Clerk of the House

Mr. Richard Puffer
Chief Clerk of the House
Legislative Hall
411 Legislative Avenue
Dover, DE 19901
P: (302) 744-4121
F: (302) 739-7854

Members of the House

Barbieri, Michael A. (D, 18)
411 Legislative Avenue
Dover, DE 19901
P: (302) 744-4279
E: michael.barbieri
@state.de.us

Baumbach, Paul S. (D, 23)
411 Legislative Avenue
Dover, DE 19901
P: (302) 744-4351
F: (302) 739-2313
E: paul.baumbach
@state.de.us

Bennett, Andria L. (D, 32)
411 Legislative Avenue
Dover, DE 19901
P: (302) 744-4351
F: (302) 739-2313
E: andria.bennett
@state.de.us

Bolden, Stephanie T. (D, 2)
411 Legislative Avenue
Dover, DE 19901
P: (302) 744-4351
F: (302) 739-2313
E: StephanieT.Bolden
@state.de.us

Brady, Gerald L. (D, 4)
411 Legislative Avenue
Dover, DE 19901
P: (302) 744-4351
E: gerald.brady@state.de.us

Carson, William J. (D, 28)
411 Legislative Avenue
Dover, DE 19901
P: (302) 744-4113
F: (302) 739-2313
E: william.carson
@state.de.us

Collins, Richard G. (R, 41)*
411 Legislative Avenue
Dover, DE 19901
P: (302) 744-4171
E: richard.collins
@state.de.us

Dukes, Timothy D. (R, 40)
411 Legislative Avenue
Dover, DE 19901
P: (302) 744-4171
E: timothy.dukes
@state.de.us

Gray, Ronald E. (R, 38)
411 Legislative Avenue
Dover, DE 19901
P: (302) 744-4171
E: ronald.gray@state.de.us

Heffernan, Debra (D, 6)
411 Legislative Avenue
Dover, DE 19901
P: (302) 744-4351
E: debra.heffernan
@state.de.us

Hensley, Kevin (R, 9)*
411 Legislative Avenue
Dover, DE 19901
P: (302) 744-4351
E: kevin.hensley
@state.de.us

Hudson, Deborah (R, 12)
411 Legislative Avenue
Dover, DE 19901
P: (302) 744-4171
E: deborah.hudson
@state.de.us

Jaques Jr., Earl G. (D, 27)
411 Legislative Avenue
Dover, DE 19901
P: (302) 744-4142
F: (302) 739-2313
E: earl.jaques@state.de.us

Johnson, James (D, 16)
411 Legislative Avenue
Dover, DE 19901
P: (302) 744-4351
F: (302) 739-2313
E: jj.johnson@state.de.us

Johnson, S. Quinton (D, 8)
411 Legislative Avenue
Dover, DE 19901
P: (302) 744-4351
F: (302) 739-2313
E: quinton.johnson
@state.de.us

Keeley, Helene M. (D, 3)
411 Legislative Avenue
Dover, DE 19901
P: (302) 744-4351
E: helene.keeley
@state.de.us

Kenton, Harvey R. (R, 36)
411 Legislative Avenue
Dover, DE 19901
P: (302) 744-4171
F: (302) 739-2773
E: harvey.kenton
@state.de.us

King, Ruth Briggs (R, 37)
411 Legislative Avenue
Dover, DE 19901
P: (302) 744-4251
F: (302) 739-2773
E: Ruth.BriggsKing@state.de.us

Kowalko Jr., John (D, 25)
411 Legislative Avenue
Dover, DE 19901
P: (302) 744-4351
F: (302) 739-2313
E: john.kowalko@state.de.us

Longhurst, Valerie (D, 15)
411 Legislative Avenue
Dover, DE 19901
P: (302) 744-4047
E: Valerie.Longhurst@state.de.us

Lynn, Sean M. (D, 31)*
411 Legislative Avenue
Dover, DE 19901
P: (302) 744-4351
E: sean.lynn@state.de.us

Matthews, Sean (D, 10)*
411 Legislative Avenue
Dover, DE 19901
P: (302) 744-4351
E: sean.matthews@state.de.us

Miro, Joseph E. (R, 22)
411 Legislative Avenue
Dover, DE 19901
P: (302) 744-4171
E: joseph.miro@state.de.us

Mitchell Jr., John L. (D, 13)
411 Legislative Avenue
Dover, DE 19901
P: (302) 744-4351
F: (302) 739-2313
E: john.l.mitchell@state.de.us

Mulrooney, Michael P. (D, 17)
411 Legislative Avenue
Dover, DE 19901
P: (302) 744-4351
E: Michael.Mulrooney@state.de.us

Osienski, Edward S. (D, 24)
411 Legislative Avenue
Dover, DE 19901
P: (302) 744-4351
F: (302) 739-2313
E: Edward.Osienski@state.de.us

Outten, William R. (R, 30)
411 Legislative Avenue
Dover, DE 19901
P: (302) 744-4083
F: (302) 739-2773
E: bobby.outten@state.de.us

Paradee, W. Charles (D, 29)
411 Legislative Avenue
Dover, DE 19901
P: (302) 744-4351
F: (302) 739-2313
E: trey.paradee@state.de.us

Peterman, Harold J. (R, 33)
411 Legislative Avenue
Dover, DE 19901
P: (302) 744-4171
F: (302) 739-2773
E: jack.peterman@state.de.us

Potter Jr., Charles (D, 1)
411 Legislative Avenue
Dover, DE 19901
P: (302) 744-4351
F: (302) 739-2313
E: Charles.Potter@state.de.us

Ramone, Michael (R, 21)
411 Legislative Avenue
Dover, DE 19901
P: (302) 744-4108
F: (302) 739-2773
E: Michael.Ramone@statc.de.us

Schwartzkopf, Peter C. (D, 14)
411 Legislative Avenue
Dover, DE 19901
P: (302) 744-4351
E: Peter.Schwartzkopf@state.de.us

Short, Bryon H. (D, 7)
411 Legislative Avenue
Dover, DE 19901
P: (302) 744-4297
E: Bryon.Short@state.de.us

Short, Daniel B. (R, 39)
411 Legislative Avenue
Dover, DE 19901
P: (302) 744-4172
F: (302) 739-2773
E: Daniel.Short@state.de.us

Smith, Melanie George (D, 5)
411 Legislative Avenue
Dover, DE 19901
P: (302) 744-4126
F: (302) 739-2313
E: melanie.g.smith@state.de.us

Smyk, Stephen T. (R, 20)
411 Legislative Avenue
Dover, DE 19901
P: (302) 744-4321
F: (302) 739-2773
E: Steve.Smyk@state.de.us

Spiegelman, Jeffrey N. (R, 11)
411 Legislative Avenue
Dover, DE 19901
P: (302) 744-4171
E: jeff.spiegelman@state.de.us

Viola, John J. (D, 26)
411 Legislative Avenue
Dover, DE 19901
P: (302) 744-4351
E: John.Viola@state.de.us

Williams, Kimberly (D, 19)
411 Legislative Avenue
Dover, DE 19901
P: (302) 744-4351
E: kimberly.williams@state.de.us

Wilson, David L. (R, 35)
411 Legislative Avenue
Dover, DE 19901
P: (302) 744-4150
F: (302) 739-2773
E: David.L.Wilson@state.de.us

Yearlck, Lyndon D. (R, 34)*
411 Legislative Avenue
Dover, DE 19901
P: (302) 744-4171

Congress

Senate

Carper, Thomas R. (D)
Coons, Christopher (D)

House

Carney Jr., John (D, At-Large)

District of Columbia

Executive

Mayor

Hon. Muriel Bowser (D)
Mayor
1350 Pennsylvania Avenue, Northwest
Suite 316
Washington, DC 20004
P: (202) 727-6300
F: (202) 727-0505
E: eom@dc.gov

Attorney General

Honourable Karl Racine (appointed)
Attorney General
441 4th Street, Northwest
Suite 1100S
Washington, DC 20001
P: (202) 727-3400
F: (202) 347-8922
E: oag@dc.gov

Auditor

Hon. Kathleen Patterson
Auditor
717 14th Street, Northwest
Suite 900
Washington, DC 20005
P: (202) 727-3600
F: (202) 724-8814
E: kathleen.patterson@dc.gov

Secretary of the District of Columbia

Hon. Lauren C. Vaughn (appointed)
Secretary of the District
1350 Pennsylvania Avenue, Northwest
Suite 419
Washington, DC 20004
P: (202) 727-6306
F: (202) 727-3582
E: secretary@dc.gov

Treasurer

Mr. Jeffrey S. DeWitt (appointed)
Chief Financial Officer
1350 Pennsylvania Avenue, Northwest
John A. Wilson Building, Suite 203
Washington, DC 20004
P: (202) 727-2476
F: (202) 727-1643
E: ocfo@dc.gov

Judiciary

Court of Appeals (FA)

Mr. Julio A. Castillo
Clerk of the Court of Appeals
Historic Courthouse
430 E Street, Northwest
Washington, DC 20001
P: (202) 879-2700

Hon. Eric T. Washington
Chief Judge
Hon. Corinne A. Beckwith
Hon. Anna Blackburne-Rigsby
Hon. Catharine F. Easterly
Hon. John R. Fisher
Hon. Stephen Glickman
Hon. Roy W. McLeese
Hon. Phyllis D. Thompson

Council of the District of Columbia

Council Chair

Conclmn. Phil Mendelson (D)
Chair
John A. Wilson Building, Suite 504
1350 Pennsylvania Avenue, Northwest
Washington, DC 20004
P: (202) 724-8032
F: (202) 724-8085
E: pmendelson@dccouncil.us

Council Chair Pro Tempore

Cnclmn. Kenyan McDuffie (D)
Chair Pro Tempore
John A. Wilson Building, Suite 506
1350 Pennsylvania Avenue, Northwest
Washington, DC 20004
P: (202) 724-8028
F: (202) 724-8076
E: kmcduffie@dccouncil.us

Secretary to the Council

Ms. Nyasha Smith
Secretary To the Council
John A. Wilson Building, Suite 5
1350 Pennsylvania Avenue Northwest
Washington, DC 20004
P: (202) 724-8080
F: (202) 347-3070
E: nsmith@dccouncil.us

Members of the Senate

Alexander, Yvette (D, 7)
John A. Wilson Building, Suite 404
1350 Pennsylvania Avenue, Northwest
Washington, DC 20004
P: (202) 724-8068
F: (202) 741-0911
E: yalexander@dccouncil.us

Allen, Charles (D, 6)*
John A. Wilson Building, Suite 406
1350 Pennsylvania Avenue, Northwest
Washington, DC 20004
P: (202) 724-8072
E: callen@dccouncil.us

Bonds, Anita (D, At-Large)
John A. Wilson Building, Suite 110
1350 Pennsylvania Avenue, Northwest
Washington, DC 20004
P: (202) 724-8064
F: (202) 724-8099
E: abonds@dccouncil.us

Cheh, Mary M. (D, 3)
John A. Wilson Building, Suite 108
1350 Pennsylvania Avenue, Northwest
Washington, DC 20004
P: (202) 724-8062
F: (202) 724-8118
E: mcheh@dccouncil.us

Evans, Jack (D, 2)
John A. Wilson Building, Suite 106
1350 Pennsylvania Avenue, Northwest
Washington, DC 20004
P: (202) 724-8058
F: (202) 727-8023
E: jevans@dccouncil.us

Grosso, David (I, At-Large)
John A. Wilson Building, Suite 402
1350 Pennsylvania Avenue, Northwest
Washington, DC 20004
P: (202) 724-8105
F: (202) 724-8071
E: dgrosso@dccouncil.us

McDuffie, Kenyan (D, 5)
John A. Wilson Building, Suite 506
1350 Pennsylvania Avenue, Northwest
Washington, DC 20004
P: (202) 724-8028
F: (202) 724-8076
E: kmcduffie@dccouncil.us

Mendelson, Phil (D, At-Large)
John A. Wilson Building, Suite 504
1350 Pennsylvania Avenue, Northwest
Washington, DC 20004
P: (202) 724-8032
F: (202) 724-8085
E: pmendelson@dccouncil.us

Nadeau, Brianne (D, 1)*
John A. Wilson Building, Suite 102
1350 Pennsylvania Avenue, Northwest
Washington, DC 20004
P: (202) 724-8181
F: (202) 724-8109
E: bnadeau@dccouncil.us

Orange Sr., Vincent B. (D, At-Large)
John A. Wilson Building, Suite 107
1350 Pennsylvania Avenue, Northwest
Washington, DC 20004
P: (202) 724-8174
F: (202) 727-8210
E: vorange@dccouncil.us

Silverman, Elissa (I, At-Large)*
John A. Wilson Building, Suite 408
1350 Pennsylvania Avenue, Northwest
Washington, DC 20004
P: (202) 724-7772
F: (202) 724-8087
E: esilverman@dccouncil.us

Congress

House Delegate

Norton, Eleanor Holmes
(D, At-Large)

Florida

Executive

Governor

Hon. Rick Scott (R)
Governor
PL 05, The Capitol
400 South Monroe Street
Tallahassee, FL 32399
P: (850) 488-7146
F: (850) 487-0801

Lieutenant Governor

Hon. Carlos Lopez-Cantera (R)
Lieutenant Governor
The State Capitol
Tallahassee, FL 32399
P: (850) 488-4711
F: (850) 921-6114

Commissioner of Agriculture & Consumer Services

Hon. Adam H. Putnam (R)
Commissioner
The Capitol, PL-10
400 South Monroe Street
Tallahassee, FL 32399
P: (850) 488-3022
F: (850) 922-4936

Attorney General

Hon. Pam Bondi (R)
Attorney General
The Capitol, PL 01
Tallahassee, FL 32399
P: (850) 414-3300
F: (954) 712-4826

Auditor

Hon. David W. Martin
(appointed by the Legislature)
Auditor General
Claude Pepper Building
111 West Madison Street
Tallahassee, FL 32399
P: (850) 412-2722
F: (850) 488-6975
E: davidmartin@aud.state.fl.us

Secretary of State

Hon. Kenneth Detzner (R)
(appointed)
Secretary of State
500 South Bronough Street
Tallahassee, FL 32399
P: (850) 245-6500
F: (850) 245-6125
E: dossecretaryofstate@dos.myflorida.com

Chief Financial Officer

Hon. Jeffrey H. Atwater (R)
Chief Financial Officer
200 East Gaines Street
Tallahassee, FL 32399
P: (877) 693-5236
F: (850) 413-2950
E: allison@jeffatwater.com

Judiciary

Supreme Court (MR)

Mr. John A. Tomasino
Clerk
500 South Duval Street
Tallahassee, FL 32399
P: (850) 488-0125
E: supremecourt@flcourts.org

Hon. Jorge Labarga
Chief Justice
Hon. Charles T. Canady
Hon. Jorge Labarga
Hon. R. Fred Lewis
Hon. Barbara J. Pariente
Hon. James E.C. Perry
Hon. Ricky Polston
Hon. Peggy A. Quince

Legislative Senate

Senate President

Sen. Andy Gardiner (R)
President
409 Senate Office Building
404 South Monroe Street
Tallahassee, FL 32399
P: (850) 487-5013
E: gardiner.andy.web@flsenate.gov

President Pro Tempore of the Senate

Sen. Garrett S. Richter (R)
President Pro Tempore
404 Senate Office Building
404 South Monroe Street
Tallahassee, FL 32399
P: (850) 487-5023
E: richter.garrett.web@flsenate.gov

Senate Majority Leader

Sen. Bill Galvano (R)
Majority Leader
330 Senate Office Building
404 South Monroe Street
Tallahassee, FL 32399
P: (850) 487-5026
E: galvano.bill.web@flsenate.gov

Senate Minority Leader

Sen. Arthenia L. Joyner (D)
Minority Leader
200 Senate Office Building
404 South Monroe Street
Tallahassee, FL 32399
P: (850) 487-5019
F: (813) 233-4280
E: joyner.arthenia.web@flsenate.gov

Secretary of the Senate

Ms. Debbie Brown
Secretary of the Senate
Suite 405, The Capitol
404 South Monroe Street
Tallahassee, FL 32399
P: (850) 487-5270
F: (850) 487-5174

Members of the Senate

Abruzzo, Joseph (D, 25)
222 Senate Office Building
404 South Monroe Street
Tallahassee, FL 32399
P: (850) 487-5025
E: abruzzo.joseph.web@flsenate.gov

Altman, Thad (R, 16)
314 Senate Office Building
404 South Monroe Street
Tallahassee, FL 32399
P: (850) 487-5016
E: altman.thad.web@flsenate.gov

Bean, Aaron P. (R, 4)
302 Senate Office Building
404 South Monroe Street
Tallahassee, FL 32399
P: (850) 487-5004
E: bean.aaron.web@flsenate.gov

Benacquisto, Lizbeth (R, 30)
326 Senate Office Building
404 South Monroe Street
Tallahassee, FL 32399
P: (850) 487-5030
E: benacquisto.lizbeth.web@flsenate.gov

Bradley, Rob (R, 7)
208 Senate Office Building
404 South Monroe Street
Tallahassee, FL 32399
P: (850) 487-5007
F: (888) 263-0641
E: bradley.rob.web@flsenate.gov

Brandes, Jeffrey P. (R, 22)
318 Senate Office Building
404 South Monroe Street
Tallahassee, FL 32399
P: (850) 487-5022
E: brandes.jeff.web@flsenate.gov

Braynon II, Oscar (D, 36)
213 Senate Office Building
404 South Monroe Street
Tallahassee, FL 32399
P: (850) 487-5036
E: braynon.oscar.web@flsenate.gov

Bullard, Dwight (D, 39)
218 Senate Office Building
404 South Monroe Street
Tallahassee, FL 32399
P: (850) 487-5039
E: bullard.dwight.web@flsenate.gov

Clemens, Jeff (D, 27)
226 Senate Office Building
404 South Monroe Street
Tallahassee, FL 32399
P: (850) 487-5027
E: clemens.jeff.web@flsenate.gov

Dean Sr., Charles S. (R, 5)
311 Senate Office Building
404 South Monroe Street
Tallahassee, FL 32399
P: (850) 487-5005
E: dean.charles.web@flsenate.gov

Detert, Nancy C. (R, 28)
416 Senate Office Building
404 South Monroe Street
Tallahassee, FL 32399
P: (850) 487-5028
E: detert.nancy.web @flsenate.gov

Diaz De La Portilla, Miguel (R, 40)
406 Senate Office Building
404 South Monroe Street
Tallahassee, FL 32399
P: (850) 487-5040
E: portilla.miguel.web @flsenate.gov

Evers, Greg (R, 2)
308 Senate Office Building
404 South Monroe Street
Tallahassee, FL 32399
P: (850) 487-5002
F: (850) 487-5276
E: evers.greg.web @flsenate.gov

Flores, Anitere (R, 37)
413 Senate Office Building
404 South Monroe Street
Tallahassee, FL 32399
P: (850) 487-5037
E: flores.anitere.web @flsenate.gov

Gaetz, Don (R, 1)
420 Senate Office Building
404 South Monroe Street
Tallahassee, FL 32399
P: (850) 487-5001
E: gaetz.don.web @flsenate.gov

Galvano, Bill (R, 26)
330 Senate Office Building
404 South Monroe Street
Tallahassee, FL 32399
P: (850) 487-5026
E: galvano.bill.web @flsenate.gov

Garcia, Rene (R, 38)
310 Senate Office Building
404 South Monroe Street
Tallahassee, FL 32399
P: (850) 487-5038
E: garcia.rene.web @flsenate.gov

Gardiner, Andy (R, 13)
409 Senate Office Building
404 South Monroe Street
Tallahassee, FL 32399
P: (850) 487-5013
E: gardiner.andy.web @flsenate.gov

Gibson, Audrey (D, 9)
205 Senate Office Building
404 South Monroe Street
Tallahassee, FL 32399
P: (850) 487-5009
E: gibson.audrey.web @flsenate.gov

Grimsley, Denise (R, 21)
306 Senate Office Building
404 South Monroe Street
Tallahassee, FL 32399
P: (850) 487-5021
E: grimsley.denise.web @flsenate.gov

Hays, D. Alan (R, 11)
320 Senate Office Building
404 South Monroe Street
Tallahassee, FL 32399
P: (850) 487-5011
E: hays.alan.web @flsenate.gov

Hukill, Dorothy L. (R, 8)
305 Senate Office Building
404 South Monroe Street
Tallahassee, FL 32399
P: (850) 487-5008
E: hukill.dorothy.web @flsenate.gov

Joyner, Arthenia L. (D, 19)
200 Senate Office Building
404 South Monroe Street
Tallahassee, FL 32399
P: (850) 487-5019
F: (813) 233-4280
E: joyner.arthenia.web @flsenate.gov

Latvala, Jack (R, 20)
408 Senate Office Building
404 South Monroe Street
Tallahassee, FL 32399
P: (850) 487-5020
E: latvala.jack.web @flsenate.gov

Lee, Tom (R, 24)
418 Senate Office Building
404 South Monroe Street
Tallahassee, FL 32399
P: (850) 487-5024
E: lee.tom.web@flsenate.gov

Legg, John (R, 17)
316 Senate Office Building
404 South Monroe Street
Tallahassee, FL 32399
P: (850) 487-5017
E: legg.john.web @flsenate.gov

Margolis, Gwen (D, 35)
414 Senate Office Building
404 South Monroe Street
Tallahassee, FL 32399
P: (850) 487-5035
E: margolis.gwen.web @flsenate.gov

Montford, William J. (D, 3)
214 Senate Office Building
404 South Monroe Street
Tallahassee, FL 32399
P: (850) 487-5003
F: (850) 487-5086
E: montford.bill.web @flsenate.gov

Negron, Joe (R, 32)
412 Senate Office Building
404 South Monroe Street
Tallahassee, FL 32399
P: (850) 487-5032
E: negron.joe.web @flsenate.gov

Richter, Garrett S. (R, 23)
404 Senate Office Building
404 South Monroe Street
Tallahassee, FL 32399
P: (850) 487-5023
E: richter.garrett.web @flsenate.gov

Ring, Jeremy (D, 29)
405 Senate Office Building
404 South Monroe Street
Tallahassee, FL 32399
P: (850) 487-5029
E: ring.jeremy.web @flsenate.gov

Sachs, Maria Lorts (D, 34)
216 Senate Office Building
404 South Monroe Street
Tallahassee, FL 32399
P: (850) 487-5034
E: sachs.maria.web @flsenate.gov

Simmons, David (R, 10)
400 Senate Office Building
404 South Monroe Street
Tallahassee, FL 32399
P: (850) 487-5010
E: simmons.david.web @flsenate.gov

Simpson, Wilton (R, 18)
322 Senate Office Building
404 South Monroe Street
Tallahassee, FL 32399
P: (850) 487-5018
E: simpson.wilton.web @flsenate.gov

Smith, Christopher L. (D, 31)
202 Senate Office Building
404 South Monroe Street
Tallahassee, FL 32399
P: (850) 487-5031
E: smith.chris.web @flsenate.gov

Sobel, Eleanor (D, 33)
410 Senate Office Building
404 South Monroe Street
Tallahassee, FL 32399
P: (850) 487-5033
F: (850) 487-5428
E: sobel.eleanor.web @flsenate.gov

Soto, Darren (D, 14)
220 Senate Office Building
404 South Monroe Street
Tallahassee, FL 32399
P: (850) 487-5014
E: soto.darren.web @flsenate.gov

Stargel, Kelli (R, 15)
324 Senate Office Building
404 South Monroe Street
Tallahassee, FL 32399
P: (850) 487-5015
E: stargel.kelli.web @flsenate.gov

Thompson, Geraldine F. (D, 12)
224 Senate Office Building
404 South Monroe Street
Tallahassee, FL 32399
P: (850) 487-5012
E: thompson.geraldine.web @flsenate.gov

House

Speaker of the House

Rep. Steve Crisafulli (R)
Speaker of the House
420 The Capitol
402 South Monroe Street
Tallahassee, FL 32399
P: (850) 717-5051
E: steve.crisafulli @myfloridahouse.gov

Florida

Speaker Pro Tempore of the House

Rep. Matt Hudson (R)
Speaker Pro Tem
418 The Capitol
402 South Monroe Street
Tallahassee, FL 32399
P: (850) 717-5080
E: matt.hudson@myfloridahouse.gov

House Majority Leader

Rep. Dana D. Young (R)
Majority Leader
322 The Capitol
402 South Monroe Street
Tallahassee, FL 32399
P: (850) 717-5060
E: dana.young@myfloridahouse.gov

House Minority Leader

Rep. Mark S. Pafford (D)
Minority Leader
316 The Capitol
402 South Monroe Street
Tallahassee, FL 32399
P: (850) 717-5086
E: mark.pafford@myfloridahouse.gov

Clerk of the House

Mr. Robert L. Ward
Clerk of the House
513 Capitol
402 South Monroe Street
Tallahassee, FL 32399
P: (850) 717-5400
E: bob.ward@myfloridahouse.gov

Members of the House

Adkins, Janet H. (R, 11)
313 House Office Building
402 South Monroe Street
Tallahassee, FL 32399
P: (850) 717-5011
E: janet.adkins@myfloridahouse.gov

Ahern, Lawrence T. (R, 66)
405 House Office Building
402 South Monroe Street
Tallahassee, FL 32399
P: (850) 717-5066
E: lawrence.ahern@myfloridahouse.gov

Albritton, Ben (R, 56)
222 The Capitol
402 South Monroe Street
Tallahassee, FL 32399
P: (850) 717-5056
E: ben.albritton@myfloridahouse.gov

Antone, Bruce (D, 46)
1401 The Capitol
402 South Monroe Street
Tallahassee, FL 32399
P: (850) 717-5046
E: bruce.antone@myfloridahouse.gov

Artiles, Frank (R, 118)
204 House Office Building
402 South Monroe Street
Tallahassee, FL 32399
P: (850) 717-5118
E: frank.artiles@myfloridahouse.gov

Avila, Bryan (R, 111)*
1301 The Capitol
402 South Monroe Street
Tallahassee, FL 32399
P: (850) 717-5111
E: bryan.avila@myfloridahouse.gov

Baxley, Dennis K. (R, 23)
317 House Office Building
402 South Monroe Street
Tallahassee, FL 32399
P: (850) 717-5023
E: dennis.baxley@myfloridahouse.gov

Berman, Lori (D, 90)
1003 The Capitol
402 South Monroe Street
Tallahassee, FL 32399
P: (850) 717-5090
E: lori.berman@myfloridahouse.gov

Beshears, Halsey (R, 7)
303 House Office Building
402 South Monroe Street
Tallahassee, FL 32399
P: (850) 717-5007
E: halsey.beshears@myfloridahouse.gov

Bileca, Michael (R, 115)
218 House Office Building
402 South Monroe Street
Tallahassee, FL 32399
P: (850) 717-5115
E: michael.bileca@myfloridahouse.gov

Boyd, Jim (R, 71)
322 The Capitol
402 South Monroe Street
Tallahassee, FL 32399
P: (850) 717-5071
E: jim.boyd@myfloridahouse.gov

Bracy, Randolph (D, 45)
1401 The Capitol
402 South Monroe Street
Tallahassee, FL 32399
P: (850) 717-5045
E: randolph.bracy@myfloridahouse.gov

Brodeur, Jason T. (R, 28)
214 House Office Building
402 South Monroe Street
Tallahassee, FL 32399
P: (850) 717-5028
E: jason.brodeur@myfloridahouse.gov

Broxson, Douglas Vaughn (R, 3)
405 House Office Building
402 South Monroe Street
Tallahassee, FL 32399
P: (850) 717-5003
E: douglas.broxson@myfloridahouse.gov

Burgess, Danny (R, 38)*
1301 The Capitol
402 South Monroe Street
Tallahassee, FL 32399
P: (850) 717-5038
E: danny.burgess@myfloridahouse.gov

Burton, Colleen (R, 40)*
1301 The Capitol
402 South Monroe Street
Tallahassee, FL 32399
P: (850) 717-5040
E: colleen.burton@myfloridahouse.gov

Caldwell, Matthew H. (R, 79)
218 House Office Building
402 South Monroe Street
Tallahassee, FL 32399
P: (850) 717-5079
E: matthew.caldwell@myfloridahouse.gov

Campbell, Daphne D. (D, 108)
1003 The Capitol
402 South Monroe Street
Tallahassee, FL 32399
P: (850) 717-5108
E: daphne.campbell@myfloridahouse.gov

Clarke-Reed, Gwyndolen (D, 92)
200 House Office Building
402 South Monroe Street
Tallahassee, FL 32399
P: (850) 717-5092
E: gwyndolen.clarke-reed@myfloridahouse.gov

Combee, Neil (R, 39)
218 House Office Building
402 South Monroe Street
Tallahassee, FL 32399
P: (850) 717-5039
E: neil.combee@myfloridahouse.gov

Corcoran, Richard (R, 37)
418 The Capitol
402 South Monroe Street
Tallahassee, FL 32399
P: (850) 717-5037
E: richard.corcoran@myfloridahouse.gov

Cortes, John (D, 43)*
1402 The Capitol
402 South Monroe Street
Tallahassee, FL 32399
P: (850) 717-5043
E: john.cortes@myfloridahouse.gov

Cortes, Robert (R, 30)*
1401 The Capitol
402 South Monroe Street
Tallahassee, FL 32399
P: (850) 717-5030

Costello, Fredrick W. (R, 25)
1301 The Capitol
402 South Monroe Street
Tallahassee, FL 32399
P: (850) 717-5025
E: fred.costello@myfloridahouse.gov

Crisafulli, Steve (R, 51)
420 The Capitol
402 South Monroe Street
Tallahassee, FL 32399
P: (850) 717-5051
E: steve.crisafulli@myfloridahouse.gov

Cruz, Janet (D, 62)
1003 The Capitol
402 South Monroe Street
Tallahassee, FL 32399
P: (850) 717-5062
E: janet.cruz@myfloridahouse.gov

Cummings, W. Travis (R, 18)
222 The Capitol
402 South Monroe Street
Tallahassee, FL 32399
P: (850) 717-5018
E: travis.cummings
@myfloridahouse.gov

Diaz, Jose Felix (R, 116)
303 House Office Building
402 South Monroe Street
Tallahassee, FL 32399
P: (850) 717-5116
E: jose.diaz
@myfloridahouse.gov

Diaz Jr., Manny (R, 103)
313 House Office Building
402 South Monroe Street
Tallahassee, FL 32399
P: (850) 717-5103
E: manny.diaz
@myfloridahouse.gov

Drake, Brad (R, 5)
1301 The Capitol
402 South Monroe Street
Tallahassee, FL 32399
P: (850) 717-5005
E: brad.drake
@myfloridahouse.gov

DuBose, Bobby (D, 94)*
1402 The Capitol
402 South Monroe Street
Tallahassee, FL 32399
P: (850) 717-5094

Dudley, Dwight Richard (D, 68)
1401 The Capitol
402 South Monroe Street
Tallahassee, FL 32399
P: (850) 717-5068
E: dwight.dudley
@myfloridahouse.gov

Eagle, Dane (R, 77)
303 House Office Building
402 South Monroe Street
Tallahassee, FL 32399
P: (850) 717-5077
E: dane.eagle
@myfloridahouse.gov

Edwards, Katie A. (D, 98)
1401 The Capitol
402 South Monroe Street
Tallahassee, FL 32399
P: (850) 717-5098
E: katie.edwards
@myfloridahouse.gov

Eisnaugle, Eric (R, 44)
1301 The Capitol
402 South Monroe Street
Tallahassee, FL 32399
P: (850) 717-5044
E: eric.eisnaugle
@myfloridahouse.gov

Fant, Jay (R, 15)*
1301 The Capitol
402 South Monroe Street
Tallahassee, FL 32399
P: (850) 717-5015
E: jay.fant
@myfloridahouse.gov

Fitzenhagen, Heather Dawes (R, 78)
319 The Capitol
402 South Monroe Street
Tallahassee, FL 32399
P: (850) 717-5078
E: heather.fitzenhagen
@myfloridahouse.gov

Fresen, Erik (R, 114)
222 The Capitol
402 South Monroe Street
Tallahassee, FL 32399
P: (850) 717-5114
E: erik.fresen
@myfloridahouse.gov

Gaetz, Matt (R, 4)
317 The Capitol
402 South Monroe Street
Tallahassee, FL 32399
P: (850) 717-5004
E: matt.gaetz
@myfloridahouse.gov

Geller, Joseph S. (D, 100)*
1402 The Capitol
402 South Monroe Street
Tallahassee, FL 32399
P: (850) 717-5100
E: joseph.geller
@myfloridahouse.gov

Gonzalez, Julio (R, 74)*
1301 The Capitol
402 South Monroe Street
Tallahassee, FL 32399
P: (850) 717-5074
E: julio.gonzalez
@myfloridahouse.gov

Goodson, Tom (R, 50)
218 House Office Building
402 South Monroe Street
Tallahassee, FL 32399
P: (850) 717-5050
E: tom.goodson
@myfloridahouse.gov

Hager, Bill (R, 89)
405 House Office Building
402 South Monroe Street
Tallahassee, FL 32399
P: (850) 717-5089
E: bill.hager
@myfloridahouse.gov

Harrell, Gayle B. (R, 83)
214 House Office Building
402 South Monroe Street
Tallahassee, FL 32399
P: (850) 717-5083
E: gayle.harrell
@myfloridahouse.gov

Harrison, Shawn (R, 63)
1102 The Capitol
402 South Monroe Street
Tallahassee, FL 32399
P: (850) 717-5063

Hill, Walter (R, 2)
1101 The Capitol
402 South Monroe Street
Tallahassee, FL 32399
P: (850) 717-5002
E: mike.hill
@myfloridahouse.gov

Hudson, Matt (R, 80)
418 The Capitol
402 South Monroe Street
Tallahassee, FL 32399
P: (850) 717-5080
E: matt.hudson
@myfloridahouse.gov

Hutson, Travis (R, 24)
1102 The Capitol
402 South Monroe Street
Tallahassee, FL 32399
P: (850) 717-5024
E: travis.hutson
@myfloridahouse.gov

Ingoglia, Blaise (R, 35)*
1101 The Capitol
402 South Monroe Street
Tallahassee, FL 32399
P: (850) 717-5035
E: blaise.ingoglia
@myfloridahouse.gov

Ingram, Clay (R, 1)
222 The Capitol
402 South Monroe Street
Tallahassee, FL 32399
P: (850) 717-5001
E: clay.ingram
@myfloridahouse.gov

Jacobs, Kristin (D, 96)*
1402 The Capitol
402 South Monroe Street
Tallahassee, FL 32399
P: (850) 717-5096
E: kristin.jacobs
@myfloridahouse.gov

Jenne, Evan (D, 99)
316 The Capitol
402 South Monroe Street
Tallahassee, FL 32399
P: (850) 717-5099
E: evan.jenne
@myfloridahouse.gov

Jones, Mia L. (D, 14)
316 The Capitol
402 South Monroe Street
Tallahassee, FL 32399
P: (850) 717-5014
E: mia.jones
@myfloridahouse.gov

Jones, Shevrin D. (D, 101)
1401 The Capitol
402 South Monroe Street
Tallahassee, FL 32399
P: (850) 717-5101
E: shevrin.jones
@myfloridahouse.gov

Kerner, Dave (D, 87)
1401 The Capitol
402 South Monroe Street
Tallahassee, FL 32399
P: (850) 717-5087
E: dave.kerner
@myfloridahouse.gov

La Rosa, Mike (R, 42)
405 House Office Building
402 South Monroe Street
Tallahassee, FL 32399
P: (850) 717-5042
E: mike.larosa
@myfloridahouse.gov

Latvala, Chris (R, 67)*
1101 The Capitol
402 South Monroe Street
Tallahassee, FL 32399
P: (850) 717-5067
E: chris.latvala
@myfloridahouse.gov

Lee Jr., Larry (D, 84)
1401 The Capitol
402 South Monroe Street
Tallahassee, FL 32399
P: (850) 717-5084
E: larry.lee
@myfloridahouse.gov

Florida

Magar, MaryLynn (R, 82)
400 House Office Building
402 South Monroe Street
Tallahassee, FL 32399
P: (850) 717-5082
E: marylynn.magar
@myfloridahouse.gov

Mayfield, Debbie (R, 54)
317 House Office Building
402 South Monroe Street
Tallahassee, FL 32399
P: (850) 717-5054
E: debbie.mayfield
@myfloridahouse.gov

McBurney, Charles (R, 16)
412 House Office Building
402 South Monroe Street
Tallahassee, FL 32399
P: (850) 717-5016
E: charles.mcburney
@myfloridahouse.gov

McGhee, Kionne L. (D, 117)
1401 The Capitol
402 South Monroe Street
Tallahassee, FL 32399
P: (850) 717-5117
E: kionne.mcghee
@myfloridahouse.gov

Metz, Larry (R, 32)
222 The Capitol
402 South Monroe Street
Tallahassee, FL 32399
P: (850) 717-5032
E: larry.metz
@myfloridahouse.gov

Miller, Mike (R, 47)*
1101 The Capitol
402 South Monroe Street
Tallahassee, FL 32399
P: (850) 717-5047
E: mike.miller
@myfloridahouse.gov

Moraitis, George Reynold (R, 93)
410 House Office Building
402 South Monroe Street
Tallahassee, FL 32399
P: (850) 717-5093
E: george.moraitis
@myfloridahouse.gov

Moskowitz, Jared Evan (D, 97)
1401 The Capitol
402 South Monroe Street
Tallahassee, FL 32399
P: (850) 717-5097
E: jared.moskowitz
@myfloridahouse.gov

Murphy, Amanda Hickman (D, 36)
1402 The Capitol
402 South Monroe Street
Tallahassee, FL 32399
P: (850) 717-5036
E: amanda.murphy
@myfloridahouse.gov

Narain, Edwin (D, 61)*
1402 The Capitol
402 South Monroe Street
Tallahassee, FL 32399
P: (850) 717-5061
E: edwin.narain
@myfloridahouse.gov

Nunez, Jeanette M. (R, 119)
222 The Capitol
402 South Monroe Street
Tallahassee, FL 32399
P: (850) 717-5119
E: jeanette.nunez
@myfloridahouse.gov

Oliva, Jose R. (R, 110)
204 House Office Building
402 South Monroe Street
Tallahassee, FL 32399
P: (850) 717-5110
E: jose.oliva
@myfloridahouse.gov

O'Toole, H. Marlene (R, 33)
313 House Office Building
402 South Monroe Street
Tallahassee, FL 32399
P: (850) 717-5033
E: marlene.o'toole
@myfloridahouse.gov

Pafford, Mark S. (D, 86)
316 The Capitol
402 South Monroe Street
Tallahassee, FL 32399
P: (850) 717-5086
E: mark.pafford
@myfloridahouse.gov

Passidomo, Kathleen (R, 106)
417 House Office Building
402 South Monroe Street
Tallahassee, FL 32399
P: (850) 717-5106
E: kathleen.passidomo
@myfloridahouse.gov

Perry, W. Keith (R, 21)
405 House Office Building
402 South Monroe Street
Tallahassee, FL 32399
P: (850) 717-5021
E: keith.perry
@myfloridahouse.gov

Peters, Kathleen M. (R, 69)
400 House Office Building
402 South Monroe Street
Tallahassee, FL 32399
P: (850) 717-5069
E: kathleen.peters
@myfloridahouse.gov

Pigman, Cary (R, 55)
214 House Office Building
402 South Monroe Street
Tallahassee, FL 32399
P: (850) 717-5055
E: cary.pigman
@myfloridahouse.gov

Pilon, Raymond A. (R, 72)
412 House Office Building
402 South Monroe Street
Tallahassee, FL 32399
P: (850) 717-5072
E: raymond.pilon
@myfloridahouse.gov

Plakon, Scott (R, 29)
1101 The Capitol
402 South Monroe Street
Tallahassee, FL 32399
P: (850) 717-5029
E: scott.plakon
@myfloridahouse.gov

Plasencia, Rene (R, 49)*
1101 The Capitol
402 South Monroe Street
Tallahassee, FL 32399
P: (850) 717-5049
E: rene.plasencia
@myfloridahouse.gov

Porter, Elizabeth W. (R, 10)
313 House Office Building
402 South Monroe Street
Tallahassee, FL 32399
P: (850) 717-5010
E: elizabeth.porter
@myfloridahouse.gov

Powell, Bobby (D, 88)
1302 The Capitol
402 South Monroe Street
Tallahassee, FL 32399
P: (850) 717-5088
E: bobby.powell
@myfloridahouse.gov

Pritchett, Sharon (D, 102)
1302 The Capitol
402 South Monroe Street
Tallahassee, FL 32399
P: (850) 717-5102
E: sharon.pritchett
@myfloridahouse.gov

Raburn, Jake (R, 57)
300 House Office Building
402 South Monroe Street
Tallahassee, FL 32399
P: (850) 717-5057
E: jake.raburn
@myfloridahouse.gov

Rader, Kevin J.G. (D, 81)
212 The Capitol
402 South Monroe Street
Tallahassee, FL 32399
P: (850) 717-5081
E: kevin.rader
@myfloridahouse.gov

Raschein, Holly Merrill (R, 120)
319 The Capitol
402 South Monroe Street
Tallahassee, FL 32399
P: (850) 717-5120
E: holly.raschein
@myfloridahouse.gov

Raulerson, Daniel D. (R, 58)
300 House Office Building
402 South Monroe Street
Tallahassee, FL 32399
P: (850) 717-5058
E: daniel.raulerson
@myfloridahouse.gov

Ray, Lake (R, 12)
422 The Capitol
402 South Monroe Street
Tallahassee, FL 32399
P: (850) 717-5012
E: lake.ray
@myfloridahouse.gov

Rehwinkel Vasilinda, Michelle (D, 9)
1001 The Capitol
402 South Monroe Street
Tallahassee, FL 32399
P: (850) 717-5009
E: michelle.vasilinda
@myfloridahouse.gov

Renuart, Ronald (R, 17)
400 House Office Building
402 South Monroe Street
Tallahassee, FL 32399
P: (850) 717-5017
E: ronald.renuart
@myfloridahouse.gov

Richardson, David (D, 113)
200 House Office Building
402 South Monroe Street
Tallahassee, FL 32399
P: (850) 717-5113
E: david.richardson
@myfloridahouse.gov

Roberson, Kenneth L. (R, 75)
214 House Office Building
402 South Monroe Street
Tallahassee, FL 32399
P: (850) 717-5075
E: kenneth.roberson@myfloridahouse.gov

Rodrigues, Ray Wesley (R, 76)
317 The Capitol
402 South Monroe Street
Tallahassee, FL 32399
P: (850) 717-5076
E: ray.rodrigues@myfloridahouse.gov

Rodriguez, Jose Javier (D, 112)
1302 The Capitol
402 South Monroe Street
Tallahassee, FL 32399
P: (850) 717-5112
E: jose.rodriguez@myfloridahouse.gov

Rogers, Hazelle (D, 95)
200 House Office Building
402 South Monroe Street
Tallahassee, FL 32399
P: (850) 717-5095
E: hazelle.rogers@myfloridahouse.gov

Rooney Jr., Patrick (R, 85)
204 House Office Building
402 South Monroe Street
Tallahassee, FL 32399
P: (850) 717-5085
E: patrick.rooney@myfloridahouse.gov

Rouson, Darryl Ervin (D, 70)
212 The Capitol
402 South Monroe Street
Tallahassee, FL 32399
P: (850) 717-5070
E: darryl.rouson@myfloridahouse.gov

Santiago, David (R, 27)
1102 The Capitol
402 South Monroe Street
Tallahassee, FL 32399
P: (850) 717-5027
E: david.santiago@myfloridahouse.gov

Slosberg, Irving L. (D, 91)
1003 The Capitol
402 South Monroe Street
Tallahassee, FL 32399
P: (850) 717-5091
E: irving.slosberg@myfloridahouse.gov

Smith, Jimmie T. (R, 34)
317 House Office Building
402 South Monroe Street
Tallahassee, FL 32399
P: (850) 717-5034
E: jimmie.smith@myfloridahouse.gov

Spano, Ross (R, 59)
1102 The Capitol
402 South Monroe Street
Tallahassee, FL 32399
P: (850) 717-5059
E: ross.spano@myfloridahouse.gov

Sprowls, Chris (R, 65)*
1101 The Capitol
402 South Monroe Street
Tallahassee, FL 32399
P: (850) 717-5065
E: chris.sprowls@myfloridahouse.gov

Stafford, Cynthia A. (D, 109)
1003 The Capitol
402 South Monroe Street
Tallahassee, FL 32399
P: (850) 717-5109
E: cynthia.stafford@myfloridahouse.gov

Stark, Richard (D, 104)
1302 The Capitol
402 South Monroe Street
Tallahassee, FL 32399
P: (850) 717-5104
E: richard.stark@myfloridahouse.gov

Steube, W. Greg (R, 73)
204 House Office Building
402 South Monroe Street
Tallahassee, FL 32399
P: (850) 717-5073
E: greg.steube@myfloridahouse.gov

Stone, Charlie (R, 22)
1102 The Capitol
402 South Monroe Street
Tallahassee, FL 32399
P: (850) 717-5022
E: charlie.stone@myfloridahouse.gov

Sullivan, Jennifer (R, 31)*
1101 The Capitol
402 South Monroe Street
Tallahassee, FL 32399
P: (850) 717-5031
E: jennifer.sullivan@myfloridahouse.gov

Taylor, Dwayne L. (D, 26)
212 The Capitol
402 South Monroe Street
Tallahassee, FL 32399
P: (850) 717-5026
E: dwayne.taylor@myfloridahouse.gov

Tobia, John (R, 53)
405 House Office Building
402 South Monroe Street
Tallahassee, FL 32399
P: (850) 717-5053
E: john.tobia@myfloridahouse.gov

Torres Jr., Victor Manuel (D, 48)
1302 The Capitol
402 South Monroe Street
Tallahassee, FL 32399
P: (850) 717-5048
E: victor.torres@myfloridahouse.gov

Trujillo, Carlos (R, 105)
417 House Office Building
402 South Monroe Street
Tallahassee, FL 32399
P: (850) 717-5105
E: carlos.trujillo@myfloridahouse.gov

Trumbull, Jay (R, 6)*
1101 The Capitol
402 South Monroe Street
Tallahassee, FL 32399
P: (850) 717-5006
E: jay.trumbull@myfloridahouse.gov

Van Zant, Charles (R, 19)
400 House Office Building
402 South Monroe Street
Tallahassee, FL 32399
P: (850) 717-5019
E: charles.vanzant@myfloridahouse.gov

Watson, Barbara (D, 107)
1003 The Capitol
402 South Monroe Street
Tallahassee, FL 32399
P: (850) 717-5107
E: barbara.watson@myfloridahouse.gov

Watson Jr., Clovis (D, 20)
1302 The Capitol
402 South Monroe Street
Tallahassee, FL 32399
P: (850) 717-5020
E: clovis.watson@myfloridahouse.gov

Williams, Alan B. (D, 8)
1001 The Capitol
402 South Monroe Street
Tallahassee, FL 32399
P: (850) 717-5008
E: alan.williams@myfloridahouse.gov

Wood, John (R, 41)
303 House Office Building
402 South Monroe Street
Tallahassee, FL 32399
P: (850) 717-5041
E: john.wood@myfloridahouse.gov

Workman, Ritch (R, 52)
422 The Capitol
402 South Monroe Street
Tallahassee, FL 32399
P: (850) 717-5052
E: ritch.workman@myfloridahouse.gov

Young, Dana D. (R, 60)
322 The Capitol
402 South Monroe Street
Tallahassee, FL 32399
P: (850) 717-5060
E: dana.young@myfloridahouse.gov

Florida

Congress

Senate

Nelson, Bill (D)
Rubio, Marco (R)

House

Bilirakis, Gus M. (R, 12)
Brown, Corrine (D, 5)
Buchanan, Vern (R, 16)
Castor, Kathy (D, 14)
Clawson, Curt (R, 19)
Crenshaw, Ander (R, 4)
Curbelo, Carlos (R, 26)
DeSantis, Ron (R, 6)
Deutch, Ted (D, 21)
Diaz-Balart, Mario (R, 25)
Frankel, Lois J. (D, 22)
Graham, Gwen (D, 2)
Grayson, Alan (D, 9)
Hastings, Alcee L. (D, 20)
Jolly, David (R, 13)
Mica, John L. (R, 7)
Miller, Jeff (R, 1)
Murphy, Patrick (D, 18)
Nugent, Richard (R, 11)
Posey, Bill (R, 8)
Rooney, Tom (R, 17)
Ros-Lehtinen, Ileana (R, 27)
Ross, Dennis A. (R, 15)
Wasserman Schultz, Debbie (D, 23)
Webster, Daniel (R, 10)
Wilson, Frederica S. (D, 24)
Yoho, Ted (R, 3)

Georgia

Executive

Governor

Hon. Nathan Deal (R)
Governor
203 State Capitol
Atlanta, GA 30334
P: (404) 656-1776
F: (404) 657-7332

Lieutenant Governor

Hon. Casey Cagle (R)
Lieutenant Governor
240 State Capitol
Atlanta, GA 30334
P: (404) 656-5030
F: (404) 656-6739

Commissioner of Agriculture

Mr. Gary Black (R)
Commissioner
19 Martin Luther King Jr. Drive, SW
204 Agricultural Building
Atlanta, GA 30334
P: (404) 656-3600
F: (404) 651-8206

Attorney General

Hon. Sam S. Olens (R)
Attorney General
40 Capitol Square, Southwest
Atlanta, GA 30334
P: (404) 656-3300
F: (404) 657-8733
E: AGOlens@law.ga.gov

Auditor

Mr. Greg S. Griffin
(appointed by the Legislature)
State Auditor
270 Washington Street, SW
Suite 1-156
Atlanta, GA 30334
P: (404) 656-2180
E: griffin@audits.ga.gov

Commissioner of Insurance

Hon. Ralph T. Hudgens (R)
Commissioner
2 Martin Luther King Jr. Drive
West Tower, Suite 704
Atlanta, GA 30334
P: (404) 656-2070
F: (404) 657-8542

Commissioner of Labor

Hon. Mark Butler (R)
Commissioner
148 International Boulevard Northeast
Atlanta, GA 30303
P: (404) 232-7300
F: (404) 656-2683
E: commissioner@gdol.ga.gov

Secretary of State

Hon. Brian Kemp (R)
Secretary of State
214 State Capitol
Atlanta, GA 30334
P: (404) 656-2881
F: (404) 656-0513
E: sos@sos.ga.gov

Superintendent of Schools

Hon. Richard L. Woods (R)
Superintendent of Public Instruction
2066 Twin Towers East
Atlanta, GA 30334
P: (404) 656-2800
F: (404) 651-8737

Treasurer

Hon. Steve McCoy
(appointed)
Treasurer & Director
200 Piedmont Avenue
Suite 1204, West Tower
Atlanta, GA 30334
P: (404) 656-2168
F: (404) 656-9048
E: OSTWeb@treasury.ga.gov

Judiciary

Supreme Court (NE)

Ms. Therese S. Barnes
Clerk
244 Washington Street
Room 572, State Office Annex Building
Atlanta, GA 30334
P: (404) 656-3470
F: (404) 656-2253

Hon. Hugh P. Thompson
Chief Justice
Hon. Robert Benham
Hon. Keith R. Blackwell
Hon. P. Harris Hines
Hon. Carol W. Hunstein
Hon. Harold D. Melton
Hon. David E. Nahmias

Legislative Senate

Senate President

Hon. Casey Cagle (R)
Lieutenant Governor
240 State Capitol
Atlanta, GA 30334
P: (404) 656-5030
F: (404) 656-6739

President Pro Tempore of the Senate

Sen. David J. Shafer (R)
President Pro Tempore
321 State Capitol
Atlanta, GA 30334
P: (404) 656-0048
F: (404) 463-5220
E: david.shafer
@senate.ga.gov

Senate Majority Leader

Sen. Bill Cowsert (R)
Majority Leader
236 State Capitol
Atlanta, GA 30334
P: (404) 463-1366
F: (404) 657-9887
E: bill.cowsert
@senate.ga.gov

Senate Minority Leader

Sen. Steve Henson (D)
Democratic Leader
121-B State Capitol
Atlanta, GA 30334
P: (404) 656-0085
F: (404) 463-2071
E: steve.henson
@senate.ga.gov

Secretary of the Senate

Mr. David A. Cook
Secretary of the Senate
353 State Capitol
Atlanta, GA 30334
P: (404) 656-5040
F: (404) 656-5043
E: David.Cook@senate.ga.gov

Members of the Senate

Albers, John (R, 56)
110-D State Capitol
Atlanta, GA 30334
P: (404) 463-8055
F: (404) 463-4161
E: john.albers
@senate.ga.gov

Beach, Brandon (R, 21)
303-B Legislative Office Building
Atlanta, GA 30334
P: (404) 463-1378
F: (404) 463-1386
E: brandon.beach
@senate.ga.gov

Bethel, Charlie (R, 54)
121-E State Capitol
Atlanta, GA 30334
P: (404) 463-1383
F: (404) 656-6484
E: charlie.bethel
@senate.ga.gov

Black, C. Ellis (D, 8)
304-A Legislative Office Building
Atlanta, GA 30334
P: (404) 656-3932
E: ellis.black@house.ga.gov

Burke, Dean (R, 11)
301-A Legislative Office Building
Atlanta, GA 30334
P: (404) 656-0040
F: (404) 657-7266
E: dean.burke@senate.ga.gov

Butler, Gloria (D, 55)
420-C State Capitol
Atlanta, GA 30334
P: (404) 656-0075
F: (404) 657-9728
E: gloria.butler
@senate.ga.gov

Cowsert, Bill (R, 46)
236 State Capitol
Atlanta, GA 30334
P: (404) 463-1366
F: (404) 657-9887
E: bill.cowsert
@senate.ga.gov

Georgia

Crane, Mike (R, 28)
325-B Legislative Office Building
Atlanta, GA 30334
P: (404) 656-6446
F: (404) 463-1381
E: mike.crane@senate.ga.gov

Davenport, Gail (D, 44)
121-C State Capitol
Atlanta, GA 30334
P: (404) 463-5260
F: (404) 656-6579
E: gail.davenport@senate.ga.gov

Dugan, Mike (R, 30)
109 State Capitol
Atlanta, GA 30334
P: (404) 656-7454
F: (404) 651-5795
E: mike.dugan@senate.ga.gov

Fort, Vincent D. (D, 39)
121-G State Capitol
Atlanta, GA 30334
P: (404) 656-5091
F: (404) 651-7078
E: vincent.fort@senate.ga.gov

Ginn, Frank (R, 47)
121-I State Capitol
Atlanta, GA 30334
P: (404) 656-4700
F: (404) 657-3248
E: frank.ginn@senate.ga.gov

Gooch, Steve (R, 51)
421-F State Capitol
Atlanta, GA 30334
P: (404) 656-9221
F: (404) 651-6768
E: steve.gooch@senate.ga.gov

Harbin, M.H. (R, 16)*
324-B Legislative Office Building
Atlanta, GA 30334
P: (404) 656-0078
F: (404) 656-6484
E: marty.harbin@senate.ga.gov

Harbison, Ed (D, 15)
431 State Capitol
Atlanta, GA 30334
P: (404) 656-0074
F: (404) 463-5547
E: ed.harbison@senate.ga.gov

Harper, Tyler (R, 7)
301-B Legislative Office Building
Atlanta, GA 30334
P: (404) 463-5263
F: (404) 463-4161
E: tyler.harper@senate.ga.gov

Heath, Bill (R, 31)
110-C State Capitol
Atlanta, GA 30334
P: (404) 656-3943
F: (404) 463-2279
E: bill.heath@senate.ga.gov

Henson, Steve (D, 41)
121-B State Capitol
Atlanta, GA 30334
P: (404) 656-0085
F: (404) 463-2071
E: steve.henson@senate.ga.gov

Hill, Hunter (R, 6)
421-B State Capitol
Atlanta, GA 30334
P: (404) 463-2518
F: (404) 651-6768
E: hunter.hill@senate.ga.gov

Hill, Jack (R, 4)
234 State Capitol
Atlanta, GA 30334
P: (404) 656-5038
F: (404) 657-7094
E: jack.hill@senate.ga.gov

Hill, Judson H. (R, 32)
421-D State Capitol
Atlanta, GA 30334
P: (404) 656-0150
F: (404) 651-6768
E: judson.hill@senate.ga.gov

Hufstetler, Chuck (R, 52)
320-A Legislative Office Building
Atlanta, GA 30334
P: (404) 656-0034
F: (404) 656-0459
E: chuck.hufstetler@senate.ga.gov

Jackson, Lester G. (D, 2)
432 State Capitol
Atlanta, GA 30334
P: (404) 463-5261
F: (404) 463-5547
E: lester.jackson@senate.ga.gov

Jackson, William S. (R, 24)
241 State Capitol
Atlanta, GA 30334
P: (404) 651-7738
F: (404) 651-5795
E: bill.jackson@senate.ga.gov

James, Donzella J. (D, 35)
121-D State Capitol
Atlanta, GA 30334
P: (404) 463-1379
F: (404) 656-6579
E: Donzella.James@senate.ga.gov

Jeffares, Rick (R, 17)
327-B Legislative Office Building
Atlanta, GA 30334
P: (404) 463-1376
F: (404) 651-5795
E: rick.jeffares@senate.ga.gov

Jones, Burt (R, 25)
327-A Legislative Office Building
Atlanta, GA 30334
P: (404) 656-0082
E: burt.jones@senate.ga.gov

Jones, Emanuel D. (D, 10)
420-D State Capitol
Atlanta, GA 30334
P: (404) 656-0502
F: (404) 657-9728
E: emanj@mindspring.com

Jones II, Harold V. (D, 22)*
323-B Legislative Office Building
Atlanta, GA 30334
P: (404) 463-3942
E: harold.jones@senate.ga.gov

Kennedy, John Flanders (R, 18)*
109 State Capitol
Atlanta, GA 30334
P: (404) 656-7454
F: (404) 651-5795
E: john.kennedy@senate.ga.gov

Kirk, Gregory Mark (R, 13)*
320-A Legislative Office Building
Atlanta, GA 30334
P: (404) 463-5258
E: greg.kirk@senate.ga.gov

Ligon Jr., William T. (R, 3)
421-C State Capitol
Atlanta, GA 30334
P: (404) 656-0045
F: (404) 651-6768
E: william.ligon@senate.ga.gov

Lucas Sr., David E. (D, 26)
305-A Legislative Office Building
Atlanta, GA 30334
P: (404) 656-5035
F: (404) 657-7266
E: david.lucas@senate.ga.gov

Martin, P. K. (R, 9)*
304-B Legislative Office Building
Atlanta, GA 30334
P: (404) 656-3933
E: p.k.martin@senate.ga.gov

McKoon, Joshua (R, 29)
319-A Legislative Office Building
Atlanta, GA 30334
P: (404) 463-3931
F: (404) 657-3217
E: josh.mckoon@senate.ga.gov

Millar, Fran (R, 40)
319-B Legislative Office Building
Atlanta, GA 30334
P: (404) 463-2260
F: (404) 657-3217
E: fran.millar@senate.ga.gov

Miller, Butch (R, 49)
109 State Capitol
Atlanta, GA 30334
P: (404) 656-7454
F: (404) 651-5795
E: butch.miller@senate.ga.gov

Mullis, Jeff E. (R, 53)
453 State Capitol
Atlanta, GA 30334
P: (404) 656-0057
F: (404) 651-6768
E: jeff.mullis@senate.ga.gov

Orrock, Nan (D, 36)
420-B State Capitol
Atlanta, GA 30334
P: (404) 463-8054
F: (404) 657-9728
E: nan.orrock@senate.ga.gov

Parent, Elena C. (D, 42)
321-B Legislative Office Building
Atlanta, GA 30334
P: (404) 656-5109
E: elena.parent@senate.ga.gov

Ramsey Sr., Ronald B. (D, 43)
303-A Legislative Office Building
Atlanta, GA 30334
P: (404) 463-2598
F: (404) 463-1386
E: ronald.ramsey@senate.ga.gov

Rhett, Michael A. (D, 33)*
321-A Legislative Office Building
Atlanta, GA 30334
P: (404) 656-0054
E: michael.rhett@senate.ga.gov

Seay, Valencia (D, 34)
420-A State Capitol
Atlanta, GA 30334
P: (404) 656-5095
F: (404) 657-9728
E: valencia.seay@senate.ga.gov

Shafer, David J. (R, 48)
321 State Capitol
Atlanta, GA 30334
P: (404) 656-0048
F: (404) 463-5220
E: david.shafer@senate.ga.gov

Sims, Freddie Powell (D, 12)
110-A State Capitol
Atlanta, GA 30334
P: (404) 463-5259
F: (404) 463-2279
E: freddie.sims@senate.ga.gov

Stone, Jesse (R, 23)
325-A Legislative Office Building
Atlanta, GA 30334
P: (404) 463-1314
F: (404) 463-1381
E: jesse.stone@senate.ga.gov

Tate, Horacena (D, 38)
121-A State Capitol
Atlanta, GA 30334
P: (404) 463-8053
F: (404) 463-7783
E: horacena.tate@senate.ga.gov

Thompson, Bruce (R, 14)
324-A Legislative Office Building
Atlanta, GA 30334
P: (404) 656-0065
F: (404) 656-6484
E: bruce.thomspon@house.ga.gov

Thompson, Curt (D, 5)
121-H State Capitol
Atlanta, GA 30334
P: (404) 463-1318
F: (404) 651-7078
E: curt@curtthompson.com

Tippins, Lindsey (R, 37)
302-B Legislative Office Building
Atlanta, GA 30334
P: (404) 657-0406
F: (404) 657-0459
E: lindsey.tippins@senate.ga.gov

Tolleson, Ross (R, 20)
121-F State Capitol
Atlanta, GA 30334
P: (404) 656-0081
F: (404) 651-6767
E: ross.tolleson@senate.ga.gov

Unterman, Renee S. (R, 45)
121-J State Capitol
Atlanta, GA 30334
P: (404) 463-1368
F: (404) 651-6767
E: renee.unterman@senate.ga.gov

Watson, Ben (R, 1)
320-B Legislative Office Building
Atlanta, GA 30334
P: (404) 656-7880
E: ben.watson@house.ga.gov

Wilkinson, John (R, 50)
421-A State Capitol
Atlanta, GA 30334
P: (404) 463-5257
F: (404) 651-6768
E: john.wilkinson@senate.ga.gov

Williams, Michael E. (R, 27)*
323-A Legislative Office Building
Atlanta, GA 30334
P: (404) 656-7127
E: michael.williams@senate.ga.gov

Williams, Tommie (R, 19)
110-B State Capitol
Atlanta, GA 30334
P: (404) 656-0089
F: (404) 463-2279
E: tommie.williams@senate.ga.gov

House

Speaker of the House

Rep. David Ralston (R)
Speaker
332 State Capitol
Atlanta, GA 30334
P: (404) 656-5020
F: (404) 656-5644
E: david.ralston@house.ga.gov

Speaker Pro Tempore of the House

Rep. Jan Jones (R)
Speaker Pro Tempore
340 State Capitol
Atlanta, GA 30334
P: (404) 656-5072
F: (404) 657-0498
E: jan.jones@house.ga.gov

House Majority Leader

Rep. Larry O'Neal (R)
Majority Leader
338 State Capitol
Atlanta, GA 30334
P: (404) 656-5052
E: larry.oneal@house.ga.gov

House Minority Leader

Rep. Stacey Abrams (D)
Minority Leader
609-F Legislative Office Building
Atlanta, GA 30334
P: (404) 656-5058
E: staceyabrams@gmail.com

Clerk of the House

Mr. William L. Reilly
Clerk of the House
309 State Capitol
Atlanta, GA 30334
P: (404) 656-5015
E: bill.reilly@house.ga.gov

Members of the House

Abrams, Stacey (D, 89)
609-F Legislative Office Building
Atlanta, GA 30334
P: (404) 656-5058
E: staceyabrams@gmail.com

Alexander, Kimberly (D, 66)
512-D Legislative Office Building
Atlanta, GA 30334
P: (404) 656-7859
E: kimberly.alexander@house.ga.gov

Allison, Stephen (R, 8)
504-A Legislative Office Building
Atlanta, GA 30334
P: (404) 656-0189
E: stephen.allison@house.ga.gov

Anderson, Tonya (D, 92)
512-F Legislative Office Building
Atlanta, GA 30334
P: (404) 656-7859
E: tonya.anderson@house.ga.gov

Atwood, Alex (R, 179)
401-A Legislative Office Building
Atlanta, GA 30334
P: (404) 656-0152
E: alex.atwood@house.ga.gov

Ballinger, Mandi (R, 23)
601-A Legislative Office Building
Atlanta, GA 30334
P: (404) 656-0254
E: mandi.ballinger@house.ga.gov

Barr, Timothy (R, 103)
612-E Legislative Office Building
Atlanta, GA 30334
P: (404) 656-0325
E: timothy.barr@house.ga.gov

Battles, Paul R. (R, 15)
401-K State Capitol
Atlanta, GA 30334
P: (404) 657-8441
E: paul.battles@house.ga.gov

Georgia

Beasley-Teague, Sharon (D, 65)
509-A Legislative Office Building
Atlanta, GA 30334
P: (404) 656-0221
F: (404) 656-7789
E: sharon.beasley-teague@house.ga.gov

Bell, Simone (D, 58)
509-D Legislative Office Building
Atlanta, GA 30334
P: (404) 656-0220
E: simone.bell@house.ga.gov

Belton, D.C. (R, 112)*
401-B Legislative Office Building
Atlanta, GA 30334
P: (404) 656-0152
E: dc.belton@house.ga.gov

Bennett, Karen (D, 94)
507-G Legislative Office Building
Atlanta, GA 30334
P: (404) 656-0202
E: karen.bennett@house.ga.gov

Bentley, Patty (D, 139)
607-C Legislative Office Building
Atlanta, GA 30334
P: (404) 656-0287
E: patty.bentley@house.ga.gov

Benton, Tommy (R, 31)
613-D Legislative Office Building
Atlanta, GA 30334
P: (404) 463-3793
F: (404) 463-2976
E: tommy.benton@house.ga.gov

Beskin, Beth (R, 54)*
601-F Legislative Office Building
Atlanta, GA 30334
P: (404) 656-0254
E: beth.beskin@house.ga.gov

Beverly, James (D, 143)
509-G Legislative Office Building
Atlanta, GA 30334
P: (404) 656-0220
E: james.beverly@house.ga.gov

Broadrick, Bruce (R, 4)
608-B Legislative Office Building
Atlanta, GA 30334
P: (404) 656-0298
E: bruce.broadrick@house.ga.gov

Brockway, Buzz (R, 102)
504-B Legislative Office Building
Atlanta, GA 30334
P: (404) 656-0188
E: buzz.brockway@house.ga.gov

Brooks Sr., Tyrone L. (D, 55)
511-H Legislative Office Building
Atlanta, GA 30334
P: (404) 656-6372
E: tyrone.brooks@house.ga.gov

Bruce, Roger B. (D, 61)
512-A Legislative Office Building
Atlanta, GA 30334
P: (404) 656-7859
E: rbruce5347@aol.com

Bryant, Bob (D, 162)
608-D Legislative Office Building
Atlanta, GA 30334
P: (404) 656-0298
F: (404) 463-4559
E: bob.bryant@house.ga.gov

Buckner, Debbie (D, 137)
409-C Legislative Office Building
Atlanta, GA 30334
P: (404) 656-0116
F: (404) 651-8086
E: debbie.buckner@house.ga.gov

Burns, Jon G. (R, 159)
228 State Capitol
Atlanta, GA 30334
P: (404) 656-5099
F: (404) 656-6897
E: jon.burns@house.ga.gov

Caldwell Jr., Johnnie (R, 131)
612-D Legislative Office Building
Atlanta, GA 30334
P: (404) 656-0325
E: johnnie.caldwell@house.ga.gov

Caldwell, Michael (R, 20)
401-F Legislative Office Building
Atlanta, GA 30334
P: (404) 656-0152
E: michael.caldwell@house.ga.gov

Cantrell, Wesley E. (R, 22)*
507-E Legislative Office Building
Atlanta, GA 30334
P: (404) 656-0202
E: wesley.cantrell@house.ga.gov

Carson, John (R, 46)
607-A Legislative Office Building
Atlanta, GA 30334
P: (404) 656-0287
E: john.carson@house.ga.gov

Carter, Amy (D, 175)
245 State Capitol
Atlanta, GA 30334
P: (404) 463-2248
E: amy.carter@house.ga.gov

Casas, David S. (R, 107)
601-H Legislative Office Building
Atlanta, GA 30334
P: (404) 656-0254
E: david.casas@house.ga.gov

Chandler, Joyce (R, 105)
601-G Legislative Office Building
Atlanta, GA 30334
P: (404) 656-0254
E: joyce.chandler@house.ga.gov

Cheokas, Mike (R, 138)
401-J State Capitol
Atlanta, GA 30334
P: (404) 656-7857
E: mike.cheokas@house.ga.gov

Clark, David (R, 98)*
612-E Legislative Office Building
Atlanta, GA 30334
P: (404) 656-0325
E: david.clark@house.ga.gov

Clark, Heath Nicholas (R, 147)*
404-C Legislative Office Building
Atlanta, GA 30334
P: (404) 656-0109
E: heath.clark@house.ga.gov

Clark, Valerie (R, 101)
507-F Legislative Office Building
Atlanta, GA 30334
P: (404) 656-0202
E: vclark123@charter.net

Coleman, Brooks P. (R, 97)
416 State Capitol
Atlanta, GA 30334
P: (404) 656-9210
F: (404) 656-5070
E: brooks.coleman@house.ga.gov

Cooke, Kevin (R, 18)
504-D Legislative Office Building
Atlanta, GA 30334
P: (404) 656-0188
E: kevin.cooke@house.ga.gov

Coomer, Christian (R, 14)
109 State Capitol
Atlanta, GA 30334
P: (404) 651-7737
F: (404) 651-5795
E: christian.coomer@house.ga.gov

Cooper, Sharon (R, 43)
436 State Capitol
Atlanta, GA 30334
P: (404) 656-5069
E: sharon.cooper@house.ga.gov

Corbett, John I. (R, 174)*
607-E Legislative Office Building
Atlanta, GA 30334
P: (404) 656-0287
E: john.corbett@house.ga.gov

Dawkins-Haigler, Dee (D, 91)
607-B Legislative Office Building
Atlanta, GA 30334
P: (404) 656-0287
E: dee.dawkins-haigler@house.ga.gov

Deffenbaugh, John (R, 1)
507-C Legislative Office Building
Atlanta, GA 30334
P: (404) 656-0202
E: john.deffenbaugh@house.ga.gov

Dempsey, Katie (R, 13)
245 State Capitol
Atlanta, GA 30334
P: (404) 463-2247
E: katie.dempsey@house.ga.gov

Dickerson, Pamela A. (D, 113)
611-E Legislative Office Building
Atlanta, GA 30334
P: (404) 656-0314
E: pam.dickerson@house.ga.gov

Dickey, Robert (R, 140)
109 State Capitol
Atlanta, GA 30334
P: (404) 651-7737
F: (404) 656-0250
E: robert.dickey@house.ga.gov

Dickson, Tom (R, 6)
245 State Capitol
Atlanta, GA 30334
P: (404) 463-2247
F: (404) 651-8086
E: tom.dickson@house.ga.gov

Dollar, Matt (R, 45)
401-K State Capitol
Atlanta, GA 30334
P: (404) 656-5138
F: (404) 651-8086
E: matt.dollar@house.ga.gov

Douglas, Demetrius (D, 78)
512-E Legislative Office Building
Atlanta, GA 30334
P: (404) 656-7859
E: demetrius.douglas@house.ga.gov

Drenner, Karla Lea (D, 85)
507-H Legislative Office Building
Atlanta, GA 30334
P: (404) 656-0202
F: (404) 651-8086
E: dren16999@aol.com

Dudgeon, Mike (R, 25)
608-C Legislative Office Building
Atlanta, GA 30334
P: (404) 656-0298
E: mike.dudgeon@house.ga.gov

Dukes, Winfred J. (D, 154)
411-H Legislative Office Building
Atlanta, GA 30334
P: (404) 656-0126
E: wdukes_2000@yahoo.com

Dunahoo, Emory (R, 30)
401-D Legislative Office Building
Atlanta, GA 30334
P: (404) 656-0152
E: emory.dunahoo@house.ga.gov

Duncan, Geoff (R, 26)
504-F Legislative Office Building
Atlanta, GA 30334
P: (404) 656-0189
E: geoff.duncan@house.ga.gov

Ealum, Darrel B. (D, 153)*
409-B Legislative Office Building
Atlanta, GA 30334
P: (404) 656-0116
E: darrel.ealum@house.ga.gov

Efstration, Chuck (R, 104)
601-C Legislative Office Building
Atlanta, GA 30334
P: (404) 656-0254
E: chuck.efstration@house.ga.gov

Ehrhart, Earl (R, 36)
245 State Capitol
Atlanta, GA 30334
P: (404) 463-2247
F: (404) 437-2601
E: earl.ehrhart@house.ga.gov

England, Terry Lamar (R, 116)
245 State Capitol
Atlanta, GA 30334
P: (404) 463-2247
E: englandhomeport2@windstream.net

Epps, Bubber (R, 144)
608-B Legislative Office Building
Atlanta, GA 30334
P: (404) 656-0298
E: bubberepps@gmail.com

Evans, Stacey (D, 42)
511-C Legislative Office Building
Atlanta, GA 30334
P: (404) 656-6372
E: stacey@staceyevans.org

Fleming, Barry A. (R, 121)
401-H Legislative Office Building
Atlanta, GA 30334
P: (404) 656-0152
E: barry.fleming@house.ga.gov

Floyd, Hugh (D, 99)
611-H Legislative Office Building
Atlanta, GA 30334
P: (404) 656-0314
F: (404) 656-0250
E: hughfloyd@mindspring.com

Fludd, Virgil (D, 64)
409-A Legislative Office Building
Atlanta, GA 30334
P: (404) 656-0116
F: (404) 651-8086
E: vfludd@mindspring.com

Frazier, Gloria (D, 126)
604-C Legislative Office Building
Atlanta, GA 30334
P: (404) 656-0265
E: frazier26@comcast.net

Frye, Spencer (D, 118)
604-B Legislative Office Building
Atlanta, GA 30334
P: (404) 656-0265
E: spencer.frye@house.ga.gov

Gardner, Pat (D, 57)
604-G Legislative Office Building
Atlanta, GA 30334
P: (404) 656-0265
F: (404) 463-2634
E: pat@patgardner.org

Gasaway, Dan (R, 28)
612-G Legislative Office Building
Atlanta, GA 30334
P: (404) 656-0325
E: dan.gasaway@house.ga.gov

Geisinger, Harry (R, 48)
408-D Legislative Office Building
Atlanta, GA 30334
P: (404) 657-1803
F: (404) 651-8086
E: harry.geisinger@house.ga.gov

Glanton, Mike (D, 75)
408-C Legislative Office Building
Atlanta, GA 30334
P: (404) 657-1803
E: mike.glanton@house.ga.gov

Golick, Rich (R, 40)
218 State Capitol
Atlanta, GA 30334
P: (404) 656-5943
E: rich.golick@house.ga.gov

Gordon, J. Craig (D, 163)
607-H Legislative Office Building
Atlanta, GA 30334
P: (404) 656-0287
E: jcraig.gordon@house.ga.gov

Gravley, Micah (R, 67)
612-F Legislative Office Building
Atlanta, GA 30334
P: (404) 656-0325
E: micah.gravley@house.ga.gov

Greene, Gerald E. (R, 151)
507-D Legislative Office Building
Atlanta, GA 30334
P: (404) 656-0202
F: (229) 732-2973
E: gerald.greene@house.ga.gov

Hamilton, Mark (R, 24)
218 State Capitol
Atlanta, GA 30334
P: (404) 656-5132
E: mark.hamilton@house.ga.gov

Harbin, Ben L. (R, 122)
614-B Legislative Office Building
Atlanta, GA 30334
P: (404) 656-3949
E: ben.harbin@house.ga.gov

Harden, Buddy (R, 148)
504-G Legislative Office Building
Atlanta, GA 30334
P: (404) 656-0188
E: bharden@planttel.net

Harrell, Brett A. (R, 106)
601-D Legislative Office Building
Atlanta, GA 30334
P: (404) 656-0254
E: brett@voteharrell.com

Georgia

Hatchett, Matt (R, 150)
415 State Capitol
Atlanta, GA 30334
P: (404) 656-5025
F: (404) 657-8278
E: matt.hatchett
@house.ga.gov

Hawkins, Lee (R, 27)
508-D Legislative Office
Building
Atlanta, GA 30334
P: (404) 656-0213
E: lee.hawkins@house.ga.gov

Henson, Michele D. (D, 86)
512-I Legislative Office
Building
Atlanta, GA 30334
P: (404) 656-7859
F: (404) 651-8086
E: michele.henson
@house.ga.gov

Hightower, Dustin (R, 68)
408-A Legislative Office
Building
Atlanta, GA 30334
P: (404) 657-1803
E: dustin.hightower
@house.ga.gov

Hitchens, Bill (R, 161)
501-A Legislative Office
Building
Atlanta, GA 30334
P: (404) 656-0178
E: bill.hitchens
@house.ga.gov

Holcomb, Scott (D, 81)
511-E Legislative Office
Building
Atlanta, GA 30334
P: (404) 656-6372
E: scott.holcomb
@house.ga.gov

Holmes, Susan (R, 129)
501-F Legislative Office
Building
Atlanta, GA 30334
P: (404) 656-0178
E: sdholmes@bellsouth.net

Houston, Penny (R, 170)
245 State Capitol
Atlanta, GA 30334
P: (404) 463-2247
F: (404) 651-8086
E: penny.houston
@house.ga.gov

Howard, Henry "Wayne" (D, 124)
511-G Legislative Office
Building
Atlanta, GA 30334
P: (404) 656-6372
E: wayne.howard
@house.ga.gov

Hugley, Carolyn Fleming (D, 136)
609-A Legislative Office
Building
Atlanta, GA 30334
P: (404) 656-5058
E: carolyn.hugley
@house.ga.gov

Jackson, Mack (D, 128)
611-F Legislative Office
Building
Atlanta, GA 30334
P: (404) 656-0314
F: (404) 656-0250
E: mack.jackson
@house.ga.gov

Jacobs, Mike (R, 80)
131 State Capitol
Atlanta, GA 30334
P: (404) 656-5116
E: repjacobs@gmail.com

Jasperse, Rick (R, 11)
504-C Legislative Office
Building
Atlanta, GA 30334
P: (404) 656-0188
E: rick.jasperse
@house.ga.gov

Jones, Jan (R, 47)
340 State Capitol
Atlanta, GA 30334
P: (404) 656-5072
F: (404) 657-0498
E: jan.jones@house.ga.gov

Jones, Jeffrey B. (R, 167)*
411-F Legislative Office
Building
Atlanta, GA 30334
P: (404) 656-0126
E: jb.jones@house.ga.gov

Jones, LaDawn (D, 62)
512-B Legislative Office
Building
Atlanta, GA 30334
P: (404) 656-7859
E: ladawn.jones
@house.ga.gov

Jones, Sheila (D, 53)
411-D Legislative Office
Building
Atlanta, GA 30334
P: (404) 656-0126
F: (404) 656-8086
E: sheila.jones
@house.ga.gov

Jordan, Darryl (D, 77)
409-E Legislative Office
Building
Atlanta, GA 30334
P: (404) 656-0116
F: (404) 651-8086
E: darryl.jordan
@house.ga.gov

Kaiser, Margaret D. (D, 59)
604-D Legislative Office
Building
Atlanta, GA 30334
P: (404) 656-0265
E: margaret.kaiser
@house.ga.gov

Kelley, Trey (R, 16)
408-B Legislative Office
Building
Atlanta, GA 30334
P: (404) 657-1803
E: trey.kelley@house.ga.gov

Kendrick, Dar'shun N. (D, 93)
404-E Legislative Office
Building
Atlanta, GA 30334
P: (404) 656-0109
F: (404) 651-8086
E: dkendrick
@kendrickforgeorgia.com

Kidd, E. Culver "Rusty" (I, 145)
507-A Legislative Office
Building
Atlanta, GA 30334
P: (404) 656-0202
E: rusty.kidd@house.ga.gov

Kirby, Tom (R, 114)
501-C Legislative Office
Building
Atlanta, GA 30334
P: (404) 656-0177
F: (404) 651-8086
E: tom.kirby@house.ga.gov

Knight, David (R, 130)
401-H State Capitol
Atlanta, GA 30334
P: (404) 656-7857
F: (404) 463-1673
E: david.knight
@house.ga.gov

Lariccia, Dominic Francis (R, 169)*
607-F Legislative Office
Building
Atlanta, GA 30334
P: (404) 656-0287
E: dominic.lariccia
@house.ga.gov

Lumsden, Eddie (R, 12)
612-B Legislative Office
Building
Atlanta, GA 30334
P: (404) 656-0325
E: eddie.lumsden
@house.ga.gov

Mabra, Ronnie (D, 63)
512-G Legislative Office
Building
Atlanta, GA 30334
P: (404) 656-7859
E: ronnie.mabra
@house.ga.gov

Marin, Pedro (D, 96)
611-A Legislative Office
Building
Atlanta, GA 30334
P: (404) 656-0314
F: (404) 651-8086
E: marinstatehouse@aol.com

Martin Jr., Charles E. (R, 49)
417-B State Capitol
Atlanta, GA 30334
P: (404) 656-5064
F: (404) 463-2249
E: chuck
@martinforgeorgia.com

Maxwell, Howard R. (R, 17)
402 State Capitol
Atlanta, GA 30334
P: (404) 656-5143
F: (404) 463-4131
E: howard.maxwell
@house.ga.gov

Mayo, Rahn (D, 84)
511-D Legislative Office
Building
Atlanta, GA 30334
P: (404) 656-6372
E: rahnmayo@gmail.com

McCall, Tom (R, 33)
228 State Capitol
Atlanta, GA 30334
P: (404) 656-5099
F: (404) 656-6897
E: tommccall@elberton.net

McClain, Dewey (D, 100)
509-B Legislative Office Building
Atlanta, GA 30334
P: (404) 656-0220
E: dewey.mcclain@house.ga.gov

Meadows III, John D. (R, 5)
HM-1 State Capitol
Atlanta, GA 30334
P: (404) 656-5141
E: john.meadows@house.ga.gov

Mitchell, Billy (D, 88)
411-A Legislative Office Building
Atlanta, GA 30334
P: (404) 656-0126
E: billy.mitchell@house.ga.gov

Morris, Greg (R, 156)
226 State Capitol
Atlanta, GA 30334
P: (404) 656-5115
F: (404) 463-4122
E: greg.morris@house.ga.gov

Mosby, Howard (D, 83)
607-D Legislative Office Building
Atlanta, GA 30334
P: (404) 656-0287
E: howard.mosby@house.ga.gov

Nimmer, Chad (R, 178)
109 State Capitol
Atlanta, GA 30334
P: (404) 651-7737
F: (404) 651-5795
E: chad.nimmer@house.ga.gov

Nix, Randy (R, 69)
402 Legislative Office Building
Atlanta, GA 30334
P: (404) 656-5087
F: (404) 463-2976
E: randy.nix@house.ga.gov

Oliver, Mary Margaret (D, 82)
604-E Legislative Office Building
Atlanta, GA 30334
P: (404) 656-0265
F: (404) 463-2634
E: mmo@mmolaw.com

O'Neal, Larry (R, 146)
338 State Capitol
Atlanta, GA 30334
P: (404) 656-5052
E: larry.oneal@house.ga.gov

Pak, B.J. (R, 108)
601-B Legislative Office Building
Atlanta, GA 30334
P: (404) 656-0254
E: votebjpak@gmail.com

Parrish, Butch (R, 158)
245 State Capitol
Atlanta, GA 30334
P: (404) 463-2247
E: butch.parrish@house.ga.gov

Parsons, Don (R, 44)
401 State Capitol
Atlanta, GA 30334
P: (404) 656-9198
E: repdon@donparsons.org

Peake, Allen (R, 141)
415 State Capitol
Atlanta, GA 30334
P: (404) 656-5025
E: allen.peake@house.ga.gov

Petrea, Jesse I. (R, 166)*
404-D Legislative Office Building
Atlanta, GA 30334
P: (404) 656-0109
E: jesse.petrea@house.ga.gov

Pezold, John David (R, 133)
504-E Legislative Office Building
Atlanta, GA 30334
P: (404) 656-0188
E: john.pezold@house.ga.gov

Powell, Alan (R, 32)
613-B Legislative Office Building
Atlanta, GA 30334
P: (404) 463-3793
F: (404) 651-8086
E: alanpowell23@hotmail.com

Powell, Jay (R, 171)
133 State Capitol
Atlanta, GA 30334
P: (404) 656-5103
E: jay.powell@house.ga.gov

Prince, Brian (D, 127)
409-D Legislative Office Building
Atlanta, GA 30334
P: (404) 656-0016
E: brian.prince@house.ga.gov

Pruett, Jimmy (R, 149)
401-D State Capitol
Atlanta, GA 30334
P: (404) 656-7855
E: jimmy.pruett@house.ga.gov

Quick, Regina (R, 117)
509-C Legislative Office Building
Atlanta, GA 30334
P: (404) 656-0220
E: regina.quick@house.ga.gov

Raffensperger, Brad (R, 50)*
612-C Legislative Office Building
Atlanta, GA 30334
P: (404) 656-0325
E: brad.raffensperger@house.ga.gov

Rakestraw, Paulette (R, 19)
501-E Legislative Office Building
Atlanta, GA 30334
P: (404) 656-0177
E: paulette.braddock@house.ga.gov

Ralston, David (R, 7)
332 State Capitol
Atlanta, GA 30334
P: (404) 656-5020
F: (404) 656-5644
E: david.ralston@house.ga.gov

Ramsey, Matt (R, 72)
415 State Capitol
Atlanta, GA 30334
P: (404) 656-5024
E: matt.ramsey@house.ga.gov

Randall, Nikki T. (D, 142)
404-A Legislative Office Building
Atlanta, GA 30334
P: (404) 656-0109
F: (404) 651-8086
E: nikki.randall@house.ga.gov

Reeves, Albert Thomas (R, 34)*
607-G Legislative Office Building
Atlanta, GA 30334
P: (404) 656-0287
E: albert.reeves@house.ga.gov

Rhodes, Trey (R, 120)*
612-B Legislative Office Building
Atlanta, GA 30334
P: (404) 656-0325
E: trey.rhodes@house.ga.gov

Rice, Tom (R, 95)
220 State Capitol
Atlanta, GA 30334
P: (404) 656-5912
E: tqgrice@aol.com

Roberts, Jay (R, 155)
218 State Capitol
Atlanta, GA 30334
P: (404) 656-7153
F: (404) 656-6700
E: jay.roberts@house.ga.gov

Rogers, Carl (R, 29)
401-C Legislative Office Building
Atlanta, GA 30334
P: (404) 656-7855
F: (404) 651-9730
E: carl.rogers@house.ga.gov

Rogers, Terry (R, 10)
501-B Legislative Office Building
Atlanta, GA 30334
P: (404) 656-0178
E: terry.rogers@house.ga.gov

Rutledge, Dale (R, 109)
404-B Legislative Office Building
Atlanta, GA 30334
P: (404) 656-0109
E: dale.rutledge@house.ga.gov

Rynders, Ed (R, 152)
218 State Capitol
Atlanta, GA 30334
P: (404) 656-6108
F: (404) 463-2249
E: erynders@bellsouth.net

Scott, Sandra G. (D, 76)
611-D Legislative Office Building
Atlanta, GA 30334
P: (404) 656-0314
E: sandra.scott@house.ga.gov

Setzler, Ed (R, 35)
401 State Capitol
Atlanta, GA 30334
P: (404) 656-7857
F: (404) 463-2976
E: ed.setzler@house.ga.gov

Georgia

Sharper, Dexter (D, 177)
411-B Legislative Office Building
Atlanta, GA 30334
P: (404) 656-0126
E: dexter.sharper@house.ga.gov

Shaw, Jason (R, 176)
508-A Legislative Office Building
Atlanta, GA 30334
P: (404) 656-0213
E: jason.shaw@house.ga.gov

Sims, Barbara (R, 119)
401-E State Capitol
Atlanta, GA 30334
P: (404) 656-7855
F: (404) 657-7775
E: barbara.sims@house.ga.gov

Smith, Earnest (D, 125)
511-F Legislative Office Building
Atlanta, GA 30334
P: (404) 656-6372
E: earnest.smith@house.ga.gov

Smith, Lynn Ratigan (R, 70)
228 State Capitol
Atlanta, GA 30334
P: (404) 656-7149
E: lynn.smith@house.ga.gov

Smith, Michael (D, 41)
604-F Legislative Office Building
Atlanta, GA 30334
P: (404) 656-0265
E: michael.smith@house.ga.gov

Smith, Richard H. (R, 134)
220 State Capitol
Atlanta, GA 30334
P: (404) 656-6831
F: (404) 463-1673
E: richard.smith@house.ga.gov

Smyre, Calvin (D, 135)
409-G Legislative Office Building
Atlanta, GA 30334
P: (404) 656-0116
F: (404) 651-8086
E: calvinsmyre@synovus.com

Spencer, Jason (R, 180)
501-D Legislative Office Building
Atlanta, GA 30334
P: (404) 656-0177
F: (404) 463-2976
E: jason.spencer@house.ga.gov

Stephens, Mickey (D, 165)
604-A Legislative Office Building
Atlanta, GA 30334
P: (404) 656-0265
E: mickey.stephens@gmail.com

Stephens, Ron (R, 164)
226-A State Capitol
Atlanta, GA 30334
P: (404) 656-5115
F: (404) 463-4122
E: ron.stephens@house.ga.gov

Stephenson, Pam (D, 90)
411-G Legislative Office Building
Atlanta, GA 30334
P: (404) 656-0126
F: (404) 656-4889
E: pam.stephenson@house.ga.gov

Stovall, Valencia (D, 74)
611-C Legislative Office Building
Atlanta, GA 30334
P: (404) 656-0314
E: valencia.stovall@house.ga.gov

Stover, David (R, 71)
501-B Legislative Office Building
Atlanta, GA 30334
P: (404) 656-0177
E: david.stover@house.ga.gov

Strickland, Brian (R, 111)
404-G Legislative Office Building
Atlanta, GA 30334
P: (404) 656-0109
E: brian.strickland@house.ga.gov

Tankersley, Jan (R, 160)
401-B State Capitol
Atlanta, GA 30334
P: (404) 656-7855
E: jan.tankersley@house.ga.gov

Tanner, Kevin (R, 9)
401-E Legisaltive Office Building
Atlanta, GA 30334
P: (404) 656-0152
E: kevin.tanner@house.ga.gov

Tarvin, Steve (R, 2)*
404-F Legislative Office Building
Atlanta, GA 30334
P: (404) 656-0109
E: steve.tarvin@house.ga.gov

Taylor, Darlene K. (R, 173)
501-G Legislative Office Building
Atlanta, GA 30334
P: (404) 656-0178
E: darlene.taylor@house.ga.gov

Taylor, Tom (R, 79)
614-A Legislative Office Building
Atlanta, GA 30334
P: (404) 656-3947
E: tom.taylor@house.ga.gov

Teasley, Sam (R, 37)
417 State Capitol
Atlanta, GA 30334
P: (404) 656-5146
E: sam.teasley@house.ga.gov

Thomas, Erica Renee (D, 39)*
512-C Legislative Office Building
Atlanta, GA 30334
P: (404) 656-7859
E: erica.thomas@house.ga.gov

Thomas, Mable (D, 56)
511-B Legislative Office Building
Atlanta, GA 30334
P: (404) 656-6372
E: mable.thomas@house.ga.gov

Trammell, Bob (D, 132)*
611-G Legislative Office Building
Atlanta, GA 30334
P: (404) 656-0314
E: bob.trammell@house.ga.gov

Turner, Scot (R, 21)
401-G Legislative Office Building
Atlanta, GA 30334
P: (404) 656-0152
E: scot.turner@house.ga.gov

Waites, Keisha (D, 60)
509-E Legislative Office Building
Atlanta, GA 30334
P: (404) 656-0220
F: (404) 651-8086
E: keisha.waites@house.ga.gov

Watson, Sam (R, 172)
508-B Legislative Office Building
Atlanta, GA 30334
P: (404) 656-0213
E: sam.watson@house.ga.gov

Welch, Andrew J. (R, 110)
508-C Legislative Office Building
Atlanta, GA 30334
P: (404) 656-0213
E: awelch@swblawfirm.com

Weldon, Tom (R, 3)
131 State Capitol
Atlanta, GA 30334
P: (404) 656-5105
E: tom.weldon@house.ga.gov

Werkheiser, Bill (R, 157)*
411-E Legislative Office Building
Atlanta, GA 30334
P: (404) 656-0126
E: bill.werkheiser@house.ga.gov

Wilkerson, David (D, 38)
409-F Legislative Office Building
Atlanta, GA 30334
P: (404) 656-0116
F: (404) 656-9645
E: david.wilkerson@house.ga.gov

Wilkinson, Joe (R, 52)
415 State Capitol
Atlanta, GA 30334
P: (404) 463-8143
F: (404) 657-8278
E: joe@joewilkinson.org

Willard, Wendell (R, 51)
132 State Capitol
Atlanta, GA 30334
P: (404) 656-5125
F: (404) 657-8277
E: wendell.willard@house.ga.gov

Williams, Al (D, 168)
511-A Legislative Office Building
Atlanta, GA 30334
P: (404) 656-6372
E: al.williams@house.ga.gov

Williams, Chuck (R, 119)
601-E Legislative Office Building
Atlanta, GA 30334
P: (404) 656-0254
E: chuck.williams@house.ga.gov

Williams, Earnest (D, 87)
507-B Legislative Office Building
Atlanta, GA 30334
P: (404) 656-0202
F: (404) 651-8086
E: earnest.williams@house.ga.gov

Williamson, Bruce (R, 115)
401-C Legislative Office Building
Atlanta, GA 30334
P: (404) 656-0152
E: bruce.williamson@house.ga.gov

Yates, John P. (R, 73)
217 State Capitol
Atlanta, GA 30334
P: (404) 656-5126
F: (404) 656-6700
E: john.yates@house.ga.gov

Congress

Senate

Isakson, Johnny (R)
Perdue, David (R)

House

Allen, Rick (R, 12)
Bishop Jr., Sanford D. (D, 2)
Carter, Buddy (R, 1)
Collins, Doug (R, 9)
Graves, Tom (R, 9)
Hice, Jody (R, 10)
Johnson Jr., Henry C. (D, 4)
Lewis, John (D, 5)
Loudermilk, Barry (R, 11)
Price, Thomas E. (R, 6)
Scott, Austin (R, 8)
Scott, David (D, 13)
Westmoreland, Lynn A. (R, 3)
Woodall, Robert (R, 7)

Guam

Executive

Governor

Hon. Eddie Baza Calvo (R)
Governor
Executive Chamber
P.O. Box 2950
Agana, GU 96932
P: (671) 472-8931
F: (671) 477-4826

Lieutenant Governor

Hon. Ray Tenorio (R)
Lieutenant Governor
R.J. Bordallo Governor's Complex
P.O. Box 2950
Hagatna, GU 96932
P: (671) 475-9380
F: (671) 477-2007
E: webmaster @guamletgovernor.net

Secretary of State

Guam does not have the office of secretary of state. Some of the duties of the secretary of state are performed by the office of the lieutenant governor.

Attorney General

Hon. Elizabeth Barrett-Anderson
Attorney General
590 South Marine Corps Drive
ITC Building, Suite 706
Tamuning, GU 96913
P: (671) 475-3324
F: (671) 472-2493
E: law@guamag.org

Auditor

Hon. Doris Flores Brooks
Public Auditor
DNA Building, Suite 401
238 Archbishop Flores Street
Hagatna, GU 96910
P: (671) 475-0390, Ext. 207
F: (671) 472-7951
E: dfbrooks@guamopa.org

Treasurer

Hon. Rose T. Fejeran
Treasurer
P.O. Box 884
Hagatna, GU 96932
P: (671) 475-1161
E: rtfejeran@doa.guam.gov

Judiciary

Supreme Court (MR)

Ms. Hannah M. Gutierrez-Arroyo
Clerk of Court
Guam Judicial Center
120 West O'Brien Drive
Hagatna, GU 96910
P: (671) 475-3162
E: hgutierrezarroyo @guamsupremecourt.com

Hon. Robert J. Torres Jr.
Chief Justice
Hon. F. Phillip Carbullido
Hon. Katherine A. Maraman

Unicameral Legislature

Senate President

Sen. Judith T. Won Pat (D)
Speaker
155 Hesler Street, Suite 201
Hagatna, GU 96910
P: (671) 472-3586
F: (671) 472-3589
E: speaker@judiwonpat.com

Vice Speaker of the Senate

Sen. Benjamin J.F. Cruz (D)
Vice Speaker
155 Hesler Street, Suite 107
Hagatna, GU 96910
P: (671) 477-2520
F: (671) 477-2522
E: senator @senatorbjcruz.com

Senate Majority Leader

Sen. Rory J. Respicio (D)
Majority Leader
155 Hesler Street, Suite 302
Hagatna, GU 96910
P: (671) 472-7679
F: (671) 472-3547
E: royforguam@gmail.com

Senate Minority Leader

Sen. V. Anthony Ada (R)
Minority Leader
140 Aspinall Avenue
Bridge Pointe Building, Suite 202
Hagatna, GU 96910
P: (671) 472-9681
F: (671) 472-9683
E: senatortonyada @guamlegislature.org

Secretary of the Senate

Ms. Rennae V. Meno
Clerk of the Legislature
155 Hesler Place
Hagatna, GU 96910
P: (671) 472-3465
F: (671) 472-3524
E: rennae @guamlegislature.org

Members of the Senate

Ada, Tom C. (D)
Suite 207, Ada Plaza Center
173 Aspinall Avenue
Hagatna, GU 96910
P: (671) 473-3301
F: (671) 473-3303
E: office@senatorada.org

Ada, V. Anthony (R)
140 Aspinall Avenue
Bridge Pointe Building, Suite 202
Hagatna, GU 96910
P: (671) 472-9681
F: (671) 472-9683
E: senatortonyada @guamlegislature.org

Aguon Jr., Frank B. (D)
238 Archebishop Flores Street
Suite 503, DNA Building
Hagatna, GU 96910
P: (671) 475-4861
E: aguon4guam@gmail.com

Blas Jr., Frank F. (R)
238 Archebishop Flores Street
Suite 801, DNA Building
Hagatna, GU 96910
P: (671) 472-2527
F: (671) 472-2528
E: frank.blasjr@gmail.com

Cruz, Benjamin J.F. (D)
155 Hesler Street, Suite 107
Hagatna, GU 96910
P: (671) 477-2520
F: (671) 477-2522
E: senator @senatorbjcruz.com

Espaldon, James V. (R)*
238 Archebishop Flores Street
Suite 801, DNA Building
Hagatna, GU 96910
P: (671) 475-4546
E: jespaldonesq@gmail.com

McCreadie, Brant (R)
De La Corte Building, Suite 102
167 East Marine Corp Drive
Hagatna, GU 96910
P: (671) 472-3462
E: brantforguam@gmail.com

Morrison, Thomas (R)
Suite 202/203B, Ada Plaza Center
173 Aspinall Avenue, Building B
Hagatna, GU 96910
P: (671) 478-8669
E: tommy @senatormorrison.com

Muña Barnes, Tina Rose (D)
155 Hesler Street, Suite 101
Hagatna, GU 96910
P: (671) 472-3455
F: (671) 472-3400
E: senator @tinamunabarnes.com

Respicio, Rory J. (D)
155 Hesler Street, Suite 302
Hagatna, GU 96910
P: (671) 472-7679
F: (671) 472-3547
E: royforguam@gmail.com

Rodriguez Jr., Dennis G. (D,)
176 Serenu Avenue, Suite 107
Tamuning, GU 96931
P: (671) 649-8638
F: (671) 649-0520
E: senatordrodriguez @gmail.com

San Nicolas, Michael F.Q. (D,)
238 Archebishop Flores Street
Suite 407, DNA Building
Hagatna, GU 96910
P: (671) 472-6453
E: senatorsannicolas @gmail.com

Torres, Mary Camacho (R)*
238 Archebishop Flores Street
Suite 801, DNA Building
Hagatna, GU 96910
E: marycamachotorres @gmail.com

**Underwood,
Nerisssa Bretania (D,)***
155 Hesler Place, Suite 104
Hagatna, GU 96910
P: (671) 969-0973
E: senatorunderwood
@guamlegislature.org

Won Pat, Judith T. (D)
155 Hesler Street, Suite 201
Hagatna, GU 96910
P: (671) 472-3586
F: (671) 472-3589
E: speaker@judiwonpat.com

Congress

House Delegate

Bordallo, Madeleine Z.
(D, At Large)

Hawaii

Executive

Governor

Hon. David Y. Ige (D)
Governor
Executive Chambers
State Capitol
Honolulu, HI 96813
P: (808) 586-0034
F: (808) 586-0006

Lieutenant Governor

Hon. Shan S. Tsutsui (D)
Lieutenant Governor
Executive Chambers
State Capitol
Honolulu, HI 96813
P: (808) 586-0255
F: (808) 586-0231
E: shan.tsusui@hawaii.gov

Secretary of State

Hawaii does not have the office of secretary of state. Some of the duties of the secretary of state are performed by the office of the lieutenant governor.

Attorney General

Hon. Doug Chin (D)
(appointed)
Attorney General
425 Queen Street
Honolulu, HI 96813
P: (808) 586-1239

Auditor

Ms. Jan K. Yamane
(appointed by the Legislature)
Acting State Auditor
465 South King Street, Room 500
Honolulu, HI 96813
P: (808) 587-0800
F: (808) 587-0830
E: auditors2
@auditor.state.hi.us

Treasurer

Hon. Wesley Machida
(appointed)
Director of Finance
P.O. Box 150
Honolulu, HI 96810
P: (808) 586-1518
F: (808) 586-1976
E: hi.budgetandfinance
@hawaii.gov

Judiciary

Supreme Court (MC)

Ms. Rochelle Hasuko
Chief Clerk
Aliiolani Hale
417 South King Street
Honolulu, HI 96813
P: (808) 539-4919
F: (808) 539-4928

Hon. Mark E. Recktenwald
Chief Justice
Hon. Sabrina S. McKenna
Hon. Paula A. Nakayama
Hon. Richard W. Pollack
Hon. Michael D. Wilson

Legislative Senate

Senate President

Sen. Donna Mercado Kim (D)
Senate President
State Capitol, Room 409
415 South Beretania Street
Honolulu, HI 96813
P: (808) 587-7200
F: (808) 587-7205
E: senkim
@capitol.hawaii.gov

Vice President of the Senate

Sen. Will Espero (D)
Vice President
State Capitol, Room 206
415 South Beretania Street
Honolulu, HI 96813
P: (808) 586-6360
F: (808) 586-6361
E: senespero
@capitol.hawaii.gov

Senate Majority Leader

Sen. J. Kalani English (D)
Majority Leader
State Capitol, Room 205
415 South Beretania Street
Honolulu, HI 96813
P: (808) 587-7225
F: (808) 587-7230
E: senenglish
@capitol.hawaii.gov

Senate Minority Leader

Sen. Sam Slom (R)
Senate Minority Floor Leader
State Capitol, Room 214
415 South Beretania Street
Honolulu, HI 96813
P: (808) 586-8420
F: (808) 586-8426
E: senslom
@capitol.hawaii.gov

Secretary of the Senate

Ms. Carol Taniguchi
Chief Clerk of the Senate
State Capitol, Room 010
415 South Beretania Street
Honolulu, HI 96813
P: (808) 586-6720
F: (808) 586-6719
E: sclerk
@Capitol.hawaii.gov

Members of the Senate

Baker, Rosalyn H. (D, 6)
State Capitol, Room 230
415 South Beretania Street
Honolulu, HI 96813
P: (808) 586-6070
F: (808) 586-6071
E: senbaker
@capitol.hawaii.gov

Chun Oakland, Suzanne (D, 13)
State Capitol, Room 226
415 South Beretania Street
Honolulu, HI 96813
P: (808) 586-6130
F: (808) 586-6131
E: senchunoakland
@capitol.hawaii.gov

Dela Cruz, Donovan M. (D, 22)
State Capitol, Room 202
415 South Beretania Street
Honolulu, HI 96813
P: (808) 586-6090
F: (808) 586-6091
E: sendelacruz
@capitol.hawaii.gov

English, J. Kalani (D, 7)
State Capitol, Room 205
415 South Beretania Street
Honolulu, HI 96813
P: (808) 587-7225
F: (808) 587-7230
E: senenglish
@capitol.hawaii.gov

Espero, Will (D, 19)
State Capitol, Room 206
415 South Beretania Street
Honolulu, HI 96813
P: (808) 586-6360
F: (808) 586-6361
E: senespero
@capitol.hawaii.gov

Gabbard, Mike (D, 20)
State Capitol, Room 201
415 South Beretania Street
Honolulu, HI 96813
P: (808) 586-6830
F: (808) 586-6679
E: sengabbard
@capitol.hawaii.gov

Galuteria, Brickwood (D, 12)
State Capitol, Room 223
415 South Beretania Street
Honolulu, HI 96813
P: (808) 586-6740
F: (808) 586-6829
E: sengaluteria
@capitol.hawaii.gov

Green, Josh (D, 3)
State Capitol, Room 407
415 South Beretania Street
Honolulu, HI 96813
P: (808) 586-9385
F: (808) 586-9391
E: sengreen
@capitol.hawaii.gov

Harimoto, Breene (D, 16)*
State Capitol, Room 215
415 South Beretania Street
Honolulu, HI 96813
P: (808) 586-6230
F: (808) 586-6231
E: senharimoto
@capitol.hawaii.gov

Ihara Jr., Les (D, 10)
State Capitol, Room 220
415 South Beretania Street
Honolulu, HI 96813
P: (808) 586-6250
F: (808) 586-6251
E: senihara@capitol.hawaii.gov

Inouye, Lorraine (D, 4)
State Capitol, Room 203
415 South Beretania Street
Honolulu, HI 96813
P: (808) 586-7335
F: (808) 586-7339
E: seninouye@capitol.hawaii.gov

Kahele, Gilbert (D, 1)
State Capitol, Room 213
415 South Beretania Street
Honolulu, HI 96813
P: (808) 586-6760
F: (808) 586-6689
E: senkahele@capitol.hawaii.gov

Keith-Agaran, Gilbert (D, 5)
State Capitol, Room 221
415 South Berctania Street
Honolulu, HI 96813
P: (808) 586-7344
F: (808) 586-7348
E: senkeithagaran@capitol.hawaii.gov

Kidani, Michelle N. (D, 18)
State Capitol, Room 228
415 South Beretania Street
Honolulu, HI 96813
P: (808) 586-7100
F: (808) 586-7109
E: senkidani@capitol.hawaii.gov

Kim, Donna Mercado (D, 14)
State Capitol, Room 409
415 South Beretania Street
Honolulu, HI 96813
P: (808) 587-7200
F: (808) 587-7205
E: senkim@capitol.hawaii.gov

Kouchi, Ronald D. (D, 8)
State Capitol, Room 210
415 South Beretania Street
Honolulu, HI 96813
P: (808) 586-6030
F: (808) 586-6031
E: senkouchi@capitol.hawaii.gov

Nishihara, Clarence K. (D, 17)
State Capitol, Room 204
415 South Beretania Street
Honolulu, HI 96813
P: (808) 586-6970
F: (808) 586-6879
E: sennishihara@capitol.hawaii.gov

Riviere, Gil (D, 23)
State Capitol, Room 217
415 South Beretania Street
Honolulu, HI 96813
P: (808) 586-7330
F: (808) 586-7334
E: senriviere@capitol.hawaii.gov

Ruderman, Russell E. (D, 2)
State Capitol, Room 218
415 South Beretania Street
Honolulu, HI 96813
P: (808) 586-6890
F: (808) 586-6899
E: senruderman@capitol.hawaii.gov

Shimabukuro, Maile S.L. (D, 21)
State Capitol, Room 222
415 South Beretania Street
Honolulu, HI 96813
P: (808) 586-7793
F: (808) 586-7797
E: senshimabukuro@capitol.hawaii.gov

Slom, Sam (R, 9)
State Capitol, Room 214
415 South Beretania Street
Honolulu, HI 96813
P: (808) 586-8420
F: (808) 586-8426
E: senslom@capitol.hawaii.gov

Taniguchi, Brian T. (D, 11)
State Capitol, Room 219
415 South Beretania Street
Honolulu, HI 96813
P: (808) 586-6460
F: (808) 586-6461
E: sentaniguchi@capitol.hawaii.gov

Thielen, Laura H. (D, 25)
State Capitol, Room 231
415 South Beretania Street
Honolulu, HI 96813
P: (808) 587-8388
F: (808) 587-7240
E: senthielen@capitol.hawaii.gov

Tokuda, Jill N. (D, 24)
State Capitol, Room 207
415 South Beretania Street
Honolulu, HI 96813
P: (808) 587-7215
F: (808) 587-7220
E: sentokuda@capitol.hawaii.gov

Wakai, Glenn (D, 15)
State Capitol, Room 216
415 South Beretania Street
Honolulu, HI 96813
P: (808) 586-8585
F: (808) 586-8588
E: senwakai@capitol.hawaii.gov

House

Speaker of the House

Rep. Joseph M. Souki (D)
Speaker
State Capitol, Room 431
415 South Beretania Street
Honolulu, HI 96813
P: (808) 586-6100
F: (808) 586-6101
E: repsouki@capitol.hawaii.gov

Vice Speaker of the House

Rep. John M. Mizuno (D)
Vice Speaker
State Capitol, Room 439
415 South Beretania Street
Honolulu, HI 96813
P: (808) 586-6050
F: (808) 586-6051
E: repmizuno@capitol.hawaii.gov

House Majority Leader

Rep. Scott K. Saiki (D)
Majority Leader
State Capitol, Room 434
415 South Beretania Street
Honolulu, HI 96813
P: (808) 586-8485
F: (808) 586-8489
E: repsaiki@capitol.hawaii.gov

House Minority Leader

Rep. Beth Fukumoto Chang (R)
Minority Leader
State Capitol, Room 333
415 South Beretania Street
Honolulu, HI 96813
P: (808) 586-9460
F: (808) 586-9466
E: repfukumoto@capitol.hawaii.gov

Clerk of the House

Mr. Brian Takashita
Clerk of the House
State Capitol, Room 027
415 South Beretania Street
Honolulu, HI 96813
P: (808) 586-6400
F: (808) 586-6401
E: hclerk@capitol.hawaii.gov

Members of the House

Aquino, Henry J.C. (D, 38)
State Capitol, Room 419
415 South Beretania Street
Honolulu, HI 96813
P: (808) 586-6520
F: (808) 586-6521
E: repaquino@capitol.hawaii.gov

Belatti, Della Au (D, 24)
State Capitol, Room 426
415 South Beretania Street
Honolulu, HI 96813
P: (808) 586-9425
F: (808) 586-9431
E: repbelatti@capitol.hawaii.gov

Brower, Tom (D, 22)
State Capitol, Room 315
415 South Beretania Street
Honolulu, HI 96813
P: (808) 586-8520
F: (808) 586-8524
E: repbrower@capitol.hawaii.gov

Cachola, Romy M. (D, 30)
State Capitol, Room 435
415 South Beretania Street
Honolulu, HI 96813
P: (808) 586-6010
F: (808) 586-6011
E: repcachola@capitol.hawaii.gov

Hawaii

Chang, Beth Fukumoto (R, 36)
State Capitol, Room 333
415 South Beretania Street
Honolulu, HI 96813
P: (808) 586-9460
F: (808) 586-9466
E: repfukumoto@capitol.hawaii.gov

Choy, Isaac W. (D, 23)
State Capitol, Room 404
415 South Beretania Street
Honolulu, HI 96813
P: (808) 586-8475
F: (808) 586-8479
E: repchoy@capitol.hawaii.gov

Creagan, Richard (D, 5)*
State Capitol, Room 331
415 South Beretania Street
Honolulu, HI 96813
P: (808) 586-9605
F: (808) 586-9608
E: repcreagan@Capitol.hawaii.gov

Cullen, Ty J.K. (D, 39)
State Capitol, Room 316
415 South Beretania Street
Honolulu, HI 96813
P: (808) 586-8490
F: (808) 586-8494
E: repcullen@capitol.hawaii.gov

DeCoite, Lynn (D, 13)*
State Capitol, Room 405
415 South Beretania Street
Honolulu, HI 96813
P: (808) 586-6790
F: (808) 586-6779
E: repdecoite@capitol.hawaii.gov

Evans, Cindy (D, 7)
State Capitol, Room 438
415 South Beretania Street
Honolulu, HI 96813
P: (808) 586-8510
F: (808) 586-8514
E: repevans@capitol.hawaii.gov

Har, Sharon E. (D, 42)
State Capitol, Room 418
415 South Beretania Street
Honolulu, HI 96813
P: (808) 586-8500
F: (808) 586-8504
E: rephar@capitol.hawaii.gov

Hashem, Mark J. (D, 18)
State Capitol, Room 326
415 South Beretania Street
Honolulu, HI 96813
P: (808) 586-6510
F: (808) 586-6511
E: rephashem@capitol.hawaii.gov

Ichiyama, Linda (D, 32)
State Capitol, Room 327
415 South Beretania Street
Honolulu, HI 96813
P: (808) 586-6220
F: (808) 586-6221
E: repichiyama@capitol.hawaii.gov

Ing, Kaniela (D, 11)
State Capitol, Room 311
415 South Beretania Street
Honolulu, HI 96813
P: (808) 586-8525
F: (808) 586-8529
E: reping@capitol.hawaii.gov

Ito, Ken (D, 49)
State Capitol, Room 432
415 South Beretania Street
Honolulu, HI 96813
P: (808) 586-8470
F: (808) 586-8474
E: repito@capitol.hawaii.gov

Johanson, Aaron Ling (R, 31)
State Capitol, Room 427
415 South Beretania Street
Honolulu, HI 96813
P: (808) 586-9470
F: (808) 586-9476
E: repjohanson@capitol.hawaii.gov

Jordan, Jo (D, 44)
State Capitol, Room 323
415 South Beretania Street
Honolulu, HI 96813
P: (808) 586-8460
F: (808) 586-8464
E: repjordan@capitol.hawaii.gov

Kawakami, Derek S.K. (D, 14)
State Capitol, Room 314
415 South Beretania Street
Honolulu, HI 96813
P: (808) 586-8435
F: (808) 586-8437
E: repkawakami@capitol.hawaii.gov

Keohokalole, Jarrett (D, 48)*
State Capitol, Room 310
415 South Beretania Street
Honolulu, HI 96813
P: (808) 586-8540
F: (808) 586-8544
E: repkeohokalole@Capitol.hawaii.gov

Kobayashi, Bertrand (D, 19)
State Capitol, Room 403
415 South Beretania Street
Honolulu, HI 96813
P: (808) 586-6310
F: (808) 586-6311
E: repkobayashi@capitol.hawaii.gov

Kong, Sam (D, 33)*
State Capitol, Room 313
415 South Beretania Street
Honolulu, HI 96813
P: (808) 586-8455
F: (808) 586-8459
E: repkong@Capitol.hawaii.gov

Lee, Chris (D, 51)
State Capitol, Room 436
415 South Beretania Street
Honolulu, HI 96813
P: (808) 586-9450
F: (808) 586-9456
E: repclee@capitol.hawaii.gov

Lopresti, Matthew (D, 41)*
State Capitol, Room 328
415 South Beretania Street
Honolulu, HI 96813
P: (808) 586-6080
F: (808) 586-6081
E: replopresti@Capitol.hawaii.gov

Lowen, Nicole E. (D, 6)
State Capitol, Room 425
415 South Beretania Street
Honolulu, HI 96813
P: (808) 586-8400
F: (808) 586-9476
E: replowen@capitol.hawaii.gov

Luke, Sylvia (D, 25)
State Capitol, Room 306
415 South Beretania Street
Honolulu, HI 96813
P: (808) 586-6200
F: (808) 586-6201
E: repluke@capitol.hawaii.gov

Matsumoto, Lauren Kealohilani (R, 45)
State Capitol, Room 303
415 South Beretania Street
Honolulu, HI 96813
P: (808) 586-9490
F: (808) 586-9496
E: repmatsumoto@capitol.hawaii.gov

McDermott, Bob (R, 40)
State Capitol, Room 330
415 South Beretania Street
Honolulu, HI 96813
P: (808) 586-9730
F: (808) 586-9738
E: repmcdermott@capitol.hawaii.gov

McKelvey, Angus L.K. (D, 10)
State Capitol, Room 320
415 South Beretania Street
Honolulu, HI 96813
P: (808) 586-6160
F: (808) 586-6161
E: repmckelvey@capitol.hawaii.gov

Mizuno, John M. (D, 28)
State Capitol, Room 439
415 South Beretania Street
Honolulu, HI 96813
P: (808) 586-6050
F: (808) 586-6051
E: repmizuno@capitol.hawaii.gov

Morikawa, Dee (D, 16)
State Capitol, Room 442
415 South Beretania Street
Honolulu, HI 96813
P: (808) 586-6280
F: (808) 586-6281
E: repmorikawa@capitol.hawaii.gov

Nakashima, Mark M. (D, 1)
State Capitol, Room 406
415 South Beretania Street
Honolulu, HI 96813
P: (808) 586-6680
F: (808) 586-6684
E: repnakashima@capitol.hawaii.gov

Nishimoto, Scott Y. (D, 21)
State Capitol, Room 421
415 South Beretania Street
Honolulu, HI 96813
P: (808) 586-8515
F: (808) 586-8519
E: repnishimoto@capitol.hawaii.gov

Ohno, Takashi (D, 27)
State Capitol, Room 332
415 South Beretania Street
Honolulu, HI 96813
P: (808) 586-9415
F: (808) 586-9421
E: repohno
@capitol.hawaii.gov

Onishi, Richard H.K. (D, 3)
State Capitol, Room 441
415 South Beretania Street
Honolulu, HI 96813
P: (808) 586-6120
F: (808) 586-6121
E: reponishi
@capitol.hawaii.gov

Oshiro, Marcus R. (D, 46)
State Capitol, Room 424
415 South Beretania Street
Honolulu, HI 96813
P: (808) 586-6700
F: (808) 586-6702
E: repmoshiro
@capitol.hawaii.gov

Oshiro, Marcus R. (D, 46)
State Capitol, Room 306
415 South Beretania Street
Honolulu, HI 96813
P: (808) 586-6200
F: (808) 586-6201
E: repmoshiro
@Capitol.hawaii.gov

Pouha, Feki (R, 47)*
State Capitol, Room 319
415 South Beretania Street
Honolulu, HI 96813
P: (808) 586-6380
F: (808) 586-6381
E: reppouha
@Capitol.hawaii.gov

Rhoads, Karl (D, 29)
State Capitol, Room 302
415 South Beretania Street
Honolulu, HI 96813
P: (808) 586-6180
F: (808) 586-6189
E: reprhoads
@capitol.hawaii.gov

Saiki, Scott K. (D, 26)
State Capitol, Room 434
415 South Beretania Street
Honolulu, HI 96813
P: (808) 586-8485
F: (808) 586-8489
E: repsaiki
@capitol.hawaii.gov

San Buenaventura, Joy (D, 4)*
State Capitol, Room 305
415 South Beretania Street
Honolulu, HI 96813
P: (808) 586-6530
F: (808) 586-6531
E: repsanbuenaventura
@Capitol.hawaii.gov

Say, Calvin K.Y. (D, 20)
State Capitol, Room 433
415 South Beretania Street
Honolulu, HI 96813
P: (808) 586-6900
F: (808) 586-6910
E: repsay
@capitol.hawaii.gov

Souki, Joseph M. (D, 8)
State Capitol, Room 431
415 South Beretania Street
Honolulu, HI 96813
P: (808) 586-6100
F: (808) 586-6101
E: repsouki
@capitol.hawaii.gov

Takayama, Gregg (D, 34)
State Capitol, Room 324
415 South Beretania Street
Honolulu, HI 96813
P: (808) 586-6340
F: (808) 586-6341
E: reptakayama
@capitol.hawaii.gov

Takumi, Roy M. (D, 35)
State Capitol, Room 444
415 South Beretania Street
Honolulu, HI 96813
P: (808) 586-6170
F: (808) 586-6171
E: reptakumi
@capitol.hawaii.gov

Thielen, Cynthia (R, 50)
State Capitol, Room 443
415 South Beretania Street
Honolulu, HI 96813
P: (808) 586-6480
F: (808) 586-6481
E: repthielen
@capitol.hawaii.gov

Tokioka, James Kunane (D, 15)
State Capitol, Room 322
415 South Beretania Street
Honolulu, HI 96813
P: (808) 586-6270
F: (808) 586-6271
E: reptokioka
@capitol.hawaii.gov

Tsuji, Clift (D, 2)
State Capitol, Room 402
415 South Beretania Street
Honolulu, HI 96813
P: (808) 586-8480
F: (808) 586-8484
E: reptsuji
@capitol.hawaii.gov

Tupola, Andria (R, 43)*
State Capitol, Room 317
415 South Beretania Street
Honolulu, HI 96813
P: (808) 586-8465
F: (808) 586-8469
E: reptupola
@Capitol.hawaii.gov

Ward, Gene (R, 17)
State Capitol, Room 318
415 South Beretania Street
Honolulu, HI 96813
P: (808) 586-6420
F: (808) 586-6421
E: repward
@capitol.hawaii.gov

Woodson, Justin (D, 9)
State Capitol, Room 304
415 South Beretania Street
Honolulu, HI 96813
P: (808) 586-6210
F: (808) 586-6211
E: repwoodson
@capitol.hawaii.gov

Yamane, Ryan I. (D, 37)
State Capitol, Room 420
415 South Beretania Street
Honolulu, HI 96813
P: (808) 586-6150
F: (808) 586-6151
E: repyamane
@capitol.hawaii.gov

Yamashita, Kyle T. (D, 12)
State Capitol, Room 422
415 South Beretania Street
Honolulu, HI 96813
P: (808) 586-6330
F: (808) 586-6331
E: repyamashita
@capitol.hawaii.gov

Congress

Senate
Hirono, Mazie K. (D)
Schatz, Brian (D)

House
Gabbard, Tulsi (D, 2)
Takai, K. Mark (D, 1)

Idaho

Executive

Governor
Hon. C.L. "Butch" Otter (R)
Governor
700 West Jefferson, Second Floor
Boise, ID 83702
P: (208) 334-2100
F: (208) 334-2175

Lieutenant Governor
Hon. Brad Little (R)
Lieutenant Governor
State Capitol
Boise, ID 83720
P: (208) 334-2200
F: (208) 334-3259

Attorney General
Hon. Lawrence Wasden (R)
Attorney General
Statehouse
Boise, ID 83720
P: (208) 334-2400
F: (208) 854-8071

Auditor
Idaho does not have the office of state auditor by a 1994 amendment to the state constitution.

Secretary of State
Hon. Lawerence Denney (R)
Secretary of State
P.O. Box 83720
Boise, ID 83720
P: (208) 334-2300
F: (208) 334-2282
E: secstate@sos.idaho.gov

Superintendent of Public Instruction
Hon. Sherri Ybarra (R)
Superintendent of Public Instruction
650 West State Street
Boise, ID 83720
P: (208) 332-6800
F: (208) 334-2228

Treasurer
Hon. Ron G. Crane (R)
State Treasurer
P.O. Box 83720
Boise, ID 83720
P: (208) 334-3200
F: (208) 332-2960
E: ron.crane@sto.idaho.gov

Judiciary

Supreme Court (NE)
Mr. Stephen W. Kenyon
Clerk of the Supreme Court
P.O. Box 83720
Boise, ID 83720
P: (208) 334-2210
F: (208) 947-7590

Hon. Roger S. Burdick
Chief Justice
Hon. Daniel T. Eismann
Hon. Joel D. Horton
Hon. Jim Jones
Hon. Warren E. Jones

Legislative Senate

Senate President
Hon. Brad Little (R)
Lieutenant Governor
State Capitol
Boise, ID 83720
P: (208) 334-2200
F: (208) 334-3259

President Pro Tempore of the Senate
Sen. Brent Hill (R)
President Pro Tempore
State Capitol Building, Room W331
P.O. Box 83720
Boise, ID 83720
P: (208) 332-1300
F: (208) 334-5397
E: bhill@senate.idaho.gov

Senate Majority Leader
Sen. Bart M. Davis (R)
Majority Leader
State Capitol Building, Room W330
P.O. Box 83720
Boise, ID 83720
P: (208) 332-1305
F: (208) 334-5397
E: bmdavis@senate.idaho.gov

Senate Minority Leader
Sen. Michelle Stennett (D)
Minority Leader
State Capitol Building, Room W304
P.O. Box 83720
Boise, ID 83720
P: (208) 332-1410
F: (208) 334-5397
E: mstennett @senate.idaho.gov

Secretary of the Senate
Ms. Jennifer Novak
Secretary of the Senate
State Capitol Building, Room W327
P.O. Box 83720
Boise, ID 83720
P: (208) 332-1309

Members of the Senate
Bair, Steve (R, 31)
State Capitol Building, Room WW37
P.O. Box 83720
Boise, ID 83720
P: (208) 332-1385
F: (208) 334-5397
E: sbair@senate.idaho.gov

Bayer, Clifford R. (R, 21)
State Capitol Building, Room WG45
P.O. Box 83720
Boise, ID 83720
P: (208) 332-1337
F: (208) 334-5397
E: cbayer@senate.idaho.gov

Brackett, Bert (R, 23)
State Capitol Building, Room WW33
P.O. Box 83720
Boise, ID 83720
P: (208) 332-1336
F: (208) 334-5397
E: bbrackett @senate.idaho.gov

Buckner-Webb, Cherie (D, 19)
State Capitol Building, Room W405
P.O. Box 83720
Boise, ID 83720
P: (208) 332-1078
F: (208) 334-5397
E: cbucknerwebb @senate.idaho.gov

Burgoyne, Grant (D, 16)
State Capitol Building, Room WG02
P.O. Box 83720
Boise, ID 83720
P: (208) 332-1409
F: (208) 334-5397
E: gburgoyne @house.idaho.gov

Cameron, Dean L. (R, 27)
State Capitol Building, Room C308
P.O. Box 83720
Boise, ID 83720
P: (208) 334-4733
F: (208) 334-5397
E: dcameron @senate.idaho.gov

Davis, Bart M. (R, 33)
State Capitol Building, Room W330
P.O. Box 83720
Boise, ID 83720
P: (208) 332-1305
F: (208) 334-5397
E: bmdavis@senate.idaho.gov

Guthrie, Jim (R, 28)
State Capitol Building, Room WW35
P.O. Box 83720
Boise, ID 83720
P: (208) 332-1348
F: (208) 334-5397
E: jguthrie @senate.idaho.gov

Hagedorn, Marv (R, 14)
State Capitol Building, Room WG54
P.O. Box 83720
Boise, ID 83720
P: (208) 332-1334
F: (208) 334-5397
E: mhagedorn @senate.idaho.gov

Hartog, Lori Den (R, 22)*
State Capitol Building, Room WG06
P.O. Box 83720
Boise, ID 83720
P: (208) 332-1340
F: (208) 334-5397
E: lhartog@senate.idaho.gov

Heider, Lee (R, 24)
State Capitol Building, Room WW35
P.O. Box 83720
Boise, ID 83720
P: (208) 332-1347
F: (208) 334-5397
E: lheider@senate.idaho.gov

Hill, Brent (R, 34)
State Capitol Building, Room W331
P.O. Box 83720
Boise, ID 83720
P: (208) 332-1300
F: (208) 334-5397
E: bhill@senate.idaho.gov

Johnson, Dan G. (R, 6)
State Capitol Building, Room WW30
P.O. Box 83720
Boise, ID 83720
P: (208) 332-1421
F: (208) 334-5397
E: djohnson@senate.idaho.gov

Keough, Shawn (R, 1)
State Capitol Building, Room WW28
P.O. Box 83720
Boise, ID 83720
P: (208) 332-1349
F: (208) 334-5397
E: skeough@senate.idaho.gov

Lacey, Roy (D, 29)
State Capitol Building, Room WG12
P.O. Box 83720
Boise, ID 83720
P: (208) 332-1406
F: (208) 334-5397
E: rlacey@senate.idaho.gov

Lakey, Todd (R, 12)
State Capitol Building, Room W435
P.O. Box 83720
Boise, ID 83720
P: (208) 332-1323
F: (208) 334-5397
E: tlakey@senate.idaho.gov

Lee, Abby (R, 9)*
State Capitol Building, Room WW27
P.O. Box 83720
Boise, ID 83720
P: (208) 332-1325
F: (208) 334-5397
E: alee@senate.idaho.gov

Lodge, Patti Anne (R, 11)
State Capitol Building, Room WW48
P.O. Box 83720
Boise, ID 83720
P: (208) 332-1320
F: (208) 334-5397
E: palodge@senate.idaho.gov

Martin, Fred (R, 15)
State Capitol Building, Room WG36
P.O. Box 83720
Boise, ID 83720
P: (208) 332-1000
F: (208) 334-5397
E: fmartin@senate.idaho.gov

McKenzie, Curt (R, 13)
State Capitol Building, Room WW42
P.O. Box 83720
Boise, ID 83720
P: (208) 332-1329
F: (208) 334-5397
E: cmckenzie@senate.idaho.gov

Mortimer, Dean M. (R, 30)
State Capitol Building, Room WG39
P.O. Box 83720
Boise, ID 83720
P: (208) 332-1358
F: (208) 334-5397
E: dmortimer@senate.idaho.gov

Nonini, Bob (R, 3)
State Capitol Building, Room W934
P.O. Box 83720
Boise, ID 83720
P: (208) 332-1338
F: (208) 334-5397
E: bnonini@senate.idaho.gov

Nuxoll, Sheryl L. (R, 7)
State Capitol Building, Room WG33
P.O. Box 83720
Boise, ID 83720
P: (208) 332-1355
F: (208) 334-5397
E: snuxoll@senate.idaho.gov

Patrick, Jim (R, 25)
State Capitol Building, Room WG44
P.O. Box 83720
Boise, ID 83720
P: (208) 332-1318
F: (208) 334-5397
E: jpatrick@senate.idaho.gov

Rice, Jim (R, 10)
State Capitol Building, Room WG31
P.O. Box 83720
Boise, ID 83720
P: (208) 332-1423
F: (208) 334-5397
E: jrice@senate.idaho.gov

Schmidt, Dan J. (D, 5)
State Capitol Building Room WG11
P.O. Box 83720
Boise, ID 83720
P: (208) 332-1405
F: (208) 334-5397
E: dschmidt@senate.idaho.gov

Siddoway, Jeff C. (R, 35)
State Capitol Building, Room WW50
P.O. Box 83720
Boise, ID 83720
P: (208) 332-1342
F: (208) 334-5397
E: jsiddoway@senate.idaho.gov

Souza, Mary (R, 4)*
State Capitol Building, Room WG04
P.O. Box 83720
Boise, ID 83720
P: (208) 332-1322
F: (208) 334-5397
E: msouza@senate.idaho.gov

Stennett, Michelle (D, 26)
State Capitol Building, Room W304
P.O. Box 83720
Boise, ID 83720
P: (208) 332-1410
F: (208) 334-5397
E: mstennett@senate.idaho.gov

Thayn, Steven P. (R, 8)
State Capitol Building, Room WG55
P.O. Box 83720
Boise, ID 83720
P: (208) 332-1344
F: (208) 334-5397
E: sthayn@senate.idaho.gov

Tippets, John (R, 32)
State Capitol Building, Room WW46
P.O. Box 83720
Boise, ID 83720
P: (208) 332-1429
F: (208) 334-5397
E: jtippets@senate.idaho.gov

Vick, Steve (R, 2)
State Capitol Building, Room WG37
P.O. Box 83720
Boise, ID 83720
P: (208) 332-1345
F: (208) 334-5397
E: sjvick@senate.idaho.gov

Ward-Engelking, Janie (D, 18)
State Capitol Building, Room WG03
P.O. Box 83720
Boise, ID 83720
P: (208) 332-1425
F: (208) 334-5397
E: jward-engelking@senate.idaho.gov

Werk, Elliot (D, 17)
State Capitol Building, Room W406
P.O. Box 83720
Boise, ID 83720
P: (208) 332-1411
F: (208) 334-5397
E: ewerk@senate.idaho.gov

Winder, Chuck (R, 20)
State Capitol Building, Room W428
P.O. Box 83720
Boise, ID 83720
P: (208) 332-1308
F: (208) 334-5397
E: cwinder@senate.idaho.gov

House

Speaker of the House

Rep. Scott Bedke (R)
Speaker
State Capitol Building, Room E303
P.O. Box 83720
Boise, ID 83720
P: (208) 332-1111
F: (208) 334-5397
E: sbedke@house.idaho.gov

House Majority Leader

Rep. Mike Moyle (R)
Majority Leader
State Capitol Building, Room E337
P.O. Box 83720
Boise, ID 83720
P: (208) 332-1120
F: (208) 334-5397
E: mmoyle@house.idaho.gov

Idaho

House Minority Leader

Rep. John Rusche (D)
Minority Leader
State Capitol Building, Room E329
P.O. Box 83720
Boise, ID 83720
P: (208) 332-1130
F: (208) 334-5397
E: jrusche@house.idaho.gov

Clerk of the House

Ms. Bonnie Alexander
Chief Clerk
State Capitol Building, Room E310
P.O. Box 83720
Boise, ID 83720
P: (208) 332-1141
F: (208) 334-5397
E: balexander@house.idaho.gov

Members of the House

Anderson, Neil (R, 31A)
State Capitol Building, Room EG67
P.O. Box 83720
Boise, ID 83720
P: (208) 332-1086
F: (208) 334-5397
E: nanderson@house.idaho.gov

Anderst, Robert (R, 12A)
State Capitol Building, Room EG46
P.O. Box 83720
Boise, ID 83720
P: (208) 332-1178
F: (208) 334-5397
E: randerst@house.idaho.gov

Andrus, Ken (R, 28A)
State Capitol Building, Room EW11
P.O. Box 83720
Boise, ID 83720
P: (208) 332-1046
F: (208) 334-5397
E: kandrus@house.idaho.gov

Barbieri, Vito (R, 2A)
State Capitol Building, Room EW57
P.O. Box 83720
Boise, ID 83720
P: (208) 332-1177
F: (208) 334-5397
E: vbarbieri@house.idaho.gov

Bateman, Linden B. (R, 33B)
State Capitol Building, Room EG65
P.O. Box 83720
Boise, ID 83720
P: (208) 332-1073
F: (208) 334-5397
E: lbateman@house.idaho.gov

Batt, Gayle (R, 11A)
State Capitol Building, Room EW38
P.O. Box 83720
Boise, ID 83720
P: (208) 332-1047
F: (208) 334-5397
E: gbatt@house.idaho.gov

Bedke, Scott (R, 27A)
State Capitol Building, Room E303
P.O. Box 83720
Boise, ID 83720
P: (208) 332-1111
F: (208) 334-5397
E: sbedke@house.idaho.gov

Bell, Maxine T. (R, 25A)
State Capitol Building, C316
P.O. Box 83720
Boise, ID 83720
P: (208) 334-4734
F: (208) 334-5397
E: mbell@house.idaho.gov

Beyeler, Merrill (R, 8B)*
State Capitol Building, Room EG61
P.O. Box 83720
Boise, ID 83720
P: (208) 332-1180
F: (208) 334-5397
E: mbeyeler@house.idaho.gov

Boyle, Judy (R, 9B)
State Capitol Building, EW29
P.O. Box 83720
Boise, ID 83720
P: (208) 332-1064
F: (208) 334-5397
E: jboyle@house.idaho.gov

Burtenshaw, Van (R, 35A)*
State Capitol Building, Room EW29
P.O. Box 83720
Boise, ID 83720
P: (208) 332-1060
F: (208) 334-5397
E: vburtenshaw@house.idaho.gov

Chaney, Greg (R, 10B)*
State Capitol Building, Room EW38
P.O. Box 1055
Boise, ID 83720
P: (208) 332-1055
F: (208) 334-5397
E: gchaney@house.idaho.gov

Cheatham, Don (R, 3B)*
State Capitol Building, Room EW29
P.O. Box 83720
Boise, ID 83720
P: (208) 332-1060
F: (208) 334-5397
E: dcheatham@house.idaho.gov

Chew, Susan B. (D, 17B)
State Capitol Building, Room EG62
P.O. Box 83720
Boise, ID 83720
P: (208) 332-1049
F: (208) 334-5397
E: schew@house.idaho.gov

Clow, Lance (R, 24A)
State Capitol Building, Room EW29
P.O. Box 83720
Boise, ID 83720
P: (208) 332-1188
F: (208) 334-5397
E: lclow@house.idaho.gov

Collins, Gary E. (R, 13B)
State Capitol Building, Room EW54
P.O. Box 83720
Boise, ID 83720
P: (208) 332-1063
F: (208) 334-5397
E: gcollins@house.idaho.gov

Crane, Brent (R, 13A)
State Capitol Building, Room E307
P.O. Box 83720
Boise, ID 83720
P: (208) 332-1120
F: (208) 334-5397
E: bcrane@house.idaho.gov

Dayley, Thomas (R, 21B)
State Capitol Building, Room EW36
P.O. Box 83720
Boise, ID 83720
P: (208) 332-1072
F: (208) 334-5397
E: tdayley@house.idaho.gov

DeMordaunt, Reed (R, 14B)
State Capitol Building, Room EW49
P.O. Box 83720
Boise, ID 83720
P: (208) 332-1057
F: (208) 334-5397
E: reedd@house.idaho.gov

Dixon, Sage (R, 1B)*
State Capitol Building, Room EW29
P.O. Box 83720
Boise, ID 83720
P: (208) 332-1185
F: (302) 334-5397
E: sdixon@house.idaho.gov

Erpelding, Mat (D, 19A)
State Capitol Building, Room E423
P.O. Box 83720
Boise, ID 83720
P: (208) 332-1078
F: (208) 334-5397
E: merpelding@house.idaho.gov

Gannon, John (D, 17A)
State Capitol Building, Room EG57
P.O. Box 83720
Boise, ID 83720
P: (208) 332-1000
F: (208) 334-5397
E: jgannon@house.idaho.gov

Gestrin, Terry (R, 8A)
State Capitol Building, Room EG32
P.O. Box 83720
Boise, ID 83720
P: (208) 332-1124
F: (208) 334-5397
E: tgestrin@house.idaho.gov

Gibbs, Marc (R, 32A)
State Capitol Building, Room EG24
P.O. Box 83720
Boise, ID 83720
P: (208) 332-1042
F: (208) 334-5397
E: mgibbs@house.idaho.gov

Harris, Steven (R, 21A)
State Capitol Building, Room EW29
P.O. Box 83720
Boise, ID 83720
P: (208) 332-1043
F: (208) 334-5397
E: sharris@house.idaho.gov

Hartgen, Stephen (R, 24B)
State Capitol Building, Room EW06
P.O. Box 83720
Boise, ID 83720
P: (208) 332-1061
F: (208) 334-5397
E: shartgen@house.idaho.gov

Hixon, Brandon (R, 10A)
State Capitol Building, Room EG25
P.O. Box 83720
Boise, ID 83720
P: (208) 332-1052
F: (208) 334-5397
E: bhixon@house.idaho.gov

Holtzclaw, James (R, 20B)
State Capitol Building, Room EG02
P.O. Box 83720
Boise, ID 83720
P: (208) 332-1041
F: (208) 334-5397
E: jholtzclaw@house.idaho.gov

Horman, Wendy (R, 30B)
State Capitol Building, Room EW37
P.O. Box 83720
Boise, ID 83720
P: (208) 332-1071
F: (208) 334-5397
E: whorman@house.idaho.gov

Jordan, Paulette E. (D, 5A)*
State Capitol Building, Room EG64
P.O. Box 83720
Boise, ID 83720
P: (208) 332-1175
F: (208) 334-5397
E: pjordan@house.idaho.gov

Kauffman, Clark (R, 25B)
State Capitol Building, Room EG40
P.O. Box 83720
Boise, ID 83720
P: (208) 332-1182
F: (208) 332-5397
E: ckauffman@house.idaho.gov

Kerby, Ryan (R, 9A)*
State Capitol Building, Room EG56
P.O. Box 83720
Boise, ID 83720
P: (208) 332-1166
F: (208) 334-5397
E: rkerby@house.idaho.gov

King, Phylis K. (D, 18B)
State Capitol Building, Room EG54
P.O. Box 83720
Boise, ID 83720
P: (208) 332-1080
F: (208) 334-5397
E: pking@house.idaho.gov

Kloc, Hy (D, 16B)
State Capitol Building, Room EG50
P.O. Box 83720
Boise, ID 83720
P: (208) 332-1075
F: (208) 334-5397
E: hkloc@house.idaho.gov

Loertscher, Thomas F. (R, 32B)
State Capitol Building, Room EW46
P.O. Box 83720
Boise, ID 83720
P: (208) 332-1183
F: (208) 334-5397
E: tloertscher@house.idaho.gov

Luker, Lynn M. (R, 15A)
State Capitol Building, Room EW06
P.O. Box 83720
Boise, ID 83720
P: (208) 332-1039
F: (208) 334-5397
E: lluker@house.idaho.gov

Malek, Luke (R, 4A)
State Capitol Building, Room EG47
P.O. Box 83720
Boise, ID 83720
P: (208) 332-1065
F: (208) 334-5397
E: lmalek@house.idaho.gov

McCrostie, John (D, 16A)*
State Capitol Building, Room EG51
P.O. Box 83720
Boise, ID 83720
P: (208) 332-1083
F: (208) 334-5397
E: jmccrostie@house.idaho.gov

McDonald, Patrick (R, 15A)
State Capitol Building, Room EG52
P.O. Box 83720
Boise, ID 83720
P: (208) 332-1176
E: pmcdonald@house.idaho.gov

McMillan, Shannon (R, 7A)
State Capitol Building, Room EW38
P.O. Box 83720
Boise, ID 83720
P: (208) 332-1033
F: (208) 334-5397
E: smcmillan@house.idaho.gov

Mendive, Ron (R, 3A)
State Capitol Building, Room EW29
P.O. Box 83720
Boise, ID 83720
P: (208) 332-1040
F: (208) 334-5397
E: rmendive@house.idaho.gov

Miller, Steven (R, 26A)
State Capitol Building, Room EG29
P.O. Box 83720
Boise, ID 83720
P: (208) 332-1174
F: (208) 334-5397
E: smiller@house.idaho.gov

Monks, Jason (R, 22B)
State Capitol Building, Room EW38
P.O. Box 83720
Boise, ID 83720
P: (208) 332-1036
F: (208) 334-5397
E: jmonks@house.idaho.gov

Moyle, Mike (R, 14A)
State Capitol Building, Room E337
P.O. Box 83720
Boise, ID 83720
P: (208) 332-1120
F: (208) 334-5397
E: mmoyle@house.idaho.gov

Nate, Ronald M. (R, 34A)*
State Capitol Building, Room EW29
P.O. Box 83720
Boise, ID 83720
P: (208) 332-1053
F: (208) 334-5397
E: rnate@house.idaho.gov

Nielsen, Peter (R, 22B)
State Capitol Building, Room EG38
P.O. Box 83720
Boise, ID 83720
P: (208) 332-1054
F: (208) 334-5397
E: pnielsen@house.idaho.gov

Nye, Mark (D, 29A)*
State Capitol Building, Room EG53
P.O. Box 83720
Boise, ID 83720
P: (208) 332-1079
F: (208) 334-5397
E: mnye@house.idaho.gov

Packer, Kelley (R, 28B)
State Capitol Building, Room EG41
P.O. Box 83720
Boise, ID 83720
P: (208) 322-1045
F: (208) 334-5397
E: kpacker@house.idaho.gov

Palmer, Joe A. (R, 20A)
State Capitol Building, Room EW60
P.O. Box 83720
Boise, ID 83720
P: (208) 332-1062
F: (208) 334-5397
E: jpalmer@house.idaho.gov

Pence, Donna L. (D, 26B)
State Capitol Building, Room E424
P.O. Box 83720
Boise, ID 83720
P: (208) 332-1130
F: (208) 334-5397
E: dpence@house.idaho.gov

Perry, Christy (R, 11B)
State Capitol Building, Room EW12
P.O. Box 83720
Boise, ID 83720
P: (208) 332-1044
F: (208) 334-5397
E: cperry@house.idaho.gov

Raybould, Dell (R, 34B)
State Capitol Building, Room EW16
P.O. Box 83720
Boise, ID 83720
P: (208) 332-1173
F: (208) 334-5397
E: draybould@house.idaho.gov

Redman, Eric (R, 2B)*
State Capitol Building, Room EG66
P.O. Box 83720
Boise, ID 83720
P: (208) 332-1070
F: (208) 334-5397
E: eredman@house.idaho.gov

Idaho

Romrell, Paul (R, 35B)
State Capitol Building, Room EG43
P.O. Box 83720
Boise, ID 83720
P: (208) 332-1056
F: (208) 334-5397
E: promrell@house.idaho.gov

Rubel, Ilana (D, 18A)
State Capitol Building, Room EG58
P.O. Box 83720
Boise, ID 83720
P: (208) 332-1034
F: (208) 334-5397
E: irubel@house.idaho.gov

Rudolph, Dan (D, 6A)*
State Capitol Building, Room EG59
P.O. Box 83720
Boise, ID 83720
P: (208) 332-1184
F: (208) 334-5397
E: drudolph@house.idaho.gov

Rusche, John (D, 6B)
State Capitol Building, Room E329
P.O. Box 83720
Boise, ID 83720
P: (208) 332-1130
F: (208) 334-5397
E: jrusche@house.idaho.gov

Scott, Heather (R, 1A)*
State Capitol Building, Room EW29
P.O. Box 83720
Boise, ID 83720
P: (208) 332-1190
F: (208) 334-5397
E: hscott@house.idaho.gov

Shepherd, Paul E. (R, 7B)
State Capitol Building, Room EW38
P.O. Box 83720
Boise, ID 83720
P: (208) 332-1067
F: (208) 334-5397
E: pshepherd@house.idaho.gov

Sims, Kathleen (R, 4B)
State Capitol Building, Room EW29
P.O. Box 83720
Boise, ID 83720
P: (208) 332-1048
F: (208) 334-5397
E: ksims@house.idaho.gov

Smith, Elaine (D, 29B)
State Capitol Building, Room EG63
P.O. Box 83720
Boise, ID 83720
P: (208) 332-1031
F: (208) 334-5397
E: esmith@house.idaho.gov

Thompson, Jeff (R, 30A)
State Capitol Building, Room EG62
P.O. Box 83720
Boise, ID 83720
P: (208) 332-1081
F: (208) 334-5397
E: jthompson@house.idaho.gov

Troy, Caroline (R, 5)*
State Capitol Building, Room EW29
P.O. Box 83720
Boise, ID 83720
P: (208) 332-1035
F: (208) 334-5397
E: ctroy@house.idaho.gov

Trujillo, Janet (R, 33A)
State Capitol Building, Room EW38
P.O. Box 83720
Boise, ID 83720
P: (208) 332-1189
F: (208) 334-5397
E: jtrujillo@house.idaho.gov

Van Orden, Julie (R, 31B)
State Capitol Building, Room EG42
P.O. Box 83720
Boise, ID 83720
P: (208) 332-1038
F: (208) 334-5397
E: jvanorden@house.idaho.gov

Vander Woude, John (R, 22A)
State Capitol Building, Room E306
P.O. Box 83720
Boise, ID 83720
P: (208) 332-1120
F: (208) 334-5397
E: jvanderwoude@house.idaho.gov

Wills, Richard (R, 22A)
State Capitol Building, Room EW56
P.O. Box 83720
Boise, ID 87320
P: (208) 332-1181
F: (208) 334-5397
E: rwills@house.idaho.gov

Wintrow, Melissa (D, 19B)*
State Capitol Building, Room EG60
P.O. Box 83720
Boise, ID 83720
P: (208) 332-1076
F: (208) 334-5397
E: mwintrow@house.idaho.gov

Wood, Fred (R, 27B)
State Capitol Building, Room EW14
P.O. Box 83720
Boise, ID 83720
P: (208) 332-1074
F: (208) 334-5397
E: fwood@house.idaho.gov

Youngblood, Rick (R, 12B)
State Capitol Building, Room EG45
P.O. Box 83720
Boise, ID 83720
P: (208) 332-1059
F: (208) 334-5397
E: ryoungblood@house.idaho.gov

Congress

Senate

Crapo, Michael D. (R)
Risch, James E. (R)

House

Labrador, Raul R. (R, 1)
Simpson, Mike (R, 2)

Illinois

Executive

Governor

Hon. Bruce Rauner (R)
Governor
207 Statehouse
Springfield, IL 62706
P: (217) 782-6830
F: (217) 524-4049

Lieutenant Governor

Hon. Evelyn Sanguinetti (R)
Lieutenant Governor
214 State House
Springfield, IL 62706
P: (217) 558-3085
F: (217) 558-3086

Attorney General

Hon. Lisa Madigan (D)
Attorney General
James R. Thompson Center
100 West Randolph Street
Chicago, IL 60601
P: (312) 814-3000

Auditor

Hon. William G. Holland
(appointed by the Legislature)
Auditor General
Iles Park Plaza
740 East Ash Street
Springfield, IL 62703
P: (217) 782-3536
F: (217) 785-8222
E: auditor@mail.state.il.us

Secretary of State

Hon. Jesse White (D)
Secretary of State
213 State Capitol
Springfield, IL 62756
P: (217) 782-2201
F: (217) 785-0358
E: jessewhite@ilsos.net

Treasurer

Hon. Michael W. Frerichs (D)
State Treasurer
219 Statehouse
Springfield, IL 62704
P: (217) 782-2211
F: (217) 785-2777

Judiciary

Supreme Court (PE)

Ms. Carolyn Taft Grosboll
Clerk of the Supreme Court
Supreme Court Building
200 East Capitol
Springfield, IL 62701
P: (217) 782-2035

Hon. Rita B. Garman
Chief Justice
Hon. Anne M. Burke
Hon. Charles E. Freeman
Hon. Lloyd A. Karmeier
Hon. Thomas L. Kilbride
Hon. Mary Jane Theis
Hon. Robert R. Thomas

Legislative Senate

Senate President

Sen. John J. Cullerton (D)
President of the Senate
327 Capitol Building
Springfield, IL 62706
P: (217) 782-2728
F: (217) 782-3242
E: john@senatorcullerton.com

President Pro Tempore of the Senate

Sen. Don Harmon (D)
Senate President Pro Tempore
329B Capitol Building
Springfield, IL 62706
P: (217) 782-8176
F: (217) 558-6013
E: info@donharmon.org

Senate Majority Leader

Sen. James F. Clayborne Jr. (D)
Senate Majority Leader
329A Capitol Building
Springfield, IL 62706
P: (217) 782-5399
F: (217) 558-6013
E: jclaybourne@senatedem.ilga.gov

Senate Minority Leader

Sen. Christine Radogno (R)
Senate Minority Leader
309G Capitol Building
Springfield, IL 62706
P: (217) 782-7730
F: (217) 782-7818
E: cradogno@sbcglobal.net

Secretary of the Senate

Mr. Tim Anderson
Secretary of the Senate
Room 401, Capitol Building
Springfield, IL 62706
P: (217) 782-5715

Members of the Senate

Althoff, Pamela J. (R, 32)
309L Capitol Building
Springfield, IL 62706
P: (217) 782-8000
F: (217) 782-9586
E: pamela@pamelaalthoff.net

Anderson, Neil (R, 36)*
Room 105-C State House
Springfield, IL 62706
P: (217) 782-5957
F: (217) 782-0116

Barickman, Jason (R, 53)
M103E Capitol Building
Springfield, IL 62706
P: (217) 782-6597
E: jason@jasonbarickman.org

Bennett, Scott M. (D, 52)*
218B Capitol Building
Springfield, IL 62706
P: (217) 782-2507

Bertino-Tarrant, Jennifer (D, 49)
119B Capitol Building
Springfield, IL 62706
P: (217) 782-0052

Biss, Daniel (D, 9)
M121 Capitol Building
Springfield, IL 62706
P: (217) 782-2119

Bivins, Tim (R, 45)
M103A Capitol Building
Springfield, IL 62706
P: (217) 782-0180
F: (217) 782-9586
E: senatorbivins@grics.net

Brady, Bill (R, 44)
103A Capitol Building
Springfield, IL 62706
P: (217) 782-6216
F: (217) 782-0116
E: billbrady@senatorbillbrady.com

Bush, Melinda (D, 31)
M120 Capitol Building
Springfield, IL 62706
P: (217) 782-7353
F: (218) 782-2115

Clayborne Jr., James F. (D, 57)
329A Capitol Building
Springfield, IL 62706
P: (217) 782-5399
F: (217) 558-6013
E: jclaybourne@senatedem.ilga.gov

Collins, Jacqueline Y. (D, 16)
M114 Capitol Building
Springfield, IL 62706
P: (217) 782-1607
F: (217) 782-2115
E: jcollins@senatedem.ilga.gov

Connelly, Michael G. (R, 21)
M103C Capitol Building
Springfield, IL 62706
P: (217) 782-8192
F: (217) 782-9586

Cullerton, John J. (D, 6)
327 Capitol Building
Springfield, IL 62706
P: (217) 782-2728
F: (217) 782-3242
E: john@senatorcullerton.com

Cullerton, Thomas (D, 23)
M118 Capitol Building
Springfield, IL 62706
P: (217) 782-9463

Cunningham, William (D, 18)
M115 Capitol Building
Springfield, IL 62706
P: (217) 782-5145
F: (217) 782-2115

Delgado, William (D, 2)
623 Capitol Building
Springfield, IL 62706
P: (217) 782-5652
F: (217) 782-1631
E: wdelgado@senatedem.ilga.gov

Duffy, Dan (R, 26)
108B Capitol Building
Springfield, IL 62706
P: (217) 782-8010
F: (217) 782-0116

Illinois

Forby, Gary (D, 59)
417B Capitol Building
Springfield, IL 62706
P: (217) 782-3088
F: (217) 782-8287
E: gforby
@senatedem.ilga.gov

Haine, William R. (D, 56)
311C Capitol Building
Springfield, IL 62706
P: (217) 782-5247
F: (217) 782-5340
E: whaine
@senatedem.ilga.gov

Harmon, Don (D, 39)
329B Capitol Building
Springfield, IL 62706
P: (217) 782-8176
F: (217) 558-6013
E: info@donharmon.org

Harris III, Napoleon (D, 15)
M122 Capitol Building
Springfield, IL 62706
P: (217) 782-8066

Hastings, Michael (D, 19)
118 Capitol Building
Springfield, IL 62706
P: (217) 782-9595

Holmes, Linda (D, 42)
129 Capitol Building
Springfield, IL 62706
P: (217) 782-0422
F: (217) 782-2115
E: info
@lindaholmesforsenate.com

Hunter, Mattie (D, 3)
619 Capitol Building
Springfield, IL 62706
P: (217) 782-5966
F: (217) 782-1631
E: mhunter
@senatedem.ilga.gov

Hutchinson, Toi W. (D, 40)
121C Capitol Building
Springfield, IL 62706
P: (217) 782-7419
F: (217) 557-3930
E: hutchinson
@senatedem.ilga.gov

Jones III, Emil (D, 14)
121D Capitol Building
Springfield, IL 62706
P: (217) 782-9573
F: (217) 557-3930
E: jones@senatedem.ilga.gov

Koehler, David (D, 46)
M113 Capitol Building
Springfield, IL 62706
P: (217) 782-8250
F: (217) 782-2115
E: dkoehler
@senatedem.ilga.gov

Kotowski, Dan (D, 28)
124 Capitol Building
Springfield, IL 62706
P: (217) 782-3875
F: (217) 782-2115
E: dan@kotowski4senate.com

LaHood, Darin M. (R, 37)
M103D Capitol Building
Springfield, IL 62706
P: (217) 782-1942
F: (217) 782-9586

Landek, Steven M. (D, 12)
113 Capitol Building
Springfield, IL 62706
P: (217) 782-0054
F: (217) 782-2331

Lightford, Kimberly A. (D, 4)
323B Capitol Building
Springfield, IL 62706
P: (212) 782-8505
F: (217) 558-2068
E: klightford
@senatedem.ilga.gov

Link, Terry (D, 30)
321 Capitol Building
Springfield, IL 62706
P: (217) 782-8181
F: (217) 782-4450
E: senator@link30.org

Luechtefeld, David (R, 58)
103B Capitol Building
Springfield, IL 62706
P: (217) 782-8137
F: (217) 782-4079
E: sendavel@midwest.net

Manar, Andy (D, 48)
119A Capitol Building
Springfield, IL 62706
P: (217) 782-0228

Martinez, Iris Y. (D, 20)
413 Capitol Building
Springfield, IL 62706
P: (217) 782-8191
F: (217) 782-3088
E: ilsenate20@sbcglobal.net

McCann, Wm. Sam (R, 50)
108E Capitol Building
Springfield, IL 62706
P: (217) 782-8206
F: (217) 782-0116

McCarter, Kyle (R, 54)
103C Capitol Building
Springfield, IL 62706
P: (217) 782-5755
F: (217) 782-0116
E: district51
@senategop.state.il.us

McConnaughay, Karen (R, 33)
103D Stratton Building
Springfield, IL 62706
P: (217) 782-1977

McGuire, Pat (D, 43)
311B Capitol Building
Springfield, IL 62706
P: (217) 782-8800
F: (217) 558-6006

Morrison, Julie A. (D, 29)
M108 Capitol Building
Springfield, IL 62706
P: (217) 782-3650

Mulroe, John G. (D, 10)
127 Capitol Building
Springfield, IL 62706
P: (217) 782-1035
F: (217) 782-2331

Munoz, Antonio (D, 1)
323A Capitol Building
Springfield, IL 62706
P: (217) 782-9415
F: (217) 558-1042
E: munoz@senatedem.ilga.gov

Murphy, Matt (R, 27)
309H Capitol Building
Springfield, IL 62706
P: (217) 782-4471
F: (217) 782-7818
E: senatormattmurphy
@sbcglobal.net

Noland, Michael (D, 22)
307B Capitol Building
Springfield, IL 62706
P: (217) 782-7746
F: (217) 557-3908
E: info@noland.org

Nybo, Chris (R, 24)
105B State House
Springfield, IL 62706
P: (217) 782-8148
F: (217) 782-0116

Oberweis, Jim (R, 25)
105A Capitol Building
Springfield, IL 62706
P: (217) 782-0471
F: (217) 782-0116

Radogno, Christine (R, 41)
309G Capitol Building
Springfield, IL 62706
P: (217) 782-7730
F: (217) 782-7818
E: cradogno@sbcglobal.net

Raoul, Kwame (D, 13)
123 Capitol Building
Springfield, IL 62706
P: (217) 782-5338
F: (217) 558-6006
E: kraoul
@senatedem.ilga.gov

Rezin, Sue (R, 38)
309I Capitol Building
Springfield, IL 62706
P: (217) 782-3840
F: (217) 782-0116

Righter, Dale A. (R, 55)
309M Capitol Building
Springfield, IL 62706
P: (217) 782-6674
F: (217) 782-7818
E: drighter
@consolidated.net

Rose, Chapin (R, 51)
M103F Capitol Building
Springfield, IL 62706
P: (217) 558-1006

Sandoval, Martin A. (D, 11)
111 Capitol Building
Spingfield, IL 62706
P: (217) 782-5304
F: (217) 558-6006
E: msandoval
@senatedem.ilga.gov

Silverstein, Ira I. (D, 8)
121B Capitol Building
Springfield, IL 62706
P: (217) 782-5500
F: (217) 782-5340
E: isilverstein
@senatedem.ilga.gov

Stadelman, Steve (D, 34)
121A Capitol Building
Springfield, IL 62706
P: (217) 782-8022

Steans, Heather (D, 7)
122 Capitol Building
Springfield, IL 62706
P: (217) 782-8492
F: (217) 782-2115
E: hsteans
@senatedem.ilga.gov

Sullivan, John M. (D, 47)
417C Capitol Building
Springfield, IL 62706
P: (217) 782-2479
F: (217) 558-0168
E: jsullivan@senatedem.ilga.gov

Syverson, Dave (R, 34)
108A Capitol Building
Springfield, IL 62706
P: (217) 782-5413
F: (217) 782-9586

Trotter, Donne E. (D, 17)
627 Capitol Building
Springfield, IL 62706
P: (217) 782-3201
F: (217) 782-8201
E: dtrotter@senatedem.ilga.gov

Van Pelt, Patricia (D, 5)
218A Capitol Building
Springfield, IL 62706
P: (217) 782-6252

House

Speaker of the House

Rep. Michael J. Madigan (D)
Speaker of the House
300 Capitol Building
Springfield, IL 62706
P: (217) 782-5350
F: (217) 524-1794
E: mmadigan@hds.ilga.gov

House Majority Leader

Rep. Barbara Flynn Currie (D)
House Majority Leader
300 Capitol Building
Springfield, IL 62706
P: (217) 782-8121
F: (217) 524-1794
E: repcurrie@sbcglobal.net

House Minority Leader

Rep. Jim B. Durkin (R)
House Minority Leader
316 Capitol Building
Springfield, IL 62706
P: (217) 782-0494
F: (217) 782-7012
E: repdurkin@hotmail.com

Clerk of the House

Mr. Tim Mapes
Clerk of the House/Chief of Staff To the Speaker
300 State House
Springfield, IL 62706
P: (217) 782-8223

Members of the House

Acevedo, Edward J. (D, 2)
109 Capitol Building
Springfield, IL 62706
P: (217) 782-2855
F: (217) 557-5148
E: acevedoed@ilga.gov

Ammons, Carol (D, 103)*
240A-W Stratton Office Building
Springfield, IL 62706
P: (217) 558-1009
E: csrepammons@gmail.com

Andersson, Steven (R, 65)*
211-N Stratton Office Building
Springfield, IL 62706
P: (217) 782-5457

Andrade Jr., Jaime M. (D, 40)
231-E Stratton Office Building
Springfield, IL 62706
P: (217) 782-8117
F: (217) 558-4551
E: staterep40@gmail.com

Anthony, John D. (R, 75)
200-2N Stratton Office Building
Springfield, IL 62706
P: (217) 782-5997
F: (217) 782-3189

Arroyo, Luis (D, 3)
274-S Stratton Building
Springfield, IL 62706
P: (217) 782-0480
F: (217) 557-9609
E: RepDistrict3@gmail.com

Batinick, Mark (R, 97)*
232-N Stratton Office Building
Springfield, IL 62706
P: (217) 782-1331

Beiser, Daniel V. (D, 111)
269-S Stratton Office Building
Springfield, IL 62706
P: (217) 782-5996
F: (217) 558-0493
E: dvbeiser@scglobal.net

Bellock, Patricia R. (R, 47)
215-N Stratton Office Building
Springfield, IL 62706
P: (217) 782-1448
F: (217) 782-2289
E: rep@pbellock.com

Bennett, Thomas (R, 106)*
222-N Stratton Office Building
Springfield, IL 62706
P: (217) 558-1039

Bourne, Avery (R, 95)*
200-2N Stratton Office Building
Springfield, IL 62706
P: (217) 782-8071
F: (217) 782-1275

Bradley, John E. (D, 117)
259-S Stratton Office Building
Springfield, IL 62706
P: (217) 782-1051
F: (217) 782-0882
E: repjohnbradley@mychoice.net

Brady, Dan (R, 105)
200-8N Stratton Office Building
Springfield, IL 62706
P: (217) 782-1118
F: (217) 558-6271
E: dan@rep-danbrady.com

Breen, Peter (R, 48)*
214-N Stratton Office Building
Springfield, IL 62706
P: (217) 782-8037

Brown, Adam (R, 102)
314 Capitol Building
Springfield, IL 62706
P: (217) 782-8398
F: (217) 782-7012

Bryant, Terri (R, 115)*
207-N Stratton Office Building
Springfield, IL 62706
P: (217) 782-0387

Burke, Daniel J. (D, 1)
233-E Stratton Office Building
Springfield, IL 62706
P: (217) 782-1117
F: (217) 782-0927
E: burkedj2@ilga.gov

Burke, Kelly (D, 36)
246-W Stratton Office Building
Springfield, IL 62706
P: (217) 782-0515
F: (217) 558-4553
E: kburke@kellyburkerep36.org

Butler, Tim (R, 87)*
1128-E Stratton Office Building
Springfield, IL 62706
P: (217) 782-0053
F: (217) 782-0897

Cabello, John (R, 68)
201-N Stratton Office Building
Springfield, IL 62706
P: (217) 782-0455
F: (217) 782-1141
E: johncabello@aol.com

Cassidy, Kelly M. (D, 14)
265-S Stratton Office Building
Springfield, IL 62706
P: (217) 782-8088
F: (217) 782-6592
E: repcassidy@gmail.com

Cavaletto, John (R, 107)
205-N Stratton Office Building
Springfield, IL 62706
P: (217) 782-0066
F: (217) 782-1336
E: john@johncavaletto.com

Chapa LaVia, Linda (D, 83)
229-E Stratton Office Building
Springfield, IL 62706
P: (217) 558-1002
F: (217) 782-0927
E: chapa-laviali@ilga.gov

Cloonen, Katherine (D, 79)
281-S Stratton Office Building
Springfield, IL 62706
P: (217) 782-5981
E: staterepcloonen79@att.net

Conroy, Deborah (D, 46)
244-W Stratton Office Building
Springfield, IL 62706
P: (217) 782-8158
E: repdebconroy@gmail.com

Costello, Jerry F. (D, 116)
200-1S Stratton Office Building
Springfield, IL 62706
P: (217) 782-1018
F: (217) 558-4502
E: staterepcostello@gmail.com

Crespo, Fred (D, 44)
255-S Stratton Office Building
Springfield, IL 62706
P: (217) 782-0347
F: (217) 557-4622
E: repfredcrespo@um.att.com

Currie, Barbara Flynn (D, 25)
300 Capitol Building
Springfield, IL 62706
P: (217) 782-8121
F: (217) 524-1794
E: repcurrie@sbcglobal.net

Illinois

D'Amico, John (D, 15)
279-S Stratton Office Building
Springfield, IL 62706
P: (217) 782-8198
F: (217) 782-2906
E: johnd@ilga.gov

Davidsmeyer, C.D. (R, 100)
220-N Stratton Office Building
Springfield, IL 62706
P: (217) 782-1840
F: (217) 558-3743
E: repcddavidsmeyer
@gmail.com

Davis, Monique D. (D, 27)
241-E Stratton Office Building
Springfield, IL 62706
P: (217) 782-0010
F: (217) 782-1795
E: davismd@ilga.gov

Davis, William (D, 30)
254-W Stratton Office Building
Springfield, IL 62706
P: (217) 782-8197
F: (217) 782-3220
E: williamd@ilga.gov

DeLuca, Anthony (D, 80)
271-S Stratton Office Building
Springfield, IL 62706
P: (217) 782-1719
F: (217) 558-4944
E: repdeluca@sbcglobal.net

Demmer, Tom (R, 90)
227-N Stratton Office Building
Springfield, IL 62706
P: (217) 782-0535
E: rep@tomdemmer.com

Drury, Scott (D, 58)
250-W Stratton Office Building
Springfield, IL 62706
P: (217) 782-0902
E: repdrury@gmail.com

Dunkin, Ken (D, 5)
278-S Stratton Office Building
Springfield, IL 62706
P: (217) 782-4535
F: (217) 782-4213
E: ken@repkendunkin.com

Durkin, Jim B. (R, 82)
316 Capitol Building
Springfield, IL 62706
P: (217) 782-0494
F: (217) 782-7012
E: repdurkin@hotmail.com

Evans Jr., Marcus C. (D, 33)
276-S Stratton Office Building
Springfield, IL 62706
P: (217) 782-8272
F: (217) 782-2404
E: repevans33@gmail.com

Feigenholtz, Sara (D, 12)
300 Capitol Building
Springfield, IL 62706
P: (217) 782-8062
F: (217) 557-7203
E: sara@staterepsara.com

Fine, Laura (D, 17)
247-E Stratton Office Building
Springfield, IL 62706
P: (217) 782-4194
F: (217) 524-0449
E: repfine@gmail.com

Flowers, Mary E. (D, 31)
251-E Stratton Office Building
Springfield, IL 62706
P: (217) 782-4207
F: (217) 782-1130
E: maryeflowers@ilga.gov

Flowers, Mary E. (D, 31)
251-E Stratton Office Building
Springfield, IL 62706
P: (217) 782-4207
F: (217) 782-1130
E: maryeflowers@ilga.gov

Ford, La Shawn K. (D, 8)
239-E Stratton Office Building
Springfield, IL 62706
P: (217) 782-5962
F: (217) 557-4502
E: repford@lashawnford.com

Fortner, Mike (R, 49)
200-4N Stratton Office Building
Springfield, IL 62706
P: (217) 782-1653
F: (217) 282-1275
E: mike.fortner
@sbcglobal.net

Franks, Jack D. (D, 63)
267-S Stratton Office Building
Springfield, IL 62706
P: (217) 782-1717
F: (217) 557-2118
E: jack@jackfranks.org

Frese, Randy (R, 94)*
230-N Stratton Office Building
Springfield, IL 62706
P: (217) 782-8096

Gabel, Robyn (D, 18)
248-W Stratton Office Building
Springfield, IL 62706
P: (217) 782-8052
F: (217) 558-4553
E: staterepgabel
@robyngabel.com

Golar, Esther (D, 6)
268-S Stratton Office Building
Springfield, IL 62706
P: (217) 782-5971
F: (217) 558-6370
E: esthergolar
@sbcglobal.net

Gordon-Booth, Jehan (D, 92)
200-8S Stratton Office Building
Springfield, IL 62706
P: (217) 782-3186
F: (217) 558-4552
E: repjgordon@gmail.com

Guzzardi, Will (D, 39)*
282-S Stratton Office Building
Springfiield, IL 62706
P: (217) 558-1032
E: will@repguzzardi.com

Hammond, Norine (R, 93)
209-N Stratton Office Building
Springfield, IL 62706
P: (217) 782-0416
F: (217) 557-4530
E: rephammond@macomb.com

Harris, David (R, 53)
221-N Stratton Office Building
Springfield, IL 62706
P: (217) 782-3739
E: repharris@yahoo.com

Harris, Greg (D, 13)
253-S Stratton Office Building
Springfield, IL 62706
P: (217) 782-3835
F: (217) 557-6470
E: greg@gregharris.org

Hays, Chad (R, 104)
202-N Stratton Office Building
Springfield, IL 62706
P: (217) 782-4811

Hernandez, Elizabeth (D, 24)
286-S Stratton Office Building
Springfield, IL 62706
P: (217) 782-8173
F: (217) 558-1844
E: repehernandez@yahoo.com

Hoffman, Jay C. (D, 113)
261-S Stratton Office Building
Springfield, IL 62706
P: (217) 782-0104
E: repjayhoffman@gmail.com

Hurley, Frances Ann (D, 35)
252-W Stratton Office Building
Springfield, IL 62706
P: (217) 782-8200
E: repfranhurley@gmail.com

Ives, Jeanne (R, 42)
218-N Stratton Office Building
Springfield, IL 62706
P: (217) 558-1037
F: (217) 782-1275
E: repjeanneives@gmail.com

Jackson Sr., Eddie Lee (D, 114)
200-7S Stratton Office Building
Springfield, IL 62706
P: (217) 782-5951
F: (217) 782-8794

Jesiel, Sheri (R, 61)*
200-5N State Office Buiding
Springfield, IL 62706
P: (217) 782-8151
F: (217) 557-7207
E: jesiel@ilhousegop.org

Jones, Thaddeus (D, 29)
240-W Stratton Office Building
Springfield, IL 62706
P: (217) 782-8087
F: (217) 558-6433
E: repjones@gmail.com

Kay, Dwight (R, 112)
223-N Stratton Office Building
Springfield, IL 62706
P: (217) 782-8018
E: dwightkay112@gmail.com

Kifowit, Stephanie (D, 84)
200-3S Stratton Office Building
Springfield, IL 62706
P: (217) 782-8028
E: stephanie.kifowit
@att.net

Lang, Lou (D, 16)
109 Capitol Building
Springfield, IL 62706
P: (217) 782-1252
F: (217) 782-9903
E: langli@ilga.gov

Leitch, David R. (R, 73)
314 Capitol Building
Springfield, IL 62706
P: (217) 782-8108
F: (217) 557-3047
E: repdavidleitch@gmail.com

Lilly, Camille Y. (D, 78)
270-S Stratton Office Building
Springfield, IL 62706
P: (217) 782-6400
F: (217) 558-1054
E: statereplilly@yahoo.com

Madigan, Michael J. (D, 22)
300 Capitol Building
Springfield, IL 62706
P: (217) 782-5350
F: (217) 524-1794
E: mmadigan@hds.ilga.gov

Manley, Natalie (D, 98)
242A-W Stratton Office Building
Springfield, IL 62706
P: (217) 782-3316
E: repmanley@gmail.com

Martwick, Robert (D, 19)
290-S Stratton Office Building
Springfield, IL 62706
P: (217) 782-8400
E: repmartwick@gmail.com

Mautino, Frank J. (D, 76)
300 Capitol Building
Springfield, IL 62706
P: (217) 782-0140
F: (217) 557-7680
E: patti76th@ivnet.com

Mayfield, Rita (D, 60)
238-W Stratton Office Building
Springfield, IL 62706
P: (217) 558-1012
F: (217) 558-1092
E: 60thdistrict@gmail.com

McAsey, Emily (D, 85)
249-E Stratton Office Building
Springfield, IL 62706
P: (217) 782-4179
F: (217) 557-7204
E: repemily@gmail.com

McAuliffe, Michael P. (R, 20)
219-N Stratton Office Building
Springfield, IL 62706
P: (217) 782-8182
F: (217) 558-1073
E: mmcauliffe20@yahoo.com

McDermed, Margo (R, 37)*
204-N Stratton Office Building
Springfield, IL 62706
P: (217) 782-0424

McSweeney, David (R, 52)
226-N Stratton Office Building
Springfield, IL 62706
P: (217) 782-1517
E: ilhouse52@gmail.com

Meier, Charles E. (R, 108)
200-7N Stratton Office Building
Springfield, IL 62706
P: (217) 782-6401
E: repcmeier@gmail.com

Mitchell, Bill (R, 101)
632 Capitol Building
Springfield, IL 62706
P: (217) 782-8163
F: (217) 557-0571
E: repmitchell@earthlink.net

Mitchell, Christian (D, 26)
260-W Stratton Office Building
Springfield, IL 62706
P: (217) 782-2023
F: (217) 558-1092
E: MitchellDistrict26@att.net

Moeller, Anna (D, 43)*
235-E Stratton Office Building
Springfield, IL 62706
P: (217) 782-8020
F: (217) 557-4459
E: staterepmoeller@gmail.com

Moffitt, Donald L. (R, 74)
217-N Stratton Office Building
Springfield, IL 62706
P: (217) 782-8032
F: (217) 557-0179
E: moffitt@grics.net

Morrison, Thomas (R, 54)
234-N Stratton Office Building
Springfield, IL 62706
P: (217) 782-8026
F: (217) 558-7016
E: Repmorrison54@gmail.com

Moylan, Martin (D, 55)
258-W Stratton Office Building
Springfield, IL 62706
P: (217) 782-8007
E: staterepmoylan@gmail.com

Mussman, Michelle (D, 56)
257-S Stratton Office Building
Springfield, IL 62706
P: (217) 782-3725
F: (217) 557-6271
E: staterepmussman@gmail.com

Nekritz, Elaine (D, 57)
245-E Stratton Office Building
Springfield, IL 62706
P: (217) 558-1004
F: (217) 558-4554
E: enekritz@repnekritz.org

Phelps, Brandon W. (D, 118)
200-9S Stratton Office Building
Springfield, IL 62706
P: (217) 782-5131
F: (217) 557-0521
E: bphelps118@gmail.com

Phillips, Reginald (R, 110)*
208-N Stratton Office Building
Springfield, IL 62706
P: (217) 558-1040

Poe, Raymond (R, 99)
E-1 Stratton Office Building
Springfield, IL 62706
P: (217) 782-0044
F: (217) 782-0897
E: RPoe@hrs.ilga.gov

Pritchard, Robert W. (R, 70)
200-3N Stratton Office Building
Springfield, IL 62706
P: (217) 782-0425
F: (217) 782-1275
E: bob@pritchardstaterep.com

Reaves-Harris, Pamela (D, 10)*
284-S Stratton Office Building
Springfield, IL 62706
P: (217) 782-8077
E: pamelar@ilga.gov

Reis, David (R, 109)
632 Capitol Building
Springfield, IL 62706
P: (217) 782-2087
F: (217) 557-0571
E: david@davidreiz.org

Riley, Al (D, 38)
262-W Stratton Office Building
Springfield, IL 62706
P: (217) 558-1007
F: (217) 557-1664
E: rep.riley38@sbcglobal.net

Rita, Robert (D, 28)
277-S Stratton Office Building
Springfield, IL 62706
P: (217) 558-1000
F: (217) 558-1091
E: ritaro@ilga.gov

Sandack, Ronald (R, 81)
632 Capitol Building
Springfield, IL 62706
P: (217) 782-6578
E: repsandack@gmail.com

Scherer, Sue (D, 96)
E-2 Stratton Office Building
Springfield, IL 62706
P: (217) 524-0353
F: (217) 524-0354
E: staterepsue@gmail.com

Sente, Carol (D, 59)
272-S Stratton Office Building
Springfield, IL 62706
P: (217) 782-0499
F: (217) 524-0443
E: repsente@gmail.com

Sims Jr., Elgie R. (D, 34)
275-S Stratton Office Building
Springfield, IL 62706
P: (217) 782-6476
F: (217) 782-0952
E: repsims34@gmail.com

Smiddy, Mike (D, 71)
200-5S Stratton Office Building
Springfield, IL 62706
P: (217) 782-3992
F: (217) 524-0443
E: RepSmiddy@gmail.com

Sommer, Keith P. (R, 88)
216-N Stratton Office Building
Springfield, IL 62706
P: (217) 782-0221
F: (217) 557-1098
E: sommer@mtco.com

Sosnowski, Joe (R, 69)
225-N Stratton Office Building
Springfield, IL 62706
P: (217) 782-0548
F: (217) 782-1141
E: repsosnowski@gmail.com

Soto, Cynthia (D, 4)
288-S Stratton Office Building
Springfield, IL 62706
P: (217) 782-0150
F: (217) 557-7210
E: 4repsoto@gmail.com

Stewart, Brian W. (R, 89)
210-N Stratton Office Building
Springfield, IL 62706
P: (217) 782-8186
F: (217) 558-7016
E: repstewart@gmail.com

Sullivan Jr., Ed (R, 51)
314 Capitol Building
Springfield, IL 62706
P: (217) 782-3696
F: (217) 558-3055
E: ILhouse51@sbcglobal.net

Tabares, Silvana (D, 21)
280-S Stratton Office Building
Springfield, IL 62706
P: (217) 782-7752
F: (217) 524-0450
E: rep.tabares@gmail.com

Thapedi, Andre (D, 32)
256-W Stratton Office Building
Springfield, IL 62706
P: (217) 782-1702
F: (217) 557-0543
E: rep32district@gmail.com

Tryon, Michael W. (R, 66)
203-N Stratton Office Building
Springfield, IL 62706
P: (217) 782-0432
F: (217) 782-1141
E: Mike@miketryon.com

Illinois

Turner, Arthur L. (D, 9)
109 Capitol Building
Springfield, IL 62706
P: (217) 782-8116
F: (217) 782-0888
E: arthurt@ilga.gov

Unes, Michael (R, 91)
224-N Stratton Office Building
Springfield, IL 62706
P: (217) 782-8152
F: (217) 782-1275
E: repunes@gmail.com

Verschoore, Patrick J. (D, 72)
263-S Stratton Office Building
Springfield, IL 62706
P: (217) 782-5970
F: (217) 558-1253
E: pverschoore@qconline.com

Wallace, Litesa (D, 67)
237-E Stratton Office Building
Springfield, IL 62706
P: (217) 782-3167
F: (217) 557-7654
E: litesa@staterepwallace.com

Walsh Jr., Lawrence M. (D, 86)
292-S Stratton Office Building
Springfield, IL 62706
P: (217) 782-8090
E: statereplarrywalshjr@gmail.com

Wehrli, Grant (R, 41)*
228-N Stratton Office Building
Springfield, IL 62706
P: (217) 782-6507

Welch, Emanuel Chris (D, 7)
266-S Stratton Office Building
Springfield, IL 62706
P: (217) 782-8120
E: repwelch@emanuelchriswelch.com

Wheeler, Barbara (R, 64)
200-1N Stratton Office Building
Springfield, IL 62706
P: (217) 782-1664
F: (217) 557-7016
E: wheeler@ilhousegop.org

Wheeler, Keith (R, 50)*
213-N Stratton Office Building
Springfield, IL 62706
P: (217) 782-1486
E: office@repkeithwheeler.org

Williams, Ann (D, 11)
273-S Stratton Office Building
Springfield, IL 62706
P: (217) 782-2458
F: (217) 557-7214
E: ann@repannwilliams.com

Willis, Kathleen (D, 77)
264-S Stratton Office Building
Springfield, IL 62706
P: (217) 782-3374
E: repwillis77@gmail.com

Winger, Christine Jennifer (R, 45)*
205A-N Stratton Office Building
Springfield, IL 62706
P: (217) 782-4014

Yingling, Sam (D, 62)
242-W Stratton Office Building
Springfield, IL 62706
P: (217) 782-7320
E: repsamyingling@gmail.com

Zalewski, Michael J. (D, 23)
243-E Stratton Office Building
Springfield, IL 62706
P: (217) 782-5280
F: (217) 524-0449
E: repzalewski@gmail.com

Congress

Senate

Durbin, Richard J. (D)
Kirk, Mark Steven (R)

House

Bost, Mike (R, 12)
Bustos, Chen (D, 17)
Davis, Danny K. (D, 7)
Davis, Rodney (R, 13)
Dold, Robert (R, 10)
Duckworth, Tammy (D, 8)
Foster, Bill (D, 11)
Gutierrez, Luis V. (D, 4)
Hultgren, Randall M. (R, 14)
Kelly, Robin (D, 2)
Kinzinger, Adam (R, 16)
Lipinski, Daniel W. (D, 3)
Quigley, Mike (D, 5)
Roskam, Peter J. (R, 6)
Rush, Bobby L. (D, 1)
Schakowsky, Janice D. (D, 9)
Schock, Aaron (R, 18)
Shimkus, John (R, 15)

Indiana

Executive

Governor

Hon. Mike Pence (R)
Governor
State House, Room 206
Indianapolis, IN 46204
P: (317) 232-4567
F: (317) 232-3443

Lieutenant Governor

Hon. Sue Ellspermann (R)
Lieutenant Governor
State Capitol, Room 333
Indianapolis, IN 46204
P: (317) 232-4545
F: (317) 232-4788

Attorney General

Hon. Greg Zoeller (R)
Attorney General
Indiana Government Center South
302 West Washington Street, 5th Floor
Indianapolis, IN 46204
P: (317) 232-6201
F: (317) 232-7979
E: Constituent@atg.in.gov

Auditor

Hon. Suzanne Crouch (R)
Auditor of State
200 West Washington Street
Suite 240
Indianapolis, IN 46204
P: (317) 232-3300
F: (317) 234-1916

Secretary of State

Hon. Connie Lawson (R)
Secretary of State
201 State House
200 West Washington Street
Indianapolis, IN 46204
P: (317) 232-6531
F: (317) 233-3283
E: sos@sos.in.gov

Superintendent of Public Instruction

Ms. Glenda Ritz (D)
Superintendent of Public Instruction
151 West Ohio Street
Indianapolis, IN 46204
P: (317) 232-6665
F: (317) 232-8004
E: superintendent@doe.in.gov

Treasurer

Hon. Kelly Mitchell (R)
State Treasurer
242 State House
Indianapolis, IN 46204
P: (317) 232-6386
F: (317) 232-5656

Judiciary

Supreme Court (MR)

Mr. Kevin Smith
Clerk/Administrator
200 West Washington Street
315 State House
Indianapolis, IN 46204
P: (317) 232-2540
F: (317) 232-8372
E: Kevin.Smith@courts.in.gov

Hon. Loretta H. Rush
Chief Justice
Hon. Steven H. David
Hon. Brent E. Dickson
Hon. Mark Massa
Hon. Robert D. Rucker

Legislative Senate

Senate President

Hon. Sue Ellspermann (R)
Lieutenant Governor
State Capitol, Room 333
Indianapolis, IN 46204
P: (317) 232-4545
F: (317) 232-4788

President Pro Tempore of the Senate

Sen. David C. Long (R)
President Pro Tempore
Indiana State Senate
200 West Washington Street
Indianapolis, IN 46204
P: (317) 232-9400
E: senator.long@iga.in.gov

Senate Majority Leader

Sen. Brandt Hershman (R)
Senate Majority Floor Leader
Indiana State Senate
200 West Washington Street
Indianapolis, IN 46204
P: (317) 232-9400
F: (317) 232-9664
E: senator.hershman@iga.in.gov

Senate Minority Leader

Sen. Tim Lanane (D)
Senate Minority Leader
Indiana State Senate
200 West Washington Street
Indianapolis, IN 46204
P: (317) 232-9400
F: (317) 233-4275
E: s25@in.gov

Secretary of the Senate

Ms. Jennifer Mertz
Principal Secretary of the Senate
200 West Washington Street
Room 3A-N
Indianapolis, IN 46204
P: (317) 232-9421
E: jmertz@iga.in.gov

Members of the Senate

Alting, Ron J. (R, 22)
Indiana State Senate
200 West Washington Street
Indianapolis, IN 46204
P: (317) 232-9400
E: senator.alting@iga.in.gov

Arnold, Jim (D, 8)
Indiana State Senate
200 West Washington Street
Indianapolis, IN 46204
P: (317) 232-9400
F: (317) 233-4275
E: s8@in.gov

Banks, Amanda (R, 27)*
Indiana State Senate
200 West Washington Street
Indianapolis, IN 46204
P: (317) 232-9400
E: senator.banks@iga.in.gov

Bassler, Eric (R, 39)*
Indiana State Senate
200 West Washington Street
Indianapolis, IN 46204
P: (317) 232-9600
E: s39@in.gov

Becker, Vaneta G. (R, 50)
Indiana State Senate
200 West Washington Street
Indianapolis, IN 46204
P: (317) 232-9400
E: s50@in.gov

Boots, Phil (R, 23)
Indiana State Senate
200 West Washington Street
Indianapolis, IN 46204
P: (317) 232-9400
E: s23@in.gov

Bray, Rodric (R, 37)
200 West Washington Street
State House
Indianapolis, IN 46204
E: senator.bray@iga.in.gov

Breaux, Jean D. (D, 34)
Indiana State Senate
200 West Washington Street
Indianapolis, IN 46204
P: (317) 232-9400
F: (317) 233-4275
E: s34@in.gov

Broden, John (D, 10)
Indiana State Senate
200 West Washington Street
Indianapolis, IN 46204
P: (317) 232-9400
F: (317) 233-4275
E: s10@in.gov

Brown, Liz (R, 15)*
Indiana State Senate
200 West Washington Street
Indianapolis, IN 46204
P: (317) 296-9400
E: s15@in.gov

Buck, Jim (R, 21)
Indiana State Senate
200 West Washington Street
Indianapolis, IN 46204
P: (317) 232-9400
E: s21@in.gov

Charbonneau, Ed (R, 5)
Indiana State Senate
200 West Washington Street
Indianapolis, IN 46204
P: (317) 232-9400
E: s5@in.gov

Crider, Michael (R, 28)
Indiana State Senate
200 West Washington Street
Indianapolis, IN 46204
P: (317) 232-9400
E: Senator.Crider@iga.in.gov

Delph, Mike (R, 29)
Indiana State Senate
200 West Washington Street
Indianapolis, IN 46204
P: (317) 232-9400
E: s29@in.gov

Indiana

Eckerty, Doug (R, 26)
Indiana State Senate
200 West Washington Street
Indianapolis, IN 46204
P: (317) 232-9400
E: s26@in.gov

Ford, Jon (R, 38)*
Indiana State Senate
200 West Washington Street
Indianapolis, IN 46204
P: (317) 296-9600
E: s38@in.gov

Glick, Susan (R, 13)
Indiana State Senate
200 West Washington Street
Indianapolis, IN 46204
P: (317) 232-9400
E: s13@in.gov

Grooms, Ron (R, 46)
Indiana State Senate
200 West Washington Street
Indianapolis, IN 46204
P: (317) 232-9400
E: s46@in.gov

Head, Randall (R, 18)
Indiana State Senate
200 West Washington Street
Indianapolis, IN 46204
P: (317) 232-9400
E: s18@in.gov

Hershman, Brandt (R, 7)
Indiana State Senate
200 West Washington Street
Indianapolis, IN 46204
P: (317) 232-9400
F: (317) 232-9664
E: senator.hershman@iga.in.gov

Holdman, Travis (R, 19)
Indiana State Senate
200 West Washington Street
Indianapolis, IN 46204
P: (317) 232-9400
E: s19@in.gov

Houchin, Erin (R, 47)*
Indiana Senate
200 West Washington Street
Indianapolis, IN 46204
P: (317) 296-9400
E: s47@in.gov

Kenley, Luke (R, 20)
Indiana State Senate
200 West Washington Street
Indianapolis, IN 46204
P: (317) 232-9400
E: s20@in.gov

Kruse, Dennis K. (R, 14)
Indiana State Senate
200 West Washington Street
Indianapolis, IN 46204
P: (317) 232-9400
E: s14@in.gov

Lanane, Tim (D, 25)
Indiana State Senate
200 West Washington Street
Indianapolis, IN 46204
P: (317) 232-9400
F: (317) 233-4275
E: s25@in.gov

Leising, Jean (R, 42)
Indiana State Senate
200 West Washington Street
Indianapolis, IN 46204
P: (317) 232-9400
E: s42@in.gov

Long, David C. (R, 16)
Indiana State Senate
200 West Washington Street
Indianapolis, IN 46204
P: (317) 232-9400
E: senator.long@iga.in.gov

Merritt Jr., James W. (R, 31)
Indiana State Senate
200 West Washington Street
Indianapolis, IN 46204
P: (317) 232-9400
E: senator.merritt@iga.in.gov

Messmer, Mark (R, 48)
Indiana Senate
200 West Washington Street
Indianapolis, IN 46204
P: (317) 232-9400
E: h63@in.gov

Miller, Patricia L. (R, 32)
Indiana State Senate
200 West Washington Street
Indianapolis, IN 46204
P: (317) 232-9400
E: senator.miller@iga.in.gov

Miller, Pete (R, 24)
Indiana State Senate
200 West Washington Street
Indianapolis, IN 46204
P: (317) 232-9400
E: sen.petemiller@iga.in.gov

Mishler, Ryan D. (R, 9)
Indiana State Senate
200 West Washington Street
Indianapolis, IN 46204
P: (317) 232-9400
E: s9@in.gov

Mrvan Jr., Frank (D, 1)
Indiana State Senate
200 West Washington Street
Indianapolis, IN 46204
P: (317) 232-9400
F: (317) 233-4275
E: s1@in.gov

Niemeyer, Rick (R, 6)
Indiana Senate
200 West Washington Street
Indianapolis, IN 46204
P: (317) 232-9400
E: h11@in.gov

Perfect, Chip (R, 43)*
Indiana State Senate
200 West Washington Street
Indianapolis, IN 46204
P: (317) 296-9400
E: s43@in.gov

Raatz, Jeff (R, 27)*
Indiana State Senate
200 West Washington Street
Indianapolis, IN 46204
P: (317) 296-9400
E: s27@in.gov

Randolph, Lonnie Marcus (D, 2)
Indiana State Senate
200 West Washington Street
Indianapolis, IN 46204
P: (317) 232-9400
F: (317) 233-4275
E: s2@in.gov

Rogers, Earline S. (D, 3)
Indiana State Senate
200 West Washington Street
Indianapolis, IN 46204
P: (317) 232-9400
F: (317) 233-4275
E: s3@in.gov

Schneider, Scott (R, 30)
Indiana State Senate
200 West Washington Street
Indianapolis, IN 46204
P: (317) 232-9400
E: s30@in.gov

Smith, Jim (R, 45)
Indiana State Senate
200 West Washington Street
Indianapolis, IN 46204
P: (317) 232-9400
E: s45@in.gov

Steele, Brent (R, 44)
Indiana State Senate
200 West Washington Street
Indianapolis, IN 46204
P: (317) 232-9400
F: (317) 232-9664
E: s44@in.gov

Stoops, Mark (D, 40)
Indiana State Senate
200 West Washington Street
Indianapolis, IN 46204
P: (317) 232-9847
E: s40@in.gov

Tallian, Karen R. (D, 4)
Indiana State Senate
200 West Washington Street
Indianapolis, IN 46204
P: (317) 232-9400
F: (317) 233-4275
E: s4@in.gov

Taylor, Greg (D, 33)
Indiana State Senate
200 West Washington Street
Indianapolis, IN 46204
P: (317) 232-9400
F: (317) 233-4275
E: s33@in.gov

Tomes, Jim (R, 49)
Indiana State Senate
200 West Washington Street
Indianapolis, IN 46204
P: (317) 232-9400
E: s49@in.gov

Walker, Greg (R, 41)
Indiana State Senate
200 West Washington Street
Indianapolis, IN 46204
P: (317) 232-9400
E: s41@in.gov

Waltz, Brent (R, 36)
Indiana State Senate
200 West Washington Street
Indianapolis, IN 46204
P: (317) 232-9400
E: s36@in.gov

Yoder, Carlin (R, 12)
Indiana State Senate
200 West Washington Street
Indianapolis, IN 46204
P: (317) 232-9400
E: s12@in.gov

Young, R. Michael (R, 35)
Indiana State Senate
200 West Washington Street
Indianapolis, IN 46204
P: (317) 232-9400
E: s35@in.gov

Zakas, Joe (R, 11)
Indiana State Senate
200 West Washington Street
Indianapolis, IN 46204
P: (317) 232-9400
E: senator.zakas@iga.in.gov

House

Speaker of the House

Rep. Brian C. Bosma (R)
Speaker of the House
Indiana House of Representatives
200 West Washington Street
Indianapolis, IN 46204
P: (317) 232-9600
E: h88@in.gov

Speaker Pro Tempore of the House

Rep. William C. Friend (R)
Speaker Pro Tem
Indiana House of Representatives
200 West Washington Street
Indianapolis, IN 46204
P: (317) 232-9600
E: h23@in.gov

House Majority Leader

Rep. Jud McMillin (R)
House Majority Floor Leader
Indiana House of Representatives
200 West Washington Street
Indianapolis, IN 46204
P: (317) 232-9600
E: h68@in.gov

House Minority Leader

Rep. Scott Pelath (D)
House Minority Leader
Indiana House of Representatives
200 West Washington Street
Indianapolis, IN 46204
P: (317) 232-9600
E: h9@in.gov

Clerk of the House

Ms. M. Carolyn Spotts
Principal House Clerk
200 West Washington Street, Room 3A-8
Indianapolis, IN 46204
P: (317) 232-9608
E: cspotts@iga.in.gov

Members of the House

Arnold, Lloyd (R, 74)
Indiana House of Representatives
200 West Washington Street
Indianapolis, IN 46204
P: (317) 232-9600
E: h74@in.gov

Austin, Terri J. (D, 36)
Indiana House of Representatives
200 West Washington Street
Indianapolis, IN 46204
P: (317) 232-9600
E: h36@in.gov

Aylesworth, Michael (R, 11)*
Indiana House of Representatives
200 West Washington Street
Indianapolis, IN 46204
P: (317) 232-9600
E: h11@in.gov

Bacon, Ron (R, 75)
Indiana House of Representatives
200 West Washington Street
Indianapolis, IN 46204
P: (317) 232-9600
E: h75@in.gov

Baird, James (R, 44)
Indiana House of Representatives
200 West Washington Street
Indianapolis, IN 46204
P: (317) 232-9600
E: h44@in.gov

Bartlett, John (D, 95)
Indiana House of Representatives
200 West Washington Street
Indianapolis, IN 46204
P: (317) 232-9600
E: h95@in.gov

Bauer, B. Patrick (D, 6)
Indiana House of Representatives
200 West Washington Street
Indianapolis, IN 46204
P: (317) 232-9600
E: h6@in.gov

Behning, Robert W. (R, 91)
Indiana House of Representatives
200 West Washington Street
Indianapolis, IN 46204
P: (317) 232-9600
E: h91@in.gov

Beumer, Greg (R, 33)
Indiana House of Representatives
200 West Washington Street
Indianapolis, IN 46204
P: (317) 232-9600
E: h33@in.gov

Borders, Bruce (R, 45)
Indiana House of Representatives
200 West Washington Street
Indianapolis, IN 46204
P: (317) 232-9600
E: h45@in.gov

Bosma, Brian C. (R, 88)
Indiana House of Representatives
200 West Washington Street
Indianapolis, IN 46204
P: (317) 232-9600
E: h88@in.gov

Braun, Mike (R, 63)*
Indiana House of Representatives
200 West Washington Street
Indianapolis, IN 46204
P: (317) 296-9600
E: h63@in.gov

Brown, Charlie (D, 3)
Indiana House of Representatives
200 West Washington Street
Indianapolis, IN 46204
P: (317) 232-9600
E: h3@in.gov

Brown, Timothy (R, 41)
Indiana House of Representatives
200 West Washington Street
Indianapolis, IN 46204
P: (317) 232-9600
E: h41@in.gov

Burton, Woody (R, 58)
Indiana House of Representatives
200 West Washington Street
Indianapolis, IN 46204
P: (317) 232-9600
E: h58@in.gov

Carbaugh, Martin (R, 81)
Indiana House of Representatives
200 West Washington Street
Indianapolis, IN 46204
P: (317) 232-9600
E: h81@in.gov

Cherry, Bob (R, 53)
Indiana House of Representatives
200 West Washington Street
Indianapolis, IN 46204
P: (317) 232-9600
E: h53@in.gov

Clere, Ed (R, 72)
Indiana House of Representatives
200 West Washington Street
Indianapolis, IN 46204
P: (317) 232-9648
E: h72@in.gov

Cook, Tony (R, 32)*
Indiana House of Representatives
200 West Washington Street
Indianapolis, IN 46204
P: (317) 232-9815
E: h32@iga.in.gov

Cox, Casey (R, 85)
Indiana House of Representatives
200 West Washington Street
Indianapolis, IN 46204
P: (317) 232-9600
E: h85@in.gov

Culver, Wesley (R, 49)
Indiana House of Representatives
200 West Washington Street
Indianapolis, IN 46204
P: (317) 232-9600
E: h49@in.gov

Davisson, Steve (R, 73)
Indiana House of Representatives
200 West Washington Street
Indianapolis, IN 46204
P: (317) 232-9600
E: h73@in.gov

DeLaney, Edward O. (D, 86)
Indiana House of Representatives
200 West Washington Street
Indianapolis, IN 46204
P: (317) 232-9600
E: h86@in.gov

Dermody, Thomas (R, 20)
Indiana House of Representatives
200 West Washington Street
Indianapolis, IN 46204
P: (317) 232-9600
E: h20@in.gov

Indiana

DeVon, Dale (R, 5)
Indiana House of Representatives
200 West Washington Street
Indianapolis, IN 46204
P: (317) 232-9600
E: h5@in.gov

Dvorak, Ryan (D, 8)
Indiana House of Representatives
200 West Washington Street
Indianapolis, IN 46204
P: (317) 232-9600
E: h8@in.gov

Eberhart, Sean (R, 57)
Indiana House of Representatives
200 West Washington Street
Indianapolis, IN 46204
P: (317) 232-9600
E: h57@in.gov

Errington, Sue (D, 34)
Indiana House of Representatives
200 West Washington Street
Indianapolis, IN 46204
P: (317) 232-9600
E: h34@in.gov

Fine, William (R, 12)*
Indiana House of Representatives
200 West Washington Street
Indianapolis, IN 46204
P: (317) 296-9600
E: h12@in.gov

Forestal, Dan (D, 100)
Indiana House of Representatives
200 West Washington Street
Indianapolis, IN 46204
P: (317) 232-9600
E: h100@in.gov

Friend, William C. (R, 23)
Indiana House of Representatives
200 West Washington Street
Indianapolis, IN 46204
P: (317) 232-9600
E: h23@in.gov

Frizzell, David N. (R, 93)
Indiana House of Representatives
200 West Washington Street
Indianapolis, IN 46204
P: (317) 232-9600
E: h93@in.gov

Frye, Randy (R, 67)
Indiana House of Representatives
200 West Washington Street
Indianapolis, IN 46204
P: (317) 232-9600
E: h67@in.gov

GiaQuinta, Phil (D, 80)
Indiana House of Representatives
200 West Washington Street
Indianapolis, IN 46204
P: (317) 232-9600
E: h80@in.gov

Goodin, Terry (D, 66)
Indiana House of Representatives
200 West Washington Street
Indianapolis, IN 46204
P: (317) 232-9600
E: h66@in.gov

Gutwein, Douglas (R, 16)
Indiana House of Representatives
200 West Washington Street
Indianapolis, IN 46204
P: (317) 232-9600
E: h16@in.gov

Hale, Christina (D, 87)
Indiana House of Representatives
200 West Washington Street
Indianapolis, IN 46204
P: (317) 232-9600
E: h87@in.gov

Hamm, Richard (R, 56)
Indiana House of Representatives
200 West Washington Street
Indianapolis, IN 46204
P: (317) 232-9600
E: h56@in.gov

Harman, Tim (R, 17)
Indiana House of Representatives
200 West Washington Street
Indianapolis, IN 46204
P: (317) 232-9600
E: h17@in.gov

Harris, Earl L. (D, 2)
Indiana House of Representatives
200 West Washington Street
Indianapolis, IN 46204
P: (317) 232-9600
E: h2@in.gov

Heaton, Bob (R, 46)
Indiana House of Representatives
200 West Washington Street
Indianapolis, IN 46204
P: (317) 232-9600
E: h46@in.gov

Huston, Todd (R, 37)
Indiana House of Representatives
200 West Washington Street
Indianapolis, IN 46204
P: (317) 232-9600
E: h37@in.gov

Judy, Christopher (R, 83)*
Indiana House of Representatives
200 West Washington Street
Indianapolis, IN 46204
P: (317) 296-9600
E: h83@in.gov

Karickhoff, Mike (R, 30)
Indiana House of Representatives
200 West Washington Street
Indianapolis, IN 46204
P: (317) 234-3827
E: h30@in.gov

Kersey, Clyde (D, 43)
Indiana House of Representatives
200 West Washington Street
Indianapolis, IN 46204
P: (317) 232-9600
E: h43@in.gov

Kersey, Clyde (D, 43)
Indiana House of Representatives
200 West Washington Street
Indianapolis, IN 46204
P: (317) 232-9600
E: h43@in.gov

Kirchhofer, Cindy (R, 89)
Indiana House of Representatives
200 West Washington Street
Indianapolis, IN 46204
P: (317) 232-9600
E: h89@in.gov

Klinker, Sheila J. (D, 27)
Indiana House of Representatives
200 West Washington Street
Indianapolis, IN 46204
P: (317) 232-9600
E: h27@in.gov

Koch, Eric (R, 65)
Indiana House of Representatives
200 West Washington Street
Indianapolis, IN 46204
P: (317) 232-9600
E: h65@in.gov

Lawson, Linda (D, 1)
Indiana House of Representatives
200 West Washington Street
Indianapolis, IN 46204
P: (317) 232-9600
E: llawsonjhornak@aol.com

Lehe, Don (R, 25)
Indiana House of Representatives
200 West Washington Street
Indianapolis, IN 46204
P: (317) 232-9600
E: h25@in.gov

Lehman, Matthew S. (R, 79)
Indiana House of Representatives
200 West Washington Street
Indianapolis, IN 46204
P: (317) 232-9600
E: h79@in.gov

Leonard, Dan (R, 50)
Indiana House of Representatives
200 West Washington Street
Indianapolis, IN 46204
P: (317) 232-9600
E: h50@in.gov

Lucas, Jim (R, 69)
Indiana House of Representatives
200 West Washington Street
Indianapolis, IN 46204
P: (317) 232-9600
E: h69@in.gov

Macer, Karlee (D, 92)
Indiana House of Representatives
200 West Washington Street
Indianapolis, IN 46204
P: (317) 232-9600
E: h92@in.gov

Mahan, Kevin (R, 31)
Indiana House of Representatives
200 West Washington Street
Indianapolis, IN 46204
P: (317) 232-9600
E: h31@in.gov

Mayfield, Peggy (R, 60)
Indiana House of Representatives
200 West Washington Street
Indianapolis, IN 46204
P: (317) 232-9600
E: h60@in.gov

McMillin, Jud (R, 68)
Indiana House of Representatives
200 West Washington Street
Indianapolis, IN 46204
P: (317) 232-9600
E: h68@in.gov

McNamara, Wendy (R, 76)
Indiana House of Representatives
200 West Washington Street
Indianapolis, IN 46204
P: (317) 232-9600
E: h76@in.gov

Miller, Doug (R, 48)*
Indiana House of Representatives
200 West Washington Street
Indianapolis, IN 46204
P: (317) 296-9600
E: h48@in.gov

Moed, Justin (D, 97)
Indiana House of Representatives
200 West Washington Street
Indianapolis, IN 46204
P: (317) 232-9600
E: h97@in.gov

Morris, Bob (R, 84)
Indiana House of Representatives
200 West Washington Street
Indianapolis, IN 46204
P: (317) 232-9600
E: h84@in.gov

Morrison, Alan (R, 42)
Indiana House of Representatives
200 West Washington Street
Indianapolis, IN 46204
P: (317) 232-9600
E: h42@in.gov

Moseley, Charles (D, 10)
Indiana House of Representatives
200 West Washington Street
Indianapolis, IN 46204
P: (317) 232-9600
E: h10@in.gov

Negele, Sharon (R, 13)
Indiana House of Representatives
200 West Washington Street
Indianapolis, IN 46204
P: (317) 232-9600
E: h13@in.gov

Niezgodski, David L. (D, 7)
Indiana House of Representatives
200 West Washington Street
Indianapolis, IN 46204
P: (317) 232-9600
E: h7@in.gov

Nisly, Curt (R, 22)*
Indiana House of Representatives
200 West Washington Street
Indianapolis, IN 46204
P: (317) 296-9600
E: h22@in.gov

Ober, David (R, 82)
Indiana House of Representatives
200 West Washington Street
Indianapolis, IN 46204
P: (317) 232-9600
E: h82@in.gov

Olthoff, Julie (R, 19)*
Indiana House of Representatives
200 West Washington Street
Indianapolis, IN 46204
P: (317) 296-9600
E: h19@in.gov

Pelath, Scott (D, 9)
Indiana House of Representatives
200 West Washington Street
Indianapolis, IN 46204
P: (317) 232-9600
E: h9@in.gov

Pierce, Matt (D, 61)
Indiana House of Representatives
200 West Washington Street
Indianapolis, IN 46204
P: (317) 232-9794
E: h61@in.gov

Porter, Gregory W. (D, 96)
Indiana House of Representatives
200 West Washington Street
Indianapolis, IN 46204
P: (317) 232-9600
F: (317) 233-8184
E: h96@in.gov

Price, John (R, 47)
Indiana House of Representatives
200 West Washington Street
Indianapolis, IN 46204
P: (317) 232-9600
E: h47@in.gov

Pryor, Cherrish S. (D, 94)
Indiana House of Representatives
200 West Washington Street
Indianapolis, IN 46204
P: (317) 232-9600
E: h94@in.gov

Rhoads, Rhonda (R, 70)
Indiana House of Representatives
200 West Washington Street
Indianapolis, IN 46204
P: (317) 232-9600
E: h70@in.gov

Richardson, Kathy Kreag (R, 29)
Indiana House of Representatives
200 West Washington Street
Indianapolis, IN 46204
P: (317) 232-9600
E: h29@in.gov

Riecken, Gail (D, 77)
Indiana House of Representatives
200 West Washington Street
Indianapolis, IN 46204
P: (317) 232-9600
E: h77@in.gov

Saunders, Thomas E. (R, 54)
Indiana House of Representatives
200 West Washington Street
Indianapolis, IN 46204
P: (317) 232-9600
E: h54@in.gov

Schaibley, Donna (R, 24)*
Indiana House of Representatives
200 West Washington Street
Indianapolis, IN 46204
P: (317) 232-9863
E: h24@iga.in.gov

Shackleford, Robin (D, 98)
Indiana House of Representatives
200 West Washington Street
Indianapolis, IN 46204
P: (317) 232-9600
E: h98@in.gov

Slager, Hal (R, 15)
Indiana House of Representatives
200 West Washington Street
Indianapolis, IN 46204
P: (317) 232-9600
E: h15@in.gov

Smaltz, Ben (R, 52)
Indiana House of Representatives
200 West Washington Street
Indianapolis, IN 46204
P: (317) 232-9600
E: h52@in.gov

Smith, Milo (R, 59)
Indiana House of Representatives
200 West Washington Street
Indianapolis, IN 46204
P: (317) 232-9600
E: h59@in.gov

Smith, Vernon G. (D, 14)
Indiana House of Representatives
200 West Washington Street
Indianapolis, IN 46204
P: (317) 232-9600
E: h14@in.gov

Soliday, Edmond (R, 4)
Indiana House of Representatives
200 West Washington Street
Indianapolis, IN 46204
P: (317) 232-9600
E: h4@in.gov

Speedy, Mike (R, 90)
Indiana House of Representatives
200 West Washington Street
Indianapolis, IN 46204
P: (317) 232-9600
E: h90@in.gov

Stemler, Steven R. (D, 71)
Indiana House of Representatives
200 West Washington Street
Indianapolis, IN 46204
P: (317) 232-9600
E: h71@in.gov

Steurwald, Greg (R, 40)
Indiana House of Representatives
200 West Washington Street
Indianapolis, IN 46204
P: (317) 232-9600
E: h40@in.gov

Indiana

Sullivan, Holli (R, 78)
Indiana House of Representatives
200 West Washington Street
Indianapolis, IN 46204
P: (317) 232-9600
E: h78@in.gov

Summers, Vanessa (D, 99)
Indiana House of Representatives
200 West Washington Street
Indianapolis, IN 46204
P: (317) 232-9600
E: h99@in.gov

Thompson, Jeff (R, 28)
Indiana House of Representatives
200 West Washington Street
Indianapolis, IN 46204
P: (317) 232-9600
E: h28@in.gov

Torr, Jerry R. (R, 39)
Indiana House of Representatives
200 West Washington Street
Indianapolis, IN 46204
P: (317) 232-9600
E: h39@in.gov

Truitt, Randy (R, 26)
Indiana House of Representatives
200 West Washington Street
Indianapolis, IN 46204
P: (317) 232-9600
E: h26@in.gov

Ubelhor, Matt (R, 62)
Indiana House of Representatives
200 West Washington Street
Indianapolis, IN 46204
P: (317) 232-9600
E: h62@in.gov

VanNatter, Heath (R, 38)
Indiana House of Representatives
200 West Washington Street
Indianapolis, IN 46204
P: (317) 232-9600
E: h38@in.gov

Washburne, Tom (R, 64)
Indiana House of Representatives
200 West Washington Street
Indianapolis, IN 46204
P: (317) 232-9600
E: h64@in.gov

Wesco, Tim (R, 21)
Indiana House of Representatives
200 West Washington Street
Indianapolis, IN 46204
P: (317) 232-9600
E: h21@in.gov

Wolkins, David A. (R, 18)
Indiana House of Representatives
200 West Washington Street
Indianapolis, IN 46204
P: (317) 232-9600
E: daw8144@gmail.com

Wright, Melanie (D, 35)*
Indiana House of Representatives
200 West Washington Street
Indianapolis, IN 46204
P: (317) 296-9600
E: h35@in.gov

Zent, Denny (R, 51)
Indiana House of Representatives
200 West Washington Street
Indianapolis, IN 46204
P: (317) 232-9600
E: h51@in.gov

Ziemke, Cindy (R, 55)
Indiana House of Representatives
200 West Washington Street
Indianapolis, IN 46204
P: (317) 232-9600
E: h55@in.gov

Congress

Senate

Coats, Daniel (R)
Donnelly, Joseph S. (D)

House

Brooks, Susan (R, 5)
Bucshon, Larry (R, 8)
Carson, Andre (D, 7)
Messer, Luke (R, 6)
Rokita, Todd (R, 4)
Stutzman, Marlin (R, 3)
Visclosky, Peter J. (D, 1)
Walorski, Jackie (R, 2)
Young, Todd (R, 9)

Iowa

Executive

Governor

Hon. Terry Branstad (R)
Governor
State Capitol
Des Moines, IA 50319
P: (515) 281-5211
F: (515) 281-6611

Lieutenant Governor

Hon. Kim Reynolds (R)
Lieutenant Governor
State Capitol, Room 9
Des Moines, IA 50319
P: (515) 281-5211
F: (515) 725-3527

Secretary of Agriculture

Mr. Bill Northey (R)
Secretary of Agriculture
Wallace Building
502 East 9th Street
Des Moines, IA 50319
P: (515) 281-5322
F: (515) 281-6236

Attorney General

Hon. Tom Miller (D)
Attorney General
Hoover State Office Building
1305 East Walnut
Des Moines, IA 50319
P: (515) 281-5164
F: (515) 281-4209

Auditor

Ms. Mary Mosiman
Auditor of State
State Capitol
1007 East Grand Avenue
Des Moines, IA 50319
P: (515) 281-5385
F: (515) 242-6134

Secretary of State

Hon. Paul Pate (R)
Secretary of State
ucas Building, 1st Floor
21 East 12th Street
Moines, IA 50319
15) 281-8993
5) 242-5952
sos.iowa.gov

Treasurer

Hon. Michael L. Fitzgerald (D)
State Treasurer
State Capitol, Room 114
Des Moines, IA 50319
P: (515) 281-5368
F: (515) 281-7562
E: mike.fitzgerald@iowa.gov

Judiciary

Supreme Court (MR)

Ms. Donna Humpal
Clerk
Iowa Judicial Branch Building
1111 East Court Avenue
Des Moines, IA 50319
P: (515) 281-5911
E: Donna.Humpal@iowacourts.gov

Hon. Mark S. Cady
Chief Justice
Hon. Brent R. Appel
Hon. Daryl L. Hecht
Hon. Edward Mansfield
Hon. Thomas D. Waterman
Hon. David S. Wiggins
Hon. Bruce Zager

Legislative Senate

Senate President

Sen. Pam Jochum (D)
Senate President
State Capitol
1007 East Grand Avenue
Des Moines, IA 50319
P: (515) 281-5804
E: pam.jochum@legis.iowa.gov

President Pro Tempore of the Senate

Sen. Steve Sodders (D)
Senate President Pro Tempore
State Capitol
1007 East Grand Avenue
Des Moines, IA 50319
P: (515) 281-5804
E: steve.sodders@legis.iowa.gov

Senate Majority Leader

Sen. Michael E. Gronstal (D)
Senate Majority Leader
State Capitol
1007 East Grand Avenue
Des Moines, IA 50319
P: (515) 281-5804
E: mike.gronstal@legis.iowa.gov

Senate Minority Leader

Sen. Bill Dix (R)
Senate Minority Leader
State Capitol
1007 East Grand Avenue
Des Moines, IA 50319
P: (515) 281-5841
E: bill.dix@legis.iowa.gov

Secretary of the Senate

Mr. Michael E. Marshall
Secretary of the Senate
State Capitol
1007 East Grand Avenue
Des Moines, IA 50319
P: (515) 281-5307
E: Mike.Marshall@legis.iowa.gov

Members of the Senate

Allen, Chaz (D, 15)*
State Capitol
1007 East Grand Avenue
Des Moines, IA 50319
P: (515) 281-3371
E: chaz.allen@legis.iowa.gov

Anderson, Bill (R, 3)
State Capitol
1007 East Grand Avenue
Des Moines, IA 50319
P: (515) 281-3371
E: bill.anderson@legis.iowa.gov

Behn, Jerry (R, 24)
State Capitol
1007 East Grand Avenue
Des Moines, IA 50319
P: (515) 281-3371
E: jerry.behn@legis.iowa.gov

Bertrand, Rick (R, 7)
State Capitol
1007 East Grand Avenue
Des Moines, IA 50319
P: (515) 281-3371
E: rick.bertrand@legis.iowa.gov

Bisignano, Tony (D, 17)*
State Capitol
1007 East Grand Avenue
Des Moines, IA 50319
P: @515) 281-3371
E: tony.bisignano@legis.iowa.gov

Bolkcom, Joe (D, 43)
State Capitol
1007 East Grand Avenue
Des Moines, IA 50319
P: (515) 281-3371
E: joe.bolkcom@legis.iowa.gov

Bowman, Tod (D, 29)
State Capitol
1007 East Grand Avenue
Des Moines, IA 50319
P: (515) 281-3371
E: tod.bowman@legis.iowa.gov

Brase, Chris (D, 46)
State Capitol
1007 East Grand Avenue
Des Moines, IA 50319
P: (515) 281-3371
E: chris.brase@legis.iowa.gov

Breitbach, Michael (R, 28)
State Capitol
1007 East Grand Avenue
Des Moines, IA 50319
P: (515) 281-3371
E: michael.breitbach@legis.iowa.gov

Chapman, Jake (R, 10)
State Capitol
1007 East Grand Avenue
Des Moines, IA 50319
P: (515) 281-3371
E: jake.chapman@legis.iowa.gov

Chelgren, Mark (R, 41)
State Capitol
1007 East Grand Avenue
Des Moines, IA 50319
P: (515) 281-3371
E: mark.chelgren@legis.iowa.gov

Iowa

Costello, Mark (R, 12)
State Capitol
1007 East Grand Avenue
Des Moines, IA 50319
P: (515) 281-3221
E: mark.costello
@legis.iowa.gov

Courtney, Thomas G. (D, 44)
State Capitol
1007 East Grand Avenue
Des Moines, IA 50319
P: (515) 281-3371
E: thomas.courtney
@legis.iowa.gov

Danielson, Jeff (D, 30)
State Capitol
1007 East Grand Avenue
Des Moines, IA 50319
P: (515) 281-3371
E: jeffdanielson@gmail.com

Dearden, Dick L. (D, 16)
State Capitol
1007 East Grand Avenue
Des Moines, IA 50319
P: (515) 281-3371
E: dick.dearden
@legis.iowa.gov

Dix, Bill (R, 25)
State Capitol
1007 East Grand Avenue
Des Moines, IA 50319
P: (515) 281-5841
E: bill.dix@legis.iowa.gov

Dotzler Jr., William A. (D, 31)
State Capitol
1007 East Grand Avenue
Des Moines, IA 50319
P: (515) 281-3371
E: bill.dotzler
@legis.iowa.gov

Dvorsky, Robert E. (D, 37)
State Capitol
1007 East Grand Avenue
Des Moines, IA 50319
P: (515) 281-3371
E: robert.dvorsky
@legis.iowa.gov

Feenstra, Randy (R, 2)
State Capitol
1007 East Grand Avenue
Des Moines, IA 50319
P: (515) 281-3371
E: randy.feenstra
@legis.iowa.gov

Garrett, Julian (R, 13)
State Capitol
1007 East Grand Avenue
Des Moines, IA 50319
P: (515) 281-3371
E: julian.garrett
@legis.iowa.gov

Gronstal, Michael E. (D, 8)
State Capitol
1007 East Grand Avenue
Des Moines, IA 50319
P: (515) 281-5804
E: mike.gronstal
@legis.iowa.gov

Guth, Dennis (R, 4)
State Capitol
1007 East Grand Avenue
Des Moines, IA 50319
P: (515) 281-3371
E: dennis.guth
@legis.iowa.gov

Hart, Rita (D, 49)
State Capitol
1007 East Grand Avenue
Des Moines, IA 50319
P: (515) 281-3371
E: rita.hart@legis.iowa.gov

Hogg, Robert M. (D, 33)
State Capitol
1007 East Grand Avenue
Des Moines, IA 50319
P: (515) 281-3371
E: rob.hogg@legis.iowa.gov

Horn, Wally E. (D, 35)
State Capitol
1007 East Grand Avenue
Des Moines, IA 50319
P: (515) 281-3371
E: wally.horn
@legis.iowa.gov

Jochum, Pam (D, 50)
State Capitol
1007 East Grand Avenue
Des Moines, IA 50319
P: (515) 281-5804
E: pam.jochum
@legis.iowa.gov

Johnson, David (R, 1)
State Capitol
1007 East Grand Avenue
Des Moines, IA 50319
P: (515) 281-3371
E: david.johnson
@legis.iowa.gov

Kapucian, Tim L. (R, 38)
State Capitol
1007 East Grand Avenue
Des Moines, IA 50319
P: (515) 281-3371
E: tim.kapucian
@legis.iowa.gov

Kinney, Kevin (D, 39)*
State Capitol
1007 East Grand Avenue
Des Moines, IA 50319
P: (515) 281-3371
E: kevin.kinney
@legis.iowa.gov

Kraayenbrink, Tim (R, 5)*
State Capitol
1007 East Grand Avenue
Des Moines, IA 50319
P: (515) 281-3371
E: tim.kraayenbrink
@legis.iowa.gov

Mathis, Liz (D, 34)
State Capitol
1007 East Grand Avenue
Des Moines, IA 50319
P: (515) 281-3371
E: liz.mathis
@legis.iowa.gov

McCoy, Matt (D, 21)
State Capitol
1007 East Grand Avenue
Des Moines, IA 50319
P: (515) 281-3371
E: matt.mccoy
@legis.iowa.gov

Petersen, Janet (D, 18)
State Capitol
1007 East Grand Avenue
Des Moines, IA 50319
P: (515) 281-3371
E: janet.petersen
@legis.iowa.gov

Quirmbach, Herman C. (D, 23)
State Capitol
1007 East Grand Avenue
Des Moines, IA 50319
P: (515) 281-3371
E: herman.quirmbach
@legis.iowa.gov

Ragan, Amanda (D, 27)
State Capitol
1007 East Grand Avenue
Des Moines, IA 50319
P: (515) 281-3371
E: amanda.ragan
@legis.iowa.gov

Rozenboom, Ken (R, 40)
State Capitol
1007 East Grand Avenue
Des Moines, IA 50319
P: (515) 281-3371
E: ken.rozenboom
@legis.iowa.gov

Schneider, Charles (R, 22)
State Capitol
1007 East Grand Avenue
Des Moines, IA 50319
P: (515) 281-3371
E: charles.schneider
@legis.iowa.gov

Schoenjahn, Brian (D, 32)
State Capitol
1007 East Grand Avenue
Des Moines, IA 50319
P: (515) 281-3371
E: brian.schoenjahn
@legis.iowa.gov

Schultz, Jason (R, 9)
State Capitol
1007 East Grand Avenue
Des Moines, IA 50319
P: (515) 281-3221
E: jason.schultz
@legis.iowa.gov

Segebart, Mark (R, 6)
State Capitol
1007 East Grand Avenue
Des Moines, IA 50319
P: (515) 281-3371
E: mark.segebart
@legis.iowa.gov

Seng, Joe M. (D, 45)
State Capitol
1007 East Grand Avenue
Des Moines, IA 50319
P: (515) 281-3371
E: joe.seng@legis.iowa.gov

Shipley, Tom (R, 11)*
State Capitol
1007 East Grand Avenue
Des Moines, IA 50319
P: (515) 281-3371
E: tom.shipley
@legis.iowa.gov

Sinclair, Amy (R, 14)
State Capitol
1007 East Grand Avenue
Des Moines, IA 50319
P: (515) 281-3371
E: amy.sinclair
@legis.iowa.g

Smith, Roby (R, 47)
State Capitol
1007 East Grand Avenue
Des Moines, IA 50319
P: (515) 281-3371
E: roby.smith
@legis.iowa.gov

Sodders, Steve (D, 36)
State Capitol
1007 East Grand Avenue
Des Moines, IA 50319
P: (515) 281-5804
E: steve.sodders
@legis.iowa.gov

Taylor, Rich (D, 42)
State Capitol
1007 East Grand Avenue
Des Moines, IA 50319
P: (515) 281-3371
E: rich.taylor
@legis.iowa.gov

Whitver, Jack (R, 19)
State Capitol
1007 East Grand Avenue
Des Moines, IA 50319
P: (515) 281-3371
E: jack.whitver
@legis.iowa.gov

Wilhelm, Mary Jo (D, 26)
State Capitol
1007 East Grand Avenue
Des Moines, IA 50319
P: (515) 281-3371
E: mary.jo.wilhelm
@legis.iowa.gov

Zaun, Brad (R, 20)
State Capitol
1007 East Grand Avenue
Des Moines, IA 50319
P: (515) 281-3371
E: brad.zaun@legis.iowa.gov

Zumbach, Dan (R, 48)
State Capitol
1007 East Grand Avenue
Des Moines, IA 50319
P: (515) 281-3371
E: dan.zumbach
@legis.iowa.gov

House

Speaker of the House

Rep. Kraig Paulsen (R)
Speaker of the House
State Capitol
1007 East Grand Avenue
Des Moines, IA 50319
P: (515) 281-5137
E: kraig.paulsen
@legis.iowa.gov

Speaker Pro Tempore of the House

Rep. Matt W. Windschitl (R)
House Speaker Pro Tem
State Capitol
1007 East Grand Avenue
Des Moines, IA 50319
P: (515) 281-3221
E: matt.windschitl
@legis.iowa.gov

House Majority Leader

Rep. Linda Upmeyer (R)
House Majority Leader
State Capitol
1007 East Grand Avenue
Des Moines, IA 50319
P: (515) 281-5137
E: linda.upmeyer
@legis.iowa.gov

House Minority Leader

Rep. Mark D. Smith (D)
House Minority Leader
State Capitol
1007 East Grand Avenue
Des Moines, IA 50319
P: (515) 281-5230
E: mark.smith
@legis.iowa.gov

Clerk of the House

Ms. Carmine Boal
Chief Clerk of the House
State Capitol
1007 East Grand Avenue
Des Moines, IA 50319
P: (515) 281-4280
F: (515) 281-4758
E: carmine.boal
@legis.iowa.gov

Members of the House

Abdul-Samad, Ako (D, 35)
State Capitol
1007 East Grand Avenue
Des Moines, IA 50319
P: (515) 281-6356
E: ako.abdul-samad
@legis.iowa.gov

Anderson, Marti (D, 36)
State Capitol
1007 East Grand Avenue
Des Moines, IA 50319
P: (515) 281-3221
E: marti.anderson
@legis.iowa.gov

Bacon, Robert (R, 48)
State Capitol
1007 East Grand Avenue
Des Moines, IA 50319
P: (515) 281-3221
E: rob.bacon@legis.iowa.gov

Baltimore, Chip (R, 47)
State Capitol
1007 East Grand Avenue
Des Moines, IA 50319
P: (515) 281-3221
E: chip.baltimore
@legis.iowa.gov

Baudler, Clel (R, 20)
State Capitol
1007 East Grand Avenue
Des Moines, IA 50319
P: (515) 281-3221
E: clel.baudler
@legis.iowa.gov

Baxter, Terry (R, 8)*
State Capitol
1007 East Grand Avenue
Des Moines, IA 50319
P: (515) 281-3221
E: terry.baxter
@legis.iowa.gov

Bearinger, Bruce (D, 64)
State Capitol
1007 East Grand Avenue
Des Moines, IA 50319
P: (515) 281-3221
E: bruce.bearinger
@legis.iowa.gov

Bennett, Liz (D, 65)*
State Capitol
1007 East Grand Avenue
Des Moines, IA 50319
P: (515) 281-3221
E: liz.bennett
@legis.iowa.gov

Berry, Deborah (D, 62)
State Capitol
1007 East Grand Avenue
Des Moines, IA 50319
P: (515) 281-3221
E: deborah.berry
@legis.iowa.gov

Best, Brian (R, 12)*
State Capitol
1007 East Grand Avenue
Des Moines, IA 50319
P: (515) 281-3221
E: brian.best
@legis.iowa.gov

Branhagen, Darrel (R, 55)*
State Capitol
1007 East Grand Avenue
Des Moines, IA 50319
P: (515) 281-3221
E: darrel.branhagen
@legis.iowa.gov

Brown-Powers, Timi (D, 61)*
State Capitol
1007 East Grand Avenue
Des Moines, IA 50319
P: (515) 281-3221
E: timi.brown-powers
@legis.iowa.gov

Byrnes, Josh (R, 51)
State Capitol
1007 East Grand Avenue
Des Moines, IA 50319
P: (515) 281-3221
E: josh.byrnes
@legis.iowa.gov

Carlson, Gary (R, 91)*
State Capitol
1007 East Grand Avenue
Des Moines, IA 50319
P: (515) 281-3221
E: gary.carlson
@legis.iowa.gov

Cohoon, Dennis (D, 87)
State Capitol
1007 East Grand Avenue
Des Moines, IA 50319
P: (515) 281-3221
E: dennis.cohoon
@legis.iowa.gov

Cownie, Peter (R, 42)
State Capitol
1007 East Grand Avenue
Des Moines, IA 50319
P: (515) 281-3221
E: peter.cownie
@legis.iowa.gov

Iowa

Dawson, Dave (D, 14)
State Capitol
1007 East Grand Avenue
Des Moines, IA 50319
P: (515) 281-3221
E: dave.dawson
@legis.iowa.gov

Deyoe, Dave (R, 49)
State Capitol
1007 East Grand Avenue
Des Moines, IA 50319
P: (515) 281-3221
E: dave.deyoe
@legis.iowa.gov

Dolecheck, Cecil (R, 24)
State Capitol
1007 East Grand Avenue
Des Moines, IA 50319
P: (515) 281-3221
E: cecil.dolecheck
@legis.iowa.gov

Drake, Jack (R, 21)
State Capitol
1007 East Grand Avenue
Des Moines, IA 50319
P: (515) 281-3221
E: jack.drake
@legis.iowa.gov

Dunkel, Nancy (D, 57)
State Capitol
1007 East Grand Avenue
Des Moines, IA 50319
P: (515) 281-3221
E: nancy.dunkel
@legis.iowa.gov

Finkenauer, Abby (D, 99)*
State Capitol
1007 East Grand Avenue
Des Moines, IA 50319
P: (515) 281-3221
E: abby.finkenaur
@legis.iowa.gov

Fisher, Dean (R, 72)
State Capitol
1007 East Grand Avenue
Des Moines, IA 50319
P: (515) 281-3221
E: dean.fisher
@legis.iowa.gov

Forbes, John (D, 40)
State Capitol
1007 East Grand Avenue
Des Moines, IA 50319
P: (515) 281-3221
E: john.forbes
@legis.iowa.gov

Forristall, Greg (R, 22)
State Capitol
1007 East Grand Avenue
Des Moines, IA 50319
P: (515) 281-3221
E: greg.forristall
@legis.iowa.gov

Fry, Joel (R, 27)
State Capitol
1007 East Grand Avenue
Des Moines, IA 50319
P: (515) 281-3221
E: joel.fry@legis.iowa.gov

Gaines, Ruth Ann (D, 32)
State Capitol
1007 East Grand Avenue
Des Moines, IA 50319
P: (515) 281-3221
E: ruthann.gaines
@legis.iowa.gov

Gaskill, Mary (D, 81)
State Capitol
1007 East Grand Avenue
Des Moines, IA 50319
P: (515) 281-3221
E: mary.gaskill
@legis.iowa.gov

Gassman, Tedd (R, 7)
State Capitol
1007 East Grand Avenue
Des Moines, IA 50319
P: (515) 281-3221
E: tedd.gassman
@legis.iowa.gov

Grassley, Pat (R, 50)
State Capitol
1007 East Grand Avenue
Des Moines, IA 50319
P: (515) 281-3221
E: pat.grassley
@legis.iowa.gov

Gustafson, Stan (R, 25)
State Capitol
1007 East Grand AVenue
Des Moines, IA 50319
P: (515) 281-3221
E: stan.gustafson
@legis.iowa.gov

Hagenow, Chris (R, 43)
State Capitol
1007 East Grand Avenue
Des Moines, IA 50319
P: (515) 281-3221
E: chris.hagenow
@legis.iowa.gov

Hall, Chris (D, 13)
State Capitol
1007 East Grand Avenue
Des Moines, IA 50319
P: (515) 281-3221
E: chris.hall
@legis.iowa.gov

Hanson, Curt (D, 82)
State Capitol
1007 East Grand Avenue
Des Moines, IA 50319
P: (515) 281-3221
E: curt.hanson
@legis.iowa.gov

Hanusa, Mary Ann (R, 16)
State Capitol
1007 East Grand Avenue
Des Moines, IA 50319
P: (515) 281-3221
E: maryann.hanusa
@legis.iowa.gov

Heartsill, Greg (R, 28)
State Capitol
1007 East Grand Avenue
Des Moines, IA 50319
P: (515) 281-3221
E: greg.heartsill
@legis.iowa.gov

Heaton, Dave E. (R, 84)
State Capitol
1007 East Grand Avenue
Des Moines, IA 50319
P: (515) 281-3221
E: dave.heaton
@legis.iowa.gov

Heddens, Lisa (D, 46)
State Capitol
1007 East Grand Avenue
Des Moines, IA 50319
P: (515) 281-3221
E: lisa.heddens
@legis.iowa.gov

Hein, Lee (R, 96)
State Capitol
1007 East Grand Avenue
Des Moines, IA 50319
P: (515) 281-3221
E: lee.hein@legis.iowa.gov

Highfill, Jake (R, 39)
State Capitol
1007 East Grand Avenue
Des Moines, IA 50319
P: (515) 281-3221
E: jake.highfill
@legis.iowa.gov

Holt, Steven (R, 18)*
State Capitol
1007 East Grand Avenue
Des Moines, IA 50319
P: (515) 281-3221
E: steven.holt
@legis.iowa.gov

Hunter, Bruce (D, 34)
State Capitol
1007 East Grand Avenue
Des Moines, IA 50319
P: (515) 281-3221
E: bruce.hunter
@legis.iowa.gov

Huseman, Daniel A. (R, 3)
State Capitol
1007 East Grand Avenue
Des Moines, IA 50319
P: (515) 281-3221
E: dan.huseman
@legis.iowa.gov

Isenhart, Charles (D, 100)
State Capitol
1007 East Grand Avenue
Des Moines, IA 50319
P: (515) 281-3221
E: charles.isenhart
@legis.iowa.gov

Jacoby, David (D, 74)
State Capitol
1007 East Grand Avenue
Des Moines, IA 50319
P: (515) 281-3221
E: david.jacoby
@legis.iowa.gov

Jones, Megan (R, 2)
State Capitol
1007 East Grand Avenue
Des Moines, IA 50319
P: (515) 281-3221
E: megan.hess
@legis.iowa.gov

Jorgensen, Ron (R, 6)
State Capitol
1007 East Grand Avenue
Des Moines, IA 50319
P: (515) 281-3221
E: ron.jorgensen
@legis.iowa.gov

Kaufmann, Bobby (R, 73)
State Capitol
1007 East Grand Avenue
Des Moines, IA 50319
P: (515) 281-3221
E: bobby.kaufmann
@legis.iowa.gov

Kearns, Jerry (D, 83)
State Capitol
1007 East Grand Avenue
Des Moines, IA 50319
P: (515) 281-3221
E: jerry.kearns
@legis.iowa.gov

Kelley, Dan (D, 29)
State Capitol
1007 East Grand Avenue
Des Moines, IA 50319
P: (515) 281-3221
E: dan.kelley
@legis.iowa.gov

Klein, Jarad (R, 78)
State Capitol
1007 East Grand Avenue
Des Moines, IA 50319
P: (515) 281-3221
E: jarad.klein
@legis.iowa.gov

Koester, Kevin (R, 38)
State Capitol
1007 East Grand Avenue
Des Moines, IA 50319
P: (515) 281-3221
E: kevin.koester
@legis.iowa.gov

Kooiker, John (R, 4)*
State Capitol
1007 East Grand Avenue
Des Moines, IA 50319
P: (515) 281-3221
E: john.kooiker
@legis.iowa.gov

Kressig, Bob (D, 59)
State Capitol
1007 East Grand Avenue
Des Moines, IA 50319
P: (515) 281-3221
E: bob.kressig
@legis.iowa.gov

Landon, John (R, 37)
State Capitol
1007 East Grand Avenue
Des Moines, IA 50319
P: (515) 281-3221
E: john.landon
@legis.iowa.gov

Lensing, Vicki (D, 85)
State Capitol
1007 East Grand Avenue
Des Moines, IA 50319
P: (515) 281-3221
E: vicki.lensing
@legis.iowa.gov

Lykam, Jim (D, 89)
State Capitol
1007 East Grand Avenue
Des Moines, IA 50319
P: (515) 281-3221
E: jim.lykam@legis.iowa.gov

Mascher, Mary (D, 86)
State Capitol
1007 East Grand Avenue
Des Moines, IA 50319
P: (515) 281-3221
E: mary.mascher
@legis.iowa.gov

Maxwell, Dave (R, 76)
State Capitol
1007 East Grand Avenue
Des Moines, IA 50319
P: (515) 281-3221
E: dave.maxwell
@legis.iowa.gov

McConkey, Charlie (D, 15)*
State Capitol
1007 East Grand Avenue
Des Moines, IA 50319
P: (515) 281-3221
E: charlie.mcconkey
@legis.iowa.gov

Meyer, Brian (D, 33)
State Capitol
1007 East Grand Avenue
Des Moines, IA 50319
P: (515) 281-3221
E: brian.meyer
@legis.iowa.gov

Miller, Helen (D, 9)
State Capitol
1007 East Grand Avenue
Des Moines, IA 50319
P: (515) 281-3221
E: helen.miller
@legis.iowa.gov

Miller, Linda J. (R, 94)
State Capitol
1007 East Grand Avenue
Des Moines, IA 50319
P: (515) 281-3221
E: linda.miller
@legis.iowa.gov

Mommsen, Norlin (R, 97)*
State Capitol
1007 East Grand Avenue
Des Moines, IA 50319
P: (515) 281-3221
E: norlin.mommsen
@legis.iowa.gov

Moore, Brian (R, 58)
State Capitol
1007 East Grand Avenue
Des Moines, IA 50319
P: (515) 281-3221
E: brian.moore
@legis.iowa.gov

Nunn, Zach (R, 30)*
State Capitol
1007 East Grand Avenue
Des Moines, IA 50319
P: (515) 281-3221
E: zach.nunn@legis.iowa.gov

Oldson, Jo (D, 41)
State Capitol
1007 East Grand Avenue
Des Moines, IA 50319
P: (515) 281-3221
E: jo.oldson@legis.iowa.gov

Olson, Rick (D, 31)
State Capitol
1007 East Grand Avenue
Des Moines, IA 50319
P: (515) 281-3221
E: rick.olson
@legis.iowa.gov

Ourth, Scott (D, 26)
State Capitol
1007 East Grand Avenue
Des Moines, IA 50319
P: (515) 281-3221
E: scott.ourth
@legis.iowa.gov

Paulsen, Kraig (R, 67)
State Capitol
1007 East Grand Avenue
Des Moines, IA 50319
P: (515) 281-5137
E: kraig.paulsen
@legis.iowa.gov

Paustian, Ross (R, 92)
State Capitol
1007 East Grand Avenue
Des Moines, IA 50319
P: (515) 281-3221
E: Ross.Paustian
@legis.state.ia.us

Pettengill, Dawn (R, 75)
State Capitol
1007 East Grand Avenue
Des Moines, IA 50319
P: (515) 281-3221
E: dawn.pettengill
@legis.iowa.gov

Prichard, Todd (D, 52)
State Capitol
1007 East Grand Avenue
Des Moines, IA 50319
P: (515) 281-3221
E: todd.prichard
@legis.iowa.gov

Rizer, Ken (R, 68)*
State Capitol
1007 East Grand Avenue
Des Moines, IA 50319
P: (515) 281-3221
E: ken.rizer@legis.iowa.gov

Rogers, Walt (R, 60)
State Capitol
1007 East Grand Avenue
Des Moines, IA 50319
P: (515) 281-3221
E: walt.rogers
@legis.iowa.gov

Ruff, Patti (D, 56)
State Capitol
1007 East Grand Avenue
Des Moines, IA 50319
P: (515) 281-3221
E: patti.ruff
@legis.iowa.gov

Running-Marquardt, Kirsten (D, 69)
State Capitol
1007 East Grand Avenue
Des Moines, IA 50319
P: (515) 281-3221
E: kirsten.
running-marquardt
@legis.iowa.gov

Salmon, Sandy (R, 63)
State Capitol
1007 East Grand Avenue
Des Moines, IA 50319
P: (515) 281-3221
E: sandy.salmon
@legis.iowa.gov

Sands, Thomas R. (R, 88)
State Capitol
1007 East Grand Avenue
Des Moines, IA 50319
P: (515) 281-3221
E: tom.sands@legis.iowa.gov

Sexton, Mike (R, 10)
State Capitol
1007 East Grand Avenue
Des Moines, IA 50319
P: (515) 281-3371
E: mike.sexton
@legis.iowa.gov

Iowa

Sheets, Larry (R, 80)
State Capitol
1007 East Grand Avenue
Des Moines, IA 50319
P: (515) 281-3221
E: larry.sheets
@legis.iowa.gov

Sieck, David (R, 23)*
State Capitol
1007 East Grand Avenue
Des Moines, IA 50319
P: (515) 281-3221
E: david.sieck
@legis.iowa.gov

Smith, Mark D. (D, 71)
State Capitol
1007 East Grand Avenue
Des Moines, IA 50319
P: (515) 281-5230
E: mark.smith
@legis.iowa.gov

Soderberg, Chuck (R, 5)
State Capitol
1007 East Grand Avenue
Des Moines, IA 50319
P: (515) 281-3221
E: chuck.soderberg
@legis.iowa.gov

Staed, Art (D, 66)
State Capitol
1007 East Grand Avenue
Des Moines, IA 50319
P: (515) 281-3221
E: art.staed@legis.iowa.gov

Stanerson, Quentin (R, 95)
State Capitol
1007 East Grand Avenue
Des Moines, IA 50319
P: (515) 281-3221
E: quentin.stanerson
@legis.iowa.gov

Steckman, Sharon (D, 53)
State Capitol
1007 East Grand Avenue
Des Moines, IA 50319
P: (515) 281-3221
E: sharon.steckman
@legis.iowa.gov

Stutsman, Sally (D, 77)
State Capitol
1007 East Grand Avenue
Des Moines, IA 50319
P: (515) 281-3221
E: sally.stutsman
@legis.iowa.gov

Taylor, Rob (R, 44)
State Capitol
1007 East Grand Avenue
Des Moines, IA 50319
P: (515) 281-3221
E: rob.taylor
@legis.iowa.gov

Taylor, Todd E. (D, 70)
State Capitol
1007 East Grand Avenue
Des Moines, IA 50319
P: (515) 281-3221
E: todd.taylor
@legis.iowa.gov

Thede, Phyllis (D, 93)
State Capitol
1007 East Grand Avenue
Des Moines, IA 50319
P: (515) 281-3221
E: phyllis.thede
@legis.iowa.gov

Upmeyer, Linda (R, 54)
State Capitol
1007 East Grand Avenue
Des Moines, IA 50319
P: (515) 281-5137
E: linda.upmeyer
@legis.iowa.gov

Vander Linden, Guy (R, 79)
State Capitol
1007 East Grand Avenue
Des Moines, IA 50319
P: (515) 281-3221
E: guy.vander.linden
@legis.iowa.gov

Watts, Ralph C. (R, 19)
State Capitol
1007 East Grand Avenue
Des Moines, IA 50319
P: (515) 281-3221
E: ralph.watts
@legis.iowa.gov

Wessel-Kroeschell, Beth (D, 45)
State Capitol
1007 East Grand Avenue
Des Moines, IA 50319
P: (515) 281-3221
E: beth.wessel-kroeschell
@legis.iowa.gov

Wills, John (R, 1)*
State Capitol
1007 East Grand Avenue
Des Moines, IA 50319
P: (515) 281-3221
E: john.wills
@legis.iowa.gov

Winckler, Cindy (D, 90)
State Capitol
1007 East Grand Avenue
Des Moines, IA 50319
P: (515) 281-3221
E: cindy.winckler
@legis.iowa.gov

Windschitl, Matt W. (R, 17)
State Capitol
1007 East Grand Avenue
Des Moines, IA 50319
P: (515) 281-3221
E: matt.windschitl
@legis.iowa.gov

Wolfe, Mary (D, 98)
State Capitol
1007 East Grand Avenue
Des Moines, IA 50319
P: (515) 281-3221
E: mary.wolfe
@legis.iowa.gov

Worthan, Gary (R, 11)
State Capitol
1007 East Grand Avenue
Des Moines, IA 50319
P: (515) 281-3221
E: gary.worthan
@legis.iowa.gov

Congress

Senate

Grassley, Chuck (R)
Harkin, Tom (D)

House

Braley, Bruce (D, 1)
King, Steve (R, 4)
Latham, Tom (R, 3)
Loebsack, Dave (D, 2)

Kansas

Executive

Governor

Hon. Sam Brownback (R)
Governor
Capitol
300 Southwest 10th Avenue,
Suite 212S
Topeka, KS 66612
P: (785) 296-3232
F: (785) 296-7973

Lieutenant Governor

Hon. Jeff Colyer M.D. (R)
Lieutenant Governor
State Capitol, 2nd Floor
300 Southwest 10th Avenue
Topeka, KS 66612
P: (785) 296-2214
F: (785) 296-5669

Attorney General

Hon. Derek Schmidt (R)
Attorney General
120 Southwest 10th Avenue,
2nd Floor
Topeka, KS 66612
P: (785) 296-2215
F: (785) 296-6296

Auditor

Mr. Scott E. Frank
(appointed by the Legislature)
Legislative Post Auditor
800 Southwest Jackson Street
Suite 1200
Topeka, KS 66612
P: (785) 296-3792
F: (785) 296-4482
E: scott.frank@lpa.ks.gov

Commissioner of Insurance

Hon. Ken Selzer (R)
Commissioner of Insurance
420 Southwest 9th Street
Topeka, KS 66612
P: (785) 296-3071
F: (785) 296-7805
E: commissioner
@ksinsurance.org

Secretary of State

Hon. Kris Kobach (R)
Secretary of State
120 Southwest 10th Avenue
Memorial Hall, 1st Floor
Topeka, KS 66612
P: (785) 296-4575
F: (785) 368-8033
E: sos@sos.ks.gov

Treasurer

Hon. Ron Estes (R)
State Treasurer
900 Southwest Jackson Street,
Suite 201
Topeka, KS 66612
P: (785) 296-3171
F: (785) 296-7950
E: ron@treasurer.ks.gov

Judiciary

Supreme Court (MR)

Ms. Heather L. Smith
Clerk of the Appellate Courts
Judicial Center
301 Southwest 10th Avenue,
Room 374
Topeka, KS 66612
P: (785) 296-3229
F: (785) 296-1028
E: appellateclerk
@kscourts.org

Hon. Lawton R. Nuss
Chief Justice
Hon. Carol A. Beier
Hon. Dan Biles
Hon. Lee A. Johnson
Hon. Marla J. Luckert
Hon. Nancy Moritz
Hon. Eric S. Rosen

Legislative Senate

Senate President

Sen. Susan Wagle (R)
Senate President
300 Southwest 10th Avenue
Room 333-E
Topeka, KS 66612
P: (785) 296-2419
E: susan.wagle
@senate.ks.gov

President Pro Tempore of the Senate

Sen. Jeff King (R)
Senate Vice President
300 Southwest 10th Avenue
Room 341-E
Topeka, KS 66612
P: (785) 296-7361
E: jeff.king@senate.ks.gov

Senate Majority Leader

Sen. Terry Bruce (R)
Senate Majority Leader
300 Southwest 10th Avenue
Room 330-E
Topeka, KS 66612
P: (785) 296-2497
E: terry.bruce
@senate.ks.gov

Senate Minority Leader

Sen. Anthony Hensley (D)
Senate Minority Leader
300 Southwest 10th Avenue
Room 318-E
Topeka, KS 66612
P: (785) 296-3245
E: anthony.hensley
@senate.ks.gov

Secretary of the Senate

Mr. Corey Carnahan
Secretary of the Senate
300 Southwest 10th Avenue
Room 325-E
Topeka, KS 66612
P: (785) 296-2456
F: (785) 276-6718
E: corey.carnahan
@senate.ks.gov

Members of the Senate

Abrams, Steve E. (R, 32)
300 Southwest 10th Avenue
Room 224-E
Topeka, KS 66612
P: (785) 296-7381
E: steve.abrams
@senate.ks.gov

Arpke, Tom (R, 24)
300 Southwest 10th Avenue
Room 135-E
Topeka, KS 66612
P: (785) 296-7369
E: tom.arpke@senate.ks.gov

Baumgardner, Molly (R, 37)*
300 Southwest 10th Avenue
Room 224-E
Topeka, KS 66612
P: (785) 296-7368
E: molly.baumgardner
@senate.ks.gov

Bowers, Elaine S. (R, 36)
300 Southwest 10th Avenue
Room 223-E
Topeka, KS 66612
P: (785) 296-7389
E: elaine.bowers
@senate.ks.gov

Bruce, Terry (R, 34)
300 Southwest 10th Avenue
Room 330-E
Topeka, KS 66612
P: (785) 296-2497
E: terry.bruce
@senate.ks.gov

Denning, Jim (R, 8)
300 Southwest 10th Avenue
Room 541-E
Topeka, KS 66612
P: (785) 296-7394
E: jim.denning
@senate.ks.gov

Donovan, Les (R, 27)
300 Southwest 10th Avenue
Room 123-E
Topeka, KS 66612
P: (785) 296-7385
E: les.donovan
@senate.ks.gov

Faust-Goudeau, Oletha (D, 29)
300 Southwest 10th Avenue
Room 124-E
Topeka, KS 66612
P: (785) 296-7387
E: oletha.faust-goudeau
@senate.ks.gov

Fitzgerald, Steve (R, 5)
300 Southwest 10th Avenue
Room 135-E
Topeka, KS 66612
P: (785) 296-7357
E: steve.fitzgerald
@senate.ks.gov

Francisco, Marci (D, 2)
300 Southwest 10th Avenue
Room 134-E
Topeka, KS 66612
P: (785) 296-7364
E: marci.francisco
@senate.ks.gov

Kansas

Haley, David (D, 4)
300 Southwest 10th Avenue
Room 134-E
Topeka, KS 66612
P: (785) 296-7376
E: david.haley
@senate.ks.gov

Hawk, Tom (D, 22)
300 Southwest 10th Avenue
Room 124-E
Topeka, KS 66612
P: (785) 296-7360
E: tom.hawk@senate.ks.gov

Hensley, Anthony (D, 19)
300 Southwest 10th Avenue
Room 318-E
Topeka, KS 66612
P: (785) 296-3245
E: anthony.hensley
@senate.ks.gov

Holland, Tom (D, 3)
300 Southwest 10th Avenue
Room 134-E
Topeka, KS 66612
P: (785) 296-7372
E: tom.holland
@senate.ks.gov

Holmes, Mitch (R, 33)
300 Southwest 10th Avenue
Room 237-E
Topeka, KS 66612
P: (785) 296-7667
E: mitch.holmes
@senate.ks.gov

Kelly, Laura (D, 18)
300 Southwest 10th Avenue
Room 125-E
Topeka, KS 66612
P: (785) 296-7365
E: laura.kelly
@senate.ks.gov

Kerschen, Dan (R, 26)
300 Southwest 10th Avenue
Room 225-E
Topeka, KS 66612
P: (785) 296-7353
E: dan.kerschen
@senate.ks.gov

King, Jeff (R, 15)
300 Southwest 10th Avenue
Room 341-E
Topeka, KS 66612
P: (785) 296-7361
E: jeff.king@senate.ks.gov

Knox, Forrest (R, 14)
300 Southwest 10th Avenue
Room 234-E
Topeka, KS 66612
P: (785) 296-7678
E: forrest.knox
@senate.ks.gov

LaTurner, Jacob (R, 13)
300 Southwest 10th Avenue
Room 135-E
Topeka, KS 66612
P: (785) 296-7370
E: jacob.laturner
@senate.ks.gov

Longbine, Jeff (R, 17)
300 Southwest 10th Avenue
Room 235-E
Topeka, KS 66612
P: (785) 296-7384
E: jeff.longbine
@senate.ks.gov

Love, Garrett (R, 38)
300 Southwest 10th Avenue
Room 237-E
Topeka, KS 66612
P: (785) 296-7359
E: garrett.love
@senate.ks.gov

Lynn, Julia (R, 9)
300 Southwest 10th Avenue
Room 445-S
Topeka, KS 66612
P: (785) 296-7382
E: julia.lynn@senate.ks.gov

Masterson, Ty (R, 16)
300 Southwest 10th Avenue
Room 545-S
Topeka, KS 66612
P: (785) 296-7388
E: ty.masterson
@senate.ks.gov

McGinn, Carolyn (R, 31)
300 Southwest 10th Avenue
Room 223-E
Topeka, KS 66612
P: (785) 296-7377
E: carolyn.mcginn
@senate.ks.gov

Melcher, Jeff (R, 11)
300 Southwest 10th Avenue
Room 541-E
Topeka, KS 66612
P: (785) 296-7301
E: jeff.melcher
@senate.ks.gov

O'Donnell, Michael (R, 25)
300 Southwest 10th Avenue
Room 225-E
Topeka, KS 66612
P: (785) 296-7391
E: michael.odonnell
@senate.ks.gov

Olson, Robert (R, 23)
300 Southwest 10th Avenue
Room 236-E
Topeka, KS 66612
P: (785) 296-7358
E: robert.olson
@senate.ks.gov

Ostmeyer, Ralph (R, 40)
300 Southwest 10th Avenue
Room 136-E
Topeka, KS 66612
P: (785) 296-7399
E: ralph.ostmeyer
@senate.ks.gov

Petersen, Mike (R, 28)
300 Southwest 10th Avenue
Room 345-S
Topeka, KS 66612
P: (785) 296-7355
E: mike.petersen
@senate.ks.gov

Pettey, Pat Huggins (D, 6)
300 Southwest 10th Avenue
Room 125-E
Topeka, KS 66612
P: (785) 296-7375
E: pat.pettey@senate.ks.gov

Pilcher-Cook, Mary (R, 10)
300 Southwest 10th Avenue
Room 441-E
Topeka, KS 66612
P: (785) 296-7362
E: mary.pilchercook
@senate.ks.gov

Powell, Larry R. (R, 39)
300 Southwest 10th Avenue
Room 237-E
Topeka, KS 66612
P: (785) 296-7694
E: larry.powell
@senate.ks.gov

Pyle, Dennis (R, 1)
300 Southwest 10th Avenue
Room 234-E
Topeka, KS 66612
P: (785) 296-7379
E: dennis.pyle
@senate.ks.gov

Schmidt, Vicki (R, 20)
300 Southwest 10th Avenue
Room 445-S
Topeka, KS 66612
P: (785) 296-7374
E: vicki.schmidt
@senate.ks.gov

Smith, Greg (R, 21)
300 Southwest 10th Avenue
Room 441-E
Topeka, KS 66612
P: (785) 296-7367
E: greg.smith@senate.ks.gov

Tyson, Caryn (R, 12)
300 Southwest 10th Avenue
Room 236-E
Topeka, KS 66612
P: (785) 296-6838
E: caryn.tyson
@senate.ks.gov

Wagle, Susan (R, 30)
300 Southwest 10th Avenue
Room 333-E
Topeka, KS 66612
P: (785) 296-2419
E: susan.wagle
@senate.ks.gov

Wilborn Esq., Richard (R, 35)*
300 Southwest 10th Avenue
Room 541-E
Topeka, KS 66612
P: (785) 296-7354
E: richard.wilborn
@senate.ks.gov

Wolf, Kay (R, 7)
300 Southwest 10th Street
Room 235-E
Topeka, KS 66612
P: (785) 296-7390
E: kay.wolf@senate.ks.gov

House

Speaker of the House

Rep. Ray Merrick (R)
Speaker of the House
300 Southwest 10th Avenue
Room 370-W
Topeka, KS 66612
P: (785) 296-2302
E: ray.merrick@house.ks.gov

Speaker Pro Tempore of the House

Rep. Peggy L. Mast (R)
House Speaker Pro Tem
300 Southwest 10th Avenue
Room 381-W
Topeka, KS 66612
P: (785) 291-3500
E: peggy.mast@house.ks.gov

House Majority Leader

Rep. Jene Vickrey (R)
House Majority Leader
300 Southwest 10th Avenue
Room 372-W
Topeka, KS 66612
P: (785) 296-7662
E: jene.vickrey
@house.ks.gov

House Minority Leader

Rep. Tom Burroughs (D)
House Minority Leader
300 Southwest 10th Avenue
Room 359-W
Topeka, KS 66612
P: (785) 296-7630
E: tom.burroughs
@house.ks.gov

Clerk of the House

Ms. Susan W. Kannarr
Chief Clerk of the House
300 Southwest 10th Avenue,
Room 272-W
Topeka, KS 66612
P: (785) 296-7633
F: (785) 291-3531
E: susan.kannarr
@house.ks.gov

Members of the House

Alcala, John (D, 57)
300 Southwest 10th Avenue
Room 173-S
Topeka, KS 66612
P: (785) 296-7371
E: john.alcala@house.ks.gov

Alford, Steve (R, 124)
300 Southwest 10th Avenue
Room 187-N
Topeka, KS 66612
P: (785) 296-7656
E: j.stephen.alford
@house.ks.gov

Anthimides, Steven (R, 98)
300 Southwest 10th Avenue
Room 519-N
Topeka, KS 66612
P: (785) 296-6824
E: steven.anthimides
@house.ks.gov

Ballard, Barbara W. (D, 44)
300 Southwest 10th Avenue
Room 451-S
Topeka, KS 66612
P: (785) 296-7697
E: barbara.ballard
@house.ks.gov

Barker, John (R, 70)
300 Southwest 10th Avenue
Room 176-W
Topeka, KS 66612
P: (785) 296-7674
E: john.barker@house.ks.gov

Barton, Tony (R, 41)*
300 Southwest 10th Avenue
Room 559-W
Topeka, KS 66612
P: (785) 296-7522
E: tony.barton@house.ks.gov

Becker, Steven (R, 104)
300 Southwest 10th Avenue
Room 512-N
Topeka, KS 66612
P: (785) 296-7196
E: steven.becker
@house.ks.gov

Billinger, Rick (R, 120)
300 Southwest 10th Avenue
Room 168-W
Topeka, KS 66612
P: (785) 296-7659
E: rick.billinger
@house.ks.gov

Boldra, Sue (R, 111)
300 Southwest 10th Avenue
Room 352-W
Topeka, KS 66612
P: (785) 296-4683
E: sue.boldra@house.ks.gov

Bollier, Barbara (R, 21)
300 Southwest 10th Avenue
Room 168-W
Topeka, KS 66612
P: (785) 296-7686
E: barbara.bollier
@house.ks.gov

Bradford, John (R, 40)
300 Southwest 10th Avenue
Room 166-W
Topeka, KS 66612
P: (785) 296-7653
E: john.bradford
@house.ks.gov

Bridges, Carolyn (D, 83)
300 Southwest 10th Avenue
Room 174-W
Topeka, KS 66612
P: (785) 296-7646
E: carolyn.bridges
@house.ks.gov

Bruchman, Rob (R, 20)
300 Southwest 10th Avenue
Room 352-S
Topeka, KS 66612
P: (785) 296-7644
E: rob.bruchman
@house.ks.gov

Brunk, Steven (R, 85)
300 Southwest 10th Avenue
Room 149-S
Topeka, KS 66612
P: (785) 296-7645
E: steve.brunk@house.ks.gov

Burroughs, Tom (D, 33)
300 Southwest 10th Avenue
Room 359-W
Topeka, KS 66612
P: (785) 296-7630
E: tom.burroughs
@house.ks.gov

Campbell, Larry (R, 26)
300 Southwest 10th Avenue
Room 452-S
Topeka, KS 66612
P: (785) 296-7632
E: larry.campbell
@house.ks.gov

Carlin, Sydney (D, 66)
300 Southwest 10th Avenue
Room 451-S
Topeka, KS 66612
P: (785) 296-7649
E: sydney.carlin
@house.ks.gov

Carmichael, John (D, 92)
300 Southwest 10th Avenue
Room 451-S
Topeka, KS 66612
P: (785) 296-7650
E: john.carmichael
@house.ks.gov

Carpenter, Blake (R, 81)*
300 Southwest 10th Avenue
Room 167-W
Topeka, KS 66612
P: (785) 296-7567
E: blake.carpenter
@house.ks.gov

Carpenter, Will (R, 75)
300 Southwest 10th Avenue
Room 352-S
Topeka, KS 66612
P: (785) 296-7673
E: will.carpenter
@house.ks.gov

Claeys, J.R. (R, 69)
300 Southwest 10th Avenue
Room 167-W
Topeka, KS 66612
P: (785) 296-7670
E: jrclaeys@house.ks.gov

Clark, Lonnie (R, 65)*
300 Southwest 10th Avenue
Room 352-S
Topeka, KS 66612
P: (785) 296-7483
E: lonnie.clark
@house.ks.gov

Clayton, Stephanie (R, 19)
300 Southwest 10th Avenue
Room 167-W
Topeka, KS 66612
P: (785) 296-7655
E: stephanie.clayton
@house.ks.gov

Concannon, Susan (R, 107)
300 Southwest 10th Avenue
Room 519-N
Topeka, KS 66612
P: (785) 296-7677
E: susan.concannon
@house.ks.gov

Corbet, Ken (R, 54)
300 Southwest 10th Avenue
Room 179-N
Topeka, KS 66612
P: (785) 296-7679
E: ken.corbet@house.ks.gov

Couture-Lovelady, Travis (R, 110)
300 Southwest 10th Avenue
Room 352-S
Topeka, KS 66612
P: (785) 296-4683
E: travis.couture-lovelady
@house.ks.gov

Curtis, Pam (D, 32)
300 Southwest 10th Avenue
Room 173-W
Topeka, KS 66612
P: (785)-296-7371
E: pam.curtis@house.ks.gov

Kansas

Dannebohm, Basil (R, 113)*
300 Southwest 10th Avenue
Room 166-W
Topeka, KS 66612
P: (785) 296-7682
E: basil.dannebohm
@house.ks.gov

Davis, Erin (R, 15)
300 Southwest 10th Avenue
Room 519-N
Topeka, KS 66612
P: (785) 296-3971
E: erin.davis@house.ks.gov

DeGraaf, Peter (R, 82)
300 Southwest 10th Avenue
Room 458-W
Topeka, KS 66612
P: (785) 296-7693
E: pete.degraaf
@house.ks.gov

Dierks, Diana (D, 71)
300 Southwest 10th Avenue
Room 519-N
Topeka, KS 66612
P: (785) 296-7642
E: diana.dierks
@house.ks.gov

Doll, John (R, 123)
300 Southwest 10th Avenue
Room 512-N
Topeka, KS 66612
P: (785) 296-7380
E: john.doll@house.ks.gov

Dove, Willie (R, 38)
300 Southwest 10th Avenue
Room 167-W
Topeka, KS 66612
P: (785) 296-7670
E: willie.dove@house.ks.gov

Edmonds, John (R, 112)
300 Southwest 10th Avenue
Room 452-S
Topeka, KS 66612
P: (785) 296-5593
E: john.edmonds
@house.ks.gov

Esau, Keith (R, 14)
300 Southwest 10th Avenue
Room 165-W
Topeka, KS 66612
P: (785) 296-7631
E: keith.esau@house.ks.gov

Estes, Bud (R, 119)
300 Southwest 10th Avenue
Room 512-N
Topeka, KS 66612
P: (785) 296-6287
E: bud.estes@house.ks.gov

Ewy, John (R, 117)
300 Southwest 10th Avenue
Room 512-N
Topeka, KS 66612
P: (785) 296-7105
E: john.ewy@house.ks.gov

Finch, Blaine (R, 59)
300 Southwest 10th Avenue
Room 167-W
Topeka, KS 66612
P: (785) 296-7655
E: blaine.finch
@house.ks.gov

Finney, Gail (D, 84)
300 Southwest 10th Avenue
Room 561-W
Topeka, KS 66612
P: (785) 296-7648
E: gail.finney@house.ks.gov

Francis, Shannon (R, 125)*
300 Southwest 10th Avenue
Room 167-W
Topeka, KS 66612
P: (785) 296-7655
E: shannon.francis
@house.ks.gov

Frownfelter, Stan S. (D, 37)
300 Southwest 10th Avenue
Room 561-W
Topeka, KS 66612
P: (785) 296-7648
E: stan.frownfelter
@house.ks.gov

Gallagher, Linda (R, 23)*
300 Southwest 10th Avenue
Room 167-W
Topeka, KS 66612
P: (785) 296-7548
E: linda.gallagher
@house.ks.gov

Garber, Randy (R, 62)
300 Southwest 10th Avenue
Room 459-W
Topeka, KS 66612
P: (785) 296-7665
E: randy.garber
@house.ks.gov

Goico, Mario (R, 94)
300 Southwest 10th Avenue
Room 276-W
Topeka, KS 66612
P: (785) 296-7663
E: mario.goico@house.ks.gov

Gonzalez, Ramon (R, 47)
300 Southwest 10th Avenue
Room 512-N
Topeka, KS 66612
P: (785) 296-7500
E: ramon.gonzalezjr
@house.ks.gov

Grosserode, Amanda (R, 16)
300 Southwest 10th Avenue
Room 274-W
Topeka, KS 66612
P: (785) 296-7659
E: amanda.grosserode
@house.ks.gov

Hawkins, Daniel (R, 100)
300 Southwest 10th Avenue
Room 165-W
Topeka, KS 66612
P: (785) 296-7631
E: dan.hawkins@house.ks.gov

Hedke, Dennis (R, 99)
300 Southwest 10th Avenue
Room 581-W
Topeka, KS 66612
P: (785) 296-7699
E: dennis.hedke
@house.ks.gov

Hemsley, Lane (R, 56)*
300 Southwest 10th Avenue
Room 165-W
Topeka, KS 66612
P: (785) 296-7460
E: lane.hemsley
@house.ks.gov

Henderson, Broderick T. (D, 35)
300 Southwest 10th Avenue
Room 451-S
Kansas City, KS 66612
P: (785) 296-7697
E: broderick.henderson
@house.ks.gov

Henry, Jerry (D, 63)
300 Southwest 10th Avenue
Room 47-S
Topeka, KS 66612
P: (785) 296-7688
E: jerry.henry@house.ks.gov

Hibbard, Larry (R, 13)
300 Southwest 10th Avenue
Room 512-N
Topeka, KS 66612
P: (785) 296-7380
E: larry.hibbard
@house.ks.gov

Highberger, Dennis (D, 46)*
300 Southwest 10th Avenue
Room 174-W .
Topeka, KS 66612
P: (785) 296-7122
E: dennis.boog.highberger
@house.ks.gov

Highland, Ron (R, 51)
300 Southwest 10th Avenue
Room 559-W
Topeka, KS 66612
P: (785) 296-7310
E: ron.highland
@house.ks.gov

Hildabrand, Brett (R, 17)
300 Southwest 10th Avenue
Room 274-W
Topeka, KS 66612
P: (785) 296-7659
E: brett.hildabrand
@house.ks.gov

Hill, Don (R, 60)
300 Southwest 10th Avenue
Room 452-S
Topeka, KS 66612
P: (785) 296-7632
E: don.hill@house.ks.gov

Hineman, Don (R, 118)
300 Southwest 10th Avenue
Room 50-S
Topeka, KS 66612
P: (785) 296-7636
E: don.hineman@house.ks.gov

Hoffman, Kyle (R, 116)
300 Southwest 10th Avenue
Room 481-W
Topeka, KS 66612
P: (785) 296-7643
E: kyle.hoffman
@house.ks.gov

Houser, Michael (R, 1)
300 Southwest 10th Avenue
Room 179-N
Topeka, KS 66612
P: (785) 296-7679
E: michael.houser
@house.ks.gov

Houston, Roderick (D, 89)
300 Southwest 10th Avenue
Room 54-S
Topeka, KS 66612
P: (785) 296-7652
E: roderick.houston
@house.ks.gov

Huebert, Steve (R, 90)
300 Southwest 10th Avenue
Room 149-S
Topeka, KS 66612
P: (785) 296-1754
E: steve.huebert@house.ks.gov

Hutchins, Becky (R, 61)
300 Southwest 10th Avenue
Room 176-W
Topeka, KS 66612
P: (785) 296-7653
E: becky.hutchins@house.ks.gov

Hutton, Mark (R, 105)
300 Southwest 10th Avenue
Room 268-W
Topeka, KS 66612
P: (785) 296-7658
E: mark.hutton@house.ks.gov

Jennings, Russell (R, 122)
300 Southwest 10th Avenue
Room 512-N
Topeka, KS 66612
P: (785) 296-7196
E: russ.jennings@house.ks.gov

Johnson, Steven (R, 108)
300 Southwest 10th Avenue
Room 286-N
Topeka, KS 66612
P: (785) 296-7696
E: steven.johnson@house.ks.gov

Jones, Dick (R, 52)*
300 Southwest 10th Avenue
Room 352-S
Topeka, KS 66612
P: (785) 296-7483
E: dick.jones@house.ks.gov

Jones, Kevin (R, 5)
300 Southwest 10th Avenue
Room 512-N
Topeka, KS 66612
P: (785) 296-6287
E: kevin.jones@house.ks.gov

Kahrs, Mark (R, 87)
300 Southwest 10th Avenue
Room 452-S
Topeka, KS 66612
P: (785) 296-5593
E: mark.kahrs@house.ks.gov

Kelley, Kasha (R, 80)
300 Southwest 10th Avenue
Room 151-S
Topeka, KS 66612
P: (785) 296-7671
E: kasha.kelley@house.ks.gov

Kelly, Jim (R, 11)
300 Southwest 10th Avenue
Room 512-N
Topeka, KS 66612
P: (785) 296-6014
E: jim.kelly@house.ks.gov

Kiegerl, S. Mike (R, 121)
300 Southwest 10th Avenue
Room 50-S
Topeka, KS 66612
P: (785) 296-7636
E: mike.kiegerl@house.ks.gov

Kleeb, Marvin (R, 48)
300 Southwest 10th Avenue
Room 286-N
Topeka, KS 66612
P: (785) 296-7680
E: marvin.kleeb@house.ks.gov

Kuether, Annie (D, 55)
300 Southwest 10th Avenue
Room 43-S
Topeka, KS 66612
P: (785) 296-7669
E: annie.kuether@house.ks.gov

Lane, Harold (D, 58)
300 Southwest 10th Avenue
Room 451-S
Topeka, KS 66612
P: (785) 296-7649
E: harold.lanc@house.ks.gov

Lunn, Jerry (R, 28)
300 Southwest 10th Avenue
Room 352-S
Topeka, KS 66612
P: (785) 296-7675
E: jerry.lunn@house.ks.gov

Lusk, Nancy (D, 22)
300 Southwest 10th Avenue
Room 54-S
Topeka, KS 66612
P: (785) 296-7651
E: nancy.lusk@house.ks.gov

Lusker, Adam (D, 2)
300 Southwest 10th Avenue
Room 43-S
Topeka, KS 66612
P: (785) 296-7698
E: adam.lusker@house.ks.gov

Macheers, Charles (R, 39)
300 Southwest 10th Avenue
Room 352-S
Topeka, KS 66612
P: (785) 296-7675
E: charles.macheers@house.ks.gov

Mason, Les (R, 73)
300 Southwest 10th Avenue
Room 268-W
Topeka, KS 66612
P: (785) 296-7640
E: les.mason@house.ks.gov

Mast, Peggy L. (R, 76)
300 Southwest 10th Avenue
Room 381-W
Topeka, KS 66612
P: (785) 291-3500
E: peggy.mast@house.ks.gov

McPherson, Craig (R, 8)
300 Southwest 10th Avenue
Room 268-W
Topeka, KS 66612
P: (785) 296-7695
E: craig.mcpherson@house.ks.gov

Merrick, Ray (R, 27)
300 Southwest 10th Avenue
Room 370-W
Topeka, KS 66612
P: (785) 296-2302
E: ray.merrick@house.ks.gov

Moxley, Tom (R, 68)
300 Southwest 10th Avenue
Room 512-N
Topeka, KS 66612
P: (785) 296-7689
E: tom.moxley@house.ks.gov

O'Brien, Connie (R, 42)
300 Southwest 10th Avenue
Room 187-N
Topeka, KS 66612
P: (785) 296-7683
E: connie.obrien@house.ks.gov

Osterman, Leslie (R, 97)
300 Southwest 10th Avenue
Room 512-N
Topeka, KS 66612
P: (785) 296-7689
E: leslie.osterman@house.ks.gov

Ousley, Jarrod (D, 24)*
300 Southwest 10th Avenue
Room 173-W
Topeka, KS 66612
P: (785) 296-7366
E: jarrod.ousley@house.ks.gov

Patton, Fred (R, 50)*
300 Southwest 10th Avenue
Room 165-W
Topeka, KS 66612
P: (785) 296-7460
E: fred.patton@house.ks.gov

Pauls, Janice L. (D, 102)
300 Southwest 10th Avenue
Room 451-S
Topeka, KS 66612
P: (785) 296-7657
E: jan.pauls@house.ks.gov

Peck Jr., Virgil (R, 12)
300 Southwest 10th Avenue
Room 274-W
Topeka, KS 66612
P: (785) 296-7641
E: virgil.peck@house.ks.gov

Phillips, Tom (R, 67)
300 Southwest 10th Avenue
Room 512-N
Topeka, KS 66612
P: (785) 296-6014
E: tom.phillips@house.ks.gov

Powell, Randy (R, 30)*
300 Southwest 10th Avenue
Room 452-S
Topeka, KS 66612
P: (785) 296-5593
E: randy.powell@house.ks.gov

Proehl, Richard J. (R, 7)
300 Southwest 10th Avenue
Room 581-W
Topeka, KS 66612
P: (785) 296-7639
E: richard.proehl@house.ks.gov

Read, Marty (R, 4)
300 Southwest 10th Avenue
Room 559-W
Topeka, KS 66612
P: (785) 296-7310
E: marty.read@house.ks.gov

Rhoades, Marc (R, 72)
300 Southwest 10th Avenue
Room 351-S
Topeka, KS 66612
P: (785) 296-7682
E: marc.rhoades@house.ks.gov

Rooker, Melissa (R, 25)
300 Southwest 10th Avenue
Room 168-W
Topeka, KS 66612
P: (785) 296-7686
E: melissa.rooker@house.ks.gov

Rubin, John (R, 18)
300 Southwest 10th Avenue
Room 151-S
Topeka, KS 66612
P: (785) 296-7690
E: john.rubin@house.ks.gov

Kansas

Ruiz, Louis E. (D, 31)
300 Southwest 10th Avenue
Room 174-W
Topeka, KS 66612
P: (785) 296-7122
E: louis.ruiz@house.ks.gov

Ryckman Jr., Ron (R, 78)
300 Southwest 10th Avenue
Room 512-N
Topeka, KS 66612
P: (785) 296-5481
E: ron.ryckman@house.ks.gov

Ryckman Sr., Ronald (R, 115)
300 Southwest 10th Avenue
Room 352-S
Topeka, KS 66612
P: (785) 296-7658
E: ronald.ryckman@house.ks.gov

Sawyer, Tom (D, 95)
300 Southwest 10th Avenue
Room 174-W
Topeka, KS 66612
P: (785) 296-7691
E: tom.sawyer@house.ks.gov

Scapa, Joseph (R, 88)
300 Southwest 10th Avenue
Room 166-W
Topeka, KS 66612
P: (785) 296-7643
E: joseph.scapa@house.ks.gov

Schroeder, Don (R, 74)
300 Southwest 10th Avenue
Room 512-N
Topeka, KS 66612
P: (785) 296-7500
E: don.schroeder@house.ks.gov

Schwab, Scott (R, 49)
300 Southwest 10th Avenue
Room 151-S
Topeka, KS 66612
P: (785) 296-7501
E: scott.schwab@house.ks.gov

Schwartz, Sharon (R, 106)
300 Southwest 10th Avenue
Room 149-S
Topeka, KS 66612
P: (785) 296-7637
E: sharon.schwartz@house.ks.gov

Seiwert, Joe (R, 101)
300 Southwest 10th Avenue
Room 521-E
Topeka, KS 66612
P: (785) 296-7647
E: joe.seiwert@house.ks.gov

Sloan, Tom (R, 45)
300 Southwest 10th Avenue
Room 149-S
Topeka, KS 66612
P: (785) 296-7654
E: tom.sloan@house.ks.gov

Smith, Charles (R, 3)*
300 Southwest 10th Avenue
Room 559-W
Topeka, KS 66612
P: (785) 296-7522
E: chuck.smith@house.ks.gov

Suellentrop, Gene (R, 91)
300 Southwest 10th Avenue
Room 186-N
Topeka, KS 66612
P: (785) 296-7681
E: gene.suellentrop@house.ks.gov

Sutton, William (R, 43)
300 Southwest 10th Avenue
Room 168-W
Topeka, KS 66612
P: (785) 296-7676
E: bill.sutton@house.ks.gov

Swanson, Susie (R, 64)*
300 Southwest 10th Avenue
Room 519-N
Topeka, KS 66612
P: (785) 296-7642
E: susie.swanson@house.ks.gov

Thimesch, Jack (R, 114)
300 Southwest 10th Avenue
Room 512-N
Topeka, KS 66612
P: (785) 296-7105
E: jack.thimesch@house.ks.gov

Thompson, Kent (R, 9)
300 Southwest 10th Avenue
Room 268-W
Topeka, KS 66612
P: (785) 296-7673
E: kent.thompson@house.ks.gov

Tietze, Annie (D, 53)
300 Southwest 10th Avenue
Room 561-W
Topeka, KS 66612
P: (785) 296-7668
E: annie.tietze@house.ks.gov

Todd, James (R, 29)
300 Southwest 10th Avenue
Room 268-W
Topeka, KS 66612
P: (785) 296-7695
E: james.todd@house.ks.gov

Trimmer, Ed (D, 79)
300 Southwest 10th Avenue
Room 174-W
Topeka, KS 66612
P: (785) 296-7122
E: ed.trimmer@house.ks.gov

Vickrey, Jene (R, 6)
300 Southwest 10th Avenue
Room 372-W
Topeka, KS 66612
P: (785) 296-7662
E: jene.vickrey@house.ks.gov

Victors, Ponka-We (D, 103)
300 Southwest 10th Avenue
Room 54-S
Topeka, KS 66612
P: (785) 296-7651
E: ponka-we.victors@house.ks.gov

Ward, Jim (D, 86)
300 Southwest 10th Avenue
Room 43-S
Topeka, KS 66612
P: (785) 296-7698
E: jim.ward@house.ks.gov

Waymaster, Troy (R, 109)
300 Southwest 10th Avenue
Room 167-W
Topeka, KS 66612
P: (785) 296-7672
E: troy.waymaster@house.ks.gov

Whipple, Brandon (D, 96)
300 Southwest 10th Avenue
Room 173-W
Topeka, KS 66612
P: (785) 296-7366
E: brandon.whipple@house.ks.gov

Whitmer, John (R, 93)*
300 Southwest 10th Avenue
Room 167-W
Topeka, KS 66612
P: (785) 296-7567
E: john.whitmer@house.ks.gov

Williams, Kristey (R, 77)*
300 Southwest 10th Avenue
Room 519-N
Topeka, KS 66612
P: (785) 296-3971
E: kristey.willliams@house.ks.gov

Wilson, John (D, 10)
300 Southwest 10th Avenue
Room 54-S
Topeka, KS 66612
P: (785) 296-7652
E: john.wilson@house.ks.gov

Winn, Valdenia C. (D, 34)
300 Southwest 10th Avenue
Room 451-S
Topeka, KS 66612
P: (785) 296-7657
E: valdenia.winn@house.ks.gov

Wolfe Moore, Kathy (D, 36)
300 Southwest 10th Avenue
Room 47-S
Topeka, KS 66612
P: (785) 296-7688
E: kathy.wolfemoore@house.ks.gov

Congress

Senate
Moran, Jerry (R)
Roberts, Pat (R)

House
Huelskamp, Tim (R, 1)
Jenkins, Lynn (R, 2)
Pompeo, Mike (R, 4)
Yoder, Kevin W. (R, 3)

Kentucky

Executive

Governor

Hon. Steve L. Beshear (D)
Governor
700 Capital Avenue, Suite 100
Frankfort, KY 40601
P: (502) 564-2611
F: (502) 564-0437

Lieutenant Governor

Hon. Crit Luallen (D)
Lieutenant Governor
700 Capitol Avenue, Suite 142
Frankfort, KY 40601
P: (502) 564-2611
F: (502) 564-2849
E: Crit.Luallen@auditor.ky.gov

Commissioner of Agriculture

Hon. James Comer (R)
Commissioner
111 Corporate Drive
Frankfort, KY 40601
P: (502) 573-0450
F: (502) 573-0046
E: james.comer@ky.gov

Attorney General

Hon. Jack Conway (D)
Attorney General
700 Capitol Avenue
Capitol Building, Suite 118
Frankfort, KY 40601
P: (502) 696-5300
F: (502) 564-2894
E: attorney.general@ag.ky.gov

Auditor

Hon. Adam Edelen (D)
Auditor of Public Accounts
209 St. Clair Street
Frankfort, KY 40601
P: (502) 564-5841
F: (502) 564-2912
E: adam.edelen@auditor.ky.gov

Secretary of State

Hon. Alison Lundergan Grimes (D)
Secretary of State
700 Capital Avenue, Suite 152
Frankfort, KY 40601
P: (502) 564-3490
F: (502) 564-5687
E: sos.secretary@ky.gov

Treasurer

Hon. Todd Hollenbach (D)
State Treasurer
1050 U.S. Highway 127 South
Suite 100
Frankfort, KY 40601
P: (502) 564-4722
F: (502) 564-6545
E: todd.hollenbach@ky.gov

Judiciary

Supreme Court (NE)

Ms. Susan Stokley Clary
Clerk of the Supreme Court
State Capitol
700 Capitol Avenue, Room 235
Frankfort, KY 40601
P: (502) 564-5444
F: (502) 564-2665

Hon. John D. Minton Jr.
Chief Justice
Hon. Lisabeth Hughes Abramson
Hon. William Cunningham
Hon. Michelle M. Keller
Hon. Mary C. Noble
Hon. Daniel J. Venters

Legislative Senate

Senate President

Sen. Robert Stivers (R)
Senate President
Capitol Annex, Room 236
702 Capitol Avenue
Frankfort, KY 40601
P: (502) 564-3120
E: robert.stivers@lrc.ky.gov

President Pro Tempore of the Senate

Sen. David Givens (R)
President Pro Tempore
Capitol Annex, Room 236
702 Capitol Avenue
Frankfort, KY 40601
P: (502) 564-3120
E: david.givens@lrc.ky.gov

Senate Majority Leader

Sen. Damon Thayer (R)
Majority Floor Leader
Capitol Annex, Room 242
702 Capitol Avenue
Frankfort, KY 40601
P: (502) 564-2450
E: Damon.Thayer@lrc.ky.gov

Senate Minority Leader

Sen. Ray S. Jones II (D)
Minority Floor Leader
Capitol Annex, Room 254
702 Capitol Avenue
Frankfort, KY 40601
P: (502) 564-2470
E: Ray.Jones@lrc.ky.gov

Secretary of the Senate

Ms. Donna Holiday
Chief Clerk of the Senate
700 Capitol Avenue
Frankfort, KY 40601
P: (502) 564-5320

Members of the Senate

Adams, Julie Raque (R, 36)
Capitol Annex, Room 209
702 Capitol Avenue
Frankfort, KY 40601
P: (502) 564-8100 Ext. 682
E: JulieRaque.Adams@lrc.ky.gov

Alvarado, Ralph (R, 28)*
Capitol Annex, Room 229
702 Capitol Avenue
Frankfort, KY 40601
P: (502) 564-8100 Ext. 681
E: Ralph.Alvarado@lrc.ky.gov

Angel, Denise Harper (D, 35)
Capitol Annex, Room 255
702 Capitol Avenue
Frankfort, KY 40601
P: (502) 564-8100 Ext. 633
E: denise.harperangel@lrc.ky.gov

Bowen, Joe R. (R, 8)
Capitol Annex, Room 228
702 Capitol Avenue
Frankfort, KY 40601
P: (502) 564-8100 Ext. 662
E: Joe.Bowen@lrc.ky.gov

Buford, Tom (R, 22)
Capitol Annex, Room 252
702 Capitol Avenue
Frankfort, KY 40601
P: (502) 564-8100 Ext. 610
F: (502) 564-2466
E: Tom.Buford@lrc.ky.gov

Carpenter, Jared (R, 34)
Capitol Annex, Room 203
702 Capitol Avenue
Frankfort, KY 40601
P: (502) 564-8100 Ext. 730
E: Jared.Carpenter@lrc.ky.gov

Carroll, Danny (R, 2)*
Capitol Annex, Room 229
702 Capitol Avenue
Frankfort, KY 40601
P: (502) 564-8100 Ext. 712

Carroll, Julian (D, 7)
Capitol Annex, Room 254
702 Capitol Avenue
Frankfort, KY 40601
P: (502) 564-2470
E: julian.carroll@lrc.ky.gov

Clark, Perry B. (D, 37)
Capitol Annex, Room 255
702 Capitol Avenue
Frankfort, KY 40601
P: (502) 564-8100 Ext. 715
E: Perry.Clark@lrc.ky.gov

Embry Jr., C.B. (R, 6)
Capitol Annex, Room 252
702 Capitol Avenue
Frankfort, KY 40601
P: (502) 564-8100 Ext. 710
E: CB.Embry@lrc.ky.gov

Gibson, Carroll (R, 5)
Capitol Annex, Room 228
702 Capitol Avenue
Frankfort, KY 40601
P: (502) 564-8100 Ext. 644
E: Carroll.Gibson@lrc.ky.gov

Girdler, Chris (R, 15)
Capitol Annex, Room 209
702 Capitol Avenue
Frankfort, KY 40601
P: (502) 564-8100 Ext. 656
E: chris.girdler@lrc.ky.gov

Givens, David (R, 9)
Capitol Annex, Room 236
702 Capitol Avenue
Frankfort, KY 40601
P: (502) 564-3120
E: david.givens@lrc.ky.gov

Kentucky

Harris, Ernie (R, 26)
Capitol Annex, Room 204
702 Capitol Avenue
Frankfort, KY 40601
P: (502) 564-8100 Ext. 605
E: Ernie.Harris@lrc.ky.gov

Higdon, Jimmy (R, 14)
Capitol Annex, Room 242
702 Capitol Avenue
Frankfort, KY 40601
P: (502) 564-2450
E: Jimmy.Higdon@lrc.ky.gov

Hornback, Paul (R, 20)
Capitol Annex, Room 203
702 Capitol Avenue
Frankfort, KY 40601
P: (502) 564-8100 Ext. 648
E: Paul.Hornback@lrc.ky.gov

Humphries, Stan (R, 1)
Capitol Annex, Room 209
702 Capitol Avenue
Frankfort, KY 40601
P: (502) 564-8100 Ext. 870
E: stan.humphries
@lrc.ky.gov

Jones II, Ray S. (D, 31)
Capitol Annex, Room 254
702 Capitol Avenue
Frankfort, KY 40601
P: (502) 564-2470
E: Ray.Jones@lrc.ky.gov

Kerr, Alice Forgy (R, 12)
Capitol Annex, Room 203
702 Capitol Avenue
Frankfort, KY 40601
P: (502) 564-8100 Ext. 625
E: alice.kerr@lrc.ky.gov

McDaniel, Christian (R, 23)
Capitol Annex, Room 204
702 Capitol Avenue
Frankfort, KY 40601
P: (502) 564-8100 Ext. 615
E: christian.mcdaniel
@lrc.ky.gov

McGarvey, Morgan (D, 19)
Capitol Annex, Room 255
702 Capitol Avenue
Frankfort, KY 40601
P: (502) 564-8100 Ext. 621
E: morgan.mcgarvey
@lrc.ky.gov

Neal, Gerald A. (D, 33)
Capitol Annex, Room 254
702 Capitol Avenue
Frankfort, KY 40601
P: (502) 564-2470
E: Gerald.Neal@lrc.ky.gov

Parrett, Dennis (D, 10)
Capitol Annex, Room 255
702 Capitol Avenue
Frankfort, KY 40601
P: (502) 564-8100 Ext. 645
E: Dennis.Parrett
@lrc.ky.gov

Ridley, Dorsey (D, 4)
Capitol Annex, Room 255
702 Capitol Avenue
Frankfort, KY 40601
P: (502) 564-8100 Ext. 655
E: Dorsey.Ridley@lrc.ky.gov

Robinson, Albert (R, 21)
Capitol Annex, Room 228
702 Capitol Avenue
Frankfort, KY 40601
P: (502) 564-8100 Ext. 604
E: Albert.Robinson
@lrc.ky.gov

Schickel, John (R, 11)
Capitol Annex, Room 209
702 Capitol Avenue
Frankfort, KY 40601
P: (502) 564-8100 Ext. 617
E: John.Schickel@lrc.ky.gov

Schroder, Wil (R, 24)*
Capitol Annex, Room 229
702 Capitol Avenue
Frankfort, KY 40601
P: (502) 564-8100 Ext. 624
E: Wil.Schroder@lrc.ky.gov

Seum, Dan (R, 38)
Capitol Annex, Room 242
702 Capitol Avenue
Frankfort, KY 40601
P: (502) 564-2450
E: dan.seum@lrc.ky.gov

Smith, Brandon (R, 30)
Capitol Annex, Room 252
702 Capitol Avenue
Frankfort, KY 40601
P: (502) 564-8100 Ext. 646
E: Brandon.Smith@lrc.ky.gov

Stivers, Robert (R, 25)
Capitol Annex, Room 236
702 Capitol Avenue
Frankfort, KY 40601
P: (502) 564-3120
E: robert.stivers
@lrc.ky.gov

Thayer, Damon (R, 17)
Capitol Annex, Room 242
702 Capitol Avenue
Frankfort, KY 40601
P: (502) 564-2450
E: Damon.Thayer@lrc.ky.gov

Thomas, Reginald (D, 13)
Capitol Annex, Room 255
702 Capitol Avenue
Frankfort, KY 40601
P: (502) 564-8100 Ext. 608
F: (502) 564-0777
E: reginald.thomas
@lrc.ky.gov

Turner, Johnny Ray (D, 29)
Capitol Annex, Room 254
702 Capitol Avenue
Frankfort, KY 40601
P: (502) 564-2470
E: JohnnyRay.Turner
@lrc.ky.gov

Webb, Robin L. (D, 18)
Capitol Annex, Room 255
702 Capitol Avenue
Frankfort, KY 40601
P: (502) 564-8100 Ext. 676
E: Robin.Webb@lrc.ky.gov

Westerfield, Whitney (R, 3)
Capitol Annex, Room 209
702 Capitol Avenue
Frankfort, KY 40601
P: (502) 564-8100 Ext. 622
E: whitney.westerfield
@lrc.ky.gov

Wilson, Mike (R, 32)
Capitol Annex, Room 204
702 Capitol Avenue
Frankfort, KY 40601
P: (502) 564-8100 Ext. 717
E: Mike.Wilson@lrc.ky.gov

Wise, Max (R, 16)*
Capitol Annex, Room 229
702 Capitol Avenue
Frankfort, KY 40601
P: (502) 564-8100 Ext. 673
E: Max.Wise@lrc.ky.gov

House

Speaker of the House

Rep. Gregory D. Stumbo (D)
Speaker
Capitol Annex, Room 303
702 Capitol Avenue
Frankfort, KY 40601
P: (502) 564-2363
E: Greg.Stumbo@lrc.ky.gov

Speaker Pro Tempore of the House

Rep. Jody Richards (D)
Speaker Pro Tempore
Capitol Annex, Room 304
702 Capitol Avenue
Frankfort, KY 40601
P: (502) 564-7520
E: Jody.Richards@lrc.ky.gov

House Majority Leader

Rep. Rocky Adkins (D)
Majority Floor Leader
Capitol Annex, Room 309
702 Capitol Avenue
Frankfort, KY 40601
P: (502) 564-5565
E: Rocky.Adkins@lrc.ky.gov

House Minority Leader

Rep. Jeffrey Hoover (R)
Minority Floor Leader
Capitol Annex, Room 472
702 Capitol Avenue
Frankfort, KY 40601
P: (502) 564-0521
E: Jeff.Hoover@lrc.ky.gov

Clerk of the House

Ms. Jean Burgin
Chief Clerk of the House
State Capitol, Room 309
700 Capital Avenue
Frankfort, KY 40601
P: (502) 564-3366
F: (502) 564-7178

Members of the House

Adkins, Rocky (D, 99)
Capitol Annex, Room 309
702 Capitol Avenue
Frankfort, KY 40601
P: (502) 564-5565
E: Rocky.Adkins@lrc.ky.gov

Bechler, Lynn (R, 4)
Capitol Annex, Room 424C
702 Capitol Avenue
Frankfort, KY 40601
P: (502) 564-8100 Ext. 665
E: lynn.bechler@lrc.ky.gov

Belcher, Linda Howlett (D, 49)
Capitol Annex, Room 352A
702 Capitol Avenue
Frankfort, KY 40601
P: (502) 564-8100 Ext. 651
E: Linda.Belcher@lrc.ky.gov

Bell, Johnny (D, 23)
Capitol Annex, Room 315
702 Capitol Avenue
Frankfort, KY 40601
P: (502) 564-7756
E: Johnny.Bell@lrc.ky.gov

Benvenuti III, Robert (R, 88)
Capitol Annex, Room 429I
702 Capitol Avenue
Frankfort, KY 40601
P: (502) 564-8100 Ext. 628
E: robert.benvenuti@lrc.ky.gov

Bratcher, Kevin D. (R, 29)
Capitol Annex, Room 429E
702 Capitol Avenue
Frankfort, KY 40601
P: (502) 564-8100 Ext. 680
E: Kevin.Bratcher@lrc.ky.gov

Brown Jr., George A. (D, 77)*
Capitol Annex, Room 332D
702 Capitol Avenue
Frankfort, KY 40601
P: (502) 564-8100 Ext. 620
E: George.Brown@lrc.ky.gov

Bunch, Regina (R, 82)
Capitol Annex, Room 424A
702 Capitol Avenue
Frankfort, KY 40601
P: (502) 564-8100 Ext. 683
E: Regina.Bunch@lrc.ky.gov

Burch, Tom (D, 30)
Capitol Annex, Room 332E
702 Capitol Avenue
Frankfort, KY 40601
P: (502) 564-8100 Ext. 601
E: Tom.Burch@lrc.ky.gov

Butler, Denny (D, 38)
Capitol Annex, Room 357C
702 Capitol Avenue
Frankfort, KY 40601
P: (502) 564-8100 Ext. 670
E: denver.butler@lrc.ky.gov

Carney, John (R, 51)
Capitol Annex, Room 401
702 Capitol Avenue
Frankfort, KY 40601
P: (502) 564-8100 Ext. 660
E: John.Carney@lrc.ky.gov

Clark, Larry (D, 46)
Capitol Annex, Room 316B
702 Capitol Avenue
Frankfort, KY 40601
P: (502) 564-8100 Ext. 699
E: Larry.Clark@lrc.ky.gov

Collins, Hubert (D, 97)
Capitol Annex, Room 329H
702 Capitol Avenue
Frankfort, KY 40601
P: (502) 564-8100 Ext. 654
E: Hubert.Collins@lrc.ky.gov

Combs, Leslie (D, 94)
Capitol Annex, Room 373C
702 Capitol Avenue
Frankfort, KY 40601
P: (502) 564-8100 Ext. 669
E: Leslie.Combs@lrc.ky.gov

Couch, Tim (R, 90)
Capitol Annex, Room 429F
702 Capitol Avenue
Frankfort, KY 40601
P: (502) 564-8100 Ext. 632
E: Tim.Couch@lrc.ky.gov

Coursey, Will (D, 6)
Capitol Annex, Room 351A
702 Capitol Avenue
Frankfort, KY 40601
P: (502) 564-8100 Ext. 659
E: Will.Coursey@lrc.ky.gov

Crimm, Ron (R, 33)
Capitol Annex, Room 416D
702 Capitol Avenue
Frankfort, KY 40601
P: (502) 564-8100 Ext. 706
E: Ron.Crimm@lrc.ky.gov

DeCesare, Jim (R, 21)
Capitol Annex, Room 472
702 Capitol Avenue
Frankfort, KY 40601
P: (502) 564-5855
E: dj951@twc.com

Denham, Mike (D, 70)
Capitol Annex, Room 329E
702 Capitol Avenue
Frankfort, KY 40601
P: (502) 564-8100 Ext. 696
E: Mike.Denham@lrc.ky.gov

DeWeese, Bob M. (R, 48)
Capitol Annex, Room 405E
702 Capitol Avenue
Frankfort, KY 40601
P: (502) 564-8100 Ext. 698
E: Bob.DeWeese@lrc.ky.gov

Donohue, Jeffrey (D, 37)
Capitol Annex, Room 324C
702 Capitol Avenue
Frankfort, KY 40601
P: (502) 564-8100 Ext. 629
E: jeffrey.donohue@lrc.ky.gov

Dossett, Myron (R, 9)
Capitol Annex, Room 424E
702 Capitol Avenue
Frankfort, KY 40601
P: (502) 564-8100 Ext. 657
E: Myron.Dossett@lrc.ky.gov

DuPlessis, Jim (R, 25)*
Capitol Annex, Room 424D
702 Capitol Avenue
Frankfort, KY 40601
P: (502) 564-8100 Ext. 650
E: Jim.DuPlessis@lrc.ky.gov

Fischer, Joseph M. (R, 68)
Capitol Annex, Room 429D
702 Capitol Avenue
Frankfort, KY 40601
P: (502) 564-8100 Ext. 742
E: Joe.Fischer@lrc.ky.gov

Flood, Kelly (D, 75)
Capitol Annex, Room 373A
702 Capitol Avenue
Frankfort, KY 40601
P: (502) 564-8100 Ext. 675
E: Kelly.Flood@lrc.ky.gov

Floyd, David W. (R, 50)
Capitol Annex, Room 432E
702 Capitol Avenue
Frankfort, KY 40601
P: (502) 564-8100 Ext. 664
E: David.Floyd@lrc.ky.gov

Glenn, Jim (D, 13)
Capitol Annex, Room 358B
702 Capitol Avenue
Frankfort, KY 40601
P: (502) 564-8100 Ext. 705
E: Jim.Glenn@lrc.ky.gov

Gooch, Jim (D, 12)
Capitol Annex, Room 370D
702 Capitol Avenue
Frankfort, KY 40601
P: (502) 564-8100 Ext. 687
E: Jim.Gooch@lrc.ky.gov

Graham, Derrick W. (D, 57)
Capitol Annex, Room 367A
702 Capitol Avenue
Frankfort, KY 40601
P: (502) 564-8100 Ext. 639
E: Derrick.Graham@lrc.ky.gov

Greer, Jeff (D, 27)
Capitol Annex, Room 367C
702 Capitol Avenue
Frankfort, KY 40601
P: (502) 564-8100 Ext. 603
E: Jeff.Greer@lrc.ky.gov

Hale, David (R, 74)*
Capitol Annex, Room 413A
702 Capitol Avenue
Frankfort, KY 40601
P: (502) 564-8100 Ext. 642
E: David.Hale@lrc.ky.gov

Harmon, Mike (R, 54)
Capitol Annex, Room 429C
702 Capitol Avenue
Frankfort, KY 40601
P: (502) 564-8100 Ext. 677
E: Mike.Harmon@lrc.ky.gov

Harris, Chris (D, 93)*
Capitol Annex, Room 329I
702 Capitol Avenue
Frankfort, KY 40601
P: (502) 564-8100 Ext. 635
E: Chris.Harris@lrc.ky.gov

Heath, Richard (R, 2)
Capitol Annex, Room 413C
702 Capitol Avenue
Frankfort, KY 40601
P: (502) 564-8100 Ext. 638
E: richard.heath@lrc.ky.gov

Hoover, Jeffrey (R, 83)
Capitol Annex, Room 472
702 Capitol Avenue
Frankfort, KY 40601
P: (502) 564-0521
E: Jeff.Hoover@lrc.ky.gov

Horlander, Dennis (D, 40)
Capitol Annex, Room 351D
702 Capitol Avenue
Frankfort, KY 40601
P: (502) 564-8100 Ext. 636
E: Dennis.Horlander@lrc.ky.gov

Howard, Cluster (D, 91)*
Capitol Annex, Room 357C
702 Capitol Avenue
Frankfort, KY 40601
P: (502) 564-8100 Ext. 641
E: cluster.howard@lrc.ky.gov

Imes, Kenny (R, 5)
Capitol Annex, Room 405D
702 Capitol Avenue
Frankfort, KY 40601
P: (502) 564-8100 Ext. 611
E: kenny.imes@lrc.ky.gov

Kentucky

Jenkins, Joni L. (D, 44)
Capitol Annex, Room 329D
702 Capitol Avenue
Frankfort, KY 40601
P: (502) 564-8100 Ext. 692
E: Joni.Jenkins@lrc.ky.gov

Kay II, James (D, 56)
Capitol Annex, Room 451A
702 Capitol Avenue
Frankfort, KY 40601
P: (502) 564-8100 Ext. 736
E: james.kay@lrc.ky.gov

Keene, Dennis (D, 67)
Capitol Annex, Room 358A
702 Capitol Avenue
Frankfort, KY 40601
P: (502) 564-8100 Ext. 626
E: Dennis.Keene@lrc.ky.gov

Kerr, Thomas (R, 64)
Capitol Annex, Room 457E
702 Capitol Avenue
Frankfort, KY 40601
P: (502) 564-8100 Ext. 694
E: thomas.kerr@lrc.ky.gov

King, Kim (R, 55)
Capitol Annex, Room 429G
702 Capitol Avenue
Frankfort, KY 40601
P: (502) 564-8100 Ext. 763
E: Kim.King@lrc.ky.gov

King, Martha Jane (D, 16)
Capitol Annex, Room 351B
702 Capitol Avenue
Frankfort, KY 40601
P: (502) 564-8100 Ext. 618
E: MarthaJane.King
@lrc.ky.gov

Koenig, Adam (R, 69)
Capitol Annex, Room 432D
702 Capitol Avenue
Frankfort, KY 40601
P: (502) 564-8100 Ext. 689
E: Adam.Koenig@lrc.ky.gov

Lee, Stan (R, 45)
Capitol Annex, Room 472
702 Capitol Avenue
Frankfort, KY 40601
P: (502) 564-4334
E: Stan.Lee@lrc.ky.gov

Linder, Brian (R, 61)
Capitol Annex, Room 424G
702 Capitol Avenue
Frankfort, KY 40601
P: (502) 564-8100 Ext. 627
E: brian.linder@lrc.ky.gov

Marzian, Mary Lou (D, 34)
Capitol Annex, Room 357E
702 Capitol Avenue
Frankfort, KY 40601
P: (502) 564-8100 Ext. 643
E: MaryLou.Marzian
@lrc.ky.gov

Mayfield, Donna (R, 73)
Capitol Annex, Room 416C
702 Capitol Avenue
Frankfort, KY 40601
P: (502) 564-8100 Ext. 630
E: Donna.Mayfield
@lrc.ky.gov

McKee, Thomas M. (D, 78)
Capitol Annex, Room 324E
702 Capitol Avenue
Frankfort, KY 40601
P: (502) 564-8100 Ext. 667
E: Tom.McKee@lrc.ky.gov

Meade, David (R, 80)
Capitol Annex, Room 405A
702 Capitol Avenue
Frankfort, KY 40601
P: (502) 564-8100 Ext. 661
E: david.meade@lrc.ky.gov

Meeks, Reginald K. (D, 42)
Capitol Annex, Room 329C
702 Capitol Avenue
Frankfort, KY 40601
P: (502) 564-8100 Ext. 653
E: Reginald.Meeks
@lrc.ky.gov

Meredith, Michael (R, 19)
Capitol Annex, Room 413G
702 Capitol Avenue
Frankfort, KY 40601
P: (502) 564-8100 Ext. 719
E: Michael.Meredit
@lrc.ky.gov

Meyer, Russ (D, 39)*
Capitol Annex, Room 457B
702 Capitol Avenue
Frankfort, KY 40601
P: (502) 564-8100 Ext. 623
E: Russ.Meyer@lrc.ky.gov

Miles, Suzanne (R, 7)
Capitol Annex, Room 451E
702 Capitol Avenue
Frankfort, KY 40601
P: (502) 564-8100 Ext. 709
E: suzanne.miles@lrc.ky.gov

Miller, Charles (D, 28)
Capitol Annex, Room 457D
702 Capitol Avenue
Frankfort, KY 40601
P: (502) 564-8100 Ext. 631
E: Charlie.Miller
@lrc.ky.gov

Miller, Jerry T. (R, 36)*
Capitol Annex, Room 429J
702 Capitol Avenue
Frankfort, KY 40601
P: (502) 564-8100 Ext. 718
E: Jerry.Miller@lrc.ky.gov

Mills, Terry (D, 24)
Capitol Annex, Room 329G
702 Capitol Avenue
Frankfort, KY 40601
P: (502) 564-8100 Ext. 684
E: Terry.Mills@lrc.ky.gov

Moffett, Phil (R, 32)*
Capitol Annex, Room 413H
702 Capitol Avenue
Frankfort, KY 40601
P: (502) 564-8100 Ext. 708
E: Phil.Moffett@lrc.ky.gov

Montell, Brad (R, 58)
Capitol Annex, Room 432C
702 Capitol Avenue
Frankfort, KY 40601
P: (502) 564-8100 Ext. 609
E: Brad.Montell@lrc.ky.gov

Moore, Tim (R, 26)
Capitol Annex, Room 432A
702 Capitol Avenue
Frankfort, KY 40601
P: (502) 564-8100 Ext. 702
E: Tim.Moore@lrc.ky.gov

Nelson, Rick (D, 87)
Capitol Annex, Room 358
702 Capitol Avenue
Frankfort, KY 40601
P: (502) 564-8100 Ext. 612
E: Rick.Nelson@lrc.ky.gov

Osborne, David (R, 59)
Capitol Annex, Room 416A
702 Capitol Avenue
Frankfort, KY 40601
P: (502) 564-8000 Ext. 679
E: David.Osborne@lrc.ky.gov

Overly, Sannie (D, 72)
Capitol Annex, Room 313
702 Capitol Avenue
Frankfort, KY 40601
P: (502) 564-2217
E: sannie.overly@lrc.ky.gov

Owens, Darryl T. (D, 43)
Capitol Annex, Room 316A
702 Capitol Avenue
Frankfort, KY 40601
P: (502) 564-8100 Ext. 685
E: Darryl.Owens@lrc.ky.gov

Palumbo, Ruth Ann (D, 76)
Capitol Annex, Room 370B
702 Capitol Avenue
Frankfort, KY 40601
P: (502) 564-8100 Ext. 600
E: RuthAnn.Palumbo
@lrc.ky.gov

Pullin, Tanya (D, 98)
Capitol Annex, Room 370A
702 Capitol Avenue
Frankfort, KY 40601
P: (502) 564-8100 Ext. 678
E: Tanya.Pullin@lrc.ky.gov

Quarles, Ryan (R, 62)
Capitol Annex, Room 405B
702 Capitol Avenue
Frankfort, KY 40601
P: (502) 564-8100 Ext. 671
E: Ryan.Quarles@lrc.ky.gov

Rader, Marie L. (R, 89)
Capitol Annex, Room 405C
702 Capitol Avenue
Frankfort, KY 40601
P: (502) 564-8100 Ext. 720
E: Marie.Rader@lrc.ky.gov

Rand, Rick (D, 47)
Capitol Annex, Room 366B
702 Capitol Avenue
Frankfort, KY 40601
P: (502) 564-8100 Ext. 619
F: (502) 564-1010
E: Rick.Rand@lrc.ky.gov

Richards, Jody (D, 20)
Capitol Annex, Room 304
702 Capitol Avenue
Frankfort, KY 40601
P: (502) 564-7520
E: Jody.Richards@lrc.ky.gov

Riggs, Steve (D, 31)
Capitol Annex, Room 370C
702 Capitol Avenue
Frankfort, KY 40601
P: (502) 564-8100 Ext. 674
F: (502) 564-6543
E: steve.riggs@lrc.ky.gov

Riner, Tom (D, 41)
Capitol Annex, Room 457C
702 Capitol Avenue
Frankfort, KY 40601
P: (502) 564-8100 Ext. 606
E: Tom.Riner@lrc.ky.gov

Rowland, Bart (R, 21)
Capitol Annex, Room 416B
702 Capitol Avenue
Frankfort, KY 40601
P: (502) 564-8100 Ext. 613
E: bart.rowland@lrc.ky.gov

Rudy, Steven J. (R, 1)
Capitol Annex, Room 413E
702 Capitol Avenue
Frankfort, KY 40601
P: (502) 564-8100 Ext. 637
E: Steven.Rudy@lrc.ky.gov

Santoro, Sal (R, 60)
Capitol Annex, Room 413D
702 Capitol Avenue
Frankfort, KY 40601
P: (502) 564-8100 Ext. 691
E: Sal.Santoro@lrc.ky.gov

Schamore, Dean (D, 10)*
Capitol Annex, Room 357A
702 Capitol Avenue
Frankfort, KY 40601
P: (502) 564-8100 Ext. 704
E: Dean.Schamore@lrc.ky.gov

Shell, Jonathan (R, 71)
Capitol Annex, Room 432B
702 Capitol Avenue
Frankfort, KY 40601
P: (502) 564-8100 Ext. 649
E: jonathan.shell
@lrc.ky.gov

Short, John (D, 92)
Capitol Annex, Room 352C
702 Capitol Avenue
Frankfort, KY 40601
P: (502) 564-8100 Ext. 668
E: John.Short@lrc.ky.gov

Simpson, Arnold (D, 65)
Capitol Annex, Room 357B
702 Capitol Avenue
Frankfort, KY 40601
P: (502) 564-8100 Ext. 695
E: Arnold.Simpson
@lrc.ky.gov

Sinnette, Kevin P. (D, 100)
Capitol Annex, Room 316C
702 Capitol Avenue
Frankfort, KY 40601
P: (502) 564-8100 Ext. 703
E: Kevin.Sinnette
@lrc.ky.gov

Smart, Rita (D, 81)
Capitol Annex, Room 367
702 Capitol Avenue
Frankfort, KY 40601
P: (502) 564-8100 Ext. 607
E: Rita.Smart@lrc.ky.gov

St. Onge, Diane (R, 63)
Capitol Annex, Room 405F
702 Capitol Avenue
Frankfort, KY 40601
P: (502) 564-8100 Ext. 701
E: Diane.StOnge@lrc.ky.gov

Steele, Fitz (D, 84)
Capitol Annex, Room 316D
702 Capitol Avenue
Frankfort, KY 40601
P: (502) 564-8100 Ext. 697
E: Fitz.Steele@lrc.ky.gov

Stewart, Jim (R, 86)
Capitol Annex, Room 429H
702 Capitol Avenue
Frankfort, KY 40601
P: (502) 564-8100 Ext. 690
E: Jim.Stewart@lrc.ky.gov

Stone, Wilson (D, 22)
Capitol Annex, Room 329F
702 Capitol Avenue
Frankfort, KY 40601
P: (502) 564-8100 Ext. 672
E: Wilson.Stone@lrc.ky.gov

Stumbo, Gregory D. (D, 95)
Capitol Annex, Room 303
702 Capitol Avenue
Frankfort, KY 40601
P: (502) 564-2363
E: Greg.Stumbo@lrc.ky.gov

Thompson, Tommy (D, 14)
Capitol Annex, Room 324D
702 Capitol Avenue
Frankfort, KY 40601
P: (502) 564-8100 Ext. 688
E: Tommy.Thompson
@lrc.ky.gov

Tilley, John (D, 8)
Capitol Annex, Room 373B
702 Capitol Avenue
Frankfort, KY 40601
P: (502) 564-8100 Ext. 658
E: John.Tilley@lrc.ky.gov

Tipton, James A. (R, 53)*
Capitol Annex, Room 429A
702 Capitol Avenue
Frankfort, KY 40601
P: (502) 564-8100 Ext. 793
E: James.Tipton@lrc.ky.gov

Turner, Tommy (R, 85)
Capitol Annex, Room 413F
702 Capitol Avenue
Frankfort, KY 40601
P: (502) 564-8100 Ext. 716
E: Tommy.Turner@lrc.ky.gov

Upchurch, Ken (R, 52)
Capitol Annex, Room 451C
702 Capitol Avenue
Frankfort, KY 40601
P: (502) 564-8100 Ext. 784
E: Ken.Upchurch@lrc.ky.gov

Watkins, David (D, 11)
Capitol Annex, Room 351C
702 Capitol Avenue
Frankfort, KY 40601
P: (502) 564-8100 Ext. 700
E: David.Watkins@lrc.ky.gov

Watkins, Gerald (D, 3)
Capitol Annex, Room 332C
702 Capitol Avenue
Frankfort, KY 40601
P: (502) 564-8100 Ext. 634

Wayne, Jim (D, 35)
Capitol Annex, Room 451B
702 Capitol Avenue
Frankfort, KY 40601
P: (502) 564-8100 Ext. 616
E: Jim.Wayne@lrc.ky.gov

Webber, Russell (R, 26)
Capitol Annex, Room 429B
702 Capitol Avenue
Frankfort, KY 40601
P: (502) 564-8100 Ext. 663
E: russell.webber
@lrc.ky.gov

Westrom, Susan (D, 79)
Capitol Annex, Room 352B
702 Capitol Avenue
Frankfort, KY 40601
P: (502) 564-8100 Ext. 740
E: Susan.Westrom@lrc.ky.gov

Wuchner, Addia (R, 66)
Capitol Annex, Room 424F
702 Capitol Avenue
Frankfort, KY 40601
P: (502) 564-8100 Ext. 707
E: AddiaKathryn.Wuchner
@lrc.ky.gov

Yonts, Brent (D, 15)
Capitol Annex, Room 366A
702 Capitol Avenue
Frankfort, KY 40601
P: (502) 564-8100 Ext. 686
E: Brent.Yonts@lrc.ky.gov

York, Jill (R, 96)
Capitol Annex, Room 451D
702 Capitol Avenue
Frankfort, KY 40601
P: (502) 564-8100 Ext. 602
E: jill.york@lrc.ky.gov

Congress

Senate

McConnell, Mitch (R)
Paul, Rand (R)

House

Barr, Andy (R, 6)
Guthrie, Brett (R, 2)
Massie, Thomas (R, 4)
Rogers, Harold (R, 5)
Whitfield, Ed (R, 1)
Yarmuth, John (D, 3)

Louisiana

Executive

Governor
Hon. Bobby Jindal (R)
Governor
P.O. Box 94004
Baton Rouge, LA 70804
P: (225) 342-7015
F: (225) 342-7099

Lieutenant Governor
Hon. Jay Dardenne (R)
Lieutenant Governor
1051 North 3rd Street
Capitol Annex Building, P.O. Box 44243
Baton Rouge, LA 70804
P: (225) 342-7009
F: (225) 342-1949
E: ltgov@crt.la.gov

Commissioner of Agriculture & Forestry
Dr. Michael G. Strain (R)
Commissioner
P.O. Box 631
Baton Rouge, LA 70821
P: (225) 922-1234
F: (225) 923-4880
E: commissioner@ldaf.state.la.us

Attorney General
Hon. James D. Caldwell (R)
Attorney General
P.O. Box 94095
Baton Rouge, LA 70804
P: (225) 326-6079
F: (225) 326-6797
E: executive@ag.state.la.us

Auditor
Louisiana does not have the office of auditor.

Commissioner of Insurance
Hon. James J. Donelon (R)
Commissioner
1702 North 3rd Street
P.O. Box 94214
Baton Rouge, LA 70804
P: (225) 342-5900
F: (225) 342-8622

Secretary of State
Hon. Tom Schedler (R)
Secretary of State
P.O. Box 94125
Baton Rouge, LA 70804
P: (225) 922-2880
F: (225) 922-2003
E: admin@sos.la.gov

Treasurer
Hon. John Neely Kennedy (R)
State Treasurer
P.O. Box 44154
Baton Rouge, LA 70804
P: (225) 342-0010
F: (225) 342-0046
E: jkennedy@treasury.state.la.us

Judiciary

Supreme Court (NE)
Mr. John Tarlton Olivier
Clerk of Court
400 Royal Street, Suite 4200
New Orleans, LA 70130
P: (504) 310-2300

Hon. Bernette J. Johnson
Chief Justice
Hon. Marcus R. Clark
Hon. Scott J. Crichton
Hon. Greg Guidry
Hon. Jefferson D. Hughes III
Hon. Jeannette Theriot Knoll
Hon. John L. Weimer

Legislative

Senate

Senate President
Sen. John A. Alario Jr. (R)
Senate President
State Capitol
P.O. Box 94183
Baton Rouge, LA 70804
P: (225) 342-2040
F: (225) 342-0617
E: alarioj@legis.la.gov

President Pro Tempore of the Senate
Sen. Sharon Weston Broome (D)
President Pro Tempore
State Capitol
P.O. Box 94183
Baton Rouge, LA 70804
P: (225) 342-2040
F: (225) 342-0617
E: broomes@legis.la.gov

Secretary of the Senate
Mr. Glenn Koepp
Secretary of the Senate
Basement, State Capitol
900 North 3rd Street
Baton Rouge, LA 70804
P: (225) 342-5997
F: (225) 342-1140
E: koeppg@legis.la.gov

Members of the Senate
Adley, Robert (R, 36)
State Capitol
P.O. Box 94183
Baton Rouge, LA 70804
P: (225) 342-2040
F: (225) 342-0617
E: adleyr@legis.la.gov

Alario Jr., John A. (R, 8)
State Capitol
P.O. Box 94183
Baton Rouge, LA 70804
P: (225) 342-2040
F: (225) 342-0617
E: alarioj@legis.la.gov

Allain II, R.L. Bret (R, 21)
State Capitol
P.O. Box 94183
Baton Rouge, LA 70804
P: (225) 342-2040
F: (225) 342-0617
E: allainb@legis.la.gov

Amedee, Jody (R, 18)
State Capitol
P.O. Box 94183
Baton Rouge, LA 70804
P: (225) 342-2040
F: (225) 342-0617
E: amedeej@legis.la.gov

Appel, Conrad (R, 9)
State Capitol
P.O. Box 94183
Baton Rouge, LA 70804
P: (225) 342-2040
F: (225) 342-0617
E: appelc@legis.la.gov

Broome, Sharon Weston (D, 15)
State Capitol
P.O. Box 94183
Baton Rouge, LA 70804
P: (225) 342-2040
F: (225) 342-0617
E: broomes@legis.la.gov

Brown, Troy E. (D, 2)
State Capitol
P.O. Box 94183
Baton Rouge, LA 70804
P: (225) 342-2040
F: (225) 342-0617
E: brownte@legis.la.gov

Buffington, Sherri Smith (R, 38)
State Capitol
P.O. Box 94183
Baton Rouge, LA 70804
P: (225) 342-2040
F: (225) 342-0617
E: smithbuffington@legis.la.gov

Chabert, Norby (R, 20)
State Capitol
P.O. Box 94183
Baton Rouge, LA 70804
P: (225) 342-2040
F: (225) 342-0617
E: chabertn@legis.la.gov

Claitor, Dan (R, 16)
State Capitol
P.O. Box 94183
Baton Rouge, LA 70804
P: (225) 342-2040
F: (225) 342-0617
E: claitord@legis.la.gov

Cortez, Patrick Page (R, 23)
State Capitol
P.O. Box 94183
Baton Rouge, LA 70804
P: (225) 342-2040
F: (225) 342-0617
E: cortezp@legis.la.gov

Crowe, A.G. (R, 1)
State Capitol
P.O. Box 94183
Baton Rouge, LA 70804
P: (225) 342-2040
F: (225) 342-0617
E: crowea@legis.la.gov

Donahue, Jack (R, 11)
State Capitol
P.O. Box 94183
Baton Rouge, LA 70804
P: (225) 342-2040
F: (225) 342-0617
E: donahuej@legis.la.gov

Dorsey-Colomb, Yvonne (D, 14)
State Capitol
P.O. Box 94183
Baton Rouge, LA 70804
P: (225) 342-2040
F: (225) 342-0617
E: dorseyy@legis.la.gov

Erdey, Dale (R, 13)
State Capitol
P.O. Box 94183
Baton Rouge, LA 70804
P: (225) 342-2040
F: (225) 342-0617
E: erdeyd@legis.la.gov

Gallot Jr., Richard (D, 29)
State Capitol
P.O. Box 94183
Baton Rouge, LA 70804
P: (225) 342-2040
F: (225) 342-0617
E: gallotr@legis.la.gov

Guillory, Elbert L. (R, 24)
State Capitol
P.O. Box 94183
Baton Rouge, LA 70804
P: (225) 342-2040
F: (225) 342-0617
E: guillorye@legis.la.gov

Heitmeier, David (D, 7)
State Capitol
P.O. Box 94183
Baton Rouge, LA 70804
P: (225) 342-2040
F: (225) 342-0617
E: HeitmeierD@legis.la.gov

Johns, Ronnie (R, 27)
State Capitol
P.O. Box 94183
Baton Rouge, LA 70804
P: (225) 342-2040
F: (225) 342-0617
E: johnsr@legis.la.gov

Kostelka, Robert W. (R, 35)
State Capitol
P.O. Box 94183
Baton Rouge, LA 70804
P: (225) 342-2040
F: (225) 342-0617
E: kostelka@legis.la.gov

LaFleur, Eric (D, 28)
State Capitol
P.O. Box 94183
Baton Rouge, LA 70804
P: (225) 342-2040
F: (225) 342-0617
E: lafleure@legis.la.gov

Long, Gerald (R, 31)
State Capitol
P.O. Box 94183
Baton Rouge, LA 70804
P: (225) 342-2040
F: (225) 342-0617
E: longg@legis.la.gov

Martiny, Daniel R. (R, 10)
State Capitol
P.O. Box 94183
Baton Rouge, LA 70804
P: (225) 342-2040
F: (225) 342-0617
E: martinyd@legis.la.gov

Mills Jr., Fred H. (R, 22)
State Capitol
P.O. Box 94183
Baton Rouge, LA 70804
P: (225) 342-2040
F: (225) 342-0617
E: millsf@legis.la.gov

Morrell, Jean-Paul J. (D, 3)
State Capitol
P.O. Box 94183
Baton Rouge, LA 70804
P: (225) 342-2040
F: (225) 342-0617
E: morrelljp@legis.la.gov

Morrish, Dan W. (R, 25)
State Capitol
P.O. Box 94183
Baton Rouge, LA 70804
P: (225) 342-2040
F: (225) 342-0617
E: morrishd@legis.la.gov

Murray, Edwin R. (D, 4)
State Capitol
P.O. Box 94183
Baton Rouge, LA 70804
P: (225) 342-2040
F: (225) 342-0617
E: murraye@legis.la.gov

Nevers, Ben (D, 12)
State Capitol
P.O. Box 94183
Baton Rouge, LA 70804
P: (225) 342-2040
F: (225) 342-0617
E: neversb@legis.la.gov

Peacock, Barrow (R, 37)
State Capitol
P.O. Box 94183
Baton Rouge, LA 70804
P: (225) 342-2040
F: (225) 342-0617
E: peacockb@legis.la.gov

Perry, Jonathan (R, 26)
State Capitol
P.O. Box 94183
Baton Rouge, LA 70804
P: (225) 342-2040
F: (225) 342-0617
E: perryj@legis.la.gov

Peterson, Karen Carter (D, 5)
State Capitol
P.O. Box 94183
Baton Rouge, LA 70804
P: (225) 342-2040
F: (225) 342-0617
E: petersonk@legis.la.gov

Riser, Neil (R, 32)
State Capitol
P.O. Box 94183
Baton Rouge, LA 70804
P: (225) 342-2040
F: (225) 342-0617
E: risern@legis.la.gov

Smith Jr., Gary L. (D, 19)
State Capitol
P.O. Box 94183
Baton Rouge, LA 70804
P: (225) 342-2040
F: (225) 342-0617
E: smithgl@legis.la.gov

Smith, John R. (R, 30)
State Capitol
P.O. Box 94183
Baton Rouge, LA 70804
P: (225) 342-2040
F: (225) 342-0617
E: smithj@legis.la.gov

Tarver Sr., Gregory W. (D, 39)
State Capitol
P.O. Box 94183
Baton Rouge, LA 70804
P: (225) 342-2040
F: (225) 342-0617
E: tarverg@legis.la.gov

Thompson, Francis C. (D, 34)
State Capitol
P.O. Box 94183
Baton Rouge, LA 70804
P: (225) 342-2040
F: (225) 342-0617
E: thompsof@legis.la.gov

Walsworth, Michael A. (R, 33)
State Capitol
P.O. Box 94183
Baton Rouge, LA 70804
P: (225) 342-2040
F: (225) 342-0617
E: walsworthm@legis.la.gov

Ward III, Rick (D, 17)
State Capitol
P.O. Box 94183
Baton Rouge, LA 70804
P: (225) 342-2040
F: (225) 342-0617
E: wardr@legis.la.gov

White Jr., Mack A. (R, 6)
State Capitol
P.O. Box 94183
Baton Rouge, LA 70804
P: (225) 342-2040
F: (225) 342-0617
E: whitem@legis.la.gov

House

Speaker of the House

Rep. Chuck Kleckley (R)
Speaker
State Capitol
P.O. Box 94062
Baton Rouge, LA 70804
P: (225) 342-7263
F: (225) 342-8336
E: larep036@legis.la.gov

Speaker Pro Tempore of the House

Rep. Walt Leger III (D)
Speaker Pro Tempore
State Capitol
P.O. Box 94062
Baton Rouge, LA 70804
P: (225) 342-6945
F: (225) 342-8336
E: legerw@legis.la.gov

Clerk of the House

Mr. Alfred W. Speer
Clerk of the House
P.O. Box 44281
Room G-106
Baton Rouge, LA 70804
P: (225) 342-7259
F: (225) 342-5045
E: speera@legis.state.la.us

Louisiana

Members of the House

Abramson, Neil (D, 98)
State Capitol
P.O. Box 94062
Baton Rouge, LA 70804
P: (225) 342-6945
F: (225) 342-8336
E: abramson@legis.la.gov

Adams, Bryan (R, 85)
State Capitol
P.O. Box 94062
Baton Rouge, LA 70804
P: (225) 342-6945
F: (225) 342-8336
E: adamsb@legis.la.gov

Anders, John F. (D, 21)
State Capitol
P.O. Box 94062
Baton Rouge, LA 70804
P: (225) 342-6945
F: (225) 342-8336
E: larep021@legis.la.gov

Armes III, James K. (D, 30)
State Capitol
P.O. Box 94062
Baton Rouge, LA 70804
P: (225) 342-6945
F: (225) 342-8336
E: armesj@legis.la.gov

Arnold, Jeffery J. (D, 102)
State Capitol
P.O. Box 94062
Baton Rouge, LA 70804
P: (225) 342-6945
F: (225) 342-8336
E: larep102@legis.la.gov

Badon, Austin J. (D, 100)
State Capitol
P.O. Box 94062
Baton Rouge, LA 70804
P: (225) 342-6945
F: (225) 342-8336
E: larep100@legis.la.gov

Barras, Taylor F. (R, 48)
State Capitol
P.O. Box 94062
Baton Rouge, LA 70804
P: (225) 342-6945
F: (225) 342-8336
E: barrast@legis.la.gov

Barrow, Regina Ashford (D, 29)
State Capitol
P.O. Box 94062
Baton Rouge, LA 70804
P: (225) 342-6945
F: (225) 342-8336
E: larep029@legis.la.gov

Berthelot, John A. (R, 88)
State Capitol
P.O. Box 94062
Baton Rouge, LA 70804
P: (225) 342-6945
F: (225) 342-8336
E: berthelotj@legis.la.gov

Billiot, Robert E. (D, 83)
State Capitol
P.O. Box 94062
Baton Rouge, LA 70804
P: (225) 342-6945
F: (225) 342-8336
E: billiotr@legis.la.gov

Bishop, Stuart J. (R, 43)
State Capitol
P.O. Box 94062
Baton Rouge, LA 70804
P: (225) 342-6945
F: (225) 342-8336
E: bishops@legis.la.gov

Bishop, Wesley T. (D, 99)
State Capitol
P.O. Box 94062
Baton Rouge, LA 70804
P: (225) 342-6945
F: (225) 342-8336
E: bishopw@legis.la.gov

Bouie Jr., Joseph (D, 97)*
State Capitol
P.O. Box 94062
Baton Rouge, LA 70804
P: (225) 342-6945
F: (225) 342-8336
E: bouiej@legis.la.gov

Broadwater, Christopher (R, 86)
State Capitol
P.O. Box 94062
Baton Rouge, LA 70804
P: (225) 342-6945
F: (225) 342-8336
E: broadwaterc@legis.la.gov

Brown, Terry R. (I, 22)
State Capitol
P.O. Box 94062
Baton Rouge, LA 70804
P: (225) 342-6945
F: (225) 342-8336
E: browntr@legis.la.gov

Burford, Richard T. (R, 7)
State Capitol
P.O. Box 94062
Baton Rouge, LA 70804
P: (225) 342-6945
F: (225) 342-8336
E: burfordr@legis.la.gov

Burns, Henry L. (R, 9)
State Capitol
P.O. Box 94062
Baton Rouge, LA 70804
P: (225) 342-6945
F: (225) 342-8336
E: burnsh@legis.la.gov

Burns, Timothy G. (R, 89)
State Capitol
P.O. Box 94062
Baton Rouge, LA 70804
P: (225) 342-6945
F: (225) 342-8336
E: larep089@legis.la.gov

Burrell, Roy (D, 2)
State Capitol
P.O. Box 94062
Baton Rouge, LA 70804
P: (225) 342-6945
F: (225) 342-8336
E: larep002@legis.la.gov

Carmody Jr., Thomas G. (R, 6)
State Capitol
P.O. Box 94062
Baton Rouge, LA 70804
P: (225) 342-6945
F: (225) 342-8336
E: carmodyt@legis.la.gov

Carter, Steve F. (R, 68)
State Capitol
P.O. Box 94062
Baton Rouge, LA 70804
P: (225) 342-6945
F: (225) 342-8336
E: carters@legis.la.gov

Chaney, Charles R. (R, 19)
State Capitol
P.O. Box 94062
Baton Rouge, LA 70804
P: (225) 342-6945
F: (225) 342-8336
E: chaneyb@legis.la.gov

Connick, Patrick (R, 84)
State Capitol
P.O. Box 94062
Baton Rouge, LA 70804
P: (225) 342-6945
F: (225) 342-8336
E: connickp@legis.la.gov

Cox, Kenny R. (D, 23)
State Capitol
P.O. Box 94062
Baton Rouge, LA 70804
P: (225) 342-6945
F: (225) 342-8336
E: coxk@legis.la.gov

Cromer, George Gregory (R, 90)
State Capitol
P.O. Box 94062
Baton Rouge, LA 70804
P: (225) 342-6945
F: (225) 342-8336
E: cromerg@legis.la.gov

Danahay, Michael E. (D, 33)
State Capitol
P.O. Box 94062
Baton Rouge, LA 70804
P: (225) 342-6945
F: (225) 342-8336
E: danahaym@legis.la.gov

Dove Sr., Gordon (R, 52)
State Capitol
P.O. Box 94062
Baton Rouge, LA 70804
P: (225) 342-6945
F: (225) 342-8336
E: larep052@legis.la.gov

Edwards, John Bel (D, 72)
State Capitol
P.O. Box 94062
Baton Rouge, LA 70804
P: (225) 342-6945
F: (225) 342-8336
E: edwardsj@legis.la.gov

Fannin, James R. (R, 13)
State Capitol
P.O. Box 94062
Baton Rouge, LA 70804
P: (225) 342-6945
F: (225) 342-8336
E: larep013@legis.la.gov

Foil, Franklin J. (R, 70)
State Capitol
P.O. Box 94062
Baton Rouge, LA 70804
P: (225) 342-6945
F: (225) 342-8336
E: foilf@legis.la.gov

Franklin, A.B. (D, 34)
State Capitol
P.O. Box 94062
Baton Rouge, LA 70804
P: (225) 342-6945
F: (225) 342-8336
E: franklina@legis.la.gov

Gaines, Randal L. (D, 57)
State Capitol
P.O. Box 94062
Baton Rouge, LA 70804
P: (225) 342-6945
F: (225) 342-8336
E: gainesr@legis.la.gov

Garofalo Jr., Raymond E. (R, 103)
State Capitol
P.O. Box 94062
Baton Rouge, LA 70804
P: (225) 342-6945
F: (225) 342-8336
E: garofalor@legis.la.gov

Geymann, Brett F. (R, 35)
State Capitol
P.O. Box 94062
Baton Rouge, LA 70804
P: (225) 342-6945
F: (225) 342-8336
E: larep035@legis.la.gov

Gisclair, Jerry (D, 54)
State Capitol
P.O. Box 94062
Baton Rouge, LA 70804
P: (225) 342-6945
F: (225) 342-8336
E: gisclairj@legis.la.gov

Guillory, Mickey J. (D, 41)
State Capitol
P.O. Box 94062
Baton Rouge, LA 70804
P: (225) 342-6945
F: (225) 342-8336
E: larep041@legis.la.gov

Guinn, John E. (R, 37)
State Capitol
P.O. Box 94062
Baton Rouge, LA 70804
P: (225) 342-6945
F: (225) 342-8336
E: guinnj@legis.la.gov

Harris, Lance (R, 25)
State Capitol
P.O. Box 94062
Baton Rouge, LA 70804
P: (225) 342-6945
F: (225) 342-8336
E: harrisl@legis.la.gov

Harrison, Joe (R, 51)
State Capitol
P.O. Box 94062
Baton Rouge, LA 70804
P: (225) 342-6945
F: (225) 342-8336
E: harrisoj@legis.la.gov

Havard, Kenneth E. (R, 62)
State Capitol
P.O. Box 94062
Baton Rouge, LA 70804
P: (225) 342-6945
F: (225) 342-8336
E: havardk@legis.la.gov

Hazel, Lowell C. (R, 27)
State Capitol
P.O. Box 94062
Baton Rouge, LA 70804
P: (225) 342-6945
F: (225) 342-8336
E: hazelc@legis.la.gov

Henry, Cameron (R, 82)
State Capitol
P.O. Box 94062
Baton Rouge, LA 70804
P: (225) 342-6945
F: (225) 342-8336
E: henryc@legis.la.gov

Hensgens, Bob (R, 47)
State Capitol
P.O. Box 94062
Baton Rouge, LA 70804
P: (225) 342-6945
F: (225) 342-8336
E: hensgensb@legis.la.gov

Hill, Dorothy Sue (D, 32)
State Capitol
P.O. Box 94062
Baton Rouge, LA 70804
P: (225) 342-6945
F: (225) 342-8336
E: hilld@legis.la.gov

Hodges, Valarie (R, 64)
State Capitol
P.O. Box 94062
Baton Rouge, LA 70804
P: (225) 342-6945
F: (225) 342-8336
E: hodgesv@legis.la.gov

Hoffmann, Frank A. (R, 15)
State Capitol
P.O. Box 94062
Baton Rouge, LA 70804
P: (225) 342-6945
F: (225) 342-8336
E: hoffmanf@legis.la.gov

Hollis, Paul B. (R, 104)
State Capitol
P.O. Box 94062
Baton Rouge, LA 70804
P: (225) 342-6945
F: (225) 342-8336
E: hollisp@legis.la.gov

Honore, Dalton W. (D, 63)
State Capitol
P.O. Box 94062
Baton Rouge, LA 70804
P: (225) 342-6945
F: (225) 342-8336
E: honored@legis.la.gov

Howard, Frank A. (R, 24)
State Capitol
P.O. Box 94062
Baton Rouge, LA 70804
P: (225) 342-6945
F: (225) 342-8336
E: howardf@legis.la.gov

Hunter, Marcus L. (D, 17)
State Capitol
P.O. Box 94062
Baton Rouge, LA 70804
P: (225) 342-6945
F: (225) 342-8336
E: hunterm@legis.la.gov

Huval, Mike (R, 46)
State Capitol
P.O. Box 94062
Baton Rouge, LA 70804
P: (225) 342-6945
F: (225) 342-8336
E: huvalm@legis.la.gov

Ivey, Barry (R, 65)
State Capitol
P.O. Box 94062
Baton Rouge, LA 70804
P: (225) 342-6945
F: (225) 342-8336
E: iveyb@legis.la.gov

Jackson, Katrina R. (D, 16)
State Capitol
P.O. Box 94062
Baton Rouge, LA 70804
P: (225) 342-6945
F: (225) 342-8336
E: jacksonk@legis.la.gov

James II, Edward C. (D, 101)
State Capitol
P.O. Box 94062
Baton Rouge, LA 70804
P: (225) 342-6945
F: (225) 342-8336
E: james.ted@legis.la.gov

Jefferson, Patrick O. (D, 11)
State Capitol
P.O. Box 94062
Baton Rouge, LA 70804
P: (225) 342-6945
F: (225) 342-8336
E: jeffersonpo@legis.la.gov

Johnson, Mike (R, 8)*
State Capitol
P.O. Box 94062
Baton Rouge, LA 70804
P: (225) 342-6945
F: (225) 342-8336
E: johnsonmi@legis.la.gov

Johnson, Robert A. (D, 28)
State Capitol
P.O. Box 94062
Baton Rouge, LA 70804
P: (225) 342-6945
F: (225) 342-8336
E: johnsoro@legis.la.gov

Jones, Sam (D, 50)
State Capitol
P.O. Box 94062
Baton Rouge, LA 70804
P: (225) 342-6945
F: (225) 342-8336
E: joness@legis.la.gov

Kleckley, Chuck (R, 36)
State Capitol
P.O. Box 94062
Baton Rouge, LA 70804
P: (225) 342-7263
F: (225) 342-8336
E: larep036@legis.la.gov

Lambert, Eddie J. (R, 59)
State Capitol
P.O. Box 94062
Baton Rouge, LA 70804
P: (225) 342-6945
F: (225) 342-8336
E: larep059@legis.la.gov

Landry, Nancy (R, 31)
State Capitol
P.O. Box 94062
Baton Rouge, LA 70804
P: (225) 342-6945
F: (225) 342-8336
E: landryn@legis.la.gov

Landry, Terry (D, 96)
State Capitol
P.O. Box 94062
Baton Rouge, LA 70804
P: (225) 342-6945
F: (225) 342-8336
E: landryt@legis.la.gov

LeBas, H. Bernard (D, 38)
State Capitol
P.O. Box 94062
Baton Rouge, LA 70804
P: (225) 342-6945
F: (225) 342-8336
E: lebasb@legis.la.gov

Leger III, Walt (D, 91)
State Capitol
P.O. Box 94062
Baton Rouge, LA 70804
P: (225) 342-6945
F: (225) 342-8336
E: legerw@legis.la.gov

Louisiana

Leopold, Christopher J. (R, 105)
State Capitol
P.O. Box 94062
Baton Rouge, LA 70804
P: (225) 342-6945
F: (225) 342-8336
E: leopoldc@legis.la.gov

Lopinto III, Joseph P. (R, 80)
State Capitol
P.O. Box 94062
Baton Rouge, LA 70804
P: (225) 342-6945
F: (225) 342-8336
E: lopintoj@legis.la.gov

Lorusso, Nicholas J. (R, 94)
State Capitol
P.O. Box 94062
Baton Rouge, LA 70804
P: (225) 342-6945
F: (225) 342-8336
E: larep094@legis.la.gov

Mack, Sherman Q. (R, 95)
State Capitol
P.O. Box 94062
Baton Rouge, LA 70804
P: (225) 342-6945
F: (225) 342-8336
E: macks@legis.la.gov

Miguez, Blake (R, 49)*
State Capitol
P.O. Box 94062
Baton Rouge, LA 70804
P: (225) 342-6945
F: (225) 342-8336
E: miguezb@legis.la.gov

Miller, Gregory A. (R, 56)
State Capitol
P.O. Box 94062
Baton Rouge, LA 70804
P: (225) 342-6945
F: (225) 342-8336
E: millerg@legis.la.gov

Montoucet, Jack (D, 42)
State Capitol
P.O. Box 94062
Baton Rouge, LA 70804
P: (225) 342-6945
F: (225) 342-8336
E: montoucj@legis.la.gov

Moreno, Helena N. (D, 93)
State Capitol
P.O. Box 94062
Baton Rouge, LA 70804
P: (225) 342-6945
F: (225) 342-8336
E: morenoh@legis.la.gov

Morris, James H. (R, 1)
State Capitol
P.O. Box 94062
Baton Rouge, LA 70804
P: (225) 342-6945
F: (225) 342-8336
E: larep001@legis.la.gov

Morris III, John C. (R, 14)
State Capitol
P.O. Box 94062
Baton Rouge, LA 70804
P: (225) 342-6945
F: (225) 342-8336
E: morrisjc@legis.la.gov

Norton, Barbara (D, 3)
State Capitol
P.O. Box 94062
Baton Rouge, LA 70804
P: (225) 342-6945
F: (225) 342-8336
E: nortonb@legis.la.gov

Ortego, Stephen J. (D, 39)
State Capitol
P.O. Box 94062
Baton Rouge, LA 70804
P: (225) 342-6945
F: (225) 342-8336
E: ortegos@legis.la.gov

Pearson, J. Kevin (R, 76)
State Capitol
P.O. Box 94062
Baton Rouge, LA 70804
P: (225) 342-6945
F: (225) 342-8336
E: pearsonk@legis.la.gov

Pierre, Vincent J. (D, 44)
State Capitol
P.O. Box 94062
Baton Rouge, LA 70804
P: (225) 342-6945
F: (225) 342-8336
E: pierrev@legis.la.gov

Ponti, Erich (R, 69)
State Capitol
P.O. Box 94062
Baton Rouge, LA 70804
P: (225) 342-6945
F: (225) 342-8336
E: pontie@legis.la.gov

Pope, J. Rogers (R, 71)
State Capitol
P.O. Box 94062
Baton Rouge, LA 70804
P: (225) 342-6945
F: (225) 342-8336
E: poper@legis.la.gov

Price, Edward J. (D, 58)
State Capitol
P.O. Box 94062
Baton Rouge, LA 70804
P: (225) 342-6945
F: (225) 342-8336
E: pricee@legis.la.gov

Pugh, Stephen E. (R, 73)
State Capitol
P.O. Box 94062
Baton Rouge, LA 94062
P: (225) 342-6945
F: (225) 342-8336
E: pughs@legis.la.gov

Pylant, Steven E. (R, 20)
State Capitol
P.O. Box 94062
Baton Rouge, LA 70804
P: (225) 342-6945
F: (225) 342-8336
E: pylants@legis.la.gov

Reynolds, H. Eugene (D, 10)
State Capitol
P.O. Box 94062
Baton Rouge, LA 70804
P: (225) 342-6945
F: (225) 342-8336
E: reynoldsg@legis.la.gov

Richard, Jerome (I, 55)
State Capitol
P.O. Box 94062
Baton Rouge, LA 70804
P: (225) 342-6945
F: (225) 342-8336
E: richardj@legis.la.gov

Ritchie, Harold L. (D, 75)
State Capitol
P.O. Box 94062
Baton Rouge, LA 70804
P: (225) 342-6945
F: (225) 342-8336
E: larep075@legis.la.gov

Robideaux, Joel C. (R, 45)
State Capitol
P.O. Box 94062
Baton Rouge, LA 70804
P: (225) 342-6945
F: (225) 342-8336
E: larep045@legis.la.gov

Schexnayder, Clay (R, 81)
State Capitol
P.O. Box 94062
Baton Rouge, LA 70804
P: (225) 342-6945
F: (225) 342-8336
E: schexnayderc@legis.la.gov

Schroder Sr., John M. (R, 77)
State Capitol
P.O. Box 94062
Baton Rouge, LA 70804
P: (225) 342-6945
F: (225) 342-8336
E: schrodej@legis.la.gov

Seabaugh, Alan (R, 5)
State Capitol
P.O. Box 94062
Baton Rouge, LA 70804
P: (225) 342-6945
F: (225) 342-8336
E: seabaugha@legis.la.gov

Shadoin, Robert E. (R, 12)
State Capitol
P.O. Box 94062
Baton Rouge, LA 70804
P: (225) 342-6945
F: (225) 342-8336
E: shadoinr@legis.la.gov

Simon, Scott (R, 74)
State Capitol
P.O. Box 94062
Baton Rouge, LA 70804
P: (225) 342-6945
F: (225) 342-8336
E: simons@legis.la.gov

Smith, Patricia Haynes (D, 67)
State Capitol
P.O. Box 94062
Baton Rouge, LA 70804
P: (225) 342-6945
F: (225) 342-8336
E: smithp@legis.la.gov

St. Germain, Karen Gaudet (D, 60)
State Capitol
P.O. Box 94062
Baton Rouge, LA 70804
P: (225) 342-6945
F: (225) 342-8336
E: larep060@legis.la.gov

Stokes, Julie (R, 79)
State Capitol
P.O. Box 94062
Baton Rouge, LA 70804
P: (225) 342-6945
F: (225) 342-8336
E: stokesj@legis.la.gov

Talbot, Kirk (R, 78)
State Capitol
P.O. Box 94062
Baton Rouge, LA 70804
P: (225) 342-6945
F: (225) 342-8336
E: talbotk@legis.la.gov

Thibaut Jr., Major (D, 18)
State Capitol
P.O. Box 94062
Baton Rouge, LA 70804
P: (225) 342-6945
F: (225) 342-8336
E: thibautm@legis.la.gov

Thierry, Ledricka Johnson (D, 40)
State Capitol
P.O. Box 94062
Baton Rouge, LA 70804
P: (225) 342-6945
F: (225) 342-8336
E: thierryl@legis.la.gov

Whitney, Lenar L. (R, 53)
State Capitol
P.O. Box 94062
Baton Rouge, LA 70804
P: (225) 342-6945
F: (225) 342-8336
E: whitneyl@legis.la.gov

Williams, Alfred C. (D, 61)
State Capitol
P.O. Box 94062
Baton Rouge, LA 70804
P: (225) 342-6945
F: (225) 342-8336
E: williamsa@legis.la.gov

Williams, Patrick C. (D, 4)
State Capitol
P.O. Box 94062
Baton Rouge, LA 70804
P: (225) 342-6945
F: (225) 342-8336
E: larep004@legis.la.gov

Willmott, Thomas P. (R, 92)
State Capitol
P.O. Box 94062
Baton Rouge, LA 70804
P: (225) 342-6945
F: (225) 342-8336
E: willmott@legis.la.gov

Woodruff, Ebony (D, 87)
State Capitol
P.O. Box 94062
Baton Rouge, LA 70804
P: (225) 342-6945
F: (225) 342-8336
E: woodruffe@legis.la.gov

Congress

Senate

Cassidy, William (R)
Vitter, David (R)

House

Abraham, Ralph (R, 5)
Boustany Jr., Charles W. (R, 3)
Fleming, John (R, 4)
Graves, Garret (R, 6)
Richmond, Cedric (D, 2)
Scalise, Steve (R, 1)

Maine

Executive

Governor

Hon. Paul LePage (R)
Governor
#1 State House Station
Augusta, ME 04333
P: (207) 287-3531
F: (207) 287-1034

Lieutenant Governor

This state does not have the office of lieutenant governor. The president (or speaker) of the Senate is next in line of succession to the governorship.

Attorney General

Hon. Janet T. Mills (D)
Attorney General
State House Station 6
Augusta, ME 04333
P: (207) 626-8800

Auditor

Hon. Pola Buckley
(elected by the Legislature)
State Auditor
66 State House Station
Augusta, ME 04333
P: (207) 624-6250
F: (207) 624-6273

Secretary of State

Hon. Matthew Dunlap (D)
Secretary of State
148 State House Station
Augusta, ME 04333
P: (207) 626-8400
F: (207) 287-8598
E: sos.office@maine.gov

Treasurer

Hon. Terry Hayes (I)
State Treasurer
39 State House, 111 Sewall Street
Cross Office Building, 3rd Floor
Augusta, ME 04333
P: (207) 624-7477
F: (207) 287-2367
E: state.treasurer@maine.gov

Judiciary

Supreme Judicial Court (GA)

Mr. Matthew Pollack
Clerk of the Law Court
205 Newbury Street, Room 139
Portland, ME 04101
P: (207) 822-4146

Hon. Leigh I. Saufley
Chief Justice
Hon. Donald G. Alexander
Hon. Ellen A. Gorman
Hon. Jeffrey L. Hjelm
Hon. Joseph M. Jabar
Hon. Jon D. Levy
Hon. Andrew M. Mead
Hon. Warren M. Silver

Legislative Senate

Senate President

Sen. Michael D. Thibodeau (R)
Senate President
3 State House Station
Augusta, ME 04333
P: (207) 287-1500
F: (207) 287-1527
E: senatorthibodeau@aol.com

Senate Majority Leader

Sen. Garrett P. Mason (R)
Majority Leader
3 State House Station
Augusta, ME 04333
P: (207) 287-1505
F: (207) 287-1527
E: SenGarrett.Mason@legislature.maine.gov

Senate Minority Leader

Sen. Justin L. Alfond (D)
Minority Leader
3 State House Station
Augusta, ME 04333
P: (207) 287-1515
F: (207) 287-1900
E: justin@justinalfond.com

Secretary of the Senate

Ms. Heather J.R. Priest
Secretary of the Senate
3 State House Station
Augusta, ME 04333
P: (207) 287-1540
F: (207) 287-1900
E: heather.priest@legislature.maine.gov

Members of the Senate

Alfond, Justin L. (D, 27)
3 State House Station
Augusta, ME 04333
P: (207) 287-1515
F: (207) 287-1900
E: justin@justinalfond.com

Baker, Linda (R, 23)*
3 State House Station
Augusta, ME 04333
P: (207) 287-1505
F: (207) 287-1527
E: bakersenate14@yahoo.com

Brakey, Eric (R, 20)*
3 State House Station
Augusta, ME 04333
P: (207) 287-1505
F: (207) 287-1527
E: eric@brakeyforsenate.com

Breen, Catherine (D, 25)*
3 State House Station
Augusta, ME 04333
P: (207) 287-1515
F: (207) 287-1900
E: cathy.breen@legislature.maine.gov

Burns, David C. (R, 29)
3 State House Station
Augusta, ME 04333
P: (207) 287-1505
F: (207) 287-1900
E: SenDavid.Burns@legislature.maine.gov

Collins, Ronald F. (R, 34)
3 State House Station
Augusta, ME 04333
P: (207) 287-1505
F: (207) 287-1527
E: RCollins7@maine.rr.com

Cushing III, Andre E. (R, 10)
3 State House Station
Augusta, ME 04333
P: (207) 287-1505
F: (207) 287-1527
E: andre@andrecushing.com

Cyrway, Scott (R, 16)*
3 State House Station
Augusta, ME 04333
P: (207) 287-1505
F: (207) 287-1527
E: scyrway@roadrunner.com

Davis Sr., Paul T. (R, 4)
3 State House Station
Augusta, ME 04333
P: (207) 287-1505
F: (207) 287-1527
E: sendavis@myottmail.com

Diamond, Bill (D, 26)
3 State House Station
Augusta, ME 04333
P: (207) 287-1515
F: (207) 287-1900
E: william.diamond@legislature.maine.gov

Dill, James F. (D, 5)
3 State House Station
Augusta, ME 04333
P: (207) 287-1515
F: (207) 287-1900
E: jdill@umext.maine.edu

Dutremble, David E. (D, 32)
3 State House Station
Augusta, ME 04333
P: (207) 287-1515
F: (207) 287-1900
E: ddutrem1@gmail.com

Edgecomb, Peter (R, 1)
3 State House Station
Augusta, ME 04333
P: (207) 287-1505
F: (207) 287-1527
E: peter.edgecomb@legislature.maine.gov

Gerzofsky, Stanley J. (D, 10)
3 State House Station
Augusta, ME 04333
P: (207) 287-1515
F: (207) 287-1900
E: stan1340@aol.com

Gratwick, Geoffrey M. (D, 32)
3 State House Station
Augusta, ME 04333
P: (207) 287-1515
F: (207) 287-1900
E: Sengeoff.gratwick@legislature.maine.gov

Hamper, James Michael (R, 19)
3 State House Station
Augusta, ME 04333
P: (207) 287-1505
F: (207) 287-1527
E: SenJames.Hamper@legislature.maine.gov

Haskell, Anne M. (D, 9)
3 State House Station
Augusta, ME 04333
P: (207) 287-1515
F: (207) 287-1900
E: annehask@maine.rr.com

Hill, Dawn (D, 35)
3 State House Station
Augusta, ME 04333
P: (207) 287-1515
F: (207) 287-1900
E: SenDawn.Hill@legislature.maine.gov

Johnson, Christopher K. (D, 13)
3 State House Station
Augusta, ME 04333
P: (207) 287-1515
F: (207) 287-1900
E: SenChris.Johnson@legislature.maine.gov

Katz, Roger J. (R, 15)
3 State House Station
Augusta, ME 04333
P: (207) 287-1505
F: (207) 287-1527
E: SenRoger.Katz@legislature.maine.gov

Langley, Brian D. (R, 7)
3 State House Station
Augusta, ME 04333
P: (207) 287-1505
F: (207) 287-1527
E: SenBrian.Langley@legislature.maine.gov

Libby, Nathan L. (D, 21)
3 State House Station
Augusta, ME 04333
P: (207) 287-1515
F: (207) 287-1900
E: nathan.libby@gmail.com

Mason, Garrett P. (R, 22)
3 State House Station
Augusta, ME 04333
P: (207) 287-1505
F: (207) 287-1527
E: SenGarrett.Mason@legislature.maine.gov

McCormick, Earle L. (R, 14)
3 State House Station
Augusta, ME 04333
P: (207) 287-1505
F: (207) 287-1527
E: demccormick@tds.net

Millett, Rebecca J. (D, 29)
3 State House Station
Augusta, ME 04333
P: (207) 287-1515
F: (207) 287-1900
E: senrebeccamillett@gmail.com

Miramant, David (D, 12)
3 State House Station
Augusta, ME 04333
P: (207) 287-1515
F: (207) 287-1900
E: davemiramant@gmail.com

Patrick, John L. (D, 18)
3 State House Station
Augusta, ME 04333
P: (207) 287-1515
F: (207) 287-1900
E: SenJohn.Patrick@legislature.maine.gov

Rosen, Kimberley C. (R, 8)
3 State House Station
Augusta, ME 04333
P: (207) 287-1505
F: (207) 287-1527
E: kimberley.rosen@legislature.maine.gov

Saviello, Thomas B. (R, 17)
3 State House Station
Augusta, ME 04333
P: (207) 287-1505
F: (207) 287-1527
E: SenThomas.Saviello@legislature.maine.gov

Thibodeau, Michael D. (R, 11)
3 State House Station
Augusta, ME 04333
P: (207) 287-1500
F: (207) 287-1527
E: senatorthibodeau@aol.com

Valentino, Linda M. (D, 31)
3 State House Station
Augusta, ME 04333
P: (207) 287-1515
F: (207) 287-1900
E: SenLinda.Valentino@legislature.maine.gov

Volk, Amy (R, 30)
3 State House Station
Augusta, ME 04333
P: (207) 287-1505
F: (207) 287-1527
E: amy.volk@legislature.maine.gov

Whittemore, Rodney L. (R, 3)
3 State House Station
Augusta, ME 04333
P: (207) 287-1505
F: (207) 287-1527
E: Rodwhittemore@gmail.com

Willette, Michael J. (R, 2)
3 State House Station
Augusta, ME 04333
P: (207) 287-1505
F: (207) 287-1527
E: mikeblackbear@gmail.com

Woodsome, David (R, 33)*
3 State House Station
Augusta, ME 04333
P: (207) 287-1505
F: (207) 287-1527
E: david.woodsome@legislature.maine.gov

House

Speaker of the House

Rep. Mark Eves (D)
Speaker
Room 333, State House
2 State House Station
Augusta, ME 04333
P: (207) 287-1430
F: (207) 287-1456
E: Mark.Eves@legislature.maine.gov

House Majority Leader

Rep. Jeffrey M. McCabe (D)
Democratic Leader
Room 333, State House
2 State House Station
Augusta, ME 04333
P: (207) 287-1430
F: (207) 287-1456
E: Jeffrey.McCabe@legislature.maine.gov

House Minority Leader

Rep. Kenneth Wade Fredette (R)
Minority Floor Leader
Room 332, State House
2 State House Station
Augusta, ME 04333
P: (207) 287-1440
F: (207) 287-1456
E: Kenneth.Fredette@legislature.maine.gov

Clerk of the House

Mr. Robert B. Hunt
Clerk of the House
Room 300, State House
2 State House Station
Augusta, ME 04333
P: (207) 287-1400
F: (207) 287-1456
E: RepRob.Hunt@legislature.maine.gov

Members of the House

Alley Sr., Robert (D, 138)*
Room 333, State House
2 State House Station
Augusta, ME 04333
P: (207) 287-1430
F: (207) 287-1456
E: Robert.Alley@legislature.maine.gov

Austin, Susan (R, 67)
Room 332, State House
2 State House Station
Augusta, ME 04333
P: (207) 287-1440
F: (207) 287-1456
E: Sue.Austin@legislature.maine.gov

Babbidge, Christopher W. (D, 8)
Room 333, State House
2 State House Station
Augusta, ME 04333
P: (207) 287-1430
F: (207) 287-1456
E: Chris.Babbidge@legislature.maine.gov

Bates, Dillon (D, 35)*
Room 333, State House
2 State House Station
Augusta, ME 04333
P: (207) 287-1430
F: (207) 287-1456
E: Dillon.Bates@legislature.maine.gov

Battle, Kevin (R, 33)*
Room 332, State House
2 State House Station
Augusta, ME 04333
P: (207) 287-1440
F: (207) 287-1456
E: Kevin.Battle@legislature.maine.gov

Bear, Henry John (TRIBAL)
2 State House Station
Augusta, ME 04333
P: (207) 287-1400
F: (207) 287-1456
E: bearlaw2@yahoo.com

Maine

Beavers, Roberta B. (D, 2)
Room 333, State House
2 State House Station
Augusta, ME 04333
P: (207) 287-1430
F: (207) 287-1456
E: Bobbi.Beavers@legislature.maine.gov

Beck, Henry E.M. (D, 110)
Room 333, State House
2 State House Station
Augusta, ME 04333
P: (207) 287-1430
F: (207) 287-1456
E: Henry.Beck@legislature.maine.gov

Bickford, Bruce A. (R, 63)
Room 332, State House
2 State House Station
Augusta, ME 04333
P: (207) 287-1440
F: (207) 287-1456
E: Bruce.Bickford@legislature.maine.gov

Black, Russell J. (R, 114)
Room 332, State House
2 State House Station
Augusta, ME 04333
P: (207) 287-1440
F: (207) 287-1456
E: Russell.Black@legislature.maine.gov

Blume, Lydia (D, 3)*
Room 333, State House
2 State House Station
Augusta, ME 04333
P: (207) 287-1430
F: (207) 287-1456
E: Lydia.Blume@legislature.maine.gov

Brooks, Heidi (D, 61)*
Room 333, State House
2 State House Station
Augusta, ME 04333
P: (207) 287-1430
F: (207) 287-1456
E: Heidi.Brooks@legislature.maine.gov

Bryant, Mark E. (D, 24)
Room 333, State House
2 State House Station
Augusta, ME 04333
P: (207) 287-1430
F: (207) 287-1456
E: Mark.Bryant@legislature.maine.gov

Buckland, Andrew (R, 113)*
Room 332, State House
2 State House Station
Augusta, ME 04333
P: (207) 287-1440
F: (207) 287-1456
E: Andrew.Buckland@legislature.maine.gov

Burstein, Christine (D, 96)*
Room 333, State House
2 State House Station
Augusta, ME 04333
P: (207) 287-1430
F: (207) 287-1456
E: Christine.Burstein@legislature.maine.gov

Campbell Sr., James J. (I, 21)
2 State House Station
Augusta, ME 04333
P: (207) 287-1400
F: (207) 287-1456
E: scampbell1936@yahoo.com

Campbell, Richard H. (R, 130)
Room 332, State House
2 State House Station
Augusta, ME 04333
P: (207) 287-1440
F: (207) 287-1456
E: Richard.Campbell@legislature.maine.gov

Chace, Paul (R, 46)*
Room 332, State House
2 State House Station
Augusta, ME 04333
P: (207) 287-1440
F: (207) 287-1456
E: Paul.Chace@legislature.maine.gov

Chapman, Ralph (D, 133)
Room 333, State House
2 State House Station
Augusta, ME 04333
P: (207) 287-1430
F: (207) 287-1456
E: Ralph.Chapman@legislature.maine.gov

Chenette, Justin Mark (D, 15)
Room 333, State House
2 State House Station
Augusta, ME 04333
P: (207) 287-1430
F: (207) 287-1456
E: Justin.Chenette@legislature.maine.gov

Chipman, Benjamin M. (I, 40)
2 State House Station
Augusta, ME 04333
P: (207) 287-1400
F: (207) 287-1456
E: Ben.Chipman@legislature.maine.gov

Cooper, Janice E. (D, 47)
Room 333, State House
2 State House Station
Augusta, ME 04333
P: (207) 287-1430
F: (207) 287-1456
E: Janice.Cooper@legislature.maine.gov

Corey, Patrick (R, 25)*
Room 332, State House
2 State House Station
Augusta, ME 04333
P: (207) 287-1440
F: (207) 287-1456
E: Patrick.Corey@legislature.maine.gov

Crafts, Dale J. (R, 56)
Room 332, State House
2 State House Station
Augusta, ME 04333
P: (207) 287-1440
F: (207) 287-1456
E: Dale.Crafts@legislature.maine.gov

Dana II, Matthew (TRIBAL, Passamaquoddy Tribe)*
2 State House Station
Augusta, ME 04333
P: (207) 287-1440
F: (207) 287-1456
E: Matthew.Dana@legislature.maine.gov

Daughtry, Matthea E. L. (D, 49)
Room 333, State House
2 State House Station
Augusta, ME 04333
P: (207) 287-1430
F: (207) 287-1456
E: mattie.daughtry@legislature.maine.gov

Davitt, James (D, 101)*
Room 333, State House
2 State House Station
Augusta, ME 04333
P: (207) 287-1430
F: (207) 287-1456
E: Jim.Davitt@legislature.maine.gov

DeChant, Jennifer (D, 52)
Room 333, State House
2 State House Station
Augusta, ME 04333
P: (207) 287-1430
F: (207) 287-1456
E: Jennifer.DeChant@legislature.maine.gov

Devin, Michael (D, 90)
Room 333, State House
2 State House Station
Augusta, ME 04333
P: (207) 287-1430
F: (207) 287-1456
E: Michael.Devin@legislature.maine.gov

Dickerson, Elizabeth E. (D, 93)
Room 333, State House
2 State House Station
Augusta, ME 04333
P: (207) 287-1430
F: (207) 287-1456
E: Elizabeth.Dickerson@legislature.maine.gov

Dillingham, Kathleen Jackson (R, 72)*
Room 332, State House
2 State House Station
Augusta, ME 04333
P: (207) 287-1440
F: (207) 287-1456
E: Kathleen.Dillingham@legislature.maine.gov

Dion, Mark N. (D, 43)
Room 333, State House
2 State House Station
Augusta, ME 04333
P: (207) 287-1430
F: (207) 287-1456
E: Mark.Dion@legislature.maine.gov

Doore, Donna (D, 85)*
Room 333, State House
2 State House Station
Augusta, ME 04333
P: (207) 287-1430
F: (207) 287-1456
E: Donna.Doore@legislature.maine.gov

Duchesne, Robert S. (D, 121)
Room 333, State House
2 State House Station
Augusta, ME 04333
P: (207) 287-1430
F: (207) 287-1456
E: Robert.Duchesne@legislature.maine.gov

Dunphy, Larry C. (R, 118)
Room 332, State House
2 State House Station
Augusta, ME 04333
P: (207) 287-1440
F: (207) 287-1456
E: Larry.Dunphy
@legislature.maine.gov

Dunphy, Michelle Ann (D, 122)*
Room 333, State House
2 State House Station
Augusta, ME 04333
P: (207) 287-1430
F: (207) 287-1456
E: Michelle.Dunphy
@legislature.maine.gov

Edgecomb, Anthony (R, 148)*
Room 332, State House
2 State House Station
Augusta, ME 04333
P: (207) 287-1440
F: (207) 287-1456
E: aj.edgecomb
@legislature.maine.gov

Espling, Eleanor M. (R, 65)
Room 332, State House
2 State House Station
Augusta, ME 04333
P: (207) 287-1440
F: (207) 287-1456
E: Ellie.Espling
@legislature.maine.gov

Evangelos, Jeffrey (U, 91)
2 State House Station
Augusta, ME 04333
P: (207) 287-1400
F: (207) 287-1456
E: Jeffrey.Evangelos
@legislature.maine.gov

Eves, Mark (D, 6)
Room 333, State House
2 State House Station
Augusta, ME 04333
P: (207) 287-1430
F: (207) 287-1456
E: Mark.Eves
@legislature.maine.gov

Farnsworth, Richard R. (D, 37)
Room 333, State House
2 State House Station
Augusta, ME 04333
P: (207) 287-1430
F: (207) 287-1456
E: Richard.Farnsworth
@legislature.maine.gov

Farrin, Bradlee (R, 111)*
Room 332, State House
2 State House Station
Augusta, ME 04333
P: (207) 287-1440
F: (207) 287-1456
E: Bradlee.Farrin
@legislature.maine.gov

Fecteau, Ryan (D, 11)*
Room 333, State House
2 State House Station
Augusta, ME 04333
P: (207) 287-1430
F: (207) 287-1456
E: Ryan.Fecteau
@legislature.maine.gov

Foley, Robert (R, 7)*
Room 332, State House
2 State House Station
Augusta, ME 04333
P: (207) 287-1440
F: (207) 287-1456
E: Robert.Foley
@legislature.maine.gov

Fowle, Lori (D, 80)
Room 333, State House
2 State House Station
Augusta, ME 04333
P: (207) 287-1430
F: (207) 287-1456
E: Lori.Fowle
@legislature.maine.gov

Fredette, Kenneth Wade (R, 100)
Room 332, State House
2 State House Station
Augusta, ME 04333
P: (207) 287-1440
F: (207) 287-1456
E: Kenneth.Fredette
@legislature.maine.gov

Frey, Aaron M. (D, 124)
Room 333, State House
2 State House Station
Augusta, ME 04333
P: (207) 287-1430
F: (207) 287-1456
E: Aaron.Frey
@legislature.maine.gov

Gattine, Drew W. (D, 34)
Room 333, State House
2 State House Station
Augusta, ME 04333
P: (207) 287-1430
F: (207) 287-1456
E: Drew.Gattine
@legislature.maine.gov

Gerrish, Karen (R, 20)*
Room 332, State House
2 State House Station
Augusta, ME 04333
P: (207) 287-1440
F: (207) 287-1456
E: Karen.Gerrish
@legislature.maine.gov

Gideon, Sara (D, 48)
Room 333, State House
2 State House Station
Augusta, ME 04333
P: (207) 287-1430
F: (207) 287-1456
E: Sara.Gideon
@legislature.maine.gov

Gilbert, Paul E. (D, 74)
Room 333, State House
2 State House Station
Augusta, ME 04333
P: (207) 287-1430
F: (207) 287-1456
E: Paul.Gilbert
@legislature.maine.gov

Gillway, James S. (R, 98)
Room 332, State House
2 State House Station
Augusta, ME 04333
P: (207) 287-1440
F: (207) 287-1456
E: James.Gillway
@legislature.maine.gov

Ginzler, Phyllis (R, 69)*
Room 332, State House
2 State House Station
Augusta, ME 04333
P: (207) 287-1440
F: (207) 287-1456
E: Phyllis.Ginzler
@legislature.maine.gov

Golden, Jared (D, 60)*
Room 333, State House
2 State House Station
Augusta, ME 04333
P: (207) 287-1430
F: (207) 287-1456
E: Jared.Golden
@legislature.maine.gov

Goode, Adam (D, 127)
Room 333, State House
2 State House Station
Augusta, ME 04333
P: (207) 287-1430
F: (207) 287-1456
E: RepAdam.Goode
@legislature.maine.gov

Grant, Gay M. (D, 83)
Room 333, State House
2 State House Station
Augusta, ME 04333
P: (207) 287-1430
F: (207) 287-1456
E: Gay.Grant
@legislature.maine.gov

Greenwood, Randall A. (R, 82)*
Room 332, State House
2 State House Station
Augusta, ME 04333
P: (207) 287-1440
F: (207) 287-1456
E: Randall.Greenwood
@legislature.maine.gov

Grohman, Martin (D, 12)*
Room 333, State House
2 State House Station
Augusta, ME 04333
P: (207) 287-1430
F: (207) 287-1456
E: Martin.Grohman
@legislature.maine.gov

Guerin, Stacey K. (R, 102)
Room 332, State House
2 State House Station
Augusta, ME 04333
P: (207) 287-1440
F: (207) 287-1456
E: Stacey.Guerin
@legislature.maine.gov

Hamann, Scott M. (D, 32)
Room 333, State House
2 State House Station
Augusta, ME 04333
P: (207) 287-1430
F: (207) 287-1456
E: Scott.Hamann
@legislature.maine.gov

Hanington, Sheldon Mark (R, 142)*
Room 332, State House
2 State House Station
Augusta, ME 04333
P: (207) 287-1440
F: (207) 287-1456
E: Sheldon.Hanington
@legislature.maine.gov

Hanley, Jeffery (R, 87)*
Room 332, State House
2 State House Station
Augusta, ME 04333
P: (207) 287-1440
F: (207) 287-1456
E: Jeff.Hanley
@legislature.maine.gov

Maine

Harlow, Denise Patricia (D, 36)
Room 333, State House
2 State House Station
Augusta, ME 04333
P: (207) 287-1430
F: (207) 287-1456
E: Denise.Harlow@legislature.maine.gov

Hawke, Stephanie (R, 89)*
Room 332, State House
2 State House Station
Augusta, ME 04333
P: (207) 287-1440
F: (207) 287-1456
E: Stephanie.Hawke@legislature.maine.gov

Head, Frances (R, 117)*
Room 332, State House
2 State House Station
Augusta, ME 04333
P: (207) 287-1440
F: (207) 287-1456
E: Frances.Head@legislature.maine.gov

Herbig, Erin D. (D, 97)
Room 333, State House
2 State House Station
Augusta, ME 04333
P: (207) 287-1430
F: (207) 287-1456
E: Erin.Herbig@legislature.maine.gov

Herrick, Lloyd (R, 73)*
Room 332, State House
2 State House Station
Augusta, ME 04333
P: (207) 287-1440
F: (207) 287-1456
E: Skip.Herrick@legislature.maine.gov

Hickman, Craig V. (D, 81)
Room 333, State House
2 State House Station
Augusta, ME 04333
P: (207) 287-1430
F: (207) 287-1456
E: Craig.Hickman@legislature.maine.gov

Higgins, Norman (R, 120)*
Room 332, State House
2 State House Station
Augusta, ME 04333
P: (207) 287-1440
F: (207) 287-1456
E: Norman.Higgins@legislature.maine.gov

Hilliard, Gary (R, 76)*
Room 332, State House
2 State House Station
Augusta, ME 04333
P: (207) 287-1440
F: (207) 287-1456
E: Gary.Hilliard@legislature.maine.gov

Hobart, Brian (R, 55)*
Room 332, State House
2 State House Station
Augusta, ME 04333
P: (207) 287-1440
F: (207) 287-1456
E: Brian.Hobart@legislature.maine.gov

Hobbins, Barry J. (D, 14)
Room 333, State House
2 State House Station
Augusta, ME 04333
P: (207) 287-1430
F: (207) 287-1456
E: Barry.Hobbins@legislature.maine.gov

Hogan, George W. (D, 13)
Room 333, State House
2 State House Station
Augusta, ME 04333
P: (207) 287-1430
F: (207) 287-1456
E: George.Hogan@legislature.maine.gov

Hubbell, Brian L. (D, 135)
Room 333, State House
2 State House Station
Augusta, ME 04333
P: (207) 287-1430
F: (207) 287-1456
E: Brian.Hubbell@legislature.maine.gov

Hymanson, Patricia (D, 4)*
Room 333, State House
2 State House Station
Augusta, ME 04333
P: (207) 287-1430
F: (207) 287-1456
E: Patricia.Hymanson@legislature.maine.gov

Jorgensen, Erik C. (D, 41)
Room 333, State House
2 State House Station
Augusta, ME 04333
P: (207) 287-1430
F: (207) 287-1456
E: Erik.Jorgensen@legislature.maine.gov

Kinney, Jonathan L. (R, 22)
Room 332, State House
2 State House Station
Augusta, ME 04333
P: (207) 287-1440
F: (207) 287-1456
E: Jonathan.Kinney@legislature.maine.gov

Kinney, Mary Anne (R, 99)*
Room 332, State House
2 State House Station
Augusta, ME 04333
P: (207) 287-1440
F: (207) 287-1456
E: MaryAnne.Kinney@legislature.maine.gov

Kornfield, Victoria P. (D, 125)
Room 333, State House
2 State House Station
Augusta, ME 04333
P: (207) 287-1430
F: (207) 287-1456
E: Tori.Kornfield@legislature.maine.gov

Kruger, Charles (D, 92)
Room 333, State House
2 State House Station
Augusta, ME 04333
P: (207) 287-1430
F: (207) 287-1456
E: Chuck.Kruger@legislature.maine.gov

Kumiega III, Walter A. (D, 134)
Room 333, State House
2 State House Station
Augusta, ME 04333
P: (207) 287-1430
F: (207) 287-1456
E: RepWalter.Kumiega@legislature.maine.gov

Lajoie, Michel A. (D, 58)
Room 333, State House
2 State House Station
Augusta, ME 04333
P: (207) 287-1430
F: (207) 287-1456
E: Michel.Lajoie@legislature.maine.gov

Lockman, Lawrence E. (R, 137)
Room 332, State House
2 State House Station
Augusta, ME 04333
P: (207) 287-1440
F: (207) 287-1456
E: Lawrence.Lockman@legislature.maine.gov

Long, Ricky D. (R, 145)
Room 332, State House
2 State House Station
Augusta, ME 04333
P: (207) 287-1440
F: (207) 287-1456
E: Ricky.Long@legislature.maine.gov

Longstaff, Thomas R.W. (D, 109)
Room 333, State House
2 State House Station
Augusta, ME 04333
P: (207) 287-1430
F: (207) 287-1456
E: Thomas.Longstaff@legislature.maine.gov

Luchini, Louis J. (D, 132)
Room 333, State House
2 State House Station
Augusta, ME 04333
P: (207) 287-1430
F: (207) 287-1456
E: Louis.Luchini@legislature.maine.gov

Lyford, Peter (R, 129)*
Room 332, State House
2 State House Station
Augusta, ME 04333
P: (207) 287-1440
F: (207) 287-1456
E: Peter.Lyford@legislature.maine.gov

Maker, Joyce A. (R, 140)
Room 332, State House
2 State House Station
Augusta, ME 04333
P: (207) 287-1440
F: (207) 287-1456
E: Joyce.Maker@legislature.maine.gov

Malaby, Richard S. (R, 136)
Room 332, State House
2 State House Station
Augusta, ME 04333
P: (207) 287-1440
F: (207) 287-1456
E: Richard.Malaby@legislature.maine.gov

Marean, Donald G. (R, 16)
Room 332, State House
2 State House Station
Augusta, ME 04333
P: (207) 287-1440
F: (207) 287-1456
E: Donald.Marean@legislature.maine.gov

Martin, John L. (D, 151)
Room 333, State House
2 State House Station
Augusta, ME 04333
P: (207) 287-1430
F: (207) 287-1456
E: John.Martin
@legislature.maine.gov

Martin, Roland Daniel (D, 150)*
Room 333, State House
2 State House Station
Augusta, ME 04333
P: (207) 287-1430
F: (207) 287-1456
E: Danny.Martin
@legislature.maine.gov

Mastraccio, Anne-Marie (D, 18)
Room 333, State House
2 State House Station
Augusta, ME 04333
P: (207) 287-1430
F: (207) 287-1456
E: Anne-Marie.Mastraccio
@legislature.maine.gov

McCabe, Jeffrey M. (D, 107)
Room 333, State House
2 State House Station
Augusta, ME 04333
P: (207) 287-1430
F: (207) 287-1456
E: Jeffrey.McCabe
@legislature.maine.gov

McClellan, Michael D. (R, 66)
Room 332, State House
2 State House Station
Augusta, ME 04333
P: (207) 287-1440
F: (207) 287-1456
E: Michael.McClellan
@legislature.maine.gov

McCreight, Joyce (D, 51)*
Room 333, State House
2 State House Station
Augusta, ME 04333
P: (207) 287-1430
F: (207) 287-1456
E: Jay.McCreight
@legislature.maine.gov

McElwee, Carol A. (R, 149)
Room 332, State House
2 State House Station
Augusta, ME 04333
P: (207) 287-1440
F: (207) 287-1456
E: Carol.McElwee
@legislature.maine.gov

McLean, Andrew J. (D, 27)
Room 333, State House
2 State House Station
Augusta, ME 04333
P: (207) 287-1430
F: (207) 287-1456
E: Andrew.McLean
@legislature.maine.gov

Melaragno, Gina (D, 62)*
Room 333, State House
2 State House Station
Augusta, ME 04333
P: (207) 287-1430
F: (207) 287-1456
E: Gina.Melaragno
@legislature.maine.gov

Mitchell, Wayne T. (TRIBAL, Penobscot Nation)
2 State House Station
Augusta, ME 04333
P: (207) 287-1400
F: (207) 287-1456
E: Wayne.Mitchell
@legislature.maine.gov

Monaghan-Derrig, Kimberly J. (D, 30)
Room 333, State House
Augusta, ME 04333
P: (207) 287-1430
F: (207) 287-1456
E: Kimberly.Monaghan
@legislature.maine.gov

Moonen, Matthew W. (D, 38)
Room 333, State House
2 State House Station
Augusta, ME 04333
P: (207) 287-1430
F: (207) 287-1456
E: Matthew.Moonen
@legislature.maine.gov

Morrison, Terry K. (D, 31)
Room 333, State House
2 State House Station
Augusta, ME 04333
P: (207) 287-1430
F: (207) 287-1456
E: Terry.Morrison
@legislature.maine.gov

Nadeau, Catherine M. (D, 78)
Room 333, State House
2 State House Station
Augusta, ME 04333
P: (207) 287-1430
F: (207) 287-1456
E: Catherine.Nadeau
@legislature.maine.gov

Noon, William F. (D, 19)
Room 333, State House
2 State House Station
Augusta, ME 04333
P: (207) 287-1430
F: (207) 287-1456
E: William.Noon
@legislature.maine.gov

Nutting, Robert W. (R, 77)
Room 332, State House
2 State House Station
Augusta, ME 04333
P: (207) 287-1440
F: (207) 287-1456
E: Bob.Nutting
@legislature.maine.gov

O'Connor, Beth A. (R, 5)
Room 332, State House
2 State House Station
Augusta, ME 04333
P: (207) 287-1440
F: (207) 287-1456
E: Beth.O'Connor
@legislature.maine.gov

Parry, Wayne R. (R, 10)
Room 332, State House
2 State House Station
Augusta, ME 04333
P: (207) 287-1440
F: (207) 287-1456
E: Wayne.Parry
@legislature.maine.gov

Peterson, Matthew J. (D, 115)
Room 333, State House
2 State House Station
Augusta, ME 04333
P: (207) 287-1430
F: (207) 287-1456
E: Matthew.Peterson
@legislature.maine.gov

Picchiotti, John J. (R, 108)
Room 332, State House
2 State House Station
Augusta, ME 04333
P: (207) 287-1440
F: (207) 287-1456
E: John.Picchiotti
@legislature.maine.gov

Pickett, Richard (R, 116)*
Room 332, State House
2 State House Station
Augusta, ME 04333
P: (207) 287-1440
F: (207) 287-1456
E: Richard.Pickett
@legislature.maine.gov

Pierce, Jeffrey (R, 53)*
Room 332, State House
2 State House Station
Augusta, ME 04333
P: (207) 287-1440
F: (207) 287-1456
E: Jeff.Pierce
@legislature.maine.gov

Pierce, Teresa (D, 44)*
Room 333, State House
2 State House Station
Augusta, ME 04333
P: (207) 287-1430
F: (207) 287-1456
E: Teresa.Pierce
@legislature.maine.gov

Pouliot, Matthew G. (R, 86)
Room 332, State House
2 State House Station
Augusta, ME 04333
P: (207) 287-1440
F: (207) 287-1456
E: Matt.Pouliot
@legislature.maine.gov

Powers, Christine B. (D, 68)
Room 333, State House
2 State House Station
Augusta, ME 04333
P: (207) 287-1430
F: (207) 287-1456
E: Christine.Powers
@legislature.maine.gov

Prescott, Dwayne (R, 17)*
Room 332, State House
2 State House Station
Augusta, ME 04333
P: (207) 287-1440
F: (207) 287-1456
E: Dwayne.Prescott
@legislature.maine.gov

Reed, Roger E. (R, 103)
Room 332, State House
2 State House Station
Augusta, ME 04333
P: (207) 287-1440
F: (207) 287-1456
E: Roger.Reed
@legislature.maine.gov

Rotundo, Margaret R. (D, 59)
Room 333, State House
2 State House Station
Augusta, ME 04333
P: (207) 287-1430
F: (207) 287-1456
E: Margaret.Rotundo
@legislature.maine.gov

Maine

Russell, Diane (D, 39)
Room 333, State House
2 State House Station
Augusta, ME 04333
P: (207) 287-1430
F: (207) 287-1456
E: Diane.Russell
@legislature.maine.gov

Rykerson, Deane (D, 1)
Room 333, State House
2 State House Station
Augusta, ME 04333
P: (207) 287-1430
F: (207) 287-1456
E: Deane.Rykerson
@legislature.maine.gov

Sanborn, Linda F. (D, 26)
Room 333, State House
2 State House Station
Augusta, ME 04333
P: (207) 287-1430
F: (207) 287-1456
E: Linda.Sanborn
@legislature.maine.gov

Sanderson, Deborah J. (R, 88)
Room 332, State House
2 State House Station
Augusta, ME 04333
P: (207) 287-1440
F: (207) 287-1456
E: Deborah.Sanderson
@legislature.maine.gov

Saucier, Robert J. (D, 147)
Room 333, State House
2 State House Station
Augusta, ME 04333
P: (207) 287-1430
F: (207) 287-1456
E: Bob.Saucier
@legislature.maine.gov

Sawicki, David (R, 64)*
Room 332, State House
2 State House Station
Augusta, ME 04333
P: (207) 287-1440
F: (207) 287-1456
E: David.Sawicki
@legislature.maine.gov

Schneck, John C. (D, 126)
Room 333, State House
2 State House Station
Augusta, ME 04333
P: (207) 287-1430
F: (207) 287-1456
E: John.Schneck
@legislature.maine.gov

Seavey, H. Stedman (R, 9)
Room 332, State House
2 State House Station
Augusta, ME 04333
P: (207) 287-1440
F: (207) 287-1456
E: Stedman.Seavey
@legislature.maine.gov

Shaw, Michael A. (D, 23)
Room 333, State House
2 State House Station
Augusta, ME 04333
P: (207) 287-1430
F: (207) 287-1456
E: Michael.Shaw
@legislature.maine.gov

Sherman, Roger L. (R, 144)
Room 332, State House
2 State House Station
Augusta, ME 04333
P: (207) 287-1440
F: (207) 287-1456
E: Rsherm
@legislature.maine.gov

Short Jr., Stanley Byron (D, 106)
Room 333, State House
2 State House Station
Augusta, ME 04333
P: (207) 287-1430
F: (207) 287-1456
E: Stanley.Short
@legislature.maine.gov

Sirocki, Heather W. (R, 28)
Room 332, State House
2 State House Station
Augusta, ME 04333
P: (207) 287-1440
F: (207) 287-1456
E: Heather.Sirocki
@legislature.maine.gov

Skolfield, Thomas (R, 112)*
Room 332, State House
2 State House Station
Augusta, ME 04333
P: (207) 287-1440
F: (207) 287-1456
E: Thomas.Skolfield
@legislature.maine.gov

Stanley, Stephen S. (D, 143)
Room 333, State House
2 State House Station
Augusta, ME 04333
P: (207) 287-1430
F: (207) 287-1456
E: Stephen.Stanley
@legislature.maine.gov

Stearns, Paul (R, 119)*
Room 332, State House
2 State House Station
Augusta, ME 04333
P: (207) 287-1440
F: (207) 287-1456
E: Paul.Stearns
@legislature.maine.gov

Stetkis, Joel (R, 105)*
Room 332, State House
2 State House Station
Augusta, ME 04333
P: (207) 287-1440
F: (207) 287-1456
E: Joel.Stetkis
@legislature.maine.gov

Stuckey, Peter C. (D, 42)
Room 333, State House
2 State House Station
Augusta, ME 04333
P: (207) 287-1430
F: (207) 287-1456
E: Peter.Stuckey
@legislature.maine.gov

Sukeforth, Gary E. (I, 95)
Room 333, State House
2 State House Station
Augusta, ME 04333
P: (207) 287-1430
F: (207) 287-1456
E: Gary.Sukeforth
@legislature.maine.gov

Tepler, Denise (D, 54)*
Room 333, State House
2 State House Station
Augusta, ME 04333
P: (207) 287-1430
F: (207) 287-1456
E: Denise.Tepler
@legislature.maine.gov

Theriault, Timothy (R, 79)*
Room 332, State House
2 State House Station
Augusta, ME 04333
P: (207) 287-1440
F: (207) 287-1456
E: tim.theriault
@legislature.maine.gov

Timberlake, Jeffrey L. (R, 75)
Room 332, State House
2 State House Station
Augusta, ME 04333
P: (207) 287-1440
F: (207) 287-1456
E: Jeffrey.Timberlake
@legislature.maine.gov

Timmons, Michael (R, 45)*
Room 332, State House
2 State House Station
Augusta, ME 04333
P: (207) 287-1440
F: (207) 287-1456
E: Michael.Timmons
@legislature.maine.gov

Tipping-Spitz, Ryan D. (D, 123)
Room 333, State House
2 State House Station
Augusta, ME 04333
P: (207) 287-1430
F: (207) 287-1456
E: Tipping-Spitz
@legislature.maine.gov

Tucker, Ralph (D, 50)*
Room 333, State House
2 State House Station
Augusta, ME 04333
P: (207) 287-1430
F: (207) 287-1456
E: Ralph.Tucker
@legislature.maine.gov

Tuell, William (R, 139)*
Room 332, State House
2 State House Station
Augusta, ME 04333
P: (207) 287-1440
F: (207) 287-1456
E: Will.Tuell
@legislature.maine.gov

Turner, Beth P. (R, 141)
Room 332, State House
2 State House Station
Augusta, ME 04333
P: (207) 287-1440
F: (207) 287-1456
E: Beth.Turner
@legislature.maine.gov

Vachon, Karen (R, 29)*
Room 332, State House
2 State House Station
Augusta, ME 04333
P: (207) 287-1440
F: (207) 287-1456
E: Karen.Vachon
@legislature.maine.gov

Verow, Arthur C. (D, 128)
Room 333, State House
2 State House Station
Augusta, ME 04333
P: (207) 287-1430
F: (207) 287-1456
E: Archie.Verow
@legislature.maine.gov

Wadsworth, Nathan (R, 70)*
Room 332, State House
2 State House Station
Augusta, ME 04333
P: (207) 287-1440
F: (207) 287-1456
E: Nathan.Wadsworth
@legislature.maine.gov

Wallace, Raymond A. (R, 104)
Room 332, State House
2 State House Station
Augusta, ME 04333
P: (207) 287-1440
F: (207) 287-1456
E: Raymond.Wallace
@legislature.maine.gov

Ward, Karleton (R, 131)*
Room 332, State House
2 State House Station
Augusta, ME 04333
P: (207) 287-1440
F: (207) 287-1456
E: Karl.Ward
@legislature.maine.gov

Warren, Charlotte (D, 84)*
Room 333, State House
2 State House Station
Augusta, ME 04333
P: (207) 287-1430
F: (207) 287-1456
E: Charlotte.Warren
@legislature.maine.gov

Welsh, Joan W. (D, 94)
Room 333, State House
2 State House Station
Augusta, ME 04333
P: (207) 287-1430
F: (207) 287-1456
E: Joan.Welsh
@legislature.maine.gov

White, Dustin Michael (R, 146)*
Room 332, State House
2 State House Station
Augusta, ME 04333
P: (207) 287-1440
F: (207) 287-1456
E: Dustin.White
@legislature.maine.gov

Winsor, Tom J. (R, 71)
Room 332, State House
2 State House Station
Augusta, ME 04333
P: (207) 287-1440
F: (207) 287-1456
E: Tom.Winsor
@legislature.maine.gov

Wood, Stephen J. (R, 57)
Room 332, State House
2 State House Station
Augusta, ME 04333
P: (207) 287-1440
F: (207) 287-1456
E: Stephen.Wood
@legislature.maine.gov

Congress

Senate

Collins, Susan (R)
King Jr., Angus S. (I)

House

Pingree, Chellie (D, 1)
Poliquin, Bruce (R, 2)

Maryland

Executive

Governor

Hon. Larry Hogan (R)
Governor
State House
100 State Circle
Annapolis, MD 21401
P: (410) 974-3901
F: (410) 974-3275

Lieutenant Governor

Hon. Boyd Rutherford (R)
Lieutenant Governor
100 State Circle
Annapolis, MD 21401
P: (410) 974-3901
F: (410) 974-2804
E: ltgov@gov.state.md.us

Attorney General

Hon. Brian E. Frosh (D)
Attorney General
200 Saint Paul Place
Baltimore, MD 21202
P: (410) 576-6300
F: (410) 576-6404
E: oag@oag.state.md.us

Auditor

Mr. Thomas J. Barnickel III
(appointed by the Legislature)
Legislative Auditor
301 West Preston Street, Room 1202
Baltimore, MD 21201
P: (410) 946-5900
F: (410) 946-5999
E: tbarnickel@ola.state.md.us

Comptroller

Hon. Peter Franchot (D)
Comptroller
80 Calvert Street
P.O. Box 466
Annapolis, MD 21404
P: (410) 260-7801
F: (410) 974-3808
E: mdcomptroller@comp.state.md.us

Secretary of State

Hon. John C. Wobensmith
(appointed)
Acting Secretary of State
16 Francis Street
Annapolis, MD 21401
P: (410) 974-5521
F: (410) 841-5527
E: mdsos@sos.state.md.us

Treasurer

Hon. Nancy K. Kopp
(elected by the Legislature)
State Treasurer
Goldstein Treasury Building
80 Calvert Street
Annapolis, MD 21401
P: (410) 260-7160
F: (410) 974-3530
E: nkopp@treasurer.state.md.us

Judiciary

Court of Appeals (MR)

Ms. Bessie M. Decker
Clerk of Court of Appeals
Robert Murphy Courts of Appeal Building
361 Rowe Boulevard
Annapolis, MD 21401
P: (410) 260-1500

Hon. Mary Ellen Barbera
Chief Judge
Hon. Sally D. Adkins
Hon. Lynne A. Battaglia
Hon. Clayton Greene Jr.
Hon. Glenn T. Harrell Jr.
Hon. Robert N. McDonald
Hon. Shirley M. Watts

Legislative Senate

Senate President

Sen. Thomas V. Mike Miller Jr. (D)
Senate President
State House, H-107
100 State Circle
Annapolis, MD 21401
P: (410) 841-3700
F: (410) 841-3910
E: thomas.v.mike.miller@senate.state.md.us

President Pro Tempore of the Senate

Sen. Nathaniel J. McFadden (D)
President Pro Tem
Miller Senate Office Building, Room 422
11 Bladen Street
Annapolis, MD 21401
P: (410) 841-3165
F: (410) 841-3138
E: nathaniel.mcfadden@senate.state.md.us

Senate Majority Leader

Sen. Catherine E. Pugh (D)
Majority Leader
Miller Senate Building, 3 East Wing
11 Bladen Street
Annapolis, MD 21401
P: (410) 841-3656
F: (410) 841-3738
E: catherine.pugh@senate.state.md.us

Senate Minority Leader

Sen. J.B. Jennings (R)
Minority Leader
James Senate Office Building, Room 423
11 Bladen Street
Annapolis, MD 21401
P: (410) 841-3706
F: (410) 841-3750
E: jb.jennings@senate.state.md.us

Secretary of the Senate

Mr. William B.C. Addison Jr.
Secretary of the Senate
Room H-105, State House
100 State Circle
Annapolis, MD 21401
P: (410) 841-3908
F: (410) 841-3910

Members of the Senate

Astle, John C. (D, 30)
James Senate Office Building, Room 123
11 Bladen Street
Annapolis, MD 21401
P: (410) 841-3578
F: (410) 841-3156
E: john.astle@senate.state.md.us

Bates, Gail H. (R, 9)
James Senate Office Building, Room 401
11 Bladen Street
Annapolis, MD 21401
P: (410) 841-3671
F: (301) 858-3571
E: gail.bates@senate.state.md.us

Benson, Joanne Claybon (D, 24)
James Senate Office Building, Room 214
11 Bladen Street
Annapolis, MD 21401
P: (410) 841-3148
F: (301) 858-3149
E: joanne.benson@senate.state.md.us

Brochin, James (D, 42)
James Senate Office Building, Room 221
11 Bladen Street
Annapolis, MD 21401
P: (410) 841-3648
F: (410) 841-3643
E: jim.brochin@senate.state.md.us

Cassilly, Bob (R, 34)*
James Senate Office Building, Room 321
11 Bladen Street
Annapolis, MD 21401
P: (410) 841-3158
E: Bob.Cassilly@senate.state.md.us

Conway, Joan Carter (D, 43)
Miller Senate Building, 2 West Wing
11 Bladen Street
Annapolis, MD 21401
P: (410) 841-3145
F: (410) 841-3135
E: joan.carter.conway@senate.state.md.us

Currie, Ulysses (D, 25)
James Senate Office Building, Room 201
11 Bladen Street
Annapolis, MD 21401
P: (410) 841-3127
F: (301) 858-3733
E: ulysses.currie@senate.state.md.us

DeGrange Sr., James E. (D, 32)
James Senate Office Building, Room 101
11 Bladen Street
Annapolis, MD 21401
P: (410) 841-3593
F: (410) 841-3589
E: james.degrange@senate.state.md.us

Eckardt, Adelaide C. (R, 37)
James Senate Office Building, Room 322
11 Bladen Street
Annapolis, MD 21401
P: (410) 841-3590
F: (410) 841-3299
E: adelaide.eckardt@house.state.md.us

Edwards, George C. (R, 1)
James Senate Office Building, Room 323
11 Bladen Street
Annapolis, MD 21401
P: (410) 841-3565
F: (301) 858-3552
E: george.edwards@senate.state.md.us

Feldman, Brian J. (D, 15)
James Senate Office Building, Room 104
11 Bladen Street
Annapolis, MD 21401
P: (410) 841-3169
F: (410) 841-3607
E: brian.feldman@senate.state.md.us

Ferguson IV, William C. (D, 46)
Miller Senate Building, Room 401
11 Bladen Street
Annapolis, MD 21401
P: (410) 841-3600
F: (410) 841-3161
E: bill.ferguson@senate.state.md.us

Gladden, Lisa A. (D, 41)
Miller Senate Building, 2 East Wing
11 Bladen Street
Annapolis, MD 21401
P: (410) 841-3697
F: (410) 841-3142
E: lisa.gladden@senate.state.md.us

Guzzone, Guy (D, 13)
James Senate Office Building, Room 121
11 Bladen Street
Annapolis, MD 21401
P: (410) 841-3572
F: (410) 841-3438
E: Bob.Cassilly@senate.state.md.us

Hershey Jr., Stephen S. (R, 36)
James Senate Office Building, Room 420
11 Bladen Street
Annapolis, MD 21401
P: (410) 841-3639
F: (410) 841-3762
E: steve.hershey@senate.state.md.us

Hough, Michael (R, 4)
James Senate Office Building, Room 403
11 Bladen Street
Annapolis, MD 21401
P: (410) 841-3704
E: michael.hough@senate.state.md.us

Jennings, J.B. (R, 7)
James Senate Office Building, Room 423
11 Bladen Street
Annapolis, MD 21401
P: (410) 841-3706
F: (410) 841-3750
E: jb.jennings@senate.state.md.us

Kagan, Cheryl C. (D, 17)
James Senate Office Building, Room 203
11 Bladen Street
Annapolis, MD 21401
P: (410) 841-3134

Kasemeyer, Edward J. (D, 12)
Miller Senate Building, 3 West Wing
11 Bladen Street
Annapolis, MD 21401
P: (410) 841-3653
F: (410) 841-3091
E: edward.kasemeyer@senate.state.md.us

Kelley, Delores Goodwin (D, 10)
James Senate Office Building, Room 302
11 Bladen Street
Annapolis, MD 21401
P: (410) 841-3606
F: (410) 841-3399
E: delores.kelley@senate.state.md.us

King, Nancy J. (D, 39)
James Senate Office Building, Room 223
11 Bladen Street
Annapolis, MD 21401
P: (301) 858-3686
F: (301) 858-6370
E: nancy.king@senate.state.md.us

Klausmeier, Katherine A. (D, 8)
James Senate Office Building, Room 103
11 Bladen Street
Annapolis, MD 21401
P: (410) 841-3620
F: (410) 841-3085
E: katherine.klausmeier@senate.state.md.us

Lee, Susan C. (D, 16)
James Senate Office Building, Room 222
11 Bladen Street
Annapolis, MD 21401
P: (410) 841-3124
F: (301) 858-3424
E: susan.lee@senate.state.md.us

Madaleno Jr., Richard Stuart (D, 18)
Miller Senate Building, 3 West Wing
11 Bladen Street
Annapolis, MD 21401
P: (410) 841-3137
F: (301) 858-3676
E: richard.madaleno@senate.state.md.us

Manno, Roger (D, 19)
James Senate Office Building, Room 102
11 Bladen Street
Annapolis, MD 21401
P: (410) 841-3151
F: (301) 858-3740
E: roger.manno@senate.state.md.us

Mathias Jr., James N. (D, 38)
James Senate Office Building, Room 216
11 Bladen Street
Annapolis, MD 21401
P: (410) 841-3645
F: (410) 841-3006
E: james.mathias@senate.state.md.us

McFadden, Nathaniel J. (D, 45)
Miller Senate Office Building, Room 422
11 Bladen Street
Annapolis, MD 21401
P: (410) 841-3165
F: (410) 841-3138
E: nathaniel.mcfadden@senate.state.md.us

Middleton, Thomas McLain (D, 28)
Miller Senate Building, 3 East Wing
11 Bladen Street
Annapolis, MD 21401
P: (410) 841-3616
F: (301) 858-3682
E: thomas.mclain.middleton@senate.state.md.us

Miller Jr., Thomas V. Mike (D, 27)
State House, H-107
100 State Circle
Annapolis, MD 21401
P: (410) 841-3700
F: (410) 841-3910
E: thomas.v.mike.miller@senate.state.md.us

Montgomery, Karen S. (D, 14)
James Senate Office Building, Room 202
11 Bladen Street
Annapolis, MD 21401
P: (410) 841-3625
F: (301) 858-3618
E: karen.montgomery@senate.state.md.us

Muse, C. Anthony (D, 26)
Miller Senate Building, Room 420
11 Bladen Street
Annapolis, MD 21401
P: (410) 841-3092
F: (301) 858-3410
E: anthony.muse@senate.state.md.us

Maryland

Nathan-Pulliam, Shirley (D, 44)
James Senate Office Building, Room 304
11 Bladen Street
Annapolis, MD 21401
P: (410) 841-3612
F: (410) 841-3100
E: shirley.nathan.pulliam@senate.state.md.us

Norman, Wayne (R, 35)
James Senate Office Building, Room 315
11 Bladen Street
Annapolis, MD 21401
P: (410) 841-3603
F: (410) 841-3190
E: wayne.norman@senate.state.md.us

Peters, Douglas J.J. (D, 23)
James Senate Office Building, Room 120
11 Bladen Street
Annapolis, MD 21401
P: (410) 841-3631
F: (301) 858-3174
E: douglas.peters@senate.state.md.us

Pinsky, Paul G. (D, 22)
James Senate Office Building, Room 220
11 Bladen Street
Annapolis, MD 21401
P: (410) 841-3155
F: (301) 858-3144
E: paul.pinsky@senate.state.md.us

Pugh, Catherine E. (D, 40)
Miller Senate Building, 3 East Wing
11 Bladen Street
Annapolis, MD 21401
P: (410) 841-3656
F: (410) 841-3738
E: catherine.pugh@senate.state.md.us

Ramirez, Victor R. (D, 47)
James Senate Office Building, Room 303
11 Bladen Street
Annapolis, MD 21401
P: (410) 841-3745
F: (301) 858-3387
E: victor.ramirez@senate.state.md.us

Raskin, Jamin B. (D, 20)
James Senate Office Building, Room 122
11 Bladen Street
Annapolis, MD 21401
P: (410) 841-3634
F: (301) 858-3166
E: jamie.raskin@senate.state.md.us

Ready, Justin D. (R, 5)
James Senate Office Building, Room 414
11 Bladen Street
Annapolis, MD 21401
P: (410) 841-3683
E: justin.ready@senate.state.md.us

Reilly, Edward R. (R, 33)
James Senate Office Building, Room 316
11 Bladen Street
Annapolis, MD 21401
P: (410) 841-3568
F: (410) 841-3067
E: edward.reilly@senate.state.md.us

Rosapepe, James C. (D, 21)
James Senate Office Building, Room 314
11 Bladen Street
Annapolis, MD 21401
P: (410) 841-3141
F: (410) 841-3195
E: jim.rosapepe@senate.state.md.us

Salling, Johnny Ray (R, 6)*
James Senate Office Building, Room 416
11 Bladen Street
Annapolis, MD 21401
P: (410) 841-3587
E: JohnnyRay.Salling@senate.state.md.us

Serafini, Andrew A. (R, 2)
James Senate Office Building, Room 402
11 Bladen Street
Annapolis, MD 21401
P: (410) 841-3903
E: andrew.serafini@senate.state.md.us

Simonaire, Bryan W. (R, 31)
James Senate Office Building, Room 320
11 Bladen Street
Annapolis, MD 21401
P: (410) 841-3658
F: (410) 841-3586
E: bryan.simonaire@senate.state.md.us

Waugh, Steve (R, 29)*
Miller Senate Building, 2 West Wing
11 Bladen Street
Annapolis, MD 21401
P: (410) 841-3673
E: Steve.Waugh@senate.state.md.us

Young, Ronald N. (D, 3)
James Senate Office Building, Room 301
11 Bladen Street
Annapolis, MD 21401
P: (410) 841-3575
F: (301) 858-3193
E: ronald.young@senate.state.md.us

Zirkin, Robert A. (D, 11)
Miller Senate Building, 2 East Wing
11 Bladen Street
Annapolis, MD 21401
P: (410) 841-3131
F: (410) 841-3737
E: bobby.zirkin@senate.state.md.us

House

Speaker of the House

Delegate Michael Erin Busch (D)
Speaker
State House, H-101
State Circle
Annapolis, MD 21401
P: (410) 841-3800
F: (410) 841-3880
E: michael.busch@house.state.md.us

Speaker Pro Tempore of the House

Delegate Adrienne A. Jones (D)
Speaker Pro Tem
House Office Building, Room 312
6 Bladen Street
Annapolis, MD 21401
P: (410) 841-3391
F: (410) 841-3157
E: adrienne.jones@house.state.md.us

House Majority Leader

Delegate Anne R. Kaiser (D)
Majority Leader
House Office Building, Room 350
6 Bladen Street
Annapolis, MD 21401
P: (410) 841-3036
F: (301) 858-3060
E: anne.kaiser@house.state.md.us

House Minority Leader

Delegate Nicholaus R. Kipke (R)
Minority Leader
House Office Building, Room 212
6 Bladen Street
Annapolis, MD 21401
P: (410) 841-3421
F: (410) 841-3553
E: nicholaus.kipke@house.state.md.us

Clerk of the House

Ms. Sylvia Siegert
Chief Clerk
Room H-104, State House
100 State Circle
Annapolis, MD 21401
P: (410) 841-3999
E: hseclerk@mlis.state.md.us

Members of the House

Adams, Christopher (R, 37B)*
House Office Building, Room 323
6 Bladen Street
Annapolis, MD 21401
P: (410) 841-3343
E: Christopher.Adams@house.state.md.us

Afzali, Kathryn L. (R, 4A)
House Office Building, Room 326
6 Bladen Street
Annapolis, MD 21401
P: (410) 841-3288
F: (301) 858-3184
E: kathy.afzali@house.state.md.us

Anderson, Curtis Stovall (D, 43)
House Office Building, Room 314
6 Bladen Street
Annapolis, MD 21401
P: (410) 841-3291
F: (410) 841-3024
E: curt.anderson@house.state.md.us

Anderton Jr., Carl (R, 38B)*
House Office Building, Room 317
6 Bladen Street
Annapolis, MD 21401
P: (410) 841-3431
E: Carl.Anderton@house.state.md.us

Angel, Angela (D, 25)*
House Office Building, Room 216
6 Bladen Street
Annapolis, MD 21401
P: (410) 841-3707
E: Angela.Angel@house.state.md.us

Arentz, Steven J. (R, 36)
House Office Building, Room 308
6 Bladen Street
Annapolis, MD 21401
P: (410) 841-3543
F: (410) 841-3098
E: steven.arentz@house.state.md.us

Atterbeary, Vanessa (D, 13)*
House Office Building, Room 216
6 Bladen Street
Annapolis, MD 21401
P: (410) 841-3471
E: Vanessa.Atterbeary@house.state.md.us

Aumann, Susan L.M. (R, 42B)
House Office Building, Room 303
6 Bladen Street
Annapolis, MD 21401
P: (410) 841-3258
F: (410) 841-3163
E: susan.aumann@house.state.md.us

Barkley, Charles E. (D, 39)
House Office Building, Room 223
6 Bladen Street
Annapolis, MD 21401
P: (301) 858-3001
F: (301) 858-3009
E: charles.barkley@house.state.md.us

Barnes, Benjamin S. (D, 21)
House Office Building, Room 151
6 Bladen Street
Annapolis, MD 21401
P: (410) 841-3046
F: (410) 841-3346
E: ben.barnes@house.state.md.us

Barnes, Darryl (D, 25)*
House Office Building, Room 206
6 Bladen Street
Annapolis, MD 21401
P: (410) 841-3557
E: Darryl.Barnes@house.state.md.us

Barron, Erek (D, 24)*
House Office Building, Room 207
6 Bladen Street
Annapolis, MD 21401
P: (410) 841-3692
E: Erek.Barron@house.state.md.us

Barve, Kumar P. (D, 17)
House Office Building, Room 251
6 Bladen Street
Annapolis, MD 21401
P: (410) 841-3990
F: (301) 858-3850
E: kumar.barve@house.state.md.us

Beidle, Pamela G. (D, 32)
House Office Building, Room 165
6 Bladen Street
Annapolis, MD 21401
P: (410) 841-3370
F: (410) 841-3347
E: pamela.beidle@house.state.md.us

Beitzel, Wendell R. (R, 1A)
House Office Building, Room 309
6 Bladen Street
Annapolis, MD 21401
P: (410) 841-3435
F: (301) 858-3040
E: wendell.beitzel@house.state.md.us

Branch, Talmadge (D, 45)
House Office Building, Room 151
6 Bladen Street
Annapolis, MD 21401
P: (410) 841-3398
F: (410) 841-3550
E: talmadge.branch@house.state.md.us

Bromwell, Eric M. (D, 8)
House Office Building, Room 415
6 Bladen Street
Annapolis, MD 21401
P: (410) 841-3766
F: (410) 841-3850
E: eric.bromwell@house.state.md.us

Brooks, Benjamin (D, 10)*
House Office Building, Room 304
6 Bladen Street
Annapolis, MD 21401
P: (410) 841-3352
E: Benjamin.Brooks@house.state.md.us

Buckel, Jason (R, 1B)
House Office Building, Room 309
6 Bladen Street
Annapolis, MD 21401
P: (410) 841-3404
E: Jason.Buckel@house.state.md.us

Busch, Michael Erin (D, 30A)
State House, H-101
State Circle
Annapolis, MD 21401
P: (410) 841-3800
F: (410) 841-3880
E: michael.busch@house.state.md.us

Campos, Will (D, 47B)*
House Office Building, Room 206
6 Bladen Street
Annapolis, MD 21401
P: (410) 841-3340
E: Will.Campos@house.state.md.us

Carey, Ned (D, 31A)*
House Office Building, Room 161
6 Bladen Street
Annapolis, MD 21401
P: (410) 841-3047
E: Ned.Carey@house.state.md.us

Carozza, Mary Beth (R, 37C)*
House Office Building, Room 203
6 Bladen Street
Annapolis, MD 21401
P: (410) 841-3356
E: MaryBeth.Carozza@house.state.md.us

Carr Jr., Alfred C. (D, 18)
House Office Building, Room 222
6 Bladen Street
Annapolis, MD 21401
P: (410) 841-3638
F: (301) 858-3053
E: alfred.carr@house.state.md.us

Carter, Jill P. (D, 41)
House Office Building, Room 416
6 Bladen Street
Annapolis, MD 21401
P: (410) 841-3268
F: (410) 841-3251
E: jill.carter@house.state.md.us

Cassilly, Andrew (R, 35B)*
House Office Building, Room 316
6 Bladen Street
Annapolis, MD 21401
P: (410) 841-3444
E: Andrew.Cassilly@house.state.md.us

Chang, Mark (D, 32)*
House Office Building, Room 160
6 Bladen Street
Annapolis, MD 21401
P: (410) 841-3511
E: Mark.Chang@house.state.md.us

Ciliberti, Barrie S. (R, 4)*
House Office Building, Room 324
6 Bladen Street
Annapolis, MD 21401
P: (410) 841-3080
E: Barrie.Ciliberti@house.state.md.us

Clippinger, Luke H. (D, 46)
House Office Building, Room 350
6 Bladen Street
Annapolis, MD 21401
P: (410) 841-3303
F: (410) 841-3537
E: luke.clippinger@house.state.md.us

Maryland

Cluster Jr., John W.E. (R, 8)
House Office Building, Room 308
6 Bladen Street
Annapolis, MD 21401
P: (410) 841-3526
F: (410) 841-3098
E: john.cluster@house.state.md.us

Conaway Jr., Frank M. (D, 40)
House Office Building, Room 314
6 Bladen Street
Annapolis, MD 21401
P: (410) 841-3189
F: (410) 841-3079
E: frank.conaway@house.state.md.us

Cullison, Bonnie L. (D, 19)
House Office Building, Room 350
6 Bladen Street
Annapolis, MD 21401
P: (410) 841-3883
F: (301) 858-3882
E: bonnie.cullison@house.state.md.us

Davis, Dereck E. (D, 25)
House Office Building, Room 231
6 Bladen Street
Annapolis, MD 21401
P: (410) 841-3519
F: (301) 858-3558
E: dereck.davis@house.state.md.us

Dumais, Kathleen M. (D, 15)
House Office Building, Room 101
6 Bladen Street
Annapolis, MD 21401
P: (410) 841-3052
F: (301) 858-3219
E: kathleen.dumais@house.state.md.us

Ebersole, Eric (D, 12)*
House Office Building, Room 305
6 Bladen Street
Annapolis, MD 21401
P: (410) 841-3328
E: Eric.Ebersole@house.state.md.us

Fennell, Diana (D, 47A)*
House Office Building, Room 209
6 Bladen Street
Annapolis, MD 21401
P: (410) 841-3478
E: Diana.Fennell@house.state.md.us

Fisher, Mark (R, 27C)
House Office Building, Room 202
6 Bladen Street
Annapolis, MD 21401
P: (410) 841-3231
F: (301) 858-3335
E: mark.fisher@house.state.md.us

Flanagan, Bob (R, 9B)
House Office Building, Room 430
6 Bladen Street
Annapolis, MD 21401
P: (410) 841-3077
E: Bob.Flanagan@house.state.md.us

Folden, William (R, 3B)*
House Office Building, Room 324
6 Bladen Street
Annapolis, MD 21401
P: (410) 841-3240
E: William.Folden@house.state.md.us

Fraser-Hidalgo, David (D, 15)
House Office Building, Room 226
6 Bladen Street
Annapolis, MD 21401
P: (410) 841-3186
F: (301) 858-3112
E: david.fraser.hidalgo@house.state.md.us

Frick, Bill (D, 16)
House Office Building, Room 350
6 Bladen Street
Annapolis, MD 21401
P: (410) 841-3454
F: (301) 858-3457
E: bill.frick@house.state.md.us

Frush, Barbara A. (D, 21)
House Office Building, Room 364
6 Bladen Street
Annapolis, MD 21401
P: (410) 841-3114
F: (410) 841-3116
E: barbara.frush@house.state.md.us

Gaines, Tawanna P. (D, 22)
House Office Building, Room 363
6 Bladen Street
Annapolis, MD 21401
P: (410) 841-3058
F: (301) 858-3119
E: tawanna.gaines@house.state.md.us

Ghrist, Jeff (R, 36)*
House Office Building, Room 410
6 Bladen Street
Annapolis, MD 21401
P: (410) 841-3555
E: Jeff.Ghrist@house.state.md.us

Gilchrist, James W. (D, 17)
House Office Building, Room 219
6 Bladen Street
Annapolis, MD 21401
P: (410) 841-3744
F: (301) 858-3057
E: jim.gilchrist@house.state.md.us

Glass, Glen (R, 34A)
House Office Building, Room 325
6 Bladen Street
Annapolis, MD 21401
P: (410) 841-3280
F: (410) 841-3754
E: glen.glass@house.state.md.us

Glenn, Cheryl D. (D, 45)
House Office Building, Room 413
6 Bladen Street
Annapolis, MD 21401
P: (410) 841-3257
F: (410) 841-3019
E: cheryl.glenn@house.state.md.us

Grammer Jr., Robin (R, 6)*
House Office Building, Room 307
6 Bladen Street
Annapolis, MD 21401
P: (410) 841-3298
E: Robin.Grammer@house.state.md.us

Gutierrez, Ana Sol (D, 18)
House Office Building, Room 404
6 Bladen Street
Annapolis, MD 21401
P: (410) 841-3181
F: (301) 858-3232
E: ana.gutierrez@house.state.md.us

Hammen, Peter A. (D, 46)
House Office Building, Room 241
6 Bladen Street
Annapolis, MD 21401
P: (410) 841-3772
F: (410) 841-3409
E: peter.hammen@house.state.md.us

Hayes, Antonio (D, 40)*
House Office Building, Room 315
6 Bladen Street
Annapolis, MD 21401
P: (410) 841-3545
E: Antonio.Hayes@house.state.md.us

Haynes, Keith E. (D, 44A)
House Office Building, Room 424
6 Bladen Street
Annapolis, MD 21401
P: (401) 841-3801
F: (410) 841-3530
E: keith.haynes@house.state.md.us

Healey, Anne (D, 22)
House Office Building, Room 361
6 Bladen Street
Annapolis, MD 21401
P: (410) 841-3961
F: (301) 858-3223
E: anne.healey@house.state.md.us

Hettleman, Shelly (D, 11)*
House Office Building, Room 311
6 Bladen Street
Annapolis, MD 21401
P: (410) 841-3833
E: Shelly.Hettleman@house.state.md.us

Hill, Terri (D, 12)*
House Office Building, Room 215
6 Bladen Street
Annapolis, MD 21401
P: (410) 841-3378
E: Terri.Hill@house.state.md.us

Hixson, Sheila Ellis (D, 20)
House Office Building, Room 131
6 Bladen Street
Annapolis, MD 21401
P: (410) 841-3469
F: (410) 841-3777
E: sheila.hixson@house.state.md.us

Holmes Jr., Marvin E. (D, 23B)
House Office Building, Room 313
6 Bladen Street
Annapolis, MD 21401
P: (410) 841-3310
F: (410) 841-3017
E: marvin.holmes@house.state.md.us

Hornberger, Kevin Bailey (R, 35A)*
House Office Building, Room 410
6 Bladen Street
Annapolis, MD 21401
P: (410) 841-3284
E: Kevin.Hornberger@house.state.md.us

Howard, Carolyn J.B. (D, 24)
House Office Building, Room 301
6 Bladen Street
Annapolis, MD 21401
P: (410) 841-3919
F: (410) 841-3925
E: carolyn.howard@house.state.md.us

Howard, Seth (R, 30B)*
House Office Building, Room 159
6 Bladen Street
Annapolis, MD 21401
P: (410) 841-3439
E: Seth.Howard@house.state.md.us

Impallaria, Richard K. (R, 7)
House Office Building, Room 310
6 Bladen Street
Annapolis, MD 21401
P: (410) 841-3289
F: (410) 841-3598
E: rick.impallaria@house.state.md.us

Jackson, Michael (D, 27B)*
House Office Building, Room 204
6 Bladen Street
Annapolis, MD 21401
P: (410) 841-3103
E: Michael.Jackson@house.state.md.us

Jacobs, Jay A. (R, 36)
House Office Building, Room 321
6 Bladen Street
Annapolis, MD 21401
P: (410) 841-3449
F: (410) 841-3093
E: jay.jacobs@house.state.md.us

Jalisi, Jay (D, 10)*
House Office Building, Room 304
6 Bladen Street
Annapolis, MD 21401
P: (410) 841-3358
F: (410) 841-3100
E: Jay.Jalisi@house.state.md.us

Jameson, Sally Young (D, 28)
House Office Building, Room 231
6 Bladen Street
Annapolis, MD 21401
P: (410) 841-3337
F: (301) 858-3277
E: sally.jameson@house.state.md.us

Jones, Adrienne A. (D, 10)
House Office Building, Room 312
6 Bladen Street
Annapolis, MD 21401
P: (410) 841-3391
F: (410) 841-3157
E: adrienne.jones@house.state.md.us

Kaiser, Anne R. (D, 14)
House Office Building, Room 350
6 Bladen Street
Annapolis, MD 21401
P: (410) 841-3036
F: (301) 858-3060
E: anne.kaiser@house.state.md.us

Kelly, Ariana B. (D, 16)
House Office Building, Room 210
6 Bladen Street
Annapolis, MD 21401
P: (410) 841-3642
F: (301) 858-3026
E: ariana.kelly@house.state.md.us

Kipke, Nicholaus R. (R, 31B)
House Office Building, Room 212
6 Bladen Street
Annapolis, MD 21401
P: (410) 841-3421
F: (410) 841-3553
E: nicholaus.kipke@house.state.md.us

Kittleman, Trent (R, 9A)*
House Office Building, Room 202
6 Bladen Street
Annapolis, MD 21401
P: (410) 841-3556
E: Trent.Kittleman@house.state.md.us

Knotts, Tony (D, 26)*
House Office Building, Room 204
6 Bladen Street
Annapolis, MD 21401
P: (410) 841-3212
E: Tony.Knotts@house.state.md.us

Korman, Marc (D, 16)*
House Office Building, Room 210
6 Bladen Street
Annapolis, MD 21401
P: (410) 841-3649
E: Marc.Korman@house.state.md.us

Kramer, Benjamin F. (D, 19)
House Office Building, Room 226
6 Bladen Street
Annapolis, MD 21401
P: (410) 841-3485
F: (301) 858-3875
E: benjamin.kramer@house.state.md.us

Krebs, Susan W. (R, 5)
House Office Building, Room 405
6 Bladen Street
Annapolis, MD 21401
P: (410) 841-3200
F: (410) 841-3349
E: susan.krebs@house.state.md.us

Krimm, Carol (D, 3A)*
House Office Building, Room 215
6 Bladen Street
Annapolis, MD 21401
P: (410) 841-3472
E: Carol.Krimm@house.state.md.us

Lafferty, Stephen W. (D, 42A)
House Office Building, Room 305
6 Bladen Street
Annapolis, MD 21401
P: (410) 841-3487
F: (410) 841-3501
E: stephen.lafferty@house.state.md.us

Lam, Clarence (D, 12)*
House Office Building, Room 214
6 Bladen Street
Annapolis, MD 21401
P: (410) 841-3205
E: Clarence.Lam@house.state.md.us

Lierman, Brooke Elizabeth (D, 46)*
House Office Building, Room 311
6 Bladen Street
Annapolis, MD 21401
P: (410) 841-3319
E: Brooke.Lierman@house.state.md.us

Lisanti, Mary Ann (D, 34A)*
House Office Building, Room 217
6 Bladen Street
Annapolis, MD 21401
P: (410) 841-3331
E: MaryAnn.Lisanti@house.state.md.us

Long, Bob (R, 6)*
House Office Building, Room 325
6 Bladen Street
Annapolis, MD 21401
P: (410) 841-3458
E: Bob.Long@house.state.md.us

Luedtke, Eric G. (D, 14)
House Office Building, Room 222
6 Bladen Street
Annapolis, MD 21401
P: (410) 841-3110
F: (301) 858-3053
E: eric.luedtke@house.state.md.us

Mautz, Johnny (R, 37B)*
House Office Building, Room 323
6 Bladen Street
Annapolis, MD 21401
P: (410) 841-3429
E: Johnny.Mautz@house.state.md.us

Maryland

McComas, Susan K. (R, 34B)
House Office Building, Room 319
6 Bladen Street
Annapolis, MD 21401
P: (410) 841-3272
F: (410) 841-3244
E: susan.mccomas@house.state.md.us

McConkey, Tony (R, 33)
House Office Building, Room 163
6 Bladen Street
Annapolis, MD 21401
P: (410) 841-3406
F: (410) 841-3209
E: tony.mcconkey@house.state.md.us

McCray, Cory (D, 45)*
House Office Building, Room 315
6 Bladen Street
Annapolis, MD 21401
P: (410) 841-3486
E: Cory.McCray@house.state.md.us

McDonough, Patrick L. (R, 7)
House Office Building, Room 310
6 Bladen Street
Annapolis, MD 21401
P: (410) 841-3334
F: (410) 841-3598
E: pat.mcdonough@house.state.md.us

McIntosh, Maggie (D, 43)
House Office Building, Room 121
6 Bladen Street
Annapolis, MD 21401
P: (410) 841-3407
F: (410) 841-3509
E: maggie.mcintosh@house.state.md.us

McKay, Mike (R, 1C)*
House Office Building, Room 322
6 Bladen Street
Annapolis, MD 21401
P: (410) 841-3321
E: Mike.McKay@house.state.md.us

McMillan, Herbert H. (R, 30A)
House Office Building, Room 164
6 Bladen Street
Annapolis, MD 21401
P: (410) 841-3211
F: (410) 841-3386
E: herb.mcmillan@house.state.md.us

Metzgar, Ric (R, 6)*
House Office Building, Room 307
6 Bladen Street
Annapolis, MD 21401
P: (410) 841-3332
E: Ric.Metzgar@house.state.md.us

Miele, Christian (R, 8)*
House Office Building, Room 316
6 Bladen Street
Annapolis, MD 21401
P: (410) 841-3365
E: Christian.Miele@house.state.md.us

Miller, Aruna (D, 15)
House Office Building, Room 426
6 Bladen Street
Annapolis, MD 21401
P: (410) 841-3090
F: (301) 858-3126
E: aruna.miller@house.state.md.us

Miller, Warren E. (R, 9A)
House Office Building, Room 403
6 Bladen Street
Annapolis, MD 21401
P: (410) 841-3582
F: (410) 841-3571
E: warren.miller@house.state.md.us

Moon, David (D, 20)*
House Office Building, Room 220
6 Bladen Street
Annapolis, MD 21401
P: (410) 841-3474
E: David.Moon@house.state.md.us

Morales, Maricé (D, 19)*
House Office Building, Room 225
6 Bladen Street
Annapolis, MD 21401
P: (410) 841-3528
E: Marice.Morales@house.state.md.us

Morgan, Matt (R, 29A)*
House Office Building, Room 317
6 Bladen Street
Annapolis, MD 21401
P: (410) 841-3170
E: Matt.Morgan@house.state.md.us

Morhaim, Dan K. (D, 11)
House Office Building, Room 362
6 Bladen Street
Annapolis, MD 21401
P: (410) 841-3054
F: (410) 841-3385
E: dan.morhaim@house.state.md.us

Oaks, Nathaniel T. (D, 41)
House Office Building, Room 411
6 Bladen Street
Annapolis, MD 21401
P: (410) 841-3283
F: (410) 841-3267
E: nathaniel.oaks@house.state.md.us

O'Donnell, Anthony J. (R, 29C)
House Office Building, Room 201
6 Bladen Street
Annapolis, MD 21401
P: (410) 841-3314
F: (410) 841-3534
E: anthony.odonnell@house.state.md.us

Otto, Charles J. (R, 38A)
House Office Building, Room 321
6 Bladen Street
Annapolis, MD 21401
P: (410) 841-3433
F: (410) 841-3463
E: charles.otto@house.state.md.us

Parrott, Neil C. (R, 2A)
House Office Building, Room 213
6 Bladen Street
Annapolis, MD 21401
P: (410) 841-3636
F: (301) 858-3308
E: neil.parrott@house.state.md.us

Patterson, Edith (D, 28)*
House Office Building, Room 221
6 Bladen Street
Annapolis, MD 21401
P: (410) 841-3247
E: Edith.Patterson@house.state.md.us

Pena-Melnyk, Joseline A. (D, 21)
House Office Building, Room 425
6 Bladen Street
Annapolis, MD 21401
P: (410) 841-3502
F: (410) 841-3342
E: joseline.pena.melnyk@house.state.md.us

Pendergrass, Shane E. (D, 13)
House Office Building, Room 241
6 Bladen Street
Annapolis, MD 21401
P: (410) 841-3139
F: (410) 841-3409
E: shane.pendergrass@house.state.md.us

Platt, Andrew (D, 17)*
House Office Building, Room 220
6 Bladen Street
Annapolis, MD 21401
P: (410) 841-3037
E: Andrew.Platt@house.state.md.us

Proctor Jr., James E. (D, 27A)
House Office Building, Room 121
6 Bladen Street
Annapolis, MD 21401
P: (410) 841-3083
F: (301) 858-3459
E: james.proctor@house.state.md.us

Reilly, Teresa (R, 35B)*
House Office Building, Room 203
6 Bladen Street
Annapolis, MD 21401
P: (410) 841-3278
F: (410) 841-3190
E: Teresa.Reilly@house.state.md.us

Rey, Deb (R, 29B)*
House Office Building, Room 319
6 Bladen Street
Annapolis, MD 21401
P: (410) 841-3227
E: Deborah.Rey
@house.state.md.us

Reznik, Kirill (D, 39)
House Office Building, Room 225
6 Bladen Street
Annapolis, MD 21401
P: (410) 841-3039
F: (301) 858-3126
E: kirill.reznik
@house.state.md.us

Robinson, A. Shane (D, 39)
House Office Building, Room 223
6 Bladen Street
Annapolis, MD 21401
P: (410) 841-3021
F: (301) 858-3375
E: shane.robinson
@house.state.md.us

Robinson, Barbara A. (D, 40)
House Office Building, Room 412
6 Bladen Street
Annapolis, MD 21401
P: (410) 841-3520
F: (410) 841-3199
E: barbara.robinson
@house.state.md.us

Rosenberg, Samuel I. (D, 41)
House Office Building, Room 365
6 Bladen Street
Annapolis, MD 21401
P: (410) 841-3297
F: (410) 841-3179
E: samuel.rosenberg
@house.state.md.us

Saab, Sid (R, 33)*
House Office Building, Room 157
6 Bladen Street
Annapolis, MD 21401
P: (410) 841-3551
E: Sid.Saab
@house.state.md.us

Sample-Hughes, Sheree (D, 37A)*
House Office Building, Room 221
6 Bladen Street
Annapolis, MD 21401
P: (410) 841-3427
E: Sheree.Sample.Hughes
@house.state.md.us

Shoemaker, Haven (R, 5)*
House Office Building, Room 320
6 Bladen Street
Annapolis, MD 21401
P: (410) 841-3359
E: Haven.Shoemaker
@house.state.md.us

Simonaire, Meagan (R, 31B)*
House Office Building, Room 156
6 Bladen Street
Annapolis, MD 21401
P: (410) 841-3206
E: Meagan.Simonaire
@house.state.md.us

Smith, Will (D, 20)*
House Office Building, Room 224
6 Bladen Street
Annapolis, MD 21401
P: (410) 841-3493
E: Will.Smith
@house.state.md.us

Sophocleus, Theodore J. (D, 32)
House Office Building, Room 162
6 Bladen Street
Annapolis, MD 21401
P: (410) 841-3372
F: (410) 841-3437
E: ted.sophocleus
@house.state.md.us

Stein, Dana M. (D, 11)
House Office Building, Room 251
6 Bladen Street
Annapolis, MD 21401
P: (410) 841-3527
F: (410) 841-3373
E: dana.stein
@house.state.md.us

Sydnor III, Charles (D, 44B)*
House Office Building, Room 306
6 Bladen Street
Annapolis, MD 21401
P: (410) 841-3802
E: Charles.Sydnor
@house.state.md.us

Szeliga, Kathy (R, 7)
House Office Building, Room 212
6 Bladen Street
Annapolis, MD 21401
P: (410) 841-3698
F: (410) 841-3023
E: kathy.szeliga
@house.state.md.us

Tarlau, Jimmy (D, 47A)*
House Office Building, Room 209
6 Bladen Street
Annapolis, MD 21401
P: (410) 841-3326
E: Jimmy.Tarlau
@house.state.md.us

Turner, Frank S. (D, 13)
House Office Building, Room 131
6 Bladen Street
Annapolis, MD 21401
P: (410) 841-3246
F: (410) 841-3986
E: frank.turner
@house.state.md.us

Valderrama, Kriselda (D, 26)
House Office Building, Room 205
6 Bladen Street
Annapolis, MD 21401
P: (410) 841-3210
F: (301) 858-3525
E: kris.valderrama
@house.state.md.us

Valentino-Smith, Geraldine (D, 23A)
House Office Building, Room 427
6 Bladen Street
Annapolis, MD 21401
P: (410) 841-3101
F: (301) 858-3294
E: geraldine.
valentino.smith
@house.state.md.us

Vallario Jr., Joseph F. (D, 23B)
House Office Building, Room 101
6 Bladen Street
Annapolis, MD 21401
P: (410) 841-3488
F: (301) 858-3495
E: joseph.vallario
@house.state.md.us

Vaughn, Michael L. (D, 24)
House Office Building, Room 423
6 Bladen Street
Annapolis, MD 21401
P: (410) 841-3691
F: (301) 858-3055
E: michael.vaughn
@house.state.md.us

Vitale, Cathy M. (R, 33)
House Office Building, Room 154
6 Bladen Street
Annapolis, MD 21401
P: (410) 841-3510
F: (410) 841-3180
E: cathy.vitale
@house.state.md.us

Vogt III, David E. (R, 4)*
House Office Building, Room 326
6 Bladen Street
Annapolis, MD 21401
P: (410) 841-3118
E: David.Vogt
@house.state.md.us

Waldstreicher, Jeffrey D. (D, 18)
House Office Building, Room 414
6 Bladen Street
Annapolis, MD 21401
P: (410) 841-3130
F: (301) 858-3233
E: jeff.waldstreicher
@house.state.md.us

Walker, Jay (D, 26)
House Office Building, Room 207
6 Bladen Street
Annapolis, MD 21401
P: (410) 841-3581
F: (301) 858-3078
E: jay.walker
@house.state.md.us

Washington, Alonzo T. (D, 22)
House Office Building, Room 205
6 Bladen Street
Annapolis, MD 21401
P: (410) 841-3652
F: (301) 858-3699
E: alonzo.washington
@house.state.md.us

Maryland

Washington, Mary L. (D, 43)
House Office Building, Room 429
6 Bladen Street
Annapolis, MD 21401
P: (410) 841-3476
F: (410) 841-3295
E: mary.washington@house.state.md.us

West, Chris (R, 42B)*
House Office Building, Room 303
6 Bladen Street
Annapolis, MD 21401
P: (410) 841-3793
E: Chris.West@house.state.md.us

Wilson, Brett (R, 2B)*
House Office Building, Room 213
6 Bladen Street
Annapolis, MD 21401
P: (410) 841-3125
E: brett.wilson@house.state.md.us

Wilson, C. T. (D, 28)
House Office Building, Room 422
6 Bladen Street
Annapolis, MD 21401
P: (410) 841-3125
F: (410) 841-3367
E: ct.wilson@house.state.md.us

Young, Karen Lewis (D, 3A)*
House Office Building, Room 217
6 Bladen Street
Annapolis, MD 21401
P: (410) 841-3436
E: Karen.Young@house.state.md.us

Young, Pat (D, 44B)*
House Office Building, Room 306
6 Bladen Street
Annapolis, MD 21401
P: (410) 841-3544
E: pat.young@house.state.md.us

Zucker, Craig J. (D, 14)
House Office Building, Room 224
6 Bladen Street
Annapolis, MD 21401
P: (410) 841-3380
F: (301) 858-3266
E: craig.zucker@house.state.md.us

Congress

Senate

Cardin, Benjamin L. (D)
Mikulski, Barbara A. (D)

House

Cummings, Elijah E. (D, 7)
Delaney, John (D, 6)
Edwards, Donna F. (D, 4)
Harris, Andy (R, 1)
Hoyer, Steny H. (D, 5)
Ruppersberger, C.A. Dutch (D, 2)
Sarbanes, John P. (D, 3)
Van Hollen Jr., Christopher (D, 8)

Massachusetts

Executive

Governor

Hon. Charles Baker (R)
Governor
State House, Room 360
Boston, MA 02133
P: (617) 725-4000
F: (617) 727-9725

Lieutenant Governor

Hon. Karyn E. Polito (R)
Lieutenant Governor
One Ashburton Place
Boston, MA 02108
P: (617) 727-7030
F: (617) 742-4528

Attorney General

Hon. Maura Healey (D)
Attorney General
1 Ashburton Place
Boston, MA 02108
P: (617) 727-2200

Auditor

Hon. Suzanne M. Bump (D)
Auditor of the Commonwealth
State House, Room 230
Boston, MA 02133
P: (617) 727-2075
F: (617) 727-2383
E: suzanne.bump@sao.state.ma.us

Secretary of the Commonwealth

Hon. William Francis Galvin (D)
Secretary of the Commonwealth
State House, Room 337
Boston, MA 02133
P: (617) 727-9180
F: (617) 742-4722
E: cis@sec.state.ma.us

Treasurer

Hon. Deb Goldberg (D)
State Treasurer
State House, Room 227
Boston, MA 02133
P: (617) 367-6900
F: (617) 248-0372

Judiciary

Supreme Judicial Court (MC)

Mr. Francis V. Kenneally
Clerk
John Adams Courthouse, Suite 1-400
One Pemberton Square
Boston, MA 02108
P: (617) 557-1020
F: (617) 557-1145
E: SJCCommClerk@sjc.state.ma.us

Hon. Ralph D. Gants
Chief Justice
Hon. Margot Botsford
Hon. Robert J. Cordy
Hon. Fernande R.V. Duffly
Hon. Geraldine S. Hines
Hon. Barbara A. Lenk
Hon. Francis X. Spina

Legislative Senate

Senate President

Sen. Stanley C. Rosenberg (D)
Senate President
Room 333, State House
Boston, MA 02133
P: (617) 722-1532
F: (617) 722-1062
E: Stan.Rosenberg@masenate.gov

President Pro Tempore of the Senate

Sen. Marc R. Pacheco (D)
President Pro Tempore
Room 312B, State House
Boston, MA 02133
P: (617) 722-1551
F: (617) 722-1074
E: Marc.Pacheco@masenate.gov

Senate Majority Leader

Sen. Harriette L. Chandler (D)
Majority Leader
Room 333, State House
Boston, MA 02133
P: (617) 722-1544
F: (617) 722-1357
E: Harriette.Chandler@masenate.gov

Senate Minority Leader

Sen. Bruce E. Tarr (R)
Minority Leader
Room 308, State House
Boston, MA 02133
P: (617) 722-1600
F: (617) 722-1310
E: Bruce.Tarr@masenate.gov

Secretary of the Senate

Mr. William F. Welch
Clerk of the Senate
Room 335, State House
24 Beacon Street
Boston, MA 02133
P: (617) 722-1276
E: william.welch@state.ma.us

Members of the Senate

Barrett, Michael (D, SP62)
Room 313A, State House
Boston, MA 02133
P: (617) 722-1572
F: (617) 626-0898
E: Mike.Barrett@masenate.gov

Brownsberger, William (D, SP186)
Room 413C, State House
Boston, MA 02133
P: (617) 722-1280
F: (617) 722-2339
E: William.Brownsberger@masenate.gov

Chandler, Harriette L. (D, SP143)
Room 333, State House
Boston, MA 02133
P: (617) 722-1544
F: (617) 722-1357
E: Harriette.Chandler@masenate.gov

Chang-Diaz, Sonia Rosa (D, SP125)
Room 312D, State House
Boston, MA 02133
P: (617) 722-1673
F: (617) 722-1079
E: Sonia.Chang-Diaz@masenate.gov

Creem, Cynthia Stone (D, SP174)
Room 312A, State House
Boston, MA 02133
P: (617) 722-1639
F: (617) 722-1266
E: Cynthia.Creem@masenate.gov

DeMacedo, Viriato Manuel (R, SP181)
Room 70, State House
Boston, MA 02133
P: (617) 722-1330
F: (617) 722-2390
E: Vinny.deMacedo@mahouse.gov

DiDomenico, Sal N. (D, SP176)
Room 218, State House
Boston, MA 02133
P: (617) 722-1650
F: (617) 722-1323
E: Sal.DiDomenico@masenate.gov

Donnelly, Kenneth J. (D, SP63)
Room 413D, State House
Boston, MA 02133
P: (617) 722-1432
F: (617) 722-1004
E: Kenneth.Donnelly@masenate.gov

Donoghue, Eileen M. (D, SP60)
Room 112, State House
Boston, MA 02133
P: (617) 722-1630
F: (617) 722-1001
E: Eileen.Donoghue@masenate.gov

Downing, Benjamin B. (D, SP161)
Room 413F, State House
Boston, MA 02133
P: (617) 722-1625
F: (617) 722-1523
E: Benjamin.Downing@masenate.gov

Eldridge, James B. (D, SP177)
Room 413A, State House
Boston, MA 02133
P: (617) 722-1120
F: (617) 722-1089
E: James.Eldridge@masenate.gov

Fattman, Ryan C. (R, SP190)
Room 111, State House
Boston, MA 02133
P: (617) 722-1420
F: (617) 722-1944
E: Ryan.Fattman@mahouse.gov

Flanagan, Jennifer L. (D, SP189)
Room 208, State House
Boston, MA 02133
P: (617) 722-1230
F: (617) 722-1130
E: Jennifer.Flanagan@masenate.gov

Massachusetts

Forry, Linda Dorcena (D, SP124)
Room 419, State House
Boston, MA 02133
P: (617) 722-1150
E: Linda.DorcenaForry@mahouse.gov

Gobi, Anne M. (D, SP188)
Room 410, State House
Boston, MA 02133
P: (617) 722-1540
F: (617) 722-1078
E: Anne.Gobi@mahouse.gov

Hedlund, Robert L. (R, SP184)
Room 313C, State House
Boston, MA 02133
P: (617) 722-1646
F: (617) 722-1028
E: Robert.Hedlund@masenate.gov

Humason Jr., Donald F. (R, SP171)
Room 213A, State House
Boston, MA 02133
P: (617) 722-1415
F: 617-722-1506
E: Donald.Humason@masenate.gov

Jehlen, Patricia D. (D, SP61)
Room 513, State House
Boston, MA 02133
P: (617) 722-1578
F: (617) 722-1117
E: Patricia.Jehlen@masenate.gov

Joyce, Brian A. (D, SP178)
Room 109D, State House
Boston, MA 02133
P: (617) 722-1643
F: (617) 722-1522
E: Brian.A.Joyce@masenate.gov

Keenan, John F. (D, SP180)
Room 413B, State House
Boston, MA 02133
P: (617) 722-1494
F: (617) 722-1055
E: John.Keenan@masenate.gov

Kennedy, Thomas P. (D, SP183)
Room 109E, State House
Boston, MA 02133
P: (617) 722-1200
F: (617) 722-1116
E: Thomas.Kennedy@masenate.gov

Lesser, Eric Philip (D, SP170)*
Room 309, State House
Boston, MA 02133
P: (617) 722-1291
F: (617) 722-1014
E: eric.lesser@masenate.gov

Lewis, Jason M. (D, SP64)
Room 511B, State House
Boston, MA 02133
P: (617) 722-1206
E: Jason.Lewis@masenate.gov

L'Italien, Barbara A. (D, SP167)
Room 416-B, State House
Boston, MA 02133
P: (617) 722-1612
F: (617) 722-1058
E: Barbara.L'Italien@mahouse.gov

Lovely, Joan (D, SP26)
Room 215, State House
Boston, MA 02133
P: (617) 722-1410
F: (617) 722-1347
E: Joan.Lovely@masenate.gov

McGee, Thomas M. (D, SP27)
Room 109C, State House
Boston, MA 02133
P: (617) 722-1350
E: Thomas.McGee@masenate.gov

Montigny, Mark C. (D, SP164)
Room 407, State House
Boston, MA 02133
P: (617) 722-1440
F: (617) 722-1068
E: Mark.Montigny@masenate.gov

Moore, Michael O. (D, SP144)
Room 109B, State House
Boston, MA 02133
P: (617) 722-1485
F: (617) 722-1066
E: Michael.Moore@masenate.gov

O'Connor Ives, Kathleen (D, SP25)
Room 519, State House
Boston, MA 02133
P: (617) 722-1604
F: (617) 722-1999
E: Kathleen.OConnorIves@masenate.gov

Pacheco, Marc R. (D, SP182)
Room 312B, State House
Boston, MA 02133
P: (617) 722-1551
F: (617) 722-1074
E: Marc.Pacheco@masenate.gov

Petruccelli, Anthony W. (D, SP185)
Room 424, State House
Boston, MA 02133
P: (617) 722-1634
F: (617) 722-1076
E: Anthony.Petruccelli@masenate.gov

Rodrigues, Michael J. (D, SP163)
Room 213B, State House
Boston, MA 02133
P: (617) 722-1114
F: (617) 722-1498
E: Michael.Rodrigues@masenate.gov

Rosenberg, Stanley C. (D, SP172)
Room 333, State House
Boston, MA 02133
P: (617) 722-1532
F: (617) 722-1062
E: Stan.Rosenberg@masenate.gov

Ross, Richard J. (R, SP179)
Room 520, State House
Boston, MA 02133
P: (617) 722-1555
F: (617) 722-1054
E: Richard.Ross@masenate.gov

Rush, Michael F. (D, SP187)
Room 504, State House
Boston, MA 02133
P: (617) 722-1348
F: (617) 722-1071
E: Mike.Rush@masenate.gov

Spilka, Karen E. (D, SP175)
Room 212, State House
Boston, MA 02133
P: (617) 722-1640
F: (617) 722-1077
E: Karen.Spilka@masenate.gov

Tarr, Bruce E. (R, SP166)
Room 308, State House
Boston, MA 02133
P: (617) 722-1600
F: (617) 722-1310
E: Bruce.Tarr@masenate.gov

Timilty, James E. (D, SP162)
Room 507, State House
Boston, MA 02133
P: (617) 722-1222
F: (617) 722-1056
E: James.Timilty@masenate.gov

Welch, James T. (D, SP169)
Room 416A, State House
Boston, MA 02133
P: (617) 722-1660
F: (413) 737-7747
E: James.Welch@masenate.gov

Wolf, Daniel A. (D, SP165)
Room 511B, State House
Boston, MA 02133
P: (617) 722-1570
F: (617) 722-1271
E: Daniel.Wolf@masenate.gov

House

Speaker of the House

Rep. Robert A. DeLeo (D)
Speaker
Room 356, State House
Boston, MA 02133
P: (617) 722-2500
F: (617) 722-2008
E: Robert.DeLeo@mahouse.gov

House Majority Leader

Rep. Ronald Mariano (D)
Majority Leader
Room 343, State House
Boston, MA 02133
P: (617) 722-2300
F: (617) 722-2750
E: Ronald.Mariano@mahouse.gov

House Minority Leader

Rep. Bradley H. Jones Jr. (R)
Minority Leader
Room 124, State House
Boston, MA 02133
P: (617) 722-2100
F: (617) 722-2390
E: Bradley.Jones@mahouse.gov

Clerk of the House

Mr. Steven T. James
Clerk of the House
Room 145, State House
24 Beacon Street
Boston, MA 02133
P: (617) 722-2356
F: (617) 722-2798
E: steven.james@hou.state.ma.us

Members of the House

Arciero, James (D, SP61)
Room 34, State House
Boston, MA 02133
P: (617) 722-2320
F: (617) 722-2798
E: James.Arciero@mahouse.gov

Ashe, Brian Michael (D, SP46)
Room 540, State House
Boston, MA 02133
P: (617) 722-2090
F: (617) 722-2848
E: Brian.Ashe@mahouse.gov

Atkins, Cory (D, SP73)
Room 195, State House
Boston, MA 02133
P: (617) 722-2015
F: (617) 722-2822
E: Cory.Atkins@mahouse.gov

Ayers, Bruce J. (D, SP97)
Room 167, State House
Boston, MA 02133
P: (617) 722-2230
E: Bruce.Ayers@mahouse.gov

Balser, Ruth B. (D, SP71)
Room 136, State House
Boston, MA 02133
P: (617) 722-2396
F: (617) 626-0119
E: Ruth.Balser@mahouse.gov

Barber, Christine P. (D, SP93)*
Room 437, State House
Boston, MA 02133
P: (617) 722-2425
E: Christine.Barber@mahouse.gov

Barrows, F. Jay (R, SP11)
Room 542, State House
Boston, MA 02133
P: (617) 722-2488
F: (617) 722-2390
E: F.JayBarrows@mahouse.gov

Benson, Jennifer (D, SP96)
Room 236, State House
Boston, MA 02133
P: (617) 722-2430
F: (617) 722-2813
E: Jennifer.Benson@mahouse.gov

Berthiaume Jr., Donald R. (R, SP147)*
Room 437, State House
Boston, MA 02133
P: (617) 722-2425
E: Donald.Berthiaume@mahouse.gov

Boldyga, Nicholas (R, SP47)
Room 167, State House
Boston, MA 02133
P: (617) 722-2810
F: (617) 626-0137
E: Nicholas.Boldyga@mahouse.gov

Bradley, Garrett J. (D, SP114)
Room 479, State House
Boston, MA 02133
P: (617) 722-2520
E: Garrett.Bradley@mahouse.gov

Brady, Michael D. (D, SP120)
Room 167, State House
Boston, MA 02133
P: (617) 722-2230
E: Michael.Brady@mahouse.gov

Brodeur, Paul A. (D, SP91)
Room 43, State House
Boston, MA 02133
P: (617) 722-2030
F: (617) 626-2215
E: Paul.Brodeur@mahouse.gov

Cabral, Antonio F.D. (D, SP23)
Room 466, State House
Boston, MA 02133
P: (617) 722-2017
F: (617) 722-2813
E: Antonio.Cabral@mahouse.gov

Calter III, Thomas J. (D, SP123)
Room 527A, State House
Boston, MA 02133
P: (617) 722-2020
F: (617) 722-2598
E: Thomas.Calter@mahouse.gov

Campanale, Kate D. (R, SP159)*
Room 437, State House
Boston, MA 02133
P: (617) 722-2425
E: Kate.Campanale@mahouse.gov

Campbell, Linda Dean (D, SP39)
Room 237, State House
Boston, MA 02133
P: (617) 722-2305
F: (617) 722-9278
E: Linda.Campbell@mahouse.gov

Cantwell, James M. (D, SP115)
Room 22, State House
Boston, MA 02133
P: (617) 722-2140
F: (617) 626-0835
E: James.Cantwell@mahouse.gov

Cariddi, Gailanne M. (D, SP7)
Room 155, State House
Boston, MA 02133
P: (617) 722-2450
F: (617) 626-0143
E: Gailanne.Cariddi@mahouse.gov

Carvalho, Evandro (D, SP128)*
Room 136, State House
Boston, MA 02133
P: (617) 722-2396
F: (617) 626-0802
E: Evandro.Carvalho@mahouse.gov

Chan, Tackey (D, SP98)
Room 26, State House
Boston, MA 02133
P: (617) 722-2080
F: (617) 626-0146
E: Tackey.Chan@mahouse.gov

Cole, Leah (R)
Room 236, State House
Boston, MA 02133
P: (617) 722-2430
F: (617) 626-0832
E: Leah.Cole@mahouse.gov

Collins, Nick (D, SP127)
Room 26, State House
Boston, MA 01233
P: (617) 722-2080
F: (617) 626-0154
E: Nick.Collins@mahouse.gov

Coppinger, Edward F. (D, SP133)
Room 160, State House
Boston, MA 02133
P: (617) 722-2304
F: (617) 626-0158
E: Edward.Coppinger@mahouse.gov

Crighton, Brendan P. (D, SP35)*
Room 437, State House
Boston, MA 02133
P: (617) 722-2425
E: brendan.crighton@mahouse.gov

Cronin, Claire (D, SP122)
Room 130, State House
Boston, MA 02133
P: (617) 722-2130
F: (617) 626-0285
E: Claire.Cronin@mahouse.gov

Cullinane, Daniel R. (D, SP135)
Room 121, State House
Boston, MA 02133
P: (617) 722-2006
F: (617) 626-0456
E: Daniel.Cullinane@mahouse.gov

Cusack, Mark J. (D, SP101)
Room 544, State House
Boston, MA 02133
P: (617) 722-2637
F: (617) 626-0159
E: Mark.Cusack@mahouse.gov

Cutler, Josh (D, SP117)
Room 39, State House
Boston, MA 02133
P: (617) 722-2014
F: (617) 626-0325
E: Josh.Cutler@mahouse.gov

Day, Michael Seamus (D, SP90)*
Room 437, State House
Boston, MA 02133
P: (617) 722-2425
E: Michael.Day@mahouse.gov

Decker, Marjorie (D, SP84)
Room 236, State House
Boston, MA 02133
P: (617) 722-2430
F: (617) 626-0337
E: Marjorie.Decker@mahouse.gov

Massachusetts

Decoste, David F. (R, SP116)*
Room 437, State House
Boston, MA 02133
P: (617) 722-2425
E: David.DeCoste@mahouse.gov

DeLeo, Robert A. (D, SP142)
Room 356, State House
Boston, MA 02133
P: (617) 722-2500
F: (617) 722-2008
E: Robert.DeLeo@mahouse.gov

D'Emilia, Angelo L. (R, SP119)
Room 548, State House
Boston, MA 02133
P: (617) 722-2488
F: (617) 626-0170
E: Angelo.D'Emilia@mahouse.gov

Dempsey, Brian S. (D, SP27)
Room 243, State House
Boston, MA 02133
P: (617) 722-2990
F: (617) 722-2215
E: Brian.Dempsey@massmail.state.ma.us

Devers, Marcos (D, SP40)
Room 146, State House
Boston, MA 02133
P: (617) 722-2011
F: (617) 727-2238
E: Marcos.Devers@mahouse.gov

Diehl, Geoffrey G. (R, SP118)
Room 167, State House
Boston, MA 02133
P: (617) 722-2810
E: Geoff.Diehl@mahouse.gov

DiNatale, Stephen (D, SP145)
Room 276, State House
Boston, MA 02133
P: (617) 722-2676
F: (617) 722-2236
E: Stephen.DiNatale@mahouse.gov

DiZoglio, Diana (D, SP38)
Room 33, State House
Boston, MA 02133
P: (617) 722-2060
F: (617) 626-0191
E: Diana.DiZoglio@mahouse.gov

Donahue, Daniel M. (D, SP158)
Room 122, State House
Boston, MA 02133
P: (617) 722-2006
F: (617) 626-0457
E: Daniel.Donahue@mahouse.gov

Donato, Paul J. (D, SP94)
Room 163, State House
Boston, MA 02133
P: (617) 722-2040
F: (617) 722-2347
E: Paul.Donato@mahouse.gov

Dooley, Shawn (R, SP105)*
Room 167, State House
Boston, MA 02133
P: (617) 722-2810
E: Shawn.Dooley@mahouse.gov

Dubois, Michelle M. (D, SP121)*
Room 437, State House
Boston, MA 02133
P: (617) 722-2425
E: michelle.dubois@mahouse.gov

Durant, Peter (R, SP148)
Room 33, State House
Boston, MA 02133
P: (617) 722-2060
E: Peter.Durant@mahouse.gov

Dwyer, James J. (D, SP89)
Room 254, State House
Boston, MA 02133
P: (617) 722-2220
F: (617) 626-0831
E: James.Dwyer@mahouse.gov

Dykema, Carolyn C. (D, SP67)
Room 473F, State House
Boston, MA 02133
P: (617) 722-2210
F: (617) 722-2239
E: Carolyn.Dykema@mahouse.gov

Ehrlich, Lori A. (D, SP32)
Room 39, State House
Boston, MA 02133
P: (617) 722-2014
E: Lori.Ehrlich@mahouse.gov

Farley-Bouvier, Tricia (D, SP9)
Room 156, State House
Boston, MA 02133
P: (617) 722-2240
E: Tricia.Farley-Bouvier@mahouse.gov

Fennell, Robert F. (D, SP34)
Room 146, State House
Boston, MA 02133
P: (617) 722-2575
F: (617) 626-0222
E: Robert.Fennell@mahouse.gov

Ferguson, Kimberly N. (R, SP143)
Room 473B, State House
Boston, MA 02133
P: (617) 722-2263
F: (617) 626-0182
E: Kimberly.Ferguson@mahouse.gov

Fernandes, John (D, SP152)
Room 254, State House
Boston, MA 02133
P: (617) 722-2220
F: (617) 626-0706
E: John.Fernandes@mahouse.gov

Ferrante, Ann-Margaret (D, SP29)
Room 36, State House
Boston, MA 02133
P: (617) 722-2370
F: (617) 722-2339
E: Ann-Margaret.Ferrante@mahouse.gov

Finn, Michael J. (D, SP50)
Room 544, State House
Boston, MA 02133
P: (617) 722-2637
F: (617) 626-0189
E: Michael.Finn@mahouse.gov

Fiola, Carole (D, SP16)
Room 443, State House
Boston, MA 02133
P: (617) 722-2460
F: (617) 626-0460
E: Carole.Fiola@mahouse.gov

Fox, Gloria L. (D, SP130)
Room 167, State House
Boston, MA 02133
P: (617) 722-2810
F: (617) 722-2846
E: Gloria.Fox@mahouse.gov

Frost, Paul K. (R, SP149)
Room 542, State House
Boston, MA 02133
P: (617) 722-2489
E: Paul.Frost@mahouse.gov

Galvin, William C. (D, SP102)
Room 448, State House
Boston, MA 02133
P: (617) 722-2582
E: William.Galvin@mahouse.gov

Garballey, Sean (D, SP82)
Room 540, State House
Boston, MA 02133
P: (617) 722-2090
F: (617) 722-2848
E: Sean.Garballey@mahouse.gov

Garlick, Denise C. (D, SP109)
Room 473G, State House
Boston, MA 02133
P: (617) 722-2070
F: (617) 626-0197
E: Denise.Garlick@mahouse.gov

Garry, Colleen M. (D, SP95)
Room 238, State House
Boston, MA 02133
P: (617) 722-2380
F: (617) 722-2847
E: Colleen.Garry@mahouse.gov

Gentile, Carmine Lawrence (D, SP72)*
Room 437, State House
Boston, MA 02133
P: (617) 722-2425
E: carmine.gentile@mahouse.gov

Gifford, Susan Williams (R, SP113)
Room 124, State House
Boston, MA 02133
P: (617) 722-2976
F: (617) 722-2848
E: Susan.Gifford@mahouse.gov

Golden Jr., Thomas A. (D, SP75)
Room 527A, State House
Boston, MA 02133
P: (617) 722-2020
F: (617) 570-6578
E: Thomas.Golden@mahouse.gov

Gonzalez, Carlos (D, SP54)*
Room 437, State House
Boston, MA 02133
P: (617) 722-2425
E: Carlos.Gonzalez@mahouse.gov

Gordon, Kenneth (D, SP80)
Room 39, State House
Boston, MA 02133
P: (617) 722-2014
F: (617) 626-0320
E: Ken.Gordon@mahouse.gov

Gregoire, Danielle W. (D, SP63)
Room 446, State House
Boston, MA 02133
P: (617) 722-2460
F: (617) 626-0323
E: Danielle.Gregoire@mahouse.gov

Haddad, Patricia A. (D, SP15)
Room 370, State House
Boston, MA 02133
P: (617) 722-2600
F: (617) 722-2313
E: Patricia.Haddad@mahouse.gov

Harrington, Sheila C. (R, SP60)
Room 237, State House
Boston, MA 02133
P: (617) 722-2305
F: (617) 626-0199
E: Sheila.Harrington@mahouse.gov

Hecht, Jonathan (D, SP88)
Room 22, State House
Boston, MA 02133
P: (617) 722-2140
F: (617) 626-0199
E: Jonathan.Hecht@mahouse.gov

Heroux, Paul (D, SP12)
Room 236, State House
Boston, MA 02133
P: (617) 722-2430
F: (617) 626-0335
E: Paul.Heroux@mahouse.gov

Hill, Bradford (R, SP28)
Room 128, State House
Boston, MA 02133
P: (617) 722-2100
E: Brad.Hill@mahouse.gov

Hogan, Kate (D, SP62)
Room 166, State House
Boston, MA 02133
P: (617) 722-2692
E: Kate.Hogan@mahouse.gov

Holmes, Russell (D, SP129)
Room 254, State House
Boston, MA 02133
P: (617) 722-2220
F: (617) 626-0205
E: Russell.Holmes@mahouse.gov

Honan, Kevin G. (D, SP140)
Room 38, State House
Boston, MA 02133
P: (617) 722-2470
F: (617) 722-2162
E: Kevin.Honan@mahouse.gov

Howitt, Steven S. (R, SP14)
Room 237, State House
Boston, MA 02133
P: (617) 722-2305
F: (617) 626-0211
E: Steven.Howitt@mahouse.gov

Hunt, Daniel (D, SP136)*
Room 33, State House
Boston, MA 02133
P: (617) 722-2060
E: Daniel.Hunt@mahouse.gov

Hunt, Randy (R, SP5)
Room 136, State House
Boston, MA 02133
P: (617) 722-2396
F: (617) 626-0218
E: Randy.Hunt@mahouse.gov

Jones Jr., Bradley H. (R, SP79)
Room 124, State House
Boston, MA 02133
P: (617) 722-2100
F: (617) 722-2390
E: Bradley.Jones@mahouse.gov

Kafka, Louis L. (D, SP104)
Room 185, State House
Boston, MA 02133
P: (617) 722-2960
F: (617) 722-2713
E: Louis.Kafka@mahouse.gov

Kaufman, Jay R. (D, SP74)
Room 34, State House
Boston, MA 02133
P: (617) 722-2320
F: (617) 722-2415
E: Jay.Kaufman@mahouse.gov

Keefe, Mary (D, SP157)
Room 473F, State House
Boston, MA 02133
P: (617) 722-2210
F: (617) 626-0286
E: Mary.Keefe@mahouse.gov

Kelcourse, James M. (R, SP25)*
Room 437, State House
Boston, MA 02133
P: (617) 722-2425
E: james.kelcourse@mahouse.gov

Khan, Kay (D, SP70)
Room 146, State House
Boston, MA 02133
P: (617) 722-2011
F: (617) 722-2238
E: Kay.Khan@mahouse.gov

Kocot, Peter V. (D, SP57)
Room 22, State House
Boston, MA 02133
P: (617) 722-2140
F: (617) 722-2347
E: Peter.Kocot@mahouse.gov

Koczera, Robert M. (D, SP21)
Room 448, State House
Boston, MA 02133
P: (617) 722-2582
E: Robert.Koczera@mahouse.gov

Kulik, Stephen (D, SP43)
Room 238, State House
Boston, MA 02133
P: (617) 722-2380
F: (617) 722-2847
E: Stephen.Kulik@mahouse.gov

Kuros, Kevin J. (R, SP150)
Room 443, State House
Boston, MA 02133
P: (617) 722-2460
F: (617) 722-2353
E: Kevin.Kuros@mahouse.gov

Lawn, John J. (D, SP69)
Room 160, State House
Boston, MA 02133
P: (617) 722-2304
F: (617) 626-0150
E: John.Lawn@mahouse.gov

Linsky, David P. (D, SP64)
Room 146, State House
Boston, MA 02133
P: (617) 722-2575
F: (617) 722-2238
E: David.Linsky@mahouse.gov

Livingstone, Jay (D, SP131)
Room 146, State House
Boston, MA 02133
P: (617) 722-2011
E: Jay.Livingstone@mahouse.gov

Lombardo, Marc T. (R, SP81)
Room 443, State House
Boston, MA 02133
P: (617) 722-2460
F: (617) 626-0240
E: Marc.Lombardo@mahouse.gov

Lyons Jr., James J. (R, SP42)
Room 39, State House
Boston, MA 02133
P: (617) 722-2014
F: (617) 626-0246
E: James.Lyons@mahouse.gov

Madden, Timothy R. (I, SP6)
Room 167, State House
Boston, MA 02133
P: (617) 722-2810
F: (617) 722-2846
E: Timothy.Madden@mahouse.gov

Mahoney, John J. (D, SP155)
Room 134, State House
Boston, MA 02133
P: (617) 722-2400
F: (617) 626-0247
E: John.Mahoney@mahouse.gov

Malia, Elizabeth A. (D, SP134)
Room 33, State House
Boston, MA 02133
P: (617) 722-2060
E: Liz.Malia@mahouse.gov

Mannal, Brian (D, SP2)
Room 448, State House
Boston, MA 02133
P: (617) 722-2582
F: (617) 626-0166
E: Brian.Mannal@mahouse.gov

Mariano, Ronald (D, SP99)
Room 343, State House
Boston, MA 02133
P: (617) 722-2300
F: (617) 722-2750
E: Ronald.Mariano@mahouse.gov

Mark, Paul W. (D, SP8)
Room 472, State House
Boston, MA 02133
P: (617) 722-2013
F: (617) 626-0249
E: Paul.Mark@mahouse.gov

Markey, Christopher (D, SP19)
Room 136, State House
Boston, MA 02133
P: (617) 722-2396
F: (617) 626-0250
E: Christopher.Markey@mahouse.gov

McGonagle, Joseph W. (D, SP87)*
Room 437, State House
Boston, MA 02133
P: (617) 722-2425
E: Joseph.McGonagle@mahouse.gov

Massachusetts

McKenna, Joseph D. (R, SP160)*
Room 437, State House
Boston, MA 02133
P: (617) 722-2425
E: joseph.mckenna@mahouse.gov

McMurtry, Paul (D, SP107)
Room 279, State House
Boston, MA 02133
P: (617) 722-2015
F: (617) 626-0413
E: Paul.McMurtry@mahouse.gov

Miceli, James R. (D, SP78)
Room 446, State House
Boston, MA 02133
P: (617) 722-2460
E: James.Miceli@mahouse.gov

Michlewitz, Aaron M. (D, SP126)
Room 156, State House
Boston, MA 02133
P: (617) 722-2240
F: (617) 570-6575
E: Aaron.M.Michlewitz@mahouse.gov

Mirra, Leonard (R, SP26)
Room 130, State House
Boston, MA 02133
P: (617) 722-2130
F: (617) 626-0339
E: Lenny.Mirra@mahouse.gov

Mom, Rady (D, SP77)*
Room 437, State House
Boston, MA 02133
P: (617) 722-2425
E: Rady.Mom@mahouse.gov

Moran, Frank (D, SP41)
Room 443, State House
Boston, MA 02133
P: (617) 722-2460
F: (617) 626-0288
E: Frank.Moran@mahouse.gov

Moran, Michael (D, SP141)
Room 39, State House
Boston, MA 02133
P: (617) 722-2014
E: Michael.Moran@mahouse.gov

Muradian Jr., David K. (R, SP151)*
Room 437, State House
Boston, MA 02133
P: (617) 722-2425
E: David.Muradian@mahouse.gov

Muratore, Mathew J. (R, SP112)*
Room 437, State House
Boston, MA 02133
P: (617) 722-2425
E: Mathew.Muratore@mahouse.gov

Murphy, James M. (D, SP100)
Room 443, State House
Boston, MA 02133
P: (617) 722-2460
E: James.Murphy@mahouse.gov

Nangle, David M. (D, SP76)
Room 146, State House
Boston, MA 02133
P: (617) 722-2575
F: (617) 722-2215
E: David.Nangle@mahouse.gov

Naughton Jr., Harold P. (D, SP154)
Room 167, State House
Boston, MA 02133
P: (617) 722-2230
F: (617) 722-9278
E: Harold.Naughton@mahouse.gov

O'Connell, Shaunna (R, SP13)
Room 237, State House
Boston, MA 02133
P: (617) 722-2305
E: Shaunna.O'Connell@mahouse.gov

O'Day, James J. (D, SP156)
Room 167, State House
Boston, MA 02133
P: (617) 722-2810
F: (617) 626-0884
E: James.O'Day@mahouse.gov

Orrall, Keiko M. (R, SP22)
Room 540, State House
Boston, MA 02133
P: (617) 722-2090
F: (617) 626-0477
E: Keiko.Orrall@mahouse.gov

Parisella, Jerald A. (D, SP30)
Room 173, State House
Boston, MA 02133
P: (617) 722-2877
F: (617) 626-0261
E: Jerald.Parisella@mahouse.gov

Peake, Sarah K. (D, SP4)
Room 540, State House
Boston, MA 02133
P: (617) 722-2090
F: (617) 722-2239
E: Sarah.Peake@mahouse.gov

Peisch, Alice Hanlon (D, SP110)
Room 473G, State House
Boston, MA 02133
P: (617) 722-2070
E: Alice.Peisch@mahouse.gov

Petrolati, Thomas M. (D, SP51)
Room 171, State House
Boston, MA 02133
P: (617) 722-2255
F: (617) 722-2846
E: Thomas.Petrolati@mahouse.gov

Pignatelli, William Smitty (D, SP10)
Room 466, State House
Boston, MA 02133
P: (617) 722-2017
F: (617) 722-2879
E: Smitty.Pignatelli@mahouse.gov

Poirier, Elizabeth A. (R, SP24)
Room 124, State House
Boston, MA 02133
P: (617) 722-2100
F: (617) 626-0108
E: Elizabeth.Poirier@mahouse.gov

Provost, Denise (D, SP86)
Room 473B, State House
Boston, MA 02133
P: (617) 722-2263
F: (617) 626-0548
E: Denise.Provost@mahouse.gov

Puppolo, Angelo (D, SP56)
Room 236, State House
Boston, MA 02133
P: (617) 722-2430
F: (617) 722-2848
E: Angelo.Puppolo@mahouse.gov

Rogers, David (D, SP83)
Room 134, State House
Boston, MA 02133
P: (617) 722-2400
F: (617) 626-0275
E: Dave.Rogers@mahouse.gov

Rogers, John H. (D, SP108)
Room 162, State House
Boston, MA 02133
P: (617) 722-2092
F: (617) 722-2347
E: John.Rogers@mahouse.gov

Rosa, Dennis A. (D, SP146)
Room 136, State House
Boston, MA 02133
P: (617) 722-2396
E: Dennis.Rosa@mahouse.gov

Roy, Jeffrey (D, SP106)
Room 134, State House
Boston, MA 02133
P: (617) 722-2400
F: (617) 626-0279
E: Jeffrey.Roy@mahouse.gov

Rushing, Byron (D, SP132)
Room 234, State House
Boston, MA 02133
P: (617) 722-2783
F: (617) 722-2238
E: Byron.Rushing@mahouse.gov

Ryan, Daniel J. (D, SP125)*
Room 136, State House
Boston, MA 02133
P: (617) 722-2396
E: Dan.Ryan@mahouse.gov

Sanchez, Jeffrey (D, SP138)
Room 130, State House
Boston, MA 02133
P: (617) 722-2130
E: Jeffrey.Sanchez@mahouse.gov

Sannicandro, Tom (D, SP66)
Room 472, State House
Boston, MA 02133
P: (617) 722-2013
F: (617) 722-2239
E: Tom.Sannicandro@mahouse.gov

Scaccia, Angelo M. (D, SP137)
Room 33, State House
Boston, MA 02133
P: (617) 722-2060
F: (617) 722-2849
E: Angelo.Scaccia@mahouse.gov

Schmid, Paul A. (D, SP18)
Room 473F, State House
Boston, MA 02133
P: (617) 722-2210
F: (617) 626-0267
E: Paul.Schmid@mahouse.gov

Scibak, John W. (D, SP58)
Room 43, State House
Boston, MA 02133
P: (617) 722-2030
F: (617) 722-2215
E: John.Scibak@mahouse.gov

Silvia, Alan (D, SP17)
Room 33, State House
Boston, MA 02133
P: (617) 722-2060
F: (617) 626-0168
E: Alan.Silvia@mahouse.gov

Smizik, Frank Israel (D, SP111)
Room 274, State House
Boston, MA 02133
P: (617) 722-2676
F: (617) 722-2239
E: Frank.Smizik@mahouse.gov

Smola, Todd M. (R, SP45)
Room 156, State House
Boston, MA 02133
P: (617) 722-2240
E: Todd.Smola@mahouse.gov

Speliotis, Theodore C. (D, SP37)
Room 20, State House
Boston, MA 02133
P: (617) 722-2410
E: Theodore.Speliotis@mahouse.gov

Stanley, Thomas M. (D, SP68)
Room 167, State House
Boston, MA 02133
P: (617) 722-2230
E: Thomas.Stanley@mahouse.gov

Story, Ellen (D, SP59)
Room 277, State House
Boston, MA 02133
P: (617) 722-2012
F: (617) 570-6577
E: Ellen.Story@mahouse.gov

Straus, William M. (D, SP20)
Room 134, State House
Boston, MA 02133
P: (617) 722-2400
F: (617) 722-2387
E: William.Straus@mahouse.gov

Swan, Benjamin (D, SP55)
Room 127, State House
Boston, MA 02133
P: (617) 722-2680
F: (617) 722-2846
E: Benjamin.Swan@mahouse.gov

Timilty, Walter F. (D, SP103)
Room 167, State House
Boston, MA 02133
P: (617) 722-2230
E: Walter.Timilty@mahouse.gov

Toomey Jr., Timothy J. (D, SP85)
Room 238, State House
Boston, MA 02133
P: (617) 722-2380
F: (617) 626-0668
E: Timothy.Toomey@mahouse.gov

Tosado, Jose F. (D, SP53)*
Room 437, State House
Boston, MA 02133
P: (617) 722-2425
E: Jose.Tosado@mahouse.gov

Tucker, Paul F. (D, SP31)*
Room 437, State House
Boston, MA 02133
P: (617) 722-2425
E: Paul.Tucker@mahouse.gov

Ultrino, Steven (D, SP92)*
Room 437, State House
Boston, MA 02133
P: (617) 722-2425
E: Steven.Ultrino@mahouse.gov

Vega, Aaron (D, SP49)
Room 134, State House
Boston, MA 02133
P: (617) 722-2400
F: (617) 626-2224
E: Aaron.Vega@mahouse.gov

Velis, John (D, SP48)*
Room 448, State House
Boston, MA 02133
P: (617) 722-2582
E: john.velis@mahouse.gov

Vieira, David T. (R, SP3)
Room 167, State House
Boston, MA 02133
P: (617) 722-2230
E: David.Vieira@mahouse.gov

Vincent, RoseLee (D, SP139)*
Room 236, State House
Boston, MA 02133
P: (617) 722-2430
E: RoseLee.Vincent@mahouse.gov

Wagner, Joseph F. (D, SP52)
Room 42, State House
Boston, MA 02133
P: (617) 722-2370
E: Joseph.Wagner@MAhouse.gov

Walsh, Chris (D, SP65)
Room 472, State House
Boston, MA 02133
P: (617) 722-2013
F: (617) 626-0291
E: Chris.Walsh@mahouse.gov

Whelan, Timothy R. (R, SP1)*
Room 437, State House
Boston, MA 02133
P: (617) 722-2425
E: Timothy.Whelan@mahouse.gov

Whipps Lee, Susannah M. (R, SP44)*
Room 437, State House
Boston, MA 02133
P: (617) 722-2425
E: Susannah.WhippsLee@mahouse.gov

Wong, Donald H. (R, SP33)
Room 542, State House
Boston, MA 02133
P: (617) 722-2488
F: (617) 626-0299
E: Donald.Wong@mahouse.gov

Zlotnik, Jonathan (D, SP144)
Room 26, State House
Boston, MA 02133
P: (617) 722-2080
F: (617) 626-0003
E: Jon.Zlotnik@mahouse.gov

Congress

Senate
Markey, Edward J. (D)
Warren, Elizabeth (D)

House
Capuano, Michael E. (D, 7)
Clark, Katherine (D, 5)
Keating, William (D, 9)
Kennedy III, Joseph P. (D, 4)
Lynch, Stephen F. (D, 8)
McGovern, James P. (D, 2)
Moulton, Seth (D, 6)
Neal, Richard (D, 1)
Tsongas, Niki (D, 3)

Michigan

Executive

Governor

Hon. Rick Snyder (R)
Governor
P.O. Box 30013
Lansing, MI 48909
P: (517) 373-3400
F: (517) 335-6863

Lieutenant Governor

Hon. Brian Calley (R)
Lieutenant Governor
P.O. Box 30013
Lansing, MI 48909
P: (517) 373-6800
F: (517) 241-5026

Attorney General

Hon. Bill Schuette (R)
Attorney General
525 West Ottawa Street
P.O. Box 30212
Lansing, MI 48909
P: (517) 373-1110

Auditor

Hon. Doug Ringler
(appointed by the Legislature)
Auditor General
201 North Washington Square
Victor Center, Suite 600
Lansing, MI 48913
P: (517) 334-8050
F: (517) 334-8079
E: dringler
@audgen.michigan.gov

Secretary of State

Hon. Ruth Johnson (R)
Secretary of State
430 West Allegan Street
Lansing, MI 48918
P: (517) 373-2510
F: (517) 373-0727
E: secretary@michigan.gov

Treasurer

Hon. Kevin Clinton
(appointed)
State Treasurer
439 West Allegan Street
Lansing, MI 48922
P: (517) 373-3223
F: (517) 335-1785
E: mistattreasurer
@michigan.gov

Judiciary

Supreme Court (NE)

Mr. Larry Royster
Clerk
P.O. Box 30052
Lansing, MI 48909
P: (517) 373-0120
E: MSC_Clerk@courts.mi.gov

Hon. Robert P. Young Jr.
Chief Justice
Hon. Richard Bernstein
Hon. Mary Beth Kelly
Hon. Stephen J. Markman
Hon. Bridget Mary McCormac
Hon. David F. Viviano
Hon. Brian Zahra

Legislative Senate

Senate President

Hon. Brian Calley (R)
Lieutenant Governor
P.O. Box 30013
Lansing, MI 48909
P: (517) 373-6800
F: (517) 241-5026

President Pro Tempore of the Senate

Sen. Tonya Schuitmaker (R)
Senate President Pro Tempore
405 Farnum Building
P.O. Box 30036
Lansing, MI 48909
P: (517) 373-0793
F: (517) 373-5607
E: SenTSchuitmaker
@senate.michigan.gov

Senate Majority Leader

Sen. Arlan Meekhof (R)
Senate Majority Leader
S-106 Capitol Builiding
P.O. Box 30036
Lansing, MI 48909
P: (517) 373-6920
F: (517) 373-2751
E: SenAMeekhof
@senate.michigan.gov

Senate Minority Leader

Sen. Jim Ananich (D)
Senate Minority Leader
S-105 Capitol Building
P.O. Box 30036
Lansing, MI 48909
P: (517) 373-0142
F: (517) 373-3938
E: SenJAnanich
@senate.michigan.gov

Secretary of the Senate

Ms. Carol Morey Viventi
Secretary of the Senate
Capitol Building, Room S-5
P.O. Box 30036
Lansing, MI 48909
P: (517) 373-2400
F: (517) 373-9635
E: cviventi
@senate.michigan.gov

Members of the Senate

Ananich, Jim (D, 27)
S-105 Capitol Building
P.O. Box 30036
Lansing, MI 48909
P: (517) 373-0142
F: (517) 373-3938
E: SenJAnanich
@senate.michigan.gov

Bieda, Steve (D, 9)
310 Farnum Building
P.O. Box 30036
Lansing, MI 48909
P: (517) 373-8360
F: (517) 373-9230
E: SenSBieda
@senate.michigan.gov

Booher, Darwin (R, 35)
720 Farnum Building
P.O. Box 30036
Lansing, MI 48909
P: (517) 373-1725
F: (517) 373-0741
E: SenDBooher
@senate.michigan.gov

Brandenburg, Jack (R, 8)
605 Farnum Building
P.O. Box 30036
Lansing, MI 48909
P: (517) 373-7670
F: (517) 373-5958
E: SenJBrandenburg
@senate.michigan.gov

Casperson, Tom (R, 38)
705 Farnum Building
P.O. Box 30014
Lansing, MI 48909
P: (517) 373-7840
F: (517) 373-3932
E: SenTCasperson
@senate.michigan.gov

Colbeck, Patrick (R, 7)
1020 Farnum Building
P.O. Box 30036
Lansing, MI 48909
P: (517) 373-7350
F: (517) 373-9228
E: SenPColbeck
@senate.michigan.gov

Emmons, Judy (R, 33)
1005 Farnum Building
P.O. Box 30036
Lansing, MI 48909
P: (517) 373-3760
F: (517) 373-8661
E: SenJEmmons
@senate.michigan.gov

Green, Mike (R, 31)
805 Farnam Building
P.O. Box 30036
Lansing, MI 48909
P: (517) 373-1777
F: (517) 373-5871
E: SenMGreen
@senate.michigan.gov

Gregory, Vincent (D, 11)
1015 Farnum Building
P.O. Box 30036
Lansing, MI 48909
P: (517) 373-7888
F: (517) 373-2983
E: SenVGregory
@senate.michigan.gov

Hansen, Goeff (R, 34)
420 Farnum Building
P.O. Box 30036
Lansing, MI 48909
P: (517) 373-1635
F: (517) 373-3300
E: SenGHansen
@senate.michigan.gov

Hertel Jr., Curtis (D, 23)*
315 Farnum Building
P.O. Box 30036
Lansing, MI 48909
P: (517) 373-1734
F: (517) 373-5397
E: senchertel
@senate.michigan.gov

Hildenbrand, Dave (R, 29)
S-324 Capitol Building
P.O. Box 30036
Lansing, MI 48909
P: (517) 373-1801
F: (517) 373-5801
E: SenDHildenbrand
@michigan.senate.gov

Hood III, Morris (D, 3)
S-9 Capitol Building
P.O. Box 30036
Lansing, MI 48909
P: (517) 373-0990
F: (517) 373-5338
E: SenMHood
@michigan.senate.gov

Hopgood, Hoon-Yung (D, 6)
515 Farnum Building
P.O. Box 30036
Lansing, MI 48909
P: (517) 373-7800
F: (517) 373-9310
E: senhhopgood
@senate.michigan.gov

Horn, Ken (R, 32)
1010 Farnum Building
P.O. Box 30036
Lansing, MI 48909
P: (517) 373-1760
F: (517) 373-3487
E: kennethhorn
@senate.mchigan.gov

Hunc, Joe (R, 22)
505 Farnum Building
P.O. Box 30036
Lansing, MI 48909
P: (517) 373-2420
F: (517) 373-2764
E: SenJHune
@michigan.senate.gov

Johnson, Bert (D, 2)
220 Farnum Building
P.O. Box 30036
Lansing, MI 48909
P: (517) 373-7748
F: (517) 373-1387
E: SenBJohnson
@senate.michigan.gov

Jones, Rick (R, 24)
915 Farnum Building
P.O. Box 30036
Lansing, MI 48909
P: (517) 373-3447
F: (517) 373-5849
E: SenRJones
@senate.michigan.gov

Knezek, David (D, 5)
610 Farnum Building
P.O. Box 30036
Lansing, MI 48909
P: (517) 373-0994
F: (517) 373-5981
E: DavidKnezek
@senate.mchigani.gov

Knollenberg, Marty (R, 13)
520 Farnum Building
P.O. Box 30036
Lansing, MI 48909
P: (517) 373-2523
F: (517) 373-5669
E: senmknollenberg
@senate.mchigani.gov

Kowall, Michael (R, 15)
S-309 Capitol Building
P.O. Box 30036
Lansing, MI 48909
P: (517) 373-1758
F: (517) 373-0938
E: SenMKowall
@senate.michigan.gov

MacGregor, Peter (R, 28)
715 Farnum Building
P.O. Box 30036
Lansing, MI 48909
P: (517) 373-0797
F: (517) 373-5236
E: senpmacgregor
@senate.michigan.gov

Marleau, James (R, 12)
S-2 Capitol Building
P.O. Box 30036
Lansing, MI 48909
P: (517) 373-2417
F: (517) 373-2694
E: senjmarleau
@senate.michigan.gov

Meekhof, Arlan (R, 30)
S-106 Capitol Builiding
P.O. Box 30036
Lansing, MI 48909
P: (517) 373-6920
F: (517) 373-2751
E: SenAMeekhof
@senate.michigan.gov

Nofs, Mike (R, 19)
S-132 Capitol Building
P.O. Box 30036
Lansing, MI 48909
P: (517) 373-2426
F: (517) 373-2964
E: SenMNofs
@senate.michigan.gov

O'Brien, Margaret E. (R, 20)
910 Farnum Building
P.O. Box 30036
Lansing, MI 48909
P: (517) 373-5100
F: (517) 373-5115
E: senmobrien
@senate.michigan.gov

Pavlov, Phillip (R, 25)
905 Farnum Building
P.O. Box 30036
Lansing, MI 48909
P: (517) 373-7708
F: (517) 373-1450
E: SenPPavlov
@senate.michigan.gov

Proos, John (R, 21)
S-8 Capitol Building
P.O. Box 30036
Lansing, MI 48909
P: (517) 373-6960
F: (517) 373-0897
E: SenJProos
@senate.michigan.gov

Robertson, David B. (R, 14)
305 Farnum Building
P.O. Box 30036
Lansing, MI 48909
P: (517) 373-1636
F: (517) 373-1453
E: SenDRobertson
@senate.michigan.gov

Rocca, Tory (R, 10)
205 Farnum Building
P.O. Box 30036
Lansing, MI 48909
P: (517) 373-7315
F: (517) 373-3126
E: SenTRocca
@senate.michigan.gov

Schmidt, Wayne A. (R, 37)
820 Farnum Building
P.O. Box 30036
Lansing, MI 48909
P: (517) 373-2413
F: (517) 373-5144
E: senwschmidt
@senate.michigan.gov

Schuitmaker, Tonya (R, 26)
405 Farnum Building
P.O. Box 30036
Lansing, MI 48909
P: (517) 373-0793
F: (517) 373-5607
E: SenTSchuitmaker
@senate.michigan.gov

Shirkey, Michael (R, 16)
320 Farnum Building
P.O. Box 30036
Lansing, MI 48909
P: (517) 373-5932
F: (517) 373-5944
E: senmshirkey
@senate.michigan.gov

Smith, Virgil (D, 4)
510 Farnum Building
P.O. Box 30036
Lansing, MI 48909
P: (517) 373-7918
F: (517) 373-5227
E: SenVSmith
@senate.michigan.gov

Stamas, Jim (R, 36)
920 Farnum Building
P.O. Box 30036
Lansing, MI 48909
P: (517) 373-7946
F: (517) 373-2678
E: senjstamas
@senate.michigan.gov

Warren, Rebekah (D, 18)
415 Farnum Building
P.O. Box 30036
Lansing, MI 48909
P: (517) 373-2406
F: (517) 373-5679
E: SenRWarren
@senate.michigan.gov

Young II, Coleman (D, 1)
410 Farnum Building
P.O. Box 30036
Lansing, MI 48909
P: (517) 373-7346
F: (517) 373-9320
E: SenCYoung
@senate.michigan.gov

Zorn, Dale (R, 17)
710 Farnum Building
P.O. Box 30036
Lansing, MI 48909
P: (517) 373-3543
F: (517) 373-0927
E: sendzorn
@senate.michigan.gov

House

Speaker of the House

Rep. Kevin Cotter (R)
Speaker of the House
164 Capitol Building
P.O. Box 30014
Lansing, MI 48909
P: (517) 373-1789
F: (517) 373-5491
E: kevincotter@house.mi.gov

Michigan

Speaker Pro Tempore of the House

Rep. Tom Leonard (R)
House Speaker Pro Tem
251 Capitol Building
P.O. Box 30014
Lansing, MI 48909
P: (517) 373-1778
E: TomLeonard@house.mi.gov

House Minority Leader

Rep. Tim Greimel (D)
House Minority Leader
167 Capitol Building
P.O. Box 30014
Lansing, MI 48909
P: (517) 373-0475
E: TimGreimel@house.mi.gov

Clerk of the House

Mr. Gary Randall
Clerk of the House
Capitol Building, Room 70
P.O. Box 30014
Lansing, MI 48909
P: (517) 373-0135
E: clerk@house.mi.gov

Members of the House

Afendoulis, Chris (R, 73)*
House Office Building, N-1092
P.O. Box 30014
Lansing, MI 48909
P: (517) 373-0218
E: chrisafendoulis@house.mi.gov

Banks, Brian (D, 1)
House Office Building, S-585
P.O. Box 30014
Lansing, MI 48909
P: (517) 373-0154
E: BrianBanks@house.mi.gov

Barrett, Tom (R, 71)*
House Office Building, N-1090
P.O. Box 30014
Lansing, MI 48909
P: (517) 373-0853
E: tombarrett@house.mi.gov

Bizon, John (R, 62)*
House Office Building, N0996
P.O. Box 30014
Lansing, MI 48909
P: (517) 373-0555
E: drjohnbizon@house.mi.gov

Brinks, Winnie (D, 76)
House Office Building, N-1095
P.O. Box 30014
Lansing, MI 48909
P: (517) 373-0822
E: winniebrinks@house.mi.gov

Brunner, Charles M. (D, 96)
House Office Building, S-1285
P.O. Box 30014
Lansing, MI 48909
P: (517) 373-0158
F: (517) 373-8881
E: charlesbrunner@house.mi.gov

Bumstead, Jon (R, 100)
House Office Building, S-1289
P.O. Box 30014
Lansing, MI 48909
P: (517) 373-7317
F: (517) 373-9469
E: jonbumstead@house.mi.gov

Byrd, Wendell L. (D, 3)*
House Office Building, S-587
P.O. Box 30014
Lansing, MI 48909
P: (517) 373-0144
E: wendellbyrd@house.mi.gov

Callton, Mike (R, 87)
House Office Building, N-1191
P.O. Box 30014
Lansing, MI 48909
P: (517) 373-0842
F: (517) 373-6979
E: mikecallton@house.mi.gov

Canfield, Edward (R, 84)*
House Office Building, S-1188
P.O. Box 30014
Lansing, MI 48909
P: (517) 373-0476
E: edwardcanfield@house.mi.gov

Chang, Stephanie (D, 6)*
House Office Building, S-685
P.O. Box 30014
Lansing, MI 48909
P: (517) 373-0823
E: stephaniechang@house.mi.gov

Chatfield, Lee (R, 107)*
House Office Building, S-1486
P.O. Box 30014
Lansing, MI 48909
P: (517) 373-2629
E: leechatfield@house.mi.gov

Chirkun, John (D, 22)*
House Office Building, S-786
P.O. Box 30014
Lansing, MI 48909
P: (517) 373-0854
E: johnchirkun@house.mi.gov

Clemente, Paul (D, 14)
House Office Building, N-693
P.O. Box 30014
Lansing, MI 48909
P: (517) 373-0140
F: (517) 373-5924
E: paulclemente@house.mi.gov

Cochran, Tom (D, 67)
House Office Building, S-1086
P.O. Box 30014
Lansing, MI 48909
P: (517) 373-0587
E: TomCochran@house.mi.gov

Cole, Triston (R, 105)*
House Office Building, S-1389
P.O. Box 30014
Lansing, MI 48909
P: (517) 373-0829
E: tristoncole@house.mi.gov

Cotter, Kevin (R, 99)
164 Capitol Building
P.O. Box 30014
Lansing, MI 48909
P: (517) 373-1789
F: (517) 373-5491
E: kevincotter@house.mi.gov

Courser, Todd (R, 82)*
House Office Building
P.O. Box 30014
Lansing, MI 48909
P: (517) 373-1800
E: toddcourser@house.mi.gov

Cox, Laura (R, 19)*
House Office Building, N-698
P.O. Box 30014
Lansing, MI 48909
P: (517) 373-3920
E: lauracox@house.mi.gov

Crawford, Kathy (R, 38)*
House Office Building, S-887
P.O. Box 30014
Lansing, MI 48909
P: (517) 373-0827
E: kathycrawford@house.mi.gov

Darany, George T. (D, 15)
House Office Building, N-694
P.O. Box 30014
Lansing, MI 48909
P: (517) 373-0847
F: (517) 373-7538
E: georgetdarany@house.mi.gov

Dianda, Scott (D, 110)
House Office Building, S-1489
P.O. Box 30014
Lansing, MI 48909
P: (517) 373-0850
E: ScottDianda@house.mi.gov

Dillon, Brandon (D, 75)
House Office Building, N-1094
P.O. Box 30014
Lansing, MI 48909
P: (517) 373-2668
F: (517) 373-5696
E: brandondillon@house.mi.gov

Driskell, Gretchen (D, 52)
House Office Building, S-986
P.O. Box 30014
Lansing, MI 48909
P: (517) 373-0828
E: GretchenDriskell@house.mi.gov

Durhal III, Fred (D, 5)*
House Office Building, S-589
P.O. Box 30014
Lansing, MI 48909
P: (517) 373-0844
E: freddurhal@house.mi.gov

Faris, Pam (D, 48)
House Office Building, N-897
P.O. Box 30014
Lansing, MI 48909
P: (517) 373-7557
E: PamFaris@house.mi.gov

Farrington, Jeff (R, 30)
House Office Building, N-794
P.O. Box 30014
Lansing, MI 48909
P: (517) 373-7768
F: (517) 373-5903
E: jefffarrington@house.mi.gov

Forlini, Anthony G. (R, 24)
House Office Building, S-788
P.O. Box 30014
Lansing, MI 48909
P: (517) 373-0113
F: (517) 373-5912
E: anthonyforlini@house.mi.gov

Franz, Ray A. (R, 101)
House Office Building, S-1385
P.O. Box 30014
Lansing, MI 48909
P: (517) 373-0825
F: (517) 373-9461
E: rayfranz@house.mi.gov

Gamrat, Cindy (R, 80)*
House Office Building, N-1099
P.O. Box 30014
Lansing, MI 48909
P: (517) 373-0836
E: cindygamrat@house.mi.gov

Garcia, Daniela (R, 90)*
House Office Building, N-1194
P.O. Box 30014
Lansing, MI 48909
P: (517) 373-0830
E: danielagarcia@house.mi.gov

Garrett, LaTanya (D, 7)*
House Office Building, S-686
P.O. Box 30014
Lansing, MI 48909
P: (517) 373-2276
E: latanyagarrett@house.mi.gov

Gay-Dagnogo, Sherry (D, 8)*
House Office Building, S-687
P.O. Box 30014
Lansing, MI 48909
P: (517) 373-3815
E: sherrygay-dagnogo@house.mi.gov

Geiss, Erika (D, 12)*
N691 House Office Building
P.O. Box 30014
Lansing, MI 48909
P: (517) 373-0852
E: erikageiss@house.mi.gov

Glardon, Ben (R, 85)
House Office Building, S-1189
P.O. Box 30014
Lansing, MI 48909
P: (517) 373-0841
F: (517) 373-7937
E: benglardon@house.mi.gov

Glenn, Gary (R, 98)*
House Office Building, S-1287
P.O. Box 30014
Lansing, MI 48909
P: (517) 373-1791
E: garyglenn@house.mi.gov

Goike, Ken (R, 33)
House Office Building, N-797
P.O. Box 30014
Lansing, MI 48909
P: (517) 373-0820
F: (517) 373-5974
E: kengoike@house.mi.gov

Graves, Joseph (R, 51)
House Office Building, S-985
P.O. Box 30014
Lansing, MI 48909
P: (517) 373-1780
E: JosephGraves@house.mi.gov

Greig, Christine (D, 37)*
House Office Building, S-886
P.O. Box 30014
Lansing, MI 48909
P: (517) 373-1793
E: christinegreig@house.mi.gov

Greimel, Tim (D, 29)
167 Capitol Building
P.O. Box 30014
Lansing, MI 48909
P: (517) 373-0475
E: TimGreimel@house.mi.gov

Guerra, Vanessa (D, 95)*
House Office Building, N-119
P.O. Box 30014
Lansing, MI 48909
P: (517) 373-0152
E: vanessaguerra@house.mi.gov

Heise, Kurt (R, 20)
House Office Building, N-699
P.O. Box 30014
Lansing, MI 48909
P: (517) 373-3816
F: (517) 373-5952
E: kurtheise@house.mi.gov

Hoadley, Jon (D, 60)*
House Office Building, N-994
P.O. Box 30014
Lansing, MI 48909
P: (517) 373-1785
E: jonhoadley@house.mi.gov

Hooker, Thomas B. (R, 77)
House Office Building, N-1096
P.O. Box 30014
Lansing, MI 48909
P: (517) 373-2277
F: (517) 373-8731
E: thomashooker@house.mi.gov

Hovey-Wright, Marcia (D, 92)
House Office Building, N-1196
P.O. Box 30014
Lansing, MI 48909
P: (517) 373-2646
F: (517) 373-9646
E: marciahoveywright@house.mi.gov

Howrylak, Martin (R, 41)
House Office Building, N-890
P.O. Box 30014
Lansing, MI 48909
P: (517) 373-1783
E: MartinHowrylak@house.mi.gov

Hughes, Holly (R, 91)
House Office Building, N-1195
P.O. Box 30014
Lansing, MI 48909
P: (517) 373-3436
F: (517) 373-9698
E: hollyhughes@house.mi.gov

Iden, Brandt (R, 61)*
House Office Building, N-995
P.O. Box 30014
Lansing, MI 48909
P: (517) 373-1774
E: brandtiden@house.mi.gov

Inman, Larry (R, 104)*
House Office Building, S-1388
P.O. Box 30014
Lansing, MI 48909
P: (517) 373-1766
E: larryinman@house.mi.gov

Irwin, Jeff (D, 53)
House Office Building, S-987
P.O. Box 30014
Lansing, MI 48909
P: (517) 373 2577
F: (517) 373-5808
E: jeffirwin@house.mi.gov

Jacobsen, Bradford C. (R, 46)
House Office Building, N-895
P.O. Box 30014
Lansing, MI 48909
P: (517) 373-1798
F: (517) 373-8574
E: bradjacobsen@house.mi.gov

Jenkins, Nancy E. (R, 57)
House Office Building, N-991
P.O. Box 30014
Lansing, MI 48909
P: (517) 373-1706
F: (517) 373-5777
E: nancyjenkins@house.mi.gov

Johnson, Joel (R, 97)
House Office Building, S-1286
P.O. Box 30014
Lansing, MI 48909
P: (517) 373-8962
F: (517) 373-7195
E: joeljohnson@house.mi.gov

Kelly, Tim (R, 94)
House Office Building, N-1198
P.O. Box 30014
Lansing, MI 48909
P: (517) 373-0837
E: TimKelly@house.mi.gov

Kesto, Klint (R, 39)
House Office Building, S-888
P.O. Box 30014
Lansing, MI 48909
P: (517) 373-1799
E: KlintKesto@house.mi.gov

Kivela, John (D, 109)
House Office Building, S-1488
P.O. Box 30014
Lansing, MI 48909
P: (517) 373-0498
E: JohnKivela@house.mi.gov

Kosowski, Robert L. (D, 16)
House Office Building, N-695
P.O. Box 30014
Lansing, MI 48909
P: (517) 373-2576
E: RobertKosowski@house.mi.gov

LaFontaine, Andrea (R, 32)
House Office Building, N-796
P.O. Box 30014
Lansing, MI 48909
P: (517) 373-8931
F: (517) 373-8637
E: andrealafontaine@house.mi.gov

Lane, Marilyn (D, 31)
House Office Building, N-795
P.O. Box 30014
Lansing, MI 48909
P: (517) 373-0159
F: (517) 373-5893
E: marilynlane@house.mi.gov

Lauwers, Dan (R, 81)
House Office Building, S-1185
P.O. Box 30014
Lansing, MI 48909
P: (517) 373-1790
E: DanLauwers@house.mi.gov

LaVoy, Bill (D, 17)
House Office Building, N-696
P.O. Box 30014
Lansing, MI 48909
P: (517) 373-1530
E: BillLaVoy@house.mi.gov

Leonard, Tom (R, 93)
251 Capitol Building
P.O. Box 30014
Lansing, MI 48909
P: (517) 373-1778
E: TomLeonard@house.mi.gov

Leutheuser, Eric (R, 58)*
House Office Building, N-992
P.O. Box 30014
Lansing, MI 48909
P: (517) 373-1794
E: ericleutheuser@house.mi.gov

Michigan

Liberati, Frank (D, 13)*
House Office Building, N-692
P.O. Box 30014
Lansing, MI 48909
P: (517) 373-0845
E: frankliberati@house.mi.gov

Love, Leslie (D, 10)*
House Office Building, S-689
P.O. Box 30014
Lansing, MI 48909
P: (517) 373-0857
E: lesllielove@house.mi.gov

Lucido, Peter (R, 36)*
House Office Building, S-885
P.O. Box 30014
Lansing, MI 48909
P: (517) 373-0843
E: peterlucido@house.mi.gov

Lyons, Lisa (R, 86)
House Office Building, N-1190
P.O. Box 30014
Lansing, MI 48909
P: (517) 373-0846
F: (517) 373-8714
E: lisalyons@house.mi.gov

Maturen, David (R, 63)*
House Office Building, N-997
P.O. Box 30014
Lansing, MI 48909
P: (517) 373-1787
E: davidmaturen@house.mi.gov

McBroom, Ed (R, 108)
House Office Building, S-1487
P.O. Box 30014
Lansing, MI 48909
P: (517) 373-0156
F: (517) 373-9370
E: edmcbroom@house.mi.gov

McCready, Mike (R, 40)
House Office Building, S-889
P.O. Box 30014
Lansing, MI 48909
P: (517) 373-8670
E: MikeMcCready@house.mi.gov

Miller, Aaron (R, 59)*
House Office Building, N-993
P.O. Box 30014
Lansing, MI 48909
P: (517) 373-0832
E: aaronmiller@house.mi.gov

Miller, Derek E. (D, 28)*
House Office Building, N-792
P.O. Box 30014
Lansing, MI 48909
P: (517) 373-1772
E: derekmiller@house.mi.gov

Moss, Jeremy (D, 35)*
House Office Building, N-799
P.O. Box 30014
Lansing, MI 48909
P: (517) 373-1788
E: jeremymoss@house.mi.gov

Muxlow, Paul (R, 83)
House Office Building, S-1187
P.O. Box 30014
Lansing, MI 48909
P: (517) 373-0835
F: (517) 373-9876
E: paulmuxlow@house.mi.gov

Neeley, Sheldon (D, 34)*
House Office Building, N-798
P.O. Box 30014
Lansing, MI 48909
P: (517) 373-8808
E: sheldonneeley@house.mi.gov

Nesbitt, Aric (R, 66)
153 Capitol Building
P.O. Box 30014
Lansing, MI 48909
P: (517) 373-0839
F: (517) 373-5940
E: aricnesbitt@house.mi.gov

Outman, Rick (R, 70)
House Office Building, S-1089
P.O. Box 30014
Lansing, MI 48909
P: (517) 373-0834
F: (517) 373-9622
E: rickoutman@house.mi.gov

Pagan, Kristy (D, 21)*
House Office Building, S-785
P.O. Box 30014
Lansing, MI 48909
P: (517) 373-2575
E: kristypagan@house.mi.gov

Pagel, David (R, 78)
House Office Building, N-1097
P.O. Box 30014
Lansing, MI 48909
P: (517) 373-1796
E: DavePagel@house.mi.gov

Pettalia, Peter (R, 106)
House Office Building, S-1485
P.O. Box 30014
Lansing, MI 48909
P: (517) 373-0833
F: (517) 373-8446
E: peterpettalia@house.mi.gov

Phelps, Phil (D, 49)
House Office Building, N-898
P.O. Box 30014
Lansing, MI 48909
P: (517) 373-7515
F: (517) 373-5817
E: RepPhelps@house.mi.gov

Plawecki, Julie (D, 11)*
House Office Building, N-690
P.O. Box 30014
Lansing, MI 48909
P: (517) 373-0849
E: julieplawecki@house.mi.gov

Poleski, Earl (R, 64)
House Office Building, N-998
P.O. Box 30014
Lansing, MI 48909
P: (517) 373-1795
F: (517) 373-5760
E: earlpoleski@house.mi.gov

Potvin, Phil (R, 102)
House Office Building, S-1386
P.O. Box 30014
Lansing, MI 48909
P: (517) 373-1747
F: (517) 373-9371
E: philpotvin@house.mi.gov

Price, Amanda (R, 89)
House Office Building, N-1193
P.O. Box 30014
Lansing, MI 48909
P: (517) 373-0838
F: (517) 373-9830
E: amandaprice@house.mi.gov

Pscholka, Al (R, 79)
351 Capitol Building
P.O. Box 30014
Lansing, MI 48909
P: (517) 373-1403
F: (517) 373-3652
E: alpscholka@house.mi.gov

Rendon, Bruce R. (R, 103)
House Office Building, S-1387
P.O. Box 30014
Lansing, MI 48909
P: (517) 373-3817
F: (517) 373-5495
E: brucerendon@house.mi.gov

Roberts, Brett (R, 65)*
House Office Building, N-999
P.O. Box 30014
Lansing, MI 48909
P: (517) 373-1775
E: brettroberts@house.mi.gov

Roberts, Sarah (D, 18)
House Office Building, N-697
P.O. Box 30014
Lansing, MI 48909
P: (517) 373-1180
E: SarahRoberts@house.mi.gov

Robinson, Rose Mary (D, 4)
House Office Building, S-588
P.O. Box 30014
Lansing, MI 48909
P: (517) 373-1008
E: RoseMaryRobinson@house.mi.gov

Runestad, Jim (R, 44)*
House Office Building, N-893
P.O. Box 30014
Lansing, MI 48909
P: (517) 373-2616
E: jimrunestad@house.mi.gov

Rutledge, David E. (D, 54)
House Office Building, S-988
P.O. Box 30014
Lansing, MI 48909
P: (517) 373-1771
F: (517) 373-5797
E: davidrutledge@house.mi.gov

Santana, Harvey (D, 9)
House Office Building, S-688
P.O. Box 30014
Lansing, MI 48909
P: (517) 373-6990
F: (517) 373-5985
E: harveysantana@house.mi.gov

Schor, Andy (D, 68)
House Office Building, S-1087
P.O. Box 30014
Lansing, MI 48909
P: (517) 373-0826
E: AndySchor@house.mi.gov

Sheppard, Jason (R, 56)*
House Office Building, N-990
P.O. Box 30014
Lansing, MI 48909
P: (517) 373-2617
E: jasonsheppard@house.mi.gov

Singh, Sam (D, 69)
141 Capitol Building
P.O. Box 30014
Lansing, MI 48909
P: (517) 373-1786
E: SamSingh@house.mi.gov

Smiley, Charles (D, 50)
House Office Building, N-899
P.O. Box 30014
Lansing, MI 48909
P: (517) 373-3906
F: (517) 373-5812
E: charlessmiley
@house.mi.gov

Somerville, Pat (R, 23)
House Office Building, S-787
P.O. Box 30014
Lansing, MI 48909
P: (517) 373-0855
F: (517) 373-5922
E: patsomerville
@house.mi.gov

Tedder, Jim (R, 43)*
House Office Building, N-892
P.O. Box 30014
Lansing, MI 48909
P: (517) 373-0615
E: jimtedder@house.mi.gov

Theis, Lana (R, 42)*
House Office Building, N-891
P.O. Box 30014
Lansing, MI 48909
P: (517) 373-1784
E: lanatheis@house.mi.gov

Tinsley-Talabi, Alberta (D, 2)
House Office Building, S-586
P.O. Box 30014
Lansing, MI 48909
P: (517) 373-1776
F: (517) 373-8502
E: albertatalabi
@house.mi.gov

Townsend, Jim (D, 26)
House Office Building, N-790
P.O. Box 30014
Lansing, MI 48909
P: (517) 373-3818
F: (517) 373-5888
E: jimtownsend@house.mi.gov

Vaupel, Henry (R, 47)*
House Office Building, N-896
P.O. Box 30014
Lansing, MI 48909
P: (517) 373-8835
E: hankvaupel@house.mi.gov

VerHeulen, Rob (R, 74)
House Office Building, N-1093
P.O. Box 30014
Lansing, MI 48909
P: (517) 373-8900
E: RobVerHeulen
@house.mi.gov

Victory, Roger (R, 88)
House Office Building, N-1192
P.O. Box 30014
Lansing, MI 48909
P: (517) 373-1830
E: RogerVictory
@house.mi.gov

Webber, Michael (R, 45)*
House Office Building, N-894
P.O. Box 30014
Lansing, MI 48909
P: (517) 373-1773
E: michaelwebber
@house.mi.gov

Wittenberg, Robert (D, 27)*
House Office Building, N-791
P.O. Box 30014
Lansing, MI 48909
P: (517) 373-0478
E: robertwittenberg
@house.mi.gov

Yanez, Henry (D, 25)
House Office Building, S-789
P.O. Box 30014
Lansing, MI 48909
P: (517) 373-2275
E: RogerVictory
@house.mi.gov

Yonker, Ken (R, 72)
House Office Building, N-1091
P.O. Box 30014
Lansing, MI 48909
P: (517) 373-0840
F: (517) 373-7590
E: kenyonker@house.mi.gov

Zemke, Adam F. (D, 55)
House Office Building, S-989
P.O. Box 30014
Lansing, MI 48909
P: (517) 373-1792
E: AdamZemke@house.mi.gov

Congress

Senate

Peters, Gary C. (D)
Stabenow, Debbie (D)

House

Amash, Justin (R, 3)
Benishek, Dan (R, 1)
Bishop, Michael (R, 8)
Conyers Jr., John (D, 13)
Dingell, John D. (D, 12)
Huizenga, Bill (R, 2)
Kildee, Dale E. (D, 5)
Lawrence, Brenda (D, 14)
Levin, Sander M. (D, 9)
Miller, Candice (R, 10)
Moolenaar, John (R, 4)
Moolenaar, John (R, 4)
Trott, Dave (R, 11)
Upton, Frederick S. (R, 6)
Walberg, Tim (R, 7)

Minnesota

Executive

Governor
Hon. Mark Dayton (D)
Governor
130 State Capitol
75 Rev. Martin Luther King Jr. Boulevard
St. Paul, MN 55155
P: (651) 201-3400
F: (651) 797-1850

Lieutenant Governor
Hon. Tina Smith (D)
Lieutenant Governor
130 State Capitol
75 Rev. Martin Luther King Jr. Boulevard
St. Paul, MN 55155
P: (651) 201-3400
F: (651) 797-1850

Attorney General
Hon. Lori Swanson (DFL)
Attorney General
State Capitol, Suite 102
St. Paul, MN 55155
P: (651) 296-3353
F: (651) 297-4193
E: attorney.general@state.mn.us

Auditor
Hon. Rebecca Otto (DFL)
State Auditor
525 Park Street, Suite 400
St. Paul, MN 55103
P: (615) 296-2551
F: (615) 296-4755
E: rebecca.otto@state.mn.us

Secretary of State
Hon. Steve Simon (DFL)
Secretary of State
180 State Office Building
100 Martin Luther King Jr. Boulevard
St. Paul, MN 55155
P: (651) 201-1328
F: (651) 269-9073
E: secretary.state@state.mn.us

Commissioner of Management & Budget
Mr. Myron Frans
(appointed)
Commissioner
400 Centennial Building
658 Cedar Street
St. Paul, MN 55155
P: (651) 201-8011
F: (651) 797-1300
E: myron.frans@state.mn.us

Judiciary

Supreme Court (NE)
Ms. AnnMarie O'Neill
Clerk of Appellate Courts
305 Minnesota Judicial Center
25 Martin Luther King Jr. Boulevard
St. Paul, MN 55155
P: (651) 296-2581

Hon. Lorie Skjerven Gildea
Chief Justice
Hon. Grant Barry Anderson
Hon. Christopher Dietzen
Hon. David L. Lillehaug
Hon. Alan C. Page
Hon. David R. Stras
Hon. Wilhelmina M. Wright

Legislative Senate

Senate President
Sen. Sandra L. Pappas (DFL)
Senate President
323 Capitol Building
75 Martin Luther King Jr. Boulevard
St. Paul, MN 55155
P: (651) 296-1802

President Pro Tempore of the Senate
Sen. Ann H. Rest (DFL)
Senate President Pro Tem
235 Capitol Building
75 Martin Luther King Jr. Boulevard
St. Paul, MN 55155
P: (651) 296-2889
E: sen.ann.rest@senate.mn

Senate Majority Leader
Sen. Thomas M. Bakk (DFL)
Senate Majority Leader
232 Capitol Building
75 Martin Luther King Jr. Boulevard
St. Paul, MN 55155
P: (651) 296-8881
E: sen.tom.bakk@senate.mn

Senate Minority Leader
Sen. David Hann (R)
Senate Minority Leader
147 State Office Building
100 Martin Luther King Jr. Boulevard
St. Paul, MN 55155
P: (651) 296-1749
E: sen.david.hann@senate.mn

Secretary of the Senate
Ms. JoAnne Zoff
Secretary of the Senate
231 State Capitol Building
75 Martin Luther King Jr. Boulevard
St. Paul, MN 55155
P: (651) 296-2344
E: joanne.zoff@senate.mn

Members of the Senate
Anderson, Bruce (R, 29)
133 State Office Building
100 Martin Luther King Jr. Boulevard
St. Paul, MN 55155
P: (651) 296-5981
E: sen.bruce.anderson@senate.mn

Bakk, Thomas M. (DFL, 3)
232 Capitol Building
75 Martin Luther King Jr. Boulevard
St. Paul, MN 55155
P: (651) 296-8881
E: sen.tom.bakk@senate.mn

Benson, Michelle R. (R, 31)
115 State Office Building
100 Martin Luther King Jr. Boulevard
St. Paul, MN 55155
P: (651) 296-3219
E: sen.michelle.benson@senate.mn

Bonoff, Terri (DFL, 44)
325 Capitol Building
75 Martin Luther King Jr. Boulevard
St. Paul, MN 55155
P: (651) 296-4314
E: sen.terri.bonoff@senate.mn

Brown, David M. (R, 15)
109 State Office Building
100 Martin Luther King Jr. Boulevard
St. Paul, MN 55155
P: (651) 296-8075
E: sen.david.brown@senate.mn

Carlson, Jim (DFL, 51)
111 Capitol Building
75 Martin Luther King Jr. Boulevard
St. Paul, MN 55155
P: (651) 297-8073
E: sen.jim.carlson@senate.mn

Chamberlain, Roger C. (R, 38)
129 State Office Building
100 Martin Luther King Jr. Boulevard
St. Paul, MN 55155
P: (651) 296-1253
E: sen.roger.chamberlain@senate.mn

Champion, Bobby Joe (DFL, 59)
306 Capitol Building
75 Martin Luther King Jr. Boulevard
St. Paul, MN 55155
P: (651) 296-9246
E: sen.bobby.champion@senate.mn

Clausen, Greg D. (DFL, 57)
303 Capitol Building
75 Martin Luther King Jr. Boulevard
St. Paul, MN 55155
P: (651) 296-4120
E: sen.greg.clausen@senate.mn

Cohen, Richard J. (DFL, 64)
301 Capitol Building
75 Martin Luther King Jr. Boulevard
St. Paul, MN 55155
P: (651) 296-5931
E: sen.richard.cohen@senate.mn

Dahle, Kevin L. (DFL, 20)
G-9 Capitol Building
75 Martin Luther King Jr. Boulevard
St. Paul, MN 55155
P: (651) 296-1279
E: sen.kevin.dahle@senate.mn

Dahms, Gary H. (R, 16)
121 State Office Building
100 Martin Luther King Jr. Boulevard
St. Paul, MN 55155
P: (651) 296-8138
E: sen.gary.dahms@senate.mn

Dibble, D. Scott (DFL, 61)
111 Capitol Building
75 Martin Luther King Jr. Boulevard
St. Paul, MN 55155
P: (651) 296-4191
E: sen.scott.dibble@senate.mn

Dziedzic, Kari (DFL, 60)
235 Capitol Building
75 Martin Luther King Jr. Boulevard
St. Paul, MN 55155
P: (651) 296-7809
E: sen.kari.dziedzic@senate.mn

Eaton, Chris A. (DFL, 40)
110 Capitol Building
75 Martin Luther King Jr. Boulevard
St. Paul, MN 55155
P: (651) 296-8869
E: sen.chris.eaton@senate.mn

Eken, Kent (DFL, 4)
303 Capitol Building
75 Martin Luther King Jr. Boulevard
St. Paul, MN 55155
P: (651) 296-3205
E: sen.kent.eken@senate.mn

Fischbach, Michelle L. (R, 13)
15 State Office Building
100 Martin Luther King Jr. Boulevard
St. Paul, MN 55155
P: (651) 296-2084
E: sen.michelle.fischbach@senate.mn

Franzen, Melisa (DFL, 49)
306 Capitol Building
75 Martin Luther King Jr. Boulevard
St. Paul, MN 55155
P: (651) 296-6238
E: sen.melisa.franzen@senate.mn

Gazelka, Paul E. (R, 9)
145 State Office Building
100 Martin Luther King Jr. Boulevard
St. Paul, MN 55155
P: (651) 296-4875
E: sen.paul.gazelka@senate.mn

Goodwin, Barb J. (DFL, 41)
110 Capitol Building
75 Martin Luther King Jr. Boulevard
St. Paul, MN 55155
P: (651) 296-4334

Hall, Dan D. (R, 56)
103 State Office Building
100 Martin Luther King Jr. Boulevard
St. Paul, MN 55155
P: (651) 296-5975
E: sen.dan.hall@senate.mn

Hann, David (R, 48)
147 State Office Building
100 Martin Luther King Jr. Boulevard
St. Paul, MN 55155
P: (651) 296-1749
E: sen.david.hann@senate.mn

Hawj, Foung (DFL, 67)
309 Capitol Building
75 Martin Luther King Jr. Boulevard
St. Paul, MN 55155
P: (651) 296-5285
E: sen.foung.hawj@senate.mn

Hayden, Jeff (DFL, 62)
208 Capitol Building
75 Martin Luther King Jr. Boulevard
St. Paul, MN 55155
P: (651) 296-4261
E: sen.jeff.hayden@senate.mn

Hoffman, John A. (DFL, 36)
Room G-24 Capitol Building
75 Martin Luther King Jr. Boulevard
St. Paul, MN 55155
P: (651) 296-4154
E: sen.john.hoffman@senate.mn

Housley, Karin (R, 39)
Room 21 State Office Building
100 Martin Luther King Jr. Boulevard
St. Paul, MN 55155
P: (651) 296-4351
E: sen.karin.housley@senate.mn

Ingebrigtsen, Bill G. (R, 8)
Room 143 State Office Building
100 Martin Luther King Jr. Boulevard
St. Paul, MN 55155
P: (651) 297-8063
E: sen.bill.ingebrigtsen@senate.mn

Jensen, Vicki (DFL, 24)
205 Capitol Building
75 Martin Luther King Jr. Boulevard
St. Paul, MN 55155
P: (651) 296-9457
E: sen.vicki.jensen@senate.mn

Johnson, Alice M. (DFL, 37)
205 Capitol Building
75 Martin Luther King Jr. Boulevard
St. Paul, MN 55155
P: (651) 296-2556
E: sen.alice.johnson@senate.mn

Kent, Susan (DFL, 53)
205 Capitol Building
75 Martin Luther King Jr. Boulevard
St. Paul, MN 55155
P: (651) 296-4166
E: sen.susan.kent@senate.mn

Kiffmeyer, Mary (R, 30)
123 State Office Building
100 Martin Luther King Jr. Boulevard
St. Paul, MN 55155
P: (651) 296-5655
E: sen.mary.kiffmeyer@senate.mn

Koenen, Lyle (DFL, 17)
G-9 Capitol Building
75 Martin Luther King Jr. Boulevard
St. Paul, MN 55155
P: (651) 296-5094
E: sen.lyle.koenen@senate.mn

Latz, Ron (DFL, 46)
303 Capitol Building
75 Martin Luther King Jr. Boulevard
St. Paul, MN 55155
P: (651) 297-8065
E: sen.ron.latz@senate.mn

Limmer, Warren (R, 34)
153 State Office Building
100 Martin Luther King Jr. Boulevard
St. Paul, MN 55155
P: (651) 296-2159
E: sen.warren.limmer@senate.mn

Lourey, Tony (DFL, 11)
G-12 Capitol Building
75 Martin Luther King Jr. Boulevard
St. Paul, MN 55155
P: (651) 296-0293
E: sen.tony.lourey@senate.mn

Marty, John (DFL, 66)
323 Capitol Building
75 Martin Luther King Jr. Boulevard
St. Paul, MN 55155
P: (651) 296-5645

Metzen, James P. (DFL, 52)
G-9 Capitol Building
75 Martin Luther King Jr. Boulevard
St. Paul, MN 55155
P: (651) 296-4370
E: sen.jim.metzen@senate.mn

Miller, Jeremy R. (R, 28)
135 State Office Building
100 Martin Luther King Jr. Boulevard
St. Paul, MN 55155
P: (651) 296-5649
E: sen.jeremy.miller@senate.mn

Nelson, Carla J. (R, 26)
117 State Office Building
100 Martin Luther King Jr. Boulevard
St. Paul, MN 55155
P: (651) 296-4848
E: sen.carla.nelson@senate.mn

Newman, Scott J. (R, 18)
141 State Office Building
100 Martin Luther King Jr. Boulevard
St. Paul, MN 55155
P: (651) 296-4131
E: sen.scott.newman@senate.mn

Minnesota

Nienow, Sean R. (R, 32)
105 State Office Building
100 Martin Luther King Jr. Boulevard
St. Paul, MN 55155
P: (651) 296-5419
E: sen.sean.nienow@senate.mn

Ortman, Julianne E. (R, 47)
119 Capitol Building
75 Martin Luther King Jr. Boulevard
St. Paul, MN 55155
P: (651) 296-4837
E: sen.julianne.ortman@senate.mn

Osmek, David J. (R, 33)
19 State Office Building
100 Martin Luther King Jr. Boulevard
St. Paul, MN 55155
P: (651) 296-1282
E: sen.david.osmek@senate.mn

Pappas, Sandra L. (DFL, 65)
323 Capitol Building
75 Martin Luther King Jr. Boulevard
St. Paul, MN 55155
P: (651) 296-1802

Pederson, John C. (R, 14)
27 State Office Building
100 Martin Luther King Jr. Boulevard
St. Paul, MN 55155
P: (651) 296-6455
E: sen.john.pederson@senate.mn

Petersen, Branden (R, 35)
127 State Office Building
100 Martin Luther King Jr. Boulevard
St. Paul, MN 55155
P: (651) 296-3733
E: sen.branden.petersen@senate.mn

Pratt, Eric R. (R, 55)
23 State Office Building
100 Martin Luther King Jr. Boulevard
St. Paul, MN 55155
P: (651) 296-4123
E: sen.eric.pratt@senate.mn

Reinert, Roger J. (DFL, 7)
325 Capitol Building
75 Martin Luther King Jr. Boulevard
St. Paul, MN 55155
P: (651) 296-4188
E: sen.roger.reinert@senate.mn

Rest, Ann H. (DFL, 45)
235 Capitol Building
75 Martin Luther King Jr. Boulevard
St. Paul, MN 55155
P: (651) 296-2889
E: sen.ann.rest@senate.mn

Rosen, Julie A. (R, 23)
139 State Office Building
100 Martin Luther King Jr. Boulevard
St. Paul, MN 55155
P: (651) 296-5713
E: sen.julie.rosen@senate.mn

Ruud, Carrie L. (R, 10)
25 State Office Building
100 Martin Luther King Jr. Boulevard
St. Paul, MN 55155
P: (651) 296-4913
E: sen.carrie.ruud@senate.mn

Saxhaug, Tom (DFL, 5)
328 Capitol Building
75 Martin Luther King Jr. Boulevard
St. Paul, MN 55155
P: (651) 296-4136
E: sen.tom.saxhaug@senate.mn

Scalze, Bev (DFL, 42)
208 Capitol Building
75 Martin Luther King Jr. Boulevard
St. Paul, MN 55155
P: (651) 296-5537
E: sen.bev.scalze@senate.mn

Schmit, Matt (DFL, 21)
306 Capitol Building
75 Martin Luther King Jr. Boulevard
St. Paul, MN 55155
P: (651) 296-4264
E: sen.matt.schmit@senate.mn

Senjem, David H. (R, 25)
113 State Office Building
100 Martin Luther King Jr. Boulevard
St. Paul, MN 55155
P: (651) 296-3903
E: sen.david.senjem@senate.mn

Sheran, Kathy (DFL, 19)
G-12 Capitol Building
75 Martin Luther King Jr. Boulevard
St. Paul, MN 55155
P: (651) 296-6153
E: sen.kathy.sheran@senate.mn

Sieben, Katie (DFL, 54)
208 Capitol Building
75 Martin Luther King Jr. Boulevard
St. Paul, MN 55155
P: (651) 297-8060
E: sen.katie.sieben@senate.mn

Skoe, Rod (DFL, 2)
235 Capitol Building
75 Martin Luther King Jr. Boulevard
St. Paul, MN 55155
P: (651) 296-4196
E: sen.rod.skoe@senate.mn

Sparks, Dan (DFL, 27)
328 Capitol Building
75 Martin Luther King Jr. Boulevard
St. Paul, MN 55155
P: (651) 296-9248
E: sen.dan.sparks@senate.mn

Stumpf, LeRoy A. (DFL, 1)
G-12 Capitol Building
75 Martin Luther King Jr. Boulevard
St. Paul, MN 55155
P: (651) 296-8660
E: sen.leroy.stumpf@senate.mn

Thompson, Dave A. (R, 58)
131 State Office Building
100 Martin Luther King Jr. Boulevard
St. Paul, MN 55155
P: (651) 296-5252
E: sen.dave.thompson@senate.mn

Tomassoni, David J. (DFL, 6)
G-9 Capitol Building
75 Martin Luther King Jr. Boulevard
St. Paul, MN 55155
P: (651) 296-8017
E: sen.david.tomassoni@senate.mn

Torres Ray, Patricia (DFL, 63)
309 Capitol Building
75 Martin Luther King Jr. Boulevard
St. Paul, MN 55155
P: (651) 296-4274
E: sen.patricia.torres.ray@senate.mn

Weber, Bill (R, 22)
125 State Office Building
100 Martin Luther King Jr. Boulevard
St. Paul, MN 55155
P: (651) 296-5650
E: sen.bill.weber@senate.mn

Westrom, Torrey N. (R, 12)
107 State Office Building
100 Martin Luther King Jr. Boulevard
St. Paul, MN 55155
P: (651) 296-3826
E: sen.torrey.westrom@senate.mn

Wiger, Charles W. (DFL, 43)
205 Capitol Building
75 Martin Luther King Jr. Boulevard
St. Paul, MN 55155
P: (651) 296-6820
E: sen.chuck.wiger@senate.mn

Wiklund, Melissa H. (DFL, 50)
303 Capitol Building
75 Martin Luther King Jr. Boulevard
St. Paul, MN 55155
P: (651) 297-8061
E: sen.melissa.wiklund@senate.mn

House

Speaker of the House

Rep. Kurt Daudt (R)
Speaker of the House
463 State Office Building
100 Martin Luther King Jr. Boulevard
St. Paul, MN 55155
P: (651) 296-5364
E: rep.kurt.daudt@house.mn

Speaker Pro Tempore of the House

Rep. Melissa Hortman (DFL)
House Deputy Minority Leader
237 State Office Building
100 Martin Luther King Jr. Boulevard
St. Paul, MN 55155
P: (651) 296-4280
E: rep.melissa.hortman@house.mn

House Majority Leader

Rep. Joyce Peppin (R)
House Majority Leader
459 State Office Building
100 Martin Luther King Jr. Boulevard
St. Paul, MN 55155
P: (651) 296-7806
E: rep.joyce.peppin@house.mn

House Minority Leader

Rep. Paul Thissen (DFL)
House Minority Leader
267 State Office Building
100 Martin Luther King Jr. Boulevard
St. Paul, MN 55155
P: (651) 296-5375
F: (651) 296-3869
E: rep.paul.thissen@house.mn

Clerk of the House

Mr. Al Mathiowetz
Chief Clerk of the House
211 State Capitol
100 Martin Luther King Jr. Boulevard
St. Paul, MN 55155
P: (651) 296-2314
E: Al.Mathiowetz@house.mn

Members of the House

Albright, Tony (R, 55B)
407 State Office Building
100 Martin Luther King Jr. Boulevard
St. Paul, MN 55155
P: (651) 296-5185
E: rep.tony.albright@house.mn

Allen, Susan (DFL, 62B)
229 State Office Building
100 Martin Luther King Jr. Boulevard
St. Paul, MN 55155
P: (651) 296-7152
E: rep.susan.allen@house.mn

Anderson, Mark (R, 9A)
579 State Office Building
100 Martin Luther King Jr. Boulevard
St. Paul, MN 55155
P: (651) 296-4293
E: rep.mark.anderson@house.mn

Anderson, Paul H. (R, 12B)
597 State Office Building
100 Martin Luther King Jr. Boulevard
St. Paul, MN 55155
P: (651) 296-4317
E: rep.paul.anderson@house.mn

Anderson, Sarah (R, 44A)
583 State Office Building
100 Martin Luther King Jr. Boulevard
St. Paul, MN 55155
P: (651) 296-5511
E: rep.sarah.anderson@house.mn

Anzelc, Tom (DFL, 5B)
317 State Office Building
100 Martin Luther King Jr. Boulevard
St. Paul, MN 55155
P: (651) 296-4936
E: rep.tom.anzelc@house.mn

Applebaum, Jon (DFL, 44B)*
223 State Office Building
100 Rev. Dr. Martin Luther King Jr. Blvd
St. Paul, MN 55155
P: (651) 296-9934
E: rep.jon.applebaum@house.mn

Atkins, Joe (DFL, 52B)
349 State Office Building
100 Martin Luther King Jr. Boulevard
St. Paul, MN 55155
P: (651) 296-4192
E: rep.joe.atkins@house.mn

Backer, Jeff (R, 12A)*
593 State Office Building
100 Rev. Dr. Martin Luther King Jr. Blvd
St. Paul, MN 55155
P: (651) 296-4929
E: rep.jeff.backer@house.mn

Baker, Dave (R, 17B)*
539 State Office Building
100 Rev. Dr. Martin Luther King Jr. Blvd
St. Paul, MN 55155
P: (651) 296-6206
E: rep.dave.baker@house.mn

Barrett, Bob (R, 32B)
567 State Office Building
100 Martin Luther King Jr. Boulevard
St. Paul, MN 55155
P: (651) 296-5377
E: rep.bob.barrett@house.mn

Bennett, Peggy (R, 27A)*
507 State Office Building
100 Rev. Dr. Martin Luther King Jr. Blvd
St. Paul, MN 55155
P: (651) 296-8216
E: rep.peggy.bennett@house.mn

Bernardy, Connie (DFL, 41A)
281 State Office Building
100 Martin Luther King Jr. Boulevard
St. Paul, MN 55155
P: (651) 296-5510
E: rep.connie.bernardy@house.mn

Bly, David (DFL, 20B)
301 State Office Building
100 Martin Luther King Jr. Boulevard
St. Paul, MN 55155
P: (651) 296-0171
E: rep.david.bly@house.mn

Carlson, Lyndon (DFL, 45A)
283 State Office Building
100 Martin Luther King Jr. Boulevard
St. Paul, MN 55155
P: (651) 296-4255
E: rep.lyndon.carlson@house.mn

Christensen, Drew (R, 56A)*
529 State Office Building
100 Rev. Dr. Martin Luther King Jr. Blvd
St. Paul, MN 55155
P: (651) 296-4212
E: rep.drew.christensen@house.mn

Clark, Karen (DFL, 62A)
273 State Office Building
100 Martin Luther King Jr. Boulevard
St. Paul, MN 55155
P: (651) 296-0294
E: rep.karen.clark@house.mn

Considine, Jack (DFL, 19B)*
323 State Office Building
100 Rev. Dr. Martin Luther King Jr. Blvd
St. Paul, MN 55155
P: (651) 296-3248
E: rep.jack.considine@house.mn

Cornish, Tony (R, 23B)
369 State Office Building
100 Martin Luther King Jr. Boulevard
St. Paul, MN 55155
P: (651) 296-4240
E: rep.tony.cornish@house.mn

Daniels, Brian (R, 24B)*
551 State Office Building
100 Rev. Dr. Martin Luther King Jr. Blvd
St. Paul, MN 55155
P: (651) 296-8237
E: rep.brian.daniels@house.mn

Daudt, Kurt (R, 31A)
463 State Office Building
100 Martin Luther King Jr. Boulevard
St. Paul, MN 55155
P: (651) 296-5364
E: rep.kurt.daudt@house.mn

Davids, Greg (R, 28B)
585 State Office Building
100 Martin Luther King Jr. Boulevard
St. Paul, MN 55155
P: (651) 296-9278
E: rep.greg.davids@house.mn

Davnie, Jim (DFL, 63A)
393 State Office Building
100 Martin Luther King Jr. Boulevard
St. Paul, MN 55155
P: (651) 296-0173
E: rep.jim.davnie@house.mn

Dean, Matt (R, 38B)
401 State Office Building
100 Martin Luther King Jr. Boulevard
St. Paul, MN 55155
P: (651) 296-3018
E: rep.matt.dean@house.mn

Dehn, Raymond (DFL, 59B)
279 State Office Building
100 Martin Luther King Jr. Boulevard
St. Paul, MN 55155
P: (651) 296-8659
E: rep.raymond.dehn@house.mn

Minnesota

Dettmer, Bob (R, 39A)
565 State Office Building
100 Martin Luther King Jr. Boulevard
St. Paul, MN 55155
P: (651) 296-4124
E: rep.bob.dettmer@house.mn

Dill, David (DFL, 3A)
311 State Office Building
100 Martin Luther King Jr. Boulevard
St. Paul, MN 55155
P: (651) 296-2190
E: rep.david.dill@house.mn

Drazkowski, Steve (R, 21B)
591 State Office Building
100 Martin Luther King Jr. Boulevard
St. Paul, MN 55155
P: (651) 296-2273
E: rep.steve.drazkowski@house.mn

Erhardt, Ron (DFL, 49A)
245 State Office Building
100 Martin Luther King Jr. Boulevard
St. Paul, MN 55155
P: (651) 296-4363
E: rep.ron.erhardt@house.mn

Erickson, Sondra (R, 15A)
479 State Office Building
100 Martin Luther King Jr. Boulevard
St. Paul, MN 55155
P: (651) 296-6746
E: rep.sondra.erickson@house.mn

Fabian, Dan (R, 1A)
429 State Office Building
100 Martin Luther King Jr. Boulevard
St. Paul, MN 55155
P: (651) 296-9635
E: rep.dan.fabian@house.mn

Fenton, Kelly (R, 53B)*
525 State Office Building
100 Rev. Dr. Martin Luther King Jr. Blvd
St. Paul, MN 55155
P: (651) 296-1147
E: rep.kelly.fenton@house.mn

Fischer, Peter (DFL, 43A)
201 State Office Building
100 Martin Luther King Jr. Boulevard
St. Paul, MN 55155
P: (651) 296-5363
E: rep.peter.fischer@house.mn

Franson, Mary (R, 8B)
517 State Office Building
100 Martin Luther King Jr. Boulevard
St. Paul, MN 55155
P: (651) 296-3201
E: rep.mary.franson@house.mn

Freiberg, Mike (DFL, 45B)
239 State Office Building
100 Martin Luther King Jr. Boulevard
St. Paul, MN 55155
P: (651) 296-4176
E: rep.mike.freiberg@house.mn

Garofalo, Patrick (R, 58B)
485 State Office Building
100 Martin Luther King Jr. Boulevard
St. Paul, MN 55155
P: (651) 296-1069
E: rep.pat.garofalo@house.mn

Green, Steve (R, 2B)
231 State Office Building
100 Martin Luther King Jr. Boulevard
St. Paul, MN 55155
P: (651) 296-9918
E: rep.steve.green@house.mn

Gruenhagen, Glenn (R, 18B)
487 State Office Building
100 Martin Luther King Jr. Boulevard
St. Paul, MN 55155
P: (651) 296-4229
E: rep.glenn.gruenhagen@house.mn

Gunther, Bob (R, 23A)
563 State Office Building
100 Martin Luther King Jr. Boulevard
St. Paul, MN 55155
P: (651) 296-3240
E: rep.bob.gunther@house.mn

Hackbarth, Tom (R, 31B)
409 State Office Building
100 Martin Luther King Jr. Boulevard
St. Paul, MN 55155
P: (651) 296-2439
E: rep.tom.hackbarth@house.mn

Halverson, Laurie (DFL, 51B)
233 State Office Building
100 Martin Luther King Jr. Boulevard
St. Paul, MN 55155
P: (651) 296-4128
E: rep.laurie.halverson@house.mn

Hamilton, Rod (R, 22B)
443 State Office Building
100 Martin Luther King Jr. Boulevard
St. Paul, MN 55155
P: (651) 296-5373
E: rep.rod.hamilton@house.mn

Hansen, Rick (DFL, 52A)
247 State Office Building
100 Martin Luther King Jr. Boulevard
St. Paul, MN 55155
P: (651) 296-6828
E: rep.rick.hansen@house.mn

Hausman, Alice (DFL, 66A)
255 State Office Building
100 Martin Luther King Jr. Boulevard
St. Paul, MN 55155
P: (651) 296-3824
E: rep.alice.hausman@house.mn

Heintzeman, Joshua (R, 10A)*
533 State Office Building
100 Rev. Dr. Martin Luther King Jr. Blvd
St. Paul, MN 55155
P: (651) 296-4333
E: rep.josh.heintzeman@house.mn

Hertaus, Jerry (R, 33A)
403 State Office Building
100 Martin Luther King Jr. Boulevard
St. Paul, MN 55155
P: (651) 296-9188
E: rep.jerry.hertaus@house.mn

Hilstrom, Debra (DFL, 40B)
377 State Office Building
100 Martin Luther King Jr. Boulevard
St. Paul, MN 55155
P: (651) 296-3709
E: rep.debra.hilstrom@house.mn

Hoppe, Joe (R, 47B)
543 State Office Building
100 Martin Luther King Jr. Boulevard
St. Paul, MN 55155
P: (651) 296-5066
E: rep.joe.hoppe@house.mn

Hornstein, Frank (DFL, 61A)
243 State Office Building
100 Martin Luther King Jr. Boulevard
St. Paul, MN 55155
P: (651) 296-9281
E: rep.frank.hornstein@house.mn

Hortman, Melissa (DFL, 36B)
237 State Office Building
100 Martin Luther King Jr. Boulevard
St. Paul, MN 55155
P: (651) 296-4280
E: rep.melissa.hortman@house.mn

Howe, Jeff (R, 13A)
527 State Office Building
100 Martin Luther King Jr. Boulevard
St. Paul, MN 55155
P: (651) 296-4373
E: rep.jeff.howe@house.mn

Isaacson, Jason (DFL, 42B)
389 State Office Building
100 Martin Luther King Jr. Boulevard
St. Paul, MN 55155
P: (651) 296-7153
E: rep.jason.isaacson@house.mn

Johnson, Brian (R, 32A)
421 State Office Building
100 Martin Luther King Jr. Boulevard
St. Paul, MN 55155
P: (651) 296-4346
E: rep.brian.johnson@house.mn

Johnson, Clark (DFL, 19A)
289 State Office Building
100 Martin Luther King Jr. Boulevard
St. Paul, MN 55155
P: (651) 296-8634
E: rep.clark.johnson@house.mn

Johnson, Sheldon (DFL, 67B)
259 State Office Building
100 Martin Luther King Jr.
Boulevard
St. Paul, MN 55155
P: (651) 296-4201
E: rep.sheldon.johnson
@house.mn

Kahn, Phyllis (DFL, 60B)
353 State Office Building
100 Martin Luther King Jr.
Boulevard
St. Paul, MN 55155
P: (651) 296-4257
E: rep.phyllis.kahn
@house.mn

Kelly, Tim (R, 21A)
559 State Office Building
100 Martin Luther King Jr.
Boulevard
St. Paul, MN 55155
P: (651) 296-8635
E: rep.tim.kelly@house.mn

Kiel, Deb (R, 1B)
537 State Office Building
100 Martin Luther King Jr.
Boulevard
St. Paul, MN 55155
P: (651) 293-5091
E: rep.deb.kiel@house.mn

Knoblach, Jim (R, 14B)
453 State Office Building
100 Rev.Dr. Martin Luther King
Jr. Blvd
St. Paul, MN 55155
P: (651) 296-6612
E: rep.jim.knoblach
@house.mn

Koznick, Jon (R, 58A)*
367 State Office Building
100 Rev. Dr. Martin Luther
King Jr. Blvd
St. Paul, MN 55155
P: (651) 296-6926
E: rep.jon.koznick@house.mn

Kresha, Ron (R, 9B)
531 State Office Building
100 Martin Luther King Jr.
Boulevard
St. Paul, MN 55155
P: (651) 296-4247
E: rep.ron.kresha@house.mn

Laine, Carolyn (DFL, 41B)
287 State Office Building
100 Martin Luther King Jr.
Boulevard
St. Paul, MN 55155
P: (651) 296-4331
E: rep.carolyn.laine
@house.mn

Lenczewski, Ann (DFL, 50B)
209 State Office Building
100 Martin Luther King Jr.
Boulevard
St. Paul, MN 55155
P: (651) 296-4218
E: rep.ann.lenczewski
@house.mn

Lesch, John (DFL, 66B)
217 State Office Building
100 Martin Luther King Jr.
Boulevard
St. Paul, MN 55155
P: (651) 296-4224
E: rep.john.lesch@house.mn

Liebling, Tina (DFL, 26A)
357 State Office Building
100 Martin Luther King Jr.
Boulevard
St. Paul, MN 55155
P: (651) 296-0573
E: rep.tina.liebling
@house.mn

Lien, Ben (DFL, 4A)
241 State Office Building
100 Martin Luther King Jr.
Boulevard
St. Paul, MN 55155
P: (651) 296-5515
E: rep.ben.lien@house.mn

Lillie, Leon (DFL, 43B)
277 State Office Building
100 Martin Luther King Jr.
Boulevard
St. Paul, MN 55155
P: (651) 296-1188
E: rep.leon.lillie@house.mn

Loeffler, Diane (DFL, 60A)
337 State Office Building
100 Martin Luther King Jr.
Boulevard
St. Paul, MN 55155
P: (651) 296-4219
E: rep.diane.loeffler
@house.mn

Lohmer, Kathy (R, 39B)
501 State Office Building
100 Martin Luther King Jr.
Boulevard
St. Paul, MN 55155
P: (651) 296-4244
E: rep.kathy.lohmer
@house.mn

Loon, Jenifer (R, 48B)
449 State Office Building
100 Martin Luther King Jr.
Boulevard
St. Paul, MN 55155
P: (651) 296-7449
E: rep.jenifer.loon
@house.mn

Loonan, Bob (R, 55A)*
523 State Office Building
100 Rev. Dr. Martin Luther
King Jr. Blvd
St. Paul, MN 55155
P: (651) 296-8872
E: rep.bob.loonan@houe.mn

Lucero, Eric (R, 30B)*
515 State Office Building
100 Rev. Dr. Martin Luther
King Jr. Blvd
St. Paul, MN 55155
P: (651) 296-1534
E: rep.eric.lucero@house.mn

Lueck, Dale K. (R, 10B)*
423 State Office Building
100 Rev. Dr. Martin Luther
King Jr. Blvd
St. Paul, MN 55155
P: (651) 296-2365
E: rep.dale.lueck@house.mn

Mack, Tara (R, 57A)
545 State Office Building
100 Martin Luther King Jr.
Boulevard
St. Paul, MN 55155
P: (651) 296-5506
E: rep.tara.mack@house.mn

Mahoney, Tim (DFL, 67A)
345 State Office Building
100 Martin Luther King Jr.
Boulevard
St. Paul, MN 55155
P: (651) 296-4277
E: rep.tim.mahoney@house.mn

Mariani, Carlos (DFL, 65B)
203 State Office Building
100 Martin Luther King Jr.
Boulevard
St. Paul, MN 55155
P: (651) 296-9714
E: rep.carlos.mariani
@house.mn

Marquart, Paul (DFL, 4B)
261 State Office Building
100 Martin Luther King Jr.
Boulevard
St. Paul, MN 55155
P: (651) 296-6829
E: rep.paul.marquart
@house.mn

Masin, Sandra (DFL, 51A)
335 State Office Building
100 Martin Luther King Jr.
Boulevard
St. Paul, MN 55155
P: (651) 296-3533
E: rep.sandra.masin
@house.mn

McDonald, Joe (R, 29A)
503 State Office Building
100 Martin Luther King Jr.
Boulevard
St. Paul, MN 55155
P: (651) 296-4336
E: rep.joe.mcdonald
@house.mn

McNamara, Denny (R, 54B)
365 State Office Building
100 Martin Luther King Jr.
Boulevard
St. Paul, MN 55155
P: (651) 296-3135
E: rep.denny.mcnamara
@house.mn

Melin, Carly (R, 6A)
315 State Office Building
100 Martin Luther King Jr.
Boulevard
St. Paul, MN 55155
P: (651) 296-0172
E: rep.carly.melin@house.mn

Metsa, Jason (DFL, 6B)
313 State Office Building
100 Martin Luther King Jr.
Boulevard
St. Paul, MN 55155
P: (651) 296-0170
E: rep.jason.metsa@house.mn

Miller, Tim (R, 17A)*
415 State Office Building
100 Rev. Dr. Martin Luther
King Jr. Blvd
St. Paul, MN 55155
P: (651) 296-4228
E: rep.tim.miller@house.mn

Moran, Rena (DFL, 65A)
329 State Office Building
100 Martin Luther King Jr.
Boulevard
St. Paul, MN 55155
P: (651) 296-5158
E: rep.rena.moran@house.mn

Mullery, Joe (DFL, 59A)
303 State Office Building
100 Martin Luther King Jr.
Boulevard
St. Paul, MN 55155
P: (651) 296-4262
E: rep.joe.mullery@house.mn

Murphy, Erin (DFL, 64A)
331 State Office Building
100 Martin Luther King Jr,
Boulevard
St. Paul, MN 55155
P: (651) 296-8799
E: rep.erin.murphy@house.mn

Minnesota

Murphy, Mary (DFL, 3B)
343 State Office Building
100 Martin Luther King Jr. Boulevard
St. Paul, MN 55155
P: (651) 296-2676
E: rep.mary.murphy@house.mn

Nash, Jim (R, 47A)*
557 State Office Building
100 Rev. Dr. Martin Luther King Jr. Blvd
St. Paul, MN 55155
P: (651) 296-4282
E: rep.jim.nash@house.mn

Nelson, Michael V. (DFL, 40A)
351 State Office Building
100 Martin Luther King Jr. Boulevard
St. Paul, MN 55155
P: (651) 296-3751
E: rep.michael.nelson@house.mn

Newberger, Jim (R, 15B)
371 State Office Building
100 Martin Luther King Jr. Boulevard
St. Paul, MN 55155
P: (651) 296-2451
E: rep.jim.newberger@house.mn

Newton, Jerry (DFL, 37A)
387 State Office Building
100 Martin Luther King Jr. Boulevard
St. Paul, MN 55155
P: (651) 296-5369
E: rep.jerry.newton@house.mn

Nornes, Bud (R, 8A)
471 State Office Building
100 Martin Luther King Jr. Boulevard
St. Paul, MN 55155
P: (651) 296-4946
E: rep.bud.nornes@house.mn

Norton, Kim (DFL, 25B)
253 State Office Building
100 Martin Luther King Jr, Boulevard
St. Paul, MN 55155
P: (651) 296-9249
E: rep.kim.norton@house.mn

O'Driscoll, Tim (R, 13B)
451 State Office Building
100 Martin Luther King Jr. Boulevard
St. Paul, MN 55155
P: (651) 296-7808
E: rep.tim.odriscoll@house.mn

O'Neill, Marion (R, 29B)
549 State Office Building
100 Martin Luther King Jr. Boulevard
St. Paul, MN 55155
P: (651) 296-5063
E: rep.marion.oneill@house.mn

Pelowski Jr., Gene (DFL, 28A)
295 State Office Building
100 Martin Luther King Jr. Boulevard
St. Paul, MN 55155
P: (651) 296-8637
E: rep.gene.pelowski@house.mn

Peppin, Joyce (R, 34A)
459 State Office Building
100 Martin Luther King Jr. Boulevard
St. Paul, MN 55155
P: (651) 296-7806
E: rep.joyce.peppin@house.mn

Persell, John (DFL, 5A)
359 State Office Building
100 Martin Luther King Jr. Boulevard
St. Paul, MN 55155
P: (651) 296-5516
E: rep.john.persell@house.mn

Petersburg, John (R, 24A)
577 State Office Building
100 Martin Luther King Jr. Boulevard
St. Paul, MN 55155
P: (651) 296-5368
E: rep.john.petersburg@house.mn

Peterson, Roz (R, 56B)*
521 State Office Building
100 Rev. Dr. Martin Luther King Jr. Blvd
St. Paul, MN 55155
P: (651) 296-5387
E: rep.roz.peterson@house.mn

Pierson, Nels T. (R, 26B)*
379 State Office Building
100 Rev. Dr. Martin Luther King Jr. Blvd
St. Paul, MN 55155
P: (651) 296-4378
E: rep.nels.pierson@house.mn

Pinto, Dave (DFL, 64B)*
321 State Office Building
100 Rev. Dr. Martin Luther King Jr. Blvd
St. Paul, MN 55155
P: (651) 296-4199
E: rep.dave.pinto@house.mn

Poppe, Jeanne (DFL, 27B)
291 State Office Building
100 Martin Luther King Jr. Boulevard
St. Paul, MN 55155
P: (651) 296-4193
E: rep.jeanne.poppe@house.mn

Pugh, Cindy (R, 33B)
411 State Office Building
100 Martin Luther King Jr. Boulevard
St. Paul, MN 55155
P: (651) 296-4315
E: rep.cindy.pugh@house.mn

Quam, Duane (R, 25A)
571 State Office Building
100 Martin Luther King Jr. Boulevard
St. Paul, MN 55155
P: (651) 296-9236
E: rep.duane.quam@house.mn

Rarick, Jason (R, 11B)*
431 State Office Building
100 Rev. Dr. Martin Luther King Jr. Blvd
St. Paul, MN 55155
P: (651) 296-0518
E: rep.jason.rarick@house.mn

Rosenthal, Paul (DFL, 49B)
213 State Office Building
100 Martin Luther King Jr. Boulevard
St. Paul, MN 55155
P: (651) 296-7803
E: rep.paul.rosenthal@house.mn

Runbeck, Linda (R, 38A)
417 State Office Building
100 Martin Luther King Jr. Boulevard
St. Paul, MN 55155
P: (651) 296-2907
E: rep.linda.runbeck@house.mn

Sanders, Tim (R, 37B)
553 State Office Building
100 Martin Luther King Jr. Boulevard
St. Paul, MN 55155
P: (651) 296-4226
E: rep.tim.sanders@house.mn

Schoen, Dan (DFL, 54A)
327 State Office Building
100 Martin Luther King Jr. Boulevard
St. Paul, MN 55155
P: (651) 296-4342
E: rep.dan.schoen@house.mn

Schomacker, Joe (R, 22A)
509 State Office Building
100 Martin Luther King Jr. Boulevard
St. Paul, MN 55155
P: (651) 296-5505
E: rep.joe.schomacker@house.mn

Schultz, Jennifer (DFL, 7A)*
215 State Office Building
100 Rev. Dr. Martin Luther King Jr. Blvd
St. Paul, MN 55155
P: (651) 296-2228
E: rep.jennifer.schultz@house.mn

Scott, Peggy (R, 35B)
437 State Office Building
100 Martin Luther King Jr. Boulevard
St. Paul, MN 55155
P: (651) 296-4231
E: rep.peggy.scott@house.mn

Selcer, Yvonne (DFL, 48A)
227 State Office Building
100 Martin Luther King Jr. Boulevard
St. Paul, MN 55155
P: (651) 296-3964
E: rep.yvonne.selcer@house.mn

Simonson, Erik (DFL, 7B)
221 State Office Building
100 Martin Luther King Jr. Boulevard
St. Paul, MN 55155
P: (651) 296-4246
E: rep.erik.simonson@house.mn

Slocum, Linda (DFL, 50A)
207 State Office Building
100 Martin Luther King Jr. Boulevard
St. Paul, MN 55155
P: (651) 296-7158
E: rep.linda.slocum@house.mn

Smith, Dennis (R, 34B)*
375 State Office Building
100 Rev. Dr. Martin Luther King Jr. Blvd
St. Paul, MN 55155
P: (651) 296-5502
E: rep.dennis.smith@house.mn

Sundin, Mike (DFL, 11A)
211 State Office Building
100 Martin Luther King Jr. Boulevard
St. Paul, MN 55155
P: (651) 296-4308
E: rep.mike.sundin@house.mn

Swedzinski, Chris (R, 16A)
491 State Office Building
100 Martin Luther King Jr. Boulevard
St. Paul, MN 55155
P: (651) 296-5374
E: rep.chris.swedzinski@house.mn

Theis, Tama (R, 14A)
445 State Office Building
100 Martin Luther King Jr. Boulevard
St. Paul, MN 55155
P: (651) 296-6316
E: rep.tama.theis@house.mn

Thissen, Paul (DFL, 61B)
267 State Office Building
100 Martin Luther King Jr. Boulevard
St. Paul, MN 55155
P: (651) 296-5375
F: (651) 296-3869
E: rep.paul.thissen@house.mn

Torkelson, Paul (R, 16B)
381 State Office Building
100 Martin Luther King Jr. Boulevard
St. Paul, MN 55155
P: (651) 296-9303
E: rep.paul.torkelson@house.mn

Uglem, Mark (R, 36A)
569 State Office Building
100 Martin Luther King Jr. Boulevard
St. Paul, MN 55155
P: (651) 296-5513
E: rep.mark.uglem@house.mn

Urdahl, Dean (R, 18A)
473 State Office Building
100 Martin Luther King Jr. Boulevard
St. Paul, MN 55155
P: (651) 296-4344
E: rep.dean.urdahl@house.mn

Vogel, Bob (R, 20A)*
581 State Office Building
100 Rev. Dr. Martin Luther King Jr. Blvd
St. Paul, MN 55155
P: (651) 296-7065
E: rep.bob.vogel@house.mn

Wagenius, Jean (DFL, 63B)
251 State Office Building
100 Martin Luther King Jr. Boulevard
St. Paul, MN 55155
P: (651) 296-4200
E: rep.jean.wagenius@house.mn

Ward, JoAnn (DFL, 53A)
531 State Office Building
100 Martin Luther King Jr. Boulevard
St. Paul, MN 55155
P: (651) 296-7807
E: rep.joann.ward@house.mn

Whelan, Abigail (R, 35A)*
439 State Office Building
100 Rev. Dr. Martin Luther King Jr. Blvd
St. Paul, MN 55155
P: (651) 296-1729
E: rep.abigail.whelan@house.mn

Wills, Anna (R, 57B)
477 State Office Building
100 Martin Luther King Jr. Boulevard
St. Paul, MN 55155
P: (651) 296-4306
E: rep.anna.wills@house.mn

Winkler, Ryan (DFL, 46A)
309 State Office Building
100 Martin Luther King Jr. Boulevard
St. Paul, MN 55155
P: (651) 296-7026
E: rep.ryan.winkler@house.mn

Yarusso, Barb (DFL, 42A)
307 State Office Building
100 Martin Luther King Jr. Boulevard
St. Paul, MN 55155
P: (651) 296-0141
E: rep.barb.yarusso@house.mn

Youakim, Cheryl (DFL, 46B)*
225 State Office Building
100 Rev. Dr. Martin Luther King Jr. Blvd
St. Paul, MN 55155
P: (651) 296-9889
E: rep.cheryl.youakim@house.mn

Zerwas, Nick (R, 30A)
433 State Office Building
100 Martin Luther King Jr. Boulevard
St. Paul, MN 55155
P: (651) 296-4237
E: rep.nick.zerwas@house.mn

Congress

Senate
Franken, Al (DFL)
Klobuchar, Amy (DFL)

House
Ellison, Keith (DFL, 5)
Emmer, Tom (R, 6)
Kline, John (R, 2)
McCollum, Betty (DFL, 4)
Nolan, Rick (DFL, 8)
Paulsen, Erik (R, 3)
Peterson, Collin C. (DFL, 7)
Walz, Tim (DFL, 1)

Mississippi

Executive

Governor

Hon. Phil Bryant (R)
Governor
P.O. Box 139
Jackson, MS 39205
P: (601) 359-3150
F: (601) 359-3741
E: governor@governor.state.ms.us

Lieutenant Governor

Hon. Tate Reeves (R)
Lieutenant Governor
New Capitol, Room 315
P.O. Box 1018
Jackson, MS 39215
P: (601) 359-3200
F: (601) 359-2001
E: ltgov@senate.ms.gov

Commissioner of Agriculture & Commerce

Hon. Cindy Hyde-Smith (R)
Commissioner
121 North Jefferson Street
Jackson, MS 39201
P: (601) 359-1100
F: (601) 354-6290

Attorney General

Hon. Jim Hood (D)
Attorney General
Department of Justice
P.O. Box 220
Jackson, MS 39205
P: (601) 359-3680
E: msag05@ago.state.ms.us

Auditor

Hon. Stacey E. Pickering (R)
State Auditor
Woolfolk Building, Suite 801
501 North West Street
Jackson, MS 39201
P: (601) 576-2800
F: (601) 576-2687
E: stacey.pickering@osa.ms.gov

Commissioner of Insurance

Hon. Mike Chaney (R)
Commissioner
1001 Woolfolk State Office Building
501 North West Street, P.O. Box 79
Jackson, MS 39201
P: (601) 359-3569
F: (601) 359-2474
E: mike.chaney@mid.state.ms.us

Secretary of State

Hon. C. Delbert Hosemann Jr. (R)
Secretary of State
P.O. Box 136
Jackson, MS 39205
P: (601) 359-1350
F: (601) 359-6700
E: delbert.hosemann@sos.ms.gov

Treasurer

Hon. Lynn Fitch (R)
State Treasurer
P.O. Box 138
Jackson, MS 39205
P: (601) 359-3600
F: (601) 359-2001

Judiciary

Supreme Court (PE)

Ms. Muriel B. Ellis
Clerk
450 High Street
P.O. Box 117
Jackson, MS 39201
P: (601) 359-3694
F: (601) 359-2407
E: sctclerk@mssc.state.ms.us

Hon. William L. Waller Jr.
Chief Justice
Hon. David Chandler
Hon. Josiah D. Coleman
Hon. Jess H. Dickinson
Hon. Leslie D. King
Hon. James W. Kitchens
Hon. Ann H. Lamar
Hon. Randy G. Pierce
Hon. Michael K. Randolph

Legislative Senate

Senate President

Hon. Tate Reeves (R)
Lieutenant Governor
New Capitol, Room 315
P.O. Box 1018
Jackson, MS 39215
P: (601) 359-3200
F: (601) 359-2001
E: ltgov@senate.ms.gov

President Pro Tempore of the Senate

Sen. Giles K. Ward (R)
President Pro Tempore
New Capitol, Room 405 B
P.O. Box 1018
Jackson, MS 39215
P: (601) 359-3250
F: (601) 359-5110
E: gkward@senate.ms.gov

Secretary of the Senate

Ms. Liz Welch
Secretary of the Senate
New Capitol, Room 308
P.O. Box 1018
Jackson, MS 39215
P: (601) 359-3202
F: (601) 359-3935

Members of the Senate

Blount, David (D, 29)
New Capitol, Room 405-D
P.O. Box 1018
Jackson, MS 39215
P: (601) 359-3232
F: (601) 359-5957
E: dblount@senate.ms.gov

Browning, Nickey (D, 3)
New Capitol, Room 213 C
P.O. Box 1018
Jackson, MS 39215
P: (601) 359-3246
F: (601) 359-3063
E: nbrowning@senate.ms.gov

Bryan, Hob (D, 7)
New Capitol, Room 409 A
P.O. Box 1018
Jackson, MS 39215
P: (601) 359-3237
F: (601) 359-2879
E: hbryan@senate.ms.gov

Burton, Terry C. (R, 31)
New Capitol, Room 215 B
P.O. Box 1018
Jackson, MS 39215
P: (601) 359-3234
F: (601) 359-5345
E: tburton@senate.ms.gov

Butler, Albert (D, 36)
New Capitol
P. O. Box 1018
Jackson, MS 39215
P: (601) 359-3232
F: (601) 359-5957
E: abutler@senate.ms.gov

Butler, Kelvin E. (D, 38)
New Capitol, Room 405 C
P.O. Box 1018
Jackson, MS 39215
P: (601) 359-3244
F: (601) 359-9210
E: kbutler@senate.ms.gov

Carmichael, Videt (R, 33)
New Capitol, Room 213 A
P.O. Box 1018
Jackson, MS 39215
P: (601) 359-3244
F: (601) 359-9210
E: vcarmichael@senate.ms.gov

Chassaniol, Lydia (R, 14)
New Capitol, Room 212 A
P.O. Box 1018
Jackson, MS 39215
P: (601) 359-3246
F: (601) 359-3063
E: lchassaniol@senate.ms.gov

Clarke, Eugene (R, 22)
New Capitol, Room 214 D
P.O. Box 1018
Jackson, MS 39215
P: (601) 359-3250
F: (601) 359-5110
E: bclarke@senate.ms.gov

Collins, Nancy Adams (R, 6)
New Capitol
P.O. Box 1018
Jackson, MS 39215
P: (601) 359-3209
F: (601) 576-2555
E: ncollins@senate.ms.gov

Dawkins, Deborah Jeanne (D, 48)
New Capitol, Room 404C
P.O. Box 1018
Jackson, MS 39215
P: (601) 359-3237
F: (601) 359-2879
E: ddawkins@senate.ms.gov

Doty, Sally (R, 39)
New Capitol
P.O. Box 1018
Jackson, MS 39215
P: (601) 359-3237
F: (601) 359-2879
E: sdoty@senate.ms.gov

Fillingane, Joey (R, 41)
New Capitol, Room 215 C
P.O. Box 1018
Jackson, MS 39215
P: (601) 359-3246
F: (601) 359-3063
E: jfillingane@senate.ms.gov

Frazier, Hillman (D, 27)
New Capitol, Room 117 A
P.O. Box 1018
Jackson, MS 39215
P: (601) 359-3246
F: (601) 359-3063
E: hfrazier@senate.ms.gov

Gandy, Phillip A. (R, 43)
New Capitol
P.O. Box 1018
Jackson, MS 39215
P: (601) 359-3250
F: (601) 359-5110
E: pgandy@senate.ms.gov

Gollott, Tommy A. (R, 50)
New Capitol, Room 408
P.O. Box 1018
Jackson, MS 39215
P: (601) 359-2886
F: (601) 359-2889
E: tgollott@senate.ms.gov

Hale, Steve (D, 10)
New Capitol
P.O. Box 1018
Jackson, MS 39215
P: (601) 359-3221
F: (601) 359-2166
E: shale@senate.ms.gov

Harkins, Josh (R, 20)
New Capitol
P.O. Box 1018
Jackson, MS 39215
P: (601) 359-2886
F: (601) 359-2889
E: jharkins@senate.ms.gov

Hill, Angela Burks (R, 40)
New Capitol
P.O. Box 1018
Jackson, MS 39215
P: (601) 359-2886
F: (601) 359-2889
E: ahill@senate.ms.gov

Hopson III, W. Briggs (R, 23)
New Capitol, Room 409 B
P.O. Box 1018
Jackson, MS 39215
P: (601) 359-3237
F: (601) 359-2879
E: bhopson@senate.ms.gov

Horhn, John (D, 26)
New Capitol, Room 212 B
P.O. Box 1018
Jackson, MS 39215
P: (601) 359-3237
F: (601) 359-2879
E: jhorhn@senate.ms.gov

Hudson, Billy (R, 45)
New Capitol
P.O. Box 1018
Jackson, MS 39215
P: (601) 359-2395
F: (601) 359-3938
E: bhudson@senate.ms.gov

Jackson, Gary (R, 15)
New Capitol, Room 212 C
P.O. Box 1018
Jackson, MS 39215
P: (601) 359-3234
F: (601) 359-5345
E: gjackson@senate.ms.gov

Jackson, Robert L. (D, 11)
New Capitol, Room 404 B
P.O. Box 1018
Jackson, MS 39215
P: (601) 359-3221
F: (601) 359-2166
E: rjackson@senate.ms.gov

Jackson II, Sampson (D, 32)
New Capitol, Room 407
P.O. Box 1018
Jackson, MS 39215
P: (601) 359-2886
F: (601) 359-2889
E: sjackson@senate.ms.gov

Jolly, Russell (D, 8)
New Capitol
P.O. Box 1018
Jackson, MS 39215
P: (601) 359-2886
F: (601) 359-2889
E: rjolly@senate.ms.gov

Jones, Kenneth Wayne (D, 21)
New Capitol, Room 213 D
P.O. Box 1018
Jackson, MS 39215
P: (601) 359-3232
F: (601) 359-5957
E: kjones@senate.ms.gov

Jordan, David (D, 24)
New Capitol, Room 405 A
P.O. Box 1018
Jackson, MS 39215
P: (601) 359-3244
F: (601) 359-9210
E: djordan@senate.ms.gov

Kirby, Dean (R, 30)
New Capitol, Room 212 D
P.O. Box 1018
Jackson, MS 39215
P: (601) 359-3234
F: (601) 359-5345
E: dkirby@senate.ms.gov

Lee, Perry (R, 35)
New Capitol, Room 213 B
P.O. Box 1018
Jackson, MS 39215
P: (601) 359-3244
F: (601) 359-9210
E: plee@senate.ms.gov

Longwitz, Will (R, 25)
New Capitol
P.O. Box 1018
Jackson, MS 39215
P: (601) 359-3232
F: (601) 359-5957
E: wlongwitz@senate.ms.gov

Massey, Chris (R, 1)
New Capitol
P.O. Box 1018
Jackson, MS 39215
P: (601) 359-2886
F: (601) 359-2889
E: cmassey@senate.ms.gov

McDaniel, Chris (R, 42)
New Capitol, Room 213 E
P.O. Box 1018
Jackson, MS 39215
P: (601) 359-3229
F: (601) 359-3935
E: cmcdaniel@senate.ms.gov

Montgomery, Haskins (D, 34)
New Capitol, Room 209 Mezz
P.O. Box 1018
Jackson, MS 39215
P: (601) 359-3234
F: (601) 359-5345
E: hmontgomery@senate.ms.gov

Moran, Philip (R, 46)
New Capitol
P.O. Box 1018
Jackson, MS 39215
P: (601) 359-3221
F: (601) 359-2166
E: pmoran@senate.ms.gov

Norwood, Sollie B. (D, 28)
P. O. Box 1018
Jackson, MS 39215
P: (601) 359-3221
F: (601) 359-2166
E: snorwood@senate.ms.gov

Parker, David (R, 19)
New Capitol
P.O. Box 1018
Jackson, MS 39215
P: (601) 359-2886
F: (601) 359-2889
E: dparker@senate.ms.gov

Parks, Rita Potts (R, 4)
New Capitol
P.O. Box 1018
Jackson, MS 39215
P: (601) 359-3232
F: (601) 359-5957
E: rparks@senate.ms.gov

Polk, John A. (R, 44)
New Capitol
P.O. Box 1018
Jackson, MS 39215
P: (601) 359-3246
F: (601) 359-3063
E: jpolk@senate.ms.gov

Simmons, Derrick T. (D, 12)
New Capitol
P.O. Box 1018
Jackson, MS 39215
P: (601) 359-3221
F: (601) 359-2166
E: dsimmons@senate.ms.gov

Simmons, Willie (D, 13)
New Capitol, Room 410
P.O. Box 1018
Jackson, MS 39215
P: (601) 359-3237
F: (601) 359-2879
E: wsimmons@senate.ms.gov

Smith, Tony (R, 47)
New Capitol
P.O. Box 1018
Jackson, MS 39215
P: (601) 359-2886
F: (601) 359-2889
E: tsmith@senate.ms.gov

Sojourner, Melanie (R, 37)
New Capitol
P.O. Box 1018
Jackson, MS 39215
P: (601) 359-3250
F: (601) 359-5110
E: msojourner@senate.ms.gov

Mississippi

Stone, Bill (D, 2)
New Capitol
P.O. Box 1018
Jackson, MS 39215
P: (601) 359-3221
F: (601) 359-2166
E: bstone@senate.ms.gov

Tindell, Sean J. (R, 49)
New Capitol
P.O. Box 1018
Jackson, MS 39215
P: (601) 359-3229
F: (601) 359-3935
E: stindell@senate.ms.gov

Tollison, Gray (R, 9)
New Capitol, Room 404 A
P.O. Box 1018
Jackson, MS 39215
P: (601) 359-3229
F: (601) 359-3935
E: gtollison@senate.ms.gov

Turner, Angela (D, 16)
New Capitol
P.O. Box 1018
Jackson, MS 39215
P: (601) 359-3237
F: (601) 359-2879
E: aturner@senate.ms.gov

Ward, Giles K. (R, 18)
New Capitol, Room 405 B
P.O. Box 1018
Jackson, MS 39215
P: (601) 359-3250
F: (601) 359-5110
E: gkward@senate.ms.gov

Watson, Michael (R, 51)
New Capitol
P.O. Box 1018
Jackson, MS 39215
P: (601) 359-3229
F: (601) 359-3935
E: mwatson@senate.ms.gov

Wiggins, Brice (R, 52)
New Capitol
P.O. Box 1018
Jackson, MS 39215
P: (601) 359-3232
F: (601) 359-5957
E: bwiggins@senate.ms.gov

Wilemon Jr., J.P. (D, 5)
New Capitol, Room 213 F
P.O. Box 1018
Jackson, MS 39215
P: (601) 359-3232
F: (601) 359-5957
E: jwilemon@senate.ms.gov

Younger, Charles (R, 17)*
New Capitol
P.O. Box 1018
Jackson, MS 39215
P: (601) 359-2395
F: (601) 359-3938
E: Cyounger@senate.ms.gov

House

Speaker of the House

Rep. Philip Gunn (R)
Speaker
New Capitol, Room: 306
P.O. Box 1018
Jackson, MS 39215
P: (601) 359-3300
E: pgunn@house.ms.gov

Speaker Pro Tempore of the House

Rep. Greg Snowden (R)
Speaker Pro Tempore
New Capitol, Room 302
P.O. Box 1018
Jackson, MS 39215
P: (601) 359-3304
E: greg@gregsnowden.com

Clerk of the House

Mr. Andrew Ketchings
Clerk of the House
305 New Capitol Building
P.O. Box 1018
Jackson, MS 39215
P: (601) 359-3360
E: aketchings@house.ms.gov

Members of the House

Alday, Gene (R, 25)
New Capitol, Room 400-F
P.O. Box 1018
Jackson, MS 39215
P: (601) 359-9488
E: galday@house.ms.gov

Aldridge, Brian (R, 17)
New Capitol, Room 400-E
P.O. Box 1018
Jackson, MS 39215
P: (601) 359-2420
E: baldridge@house.ms.gov

Anderson, Jeramey D. (D, 110)
New Capitol
P.O. Box 1018
Jackson, MS 39215
E: janderson@house.ms.gov

Arnold, William Tracy (R, 3)
New Capitol, Room 400-F
P.O. Box 1018
Jackson, MS 39215
P: (601) 359-2438
E: warnold@house.ms.gov

Bailey, Willie L. (D, 49)
New Capitol, Room 100-C
P.O. Box 1018
Jackson, MS 39215
P: (601) 359-9311
E: wbailey@house.ms.gov

Bain, Nick (D, 2)
New Capitol, Room 400-F
P.O. Box 1018
Jackson, MS 39215
P: (601) 359-3338
E: nbain@house.ms.gov

Baker, Mark (R, 74)
New Capitol, Room 112-A
P.O. Box 1018
Jackson, MS 39215
P: (601) 359-3388
E: mbaker@house.ms.gov

Banks, Earle S. (D, 67)
New Capitol, Room 100-C
P.O. Box 1018
Jackson, MS 39215
P: (601) 359-9392
E: ebanksjax@aol.com

Baria, David (D, 122)
New Capitol, Room 201
P.O. Box 1018
Jackson, MS 39215
P: (601) 359-3133
E: dbaria@house.ms.gov

Barker, Toby (R, 102)
New Capitol, Room 100
P.O. Box 1018
Jackson, MS 39215
P: (601) 359-3362
E: tbarker@house.ms.gov

Barton, Manly (R, 109)
New Capitol, Room BSMNT
P.O. Box 1018
Jackson, MS 39215
P: (601) 359-3354
E: mbarton@house.ms.gov

Beckett, Charles Jim (R, 23)
New Capitol, Room 205-C
P.O. Box 1018
Jackson, MS 39215
P: (601) 359-3335
E: jbeckett@house.ms.gov

Bell, Donnie (R, 21)
New Capitol, Room 400-B
P.O. Box 1018
Jackson, MS 39215
P: (601) 359-3396
E: dbell@house.ms.gov

Bennett, Richard (R, 120)
New Capitol, Room 201-M5
P.O. Box 1018
Jackson, MS 39215
P: (601) 359-2860
E: rbennett@house.ms.gov

Blackmon Jr., Edward (D, 57)
New Capitol, Room 400-H
P.O. Box 1018
Jackson, MS 39215
P: (601) 359-3371
E: eblackmon@house.ms.gov

Bounds, C. Scott (D, 44)
New Capitol, Room 115-B
P.O. Box 1018
Jackson, MS 39215
P: (601) 359-3334
E: sbounds@house.ms.gov

Boyd, Randy P. (R, 19)
New Capitol, Room 400-F
P.O. Box 1018
Jackson, MS 39215
P: (601) 359-2435
E: rboyd@house.ms.gov

Brown, Cecil (D, 66)
New Capitol, Room 201-M6
P.O. Box 1018
Jackson, MS 39215
P: (601) 359-9396
E: cbrown@house.ms.gov

Brown, Chris (R, 20)
New Capitol, Room 400-F
P.O. Box 1018
Jackson, MS 39215
P: (601) 359-2434
E: crbrown@house.ms.gov

Burnett, Clara Henderson (D, 9)
New Capitol, Room 400-E
P.O. Box 1018
Jackson, MS 39215
P: (601) 359-2422
E: cburnett@house.ms.gov

Busby, Charles (R, 111)
New Capitol, Room 400-E
P.O. Box 1018
Jackson, MS 39215
P: (601) 359-2419
E: cbusby@house.ms.gov

Byrd, Larry (R, 104)
New Capitol, Room 201-M7
P.O. Box 1018
Jackson, MS 39215
P: (601) 359-3352
E: lbyrd@house.ms.gov

Calhoun, Credell (D, 68)
New Capitol, Room 102-C
P.O. Box 1018
Jackson, MS 39215
P: (601) 359-2429
E: ccalhoun@house.ms.gov

Campbell, Kimberly (D, 72)
New Capitol, Room BSMNT
P.O. Box 1018
Jackson, MS 39215
P: (601) 359-4083
E: kcampbell@house.ms.gov

Carpenter, Lester (R, 1)
New Capitol, Room 119-A
P.O. Box 1018
Jackson, MS 39215
P: (601) 359-3366
E: lcarpenter@house.ms.gov

Chism, Gary A. (R, 37)
New Capitol, Room 400-G
P.O. Box 1018
Jackson, MS 39215
P: (601) 359-3364
E: gchism@house.ms.gov

Clark, Bryant W. (D, 47)
New Capitol, Room BSMNT-B
P.O. Box 1018
Jackson, MS 39215
P: (601) 359-2845
E: bclark@house.ms.gov

Clarke, Alyce Griffin (D, 69)
New Capitol, Room 204-D
P.O. Box 1018
Jackson, MS 39215
P: (601) 359-9465
E: aclarke@house.ms.gov

Cockerham, Angela (D, 96)
State Capitol, Room 201
P.O. Box 1018
Jackson, MS 39215
P: (601) 359-3333
E: acockerham@house.ms.gov

Coleman, Linda F. (D, 29)
New Capitol, Room BSMNT
P.O. Box 1018
Jackson, MS 39215
P: (601) 359-4082
E: lcoleman@house.ms.gov

Coleman, Mary H. (D, 65)
New Capitol, Room BSMNT
P.O. Box 1018
Jackson, MS 39215
P: (601) 359-9395
E: mcoleman@house.ms.gov

Crawford, Carolyn (R, 121)
New Capitol, Room 400-F
P.O. Box 1018
Jackson, MS 39215
P: (601) 359-2430
E: ccrawford@house.ms.gov

Currie, Becky (R, 92)
New Capitol, Room 401-C
P.O. Box 1018
Jackson, MS 39215
P: (601) 359-5334
E: bcurrie@house.ms.gov

DeBar, Dennis (R, 105)
New Capitol, Room 400-F
P.O. Box 1018
Jackson, MS 39215
P: (601) 359-2436
E: ddebar@house.ms.gov

DeLano, Scott (R, 117)
New Capitol, Room 401-B
P.O. Box 1018
Jackson, MS 39215
P: (601) 359-3349
E: sdelano@house.ms.gov

Denny Jr., Bill C. (R, 64)
New Capitol, Room 400-D
P.O. Box 1018
Jackson, MS 39215
P: (601) 359-3369
E: bdenny@house.ms.gov

Denton, Oscar (D, 55)
New Capitol
P.O. Box 1018
Jackson, MS 39215
E: odenton@house.ms.gov

Dickson, Reecy L. (D, 42)
New Capitol, Room 400-F
P.O. Box 1018
Jackson, MS 39215
P: (601) 359-2433
E: rdickson@house.ms.gov

Dixon, Deborah Butler (D, 63)
New Capitol, Room 400-F
P.O. Box 1018
Jackson, MS 39215
P: (601) 359-3339
E: ddixon@house.ms.gov

Eaton, Blaine (D, 79)
New Capitol, Room 400-F
P.O. Box 1018
Jackson, MS 39215
P: (601) 359-2430
E: beaton@house.ms.gov

Ellis, Tyrone (D, 38)
New Capitol, Room BSMNT
P.O. Box 1018
Jackson, MS 39215
P: (601) 359-4084
E: tellis@house.ms.gov

Espy, Chuck (D, 26)
New Capitol, Room 100-C
P.O. Box 1018
Jackson, MS 39215
P: (601) 359-9391
E: cespy3@gmail.com

Eure, Casey (R, 116)
New Capitol, Room 119-B
P.O. Box 1018
Jackson, MS 39215
P: (601) 359-9466
E: ceure@house.ms.gov

Evans, Bob (D, 91)
New Capitol, Room BSMNT
P.O. Box 1018
Jackson, MS 39215
P: (601) 359-3354
E: bevans@house.ms.gov

Evans, James (D, 70)
New Capitol, Room 201-M7
P.O. Box 1018
Jackson, MS 39215
P: (601) 359-2461
E: jevans@house.ms.gov

Evans, Michael T. (D, 43)
New Capitol, Room 400-F
P.O. Box 1018
Jackson, MS 39215
P: (601) 359-3311
E: mevans@house.ms.gov

Faulkner, John G. (D, 5)
New Capitol
P.O. Box 1018
Jackson, MS 39215
E: jfaulkner@house.ms.gov

Formby, Mark (R, 108)
New Capitol, Room 402-B
P.O. Box 1018
Jackson, MS 39215
P: (601) 359-3359
E: mformby@house.ms.gov

Frierson, Herb (R, 106)
New Capitol, Room 201-C
P.O. Box 1018
Jackson, MS 39215
P: (601) 359-3340
E: hfrierson@house.ms.gov

Gibbs, Karl (D, 36)
New Capitol
P. O. Box 1018
Jackson, MS 39215
E: kgibbs@house.ms.gov

Gipson, Andy (R, 77)
New Capitol, Room 112-B
P.O. Box 1018
Jackson, MS 39215
P: (601) 359-1541
E: agipson@house.ms.gov

Guice, Jeffrey S. (R, 114)
New Capitol, Room 119
P.O. Box 1018
Jackson, MS 39215
P: (601) 359-2508
E: jguice@house.ms.gov

Gunn, Philip (R, 56)
New Capitol, Room: 306
P.O. Box 1018
Jackson, MS 39215
P: (601) 359-3300
E: pgunn@house.ms.gov

Hamilton, Eugene Forrest (R, 6)
New Capitol, Room 100-C
P.O. Box 1018
Jackson, MS 39215
P: (601) 359-4075
E: efhamilton@house.ms.gov

Haney, Greg (R, 118)
New Capitol, Room 400-F
P.O. Box 1018
Jackson, MS 39215
P: (601) 359-3338
E: ghaney@house.ms.gov

Harrison, Esther M. (D, 41)
New Capitol
P.O. Box 1018
Jackson, MS 39215
P: (601) 359-9390
E: eharrison@house.ms.gov

Hines Sr., John W. (D, 50)
New Capitol, Room 112-D
P.O. Box 1018
Jackson, MS 39215
P: (601) 359-3755
E: jhines@house.ms.gov

Holland, D. Stephen (D, 16)
New Capitol, Room 201
P.O. Box 1018
Jackson, MS 39215
P: (601) 359-3348
E: sholland@house.ms.gov

Holloway Sr., Gregory (D, 76)
New Capitol, Room 400-F
P.O. Box 1018
Jackson, MS 39215
P: (601) 359-2435
E: gholloway@house.ms.gov

Mississippi

Hood, Joey (R, 35)
New Capitol, Room 102-C
P.O. Box 1018
Jackson, MS 39215
P: (601) 359-2425
E: jhood@house.ms.gov

Horan, Kevin (D, 24)
New Capitol, Room 400-F
P.O. Box 1018
Jackson, MS 39215
P: (601) 359-2438
E: khoran@house.ms.gov

Horne, Steve A. (R, 81)
New Capitol, Room 400-E
P.O. Box 1018
Jackson, MS 39215
P: (601) 359-2424
E: shorne@house.ms.gov

Howell, Bobby B. (R, 46)
New Capitol, Room 104-A
P.O. Box 1018
Jackson, MS 39215
P: (601) 359-2428
E: bhowell@house.ms.gov

Huddleston, Mac (R, 15)
New Capitol, Room 201
P.O. Box 1018
Jackson, MS 39215
P: (601) 359-3340
E: mhuddleston@house.ms.gov

Huddleston, Robert E. (D, 30)
New Capitol, Room 400-E
P.O. Box 1018
Jackson, MS 39215
P: (601) 359-2418
E: rhuddleston@house.ms.gov

Jackson, Lataisha (D, 11)
New Capitol
P.O. Box 1018
Jackson, MS 39215
E: ljackson@house.ms.gov

Jennings, Wanda Taylor (R, 7)
New Capitol, Room 100-A
P.O. Box 1018
Jackson, MS 39215
P: (601) 359-3327
E: wjennings@house.ms.gov

Johnson III, Robert L. (D, 94)
New Capitol, Room 100-D
P.O. Box 1018
Jackson, MS 39215
P: (601) 359-3355
E: rjohnson@house.ms.gov

Kinkade, Bill (R, 52)
New Capitol
P.O. Box 1018
Jackson, MS 39215
E: bkinkade@house.ms.gov

Ladner, Timmy (R, 93)
New Capitol, Room 400-F
P.O. Box 1018
Jackson, MS 39215
P: (601) 359-2438
E: tladner@house.ms.gov

Lamar, John Thomas (R, 8)
New Capitol, Room 400-F
P.O. Box 1018
Jackson, MS 39215
P: (601) 359-2431
E: jlamar@house.ms.gov

Lane, Sherra Hillman (D, 86)
State Capitol, Room 102-C
P.O. Box 1018
Jackson, MS 39215
P: (601) 359-9485
E: slane@house.ms.gov

Lott, Hank (R, 101)
New Capitol, Room 102-C
P.O. Box 1018
Jackson, MS 39215
P: (601) 359-2435
E: hlott@house.ms.gov

Malone, Bennett (D, 45)
New Capitol, Room BSMNT
P.O. Box 1018
Jackson, MS 39215
P: (601) 359-4073
E: bmalone@house.ms.gov

Martinson, Rita (R, 58)
State Capitol, Room 201-M3
P.O. Box 1018
Jackson, MS 39215
P: (601) 359-3131
E: rmartinson@house.ms.gov

Massengill, Steve (R, 13)
New Capitol, Room 400-F
P.O. Box 1018
Jackson, MS 39215
P: (601) 359-3338
E: smassengill@house.ms.gov

Mayo, Brad (R, 12)
New Capitol, Room 400-F
P.O. Box 1018
Jackson, MS 39215
P: (601) 359-2431
E: bmayo@house.ms.gov

McLeod, Doug (R, 107)
New Capitol, Room 400-F
P.O. Box 1018
Jackson, MS 39215
P: (601) 359-3311
E: dmcleod@house.ms.gov

Mettetal, Nolan (R, 10)
New Capitol, Room 205-A
P.O. Box 1018
Jackson, MS 39215
P: (601) 359-3331
E: nmettetal@house.ms.gov

Middleton, America Chuck (D, 85)
New Capitol, Room 400-F
P.O. Box 1018
Jackson, MS 39215
P: (601) 359-2436
E: amiddleton@house.ms.gov

Miles, Tom (D, 75)
New Capitol, Room 400-F
P.O. Box 1018
Jackson, MS 39215
P: (601) 359-3311
E: tmiles@house.ms.gov

Mims, Sam C. (R, 97)
New Capitol, Room 104-B
P.O. Box 1018
Jackson, MS 39215
P: (601) 359-3320
E: smims@house.ms.gov

Moak, Bobby (D, 53)
New Capitol, Room 201
P.O. Box 1018
Jackson, MS 39215
P: (601) 359-3133
E: bmoak@locnet.net

Monsour, Alex (R, 54)
New Capitol, Room 102-B
P.O. Box 1018
Jackson, MS 39215
P: (601) 359-9382
E: amonsour@house.ms.gov

Moore, John L. (R, 60)
New Capitol, Room 205-B
P.O. Box 1018
Jackson, MS 39215
P: (601) 359-3330
E: jmoore@house.ms.gov

Morgan, Ken (R, 100)
New Capitol, Room 102-C
P.O. Box 1018
Jackson, MS 39215
P: (601) 359-2426
E: kmorgan@house.ms.gov

Myers, David W. (D, 98)
New Capitol, Room 201-M6
P.O. Box 1018
Jackson, MS 39215
P: (601) 359-9393
E: dmyers@house.ms.gov

Nelson, Pat (R, 40)
New Capitol, Room 400-F
P.O. Box 1018
Jackson, MS 39215
P: (601) 359-3339
E: pnelson@house.ms.gov

Oberhousen, Brad A. (D, 73)
New Capitol, Room 400-F
P.O. Box 1018
Jackson, MS 39215
P: (601) 359-2439
E: boberhousen@house.ms.gov

Patterson, Randall H. (D, 115)
New Capitol, BSMNT
P.O. Box 1018
Jackson, MS 39215
P: (601) 359-4074
E: rhpatterson@house.ms.gov

Perkins Sr., Willie J. (D, 32)
New Capitol, Room BSMNT
P.O. Box 1018
Jackson, MS 39215
P: (601) 359-4082
E: wperkins@house.ms.gov

Pigott, Bill (R, 99)
New Capitol, Room 201-M7
P.O. Box 1018
Jackson, MS 39215
P: (601) 359-5140
E: bpigott@house.ms.gov

Powell, Brent (R, 59)
New Capitol
P.O. Box 1018
Jackson, MS 39215
E: bpowell@house.ms.gov

Read, John O. (R, 112)
New Capitol, Room 201-M2
P.O. Box 1018
Jackson, MS 39215
P: (601) 359-3321
E: jread@house.ms.gov

Reynolds, Thomas U. (D, 33)
New Capitol, Room 201-M6
P.O. Box 1018
Jackson, MS 39215
P: (601) 359-9394
E: treynolds@house.ms.gov

Rogers, Margaret Ellis (D, 14)
New Capitol, Room 100-C
P.O. Box 1018
Jackson, MS 39215
P: (601) 359-9390
E: mrogers@house.ms.gov

Rogers, Ray (R, 61)
New Capitol, Room 201
P.O. Box 1018
Jackson, MS 39215
P: (601) 359-3343
E: rrogers@house.ms.gov

Rushing, Randal (R, 78)
New Capitol, Room 400-F
P.O. Box 1018
Jackson, MS 39215
P: (601) 359-2435
E: rrushing@house.ms.gov

Scott, Omeria (D, 80)
New Capitol
P.O. Box 1018
Jackson, MS 39215
P: (601) 359-3362
E: oscott@house.ms.gov

Shirley, William (R, 84)
New Capitol, Room 400-F
P.O. Box 1018
Jackson, MS 39215
P: (601) 359-2434
E: wshirley@house.ms.gov

Shows, Bobby (R, 89)
New Capitol, Room 400-A
P.O. Box 1018
Jackson, MS 39215
P: (601) 359-3337
E: bshows@house.ms.gov

Smith, Ferr (D, 27)
New Capitol, Room BSMNT
P.O. Box 1018
Jackson, MS 39215
P: (601) 359-9395
E: fsmith@house.ms.gov

Smith, Jeffrey C. (R, 39)
New Capitol, Room 201-F
P.O. Box 1018
Jackson, MS 39215
P: (601) 359-3343
E: jsmith@house.ms.gov

Snowden, Greg (R, 83)
New Capitol, Room 302
P.O. Box 1018
Jackson, MS 39215
P: (601) 359-3304
E: greg@gregsnowden.com

Staples, Gary V. (R, 88)
New Capitol, Room 201-M4
P.O. Box 1018
Jackson, MS 39215
P: (601) 359-3017
E: gstaples@house.ms.gov

Steverson, Jody (D, 4)
New Capitol, Room 400-F
P.O. Box 1018
Jackson, MS 39215
P: (601) 359-2435
E: jsteverson@house.ms.gov

Straughter, Rufus E. (D, 51)
New Capitol, Room 400-E
P.O. Box 1018
Jackson, MS 39215
P: (601) 359-2421
E: rstraughter@house.ms.gov

Stringer, Johnny W. (D, 87)
New Capitol, Room 201-M6
P.O. Box 1018
Jackson, MS 39215
P: (601) 359-9397
E: jstringer@house.ms.gov

Sullivan, Preston E. (D, 22)
New Capitol, Room 202
P.O. Box 1018
Jackson, MS 39215
P: (601) 359-3332
E: psullivan@house.ms.gov

Taylor, Tommy (R, 28)
New Capitol
P.O. Box 1018
Jackson, MS 39215
P: (601) 359-3360
E: ttaylor@house.ms.gov

Thomas, Sara Richardson (D, 31)
New Capitol, Room BSMNT
P.O. Box 1018
Jackson, MS 39215
P: (601) 359-2845
E: sthomas@house.ms.gov

Turner, Jerry R. (R, 18)
New Capitol, Room 201-M4
P.O. Box 1018
Jackson, MS 39215
P: (601) 359-9473
E: jturner@house.ms.gov

Warren, Joseph L. (D, 90)
New Capitol, Room 203
P.O. Box 1018
Jackson, MS 39215
P: (601) 359-3014
E: jwarren@house.ms.gov

Watson, Percy W. (D, 103)
New Capitol, Room 119-C
P.O. Box 1018
Jackson, MS 39215
P: (601) 359-3096
E: pwatson@house.ms.gov

Weathersby, Tom (R, 62)
New Capitol, Room 115-A
P.O. Box 1018
Jackson, MS 39215
P: (601) 359-3336
E: tweathersby@house.ms.gov

White, Jason (R, 48)
New Capitol, Room BSMNT-B
P.O. Box 1018
Jackson, MS 39215
P: (601) 359-2861
E: jwhite@house.ms.gov

Whittington, Linda (D, 34)
New Capitol, Room 400-F
P.O. Box 1018
Jackson, MS 39215
P: (601) 359-9492
E: lwhittington@house.ms.gov

Williams-Barnes, Sonya (D, 119)
New Capitol, Room 400-F
P.O. Box 1018
Jackson, MS 39215
P: (601) 359-2432
E: swilliams-barnes@house.ms.gov

Willis, Patricia H. (R, 95)
New Capitol
P. O. Box 1018
Jackson, MS 39215
E: pwillis@house.ms.gov

Wooten, Adrienne (D, 71)
New Capitol, Room 400-F
P.O. Box 1018
Jackson, MS 39215
P: (601) 359-2433
E: adrienneahooper@yahoo.com

Young Jr., Charles (D, 82)
New Capitol, Room 400-F
P.O. Box 1018
Jackson, MS 39215
P: (601) 359-2432
E: cyoung@house.ms.gov

Zuber III, Henry (R, 113)
New Capitol, Room 402-C
P.O. Box 1018
Jackson, MS 39215
P: (601) 359-3328
E: hzuber@house.ms.gov

Congress

Senate

Cochran, Thad (R)
Wicker, Roger F. (R)

House

Harper, Gregg (R, 3)
Palazzo, Steven (R, 4)
Thompson, Bennie G. (D, 2)

Missouri

Executive

Governor
Hon. Jay Nixon (D)
Governor
Capitol Building, Room 216
P.O. Box 720
Jefferson City, MO 65102
P: (573) 751-3222
F: (573) 526-3291

Lieutenant Governor
Hon. Peter Kinder (R)
Lieutenant Governor
State Capitol, Room 224
Jefferson City, MO 65101
P: (573) 751-4727
F: (573) 751-9422
E: ltgovinfo@mail.mo.gov

Attorney General
Hon. Chris Koster (D)
Attorney General
Supreme Court Building
207 West High Street
Jefferson City, MO 65101
P: (573) 751-3321
F: (573) 751-0774

Auditor
Hon. John Watson (R)
State Auditor
State Capitol, Room 121
Jefferson City, MO 65101
P: (573) 751-4824
F: (573) 751-6539
E: moaudit@auditor.mo.gov

Secretary of State
Hon. Jason Kander (D)
Secretary of State
600 West Main
P.O. Box 1767
Jefferson City, MO 65101
P: (573) 751-4936
F: (573) 526-4903
E: info@sos.mo.gov

Treasurer
Hon. Clint Zweifel (D)
State Treasurer
P.O. Box 210
Jefferson City, MO 65102
P: (573) 751-2411
F: (573) 751-9443
E: clint.zweifel
@treasurer.mo.gov

Judiciary

Supreme Court (MR)
Mr. Bill Thompson
Supreme Court Clerk
P.O. Box 150
Jefferson City, MO 65102
P: (573) 751-4144

Hon. Mary Russell
Chief Justice
Hon. Patricia Breckenridge
Hon. George W. Draper III
Hon. Zel M. Fischer
Hon. Laura Denvir Stith
Hon. Richard B. Teitelman
Hon. Paul C. Wilson

Legislative Senate

Senate President
Hon. Peter Kinder (R)
Lieutenant Governor
State Capitol, Room 224
Jefferson City, MO 65101
P: (573) 751-4727
F: (573) 751-9422
E: ltgovinfo@mail.mo.gov

President Pro Tempore of the Senate
Sen. Tom Dempsey (R)
President Pro Tempore
State Capitol, Room 326
201 West Capitol Avenue
Jefferson City, MO 65101
P: (573) 751-1141
F: (573) 522-3383
E: Tom.Dempsey
@senate.mo.gov

Senate Majority Leader
Sen. Ron Richard (R)
Majority Floor Leader
State Capitol, Room 321
201 West Capitol Avenue
Jefferson City, MO 65101
P: (573) 751-2173
F: (573) 526-5813
E: Ron.Richard
@senate.mo.gov

Senate Minority Leader
Sen. Joseph Keaveny (D)
Minority Floor Leader
State Capitol, Room 333
201 West Capitol Avenue
Jefferson City, MO 65101
P: (573) 751-3599
F: (573) 751-0266
E: Joseph.Keaveny
@senate.mo.gov

Secretary of the Senate
Ms. Terry L. Spieler
Secretary of the Senate
State Capitol, Room 325
201 West Capitol Avenue
Jefferson City, MO 65101
P: (573) 751-3766
E: tspieler@senate.mo.gov

Members of the Senate
Brown, Dan W. (R, 16)
State Capitol, Room 422
201 West Capitol Avenue
Jefferson City, MO 65101
P: (573) 751-5713
F: (573) 751-0733
E: Dan.Brown@senate.mo.gov

Chappelle-Nadal, Maria (D, 14)
State Capitol, Room 428
201 West Capitol Avenue
Jefferson City, MO 65101
P: (573) 751-4106
F: (573) 751-0467

Cunningham, Mike (R, 33)
State Capitol, Room 331
201 West Capitol Avenue
Jefferson City, MO 65101
P: (573) 751-1882
E: Mike.Cunningham
@senate.mo.gov

Curls, Shalonn Kiki (D, 9)
State Capitol, Room 434
201 West Capitol Avenue
Jefferson City, MO 65101
P: (573) 751-3158
E: Shalonn.Curls
@senate.mo.gov

Dempsey, Tom (R, 23)
State Capitol, Room 326
201 West Capitol Avenue
Jefferson City, MO 65101
P: (573) 751-1141
F: (573) 522-3383
E: Tom.Dempsey
@senate.mo.gov

Dixon, Bob (R, 30)
State Capitol, Room 221
201 West Capitol Avenue
Jefferson City, MO 65101
P: (573) 751-2583
F: (573) 526-1305
E: Bob.Dixon@senate.mo.gov

Emery, Ed (R, 31)
State Capitol, Room 426
201 West Capitol Avenue
Jefferson City, MO 65101
P: (573) 751-2108
E: Ed.Emery@senate.mo.gov

Hegeman, Daniel J. (R, 12)
State Capitol, Room 332
201 West Capitol Avenue
Jefferson City, MO 65101
P: (573) 751-1415
E: Dan.Hegeman
@senate.mo.gov

Holsman, Jason R. (D, 7)
State Capitol, Room 421
201 West Capitol Avenue
Jefferson City, MO 65101
P: (573) 751-6607
F: (573) 522-9495
E: Jason.Holsman
@senate.mo.gov

Keaveny, Joseph (D, 4)
State Capitol, Room 333
201 West Capitol Avenue
Jefferson City, MO 65101
P: (573) 751-3599
F: (573) 751-0266
E: Joseph.Keaveny
@senate.mo.gov

Kehoe, Mike (R, 6)
State Capitol, Room 220
201 West Capitol Avenue
Jefferson City, MO 65101
P: (573) 751-2076
F: (573) 751-2582
E: Mike.Kehoe@senate.mo.gov

Kraus, Will (R, 8)
State Capitol, Room 418
201 West Capitol Avenue
Jefferson City, MO 65101
P: (573) 751-1464
E: Will.Kraus@senate.mo.gov

LeVota, Paul (D, 11)
State Capitol, Room 330
201 West Capitol Avenue
Jefferson City, MO 65101
P: (573) 751-3074
E: Paul.LeVota
@senate.mo.gov

Libla, Doug (R, 25)
State Capitol, Room 219
201 West Capitol Avenue
Jefferson City, MO 65101
P: (573) 751-4843
E: Doug.Libla@senate.mo.gov

Munzlinger, Brian (R, 18)
State Capitol, Room 319
201 West Capitol Avenue
Jefferson City, MO 65101
P: (573) 751-7985
F: (573) 522-3722
E: Brian.Munzlinger
@senate.mo.gov

Nasheed, Jamilah (D, 5)
State Capitol, Room 328
201 West Capitol Avenue
Jefferson City, MO 65101
P: (573) 751-4415
F: (573) 522-9180
E: Jamilah.Nasheed
@senate.mo.gov

Onder Jr., Robert F. (R, 2)
State Capitol, Room 226
201 West Capitol Avenue
Jefferson City, MO 65101
P: (573) 751-1282
E: Robert.Onder
@senate.mo.gov

Parson, Michael (R, 28)
State Capitol, Room 420
201 West Capitol Avenuc
Jefferson City, MO 65101
P: (573) 751-8793
F: (573) 526-8793
E: mparson@senate.mo.gov

Pearce, David (R, 21)
State Capitol, Room 227
201 West Capitol Avenue
Jefferson City, MO 65101
P: (573) 751-2272
F: (573) 526-7381
E: David.Pearce
@senate.mo.gov

Richard, Ron (R, 32)
State Capitol, Room 321
201 West Capitol Avenue
Jefferson City, MO 65101
P: (573) 751-2173
F: (573) 526-5813
E: Ron.Richard
@senate.mo.gov

Riddle, Jeanie (R, 10)
State Capitol, Room 431
201 West Capitol Avenue
Jefferson City, MO 65101
P: (573) 751-2757
E: Jeanie.Riddle
@senate.mo.gov

Romine, Gary (R, 3)
State Capitol, Room 429
201 West Capitol Avenue
Jefferson City, MO 65101
P: (573) 751-4008
E: Gary.Romine
@senate.mo.gov

Sater, David (R, 29)
State Capitol, Room 419
201 West Capitol Avenue
Jefferson City, MO 65101
P: (573) 751-1480
F: (573) 522-1466
E: David.Sater
@senate.mo.gov

Schaaf, Robert (R, 34)
State Capitol, Room 423
201 West Capitol Avenue
Jefferson City, MO 65101
P: (573) 751-2183
F: (573) 526-9851
E: Robert,Schaaf
@senate.mo.gov

Schaefer, Kurt (R, 19)
State Capitol, Room 416
201 West Capitol Avenue
Jefferson City, MO 65101
P: (573) 751-3931
F: (573) 751-4320
E: Kurt.Schaefer
@senate.mo.gov

Schatz, Dave (R, 26)
State Capitol, Room 433
201 West Capitol Avenue
Jefferson City, MO 65101
P: (573) 751-3678
E: Dave.Schatz
@senate.mo.gov

Schmitt, Eric (R, 15)
State Capitol, Room 320
201 West Capitol Avenue
Jefferson City, MO 65101
P: (573) 751-2853
E: eschmitt@senate.mo.gov

Schupp, Jill (D, 24)
State Capitol, Room 425
201 West Capitol Avenue
Jefferson City, MO 65101
P: (573) 751-9762
E: Jill.Schupp@house.mo.gov

Sifton, Scott (D, 1)
State Capitol, Room 329
201 West Capitol Avenue
Jefferson City, MO 65101
P: (573) 751-0220
F: (573) 751-4564
E: Scott.Sifton
@senate.mo.gov

Silvey, Ryan (R, 17)
State Capitol, Room 331A
201 West Capitol Avenue
Jefferson City, MO 65101
P: (573) 751-5282
E: Ryan.Silvey
@senate.mo.gov

Wallingford, Wayne (R, 27)
State Capitol, Room 225
201 West Capitol Avenue
Jefferson City, MO 65101
P: (573) 751-2459
E: Wayne.Wallingford
@senate.mo.gov

Walsh, Gina (D, 13)
State Capitol, Room 427
201 West Capitol Avenue
Jefferson City, MO 65101
P: (573) 751-2420
F: (573) 751-1598
E: Gina.Walsh@senate.mo.gov

Wasson, Jay (R, 20)
State Capitol, Room 323
201 West Capitol Avenue
Jefferson City, MO 65101
P: (573) 751-1503
F: (573) 522-6233
E: Jay.Wasson@senate.mo.gov

Wieland, Paul (R, 22)
State Capitol, Room 334
201 West Capitol Avenue
Jefferson City, MO 65101
P: (573) 751-1492
E: Paul.Wieland
@senate.mo.gov

House

Speaker of the House

Rep. John J. Diehl Jr. (R)
Speaker of the House
State Capitol, Room 308
201 West Capitol Avenue
Jefferson City, MO 65101
P: (573) 751-1544
F: (573) 526-0947
E: John.Diehl@house.mo.gov

Speaker Pro Tempore of the House

Rep. Denny L. Hoskins (R)
Speaker Pro Tem
State Capitol, Room 301
201 West Capitol Avenue
Jefferson City, MO 65101
P: (573) 751-4302
F: (573) 522-2630
E: Denny.Hoskins
@house.mo.gov

House Majority Leader

Rep. Todd Richardson (R)
Majority Floor Leader
State Capitol, Room 302A
201 West Capitol Avenue
Jefferson City, MO 65101
P: (573) 751-4039
F: (573) 751-5271
E: Todd.Richardson
@house.mo.gov

House Minority Leader

Rep. Jacob Hummel (D)
House Minority Floor Leader
State Capitol, Room 204
201 West Capitol Avenue
Jefferson City, MO 65101
P: (573) 751-0438
F: (573) 526-2038
E: Jake.Hummel@house.mo.gov

Clerk of the House

Mr. D. Adam Crumbliss
Chief Clerk
State Capitol, Room 306C
201 West Capitol Avenue
Jefferson City, MO 65101
P: (573) 751-4017
E: adam.crumbliss
@house.mo.gov

Members of the House

Adams, Joe (D, 86)*
State Capitol, Room 105H
201 West Capitol Avenue
Jefferson City, MO 65101
P: (573) 751-4265
E: Joe.Adams@house.mo.gov

Alferman, Justin (R, 61)*
State Capitol, Room 116-2
201 West Capitol Avenue
Jefferson City, MO 65101
P: (573) 751-6668
E: Justin.Alferman
@house.mo.gov

Allen, Sue (R, 100)
State Capitol, Room 310
201 West Capitol Avenue
Jefferson City, MO 65101
P: (573) 751-9765
F: (573) 522-9206
E: Sue.Allen@house.mo.gov

Missouri

Anders, Ira (D, 21)
State Capitol, Room 101E
201 West Capitol Avenue
Jefferson City, MO 65101
P: (573) 751-5701
F: (573) 526-7337
E: Ira.Anders@house.mo.gov

Anderson, Sonya (R, 131)
State Capitol, Room 233A
201 West Capitol Avenue
Jefferson City, MO 65101
P: (573) 751-2948
E: Sonya.Anderson@house.mo.gov

Andrews, Allen (R, 1)*
State Capitol, Room 135AB
201 West Capitol Avenue
Jefferson City, MO 65101
P: (573) 751-9465
E: Allen.Andrews@house.mo.gov

Arthur, Lauren (D, 18)*
State Capitol, Room 109H
201 West Capitol Avenue
Jefferson City, MO 65101
P: (573) 751-2199
E: Lauren.Arthur@house.mo.gov

Austin, Kevin (R, 136)
State Capitol, Room 410B
201 West Capitol Avenue
Jefferson City, MO 65101
P: (573) 751-0232
E: Kevin.Austin@house.mo.gov

Bahr, Kurt (R, 102)
State Capitol, Room 408B
201 West Capitol Avenue
Jefferson City, MO 65101
P: (573) 751-9768
F: (573) 526-1423
E: Kurt.Bahr@house.mo.gov

Barnes, Jay (R, 60)
State Capitol, Room 306A
201 West Capitol Avenue
Jefferson City, MO 65101
P: (573) 751-2412
F: (573) 526-9774
E: Jay.Barnes@house.mo.gov

Basye, Chuck (R, 47)*
State Capitol, Room 201G
201 West Capitol Avenue
Jefferson City, MO 65101
P: (573) 751-1501
E: Chuck.Basye@house.mo.gov

Beard, Nathan (R, 52)*
State Capitol, Room 409A
201 West Capitol Avenue
Jefferson City, MO 65101
P: (573) 751-9774
E: Nathan.Beard@house.mo.gov

Beatty, Gail McCann (D, 26)
State Capitol, Room 130DB
201 West Capitol Avenue
Jefferson City, MO 65101
P: (573) 751-2124
F: (573) 522-9796
E: Gail.Beatty@house.mo.gov

Bernskoetter, Mike (R, 59)
State Capitol, Room 414
201 West Capitol Avenue
Jefferson City, MO 65101
P: (573) 751-0665
F: (573) 526-3278
E: Mike.Bernskoetter@house.mo.gov

Berry, T.J. (R, 38)
State Capitol, Room 205
201 West Capitol Avenue
Jefferson City, MO 65101
P: (573) 751-2238
F: (573) 522-9320
E: TJ.Berry@house.mo.gov

Black, Linda (D, 117)
State Capitol, Room 411-2
201 West Capitol Avenue
Jefferson City, MO 65101
P: (573) 751-2317
F: (573) 522-6297
E: Linda.Black@house.mo.gov

Bondon, Jack (R, 56)*
State Capitol, Room 201F
201 West Capitol Avenue
Jefferson City, MO 65101
P: (573) 751-2175
E: Jack.Bondon@house.mo.gov

Brattin, Rick (R, 55)
State Capitol, Room 114C
201 West Capitol Avenue
Jefferson City, MO 65101
P: (573) 751-3783
F: (573) 522-6078
E: Rick.Brattin@house.mo.gov

Brown, Cloria (R, 94)
State Capitol, Room 406A
201 West Capitol Avenue
Jefferson City, MO 65101
P: (573) 751-3719
F: (573) 522-2628
E: Cloria.Brown@house.mo.gov

Brown, Wanda (R, 57)
State Capitol, Room 412C
201 West Capitol Avenue
Jefferson City, MO 65101
P: (573) 751-3971
F: (573) 526-1889
E: Wanda.Brown@house.mo.gov

Burlison, Eric (R, 133)
State Capitol, Room 316
201 West Capitol Avenue
Jefferson City, MO 65101
P: (573) 751-0136
F: (573) 526-9791
E: Eric.Burlison@house.mo.gov

Burns, Bob (D, 93)
State Capitol, Room 109E
201 West Capitol Avenue
Jefferson City, MO 65101
P: (573) 751-0211
E: Bob.Burns@house.mo.gov

Butler, Michael (D, 79)
State Capitol, Room 109D
201 West Capitol Avenue
Jefferson City, MO 65101
P: (573) 751-6800
E: Michael.Butler@house.mo.gov

Carpenter, Jon (D, 15)
State Capitol, Room 101I
201 West Capitol Avenue
Jefferson City, MO 65101
P: (573) 751-4787
E: Jon.Carpenter@house.mo.gov

Chipman, Jason (R, 120)*
State Capitol, Room 115H
201 West Capitol Avenue
Jefferson City, MO 65101
P: (573) 751-1688
E: Jason.Chipman@house.mo.gov

Cierpiot, Mike (R, 30)
State Capitol, Room 302B
201 West Capitol Avenue
Jefferson City, MO 65101
P: (573) 751-0907
E: Mike.Cierpiot@house.mo.gov

Colona, Mike (D, 80)
State Capitol, Room 107
201 West Capitol Avenue
Jefferson City, MO 65101
P: (573) 751-6736
F: (573) 526-9844
E: Mike.Colona@house.mo.gov

Conway, Kathie (R, 104)
State Capitol, Room 114B
201 West Capitol Avenue
Jefferson City, MO 65101
P: (573) 751-2250
F: (573) 522-2070
E: Kathie.Conway@house.mo.gov

Conway, Pat (D, 10)
State Capitol, Room 109B
201 West Capitol Avenue
Jefferson City, MO 65101
P: (573) 751-9755
F: (573) 526-1965
E: Pat.Conway@house.mo.gov

Cookson, Steve (R, 153)
State Capitol, Room 403A
201 West Capitol Avenue
Jefferson City, MO 65101
P: (573) 751-1066
F: (573) 526-9842
E: Steve.Cookson@house.mo.gov

Corlew, Kevin (R, 14)*
State Capitol, Room 201A
201 West Capitol Avenue
Jefferson City, MO 65101
P: (573) 751-3618
E: Kevin.Corlew@house.mo.gov

Cornejo, Robert (R, 64)
State Capitol, Room 115B
201 West Capitol Avenue
Jefferson City, MO 65101
P: (573) 751-1484
E: Robert.Cornejo@house.mo.gov

Crawford, Sandy (R, 129)
State Capitol, Room 207B
201 West Capitol Avenue
Jefferson City, MO 65101
P: (573) 751-1167
F: (573) 526-0821
E: Sandy.Crawford@house.mo.gov

Cross, Gary (R, 35)
State Capitol, Room 112
201 West Capitol Avenue
Jefferson City, MO 65101
P: (573) 751-1459
F: (573) 526-0932
E: Gary.Cross@house.mo.gov

Curtis, Courtney Allen (D, 73)
State Capitol, Room 135BB
201 West Capitol Avenue
Jefferson City, MO 65101
P: (573) 751-0855
E: Courtney.Curtis@house.mo.gov

Curtman, Paul (R, 109)
State Capitol, Room 306B
201 West Capitol Avenue
Jefferson City, MO 65101
P: (573) 751-3776
E: Paul.Curtman
@house.mo.gov

Davis, Charlie (R, 162)
State Capitol, Room 234
201 West Capitol Avenue
Jefferson City, MO 65101
P: (573) 751-7082
F: (573) 526-9847
E: Charlie.Davis
@house.mo.gov

Diehl Jr., John J. (R, 89)
State Capitol, Room 308
201 West Capitol Avenue
Jefferson City, MO 65101
P: (573) 751-1544
F: (573) 526-0947
E: John.Diehl@house.mo.gov

Dogan, Shamed (R, 98)*
State Capitol, Room 201C
201 West Capitol Avenue
Jefferson City, MO 65101
P: (573) 751-4392
E: Shamed.Dogan
@house.mo.gov

Dohrman, Dean (R, 51)
State Capitol, Room 115G
201 West Capitol Avenue
Jefferson City, MO 65101
P: (573) 751-2204
E: Dean.Dohrman
@house.mo.gov

Dugger, Tony (R, 141)
State Capitol, Room 300
201 West Capitol Avenue
Jefferson City, MO 65101
P: (573) 751-2205
F: (573) 526-9840
E: Tony.Dugger@house.mo.gov

Dunn, Randy (D, 23)
State Capitol, Room 135BA
201 West Capitol Avenue
Jefferson City, MO 65101
P: (573) 751-0538
E: Randy.Dunn@house.mo.gov

Eggleston, J. (R, 2)*
State Capitol, Room 406B
201 West Capitol Avenue
Jefferson City, MO 65101
P: (573) 751-4285
E: J.Eggleston@house.mo.gov

Ellington, Brandon (D, 22)
State Capitol, Room 101C
201 West Capitol Avenue
Jefferson City, MO 65101
P: (573) 751-3129
E: Brandon.Ellington
@house.mo.gov

Engler, Kevin (R, 116)
State Capitol, Room 313-3
201 West Capitol Avenue
Jefferson City, MO 65101
P: (573) 751-3455
E: Kevin.Engler
@house.mo.gov

English, Keith (D, 68)
State Capitol, Room 317-A
201 West Capitol Avenue
Jefferson City, MO 65101
P: (573) 751-9628
E: Keith.English
@house.mo.gov

Entlicher, Sue (R, 128)
State Capitol, Room 207A
201 West Capitol Avenue
Jefferson City, MO 65101
P: (573) 751-1347
F: (573) 522-9179
E: Sue.Entlicher
@house.mo.gov

Fitzpatrick, Scott (R, 158)
State Capitol, Room 415A
201 West Capitol Avenue
Jefferson City, MO 65101
P: (573) 751-1488
E: Scott.Fitzpatrick
@house.mo.gov

Fitzwater, Paul (R, 144)
State Capitol, Room 110B
201 West Capitol Avenue
Jefferson City, MO 65101
P: (573) 751-2112
F: (573) 526-6856
E: Paul.Fitzwater
@house.mo.gov

Fitzwater, Travis (R, 49)*
State Capitol, Room 116A2
201 West Capitol Avenue
Jefferson City, MO 65101
P: (573) 751-5226
E: Travis.Fitzwater
@house.mo.gov

Flanigan, Tom (R, 163)
State Capitol, Room 309
201 West Capitol Avenue
Jefferson City, MO 65101
P: (573) 751-5458
F: (573) 526-9773
E: Thomas.Flanigan
@house.mo.gov

Fraker, Lyndall (R, 137)
State Capitol, Room 304A
201 West Capitol Avenue
Jefferson City, MO 65101
P: (573) 751-3819
F: (573) 526-1888
E: Lyndall.Fraker
@house.mo.gov

Franklin, Diane (R, 123)
State Capitol, Room 206B
201 West Capitol Avenue
Jefferson City, MO 65101
P: (573) 751-1119
F: (573) 526-9803
E: Diane.Franklin
@house.mo.gov

Frederick, Keith (R, 121)
State Capitol, Room 403B
201 West Capitol Avenue
Jefferson City, MO 65101
P: (573) 751-3834
F: (573) 751-0733
E: Keith.Frederick
@house.mo.gov

Gannon, Elaine (R, 115)
State Capitol, Room 304B
201 West Capitol Avenue
Jefferson City, MO 65101
P: (573) 751-7735
E: Elaine.Gannon
@house.mo.gov

Gardner, Kimberly (D, 77)
State Capitol, Room 109I
201 West Capitol Avenue
Jefferson City, MO 65101
P: (573) 751-1400
E: Kimberly.Gardner
@house.mo.gov

Gosen, Don (R, 101)
State Capitol, Room 311
201 West Capitol Avenue
Jefferson City, MO 65101
P: (573) 751-1247
F: (573) 751-2728
E: Don.Gosen@house.mo.gov

Gray, Rochelle Walton (D, 75)
State Capitol, Room 105F
201 West Capitol Avenue
Jefferson City, MO 65101
P: (573) 751-5538
F: (573) 526-0572
E: Rochelle.Gray
@house.mo.gov

Green, Alan (D, 67)*
State Capitol, Room 102BA
201 West Capitol Avenue
Jefferson City, MO 65101
P: (573) 751-2135
E: Alan.Green@house.mo.gov

Haahr, Elijah (R, 134)
State Capitol, Room 410A
201 West Capitol Avenue
Jefferson City, MO 65101
P: (573) 751-2210
E: Elijah.Haahr
@house.mo.gov

Haefner, Marsha (R, 95)
State Capitol, Room 305A
201 West Capitol Avenue
Jefferson City, MO 65101
P: (573) 751-3762
F: (573) 526-4767
E: Marsha.Haefner
@house.mo.gov

Hansen, Jim (R, 40)
State Capitol, Room 405A
201 West Capitol Avenue
Jefferson City, MO 65101
P: (573) 751-4028
E: Jim.Hansen@house.mo.gov

Harris, Ben (D, 118)
State Capitol, Room 105A
201 West Capitol Avenue
Jefferson City, MO 65101
P: (573) 751-2398
F: (573) 526-1963
E: Ben.Harris@house.mo.gov

Hicks, Ron (R, 107)
State Capitol, Room 115E
201 West Capitol Avenue
Jefferson City, MO 65101
P: (573) 751-1470
E: Ron.Hicks@house.mo.gov

Higdon, Galen (R, 11)
State Capitol, Room 412A
201 West Capitol Avenue
Jefferson City, MO 65101
P: (573) 751-3643
F: (573) 522-5025
E: Galen.Higdon
@house.mo.gov

Hill, Justin (R, 108)*
State Capitol, Room 116-A1
201 West Capitol Avenue
Jefferson City, MO 65101
P: (573) 751-3572
E: Justin.Hill@house.mo.gov

Hinson, Dave (R, 119)
State Capitol, Room 411A
201 West Capitol Avenue
Jefferson City, MO 65101
P: (573) 751-0549
F: (573) 526-9846
E: Dave.Hinson@house.mo.gov

Missouri

Hoskins, Denny L. (R, 54)
State Capitol, Room 301
201 West Capitol Avenue
Jefferson City, MO 65101
P: (573) 751-4302
F: (573) 522-2630
E: Denny.Hoskins@house.mo.gov

Hough, Lincoln (R, 135)
State Capitol, Room 411B
201 West Capitol Avenue
Jefferson City, MO 65101
P: (573) 751-9809
F: (573) 526-8965
E: Lincoln.Hough@house.mo.gov

Houghton, Jay (R, 43)
State Capitol, Room 412B
201 West Capitol Avenue
Jefferson City, MO 65101
P: (573) 751-3649
F: (573) 526-0905
E: Jay.Houghton@house.mo.gov

Hubbard, Penny (D, 78)
State Capitol, Room 105B
201 West Capitol Avenue
Jefferson City, MO 65101
P: (573) 751-2383
F: (573) 526-0568
E: Penny.Hubbard@house.mo.gov

Hubrecht, Tila (R, 151)*
State Capitol, Room 407C
201 West Capitol Avenue
Jefferson City, MO 65101
P: (573) 751-1494
E: Tila.Hubrecht@house.mo.gov

Hummel, Jacob (D, 81)
State Capitol, Room 204
201 West Capitol Avenue
Jefferson City, MO 65101
P: (573) 751-0438
F: (573) 526-2038
E: Jake.Hummel@house.mo.gov

Hurst, Tom (R, 62)
State Capitol, Room 206C
201 West Capitol Avenue
Jefferson City, MO 65101
P: (573) 751-1344
E: Tom.Hurst@house.mo.gov

Johnson, Delus (R, 9)
State Capitol, Room 302-1
201 West Capitol Avenue
Jefferson City, MO 65101
P: (573) 751-3666
E: Delus.Johnson@house.mo.gov

Jones, Caleb (R, 50)
State Capitol, Room 303A
201 West Capitol Avenue
Jefferson City, MO 65101
P: (573) 751-2134
F: (573) 526-3994
E: Caleb.Jones@house.mo.gov

Justus, Jeffery (R, 156)
State Capitol, Room 115D
201 West Capitol Avenue
Jefferson City, MO 65101
P: (573) 751-1309
E: Jeffery.Justus@house.mo.gov

Keeney, Shelley (R, 145)
State Capitol, Room 313-1
201 West Capitol Avenue
Jefferson City, MO 65101
P: (573) 751-5912
F: (573) 526-9804
E: Shelley.Keeney@house.mo.gov

Kelley, Mike (R, 127)
State Capitol, Room 235
201 West Capitol Avenue
Jefferson City, MO 65101
P: (573) 751-2165
F: (573) 526-2577
E: Mike.Kelley@house.mo.gov

Kendrick, Kip (D, 45)*
State Capitol, Room 106B
201 West Capitol Avenue
Jefferson City, MO 65101
P: (573) 751-4189
E: Kip.Kendrick@house.mo.gov

Kidd, Bill (R, 20)*
State Capitol, Room 201E
201 West Capitol Avenue
Jefferson City, MO 65101
P: (573) 751-3674
E: Bill.Kidd@house.mo.gov

King, Nick (R, 17)*
State Capitol, Room 201-CA
201 West Capitol Avenue
Jefferson City, MO 65101
P: (573) 751-1218
E: Nick.King@house.mo.gov

Kirkton, Jeanne (D, 91)
State Capitol, Room 135BC
201 West Capitol Avenue
Jefferson City, MO 65101
P: (573) 751-1285
F: (573) 522-9394
E: Jeanne.Kirkton@house.mo.gov

Koenig, Andrew (R, 99)
State Capitol, Room 312
201 West Capitol Avenue
Jefferson City, MO 65101
P: (573) 751-5568
F: (573) 522-9204
E: Andrew.Koenig@house.mo.gov

Kolkmeyer, Glen (R, 53)
State Capitol, Room 400CA
201 West Capitol Avenue
Jefferson City, MO 65101
P: (573) 751-1462
E: Glen.Kolkmeyer@house.mo.gov

Korman, Bart (R, 42)
State Capitol, Room 113
201 West Capitol Avenue
Jefferson City, MO 65101
P: (573) 751-2689
F: (573) 526-0559
E: Bart.Korman@house.mo.gov

Kratky, Michele (D, 82)
State Capitol, Room 109C
201 West Capitol Avenue
Jefferson City, MO 65101
P: (573) 751-4220
F: (573) 522-6170
E: Michele.Kratky@house.mo.gov

LaFaver, Jeremy (D, 25)
State Capitol, Room 105J
201 West Capitol Avenue
Jefferson City, MO 65101
P: (573) 751-2437
E: Jeremy.LaFaver@house.mo.gov

Lair, Mike (R, 7)
State Capitol, Room 402
201 West Capitol Avenue
Jefferson City, MO 65101
P: (573) 751-2917
F: (573) 526-9775
E: Mike.Lair@house.mo.gov

Lant, Bill (R, 159)
State Capitol, Room 400
201 West Capitol Avenue
Jefferson City, MO 65101
P: (573) 751-9801
F: (573) 522-5505
E: Bill.Lant@house.mo.gov

Lauer, Jeanie (R, 32)
State Capitol, Room 413B
201 West Capitol Avenue
Jefferson City, MO 65101
P: (573) 751-1487
F: (573) 526-2619
E: Jeanie.Lauer@house.mo.gov

Lavender, Deb (D, 90)*
State Capitol, Room 109F
201 West Capitol Avenue
Jefferson City, MO 65101
P: (573) 751-4069
E: Deb.Lavender@house.mo.gov

Leara, Mike (R, 96)
State Capitol, Room 313-2
201 West Capitol Avenue
Jefferson City, MO 65101
P: (573) 751-2150
F: (573) 526-8794
E: Mike.Leara@house.mo.gov

Lichtenegger, Donna (R, 146)
State Capitol, Room 314
201 West Capitol Avenue
Jefferson City, MO 65101
P: (573) 751-6662
F: (573) 522-6191
E: Donna.Lichtenegger@house.mo.gov

Love, Warren (R, 125)
State Capitol, Room 235BA
201 West Capitol Avenue
Jefferson City, MO 65101
P: (573) 751-4065
E: Warren.Love@house.mo.gov

Lynch, Steve (R, 122)
State Capitol, Room 203C
201 West Capitol Avenue
Jefferson City, MO 65101
P: (573) 751-1446
E: Steve.Lynch@house.mo.gov

Marshall, Nick (R, 13)
State Capitol, Room 134
201 West Capitol Avenue
Jefferson City, MO 65101
P: (573) 751-6593
F: (573) 522-9278
E: Nick.Marshall@house.mo.gov

Mathews, Kirk (R, 110)*
State Capitol, Room 203A
201 West Capitol Avenue
Jefferson City, MO 65101
P: (573) 751-0562
E: Kirk.Mathews@house.mo.gov

May, Karla (D, 84)
State Capitol, Room 101J
201 West Capitol Avenue
Jefferson City, MO 65101
P: (573) 751-2198
F: (573) 526-9004
E: Karla.May@house.mo.gov

McCaherty, John (R, 97)
State Capitol, Room 401B
201 West Capitol Avenue
Jefferson City, MO 65101
P: (573) 751-3751
F: (573) 522-1582
E: John.McCaherty
@house.mo.gov

McCreery, Tracy (D, 88)
State Capitol, Room 105E
201 West Capitol Avenue
Jefferson City, MO 65101
P: (573) 751-9762
E: Tracy.McCreery
@house.mo.gov

McDaniel, Andrew (R, 150)*
State Capitol, Room 115I
201 West Capitol Avenue
Jefferson City, MO 65101
P: (573) 751-3629
E: Andrew.McDaniel
@house.mo.gov

McDonald, Tom (D, 28)
State Capitol, Room 109A
201 West Capitol Avenue
Jefferson City, MO 65101
P: (573) 751-9851
F: (573) 522-8172
E: Tom.McDonald
@house.mo.gov

McGaugh, Joe Don (R, 39)
State Capitol, Room 236A
201 West Capitol Avenue
Jefferson City, MO 65101
P: (573) 751-1468
E: JoeDon.McGaugh
@house.mo.gov

McManus, Kevin (D, 36)
State Capitol, Room 101D
201 West Capitol Avenue
Jefferson City, MO 65101
P: (573) 751-9469
F: (573) 751-6688
E: Kevin.McManus
@house.mo.gov

McNeil, Margo (D, 69)
State Capitol, Room 103DC
201 West Capitol Avenue
Jefferson City, MO 65101
P: (573) 751-5365
F: (573) 526-9776
E: Margo.McNeil
@house.mo.gov

Meredith, Sue (D, 71)
State Capitol, Room 103BB
201 West Capitol Avenue
Jefferson City, MO 65101
P: (573) 751-4183
E: Susan.Meredith
@house.mo.gov

Messenger, Jeffrey (R, 130)
State Capitol, Room 407A
201 West Capitol Avenue
Jefferson City, MO 65101
P: (573) 751-2381
E: Jeff.Messenger
@house.mo.gov

Miller, Rocky (R, 124)
State Capitol, Room 233B
201 West Capitol Avenue
Jefferson City, MO 65101
P: (573) 751-3604
E: Rocky.Miller
@house.mo.gov

Mims, Bonnaye (D, 27)
State Capitol, Room 103BA
201 West Capitol Avenue
Jefferson City, MO 65101
P: (573) 751-7639
E: Bonnaye.Mims
@house.mo.gov

Mitten, Gina (D, 83)
State Capitol, Room 101B
201 West Capitol Avenue
Jefferson City, MO 65101
P: (573) 751-2883
E: Gina.Mitten@house.mo.gov

Montecillo, Genise (D, 92)
State Capitol, Room 130D-A
201 West Capitol Avenue
Jefferson City, MO 65101
P: (573) 751-9472
F: (573) 522-3369
E: Genise.Montecillo
@house.mo.gov

Moon, Mike (R, 157)
State Capitol, Room 203B
201 West Capitol Avenue
Jefferson City, MO 65101
P: (573) 751-4077
E: Mike.Moon@house.mo.gov

Morgan, Judy (D, 24)
State Capitol, Room 101G
201 West Capitol Avenue
Jefferson City, MO 65101
P: (573) 751-4485
E: Judy.Morgan@house.mo.gov

Morris, Lynn A. (R, 140)
State Capitol, Room 200BC
201 West Capitol Avenue
Jefferson City, MO 65101
P: (573) 751-2565
E: Lynn.Morris@house.mo.gov

Muntzel, Dave (R, 48)
State Capitol, Room 235BB
201 West Capitol Avenue
Jefferson City, MO 65101
P: (573) 751-0169
E: Dave.Muntzel
@house.mo.gov

Neely, Jim (R, 8)
State Capitol, Room 110A
201 West Capitol Avenue
Jefferson City, MO 65101
P: (573) 751-0246
E: Jim.Neely@house.mo.gov

Newman, Stacey (D, 87)
State Capitol, Room 101K
201 West Capitol Avenue
Jefferson City, MO 65101
P: (573) 751-0100
F: (573) 526-9866
E: Stacey.Newman
@house.mo.gov

Nichols, Mary (D, 72)
State Capitol, Room 101A
201 West Capitol Avenue
Jefferson City, MO 65101
P: (573) 751-1832
F: (573) 526-2649
E: Mary.Nichols
@house.mo.gov

Norr, Charlie (D, 132)
State Capitol, Room 105D
201 West Capitol Avenue
Jefferson City, MO 65101
P: (573) 751-3795
E: Charlie.Norr
@house.mo.gov

Otto, Bill (D, 70)
State Capitol, Room 103BC
201 West Capitol Avenue
Jefferson City, MO 65101
P: (573) 751-4163
E: Bill.Otto@house.mo.gov

Pace, Sharon L. (D, 74)
State Capitol, Room 105G
201 West Capitol Avenue
Jefferson City, MO 65101
P: (573) 751-4726
F: (573) 526-9836
E: Sharon.Pace@house.mo.gov

Parkinson, Mark (R, 105)
State Capitol, Room 200A
201 West Capitol Avenue
Jefferson City, MO 65101
P: (573) 751-2949
F: (573) 526-4880
E: Mark.Parkinson
@house.mo.gov

Peters, Joshua (D, 76)
State Capitol, Room 105I
201 West Capitol Avenue
Jefferson City, MO 65101
P: (573) 751-7605
E: Joshua.Peters
@house.mo.gov

Pfautsch, Donna (R, 33)
State Capitol, Room 236B
201 West Capitol Avenue
Jefferson City, MO 65101
P: (573) 751-9766
E: Donna.Pfautsch
@house.mo.gov

Phillips, Don (R, 138)
State Capitol, Room 135
201 West Capitol Avenue
Jefferson City, MO 65101
P: (573) 751-3851
F: (573) 526-9794
E: Don.Phillips
@house.mo.gov

Pierson, Tommie (D, 66)
State Capitol, Room 101H
201 West Capitol Avenue
Jefferson City, MO 65101
P: (573) 751-6845
F: (573) 526-1571
E: Tommie.Pierson
@house.mo.gov

Pietzman, Randy (R, 41)*
State Capitol,Room 201D
201 West Capitol Avenue
Jefferson City, MO 65101
P: (573) 751-9459
E: Randy.Pietzman
@house.mo.gov

Pike, Patricia (R, 126)*
State Capitol, Room 400CB
201 West Capitol Avenue
Jefferson City, MO 65101
P: (573) 751-5388
E: Patricia.Pike
@house.mo.gov

Pogue, Jeff (R, 143)
State Capitol, Room 400CC
201 West Capitol Avenue
Jefferson City, MO 65101
P: (573) 751-2264
E: Jeff.Pogue@house.mo.gov

Redmon, Craig (R, 4)
State Capitol, Room 111
201 West Capitol Avenue
Jefferson City, MO 65101
P: (573) 751-3644
E: Craig.Redmon
@house.mo.gov

Rehder, Holly (R, 148)
State Capitol, Room 404B
201 West Capitol Avenue
Jefferson City, MO 65101
P: (573) 751-5471
E: Holly.Rehder
@house.mo.gov

Missouri

Reibolt, Bill (R, 130)
State Capitol, Room 303B
201 West Capitol Avenue
Jefferson City, MO 65101
P: (573) 751-9781
F: (573) 522-9287
E: Bill.Reiboldt
@house.mo.gov

Remole, Tim (R, 6)
State Capitol, Room 201BA
201 West Capitol Avenue
Jefferson City, MO 65101
P: (573) 751-6566
E: Tim.Remole@house.mo.gov

Rhoads, Shawn (R, 154)
State Capitol, Room 407B
201 West Capitol Avenue
Jefferson City, MO 65101
P: (573) 751-1455
E: Shawn.Rhoads
@house.mo.gov

Richardson, Todd (R, 152)
State Capitol, Room 302A
201 West Capitol Avenue
Jefferson City, MO 65101
P: (573) 751-4039
F: (573) 751-5271
E: Todd.Richardson
@house.mo.gov

Rizzo, John (D, 19)
State Capitol, Room 102BB
201 West Capitol Avenue
Jefferson City, MO 65101
P: (573) 751-3310
F: (573) 526-1947
E: John.Rizzo@house.mo.gov

Roden, Shane (R, 111)*
State Capitol, Room 115J
201 West Capitol Avenue
Jefferson City, MO 65101
P: (573) 751-4567
E: Shane.Roden@house.mo.gov

Roeber, Rebecca (R, 34)*
State Capitol, Room 116-3
201 West Capitol Avenue
Jefferson City, MO 65101
P: (573) 751-1456
E: Rebecca.Roeber
@house.mo.gov

Rone, Don (R, 149)*
State Capitol, Room 116-1
201 West Capitol Avenue
Jefferson City, MO 65101
P: (573) 751-4085
E: Don.Rone@house.mo.gov

Ross, Robert (R, 142)
State Capitol, Room 114A
201 West Capitol Avenue
Jefferson City, MO 65101
P: (573) 751-1490
E: Robert.Ross@house.mo.gov

Rowden, Caleb (R, 44)
State Capitol, Room 415B
201 West Capitol Avenue
Jefferson City, MO 65101
P: (573) 751-1169
E: Caleb.Rowden
@house.mo.gov

Rowland, Lyle (R, 155)
State Capitol, Room 413A
201 West Capitol Avenue
Jefferson City, MO 65101
P: (573) 751-2042
F: (573) 526-0575
E: Lyle.Rowland
@house.mo.gov

Runions, Joe (D, 37)
State Capitol, Room 101F
201 West Capitol Avenue
Jefferson City, MO 65101
P: (573) 751-0238
E: Joe.Runions@house.mo.gov

Ruth, Becky (R, 114)*
State Capitol, Room 115F
201 West Capitol Avenue
Jefferson City, MO 65101
P: (573) 751-4451
E: Becky.Ruth@house.mo.gov

Shaul, Dan (R, 113)*
State Capitol, Room 116-5
201 West Capitol Avenue
Jefferson City, MO 65101
P: (573) 751-2504
E: Dan.Shaul@house.mo.gov

Shull, Noel (R, 16)
State Capitol, Room 201B
201 West Capitol Avenue
Jefferson City, MO 65101
P: (573) 751-9458
E: Noel.Shull@house.mo.gov

Shumake, Lindell F. (R, 5)
State Capitol, Room 404A
201 West Capitol Avenue
Jefferson City, MO 65101
P: (573) 751-3613
F: (573) 751-7928
E: Lindell.Shumake
@house.mo.gov

Smith, Clem (D, 85)
State Capitol, Room 105C
201 West Capitol Avenue
Jefferson City, MO 65101
P: (573) 751-4468
F: (573) 526-1239
E: Clem.Smith@house.mo.gov

Solon, Sheila (R, 31)
State Capitol, Room 305B
201 West Capitol Avenue
Jefferson City, MO 65101
P: (573) 751-8636
F: (573) 522-1178
E: Sheila.Solon
@house.mo.gov

Sommer, Chrissy (R, 106)
State Capitol, Room 401A
201 West Capitol Avenue
Jefferson City, MO 65101
P: (573) 751-1452
E: Chrissy.Sommer
@house.mo.gov

Spencer, Bryan (R, 63)
State Capitol, Room 200B
201 West Capitol Avenue
Jefferson City, MO 65101
P: (573) 751-1460
E: Bryan.Spencer
@house.mo.gov

Swan, Kathryn (R, 147)
State Capitol, Room 115C
201 West Capitol Avenue
Jefferson City, MO 65101
P: (573) 751-1443
E: Kathryn.Swan
@house.mo.gov

Taylor, Jered (R, 139)*
State Capitol, Room 116-4
201 West Capitol Avenue
Jefferson City, MO 65101
P: (573) 751-3833
E: Jered.Taylor
@house.mo.gov

Vescovo, Rob (R, 112)*
State Capitol, Room 409B
201 West Capitol Avenue
Jefferson City, MO 65101
P: (573) 751-3607
E: Rob.Vescovo@house.mo.gov

Walker, Nate (R, 3)
State Capitol, Room 405B
201 West Capitol Avenue
Jefferson City, MO 65101
P: (573) 751-3647
E: Nate.Walker@house.mo.gov

Webber, Stephen (D, 46)
State Capitol, Room 106A
201 West Capitol Avenue
Jefferson City, MO 65101
P: (573) 751-9753
F: (573) 526-0750
E: Stephen.Webber
@house.mo.gov

White, Bill (R, 161)
State Capitol, Room 408A
201 West Capitol Avenue
Jefferson City, MO 65101
P: (573) 751-3791
E: Bill.White@house.mo.gov

Wiemann, John (R, 103)*
State Capitol, Room 135AC
201 West Capitol Avenue
Jefferson City, MO 65101
P: (573) 751-2176

Wilson, Kenneth (R, 12)
State Capitol, Room 206A
201 West Capitol Avenue
Jefferson City, MO 65101
P: (573) 751-9760
E: Ken.Wilson@house.mo.gov

Wood, David (R, 58)
State Capitol, Room 115A
201 West Capitol Avenue
Jefferson City, MO 65101
P: (573) 751-2077
E: David.Wood@house.mo.gov

Zerr, Anne (R, 65)
State Capitol, Room 315
201 West Capitol Avenue
Jefferson City, MO 65101
P: (573) 751-3717
E: Anne.Zerr@house.mo.gov

Congress

Senate

Blunt, Roy (R)
McCaskill, Claire (D)

House

Clay, William L. (D, 1)
Cleaver, Emanuel (D, 5)
Graves Jr., Sam B. (R, 6)
Hartzler, Vicky (R, 4)
Long, Billy (R, 7)
Luetkemeyer, Blaine (R, 3)
Smith, Jason T. (R, 8)
Wagner, Ann (R, 2)

Montana

Executive

Governor

Hon. Steve Bullock (D)
Governor
State Capitol
Helena, MT 59620
P: (406) 444-3111
F: (404) 444-5529

Lieutenant Governor

Hon. Angela McLean (D)
Lieutenant Governor
Capitol Station, Room 207
P.O. Box 200801
Helena, MT 59620
P: (406) 444-5665
F: (406) 444-4648

Attorney General

Hon. Tim Fox (R)
Attorney General
Justice Building
215 North Sanders
Helena, MT 59620
P: (406) 444-2026
F: (406) 444-3549
E: contactdoj@mt.gov

Auditor

Hon. Monica J. Lindeen (D)
Commissioner of Securities & Insurance, State Auditor
840 Helena Avenue
Helena, MT 59601
P: (406) 444-2040
F: (406) 444-3497
E: stateauditor@mt.gov

Hon. Brad Johnson (R)
Commissioner
1701 Prospect Avenue
P.O. Box 202601
Helena, MT 59620
P: (406) 444-6169
F: (406) 444-7618

Secretary of State

Hon. Linda McCulloch (D)
Secretary of State
P.O. Box 202801
Helena, MT 59620
P: (406) 444-2034
F: (406) 444-4249
E: sos@mt.gov

Superintendent of Public Instruction

Hon. Denise Juneau (D)
Superintendent of Public Instruction
P.O. Box 202501
Helena, MT 59620
P: (406) 444-3095
F: (406) 444-9299
E: OPISupt@mt.gov

Treasurer

Hon. Sheila Hogan (appointed)
Director
125 North Roberts Street
P.O. Box 200101
Helena, MT 59620
P: (406) 444-2032
F: (406) 444-6194
E: shogan@mt.gov

Judiciary

Supreme Court (NE)

Mr. Ed Smith
Clerk
215 North Sanders, Room 323
P.O. Box 203003
Helena, MT 59620
P: (406) 444-3858
F: (406) 444-5705

Hon. Mike McGrath
Chief Justice
Hon. Beth Baker
Hon. Patricia O'Brien Cotter
Hon. Laurie McKinnon
Hon. James A. Rice
Hon. James Jeremiah Shea
Hon. Michael Wheat

Legislative Senate

Senate President

Sen. Debby Barrett (R)
Senate President
P.O. Box 200500
Helena, MT 59620
P: (406) 444-4800
F: (406) 444-4875
E: Sen.Debby.Barrett@mt.gov

President Pro Tempore of the Senate

Sen. Eric Moore (R)
President Pro Tempore
P.O. Box 200500
Helena, MT 59620
P: (406) 444-4800
F: (406) 444-4875
E: mail @senatorericmoore.com

Senate Majority Leader

Sen. Matt Rosendale (R)
Majority Leader
P.O. Box 200500
Helena, MT 59620
P: (406) 444-4800
F: (406) 444-4875
E: mattrosendale @midrivers.com

Senate Minority Leader

Sen. Jon Sesso (D)
Minority Leader
P.O. Box 200500
Helena, MT 59620
P: (406) 444-4800
F: (406) 444-4875
E: jonsesso@yahoo.com

Secretary of the Senate

Ms. Marilyn Miller
Secretary of the Senate
Room 302B, State Capitol
P.O. Box 200500
Helena, MT 59620
P: (406) 444-4801
F: (406) 444-4875
E: mmiller2@mt.gov

Members of the Senate

Ankney, Duane (R, 20)
P.O. Box 200500
Helena, MT 59620
P: (406) 444-4800
F: (406) 444-4875
E: goodwind1.duane @gmail.com

Arntzen, Elsie (R, 26)
P.O. Box 200500
Helena, MT 59620
P: (406) 444-4800
F: (406) 444-4875
E: emarntzen@gmail.com

Barrett, Debby (R, 36)
P.O. Box 200500
Helena, MT 59620
P: (406) 444-4800
F: (406) 444-4875
E: Sen.Debby.Barrett@mt.gov

Barrett, Dick (D, 45)
P.O. Box 200500
Helena, MT 59620
P: (406) 444-4800
F: (406) 444-4875
E: rnewbar@gmail.com

Blasdel, Mark (R, 4)
P.O. Box 200500
Helena, MT 59620
P: (406) 444-4800
F: (406) 444-4875
E: Sen.Mark.Blasdel@mt.gov

Brenden, John C. (R, 17)
P.O. Box 200500
Helena, MT 59620
P: (406) 444-4800
F: (406) 444-4875
E: senatorbrenden@gmail.com

Brown, Dee L. (R, 2)
P.O. Box 200500
Helena, MT 59620
P: (406) 444-4800
F: (406) 444-4875
E: Sen.Dee.Brown@mt.gov

Brown, Taylor (R, 28)
P.O. Box 200500
Helena, MT 59620
P: (406) 444-4800
F: (406) 444-4875
E: taylor @northernbroadcasting.com

Buttrey, Edward (R, 11)
P.O. Box 200500
Helena, MT 59620
P: (406) 444-4800
F: (406) 444-4875
E: ebuttrey@senate13.com

Caferro, Mary (D, 41)
P.O. Box 200500
Helena, MT 59620
P: (406) 444-4800
F: (406) 444-4875
E: marycaferro@gmail.com

Cohenour, Jill (D, 42)
P.O. Box 200500
Helena, MT 59620
P: (406) 444-4800
F: (406) 444-4875
E: Sen.Jill.Cohenour@mt.gov

Connell, Pat (R, 43)
P.O. Box 200500
Helena, MT 59620
P: (406) 444-4800
F: (406) 444-4875
E: connell4sd43@yahoo.com

Montana

Driscoll, Robyn (D, 25)
P.O. Box 200500
Helena, MT 59620
P: (406) 444-4800
F: (406) 444-4875
E: Sen.Robyn.Driscoll@mt.gov

Facey, Tom (D, 50)
P.O. Box 200500
Helena, MT 59620
P: (406) 444-4800
F: (406) 444-4875
E: facey_tom@hotmail.com

Fielder, Jennifer (R, 7)
P.O. Box 200500
Helena, MT 59620
P: (406) 444-4800
F: (406) 444-4875
E: Sen.Jennifer.Fielder@mt.gov

Hamlett, Bradley Maxon (D, 15)
P.O. Box 200500
Helena, MT 59620
P: (406) 444-4800
F: (406) 444-4875
E: Sen.Bradley.Hamlett@mt.gov

Hansen, Kristin (R, 14)
P.O. Box 200500
Helena, MT 59620
P: (406) 444-4800
F: (406) 444-4875
E: Sen.Kris.Hansen@mt.gov

Hinkle, Jedediah (R, 32)*
P.O. Box 200500
Helena, MT 59620
P: (406) 444-4800
F: (406) 444-4875
E: Sen.Jedediah.Hinkle@mt.gov

Hoven, Brian E. (R, 13)
P.O. Box 200500
Helena, MT 59620
P: (406) 444-4800
F: (406) 444-4875
E: brian@hovenequipment.com

Howard, David (R, 29)
P.O. Box 200500
Helena, MT 59620
P: (406) 444-4800
F: (406) 444-4875
E: sendavidhoward@gmail.com

Jones, Llew (R, 9)
P.O. Box 200500
Helena, MT 59620
P: (406) 444-4800
F: (406) 444-4875
E: ljones@mtbus.net

Kary, Douglas (R, 22)
P.O. Box 200500
Helena, MT 59620
P: (406) 444-4800
F: (406) 444-4875
E: Sen.Doug.Kary@mt.gov

Kaufmann, Christine (D, 40)
P.O. Box 200500
Helena, MT 59620
P: (406) 444-4800
F: (406) 444-4875
E: kaufmann@mt.net

Keane, Jim (D, 38)
P.O. Box 200500
Helena, MT 59620
P: (406) 444-4800
F: (406) 444-4875

Keenan, Bob (R, 5)
P.O. Box 200500
Helena, MT 59620
P: (406) 444-4800
F: (406) 444-4875
E: bob@bobkeenan.us

Larsen, Cliff (D, 47)
P.O. Box 200500
Helena, MT 59620
P: (406) 444-4800
F: (406) 444-4875
E: cliff@larsenusa.com

Malek, Sue (D, 46)
P.O. Box 200500
Helena, MT 59620
P: (406) 444-4800
F: (406) 444-4875
E: suemalek@gmail.com

McNally, Mary (D, 24)
P.O. Box 200500
Helena, MT 59620
P: (406) 444-4800
F: (406) 444-4875
E: Sen.Mary.McNally@mt.gov

Moe, Mary Sheehy (D, 12)*
P.O. Box 200500
Helena, MT 59620
P: (406) 444-4800
F: (406) 444-4875
E: moe.mt.senate@gmail.com

Moore, Eric (R, 19)
P.O. Box 200500
Helena, MT 59620
P: (406) 444-4800
F: (406) 444-4875
E: mail@senatorericmoore.com

Phillips, Mike (D, 31)
P.O. Box 200500
Helena, MT 59620
P: (406) 444-4800
F: (406) 444-4875
E: mikephillips@montana.net

Pomnichowski, J.P. (D, 33)
P.O. Box 200500
Helena, MT 59620
P: (406) 444-4800
F: (406) 444-4875
E: Sen.JP@mt.gov

Ripley, Rick (R, 10)
P.O. Box 200500
Helena, MT 59620
P: (406) 444-4800
F: (406) 444-4875
E: ripley@3rivers.net

Rosendale, Matt (R, 18)
P.O. Box 200500
Helena, MT 59620
P: (406) 444-4800
F: (406) 444-4875
E: mattrosendale@midrivers.com

Sales, Scott (R, 35)
P.O. Box 200500
Helena, MT 59620
P: (406) 444-4800
F: (406) 444-4875
E: sales4mtsenate@hotmail.com

Sands, Diane (D, 49)
P.O. Box 200500
Helena, MT 59620
P: (406) 444-4800
F: (406) 444-4875
E: senatorsands@gmail.com

Sesso, Jon (D, 37)
P.O. Box 200500
Helena, MT 59620
P: (406) 444-4800
F: (406) 444-4875
E: jonsesso@yahoo.com

Smith, Cary L. (R, 27)
P.O. Box 200500
Helena, MT 59620
P: (406) 444-4800
F: (406) 444-4875
E: Sen.Cary.Smith@mt.gov

Stewart-Peregoy, Sharon (D, 21)
P.O. Box 200500
Helena, MT 59620
P: (406) 444-4800
F: (406) 444-4875
E: Sen.Sharon.Stewart-Peregoy@mt.gov

Swandal, Nels (R, 30)*
P.O. Box 200500
Helena, MT 59620
P: (406) 444-4800
F: (406) 444-4875
E: Sen.Nels.Swandal@mt.gov

Taylor, Janna (R, 6)
P.O. Box 200500
Helena, MT 59620
P: (406) 444-4800
F: (406) 444-4875
E: Sen.Janna.Taylor@mt.gov

Thomas, Fred (R, 44)
P.O. Box 200500
Helena, MT 59620
P: (406) 444-4800
F: (406) 444-4875
E: sfredthomas@yahoo.com

Tutvedt, Bruce (R, 3)
P.O. Box 200500
Helena, MT 59620
P: (406) 444-4800
F: (406) 444-4875
E: Tutvedt@montanasky.us

Vance, Gordon (R, 34)
P.O. Box 200500
Helena, MT 59620
P: (406) 444-4800
F: (406) 444-4875
E: vancesd34@gmail.com

Vincent, Chas V. (R, 1)
P.O. Box 200500
Helena, MT 59620
P: (406) 444-4800
F: (406) 444-4875
E: cvvincent@hotmail.com

Vuckovich, Gene (D, 39)
P.O. Box 200500
Helena, MT 59620
P: (406) 444-4800
F: (406) 444-4875
E: Sen.Gene.Vuckovich@mt.gov

Webb, Roger (R, 23)
P.O. Box 200500
Helena, MT 59620
P: (406) 444-4800
F: (406) 444-4875
E: webb4mt@hotmail.com

Whitford, Lea (D, 8)
P.O. Box 200500
Helena, MT 59620
P: (406) 444-4800
F: (406) 444-4875
E: Sen.Lea.Whitford@mt.gov

Windy Boy, Jonathan (D, 16)
P.O. Box 200500
Helena, MT 59620
P: (406) 444-4800
F: (406) 444-4875
E: SenatorJWB@gmail.com

Wolken, Cynthia (D, 48)*
P.O. Box 200500
Helena, MT 59620
P: (406) 444-4800
F: (406) 444-4875
E: Sen.Cynthia.Wolken
@mt.gov

House

Speaker of the House

Rep. Austin Knudsen (R)
Speaker of the House
P.O. Box 200400
Helena, MT 59620
P: (406) 444-4800
F: (406) 444-4825
E: austinforhouse@yahoo.com

Speaker Pro Tempore of the House

Rep. Lee Randall (R)
Speaker Pro Tempore
P.O. Box 200400
Helena, MT 59620
P: (406) 444-4800
F: (406) 444-4825
E: leerandall_2003
@hotmail.com

House Majority Leader

Rep. Keith Regier (R)
Majority Leader
P.O. Box 200400
Helena, MT 59620
P: (406) 444-4800
F: (406) 444-4825
E: Rep.Keith.Regier@mt.gov

House Minority Leader

Rep. Chuck Hunter (D)
Minority Leader
P.O. Box 200400
Helena, MT 59620
P: (406) 444-4800
F: (406) 444-4825
E: Rep.Chuck.Hunter@mt.gov

Clerk of the House

Ms. Lindsey Grovom
Chief Clerk of the House
Room 370, State Capitol
P.O. Box 200400
Helena, MT 59620
P: (406) 444-4819
F: (406) 444-4825
E: lgrovom@mt.gov

Members of the House

Ballance, Nancy (R, 87)
P.O. Box 200400
Helena, MT 59620
P: (406) 444-4800
F: (406) 444-4825
E: nancyballance@aol.com

Bennett, Bryce (D, 91)
P.O. Box 200400
Helena, MT 59620
P: (406) 444-4800
F: (406) 444-4825
E: bennettforhouse
@gmail.com

Bennett, Jerry A. (R, 1)
P.O. Box 200400
Helena, MT 59620
P: (406) 444-4800
F: (406) 444-4825
E: jbenhd1@hotmail.com

Berglee, Seth (R, 58)*
P.O. Box 200400
Helena, MT 59620
P: (406) 444-4800
F: (406) 444-4825
E: Rep.Seth.Berglee@mt.gov

Berry, Tom (R, 40)
P.O. Box 200400
Helena, MT 59620
P: (406) 444-4800
F: (406) 444-4825
E: tom@tomberrymt.com

Brodehl, Randy (R, 9)
P.O. Box 200400
Helena, MT 59620
P: (406) 444-4800
F: (406) 444-4825
E: randybrodehl57@gmail.com

Brown, Bob (R, 13)*
P.O. Box 200400
Helena, MT 59620
P: (406) 444-4800
F: (406) 444-4825
E: Rep.Bob.Brown@mt.gov

Brown, Zach D. (D, 63)*
P.O. Box 200400
Helena, MT 59620
P: (406) 444-4800
F: (406) 444-4825
E: brownformontana
@gmail.com

Burnett, Tom (R, 67)
P.O. Box 200400
Helena, MT 59620
P: (406) 444-4800
F: (406) 444-4825
E: burnetthd67@gmail.com

Clark, Christy (R, 17)
P.O. Box 200400
Helena, MT 59620
P: (406) 444-4800
F: (406) 444-4825
E: christy_clark@ymail.com

Cook, Rob (R, 18)
P.O. Box 200400
Helena, MT 59620
P: (406) 444-4800
F: (406) 444-4825
E: Rep.Rob.Cook@mt.gov

Court, Virginia (D, 50)
P.O. Box 200400
Helena, MT 59620
P: (406) 444-4800
F: (406) 444-4825
E: Rep.Virginia.Court
@mt.gov

Cuffe, Mike (R, 2)
P.O. Box 200400
Helena, MT 59620
P: (406) 444-4800
F: (406) 444-4825
E: Rep.Mike.Cuffe@mt.gov

Curdy, Willis (D, 98)*
P.O. Box 200400
Helena, MT 59620
P: (406) 444-4800
F: (406) 444-4825
E: Rep.Willis.Curdy@mt.gov

Custer, Geraldine (R, 39)*
P.O. Box 200400
Helena, MT 59620
P: (406) 444-4800
F: (406) 444-4825
E: Rep.Geraldine.Custer
@mt.gov

Doane, Alan (R, 36)
P.O. Box 200400
Helena, MT 59620
P: (406) 444-4800
F: (406) 444-4825
E: alandoane@midrivers.com

Dudik, Kimberly (D, 94)
P.O. Box 200400
Helena, MT 59620
P: (406) 444-4800
F: (406) 444-4825
E: kimberly.dudik@gmail.com

Dunwell, Mary Ann (D, 84)*
P.O. Box 200400
Helena, MT 59620
P: (406) 444-4800
F: (406) 444-4825
E: Rep.MaryAnn.Dunwell
@mt.gov

Eck, Jenny (D, 79)
P.O. Box 200400
Helena, MT 59620
P: (406) 444-4800
F: (406) 444-4825
E: jennyeck4mt@gmail.com

Ehli, Ron (R, 86)
P.O. Box 200400
Helena, MT 59620
P: (406) 444-4800
F: (406) 444-4825
E: Rep.Ron.Ehli@mt.gov

Ellis, Janet (D, 81)*
P.O. Box 200400
Helena, MT 59620
P: (406) 444-4800
F: (406) 444-4825
E: Rep.Janet.Ellis@mt.gov

Essmann, Jeff (R, 54)
P.O. Box 200400
Helena, MT 59620
P: (406) 444-4800
F: (406) 444-4825
E: jessmann@mt.gov

Fiscus, Clayton (R, 43)
P.O. Box 200400
Helena, MT 59620
P: (406) 444-4800
F: (406) 444-4825
E: clayton
@fiscusforthepeople.com

Fitzpatrick, Steve (R, 20)
P.O. Box 200400
Helena, MT 59620
P: (406) 444-4800
F: (406) 444-4825
E: Rep.Steve.Fitzpatrick
@mt.gov

Flynn, Kelly (R, 70)
P.O. Box 200400
Helena, MT 59620
P: (406) 444-4800
F: (406) 444-4825
E: Rep.Kelly.Flynn@mt.gov

Funk, Moffie (D, 82)*
P.O. Box 200400
Helena, MT 59620
P: (406) 444-4800
F: (406) 444-4825
E: Rep.Moffie.Funk@mt.gov

Garner, Frank (R, 7)*
P.O. Box 200400
Helena, MT 59620
P: (406) 444-4800
F: (406) 444-4825

Montana

Glimm, Carl (R, 6)
P.O. Box 200400
Helena, MT 59620
P: (406) 444-4800
F: (406) 444-4825
E: Rep.Carl.Glimm@mt.gov

Greef, Edward (R, 88)
P.O. Box 200400
Helena, MT 59620
P: (406) 444-4800
F: (406) 444-4825
E: edgreef@hotmail.com

Hagstrom, Dave (R, 52)
P.O. Box 200400
Helena, MT 59620
P: (406) 444-4800
F: (406) 444-4825
E: drhagstrom@reagan.com

Harris, Bill (R, 29)
P.O. Box 200400
Helena, MT 59620
P: (406) 444-4800
F: (406) 444-4825
E: harris@midrivers.com

Hayman, Denise (D, 66)*
P.O. Box 200400
Helena, MT 59620
P: (406) 444-4800
F: (406) 444-4825
E: Rep.Denise.Hayman@mt.gov

Hertz, Greg (R, 12)
P.O. Box 200400
Helena, MT 59620
P: (406) 444-4800
F: (406) 444-4825
E: greghertz11@gmail.com

Hess, Stephanie (R, 28)*
P.O. Box 200400
Helena, MT 59620
P: (406) 444-4800
F: (406) 444-4825
E: Stephhess28@gmail.com

Hill, Ellie Boldman (D, 90)
P.O. Box 200400
Helena, MT 59620
P: (406) 444-4800
F: (406) 444-4825
E: elliehillhd94@gmail.com

Hollandsworth, Roy (R, 27)
P.O. Box 200400
Helena, MT 59620
P: (406) 444-4800
F: (406) 444-4825
E: hgrain@3rivers.net

Holmlund, Kenneth (R, 38)*
P.O. Box 200400
Helena, MT 59620
P: (406) 444-4800
F: (406) 444-4825
E: Rep.Ken.Holmlund@mt.gov

Hunter, Chuck (D, 83)
P.O. Box 200400
Helena, MT 59620
P: (406) 444-4800
F: (406) 444-4825
E: Rep.Chuck.Hunter@mt.gov

Jacobson, Tom (D, 21)
P.O. Box 200400
Helena, MT 59620
P: (406) 444-4800
F: (406) 444-4825
E: tomjacobsonmt@gmail.com

Jones, Donald W. (R, 46)
P.O. Box 200400
Helena, MT 59620
P: (406) 444-4800
F: (406) 444-4825
E: donjonesmt@gmail.com

Karjala, Jessica (D, 48)*
P.O. Box 200400
Helena, MT 59620
P: (406) 444-4800
F: (406) 444-4825
E: Rep.Jessica.Karjala
@mt.gov

Kelker, Katharin A. (D, 47)*
P.O. Box 200400
Helena, MT 59620
P: (406) 444-4800
F: (406) 444-4825
E: Rep.Kathy.Kelker@mt.gov

Kipp III, George G. (D, 15)*
P.O. Box 200400
Helena, MT 59620
P: (406) 444-4800
F: (406) 444-4825
E: Rep.George.Kipp@mt.gov

Knudsen, Austin (R, 34)
P.O. Box 200400
Helena, MT 59620
P: (406) 444-4800
F: (406) 444-4825
E: austinforhouse@yahoo.com

Lamm, Debra (R, 60)*
P.O. Box 200400
Helena, MT 59620
P: (406) 444-4800
F: (406) 444-4825
E: Rep.Debra.Lamm@mt.gov

Lang, Mike (R, 33)
P.O. Box 200400
Helena, MT 59620
P: (406) 444-4800
F: (406) 444-4825
E: Rep.Mike.Lang@mt.gov

Laszloffy, Sarah (R, 53)
P.O. Box 200400
Helena, MT 59620
P: (406) 444-4800
F: (406) 444-4825
E: Rep.Sarah.Laszloffy
@mt.gov

Lavin, Steve (R, 8)
P.O. Box 200400
Helena, MT 59620
P: (406) 444-4800
F: (406) 444-4825
E: Rep.Steve.Lavin@mt.gov

Lieser, Ed (D, 5)
P.O. Box 200400
Helena, MT 59620
P: (406) 444-4800
F: (406) 444-4825
E: liesered@yahoo.com

Lynch, Ryan (D, 76)
P.O. Box 200400
Helena, MT 59620
P: (406) 444-4800
F: (406) 444-4825
E: Rep.Ryan.Lynch@mt.gov

MacDonald, Margie (D, 51)
P.O. Box 200400
Helena, MT 59620
P: (406) 444-4800
F: (406) 444-4825
E: Rep.Margie.MacDonald
@mt.gov

Mandeville, Forrest J. (R, 57)*
P.O. Box 200400
Helena, MT 59620
P: (406) 444-4800
F: (406) 444-4825
E: Rep.Forrest.Mandeville
@mt.gov

Manzella, Theresa (R, 85)*
P.O. Box 200400
Helena, MT 59620
P: (406) 444-4800
F: (406) 444-4825
E: Rep.Theresa.Manzella
@mt.gov

McCarthy, Kelly (D, 49)
P.O. Box 200400
Helena, MT 59620
P: (406) 444-4800
F: (406) 444-4825
E: kelly
@kellyformontana.org

McClafferty, Edie L. (D, 73)
P.O. Box 200400
Helena, MT 59620
P: (406) 444-4800
F: (406) 444-4825
E: ediemcclafferty
@gmail.com

McConnell, Nate (D, 89)*
P.O. Box 200400
Helena, MT 59620
P: (406) 444-4800
F: (406) 444-4825
E: Rep.Nate.McConnell
@mt.gov

McKamey, Wendy (R, 23)*
P.O. Box 200400
Helena, MT 59620
P: (406) 444-4800
F: (406) 444-4825
E: Rep.Wendy.McKamey@mt.go

Mehlhoff, Robert (D, 22)
P.O. Box 200400
Helena, MT 59620
P: (406) 444-4800
F: (406) 444-4825
E: rmehlhoff@yahoo.com

Meyers, Gilbert Bruce (R, 32)*
P.O. Box 200400
Helena, MT 59620
P: (406) 444-4800
F: (406) 444-4825
E: Rep.GBruce.Meyers@mt.gov

Miller, Mike (R, 80)
P.O. Box 200400
Helena, MT 59620
P: (406) 444-4800
F: (406) 444-4825
E: mike4hd84@blackfoot.net

Monforton, Matthew (R, 69)*
P.O. Box 200400
Helena, MT 59620
P: (406) 444-4800
F: (406) 444-4825
E: Rep.Matthew.Monforton
@mt.gov

Moore, David Doc (R, 92)
P.O. Box 200400
Helena, MT 59620
P: (406) 444-4800
F: (406) 444-4825
E: Rep.David.Moore@mt.gov

Mortensen, Dale (R, 44)*
P.O. Box 200400
Helena, MT 59620
P: (406) 444-4800
F: (406) 444-4825
E: Rep.Dale.Mortensen
@mt.gov

Noland, Mark R. (R, 10)*
P.O. Box 200400
Helena, MT 59620
P: (406) 444-4800
F: (406) 444-4825
E: marknolandhd10@gmail.com

Noonan, Pat (D, 74)
P.O. Box 200400
Helena, MT 59620
P: (406) 444-4800
F: (406) 444-4825
E: pnoonan73@yahoo.com

Olsen, Andrea (D, 100)*
P.O. Box 200400
Helena, MT 59620
P: (406) 444-4800
F: (406) 444-4825
E: Rep.Andrea.Olsen@mt.gov

Olszewski, Albert D. (R, 11)*
P.O. Box 200400
Helena, MT 59620
P: (406) 444-4800
F: (406) 444-4825
E: Rep.Albert.Olszewski@mt.gov

Osmundson, Ryan (R, 30)
P.O. Box 200400
Helena, MT 59620
P: (406) 444-4800
F: (406) 444-4825
E: ryanosmundson@gmail.com

Pease-Lopez, Carolyn (D, 42)
P.O. Box 200400
Helena, MT 59620
P: (406) 444-4800
F: (406) 444-4825
E: Rep.Carolyn.Pease-Lopez@mt.gov

Peppers, Patricia Rae (D, 41)
P.O. Box 200400
Helena, MT 59620
P: (406) 444-4800
F: (406) 444-4825
E: Rep.Rae.Peppers@mt.gov

Perry, Zac (D, 3)*
P.O. Box 200400
Helena, MT 59620
P: (406) 444-4800
F: (406) 444-4825
E: Rep.Zac.Perry@mt.gov

Person, Andrew (D, 96)
P.O. Box 200400
Helena, MT 59620
P: (406) 444-4800
F: (406) 444-4825
E: james.a.person@gmail.com

Pierson, Gordon (D, 78)
P.O. Box 200400
Helena, MT 59620
P: (406) 444-4800
F: (406) 444-4825
E: Rep.Gordon.Pierson@mt.gov

Pinocci, Randy (R, 19)*
P.O. Box 200400
Helena, MT 59620
P: (406) 444-4800
F: (406) 444-4825
E: Rep.Randall.Pinocci@mt.gov

Pope, Christopher (D, 65)*
P.O. Box 200400
Helena, MT 59620
P: (406) 444-4800
F: (406) 444-4825
E: Rep.Christopher.Pope@mt.gov

Price, Jean (D, 24)
P.O. Box 200400
Helena, MT 59620
P: (406) 444-4800
F: (406) 444-4825
E: jeanbigskybigwin@gmail.com

Randall, Lee (R, 37)
P.O. Box 200400
Helena, MT 59620
P: (406) 444-4800
F: (406) 444-4825
E: leerandall_2003@hotmail.com

Redfield, Alan (R, 59)
P.O. Box 200400
Helena, MT 59620
P: (406) 444-4800
F: (406) 444-4825
E: Rep.Alan.Redfield@mt.gov

Regier, Keith (R, 4)
P.O. Box 200400
Helena, MT 59620
P: (406) 444-4800
F: (406) 444-4825
E: Rep.Keith.Regier@mt.gov

Ricci, Vince (R, 55)*
P.O. Box 200400
Helena, MT 59620
P: (406) 444-4800
F: (406) 444-4825
E: Rep.Vince.Ricci@mt.gov

Richmond, Tom (R, 56)*
P.O. Box 200400
Helena, MT 59620
P: (406) 444-4800
F: (406) 444-4825
E: tomrichmondmt@gmail.com

Salomon, Daniel (R, 93)
P.O. Box 200400
Helena, MT 59620
P: (406) 444-4800
F: (406) 444-4825
E: dansalomon12@gmail.com

Schreiner, Casey (D, 25)
P.O. Box 200400
Helena, MT 59620
P: (406) 444-4800
F: (406) 444-4825
E: Rep.Casey.Schreiner@mt.gov

Schwaderer, Nicholas (R, 14)
P.O. Box 200400
Helena, MT 59620
P: (406) 444-4800
F: (406) 444-4825
E: nick.schwadererhd14@gmail.com

Shaw, Ray (R, 71)
P.O. Box 200400
Helena, MT 59620
P: (406) 444-4800
F: (406) 444-4825
E: Rep.Ray.Shaw@mt.gov

Smith, Bridget (D, 31)
P.O. Box 200400
Helena, MT 59620
P: (406) 444-4800
F: (406) 444-4825
E: repbsmith@gmail.com

Staffanson, Scott (R, 35)
P.O. Box 200400
Helena, MT 59620
P: (406) 444-4800
F: (406) 444-4825
E: scottstaffanson@gmail.com

Steenberg, Tom (D, 99)
P.O. Box 200400
Helena, MT 59620
P: (406) 444-4800
F: (406) 444-4825
E: mtsteenberg@bresnan.net

Swanson, Kathy (D, 77)
P.O. Box 200400
Helena, MT 59620
P: (406) 444-4800
F: (406) 444-4825
E: Rep.Kathy.Swanson@mt.gov

Tropila, Mitch (D, 26)
P.O. Box 200400
Helena, MT 59620
P: (406) 444-4800
F: (406) 444-4825
E: tropila@mt.net

Tschida, Brad (R, 97)*
P.O. Box 200400
Helena, MT 59620
P: (406) 444-4800
F: (406) 444-4825
E: Rep.Brad.Tschida@mt.gov

Wagoner, Kirk (R, 75)
P.O. Box 200400
Helena, MT 59620
P: (406) 444-4800
F: (406) 444-4825
E: kirk@kirkbwagoner.org

Webber, Susan A. (D, 16)*
P.O. Box 200400
Helena, MT 59620
P: (406) 444-4800
F: (406) 444-4825
E: Rep.Susan.Webber@mt.gov

Welborn, Jeffrey W. (R, 72)
P.O. Box 200400
Helena, MT 59620
P: (406) 444-4800
F: (406) 444-4825
E: jeffwelborn@hotmail.com

White, Kerry (R, 64)
P.O. Box 200400
Helena, MT 59620
P: (406) 444-4800
F: (406) 444-4825
E: winwithwhite@gmail.com

Williams, Kathleen (D, 61)
P.O. Box 200400
Helena, MT 59620
P: (406) 444-4800
F: (406) 444-4825
E: Rep.Kathleen.Williams@mt.gov

Wilson, Nancy (D, 95)
P.O. Box 200400
Helena, MT 59620
P: (406) 444-4800
F: (406) 444-4825
E: nwilsonhd95@gmail.com

Wittich, Art (R, 68)
P.O. Box 200400
Helena, MT 59620
P: (406) 444-4800
F: (406) 444-4825
E: Rep.Art.Wittich@mt.gov

Woods, Tom (D, 64)
P.O. Box 200400
Helena, MT 59620
P: (406) 444-4800
F: (406) 444-4825
E: tomwoods4mt@gmail.com

Montana

Zolnikov, Daniel (R, 45)
P.O. Box 200400
Helena, MT 59620
P: (406) 444-4800
F: (406) 444-4825
E: Rep.Daniel.Zolnikov
@mt.gov

Congress

Senate
Daines, Steve (R)
Tester, Jon (D)

House
Zinke, Ryan K. (R, At-Large)

Nebraska

Executive

Governor

Hon. Pete Ricketts (R)
Governor
P.O. Box 94848
Lincoln, NE 68509
P: (402) 471-2244
F: (402) 741-6031

Lieutenant Governor

Hon. Mike Foley (R)
Lieutenant Governor
State Capitol, Room 2315
P.O. Box 94863
Lincoln, NE 68509
P: (402) 471-2256
F: (402) 471-6031
E: mike.foley@nebraska.gov

Attorney General

Hon. Doug Peterson (R)
Attorney General
State Capitol
P.O. Box 98920
Lincoln, NE 68509
P: (402) 471-2682
F: (402) 471-3297

Auditor

Hon. Charlie Janssen (R)
Auditor of Public Accounts
State Capitol, Suite 2303
P.O. Box 98917
Lincoln, NE 68509
P: (402) 471-2111
F: (402) 471-3301
E: charlie.janssen@nebraska.gov

Secretary of State

Hon. John A. Gale (R)
Secretary of State
P.O. Box 94608
Lincoln, NE 68509
P: (402) 471-2554
F: (402) 471-3237
E: Sos.info@nebraska.gov

Treasurer

Hon. Don B. Stenberg (R)
State Treasurer
2005 State Capitol
P.O. Box 94788
Lincoln, NE 68509
P: (402) 471-2455
F: (402) 471-4390
E: Don.Stenberg@nebraska.gov

Judiciary

Supreme Court (MR)

Ms. Teresa Brown
Clerk
2413 State Capitol
P.O. Box 98910
Lincoln, NE 68509
P: (402) 471-3731
F: (402) 471-3480
E: terri.a.brown@nebraska.gov

Hon. Michael G. Heavican
Chief Justice
Hon. William B. Cassel
Hon. William Connolly
Hon. Michael McCormack
Hon. Lindsey Miller-Lerman
Hon. Kenneth C. Stephan
Hon. John F. Wright

Unicameral Legislature

Speaker of the Legislature

Speaker Galen Hadley (NP)
Speaker of the Legislature
State Capitol, Room 2103
P.O. Box 94604
Lincoln, NE 68509
P: (401) 471-2726
F: (402) 471-2126
E: ghadley@leg.ne.gov

Chairperson of the Executive Board

Sen. Bob Krist (NP)
Chair of the Executive Board
State Capitol, Room 2108
P.O. Box 94604
Lincoln, NE 68509
P: (402) 471-2718
F: (402) 471-2126
E: bkrist@leg.ne.gov

Clerk of the Legislature

Mr. Patrick J. O'Donnell
Clerk of the Legislature
State Capitol, Room 2018
P.O. Box 94604
Lincoln, NE 68509
P: (402) 471-2271
F: (402) 471-2126
E: podonnell@leg.ne.gov

Members of the Senate

Baker, Roy (NP, 30)*
Room 1522, State Capitol
P.O. Box 94604
Lincoln, NE 68509
P: (402) 471-2620
E: rbaker@leg.ne.gov

Bloomfield, Dave (NP, 17)
State Capitol, Room 1206
P.O. Box 94604
Lincoln, NE 68509
P: (402) 471-2716
F: (402) 471-2126
E: dbloomfield@lcg.ne.gov

Bolz, Kate (NP, 29)
State Capitol, Room 1120
P.O. Box 94604
Lincoln, NE 68509
P: (402) 471-2734
F: (402) 471-2126
E: kbolz@leg.ne.gov

Brasch, Lydia (NP, 16)
State Capitol, Room 1016
P.O. Box 94604
Lincoln, NE 68509
P: (402) 471-2728
F: (402) 471-2126
E: lbrasch@leg.ne.gov

Campbell, Kathy (NP, 25)
State Capitol, Room 1402
P.O. Box 94604
Lincoln, NE 68509
P: (402) 471-2731
F: (402) 471-2126
E: kcampbell@leg.ne.gov

Chambers, Ernie (NP, 11)
State Capitol, Room 1114
P.O. Box 94604
Lincoln, NE 68509
P: (402) 471-2612
F: (402) 471-2126
E: echambers@le.ne.gov

Coash, Colby (NP, 27)
State Capitol, Room 2028
P.O. Box 94604
Lincoln, NE 68509
P: (402) 471-2632
F: (402) 471-2126
E: ccoash@leg.ne.gov

Cook, Tanya (NP, 13)
State Capitol, Room 2011
P.O. Box 94604
Lincoln, NE 68509
P: (402) 471-2727
F: (402) 471-2126
E: tcook@leg.ne.gov

Craighead, Joni (NP, 6)*
Room 1529, State Capitol
P.O. Box 94604
Lincoln, NE 68509
P: (402) 471-2714
E: jcraighead@leg.ne.gov

Crawford, Sue (NP, 45)
State Capitol, Room 1021
P.O. Box 94604
Lincoln, NE 68509
P: (402) 471-2628
F: (402) 471-2126
E: scrawford@leg.ne.gov

Davis, Al (NP, 43)
State Capitol, Room 1117
P.O. Box 94604
Lincoln, NE 68509
P: (402) 471-2628
F: (402) 471-2126
E: adavis@leg.ne.gov

Ebke, Laura (NP, 32)*
Room 1101, State Capitol
P.O. Box 94604
Lincoln, NE 68509
P: (402) 471-2711
E: lebke@leg.ne.gov

Friesen, Curt (NP, 34)*
Room 1403, State Capitol
P.O. Box 94604
Lincoln, NE 68509
P: (402) 471-2630
E: cfriesen@leg.ne.gov

Garrett, Tommy L. (NP, 3)
State Capitol, Room 1208
P.O. Box 94604
Lincoln, NE 68509
P: (402) 471-2627
F: (402) 471-2126
E: tgarrett@leg.ne.gov

Gloor, Mike (NP, 35)
State Capitol, Room 1401
P.O. Box 94604
Lincoln, NE 68509
P: (402) 471-2617
F: (402) 471-2126
E: mgloor@leg.ne.gov

Groene, Michael (NP, 42)*
Room 1101, State Capitol
P.O. Box 94604
Lincoln, NE 68509
P: (402) 471-2729
E: mgroene@leg.ne.gov

Nebraska

Haar, Ken (NP, 21)
State Capitol, Room 1015
P.O. Box 94604
Lincoln, NE 68509
P: (402) 471-2673
F: (402) 471-2126
E: khaar@leg.ne.gov

Hadley, Galen (NP, 37)
State Capitol, Room 2103
P.O. Box 94604
Lincoln, NE 68509
P: (401) 471-2726
F: (402) 471-2126
E: ghadley@leg.ne.gov

Hansen, Matt (NP, 26)*
Room 1404, State Capitol
P.O. Box 94604
Lincoln, NE 68509
P: (402) 471-2610
E: mhansen@leg.ne.gov

Harr, Burke (NP, 8)
State Capitol, Room 2010
P.O. Box 94604
Lincoln, NE 68509
P: (402) 471-2722
F: (402) 471-2126
E: bharr@leg.ne.gov

Hilkemann, Robert (NP, 4)*
Room 1115, State Capitol
P.O. Box 94604
Lincoln, NE 68509
P: (402) 471-2621
E: rhilkemann@leg.ne.gov

Howard, Sara (NP, 9)
State Capitol, Room 1012
P.O. Box 94604
Lincoln, NE 68509
P: (402) 471-2723
F: (402) 471-2126
E: showard@leg.ne.gov

Hughes, Dan (NP, 44)*
Room 1117, State Capitol
P.O. Box 94604
Lincoln, NE 68509
P: (402) 471-2805
E: dhughes@leg.ne.gov

Johnson, Jerry (NP, 23)
State Capitol, Room 1022
P.O. Box 94604
Lincoln, NE 68509
P: (402) 471-2719
F: (402) 471-2126
E: jjohnson@leg.ne.gov

Kintner, Bill (NP, 2)
State Capitol, Room 1000
P.O. Box 94604
Lincoln, NE 68509
P: (402) 471-2613
F: (402) 471-2126
E: bkinter@leg.ne.gov

Kolowski, Rick (NP, 31)
State Capitol, Room 1018
P.O. Box 94604
Lincoln, NE 68509
P: (402) 471-2327
F: (402) 471-2126
E: rkolowski@leg.ne.gov

Kolterman, Mark (NP, 24)*
Room 1115, State Capitol
P.O. Box 94604
Lincoln, NE 68509
P: (402) 471-2756
E: mkolterman@leg.ne.gov

Krist, Bob (NP, 10)
State Capitol, Room 2108
P.O. Box 94604
Lincoln, NE 68509
P: (402) 471-2718
F: (402) 471-2126
E: bkrist@leg.ne.gov

Kuehn, John (NP, 38)*
Room 1117, State Capitol
P.O. Box 94604
Lincoln, NE 68509
P: (402) 471-2732
E: jkkuehn@leg.ne.gov

Larson, Tyson (NP, 40)
State Capitol, Room 1019
P.O. Box 94604
Lincoln, NE 68509
P: (402) 471-2801
F: (402) 471-2126
E: tlarson@leg.ne.gov

Lindstrom, Brett (NP, 18)*
Room 1202, State Capitol
P.O. Box 94604
Lincoln, NE 68509
P: (402) 471-2618
E: blindstrom@leg.ne.gov

McCollister, John (NP, 20)*
Room 1017, State Capitol
P.O. Box 94604
Lincoln, NE 68509
P: (402) 471-2622
E: jmccollister@leg.ne.gov

McCoy, Beau (NP, 39)
State Capitol, Room 2107
P.O. Box 94604
Lincoln, NE 68509
P: (401) 471-2885
F: (402) 471-2126
E: bmccoy@leg.ne.gov

Mello, Heath (NP, 5)
State Capitol, Room 1004
P.O. Box 94604
Lincoln, NE 68509
P: (402) 471-2710
F: (402) 471-2126
E: hmello@leg.ne.gov

Morfeld, Adam (NP, 46)*
Room 1008, State Capitol
P.O. Box 94604
Lincoln, NE 68509
P: (402) 471-2720
E: amorfeld@leg.ne.gov

Murante, John (NP, 49)
State Capitol, Room 1423
P.O. Box 94604
Lincoln, NE 68509
P: (402) 471-2725
F: (402) 471-2126
E: jmurante@leg.ne.gov

Nordquist, Jeremy J. (NP, 7)
State Capitol, Room 2004
P.O. Box 94604
Lincoln, NE 68509
P: (402) 471-2721
F: (402) 471-2126
E: jnordquist@leg.ne.gov

Pansing Brooks, Patty (NP, 28)*
Room 1523, State Capitol
P.O. Box 94604
Lincoln, NE 68509
P: (402) 471-2633
E: ppansingbrooks@leg.ne.gov

Riepe, Merv (NP, 12)*
Room 1528, State Capitol
P.O. Box 94604
Lincoln, NE 68509
P: (402) 471-2623
E: mriepe@leg.ne.gov

Scheer, Jim (NP, 19)
State Capitol, Room 1401
P.O. Box 94604
Lincoln, NE 68509
P: (402) 471-2929
F: (402) 471-2126
E: jscheer@leg.ne.gov

Schilz, Ken (NP, 47)
State Capitol, Room 1210
P.O. Box 94604
Lincoln, NE 68509
P: (402) 471-2616
F: (402) 471-2126
E: kschilz@leg.ne.gov

Schnoor, David*
Room 1118, State Capitol
P.O. Box 94604
Lincoln, NE 68509
P: (402) 471-2625
E: dschnoor@leg.ne.gov

Schumacher, Paul (NP, 22)
State Capitol, Room 1124
P.O. Box 94604
Lincoln, NE 68509
P: (402) 471-2715
F: (402) 471-2126
E: pschumacher@leg.ne.gov

Seiler, Les (NP, 33)
State Capitol, Room 1017
P.O. Box 94604
Lincoln, NE 68509
P: (402) 471-2712
F: (402) 471-2126
E: lseiler@leg.ne.gov

Smith, Jim (NP, 14)
State Capitol, Room 1110
P.O. Box 94604
Lincoln, NE 68509
P: (402) 471-2730
F: (402) 471-2126
E: jsmith@leg.ne.gov

Stinner Sr., John (NP, 48)*
Room 1406, State Capitol
P.O. Box 94604
Lincoln, NE 68509
P: (402) 471-2802
E: jstinner@leg.ne.gov

Sullivan, Kate (NP, 41)
State Capitol, Room 1107
P.O. Box 94604
Lincoln, NE 68509
P: (402) 471-2631
F: (402) 471-2126
E: ksullivan@leg.ne.gov

Watermeier, Dan (NP, 1)
State Capitol, Room 2000
P.O. Box 94604
Lincoln, NE 68509
P: (402) 471-2733
F: (402) 471-2126
E: dwatermeier@leg.ne.gov

Williams, Matt (NP, 36)*
Room 2015, State Capitol
P.O. Box 94604
Lincoln, NE 68509
P: (402) 471-2642
E: mwilliams@leg.ne.gov

Congress

Senate
Fischer, Deb (R)
Sasse, Ben (R)

House
Ashford, Brad (D, 2)
Fortenberry, Jeff (R, 1)
Smith, Adrian M. (R, 3)

Nevada

Executive

Governor

Hon. Brian Sandoval (R)
Governor
Capitol Building
Carson City, NV 89701
P: (775) 684-5670
F: (775) 684-5683

Lieutenant Governor

Hon. Mark Hutchison (R)
Lieutenant Governor
101 North Carson Street, Suite 2
Carson City, NV 89701
P: (775) 684-7111
F: (775) 684-7110

Attorney General

Hon. Adam Laxalt (R)
Attorney General
Old State Capitol Building
100 North Carson Street
Carson City, NV 89701
P: (775) 684-1100
F: (775) 684-1108
E: aginfo@ag.state.nv.us

Auditor

Hon. Paul V. Townsend
(appointed by the Legislature)
Legislative Auditor
Audit Division
401 South Carson Street
Carson City, NV 89701
P: (775) 684-6815
F: (775) 684-6435
E: townsend@lcb.state.nv.us

Controller

Hon. Ron Knecht (R)
State Controller
101 North Carson Street, Suite 5
Carson City, NV 89701
P: (775) 684-5632
F: (775) 684-5695

Secretary of State

Hon. Barbara Cegavske (R)
Secretary of State
101 North Carson Stree, Suite 3
Carson City, NV 89701
P: (775) 684-5708
F: (775) 684-5724
E: sosmail@sos.nv.gov

Treasurer

Hon. Dan Schwartz (R)
State Treasurer
101 North Carson Street, Suite 4
Carson City, NV 89701
P: (775) 684-5600
F: (775) 684-5781
E: statetreasurer
@nevadatreasurer.gov

Judiciary

Supreme Court (NE)

Ms. Tracie K. Lindeman
Chief Clerk
201 South Carson Street
Carson City, NV 89701
P: (775) 684-1600
F: (775) 684-1601
E: nvscclerk
@nvcourts.nv.gov

Hon. James W. Hardesty
Chief Justice
Hon. Michael A. Cherry
Hon. Michael L. Douglas
Hon. Mark Gibbons
Hon. Ron Parraguirre
Hon. Kristina Pickering
Hon. Nancy Saitta

Legislative Senate

Senate President

Hon. Mark Hutchison (R)
Lieutenant Governor
101 North Carson Street, Suite 2
Carson City, NV 89701
P: (775) 684-7111
F: (775) 684-7110

President Pro Tempore of the Senate

Sen. Joseph P. Hardy (R)
President Pro Tempore
Room 2132
401 South Carson Street
Carson City, NV 89701
P: (775) 684-1462
F: (775) 684-6522
E: Joe.Hardy
@sen.state.nv.us

Senate Majority Leader

Sen. Michael Roberson (R)
Majority Leader
Room 1222
401 South Carson Street
Carson City, NV 89701
P: (775) 684-1481
F: (775) 684-6522
E: Michael.Roberson
@sen.state.nv.us

Senate Minority Leader

Sen. Aaron D. Ford (D)
Minority Leader
Room 2160
401 South Carson Street
Carson City, NV 89701
P: (775) 684-6502
F: (775) 684-6522
E: Aaron.Ford
@sen.state.nv.us

Secretary of the Senate

Mr. David A. Byerman
Secretary of the Senate
401 South Carson Street
Carson City, NV 89701
P: (775) 684-1401
F: (775) 684-6522
E: David.Byerman
@sen.state.nv.us

Members of the Senate

Atkinson, Kelvin D. (D, 4)
Room 2158
401 South Carson Street
Carson City, NV 89701
P: (775) 684-1429
F: (775) 684-6522
E: Kelvin.Atkinson
@sen.state.nv.us

Brower, Greg (R, 15)
Room 2129
401 South Carson Street
Carson City, NV 89701
P: (775) 684-1419
F: (775) 684-6522
E: Greg.Brower
@sen.state.nv.us

Denis, Mo (D, 2)
Room 2104
401 South Carson Street
Carson City, NV 89701
P: (775) 684-1431
F: (775) 684-6522
E: Moises.Denis
@sen.state.nv.us

Farley, Patricia (R, 8)*
Room 2121
401 South Carson Street
Carson City, NV 89701
P: (775) 684-1445
F: (775) 684-6522
E: Patricia.Farley
@sen.state.nv.us

Ford, Aaron D. (D, 11)
Room 2160
401 South Carson Street
Carson City, NV 89701
P: (775) 684-6502
F: (775) 684-6522
E: Aaron.Ford
@sen.state.nv.us

Goicoechea, Pete (R, 19)
Room 2128
401 South Carson Street
Carson City, NV 89701
P: (775) 684-1447
F: (775) 684-6522
E: Pete.Goicoechea
@sen.state.nv.us

Gustavson, Donald G. (R, 14)
Room 2126
401 South Carson Street
Carson City, NV 89701
P: (775) 684-1480
F: (775) 684-6522
E: Don.Gustavson
@sen.state.nv.us

Hammond, Scott (R, 18)
Room 2124
401 South Carson Street
Carson City, NV 89701
P: (775) 684-1442
F: (775) 684-6522
E: Scott.Hammond
@sen.state.nv.us

Hardy, Joseph P. (R, 12)
Room 2132
401 South Carson Street
Carson City, NV 89701
P: (775) 684-1462
F: (775) 684-6522
E: Joe.Hardy
@sen.state.nv.us

Harris, Becky (R, 9)*
Room 2143
401 South Carson Street
Carson City, NV 89701
P: (775) 684-1421
F: (775) 684-6522
E: Becky.Harris
@sen.state.nv.us

Kieckhefer, Ben (R, 16)
Room 1224
401 South Carson Street
Carson City, NV 89701
P: (775) 684-1450
F: (775) 684-6522
E: Ben.Kieckhefer
@sen.state.nv.us

Kihuen, Ruben (D, 10)
Room 2107
401 South Carson Street
Carson City, NV 89701
P: (775) 684-1427
F: (775) 684-6522
E: Ruben.Kihuen
@sen.state.nv.us

Lipparelli, Mark A. (R, 6)*
Room 2127
401 South Carson Street
Carson City, NV 89701
P: (775) 684-1475
F: (775) 684-6522
E: Mark.Lipparelli
@sen.state.nv.us

Manendo, Mark A. (D, 21)
Room 2103
401 South Carson Street
Carson City, NV 89701
P: (775) 684-6503
F: (775) 684-6522
E: Mark.Manendo
@sen.state.nv.us

Parks, David R. (D, 7)
Room 2100
401 South Carson Street
Carson City, NV 89701
P: (775) 684-6504
F: 775) 684-6522
E: David.Parks
@sen.state.nv.us

Roberson, Michael (R, 20)
Room 1222
401 South Carson Street
Carson City, NV 89701
P: (775) 684-1481
F: (775) 684-6522
E: Michael.Roberson
@sen.state.nv.us

Segerblom, Tick (D, 3)
Room 2145
401 South Carson Street
Carson City, NV 89701
P: (775) 684-1422
F: (775) 684-6522
E: Tick.Segerblom
@sen.state.nv.us

Settelmeyer, James (R, 17)
Room 2125
401 South Carson Street
Carson City, NV 89701
P: (775) 684-1470
F: (775) 684-6522
E: James.Settelmeyer
@sen.state.nv.us

Smith, Debbie (D, 13)
Room 2160
401 South Carson Street
Carson City, NV 89701
P: (775) 684-1433
F: (775) 684-6522
E: Debbie.Smith
@sen.state.nv.us

Spearman, Pat (D, 1)
Room 2102
401 South Carson Street
Carson City, NV 89701
P: (775) 684-1424
F: (775) 684-6522
E: Pat.Spearman
@sen.state.nv.us

Woodhouse, Joyce (D, 5)
Room 2101
401 South Carson Street
Carson City, NV 89701
P: (775) 684-1457
F: (775) 684-6522
E: Joyce.Woodhouse
@sen.state.nv.us

Assembly

Speaker of the Assembly

Asmblymn. John Hambrick (R
Speaker of the Assembly
Room 1100
401 South Carson Street
Carson City, NV 89701
P: (775) 684-8827
F: (775) 684-8533
E: John.Hambrick
@asm.state.nv.us

Speaker Pro Tempore of the Assembly

Asmblymn. John Ellison (R)
Speaker Pro Tem
Room 4115
401 South Carson Street
Carson City, NV 89701
P: (775) 684-8831
F: (775) 684-8533
E: John.Ellison
@asm.state.nv.us

Assembly Majority Leader

Asmblymn. Paul Anderson (R)
Majority Floor Leader
Room 1102
401 South Carson Street
Carson City, NV 89701
P: (775) 684-8853
F: (775) 684-8533
E: Paul.Anderson
@asm.state.nv.us

Assembly Minority Leader

Asmblywmn. Marilyn Kirkpatrick (D)
Minority Floor Leader
Room 3105
401 South Carson Street
Carson City, NV 89701
P: (775) 684-8509
F: (775) 684-8533
E: Marilyn.Kirkpatrick
@asm.state.nv.us

Clerk of the Assembly

Ms. Susan Furlong
Chief Clerk of the Assembly
401 South Carson Street
Carson City, NV 89701
P: (775) 684-8555
E: Susan.Furlong
@asm.state.nv.us

Members of the Assembly

Anderson, Elliot T. (D, 15)
Room 4110
401 South Carson Street
Carson City, NV 89701
P: (775) 684-8835
F: (775) 684-8533
E: Elliot.Anderson
@asm.state.nv.us

Anderson, Paul (R, 13)
Room 1102
401 South Carson Street
Carson City, NV 89701
P: (775) 684-8853
F: (775) 684-8533
E: Paul.Anderson
@asm.state.nv.us

Araujo, Nelson (D, 3)*
Room 3129
401 South Carson Street
Carson City, NV 89701
P: (775) 684-8599
F: (775) 684-8533
E: Nelson.Araujo
@asm.state.nv.us

Armstrong, Derek W. (R, 21)*
Room 4109
401 South Carson Street
Carson City, NV 89701
P: (775) 684-8839
F: (775) 684-8533
E: Derek.Armstrong
@asm.state.nv.us

Benitez-Thompson, Teresa (D, 27)
Room 3105
401 South Carson Street
Carson City, NV 89701
P: (775) 684-8845
F: (775) 684-8533
E: Teresa.BenitezThompson
@asm.state.nv.us

Bustamante Adams, Irene (D, 42)
Room 3156
401 South Carson Street
Carson City, NV 89701
P: (775) 684-8803
F: (775) 684-8533
E: Irene.BustamanteAdams
@asm.state.nv.us

Carlton, Maggie (D, 14)
Room 3105
401 South Carson Street
Carson City, NV 89701
P: (775) 684-8597
F: (775) 684-8533
E: Maggie.Carlton
@asm.state.nv.us

Carrillo, Richard (D, 18)
Room 3130
401 South Carson Street
Carson City, NV 89701
P: (775) 684-8801
F: (775) 684-8533
E: Richard.Carrillo
@asm.state.nv.us

Diaz, Olivia (D, 11)
Room 4122
401 South Carson Street
Carson City, NV 89701
P: (775) 684-8553
F: (775) 684-8533
E: Olivia.Diaz
@asm.state.nv.us

Nevada

Dickman, Jill (R, 31)*
Room 4123
401 South Carson Street
Carson City, NV 89701
P: (775) 684-8563
F: (775) 684-8533
E: Jill.Dickman
@asm.state.nv.us

Dooling, Vicki (R, 41)*
Room 3160
401 South Carson Street
Carson City, NV 89701
P: (775) 684-8821
F: (775) 684-8533
E: Vicki.Dooling
@asm.state.nv.us

Edwards, Chris (R, 19)*
Room 4111
401 South Carson Street
Carson City, NV 89701
P: (775) 684-8857
F: (775) 684-8533
E: Chris.Edwards
@asm.state.nv.us

Ellison, John (R, 33)
Room 4115
401 South Carson Street
Carson City, NV 89701
P: (775) 684-8831
F: (775) 684-8533
E: John.Ellison
@asm.state.nv.us

Fiore, Michele (R, 4)
Room 4112
401 South Carson Street
Carson City, NV 89701
P: (775) 684-8829
F: (775) 684-8533
E: michele.fiore
@asm.state.nv.us

Flores, Edgar R. (D, 28)*
Room 3124
401 South Carson Street
Carson City, NV 89701
P: (775) 684-8583
F: (775) 684-8533
E: Edgar.Flores
@asm.state.nv.us

Gardner, David M. (R, 9)*
Room 4121
401 South Carson Street
Carson City, NV 89701
P: (775) 684-8549
F: (775) 684-8533
E: David.Gardner
@asm.state.nv.us

Hambrick, John (R, 2)
Room 1100
401 South Carson Street
Carson City, NV 89701
P: (775) 684-8827
F: (775) 684-8533
E: John.Hambrick
@asm.state.nv.us

Hansen, Ira (R, 32)
Room 3127
401 South Carson Street
Carson City, NV 89701
P: (775) 684-8851
F: (775) 684-8533
E: Ira.Hansen
@asm.state.nv.us

Hickey, Pat (R, 25)
Room 3133
401 South Carson Street
Carson City, NV 89701
P: (775) 684-8837
F: (775) 684-8533
E: Pat.Hickey
@asm.state.nv.us

Joiner, Amber J. (D, 24)*
Room 3131
401 South Carson Street
Carson City, NV 89701
P: (775) 684-8559
F: (775) 684-8533
E: Amber.Joiner
@asm.state.nv.us

Jones, Brent A. (R, 35)*
Room 4107
401 South Carson Street
Carson City, NV 89701
P: (775) 684-8573
F: (775) 684-8533
E: Brent.Jones
@asm.state.nv.us

Kirkpatrick, Marilyn (D, 1)
Room 3105
401 South Carson Street
Carson City, NV 89701
P: (775) 684-8509
F: (775) 684-8533
E: Marilyn.Kirkpatrick
@asm.state.nv.us

Kirner, Randy (R, 26)
Room 4108
401 South Carson Street
Carson City, NV 89701
P: (775) 684-8848
F: (775) 684-8533
E: Randy.Kirner
@asm.state.nv.us

Moore, John (R, 8)*
Room 4113
401 South Carson Street
Carson City, NV 89701
P: (775) 684-8537
F: (775) 684-8533
E: John.Moore
@asm.state.nv.us

Munford, Harvey J. (D, 6)
Room 3140
401 South Carson Street
Carson City, NV 89701
P: (775) 684-8545
F: (775) 684-8533
E: Harvey.Munford
@asm.state.nv.us

Neal, Dina (D, 7)
Room 4102
401 South Carson Street
Carson City, NV 89701
P: (775) 684-8587
F: (775) 684-8533
E: Dina.Neal
@asm.state.nv.us

Nelson, Erv (R, 5)*
Room 4117
401 South Carson Street
Carson City, NV 89701
P: (775) 684-8833
F: (775) 684-8533
E: Erven.Nelson
@asm.state.nv.us

Ohrenschall, James (D, 12)
Room 4103
401 South Carson Street
Carson City, NV 89701
P: (775) 684-8819
F: (775) 684-8533
E: James.Ohrenschall
@asm.state.nv.us

O'Neill, Philip (R, 40)*
Room 3116
401 South Carson Street
Carson City, NV 89701
P: (775) 684-8825
F: (775) 684-8533
E: PK.Oneill
@asm.state.nv.us

Oscarson, James (R, 36)
Room 3132
401 South Carson Street
Carson City, NV 89701
P: (775) 684-8805
F: (775) 684-8533
E: James.Oscarson
@asm.state.nv.us

Seaman, Victoria (R, 34)*
Room 3123
401 South Carson Street
Carson City, NV 89701
P: (775) 684-8847
F: (775) 684-8533
E: Victoria.Seaman
@asm.state.nv.us

Shelton, Shelly M. (R, 10)*
Room 4118
401 South Carson Street
Carson City, NV 89701
P: (775) 684-8541
F: (775) 684-8533
E: Shelly.Shelton
@asm.state.nv.us

Silberkraus, Stephen (R, 29)*
Room 3153
401 South Carson Street
Carson City, NV 89701
P: (775) 684-8855
F: (775) 684-8533
E: Stephen.Silberkraus
@asm.state.nv.us

Spiegel, Ellen B. (D, 20)
Room 3134
401 South Carson Street
Carson City, NV 89701
P: (775) 684-8577
F: (775) 684-8533
E: Ellen.Spiegel
@asm.state.nv.us

Sprinkle, Michael (D, 30)
Room 3125
401 South Carson Street
Carson City, NV 89701
P: (775) 684-8841
F: (775) 684-8533
E: Mike.Sprinkle
@asm.state.nv.us

Stewart, Lynn D. (R, 22)
Room 3128
401 South Carson Street
Carson City, NV 89701
P: (775) 684-8823
F: (775) 684-8533
E: Lynn.Stewart
@asm.state.nv.us

Swank, Heidi (D, 16)
Room 4105
401 South Carson Street
Carson City, NV 89701
P: (775) 684-8595
F: (775) 684-8533
E: Heidi.Swank
@asm.state.nv.us

Thompson, Tyrone (D, 17)
Room 3159
401 South Carson Street
Carson City, NV 89701
P: (775) 684-8569
E: Tyrone.Thompson
@asm.state.nv.us

Titus, Robin I. (R, 38)*
Room 3158
401 South Carson Street
Carson City, NV 89701
P: (775) 684-8507
F: (775) 684-8533
E: Robin.Titus
@asm.state.nv.us

Trowbridge, Glenn E. (R, 37)*
Room 4104
401 South Carson Street
Carson City, NV 89701
P: (775) 684-8505
F: (775) 684-8533
E: Glenn.Trowbridge
@asm.state.nv.us

Wheeler, Jim (R, 39)
Room 3119
401 South Carson Street
Carson City, NV 89701
P: (775) 684-8843
F: (775) 684-8533
E: Jim.Wheeler
@asm.state.nv.us

Woodbury, Melissa (R, 23)
Room 4114
401 South Carson Street
Carson City, NV 89701
P: (775) 684-8503
F: (775) 684-8533
E: Melissa.Woodbury
@asm.state.nv.us

Congress

Senate

Heller, Dean (R)
Reid, Harry (D)

House

Amodei, Mark E. (R, 2)
Heck, Joe (R, 3)
Titus, Dina (D, 1)

New Hampshire

Executive

Governor

Hon. Maggie Hassan (D)
Governor
107 North Main Street, Room 208
Concord, NH 03301
P: (603) 271-2121
F: (603) 271-7640

Lieutenant Governor

This state does not have the office of lieutenant governor. The president (or speaker) of the Senate is next in line of succession to the governorship.

Attorney General

Hon. Joseph Foster
(appointed)
Attorney General
33 Capitol Street
Concord, NH 03301
P: (603) 271-3658
F: (603) 271-2110
E: attorneygeneral@doj.nh.gov

Auditor

Mr. Jeffry A. Pattison
(appointed by the Legislature)
Legislative Budget Assistant
State House, Room 102
107 North Main Street
Concord, NH 03301
P: (603) 271-3161
F: (603) 271-1097
E: jeff.pattison@leg.state.nh.us

Secretary of State

Hon. William M. Gardner
(elected by the Legislature)
Secretary of State
State House, Room 204
Concord, NH 03301
P: (603) 271-3242
F: (603) 271-6316
E: kladd@sos.state.nh.us

Treasurer

Hon. Catherine Provencher
(elected by the Legislature)
State Treasurer
25 Capitol Street, Room 121
Concord, NH 03301
P: (603) 271-2621
F: (603) 271-3922
E: cprovencher@treasury.state.nh.us

Judiciary

Supreme Court (GA)

Ms. Eileen Fox
Clerk of Court
Supreme Court Building
One Charles Doe Drive
Concord, NH 03301
P: (603) 271-2646
F: (603) 271-6630

Hon. Linda S. Dalianis
Chief Justice
Hon. James P. Bassett
Hon. Carol Ann Conboy
Hon. Gary E. Hicks
Hon. Robert J. Lynn

Legislative Senate

Senate President

Sen. Chuck Morse (R)
Senate President
State House, Room 302
107 North Main Street
Concord, NH 03301
P: (603) 271-8472
E: chuck.morse@leg.state.nh.us

President Pro Tempore of the Senate

Sen. Sharon M. Carson (R)
President Pro Tempore
State House, Room 106
107 North Main Street
Concord, NH 03301
P: (603) 271-1403
E: sharon.carson@leg.state.nh.us

Senate Majority Leader

Sen. Jeb E. Bradley (R)
Majority Leader
State House, Room 302
107 North Main Street
Concord, NH 03301
P: (603) 271-2106
E: jeb.bradley@leg.state.nh.us

Secretary of the Senate

Ms. Tammy L. Wright
Clerk of the Senate
Senate Chamber
107 North Main Street
Concord, NH 03301
P: (603) 271-3420
F: (603) 271-2545
E: tammy.wright@leg.state.nh.us

Members of the Senate

Avard, Kevin A (R, 12)
State House, Room 105-A
107 North Main Street
Concord, NH 03301
P: (603) 271-4151
F: (603) 521-7657
E: kevin.avard@leg.state.nh.us

Birdsell, Regina M. (R, 19)
State House, Room 105-A
107 North Main Street
Concord, NH 03301
P: (603) 271-4151
E: regina.birdsell@leg.state.nh.us

Boutin, David R. (R, 16)
Legislative Office Building, Room 102-A
33 North State Street
Concord, NH 03301
P: (603) 271-3092
E: dboutin1465@comcast.net

Bradley, Jeb E. (R, 3)
State House, Room 302
107 North Main Street
Concord, NH 03301
P: (603) 271-2106
E: jeb.bradley@leg.state.nh.us

Carson, Sharon M. (R, 14)
State House, Room 106
107 North Main Street
Concord, NH 03301
P: (603) 271-1403
E: sharon.carson@leg.state.nh.us

Cataldo, Sam A. (R, 6)
State House, Room 107
107 North Main Street
Concord, NH 03301
P: (603) 271-4063
E: sam.cataldo@leg.state.nh.us

Clark, Martha Fuller (D, 21)
State House, Room 115
107 North Main Street
Concord, NH 03301
P: (603) 271-3076
E: martha.fullerclark@leg.state.nh.us

D'Allesandro, Lou (D, 20)
State House, Room 117
107 North Main Street
Concord, NH 03301
P: (603) 271-2117
E: dalas@leg.state.nh.us

Daniels, Gary L. (R, 11)
State House, Room 302
107 North Main Street
Concord, NH 03301
P: (603) 271-2609
E: Gary.Daniels@leg.state.nh.us

Feltes, Dan (D, 15)*
Legislative Office Building, Room 5
33 North State Street
Concord, NH 03301
P: (603) 271-3067
E: Dan.Feltes@leg.state.nh.us

Forrester, Jeanie (R, 2)
State House, Room 105
107 North Main Street
Concord, NH 03301
P: (603) 271-4980
E: jeanie.forrester@leg.state.nh.us

Hosmer, Andrew J. (D, 7)
Legislative Office Building, Room 101-A
33 North State Street
Concord, NH 03301
P: (603) 271-8631
E: andrew.hosmer@leg.state.nh.us

Kelly, Molly (D, 10)
State House, Room 120
107 North Main Street
Concord, NH 03301
P: (603) 271-3207
E: molly.kelly@leg.state.nh.us

Lasky, Bette R. (D, 13)
State House, Room 124
107 North Main Street
Concord, NH 03301
P: (603) 271-3091
E: Bette.Lasky
@leg.state.nh.us

Little, Jerry (R, 8)*
State House, Room 105-A
107 North Main Street
Concord, NH 03301
P: (603) 271-4151
E: Jerry.Little
@leg.state.nh.us

Morse, Chuck (R, 22)
State House, Room 302
107 North Main Street
Concord, NH 03301
P: (603) 271-8472
E: chuck.morse
@leg.state.nh.us

Pierce, David M. (D, 5)
Legislative Office Building,
Room 5
33 North State Street
Concord, NH 03301
P: (603) 271-3067
E: david.pierce
@leg.state.nh.us

Prescott, Russell (R, 23)
State House, Room 302
107 North Main Street
Concord, NH 03301
P: (603) 271-3074
E: represcott
@represcott.com

Reagan, John (R, 17)
State House, Room 107
107 North Main Street
Concord, NH 03301
P: (603) 271-4063
E: john.reagan111@gmail.com

Sanborn, Andy (R, 9)
State House, Room 302
107 North Main Street
Concord, NH 03301
P: (603) 271-2609
E: andy.sanborn
@leg.state.nh.us

Soucy, Donna M. (D, 18)
State House, Room 120
107 North Main Street
Concord, NH 03301
P: (603) 271-3207
E: donna.soucy
@leg.state.nh.us

Stiles, Nancy F. (R, 24)
State House, Room 103-A
33 North State Street
Concord, NH 03301
P: (603) 271-3093
E: nancy.stiles
@leg.state.nh.us

Watters, David H. (D, 4)
Legislative Office Building,
Room 101-A
33 North State Street
Concord, NH 03301
P: (603) 271-8631
E: david.watters
@leg.state.nh.us

Woodburn, Jeff (D, 1)
State House, Room 120
107 North Main Street
Concord, NH 03301
P: (603) 271-3207
E: Jeff.Woodburn
@leg.state.nh.us

House

Speaker of the House

Rep. Shawn N. Jasper (R)
Speaker of the House
83 Old Derry Road
Hudson, NH 03051
P: (603) 595-9621
F: (603) 882-2056
E: shawn.jasper
@leg.state.nh.us

Deputy Speaker of the House

Rep. Naida L. Kaen (D)
Deputy Speaker
22 Toon Lane
Lee, NH 03861
P: (603) 659-2205
E: naidakaen@gmail.com

House Majority Leader

Rep. Stephen J. Shurtleff (D)
Majority Leader
11 Vinton Drive
Penacook, NH 03303
P: (603) 753-4563
E: steve.shurtleff
@leg.state.nh.us

House Minority Leader

Rep. Gene G. Chandler (R)
Minority Leader
P.O. Box 296
Bartlett, NH 03812
P: (603) 374-6603
E: gene.chandler
@leg.state.nh.us

Clerk of the House

Ms. Karen O. Wadsworth
Clerk of the House
State House, Room 317
107 North Main Street
Concord, NH 03301
P: (603) 271-2548
F: (603) 271-3309
E: karen.wadsworth
@leg.state.nh.us

Members of the House

Abbott, Michael D. (D, SP18)*
P.O. Box 174
Hinsdale, NH 03451
P: (603) 336-7090
E: Michael.Abbott
@leg.state.nh.us

Abel, Richard (D, SP53)*
112 Bank Street
Lebanon, NH 03766
P: (603) 448-5831
E: Richard.Abel
@leg.state.nh.us

Abrami, Patrick F. (R, SP150)
9 Tall Pines Drive
Stratham, NH 03885
P: (603) 772-3489
F: (781) 272-5666
E: patrick.abrami
@leg.state.nh.us

Abramson, Max (R, SP151)*
14 Charles Henry Way
Seabrook, NH 03874
P: (603) 760-7090

Adams, Christopher R. (R, SP83)*
10 Sargent Road
Brookline, NH 03033
P: (603) 673-3212
E: cradams13@charter.net

Aldrich, Glen (R, SP2)*
343 Old Lakeshore Road, Lot 43
Gilford, NH 03249
P: (603) 527-8726
E: glenaldrich@gmail.com

Alicea, Caroletta C. (D, SP110)
4 Stirrup Iron Road
Boscawen, NH 03303
P: (603) 796-6119
E: caroletta.alicea
@leg.state.nh.us

Allen, Mary M. (R, SP146)
39 Pond Street
Newton, NH 03858
P: (603) 382-5665

Almy, Susan W. (D, SP53)
266 Poverty Lane, Unit 4B
Lebanon, NH 03766
P: (603) 448-4769
E: susan.almy@comcast.net

Ames, Richard (D, SP26)
12 Blackberry Lane
Jaffrey, NH 03452
P: (603) 532-6781
E: Richard.Ames
@leg.state.nh.us

Ammon, Keith (R, SP97)*
P.O. Box 38
New Boston, NH 03070
P: (603) 296-9879
E: Keith.Ammon
@leg.state.nh.us

Avellani, Lino (R, SP14)*
P.O. Box 516
Sanbornville, NH 03872
P: (603) 858-5196
E: lino.avellani
@leg.state.nh.us

Azarian, Gary S. (R, SP139)
34 Tickle Fancy Lane
Salem, NH 03079
P: (603) 890-8669
E: gazarian@comcast.net

Baber, William S. (D, SP182)
5 Gerry's Lane
Dover, NH 03820
P: (603) 749-5969
E: bill.baber
@leg.state.nh.us

Backus, Robert A. (D, SP76)
1318 Goffstown Drive
Manchester, NH 03102
P: (603) 232-0525
E: robert.backus
@leg.state.nh.us

New Hampshire

Bailey, Brad (R, SP54)
101 Smutty Hollow Road
Monroe, NH 03771
P: (603) 638-2118
E: brad.bailey
@leg.state.nh.us

Balcom, John L. (R, SP78)
85 Pond View Drive
Merrimack, NH 03054
P: (603) 424-8422
F: (603) 424-7854
E: john.balcom
@leg.state.nh.us

Baldasaro, Alfred P. (R, SP136)
41 Hall Road
Londonderry, NH 03053
P: (603) 425-6997
E: al.baldasaro
@leg.state.nh.us

Barnes III, Arthur E. (R, SP139)*
174 Pelham Road
Salem, NH 03079
P: (893) 475-4754
E: arthur.barnes
@leg.state.nh.us

Baroody, Benjamin C. (D, SP100)
1175 Bridge Street
Manchester, NH 03104
P: (603) 627-1122
F: (603) 218-6780
E: ben.baroody
@leg.state.nh.us

Barry, Richard W. (R, SP78)
12 Kyle Road
Merrimack, NH 03054
P: (603) 880-3731
F: (603) 880-0582
E: richardbarry
@leg.state.nh.us

Bartlett, Christy D. (D, SP121)
77 Sanborn Road
Concord, NH 03301
P: (603) 224-3172
E: christydbartlett
@gmail.com

Bates, David (R, SP138)
12 Range Road
Windham, NH 03087
P: (603) 894-6987
E: rep.bates@live.com

Beaudoin, Steven P. (R, SP177)
24 Hemlock Street
Rochester, NH 03867
P: (603) 332-9458
E: steven.beaudoin
@leg.state.nh.us

Beaulieu, Jane E. (D, SP102)
609 South Main Street
Manchester, NH 03102
P: (603) 626-1260
E: jane.beaulieu
@leg.state.nh.us

Belanger, James P. (R, SP84)
32 Plain Road
Hollis, NH 03049
P: (603) 465-2301
E: jim.belanger
@leg.state.nh.us

Belanger, Ronald J. (R, SP139)
8 Braemoor Woods Road
Apartment 201
Salem, NH 03079
P: (603) 893-0659
E: ron.belanger
@leg.state.nh.us

Bennett, Travis (D, SP48)*
4C Pleasant Street
Plymouth, NH 03264
P: (603) 686-0625
E: travisrbennett1
@gmail.com

Berch, Paul S. (D, SP18)
956 River Road
Westmoreland, NH 03467
P: (603) 399-4960
E: pberch@myfairpoint.net

Berrien, Skip (D, SP149)*
7 Coach Road
Exeter, NH 03833
E: skip.berrien
@leg.state.nh.us

Berube, Roger R. (D, SP186)
15 Stackpole Road
Somersworth, NH 03878
P: (603) 692-5653
E: rogerrberube@hotmail.com

Bickford, David A. (R, SP171)
183 Brackett Road
New Durham, NH 03855
P: (603) 859-7899
E: davidabickford51
@yahoo.com

Biggie, Barbara (R, SP80)*
P.O. Box 962
Milford, NH 03055
P: (603) 930-5600
E: barbara.biggie
@leg.state.nh.us

Bixby, Peter W. (D, SP185)
69 Glenwood Avenue
Dover, NH 03820
P: (603) 749-5659
E: peter.bixby
@leg.state.nh.us

Boehm, Ralph G. (R, SP77)
6 Gibson Drive
Litchfield, NH 03052
P: (603) 860-6309
E: ralph.boehm
@leg.state.nh.us

Booras, Efstathia C. (D, SP90)
44 Balcom Street
Nashua, NH 03060
P: (603) 886-5886
E: efstathia.booras
@leg.state.nh.us

Borden, David A. (D, SP155)
P.O. Box 167
New Castle, NH 03854
P: (603) 436-4132
E: david@davidbordennh.com

Bordenet, John (D, SP22)*
22 Woodbury Street
Keene, NH 03431
P: (603) 352-0680
E: John.Bordenet
@leg.state.nh.us

Bouldin, Amanda (D, SP69)*
412 Central Street, Floor 2
Manchester, NH 03103
E: Amanda.Bouldin
@leg.state.nh.us

Bradley, Paula E. (D, SP120)
33 Christian Avenue, #43
Concord, NH 03301
P: (603) 466-2574
F: (603) 466-5883
E: Paula.Bradley
@leg.state.nh.us

Brewster, Michael (R, SP123)*
P.O. Box 94
Barnstead, NH 03218
P: (603) 491-5927

Bridge, Ernest H. (R, SP199)*
392 Lear Hill Road
Unity, NH 03773
P: (603) 863-7203
E: YankeeErnie@gmail.com

Brown, Chris (D, SP52)*
5 Mink Drive
Hanover, NH 03755
P: (603) 643-2032
E: Chris.Brown
@leg.state.nh.us

Brown, Duane R. (R, SP56)*
1199 Mt. Moosilauke Highway
Wentworth, NH 03283
P: (603) 764-5902
E: duane.brown
@leg.state.nh.us

Brown, Pamela (D, SP88)
2 Clocktower Place, Apartment 434
Nashua, NH 03060
P: (603) 930-6999
E: pam.brown
@leg.state.nh.us

Brown, Rebecca A. (D, SP42)
80 Post Road
Sugar Hill, NH 03586
P: (603) 823-8119
E: rebecca.brown
@leg.state.nh.us

Buco, Thomas L. (D, SP11)
P.O. Box 3149
Conway, NH 03818
P: (603) 986-5629
E: tom.buco@leg.state.nh.us

Burt, John A. (R, SP96)
7 Bay Street
Goffstown, NH 03045
P: (603) 624-5084
F: (603) 641-1135
E: john.burt
@leg.state.nh.us

Burton, Wayne M. (D, SP174)*
106 Madbury Road
Durham, NH 03824
P: (603) 868-5037
E: Wayne.Burton
@leg.state.nh.us

Bush, Carol (R, SP162)*
40 Hannah Lane
Newington, NH 03801
P: (603) 436-3980
E: carol.bush
@leg.state.nh.us

Butler, Edward A. (D, SP16)
2 Morey Road
Harts Location, NH 03812
P: (603) 374-6131
F: (603) 374-6168
E: Edward.Butler
@leg.state.nh.us

Byron, Frank A. (R, SP77)
8 Mallard Court
Litchfield, NH 03052
P: (603) 889-7424
E: frank.byron
@leg.state.nh.us

Cahill, Michael D. (D, SP148)
328 Ash Swamp Road
Newmarket, NH 03857
P: (603) 659-2355
E: michael.cahill
@leg.state.nh.us

Cali-Pitts, Jacqueline A. (D, SP161)
40 Bedford Way, Apartment 112
Portsmouth, NH 03801
P: (603) 431-7657
E: cali0917@aol.com

Cardon, G. Thomas (R, SP137)*
2 Cunningham Drive
Derry, NH 03038
P: (607) 437-4847
E: thomas.cardon
@leg.state.nh.us

Carson, Clyde J. (D, SP109)
33 Kearsarge Mountain Road
Warner, NH 03278
P: (603) 456-2562
E: clyde.carson
@leg.state.nh.us

Chandler, Gene G. (R, SP10)
P.O. Box 296
Bartlett, NH 03812
P: (603) 374-6603
E: gene.chandler
@leg.state.nh.us

Chase, Cynthia (D, SP25)
110 Arch Street, #38
Keene, NH 03431
P: (603) 357-2381
E: cyndychase25@gmail.com

Chase, Francis (R, SP151)*
14 Lighthouse Way
Seabrook, NH 03874
P: (603) 944-0830
E: CHD5100@outlook.com

Cheney, Catherine (R, SP185)*
9 Snows Court
Dover, NH 03820
P: (603) 740-4697
E: catherine.cheney
@leg.state.nh.us

Chirichiello, Brian (R, SP137)
6 Rollins Street
Derry, NH 03038
P: (603) 432-0799
E: brian.chirichiello
@verani.com

Christensen, Chris (R, SP78)*
27 Greatstone Drive
Merrimack, NH 03054
P: (603) 424-2542
E: c.christensen
@leg.state.nh.us

Christiansen, Lars T. (R, SP94)
1 Stone Wood Lane
Hudson, NH 03051
P: (603) 889-0481
E: lars@taybre.net

Christie Jr., Andrew (R, SP168)*
185 Kensington Road
Hampton Falls, NH 03844
P: (603) 926-7106
E: andrew.christie
@leg.state.nh.us

Christie, Rick (R, SP63)*
149 Moose Club Park Road
Goffstown, NH 03045
P: (603) 626-5743
E: rickchristie2014
@gmail.com

Cilley, Jacalyn L. (D, SP172)
2 Oak Hill Road
Barrington, NH 03825
P: (603) 664-5597
E: jcilley@aol.com

Cloutier, John R. (D, SP203)
10 Spruce Avenue, Apartment #1
Claremont, NH 03743
P: (603) 542-6290
E: jocloutier@comcast.net

Coffey, James (R, SP82)
63 Wilson Hill Road
New Ipswich, NH 03071
P: (603) 878-4858
E: james.coffey
@leg.state.nh.us

Cohen, Alan (D, SP87)*
4 Monterey Avenue
Nashua, NH 03064
P: (603) 889-0965
E: Alan.Cohen
@leg.state.nh.us

Comeau, Ed (R, SP14)*
212 Stoneham Road
Brookfield, NH 03872
P: (603) 522-2275
E: ed@edcomeau.org

Comtois, Guy (R, SP7)
P.O. Box 186
Center Barnstead, NH 03225
P: (603) 776-8989
E: gcomtois2010@gmail.com

Converse, Larry (D, SP197)
7 Clover Street
Claremont, NH 03743
P: (603) 542-2180
E: lcallcone@aol.com

Cook, Allen W. (R, SP142)*
153-B Pickpocket Road
Brentwood, NH 03833
P: (603) 772-6430
E: Allen.cook
@leg.state.nh.us

Cooney, Mary R. (D, SP48)
78 Highland Street
Plymouth, NH 03264
P: (603) 536-1141
E: mary.cooney
@leg.state.nh.us

Cordelli, Glenn (R, SP13)
P.O. Box 209
Tuftonboro, NH 03816
P: (603) 515-0008
E: glenn.cordelli
@leg.state.nh.us

Cornell, Patricia (D, SP75)*
787 Montgomery Street
Manchester, NH 03102
P: (603) 644-5480
E: patricia.cornell
@leg.state.nh.us

Cote, David E. (D, SP56)
96 West Hollis Street
Nashua, NH 03060
P: (603) 882-2244
E: david.cote
@leg.state.nh.us

Crawford, Karel A. (R, SP13)
P.O. Box 825
Center Harbor, NH 03226
P: (603) 253-7857
E: karel.crawford
@leg.state.nh.us

Cushing, Robert R. (D, SP152)
395 Winnacunnet Road
Hampton, NH 03842
P: (617) 926-2737
E: renny.cushing
@leg.state.nh.us

Danielson, David J. (R, SP64)
9 Darby Lane
Bedford, NH 03110
P: (603) 472-3833
E: david.danielson
@leg.state.nh.us

Darrow, Stephen (R, SP57)*
463 Slab City Road
Grafton, NH 03240
P: (603) 523-4678
E: stephen.darrow
@leg.state.nh.us

DeLemus, Susan (R, SP179)
14 Dustin Homestead
Rochester, NH 03867
P: (603) 335-5119
E: susan.delemus
@leg.state.nh.us

Deloge, Helen (D, SP118)
30 Wilson Avenue
Concord, NH 03301
P: (603) 224-3628
E: helen.deloge@gmail.com

DeSimone, Debra L. (R, SP145)
11 Providence Hill Road
Atkinson, NH 03811
P: (603) 362-4314
E: debra.desimone
@leg.state.nh.us

Devine, James E. (R, SP135)
54 Hampstead Road
Sandown, NH 03873
P: (603) 887-3569
F: (603) 887-4923
E: jim.devine
@leg.state.nh.us

DiFranco, Debbie (D, SP158)*
380 Ocean Road, #21
Portsmouth, NH 03801
P: (603) 319-8428
E: Debbie.DiFranco
@leg.state.nh.us

DiSesa, Len (D, SP184)*
29 Pleasant Valley Road
Dover, NH 03820
P: (603) 343-4344
E: Len.DiSesa
@leg.state.nh.us

New Hampshire

DiSilvestro, Linda A. (D, SP66)
145 Fox Hollow Way
Manchester, NH 03104
P: (603) 645-6729
E: linda.disilvestro@leg.state.nh.us

Dobson, Brian F. (R, SP163)*
99 Old Turnpike Road
Nottingham, NH 03290
P: (603) 608-1170
E: Briandobson1983@gmail.com

Doherty, David (D, SP122)*
242 Fourth Range Road
Pembroke, NH 03275
P: (603) 485-2788
E: David.Doherty@leg.state.nh.us

Donovan, Daniel A. (R, SP59)
P.O. Box 697
Deering, NH 03244
P: (603) 464-5805
F: (603) 487-3591
E: daniel.donovan@leg.state.nh.us

Doucette, Fred (R, SP139)*
P.O. Box 862
Salem, NH 03079
P: (603) 553-6460
E: fred.doucette@leg.state.nh.us

Duarte, Joe (R, SP133)
10 Critchett Road
Candia, NH 03034
P: (603) 483-8454
E: joe.duarte@leg.state.nh.us

Dumais, Russell (R, SP2)*
6 Glidden Road
Gilford, NH 03249
P: (603) 293-2014

Eastman, Eric R. (R, SP85)*
54 Coburn Woods
Nashua, NH 03063
P: (603) 879-0009
E: eric.eastman@leg.state.nh.us

Eaton, Daniel A. (D, SP20)
1 Shedd Hill Road
Stoddard, NH 03464
P: (603) 446-3535
F: (603) 446-3535
E: Daniel.Eaton@leg.state.nh.us

Ebel, Karen E. (D, SP107)
P.O. Box 714
New London, NH 03257
P: (603) 748-3876
E: karen.ebel@leg.state.nh.us

Edelblut, Frank (R, SP95)*
99 Badger Farm Road
Wilton, NH 03086
P: (603) 661-7730
E: frank.edelblut@leg.state.nh.us

Edwards, Elizabeth (D, SP68)*
524 Wilson Street, #5
Manchester, NH 03103

Elliott, Robert J. (R, SP139)
44 Centerville Drive
Salem, NH 03079
P: (603) 893-0402
E: bob.elliott@leg.state.nh.us

Emerick, J. Tracy (R, SP152)
207 North Shore Road
Hampton, NH 03842
P: (603) 926-8316
E: tracy.emerick@leg.state.nh.us

Emerson, Susan (R, SP28)
P.O. Box 646
Rindge, NH 03461
P: (603) 899-6529
E: semerson435@aol.com

Estevez, Eric P. (R, SP94)*
P.O. Box 22
Pelham, NH 03076
P: (603) 402-0920
E: Eric.Estevez@leg.state.nh.us

Ferrante, Beverly Ann (R, SP137)
68 Chester Road
Derry, NH 03038
P: (603) 434-8974
E: bevferrante@yahoo.com

Ferreira, Elizabeth (R, SP85)*
325 Broad Street
Nashua, NH 03063

Fesh, Bob M. (R, SP137)
27 Claire Avenue
Derry, NH 03038
P: (603) 434-1550
E: rmfesh@comcast.net

Fields, Dennis H. (R, SP4)
429 Lower Bay Road
Sanbornton, NH 03269
P: (603) 528-6224
E: dennis.fields@leg.state.nh.us

Fisher, Robert (R, SP9)*
58 Adams Street
Laconia, NH 03246
P: (802) 727-0441
E: robert.fisher@leg.state.nh.us

Flanagan, Jack B. (R, SP83)
4 Sawtelle Road
Brookline, NH 03033
P: (603) 672-7175
E: jack.flanagan@leg.state.nh.us

Flanders, Donald H. (R, SP3)
19 Kensington Drive
Laconia, NH 03246
P: (603) 524-5369
F: (603) 524-0748
E: dflanders@metrocast.net

Ford, Susan (D, SP42)
557 Sugar Hill Road
Easton, NH 03580
P: (603) 823-5609
E: susan.ford@leg.state.nh.us

Forest, Armand D. (D, SP75)
692 Montgomery Street
Manchester, NH 03102
P: (603) 669-0646
E: armand.forest@leg.state.nh.us

Fothergill, John (R, SP34)*
37 Colby Street
Colebrook, NH 03576
P: (603) 915-1220
E: john.Fothergill@leg.state.nh.us

Francese, Paula (D, SP149)*
181 High Street
Exeter, NH 03833
P: (603) 778-1726
E: Paula.Francese@leg.state.nh.us

Fraser, Valerie (R, SP1)*
348 Pinnacle Hill Road
New Hampton, NH 03256
P: (603) 744-0107
E: valerie.fraser@leg.state.nh.us

Frazer, June M. (D, SP115)
27 Piscataqua Road
Concord, NH 03301
P: (603) 228-0048
E: June.Frazer@leg.state.nh.us

Freitas, Mary C. (D, SP71)*
279 Candia Road
Manchester, NH 03109
P: (603) 622-9056
E: mfreitas279@myfairpoint.net

French, Barbara C. (D, SP108)
81 Fairview Avenue
Henniker, NH 03242
P: (603) 428-3366

French, Harold F. (R, SP104)*
232 South Main Street
Franklin, NH 03235
P: (603) 848-8588
E: harold.french@leg.state.nh.us

Friel, William G. (R, SP145)
5 Kelly Lane
Atkinson, NH 03811
P: (617) 960-7445
E: william.friel@leg.state.nh.us

Fromuth, Bart (R, SP64)*
38 Hawthorne Drive, Unit G 201
Bedford, NH 03110
P: (603) 203-1379
E: bart@voteforbart.com

Gagne, Larry (R, SP70)
126 Lakeside Drive
Manchester, NH 03104
P: (603) 625-9692
E: lgagne25@comcast.net

Gagnon, Raymond G. (D, SP198)
4 Warren Street
Claremont, NH 03743
P: (603) 542-7286
E: raymond.gagnon@leg.state.nh.us

Gallagher, Brian S. (R, SP4)*
292 Hueber Drive
Sanbornton, NH 03269
P: (603) 530-2651
E: brian.gallagher@leg.state.nh.us

Gallagher, Brian S. (R, SP4)*
292 Hueber Drive
Sanbornton, NH 03269
P: (603) 530-2651
E: brian.gallagher@leg.state.nh.us

Gannon, William M. (R, SP135)*
P.O. Box 71
Sandown, NH 03873

Gardner, Janice S. (D, SP183)
165 Dover Point Road
Dover, NH 03820
P: (603) 742-0205
E: janice.gardner@leg.state.nh.us

Gargasz, Carolyn M. (R, SP84)
P.O. Box 1223
Hollis, NH 03049
P: (603) 465-7463
F: (603) 465-7463
E: carolyn.gargasz@leg.state.nh.us

Gidge, Kenneth N. (D, SP90)
22 Hayden Street
Nashua, NH 03060
P: (603) 888-2355
E: kgidge@aol.com

Gile, Mary Stuart (D, SP129)
35 Penacook Street
Concord, NH 03301
P: (603) 224-2278
E: mary.gile@leg.state.nh.us

Gionet, Edmond D. (R, SP45)
P.O. Box 414
Lincoln, NH 03251
P: (603) 745-2240
E: edmond.gionet@leg.state.nh.us

Goley, Jeff P. (D, SP65)
1683 River Road
Manchester, NH 03104
P: (603) 626-6659
E: jeff.goley@leg.state.nh.us

Gonzalez, Carlos E. (R, SP102)
P.O. Box 154
Manchester, NH 03105
P: (603) 674-9696
E: cegonzalezj@comcast.net

Gordon, Pamela S. (D, SP160)*
215 Washington Street
Portsmouth, NH 03801
P: (603) 319-8398
E: Pamela.Gordon@leg.state.nh.us

Gordon, Richard E. (R, SP166)
4 Burnt Swamp Road
East Kingston, NH 03827
P: (603) 642-7252
E: dick.gordon@leg.state.nh.us

Gorman, Mary J. (D, SP88)
44 1/2 Amherst Street
Nashua, NH 03064
P: (603) 886-1652
E: mqgorman@comcast.net

Gottling, Suzanne H. (D, SP195)
173 Lake Avenue
Sunapee, NH 03782
P: (603) 763-5904
E: sgottling@comcast.net

Gould, Linda (R, SP64)*
2 Elder Williams Road
Bedford, NH 03110
P: (603) 472-3877
E: linda.gould@leg.state.nh.us

Goulette, Bill (R, SP80)*
416 Osgood Road
Milford, NH 03055
P: (603) 801-3060
E: bill.goulette@leg.state.nh.us

Gray, James P. (R, SP176)
21 Roulx Drive
Rochester, NH 03867
P: (603) 332-7144
E: james.gray@leg.state.nh.us

Grenier, James L. (R, SP200)
P.O. Box 247
Goshen, NH 03605
P: (603) 863-5681
E: jimgreniersullivan7@gmail.com

Griffin, Barbara (R, SP63)*
84 Merrill Road
Goffstown, NH 03045
P: (603) 497-8286
E: barbara.griffin@leg.state.nh.us

Griffin, Mary E. (R, SP138)
4 Wynridge Road
Windham, NH 03087
P: (603) 432-0959
E: mary.griffin@leg.state.nh.us

Groen, Warren (R, SP178)
17 Alice Lane
Rochester, NH 03867
P: (603) 817-9353
E: warren.groen@leg.state.nh.us

Guerette, Lee (D, SP90)*
22 Hayden
Nashua, NH 03060
P: (603) 888-2355
E: Leeguerette@comcast.net

Guthrie, Joseph A. (R, SP144)
15 Madison Drive
Hampstead, NH 03841
P: (603) 489-1228
E: joseph.guthrie@leg.state.nh.us

Haefner, Robert H. (R, SP94)
1 St. John Street
Hudson, NH 03051
P: (603) 889-1553
E: bob.haefner@leg.state.nh.us

Hagan, Joseph M. (R, SP135)
30 Chester Street
Chester, NH 03036
P: (603) 887-4280

Halstead, Carolyn (R, SP80)*
79 Ruonala Road
Milford, NH 03055
P: (603) 672-7141
E: carolyn.halstead@leg.state.nh.us

Hannon, Joe (R, SP193)*
1 Thornton Lane
Lee, NH 03861
P: (603) 292-5852
E: joehannon4nh@gmail.com

Hansberry, Daniel C. (D, SP92)
20 Shelley Drive
Nashua, NH 03062
P: (603) 888-5634
E: daniel.hansberry@leg.state.nh.us

Hansen, Peter (R, SP79)
82 Amherst Street
Amherst, NH 03031
P: (603) 673-5987
E: peter.hansen@leg.state.nh.us

Harris, Jeffrey F. (R, SP140)
146 Exeter Road
Epping, NH 03042
P: (603) 679-2331
E: jeffrey.harris@leg.state.nh.us

Harvey, Suzanne (D, SP86)
8 Crawford Lane
Nashua, NH 03063
P: (603) 598-0582
E: suzanne.harvey@leg.state.nh.us

Hatch, William A. (D, SP39)
79 Promenade Street
Gorham, NH 03581
P: (603) 466-9491
E: William.Hatch@leg.state.nh.us

Heath, Mary (D, SP71)
76 Island Pond Road
Manchester, NH 03109
P: (603) 622-0895
E: mary.heath@leg.state.nh.us

Heffron, Frank H. (D, SP149)
4 Minuteman Lane
Exeter, NH 03833
P: (603) 772-4659
E: frank.heffron@leg.state.nh.us

Henle, Paul J. (D, SP114)
11-2 Cabernet Drive
Concord, NH 03303
P: (603) 986-9620
E: paul.henle@leg.state.nh.us

Hennessey, Erin Tapper (R, SP41)*
88 Lilac Lane
Littleton, NH 03561
P: (603) 991-7572
E: erin.hennessey@leg.state.nh.us

Hennessey, Martha (D, SP52)*
4 Webster Terrace
Hanover, NH 03755
P: (603) 643-8640
E: martha.hennessey@leg.state.nh.us

New Hampshire

Herbert, Christopher J. (D, SP100)*
85 Watts Street
Manchester, NH 03104
P: (603) 669-2838
E: cherb55@comcast.net

Hess, David W. (R, SP126)
68 Pine Street
Hooksett, NH 03106
P: (603) 485-9027
F: (603) 647-0900
E: dave.hess@leg.state.nh.us

Higgins, Patricia C. (D, SP52)
8 Mink Drive
Hanover, NH 03755
P: (603) 643-3989
E: patricia.higgins@leg.state.nh.us

Hill, Gregory (R, SP105)
1 Knowles Farm Road
Northfield, NH 03276
P: (603) 286-7329
E: greg.hill@leg.state.nh.us

Hinch, Richard W. (R, SP78)
14 Ichabod Drive
Merrimack, NH 03054
P: (603) 261-6317
E: dick.hinch@leg.state.nh.us

Hirsch, Geoffrey D. (D, SP108)
P.O. Box 385
Bradford, NH 03221
P: (603) 938-2833
E: geoffrey.hirsch@leg.state.nh.us

Hodgdon, Bruce E. (R, SP132)
P.O. Box 323
Northwood, NH 03261
P: (603) 942-5264
E: bruce.hodgdon@leg.state.nh.us

Hoell, J.R. (R, SP125)
32 Ordway Road
Dunbarton, NH 03046
P: (603) 315-9002
E: jr.hoell@leg.state.nh.us

Hoelzel, Kathleen M. (R, SP134)
15 Dudley Road
Raymond, NH 03077
P: (603) 895-4172
E: kathleen.hoelzel@leg.state.nh.us

Hogan, Edith R. (R, SP91)
34 Dearborn Street
Nashua, NH 03060
P: (603) 883-5320
E: dee-hogan@hotmail.com

Hopper, Gary S. (R, SP59)
107 Buxton School Road
Weare, NH 03281
P: (603) 529-7728
E: gary.hopper@leg.state.nh.us

Horn, Werner D. (R, SP104)*
137 Winnipesaukee Street
Franklin, NH 03235
P: (603) 470-9667
E: werner.horn@leg.state.nh.us

Horrigan, Timothy (D, SP174)
7-A Faculty Road
Durham, NH 03824
P: (603) 868-3342
F: (866) 542-0665
E: Timothy.Horrigan@leg.state.nh.us

Howard, Raymond (R, SP8)*
311 Stockbridge Corner Road
Alton, NH 03809
P: (603) 875-4115
E: brhowardjr@yahoo.com

Howe, Ann M. (R, SP144)*
60 Ellyson Avenue
East Hampstead, NH 03826
E: ann.howe@leg.state.nh.us

Hull, Robert (R, SP49)*
12 Liberty Lane
Grafton, NH 03240
P: (603) 780-4244
E: robert.hull@leg.state.nh.us

Hunt, John B. (R, SP28)
165 Sunridge Road
Rindge, NH 03461
P: (603) 899-6000
F: (603) 899-6160
E: jbhunt@prodigy.net

Hurt, George (R, SP2)*
P.O. Box 7481
Gilford, NH 03247
E: gfhurt@gmail.com

Infantine, William J. (R, SP70)
89 Winward Lane
Manchester, NH 03104
P: (603) 622-3325
E: Repinfantine@gmail.com

Ingbretson, Paul C. (R, SP55)
P.O. Box 296
Pike, NH 03780
P: (603) 989-3092
E: ingbretson_studio@yahoo.com

Introne Jr., Robert E. (R, SP136)
8 Everts Street
Londonderry, NH 03053
P: (603) 432-0345
F: (603) 434-6266
E: REIntrone@aol.com

Irwin, Virginia (D, SP199)
182 Fletcher Road
Newport, NH 03773
P: (603) 863-3582
E: virginia.irwin@leg.state.nh.us

Itse, Daniel C. (R, SP141)
P.O. Box 70
Fremont, NH 03044
P: (603) 642-9403
E: daniel.itse@leg.state.nh.us

Jack, Martin L. (D, SP93)
83 Cadogan Way
Nashua, NH 03062
P: (603) 318-0457
E: martin.jack@leg.state.nh.us

Jasper, Shawn N. (R, SP94)
83 Old Derry Road
Hudson, NH 03051
P: (603) 595-9621
F: (603) 882-2056
E: shawn.jasper@leg.state.nh.us

Jeudy, Jean L. (D, SP67)
134 Calef Road
Manchester, NH 03103
P: (603) 645-5290
E: Jean.jeudy@gmail.com

Johnsen, Gladys (D, SP24)
417 Pako Avenue
Keene, NH 03431
P: (603) 358-5164
F: (603) 398-5164
E: johnsengladys@gmail.com

Johnson, Eric (R)
2249 US Route 3
Campton, NH 03223
P: (603) 726-4980
E: eric.johnson@leg.sate.nh.us

Jones, Laura (R, SP192)
9 Jackson Street
Rochester, NH 03867
P: (603) 948-2264
E: laurajonesnh@gmail.com

Kaczynski Jr., Thomas L. (R, SP190)*
112 Whitehall Road
Rochester, NH 03868
P: (603) 332-7310
E: hampoul@metrocast.net

Kaen, Naida L. (D, SP173)
22 Toon Lane
Lee, NH 03861
P: (603) 659-2205
E: naidakaen@gmail.com

Kappler, Lawrence M. (R, SP134)
18 Agent Road
Raymond, NH 03077
P: (603) 303-8959
E: lawrence.Kappler@leg.state.nh.us

Karrick, David B. (D, SP127)
P.O. Box 328
Warner, NH 03278
P: (603) 456-2772
E: david.karrick@leg.state.nh.us

Katsakiores, Phyllis M. (R, SP137)
1 Bradford Street
Derry, NH 03038
P: (603) 434-9587
E: pkatsakiores@comcast.net

Katsiantonis, Thomas (D, SP72)
45 Glen Bloom Drive
Manchester, NH 03109
P: (603) 627-9652
E: thomaskatsiantonis@gmail.com

Kellogg, Shem (R, SP145)*
48 Westville Road, Unit 4-2
Plaistow, NH 03865
P: (603) 560-8621
E: shem.kellogg@leg.state.nh.us

Kenison, Linda B. (D, SP117)*
10 Marshall Street
Concord, NH 03301
P: (603) 228-8348
E: Linda.Kenison@leg.state.nh.us

Kidder, David H. (R, SP107)
34 Blueberry Lane
New London, NH 03257
P: (603) 526-4767
E: david.kidder
@leg.state.nh.us

Knowles, Robert (R, SP180)*
22 Meadowbrook Village
Rochester, NH 03867
P: (603) 335-0373
E: RKnowles@metrocast.net

Kolodziej, Walter (R, SP138)
8 Kent Street
Windham, NH 03087
P: (603) 437-7936

Kotowski, Frank R. (R, SP126)
21 Pleasant Street
Hooksett, NH 03106
P: (603) 485-9579
E: frkotowski@comcast.net

Kuch, Bill (R, SP125)*
82 Page Road
Bow, NH 03304
P: (603) 856-0957
E: Bill.Kuch
@leg.state.nh.us

Kurk, Neal M. (R, SP59)
R.R.1
Weare, NH 03281
P: (603) 529-7253
E: rep03281@aol.com

Lachance, Joseph (R, SP65)*
105 Brae Burn Drive
Manchester, NH 03104

Ladd, Rick (R, SP44)
P.O. Box 67
Haverhill, NH 03765
P: (603) 989-3268
E: ladd.nhhouse@charter.net

Laware, Thomas (R, SP201)
398 River Road
Charlestown, NH 03603
P: (603) 826-3137
F: (603) 826-3137
E: thomas.laware
@leg.state.nh.us

Lebreche, Shari (R, SP6)*
64 Tioga Drive
Belmont, NH 03220
P: (603) 455-6186
E: shari.lebreche
@leg.state.nh.us

LeBrun, Donald (R, SP89)
333 Candlewood Park
Nashua, NH 03062
P: (603) 886-1725
E: donald.lebrun
@leg.state.nh.us

Leeman, Don E. (R, SP191)*
14 Partridge Green Way
Rochester, NH 03867
P: (603) 973-6009
E: Don.Leeman
@leg.state.nh.us

Leishman, Peter R. (D, SP81)
39 Birch Road
Peterborough, NH 03458
P: (603) 924-0004
E: PRLeishman@aol.com

Ley, Douglas A. (D, SP26)
28 School Street
Jaffrey, NH 03452
P: (603) 532-8556
E: douglas.ley
@leg.state.nh.us

Lincoln Froburg, Alethea (D, SP36)*
437 Second Avenue
Berlin, NH 03570
P: (603) 752-3867
E: Alethea.Froburg
@leg.state.nh.us

Long, Douglas B. (R, SP106)*
12 French Road
Wilmot, NH 03287
P: (603) 927-4137
E: longbroscon
@mcttelecom.com

Lovejoy, Patricia (D, SP167)
21 Coach Road
Stratham, NH 03885
P: (603) 778-9662
E: patty.lovejoy
@leg.state.nh.us

Lundgren, David C. (R, SP136)
21 King John Drive
Londonderry, NH 03053
P: (603) 432-3499
F: (603) 432-4142
E: qtipnh@aol.com

Luneau, David (I, SP112)*
211 Putney Hill Road
Hopkinton, NH 03229
P: (603) 746-6484
E: dluneauNH@gmail.com

Luther, Robert (R, SP3)
152 Court Street
Laconia, NH 03246
P: (603) 524-4692
E: robert.luther
@leg.state.nh.us

MacKay, James R. (R, SP116)
139 North State Street
Concord, NH 03301
P: (603) 224-0623
E: james.mackay@mygait.com

Maes, Kevin G. (D, SP46)*
P.O. Box 205
Rumney, NH 03266
P: (603) 786-9705
E: Kevin.Maes
@leg.state.nh.us

Major, Norman L. (R, SP145)
12 Kingston Road
Plaistow, NH 03865
P: (603) 382-5429
F: (603) 382-8117
E: norman.major
@leg.state.nh.us

Mangipudi, Latha (D, SP92)
20 Salmon Brook Drive
Nashua, NH 03062
P: (603) 891-1239
E: Latha.Mangipudi
@leg.state.nh.us

Manley, Jonathan F. (D, SP60)
227 Bible Hill Road
Bennington, NH 03442
P: (603) 588-2427
E: jonathan.manley
@leg.state.nh.us

Mann, John E. (D, SP19)
35 Prentice Hill Road
Alstead, NH 03602
P: (603) 835-9095
E: john.mann
@leg.state.nh.us

Manning Jr., John J. (R, SP139)
30 Maclarnon Road
Salem, NH 03079
P: (603) 818-3188
E: john.manning
@leg.state.nh.us

Marple, Richard (R, SP126)
11 Dartmouth Street
Hooksett, NH 03106
P: (603) 627-1837
F: (603) 627-1837
E: dick.marple
@leg.state.nh.us

Marston, Dick (R, SP76)
25 English Village Road, #304
Manchester, NH 03102
P: (603) 666-7334
E: dick.marston.nhstaterep
@gmail.com

Martel, Andre A. (R, SP101)
81 Maurice Street
Manchester, NH 03103
P: (603) 218-3370
E: martel.andy@yahoo.com

Martin, John (R, SP125)*
96 Woodhill Road
Bow, NH 03304
P: (603) 774-3098
E: john.martin
@leg.state.nh.us

Massimilla, Linda (D, SP41)
197 Orchard Hill Road
LIttleton, NH 03561
P: (603) 444-5270
E: linda.massimilla
@leg.state.nh.us

Matthews, Carolyn L. (R, SP134)*
12 Ann Logan Circle
Raymond, NH 03077
P: (603) 244-2027
E: Carolyn.Matthews
@leg.state.nh.us

McBeath, Rebecca (D, SP157)*
243 Middle Road
Portsmouth, NH 03801
P: (603) 834-3291
E: Rebecca.McBeath
@leg.state.nh.us

McCarthy, Frank (R, SP11)
P.O. Box 876
Conway, NH 03818
P: (603) 356-9160
E: frank.mccarthy
@leg.state.nh.us

McCarthy, Peggy (R, SP86)*
34 Terry Street
Nashua, NH 03064
P: (603) 598-4966
E: Mccarthy.Peggy@gmail.com

McClarren, Donald B. (R, SP86)
39 Monza Road
Nashua, NH 03064
P: (603) 883-9245
E: donald.mcclarren
@leg.state.nh.us

New Hampshire

McConkey, Mark E. (R, SP12)
10 Clover Lane
Freedom, NH 03836
P: (603) 520-8275
E: mcconkey2@hotmail.com

McConnell, Jim (R, SP29)*
P.O. Box G
Keene, NH 03431
P: (603) 357-7150
E: Jim.McConnell
@leg.state.nh.us

McGuire, Carol (R, SP131)
700 Suncook Valley Highway
Epsom, NH 03234
P: (603) 782-4918
E: carol@mcguire4house.com

McGuire, Dan (R, SP123)
700 Suncook Valley Highway
Epsom, NH 03234
P: (603) 782-4918
E: dan@mcguire4house.com

McKinney, Betsy (R, SP136)
3 Leelynn Circle
Londonderry, NH 03053
P: (603) 432-5232
E: betsy.mckinney
@leg.state.nh.us

McLean, Mark (R, SP72)*
43 Forest Hill Way
Manchester, NH 03109
P: (603) 668-0076
E: mark.mclean
@leg.state.nh.us

McMahon, Charles E. (R, SP138)
11 Floral Street
Windham, NH 03087
P: (603) 432-8877
F: (603) 432-6854
E: cmcmahon55@gmail.com

McNamara, Richard D. (D, SP95)
P.O. Box 1891
Hillsborough, NH 03244
P: (508) 728-9836
E: richard.mcnamara
@leg.state.nh.us

Milz, David E. (R, SP137)
12R Bonnie Lane
Derry, NH 03038
P: (603) 437-0030
E: david.milz
@leg.state.nh.us

Moffett, Howard M. (D, SP111)
66 Cogswell Hill Road
Canterbury, NH 03224
P: (603) 782-4993
E: howard.moffett
@leg.state.nh.us

Moody, Marcia G. (D, SP148)
1 Maple Street
Newmarket, NH 03857
P: (603) 659-7106
E: Marcia.Moody
@leg.state.nh.us

Moore, Josh (R, SP78)*
14 Buttonwood Lane
Merrimack, NH 03054
P: (603) 361-0955
E: josh.moore
@leg.state.nh.us

Moynihan, Wayne T. (D, SP35)
138 Plain Road
Dummer, NH 03588
P: (603) 449-2058
E: wayne.moynihan
@leg.state.nh.us

Mullen, John A. (R, SP169)
34 Shore Drive
Middleton, NH 03887
P: (603) 755-9062
E: john.mullen
@leg.state.nh.us

Murotake, David K. (R, SP89)
17 Port Chester Drive
Nashua, NH 03062
P: (603) 889-4568
E: david.murotake
@leg.state.nh.us

Murphy, Keith (R, SP64)
5 Rachel Way
Bedford, NH 03110
P: (603) 488-2347
F: (603) 644-3537
E: rep.keithmurphy
@gmail.com

Myler, Mel (D, SP112)
P.O. Box 82
Contoocook, NH 03229
P: (603) 746-5294
E: mel.myler
@leg.state.nh.us

Nelson, Bill G. (R, SP14)
98 Lyford Road
Brookfield, NH 03872
P: (603) 522-5279
E: bill.nelson
@leg.state.nh.us

Nigrello, Robert L. (R, SP147)
2 Pine Woods
East Kingston, NH 03827
P: (603) 394-7591
E: bob.nigrello
@leg.state.nh.us

Nordgren, Sharon L. (D, SP52)
23 Rope Ferry Road
Hanover, NH 03755
P: (603) 643-5068
F: (603) 643-8567
E: sharon.nordgren
@leg.state.nh.us

Notter, Jeanine (R, SP78)
19 Whittier Road
Merrimack, NH 03054
P: (603) 423-0408
E: jeanine.notter
@leg.state.nh.us

Ober, Lynne M. (R, SP94)
3 Heritage Circle
Hudson, NH 03051
P: (603) 883-9654
E: lynne.ober@comcast.net

Ober III, Russell T. (R, SP94)
3 Heritage Circle
Hudson, NH 03051
P: (603) 883-9654

O'Brien Sr., Michael B. (D, SP93)
4 Woodfield Street
Nashua, NH 03062
P: (603) 888-8051
E: michael.o'brien
@leg.state.nh.us

O'Brien, William L. (R, SP62)
P.O. Box 154
Mont Vernon, NH 03057
P: (603) 271-3661
E: william.obrien
@leg.state.nh.us

O'Connor, John T. (R, SP137)
13 Arrowhead Road
Derry, NH 03038
P: (603) 434-8393
E: john.o'connor
@leg.state.nh.us

O'Hearne, Andrew S. (D, SP196)
120 Main Street
Claremont, NH 03743
P: (603) 558-1038
E: andrew.ohearne
@leg.state.nh.us

Ohm, Bill (R, SP93)
18 Mount Laurels Drive, Apartment 403
Nashua, NH 03062
P: (603) 891-2306
F: (413) 691-6187
E: bill.ohm@leg.state.nh.us

Oligny, Jeffrey (R, SP165)
28 Main Street
Plaistow, NH 03865
P: (205) 351-8003
E: jeffrey.oligny
@leg.state.nh.us

O'Neil, William (D, SP66)
309 Ash Street
Manchester, NH 03104
P: (603) 644-5277
E: william.oneil
@leg.state.nh.us

Osborne, Jason (R, SP135)*
65 Miner Road
Auburn, NH 03032
P: (603) 391-2138
E: Jason@Osborne4NH.com

Oxenham, Lee Walker (D, SP194)*
92 Methodist Hill Road
Plainfield, NH 03781
P: (603) 727-9368
E: Lee.Oxenham
@leg.state.nh.us

Packard, Sherman A. (R, SP136)
70 Old Derry Road
Londonderry, NH 03053
P: (603) 432-3391
F: (603) 421-0902
E: sherman.packard
@leg.state.nh.us

Palmer, Barry (R, SP89)
123 Shore Drive
Nashua, NH 03062
P: (603) 889-0288

Pantelakos, Laura C. (D, SP156)
528 Dennett Street
Portsmouth, NH 03801
P: (603) 436-2148
E: lcpantelakos@comcast.net

Parent, Jason R. (R, SP128)*
40 Twin Bridge Road
Northfield, NH 03276
P: (603) 387-4626
E: Jason.Parent
@leg.state.nh.us

Parison, James (R, SP82)
40 Old Rindge Road
New Ipswich, NH 03071
P: (603) 878-5001
E: james.parison
@leg.state.nh.us

Parker, Harold B. (R, SP15)*
P.O. Box 742
Wolfeboro Falls, NH 03896
P: (603) 491-6807
E: hbpcd6@gmail.com

Parkhurst, Henry A.L. (D, SP30)
One Parkhurst Place
Winchester, NH 03470
P: (603) 239-8945
E: hank.parkhurst@leg.state.nh.us

Parsons, Robbie (R, SP169)
221 Old Wakefield Road
Milton, NH 03851
P: (603) 652-9009

Patten, Dick (D, SP119)
30 Pinewood Trail
Concord, NH 03301
P: (603) 228-1803
F: (603) 715-1648
E: Dick.Patten@leg.state.nh.us

Pearson, William (D, SP21)*
31 Elliot Street
Keene, NH 03431
P: (603) 714-9075
E: William.Pearson@leg.state.nh.us

Peckham, Michele (R, SP153)
82 Atlantic Avenue
North Hampton, NH 03862
P: (603) 997-1120
F: (603) 964-3744
E: michele.peckham@leg.state.nh.us

Pellegrino, Tony J. (R, SP78)
35 Amherst Road
Merrimack, NH 03054
P: (603) 424-7095
E: anthony.pellegrino@leg.state.nh.us

Peterson, Ken (R, SP64)*
43 Brick Mill Road
Bedford, NH 03110
P: (603) 472-2913
E: ken.peterson@leg.state.nh.us

Phillips, Larry R. (D, SP22)
171 Roxbury Street
Keene, NH 03431
P: (603) 357-4315
E: larry.phillips@leg.state.nh.us

Pierce, David W. (R, SP63)*
21 Mill Street
Goffstown, NH 03045
P: (603) 497-8278
E: david.w.pierce@leg.state.nh.us

Piper, Wendy A. (D, SP50)
P.O. Box 311
Enfield, NH 03748
P: (603) 632-7179
E: wendy.piper@leg.state.nh.us

Pitre, Joseph (R, SP170)
76 Cocheco Road
Farmington, NH 03835
P: (603) 755-2447
F: (603) 755-2447
E: joe.pitre@leg.state.nh.us

Porter, Marjorie A. (D, SP58)
64 School Street
Hillsborough, NH 03244
P: (603) 464-0225
E: marjorie.porter@leg.state.nh.us

Potucek, John (R, SP137)*
18 Sunset Avenue
Derry, NH 03038
P: (603) 432-9049
E: john.potucek@leg.state.nh.us

Priestley, Anne K. (R, SP139)
4 Bluff Street
Salem, NH 03079
P: (603) 893-1214
E: kpanne@gmail.com

Proulx, Mark (R, SP101)
76 Janet Court
Manchester, NH 03103
P: (603) 669-7179
F: (603) 669-7179
E: mark.proulx@leg.state.nh.us

Prudhomme-O'Brien, Katherine (R, SP137)*
19 Beacon Hill Road
Derry, NH 03038
P: (603) 425-6605
E: kpo@leg.state.nh.us

Rappaport, Laurence M. (R, SP34)
P.O. Box 158
Colebrook, NH 03576
P: (603) 237-4429
E: larry.rappaport@leg.state.nh.us

Ratzki, Mario F. (D, SP103)
P.O. Box 213
East Andover, NH 03231
P: (603) 735-5440
E: Mario.Ratzki@leg.state.nh.us

Rice, Chip L. (D, SP129)
23 Wilson Avenue
Concord, NH 03301
P: (603) 224-2886
E: chip.rice@leg.state.nh.us

Rice, Frederick (R, SP152)
15 Heather Lane
Hampton, NH 03842
P: (603) 929-1517
F: (603) 929-9511
E: fred.rice@leg.state.nh.us

Rice, Kimberly (R, SP94)*
51 Belknap Road
Hudson, NH 03051
P: (603) 943-3369
E: kimberly.rice@leg.state.nh.us

Richardson, Herbert D. (R, SP37)
2 First Street
Lancaster, NH 03584
P: (603) 788-2442
E: herb.richardson@leg.state.nh.us

Rideout, Leon H. (R, SP40)
28 Causeway Street
Lancaster, NH 03584
P: (603) 684-1102
E: leon.rideout@leg.state.nh.us

Roberts, Carol R. (D, SP61)*
31 Curtis Farm Road
Wilton, NH 03836
P: (603) 654-6922
E: Carol.Roberts@leg.state.nh.us

Roberts, Kris E. (D, SP21)
58 Grove Street
Keene, NH 03431
P: (603) 352-1105
E: kriseroberts@icloud.com

Robertson, Timothy N. (D, SP23)
3 James Hill Drive
Keene, NH 03431
P: (603) 352-7006
E: timothyrbrtsn2@gmail.com

Rogers, Katherine D. (D, SP130)
4 Jay Drive
Concord, NH 03301
P: (603) 496-8521
E: katherine.rogers@leg.state.nh.us

Rokas, Theodoros (D, SP69)
393 Wilson Street
Manchester, NH 03103
P: (603) 620-2228
E: ted.rokas@leg.state.nh.us

Rollins, Skip (R, SP199)
5 Willow Street
Newport, NH 03773
P: (603) 863-6340
E: skip@lavalleys.com

Rollo, Deanna S. (D, SP186)
23 Heritage Drive
Rollinsford, NH 03869
P: (603) 742-7511
E: deanna1214@aol.com

Rosenwald, Cindy (D, SP87)
101 Wellington Street
Nashua, NH 03064
P: (603) 595-9896
E: cindy.rosenwald@leg.state.nh.us

Rouillard, Claire (R, SP63)*
14 Jasmine Lane
Goffstown, NH 03045
P: (603) 494-6144
E: Claire.Rouillard@leg.state.nh.us

Rowe, Robert H. (R, SP79)
P.O. Box 1117
Amherst, NH 03031
P: (603) 673-2693
E: rh.rowe@comcast.net

Russell, David H. (R, SP5)
P.O. Box 60
Gilmanton Iron Works, NH 03837
P: (603) 364-7449
F: (603) 364-7448
E: russells@metrocast.net

Russell, David H. (R, SP5)
P.O. Box 60
Gilmanton Iron Works, NH 03837
P: (603) 364-7449
F: (603) 364-7448
E: russells@metrocast.net

New Hampshire

Sad, Tara A. (D, SP18)
82 North Road
Walpole, NH 03608
P: (603) 756-4861
E: tara.eric@gmail.com

Sanborn, Laurie J. (R, SP98)
71 Eagle Drive
Bedford, NH 03110
P: (603) 682-1557
E: repsanborn@gmail.com

Sanders, Elisabeth N. (R, SP143)
61 Beach Plain Road
Danville, NH 03819
P: (603) 642-5070
E: elisabeth.sanders@leg.state.nh.us

Saunderson, George (D, SP111)*
615 Lovejoy Road
Loudon, NH 03307
P: (603) 783-4750
E: George.Saunderson@leg.state.nh.us

Schleien, Eric (R, SP94)*
825 Fox Hollow Drive
Hudson, NH 03051
P: (914) 275-5696
E: eric.schleien@leg.state.nh.us

Schmidt, Andrew (D, SP194)
P.O. Box 1747
Grantham, NH 03753
P: (603) 863-1247
E: andrew.schmidt@leg.state.nh.us

Schmidt, Peter B. (D, SP187)
P.O. Box 1468
Dover, NH 03821
P: (603) 743-3751
E: reppbs@ttlc.net

Schmidt, Stephen (R, SP15)
59 Spruce Road
Wolfeboro, NH 03894
P: (603) 569-0848
E: stephen.schmidt@leg.state.nh.us

Schroadter, Adam (R, SP148)
P.O. Box 564
Newmarket, NH 03857
P: (603) 292-6058
F: (310) 919-2845
E: repschroadter@gmail.com

Schuett, Dianne E. (D, SP122)
533 Pembroke Street
Pembroke, NH 03275
P: (603) 224-0314
E: dianne.schuett@leg.state.nh.us

Scontsas, Lisa E. (R, SP87)
24 Courtland Street
Nashua, NH 03064
P: (603) 883-6869
E: lscontsas@gmail.com

Seaworth, G. Brian (R, SP122)
161 Buck Street
Pembroke, NH 03275
P: (603) 485-8030
E: brian.seaworth@leg.state.nh.us

Seidel, Carl W. (R, SP85)
39 Pilgrim Circle
Nashua, NH 03063
P: (603) 598-2795
F: (603) 598-3412
E: carl.seidel@leg.state.nh.us

Shackett, Jeffrey (R, SP49)
181 Whittemore Point Road South
Bridgewater, NH 03222
P: (603) 744-5895
E: jeffrey.shackett@leg.state.nh.us

Shattuck, Gilman C. (D, SP58)
571 Center Road
Hillsborough, NH 03244
P: (603) 464-3850
E: gilman.shattuck@leg.state.nh.us

Shaw, Barbara E. (D, SP73)
45 Randall Street
Manchester, NH 03103
P: (603) 626-4681
E: beshaw3@comcast.net

Shepardson, Marjorie J. (D, SP27)
94 Pleasant Street
Marlborough, NH 03455
P: (603) 876-4027
E: marge.shepardson@gmail.com

Sherman, Thomas M. (D, SP155)
296 Harbor Road
Rye, NH 03870
P: (603) 379-2248
E: thomas.sherman@leg.state.nh.us

Shurtleff, Stephen J. (D, SP113)
11 Vinton Drive
Penacook, NH 03303
P: (603) 753-4563
E: steve.shurtleff@leg.state.nh.us

Silva, Peter (R, SP92)
18 Masefield Road
Nashua, NH 03062
P: (603) 888-0558
F: (781) 828-0223
E: psilva.nhstaterep@gmail.com

Simmons, Tammy (R, SP74)
142 Parker Street
Manchester, NH 03102
P: (603) 235-9998
E: tammy.simmons@leg.state.nh.us

Simpson, Alexis (D, SP149)*
20 Main Street, #2400
Exeter, NH 03833
P: (603) 303-4722

Smith, Gregory (R, SP94)*
3 Mountain View Road
Pelham, NH 03076
P: (603) 635-3835
E: gregory.smith@leg.state.nh.us

Smith, Marjorie K. (D, SP174)
P.O. Box 136
Durham, NH 03824
P: (603) 868-7500
E: Marjorie.Smith@leg.state.nh.us

Smith, Steven (R, SP204)
P.O. Box 624
Charlestown, NH 03603
P: (603) 826-5940
E: nhfirst@gmail.com

Smith, Suzanne (D, SP48)
20 Brookside Lane
Hebron, NH 03241
P: (603) 744-9064
E: suzanne.smith@leg.state.nh.us

Smith, Timothy J. (D, SP74)
494 South Main Street, Apartment 1
Manchester, NH 03102
P: (603) 657-0324
E: tim.smith@leg.state.nh.us

Snow, Kendall A. (D, SP99)*
150 Birchwood Road
Manchester, NH 03104
P: (603) 669-1075
E: Ken.Snow@leg.state.nh.us

Soucy, Timothy (D, SP91)
33 Gillis Street
Nashua, NH 03060
P: (603) 305-5012
E: timothy.soucy@leg.state.nh.us

Southworth, Tom (D, SP188)*
56 Durham Road, Unit 26
Dover, NH 03820
P: (603) 742-0556
E: Thomas.Southworth@leg.state.nh.us

Souza, Kathleen F. (R, SP100)
628 Belmont Street
Manchester, NH 03104
P: (603) 645-6131
E: irishsouza@netscape.com

Spang, Judith T. (D, SP174)
55 Wiswall Road
Durham, NH 03824
P: (603) 659-5936
E: Judith.Spang@leg.state.nh.us

Spanos, Peter (R, SP3)*
P.O. Box 102
Winnisquam, NH 03289
P: (603) 524-2960
E: peterjspanos@gmail.com

Spillane, James (R, SP133)*
16 Swamp Road
Deerfield, NH 03037
P: (603) 463-5623
E: james@jamesspillane.org

Sprague, Dale R. (D, SP186)
35 Page Street
Somersworth, NH 03878
P: (603) 692-3440
E: dale.sprague@leg.state.nh.us

Stepanek, Stephen B. (R, SP79)
P.O. Box 1015
Milford, NH 03055
P: (603) 673-7658
F: (603) 672-9392
E: stephen.stepanek@leg.state.nh.us

Sterling Jr., Franklin W. (R, SP31)
63 Monadnock View Drive
Jaffrey, NH 03452
P: (603) 532-8284
E: fwsterling@comcast.net

Stevens, Audrey M. (D, SP175)
8 Lisa Lane
Rochester, NH 03868
P: (603) 332-3863
E: audrey.stevens@leg.state.nh.us

Straight, Philip N. (R, SP78)
11 Spruce Street
Merrimack, NH 03054
P: (603) 424-2043
E: phil.straight@leg.state.nh.us

Sullivan, Daniel J. (D, SP99)
172 Arah Street
Manchester, NH 03104
P: (603) 627-5044
E: dan.sullivan@leg.state.nh.us

Sullivan, Victoria L. (R, SP73)*
1056 South Beech Street
Manchester, NH 03103
P: (603) 232-4382
E: patchessul@comcast.net

Sweeney, Dennis B. (R, SP151)*
73 Black Snake Road
Seabrook, NH 03874
P: (603) 343-3067
E: dennissweeney6r@gmail.com

Sweeney, Joe (R, SP139)
29 Hunters Run
Salem, NH 03079
P: (603) 327-7184
E: josephfsweeney@gmail.com

Sweeney, Shawn P. (R, SP80)
33 Orchard Street
Milford, NH 03055
P: (603) 265-0319
E: shawn.sweeney@leg.state.nh.us

Sykes, George E. (D, SP53)
3 Avon Avenue
Lebanon, NH 03766
P: (603) 448-0319
E: george.sykes@leg.state.nh.us

Sylvia, Michael J. (R, SP6)
216 Farrarville Road
Belmont, NH 03220
P: (603) 707-8594
E: mike.sylvia@leg.state.nh.us

Sytek, John J. (R, SP139)
34 Town Village Drive
Salem, NH 03079
P: (603) 893-8889
F: (603) 893-0000
E: john.sytek@leg.state.nh.us

Takesian, Charlene F. (R, SP94)
114 Jeremy Hill Road
Pelham, NH 03076
P: (603) 635-7215
E: charlene.takesian@leg.state.nh.us

Tamburello, Daniel (R, SP136)
3 Royal Lane
Londonderry, NH 03053
P: (603) 434-2940
E: daniel.tamburello@leg.state.nh.us

Tasker, Kyle J. (R, SP133)
87 Smoke Street
Nottingham, NH 03290
P: (603) 724-4716
E: kjtasker@gmail.com

Tatro, Bruce (D, SP32)
208 Old Richmond Road
Swanzey, NH 03446
P: (603) 352-3904
E: bruce.tatro@leg.state.nh.us

Theberge, Robert L. (D, SP36)
P.O. Box 271
Berlin, NH 03570
P: (603) 752-5672
E: robert.theberge@leg.state.nh.us

Tholl Jr., John E. (R, SP38)
41 Kimball Hill Road
Whitefield, NH 03598
P: (603) 837-2278
E: jetjr2@msn.com

Thomas, Doug (R, SP136)*
132 Mammoth Road
Londonderry, NH 03053
P: (603) 437-6090
E: doug.thomasnh@gmail.com

Thomas, Yvonne D. (D, SP36)
557 Norway Street
Berlin, NH 03570
P: (603) 752-1816
E: yvonne.thomas@leg.state.nh.us

Ticehurst, Susan J. (D, SP12)
334 Pease Hill Road
Tamworth, NH 03886
P: (603) 323-8040
E: ticehurstnhhouse@gmail.com

Tilton, Ben (D, SP29)*
840 Old Homestead
Swanzey, NH 03446
P: (603) 726-0664
E: swanzeygovbltilton@gmail.com

Tilton, Franklin T. (R, SP3)
56 Orchard Street
Laconia, NH 03246
P: (603) 528-8466
E: frank.tilton@leg.state.nh.us

Townsend, Chuck (D, SP51)
49 Hall Road
Canaan, NH 03741
P: (603) 632-7493
F: (603) 632-4471
E: chuck.townsend@leg.state.nh.us

Treleaven, Susan (D, SP185)*
454 Sixth Street
Dover, NH 03820
P: (603) 749-2347
E: streleaven@comcast.net

True, Chris (R, SP135)*
41 Hunt Pond Road
Sandown, NH 03873
P: (603) 887-2793
E: chris.true@leg.state.nh.us

Tucker, Pamela (R, SP154)
15 Eagle Court
Greenland, NH 03840
P: (603) 431-8982
E: pam.tucker@leg.state.nh.us

Turcotte, Alan J. (D, SP124)
3 High Ridge Trail
Allenstown, NH 03275
P: (603) 485-2349
E: alanturcotte4rep@gmail.com

Turcotte, Len (R, SP172)*
143 Beauty Hill Road
Barrington, NH 03825
P: (603) 664-7715
E: len.turcotte@leg.state.nh.us

Twombly, Timothy L. (R, SP91)
120 East Hobart Street
Nashua, NH 03060
P: (603) 888-4466
F: (603) 888-4466
E: timothy.twombly@leg.state.nh.us

Ulery, Jordan G. (R, SP94)
P.O. Box 15
Hudson, NH 03051
P: (603) 882-8979
F: (603) 882-6863
E: Repulery@myfairpoint.net

Umberger, Karen C. (R, SP11)
P.O. Box 186
Kearsarge, NH 03847
P: (603) 356-6881
E: karen.umberger@leg.state.nh.us

Vadney, Herbert R. (R, SP2)
10 Sleepy Hollow Road
Meredith, NH 03253
P: (603) 279-1141
E: herb.vadney@leg.state.nh.us

Vann, Ivy (D, SP81)*
50 Summer Street
Peterborough, NH 03458
P: (603) 533-0357
E: Ivy.Vann@leg.state.nh.us

Varney, Peter (R, SP5)*
P.O. 1059
Alton, NH 03809
P: (603) 765-6380
E: pvarney@atsnh.com

Varney, Peter (R, SP5)*
P.O. 1059
Alton, NH 03809
P: (603) 765-6380
E: pvarney@atsnh.com

Verschueren, James (D, SP181)
102-B Sixth Street
Dover, NH 03820
P: (603) 343-4652
E: james.verschueren@leg.state.nh.us

Vose, Michael (R, SP140)*
75 Olde Bridge Lane
Epping, NH 03042
P: (603) 734-4084
E: michael.vose@leg.state.nh.us

New Hampshire

Wall, Janet G. (D, SP174)
9 Kelley Road
Madbury, NH 03823
P: (603) 749-3051
F: (603) 749-3051
E: janet.wall
@leg.state.nh.us

Wallner, Mary Jane (D, SP112)
4 Chestnut Pasture Road
Concord, NH 03301
P: (603) 225-5249
E: Maryjane.Wallner
@leg.state.nh.us

Walsh, Robert M. (D, SP68)
114 Weston Street
Manchester, NH 03104
P: (603) 622-1023
E: bob.walsh
@leg.state.nh.us

Walsh, Thomas C. (R, SP126)
15 Berry Hill Road
Hooksett, NH 03106
P: (603) 623-4104
E: tcwiv1966@aol.com

Ward, Gerald W.R. (D, SP159)
16 Nixon Pike
Portsmouth, NH 03801
P: (603) 436-6142
E: ward4staterep@gmail.com

Ward, Joanne (R, SP150)
6 Wedgewood Drive
Stratham, NH 03885
P: (603) 772-5145
F: (603) 431-2530
E: joanne.ward
@leg.state.nh.us

Ward, Kenneth (D, SP189)
P.O. Box 602
Rollinsford, NH 03869
P: (603) 988-7580
E: ken.ward@leg.state.nh.us

Webb, James (R, SP137)
6 Independence Avenue
Derry, NH 03038
P: (603) 845-3454
E: james.webb
@leg.state.nh.us

Weber, Lucy McV. (D, SP18)
217 Old Keene Road
Walpole, NH 03608
P: (603) 756-4338
E: lwmcv@comcast.net

Welch, David A. (R, SP144)
P.O. Box 570
Kingston, NH 03848
P: (603) 642-4402
E: david.welch
@leg.state.nh.us

Weyler, Kenneth L. (R, SP144)
23 Scotland Road
Kingston, NH 03848
P: (603) 642-3518
E: kweyler@aol.com

Wheeler, Deborah H. (D, SP105)
38 Bay Street
Northfield, NH 03276
P: (603) 286-8212
E: deborah.wheeler
@leg.state.nh.us

White, Andrew (D, SP53)
18 Garnet Street
Lebanon, NH 03766
P: (603) 722-0348
E: andrew.white
@leg.state.nh.us

Whitehouse, Joshua (R, SP170)*
45 Foxtrot Drive
Farmington, NH 03835
P: (603) 497-7091
E: jwhitehouse@outlook.com

Williams, Kermit R. (D, SP61)
55 Burns Hill Road
Wilton, NH 03086
P: (603) 654-7684
E: kermit.williams
@leg.state.nh.us

Woitkun, Steven J. (R, SP164)*
85 Fairview Drive
Danville, NH 03819
P: (603) 642-5154
E: steven.woitkun
@leg.state.nh.us

Wolf, Terry (R, SP64)*
61 Bracken Circle
Bedford, NH 03110
P: (603) 471-0240
E: terry.wolf
@leg.state.nh.us

Wood, David (R, SP152)*
4 Ruth Lane
Hampton, NH 03842
P: (603) 926-8822
E: david.wood
@leg.state.nh.us

Woodbury, David (D, SP62)
37 McCurdy Road
New Boston, NH 03070
P: (603) 487-2634
E: david.woodbury
@leg.state.nh.us

Wright, Donald S. (R, SP17)
160 Sodom Road
Moultonborough, NH 03254
P: (603) 707-7869
E: ted.wright
@leg.state.nh.us

Wuelper, Kurt (R, SP171)*
1336 Parker Mountain Road
Strafford, NH

Zaricki, Nick (R, SP63)*
11 Hoyt Road
Goffstown, NH 03045
P: (603) 660-3872
E: nick.zaricki
@leg.state.nh.us

Congress

Senate

Ayotte, Kelly (R)
Shaheen, Jeanne (D)

House

Kuster, Ann (D, 2)
Shea-Porter, Carol (D, 1)

New Jersey

Executive

Governor

Hon. Chris Christie (R)
Governor
The State House
P.O. Box 001
Trenton, NJ 08625
P: (609) 292-6000
F: (609) 777-2922

Lieutenant Governor

Hon. Kim Guadagno (R)
Lieutenant Governor/Secretary of State
P.O. Box 001
Trenton, NJ 08625
P: (609) 292-6000
F: (609) 292-3454
E: lt.governor@gov.state.nj.us

Attorney General

Hon. John Jay Hoffman
(appointed)
Acting Attorney General
Hughes Justice Complex, 25 Market Street
P.O. Box 080
Trenton, NJ 08625
P: (609) 292-8740

Auditor

Hon. Stephen M. Eells
(appointed by the Legislature)
State Auditor
125 South Warren Street
P.O. Box 067
Trenton, NJ 08625
P: (609) 847-3470
F: (609) 633-0834
E: seells@njleg.org

Secretary of State

Hon. Kim Guadagno
(appointed)
Lieutenant Governor/Secretary of State
P.O. Box 001
Trenton, NJ 08625
P: (609) 292-6000
F: (609) 292-3454
E: lt.governor@gov.state.nj.us

Treasurer

Hon. Andrew P. Sidamon-Eristoff
(appointed)
State Treasurer
State House
P.O. Box 002
Trenton, NJ 08625
P: (608) 292-6748
F: (609) 984-3888

Judiciary

Supreme Court (GA)

Mr. Mark Neary
Clerk
Richard J. Hughes Justice Complex
P.O. Box 970
Trenton, NJ 08625
P: (609) 292-4837

Hon. Stuart Rabner
Chief Justice
Hon. Barry T. Albin
Hon. Mary Catherine Cuff
Hon. Faustino J. Fernandez-Vina
Hon. Jaynee LaVecchia
Hon. Anne M. Patterson
Hon. Lee A. Solomon

Legislative Senate

Senate President

Sen. Stephen M. Sweeney (D)
Senate President
State House
P.O. Box 099
Trenton, NJ 08625
P: (609) 847-3700
F: (609) 984-1235
E: SenSweeney@njleg.org

President Pro Tempore of the Senate

Sen. Nia H. Gill (D)
President Pro Tempore
State House
P.O. Box 099
Trenton, NJ 08625
P: (609) 847-3700
F: (609) 984-1235
E: SenGill@njleg.org

Senate Majority Leader

Sen. Loretta Weinberg (D)
Majority Leader
State House
P.O. Box 099
Trenton, NJ 08625
P: (609) 847-3700
F: (609) 984-1235
E: SenWeinberg@njleg.org

Senate Minority Leader

Sen. Thomas H. Kean Jr. (R)
Republican Leader
State House
P.O. Box 099
Trenton, NJ 08625
P: (609) 847-3600
F: (609) 984-8148
E: SenKean@njleg.org

Secretary of the Senate

Ms. Jennifer A. McQuaid
Secretary of the Senate
State House, Room 115
P.O. Box 099
Trenton, NJ 08625
P: (609) 847-3915

Members of the Senate

Addiego, Dawn Marie (R, 8)
State House
P.O. Box 099
Trenton, NJ 08625
P: (609) 847-3600
F: (609) 984-8148
E: SenAddiego@njleg.org

Allen, Diane B. (R, 7)
State House
P.O. Box 099
Trenton, NJ 08625
P: (609) 847-3600
F: (609) 984-8148
E: SenAllen@njleg.org

Barnes III, Peter J. (D, 18)
State House
P.O. Box 099
Trenton, NJ 08625
P: (609) 847-3700
F: (609) 984-1235
E: senbarnes@njleg.org

Bateman, Christopher (R, 16)
State House
P.O. Box 099
Trenton, NJ 08625
P: (609) 847-3600
F: (609) 984-8148
E: SenBateman@njleg.org

Beach, James (D, 6)
State House
P.O. Box 099
Trenton, NJ 08625
P: (609) 847-3700
F: (609) 984-1235
E: SenBeach@njleg.org

Beck, Jennifer (R, 11)
State House
P.O. Box 099
Trenton, NJ 08625
P: (609) 847-3600
F: (609) 984-8148
E: SenBeck@njleg.org

Bucco, Anthony R. (R, 25)
State House
P.O. Box 099
Trenton, NJ 08625
P: (609) 847-3600
F: (609) 984-8148
E: SenBucco@njleg.org

Cardinale, Gerald (R, 39)
State House
P.O. Box 099
Trenton, NJ 08625
P: (609) 847-3600
F: (609) 984-8148
E: SenCardinale@njleg.org

Codey, Richard J. (D, 27)
State House
P.O. Box 099
Trenton, NJ 08625
P: (609) 847-3700
F: (609) 984-1235
E: SenCodey@njleg.org

Connors, Christopher J. (R, 9)
State House
P.O. Box 099
Trenton, NJ 08625
P: (609) 847-3600
F: (609) 984-8148
E: SenConnors@njleg.org

Cruz-Perez, Nilsa (D, 5)
State House
P.O. Box 099
Trenton, NJ 08625
P: (609) 847-3700
F: (609) 984-1235
E: sencruzperez@njleg.org

New Jersey

Cunningham, Sandra Bolden (D, 31)
State House
P.O. Box 099
Trenton, NJ 08625
P: (609) 847-3700
F: (609) 984-1235
E: SenCunningham@njleg.org

Doherty, Michael J. (R, 23)
State House
P.O. Box 099
Trenton, NJ 08625
P: (609) 847-3600
F: (609) 984-8148
E: SenDoherty@njleg.org

Gill, Nia H. (D, 34)
State House
P.O. Box 099
Trenton, NJ 08625
P: (609) 847-3700
F: (609) 984-1235
E: SenGill@njleg.org

Gordon, Robert M. (D, 38)
State House
P.O. Box 099
Trenton, NJ 08625
P: (609) 847-3700
F: (609) 984-1235
E: SenGordon@njleg.org

Greenstein, Linda R. (D, 14)
State House
P.O. Box 099
Trenton, NJ 08625
P: (609) 847-3700
F: (609) 984-1235
E: SenGreenstein@njleg.org

Holzapfel, James W. (R, 10)
State House
P.O. Box 099
Trenton, NJ 08625
P: (609) 847-3600
F: (609) 984-8148
E: SenHolzapfel@njleg.org

Kean Jr., Thomas H. (R, 21)
State House
P.O. Box 099
Trenton, NJ 08625
P: (609) 847-3600
F: (609) 984-8148
E: SenKean@njleg.org

Kyrillos Jr., Joseph M. (R, 13)
State House
P.O. Box 099
Trenton, NJ 08625
P: (609) 847-3600
F: (609) 984-8148
E: SenKyrillos@njleg.org

Lesniak, Raymond J. (D, 20)
State House
P.O. Box 099
Trenton, NJ 08625
P: (609) 847-3700
F: (609) 984-1235
E: SenLesniak@njleg.org

Madden Jr., Fred H. (D, 4)
State House
P.O. Box 099
Trenton, NJ 08625
P: (609) 847-3700
F: (609) 984-1235
E: SenMadden@njleg.org

Oroho, Steven V. (R, 24)
State House
P.O. Box 099
Trenton, NJ 08625
P: (609) 847-3600
F: (609) 984-8148
E: SenOroho@njleg.org

O'Toole, Kevin J. (R, 40)
State House
P.O. Box 099
Trenton, NJ 08625
P: (609) 847-3600
F: (609) 984-8148
E: SenOToole@njleg.org

Pennacchio, Joseph (R, 26)
State House
P.O. Box 099
Trenton, NJ 08625
P: (609) 847-3600
F: (609) 984-8148
E: SenPennacchio@njleg.org

Pou, Nellie (D, 35)
State House
P.O. Box 099
Trenton, NJ 08625
P: (609) 847-3700
F: (609) 984-1235
E: SenPou@njleg.org

Rice, Ronald L. (D, 28)
State House
P.O. Box 099
Trenton, NJ 08625
P: (609) 847-3700
F: (609) 984-1235
E: SenRice@njleg.org

Ruiz, M. Teresa (D, 29)
State House
P.O. Box 099
Trenton, NJ 08625
P: (609) 847-3700
F: (609) 984-1235
E: SenRuiz@njleg.org

Sacco, Nicholas J. (D, 32)
State House
P.O. Box 099
Trenton, NJ 08625
P: (609) 847-3700
F: (609) 984-1235
E: SenSacco@njleg.org

Sarlo, Paul A. (D, 36)
State House
P.O. Box 099
Trenton, NJ 08625
P: (609) 847-3700
F: (609) 984-1235
E: SenSarlo@njleg.org

Scutari, Nicholas P. (D, 22)
State House
P.O. Box 099
Trenton, NJ 08625
P: (609) 847-3700
F: (609) 984-1235
E: SenScutari@njleg.org

Singer, Robert W. (R, 30)
State House
P.O. Box 099
Trenton, NJ 08625
P: (609) 847-3600
F: (609) 984-8148
E: SenSinger@njleg.org

Smith, Bob (D, 17)
State House
P.O. Box 099
Trenton, NJ 08625
P: (609) 847-3700
F: (609) 984-1235
E: senbsmith@njleg.org

Stack, Brian P. (D, 33)
State House
P.O. Box 099
Trenton, NJ 08625
P: (609) 847-3700
F: (609) 984-1235
E: SenStack@njleg.org

Sweeney, Stephen M. (D, 3)
State House
P.O. Box 099
Trenton, NJ 08625
P: (609) 847-3700
F: (609) 984-1235
E: SenSweeney@njleg.org

Thompson, Samuel D. (R, 12)
State House
P.O. Box 099
Trenton, NJ 08625
P: (609) 847-3600
F: (609) 984-8148
E: SenThompson@njleg.org

Turner, Shirley K. (D, 15)
State House
P.O. Box 099
Trenton, NJ 08625
P: (609) 847-3700
F: (609) 984-1235
E: SenTurner@njleg.org

Van Drew, Jeff (D, 1)
State House
P.O. Box 099
Trenton, NJ 08625
P: (609) 847-3700
F: (609) 984-1235
E: SenVanDrew@njleg.org

Vitale, Joseph F. (D, 19)
State House
P.O. Box 099
Trenton, NJ 08625
P: (609) 847-3700
F: (609) 984-1235
E: SenVitale@njleg.org

Weinberg, Loretta (D, 37)
State House
P.O. Box 099
Trenton, NJ 08625
P: (609) 847-3700
F: (609) 984-1235
E: SenWeinberg@njleg.org

Whelan, Jim (D, 2)
State House
P.O. Box 099
Trenton, NJ 08625
P: (609) 847-3700
F: (609) 984-1235
E: SenWhelan@njleg.org

General Assembly

Speaker of the General Assembly

Asmblymn. Vincent Prieto (D)
Assembly Speaker
State House
P.O. Box 098
Trenton, NJ 08625
P: (609) 847-3500
F: (609) 292-2386
E: AsmPrieto@njleg.org

Speaker Pro Tempore of the General Assembly

Asmblymn. Jerry Green (D)
Speaker Pro Tempore
State House
P.O. Box 098
Trenton, NJ 08625
P: (609) 847-3500
F: (609) 292-2386
E: AsmGreen@njleg.org

General Assembly Majority Leader

Asmblymn. Louis D. Greenwald (D)
Majority Leader
State House
P.O. Box 098
Trenton, NJ 08625
P: (609) 847-3500
F: (609) 292-2386
E: AsmGreenwald@njleg.org

General Assembly Minority Leader

Asmblymn. Jon M. Bramnick (R)
Republican Leader
State House
P.O. Box 098
Trenton, NJ 08625
P: (609) 847-3400
F: (609) 633-9806
E: AsmBramnick@njleg.org

Clerk of the General Assembly

Ms. Dana M. Burley
Clerk of the General Assembly
State House, Room 214
P.O. Box 098
Trenton, NJ 08625
P: (609) 847-3115

Members of the General Assembly

Andrzejczak, Bob (D, 1)
State House
P.O. Box 098
Trenton, NJ 08625
P: (609) 847-3500
F: (609) 292-2386
E: AsmAndrzejczak@njleg.org

Angelini, Mary Pat (R, 11)
State House
P.O. Box 098
Trenton, NJ 08625
P: (609) 847-3400
F: (609) 633-9806
E: AswAngelini@njleg.org

Auth, Robert (R, 39)
State House
P.O. Box 098
Trenton, NJ 08625
P: (609) 847-3400
F: (609) 633-9806
E: AsmAuth@njleg.org

Benson, Daniel R. (D, 14)
State House
P.O. Box 098
Trenton, NJ 08625
P: (609) 847-3500
F: (609) 292-2386
E: AsmBenson@njleg.org

Bramnick, Jon M. (R, 21)
State House
P.O. Box 098
Trenton, NJ 08625
P: (609) 847-3400
F: (609) 633-9806
E: AsmBramnick@njleg.org

Brown, Chris A. (R, 2)
State House
P.O. Box 098
Trenton, NJ 08625
P: (609) 847-3400
F: (609) 633-9806
E: asmchrisabrown@njleg.org

Brown, Christopher J. (R, 8)
State House
P.O. Box 098
Trenton, NJ 08625
P: (609) 847-3400
F: (609) 633-9806
E: asmchristopherjbrown@njleg.org

Bucco, Anthony M. (R, 25)
State House
P.O. Box 098
Trenton, NJ 08625
P: (609) 847-3400
F: (609) 633-9806
E: AsmBucco@njleg.org

Burzichelli, John J. (D, 3)
State House
P.O. Box 098
Trenton, NJ 08625
P: (609) 847-3500
F: (609) 292-2386
E: AsmBurzichelli@njleg.org

Caputo, Ralph R. (D, 28)
State House
P.O. Box 098
Trenton, NJ 08625
P: (609) 847-3500
F: (609) 292-2386
E: AsmCaputo@njleg.org

Caride, Marlene (D, 36)
State House
P.O. Box 098
Trenton, NJ 08625
P: (609) 292-7065
F: (609) 292-2386
E: AswCaride@njleg.org

Carroll, Michael Patrick (R, 25)
State House
P.O. Box 098
Trenton, NJ 08625
P: (609) 847-3400
F: (609) 633-9806
E: AsmCarroll@njleg.org

Casagrande, Caroline (R, 11)
State House
P.O. Box 098
Trenton, NJ 08625
P: (609) 847-3400
F: (609) 633-9806
E: AswCasagrande@njleg.org

Ciattarelli, Jack M. (R, 16)
State House
P.O. Box 098
Trenton, NJ 08625
P: (609) 847-3400
F: (609) 633-9806
E: AsmCiattarelli@njleg.org

Clifton, Robert (R, 12)
State House
P.O. Box 098
Trenton, NJ 08625
P: (609) 847-3400
F: (609) 633-9806
E: AsmClifton@njleg.org

Conaway Jr., Herb (D, 7)
State House
P.O. Box 098
Trenton, NJ 08625
P: (609) 847-3500
F: (609) 292-2386
E: AsmConaway@njleg.org

Coughlin, Craig J. (D, 19)
State House
P.O. Box 098
Trenton, NJ 08625
P: (609) 847-3500
F: (609) 292-2386
E: AsmCoughlin@njleg.org

Dancer, Ronald S. (R, 12)
State House
P.O. Box 098
Trenton, NJ 08625
P: (609) 847-3400
F: (609) 633-9806
E: AsmDancer@njleg.org

Danielsen, Joseph (D, 17)*
State House
P.O. Box 098
Trenton, NJ 08625
P: (609) 847-3500
F: (609) 292-2386
E: AsmDanielsen@njleg.org

DeAngelo, Wayne P. (D, 14)
State House
P.O. Box 098
Trenton, NJ 08625
P: (609) 847-3500
F: (609) 292-2386
E: AsmDeAngelo@njleg.org

DeCroce, BettyLou (R, 26)
State House
P.O. Box 098
Trenton, NJ 08625
P: (609) 847-3400
F: (609) 633-9806
E: AswDeCroce@njleg.org

Diegnan Jr., Patrick J. (D, 18)
State House
P.O. Box 098
Trenton, NJ 08625
P: (609) 847-3500
F: (609) 292-2386
E: AsmDiegnan@njleg.org

DiMaio, John (R, 23)
State House
P.O. Box 098
Trenton, NJ 08625
P: (609) 847-3400
F: (609) 633-9806
E: AsmDiMaio@njleg.org

Egan, Joseph V. (D, 17)
State House
P.O. Box 098
Trenton, NJ 08625
P: (609) 847-3500
F: (609) 292-2386
E: AsmEgan@njleg.org

Eustace, Timothy J. (D, 38)
State House
P.O. Box 098
Trenton, NJ 08625
P: (609) 847-3500
F: (609) 292-2386
E: AsmEustace@njleg.org

New Jersey

Fiocchi, Sam (R, 1)
State House
P.O. Box 098
Trenton, NJ 08625
P: (609) 847-3400
F: (609) 633-9806
E: AsmFiocchi@njleg.org

Fuentes, Angel (D, 5)
State House
P.O. Box 098
Trenton, NJ 08625
P: (609) 847-3500
F: (609) 292-2386
E: AsmFuentes@njleg.org

Garcia, Carmelo G. (D, 33)
State House
P.O. Box 098
Trenton, NJ 08625
P: (609) 847-3500
F: (609) 292-2386
E: AsmGarcia@njleg.org

Giblin, Thomas P. (D, 34)
State House
P.O. Box 098
Trenton, NJ 08625
P: (609) 847-3500
F: (609) 292-2386
E: AsmGiblin@njleg.org

Gove, Dianne C. (R, 9)
State House
P.O. Box 098
Trenton, NJ 08625
P: (609) 847-3400
F: (609) 633-9806
E: AswGove@njleg.org

Green, Jerry (D, 22)
State House
P.O. Box 098
Trenton, NJ 08625
P: (609) 847-3500
F: (609) 292-2386
E: AsmGreen@njleg.org

Greenwald, Louis D. (D, 6)
State House
P.O. Box 098
Trenton, NJ 08625
P: (609) 847-3500
F: (609) 292-2386
E: AsmGreenwald@njleg.org

Gusciora, Reed (D, 15)
State House
P.O. Box 098
Trenton, NJ 08625
P: (609) 847-3500
F: (609) 292-2386
E: AsmGusciora@njleg.org

Handlin, Amy H. (R, 13)
State House
P.O. Box 098
Trenton, NJ 08625
P: (609) 847-3400
F: (609) 633-9806
E: AswHandlin@njleg.org

Huttle, Valerie Vainieri (D, 37)
State House
P.O. Box 098
Trenton, NJ 08625
P: (609) 847-3500
F: (609) 292-2386
E: AswVainieriHuttle@njleg.org

Jasey, Mila M. (D, 27)
State House
P.O. Box 098
Trenton, NJ 08625
P: (609) 847-3500
F: (609) 292-2386
E: AswJasey@njleg.org

Jimenez, Angelica M. (D, 32)
State House
P.O. Box 098
Trenton, NJ 08625
P: (609) 847-3500
F: (609) 292-2386
E: AswJimenez@njleg.org

Johnson, Gordon M. (D, 37)
State House
P.O. Box 098
Trenton, NJ 08625
P: (609) 847-3500
F: (609) 292-2386
E: AsmJohnson@njleg.org

Kean, Sean T. (R, 30)
State House
P.O. Box 098
Trenton, NJ 08625
P: (609) 847-3400
F: (609) 633-9806
E: AsmKean@njleg.org

Lagana, Joseph A. (D, 38)
State House
P.O. Box 098
Trenton, NJ 08625
P: (609) 847-3500
F: (609) 292-2386
E: AsmLagana@njleg.org

Lampitt, Pamela Rosen (D, 6)
State House
P.O. Box 098
Trenton, NJ 08625
P: (609) 847-3500
F: (609) 292-2386
E: AswLampitt@njleg.org

Mainor, Charles (D, 31)
State House
P.O. Box 098
Trenton, NJ 08625
P: (609) 847-3500
F: (609) 292-2386
E: AsmMainor@njleg.org

Mazzeo, Vincent (D, 2)
State House
P.O. Box 098
Trenton, NJ 08625
P: (609) 847-3500
F: (609) 292-2386
E: AsmMazzeo@njleg.org

McGuckin, Gregory P. (R, 10)
State House
P.O. Box 098
Trenton, NJ 08625
P: (609) 847-3400
F: (609) 633-9806
E: AsmMcGuckin@njleg.org

McHose, Alison (R, 24)
State House
P.O. Box 098
Trenton, NJ 08625
P: (609) 847-3400
F: (609) 633-9806
E: AswMcHose@njleg.org

McKeon, John F. (D, 27)
State House
P.O. Box 098
Trenton, NJ 08625
P: (609) 847-3500
F: (609) 292-2386
E: AsmMcKeon@njleg.org

Moriarty, Paul D. (D, 4)
State House
P.O. Box 098
Trenton, NJ 08625
P: (609) 847-3500
F: (609) 292-2386
E: AsmMoriarty@njleg.org

Mosquera, Gabriela (D, 4)
State House
P.O. Box 098
Trenton, NJ 08625
P: (609) 847-3500
F: (609) 292-2386
E: AswMosquera@njleg.org

Mukherji, Raj (D, 33)
State House
P.O. Box 098
Trenton, NJ 08625
P: (609) 847-3500
F: (609) 292-2386
E: AsmMukherji@njleg.org

Munoz, Nancy (R, 21)
State House
P.O. Box 098
Trenton, NJ 08625
P: (609) 847-3400
F: (609) 633-9806
E: AswMunoz@njleg.org

Muoio, Elizabeth Mahar (D, 15)*
State House
P.O. Box 98
Trenton, NJ 08625
P: (609) 847-3500
F: (609) 292-2386
E: AswMuoio@njleg.org

O'Donnell, Jason (D, 31)
State House
P.O. Box 098
Trenton, NJ 08625
P: (609) 847-3500
F: (609) 292-2386
E: AsmODonnell@njleg.org

Oliver, Sheila Y. (D, 34)
State House
P.O. Box 098
Trenton, NJ 08625
P: (609) 847-3500
F: (609) 292-2386
E: AswOliver@njleg.org

O'Scanlon Jr., Declan (R, 13)
State House
P.O. Box 098
Trenton, NJ 08625
P: (609) 847-3400
F: (609) 633-9806
E: AsmOScanlon@njleg.org

Peterson, Erik (R, 23)
State House
P.O. Box 098
Trenton, NJ 08625
P: (609) 847-3400
F: (609) 633-9806
E: AsmPeterson@njleg.org

Pinkin, Nancy J. (D, 18)
State House
P.O. Box 098
Trenton, NJ 08625
P: (609) 847-3500
F: (609) 292-2386
E: AswPinkin@njleg.org

Pintor Marin, Eliana (D, 29)
State House
P.O. Box 098
Trenton, NJ 08625
P: (609) 847-3500
F: (609) 292-2386
E: AswPintorMarin@njleg.org

Prieto, Vincent (D, 32)
State House
P.O. Box 098
Trenton, NJ 08625
P: (609) 847-3500
F: (609) 292-2386
E: AsmPrieto@njleg.org

Quijano, Annette (D, 20)
State House
P.O. Box 098
Trenton, NJ 08625
P: (609) 847-3500
F: (609) 292-2386
E: AswQuijano@njleg.org

Rible, David P. (R, 30)
State House
P.O. Box 098
Trenton, NJ 08625
P: (609) 847-3400
F: (609) 633-9806
E: AsmRible@njleg.org

Rodriguez-Gregg, Maria (R, 8)
State House
P.O. Box 098
Trenton, NJ 08625
P: (609) 847-3400
F: (609) 633-9806
E: AswRodriguez-Gregg@njleg.org

Rumana, Scott T. (R, 40)
State House
P.O. Box 098
Trenton, NJ 08625
P: (609) 847-3400
F: (609) 633-9806
E: AsmRumana@njleg.org

Rumpf, Brian E. (R, 9)
State House
P.O. Box 098
Trenton, NJ 08625
P: (609) 847-3400
F: (609) 633-9806
E: AsmRumpf@njleg.org

Russo, David C. (R, 40)
State House
P.O. Box 098
Trenton, NJ 08625
P: (609) 847-3400
F: (609) 633-9806
E: AsmRusso@njleg.org

Schaer, Gary S. (D, 36)
State House
P.O. Box 098
Trenton, NJ 08625
P: (609) 847-3500
F: (609) 292-2386
E: AsmSchaer@njleg.org

Schepisi, Holly (R, 39)
State House
P.O. Box 098
Trenton, NJ 08625
P: (609) 847-3400
F: (609) 633-9806
E: AswSchepisi@njleg.org

Simon, Donna M. (R, 16)
State House
P.O. Box 098
Trenton, NJ 08625
P: (609) 847-3400
F: (609) 633-9806
E: AswSimon@njleg.org

Singleton, Troy (D, 7)
State House
P.O. Box 098
Trenton, NJ 08625
P: (609) 847-3500
F: (609) 292-2386
E: AsmSingleton@njleg.org

Space, Parker (R, 24)
State House
P.O. Box 098
Trenton, NJ 08625
P: (609) 847-3400
F: (609) 633-9806
E: asmspace@njleg.org

Spencer, L. Grace (D, 29)
State House
P.O. Box 098
Trenton, NJ 08625
P: (609) 847-3500
F: (609) 292-2386
E: AswSpencer@njleg.org

Stender, Linda (D, 22)
State House
P.O. Box 098
Trenton, NJ 08625
P: (609) 847-3500
F: (609) 292-2386
E: AswStender@njleg.org

Sumter, Shavonda E. (D, 35)
State House
P.O. Box 098
Trenton, NJ 08625
P: (609) 847-3500
F: (609) 292-2386
E: AswSumter@njleg.org

Taliaferro, Adam (D, 3)*
State House
P.O. Box 98
Trenton, NJ 08625
P: (609) 847-3500
F: (609) 292-2386
E: AsmTaliaferro@njleg.org

Tucker, Cleopatra G. (D, 28)
State House
P.O. Box 098
Trenton, NJ 08625
P: (609) 847-3500
F: (609) 292-2386
E: AswTucker@njleg.org

Webber, Jay (R, 26)
State House
P.O. Box 098
Trenton, NJ 08625
P: (609) 847-3400
F: (609) 633-9806
E: AsmWebber@njleg.org

Wilson, Gilbert L. (D, 5)
State House
P.O. Box 098
Trenton, NJ 08625
P: (609) 847-3500
F: (609) 292-2386
E: AsmWilson@njleg.org

Wimberly, Benjie E. (D, 35)
State House
P.O. Box 098
Trenton, NJ 08625
P: (609) 847-3500
F: (609) 292-2386
E: AsmWimberly@njleg.org

Wisniewski, John S. (D, 19)
State House
P.O. Box 098
Trenton, NJ 08625
P: (609) 847-3500
F: (609) 292-2386
E: AsmWisniewski@njleg.org

Wolfe, David W. (R, 10)
State House
P.O. Box 098
Trenton, NJ 08625
P: (609) 847-3400
F: (609) 633-9806
E: AsmWolfe@njleg.org

Congress

Senate

Booker, Cory A. (D)
Menendez, Robert (D)

House

Coleman, Bonnie Watson (D, 12)
Frelinghuysen, Rodney P. (R, 11)
Garrett, Scott (R, 5)
Lance, Leonard (R, 7)
LoBiondo, Frank A. (R, 2)
MacArthur, Tom (R, 3)
Norcross, Donald (D, 1)
Pallone Jr., Frank (D, 6)
Pascrell Jr., William (D, 9)
Payne, Donald M. (D, 10)
Sires, Albio (D, 8)
Smith, Chris H. (R, 4)

New Mexico

Executive

Governor

Hon. Susana Martinez (R)
Governor
State Capitol, Fourth Floor
Santa Fe, NM 87501
P: (505) 476-2200
F: (505) 476-2226

Lieutenant Governor

Hon. John A. Sanchez (R)
Lieutenant Governor
State Capitol, Suite 417
Santa Fe, NM 87501
P: (505) 476-2250
F: (505) 476-2257

Attorney General

Hon. Hector H. Balderas (D)
Attorney General
P.O. Drawer 1508
Santa Fe, NM 87504
P: (505) 827-6000
F: (505) 827-5826

Auditor

Hon. Timothy Keller (D)
State Auditor
2540 Camino Edwward Ortiz, Suite A
Santa Fe, NM 87507
P: (505) 476-3800
F: (505) 827-3512

Commissioner of Public Lands

Hon. Aubrey Dunn (R)
310 Old Santa Fe Trail
P.O. Box 1148
Santa Fe, NM 87504
P: (505) 827-5761
F: (505) 827-5761
E: commissioner@slo.state.nm.us

Secretary of State

Hon. Dianna J. Duran (R)
Secretary of State
325 Don Gaspar, Suite 300
Capitol Annex
Santa Fe, NM 87501
P: (505) 827-3600
F: (505) 827-8081
E: diannaj.duran@state.nm.us

Treasurer

Hon. Tim Eichenberg (D)
State Treasurer
P.O. Box 5135
Santa Fe, NM 87505
P: (505) 955-1120
F: (505) 955-1195

Judiciary

Supreme Court (PE)

Mr. Joey D. Moya
Chief Clerk
237 Don Gaspar Avenue, Room 104
P.O. Box 848
Santa Fe, NM 87504
P: (505) 827-4860
F: (505) 827-4837

Hon. Barbara J. Vigil
Chief Justice
Hon. Richard C. Bosson
Hon. Edward L. Chavez
Hon. Charles W. Daniels
Hon. Petra Jimenez Maes

Legislative Senate

Senate President

Hon. John A. Sanchez (R)
Lieutenant Governor
State Capitol, Suite 417
Santa Fe, NM 87501
P: (505) 476-2250
F: (505) 476-2257

President Pro Tempore of the Senate

Sen. Mary Kay Papen (D)
President Pro Tempore
State Capitol Building, Room 105
Santa Fe, NM 87501
P: (505) 986-4733
E: marykay.papen@nmlegis.gov

Senate Majority Leader

Sen. Michael S. Sanchez (D)
Majority Floor Leader
State Capitol Building, Room 119
Santa Fe, NM 87501
P: (505) 986-4727
E: michael.sanchez@nmlegis.gov

Senate Minority Leader

Sen. Stuart Ingle (R)
Minority Floor Leader
State Capitol Building, Room 109A
Santa Fe, NM 87501
P: (505) 986-4702
E: stuart.ingle@nmlegis.gov

Secretary of the Senate

Ms. Lenore Naranjo
Chief Clerk of the Senate
State Capitol Building, Room 115
Santa Fe, NM 87501
P: (505) 986-4714
F: (505) 986-4280
E: lenore.naranjo@nmlegis.gov

Members of the Senate

Beffort, Sue Wilson (R, 19)
State Capitol Building, Room 415G
Santa Fe, NM 87501
P: (505) 986-4395
E: sue.beffort@nmlegis.gov

Brandt, Craig (R, 40)
State Capitol Building, Room 416F
Santa Fe, NM 87501
P: (505) 986-4267
E: craig.brandt@nmlegis.gov

Burt, William F. (R, 33)
State Capitol Building, Room 415A
Santa Fe, NM 87501
P: (505) 986-4366
E: bill.burt@nmlegis.gov

Campos, Pete (D, 8)
State Capitol Building, Room 302B
Santa Fe, NM 87501
P: (505) 986-4311
E: pete.campos@nmlegis.gov

Candelaria, Jacob (D, 26)
State Capitol Building, Room 414A
Santa Fe, NM 87501
P: (505) 986-4391
E: jacob.candelaria@nmlegis.gov

Cervantes, Joseph (D, 31)
State Capitol Building, Room 414D
Santa Fe, NM 87501
P: (505) 986-4385
E: Joseph@cervanteslawnm.com

Cisneros, Carlos R. (D, 6)
State Capitol Building, Room 325B
Santa Fe, NM 87501
P: (505) 986-4362
E: carlos.cisneros@nmlegis.gov

Cotter, Lee (R, 36)
State Capitol Building, Room 416C
Santa Fe, NM 87501
P: (505) 986-4377
E: lee.cotter@nmlegis.gov

Griego, Phil A. (D, 39)
State Capitol Building, Room 323
Santa Fe, NM 87501
P: (505) 986-4513
E: senatorgriego@yahoo.com

Griggs, Ron (R, 34)
State Capitol Building, Room 416B
Santa Fe, NM 87501
P: (505) 986-4276
E: ron.griggs@nmlegis.gov

Ingle, Stuart (R, 27)
State Capitol Building, Room 109A
Santa Fe, NM 87501
P: (505) 986-4702
E: stuart.ingle@nmlegis.gov

Ivey-Soto, Daniel A. (D, 15)
State Capitol Building, Room 300B
Santa Fe, NM 87501
P: (505) 986-4270
E: daniel.ivey-soto@nmlegis.gov

Kernan, Gay G. (R, 42)
State Capitol Building, Room 415E
Santa Fe, NM 87501
P: (505) 986-4274
E: ggkern@valornet.com

Leavell, Carroll H. (R, 41)
State Capitol Building, Room 415C
Santa Fe, NM 87501
P: (505) 986-4278
E: leavell4@leaco.net

Lopez, Linda M. (D, 11)
State Capitol Building, Room 320
Santa Fe, NM 87501
P: (505) 986-4737
E: linda.lopez@nmlegis.gov

Martinez, Richard C. (D, 5)
State Capitol Building, Room 319
Santa Fe, NM 87501
P: (505) 986-4487
E: richard.martinez@nmlegis.gov

McSorley, Cisco (D, 16)
State Capitol Building, Room 217
Santa Fe, NM 87501
P: (505) 986-4389
E: cisco.mcsorley@nmlegis.gov

Moores, Mark (R, 21)
State Capitol Building, Room 416D
Santa Fe, NM 87501
P: (505) 986-4859
E: mark.moores@nmlegis.gov

Morales, Howie C. (D, 28)
State Capitol Building, Room 300D
Santa Fe, NM 87501
P: (505) 986-4863
E: hcm260@gmail.com

Munoz, George K. (D, 4)
State Capitol Building, Room 218A
Santa Fe, NM 87501
P: (505) 986-4371
E: munozgeo@gmail.com

Neville, Steven P. (R, 2)
State Capitol Building, Room 109C
Santa Fe, NM 87501
P: (505) 986-4701
E: steven.neville@nmlegis.gov

O'Neill, Bill B. (D, 13)
State Capitol Building, Room 300C
Santa Fe, NM 87501
P: (505) 986-4260
E: oneillsd13@billoneillfornm.com

Ortiz Y Pino, Gerald P. (D, 12)
State Capitol Building, Room 300A
Santa Fe, NM 87501
P: (505) 986-4482
E: jortizyp@msn.com

Padilla, Michael (D, 14)
State Capitol Building, Room 120
Santa Fe, NM 87501
P: (505) 986-4726
E: michael.padilla@nmlegis.gov

Papen, Mary Kay (D, 38)
State Capitol Building, Room 105
Santa Fe, NM 87501
P: (505) 986-4733
E: marykay.papen@nmlegis.gov

Payne, William H. (R, 20)
State Capitol Building, Room 109B
Santa Fe, NM 87501
P: (505) 986-4703
E: william.payne@nmlegis.gov

Pinto, John (D, 3)
State Capitol Building, Room 301B
Santa Fe, NM 87501
P: (505) 986-4835
E: john.pinto@nmlegis.gov

Pirtle, Cliff R. (R, 32)
State Capitol Building, Room 416E
Santa Fe, NM 87501
P: (505) 986-4862
E: cliff.pirtle@nmlegis.gov

Rodriguez, Nancy (D, 24)
State Capitol Building, Room 301A
Santa Fe, NM 87501
P: (505) 986-4264
E: nancy.rodriguez@nmlegis.gov

Rue, Sander (R, 23)
State Capitol Building, Room 415B
Santa Fe, NM 87501
P: (505) 986-4375
E: sander.rue@nmlegis.gov

Ryan, John C. (R, 10)
State Capitol Building, Room 416G
Santa Fe, NM 87501
P: (505) 986-4373
E: john.ryan@nmlegis.gov

Sanchez, Clemente (D, 30)
State Capitol Building, Room 414B
Santa Fe, NM 87501
P: (505) 986-4369
E: clemente.sanchez@nmlegis.gov

Sanchez, Michael S. (D, 29)
State Capitol Building, Room 119
Santa Fe, NM 87501
P: (505) 986-4727
E: michael.sanchez@nmlegis.gov

Sapien, John M. (D, 9)
State Capitol Building, Room 328A
Santa Fe, NM 87501
P: (505) 986-4834
E: john.sapien@nmlegis.gov

Sharer, William E. (R, 1)
State Capitol Building, Room 415H
Santa Fe, NM 87501
P: (505) 986-4381
E: bill@williamsharer.com

Shendo Jr., Benny (D, 22)
State Capitol Building, Room 302A
Santa Fe, NM 87501
P: (505) 986-4310
E: benny.shendo@nmlegis.gov

Smith, John Arthur (D, 35)
State Capitol Building, Room 325A
Santa Fe, NM 87501
P: (505) 986-4365
E: john.smith@nmlegis.gov

Soules, William P. (D, 37)
State Capitol Building, Room 218B
Santa Fe, NM 87501
P: (505) 986-4380
E: bill.soules@nmlegis.gov

Stewart, Mimi (D, 17)
State Capitol Building, Room 414C
Santa Fe, NM 87501
P: (505) 986-4856
E: mimi.stewart@nmlegis.gov

Torraco, Lisa A. (R, 18)
State Capitol Building, Room 415F
Santa Fe, NM 87501
P: (505) 986-4266
E: lisa.torraco@nmlegis.gov

Wirth, Peter (D, 25)
State Capitol Building, Room 328B
Santa Fe, NM 87501
P: (505) 986-4861
E: peter.wirth@nmlegis.gov

Woods, Pat (R, 7)
State Capitol Building, Room 415D
Santa Fe, NM 87501
P: (505) 986-4393
E: pat.woods@nmlegis.gov

House

Speaker of the House

Rep. Don L. Tripp (R)
Speaker
State Capitol Building, Room 100
Santa Fe, NM 87501
P: (505) 986-4782
E: trippsdon@netscape.net

House Majority Leader

Rep. Nate Gentry (R)
Majority Floor Leader
State Capitol Building, Room 134
Santa Fe, NM 87501
P: (505) 986-4776
E: natefornm@gmail.com

House Minority Leader

Rep. Brian F. Egolf Jr. (D)
Minority Floor Leader
State Capitol Building, Room 125
Santa Fe, NM 87501
P: (505) 986-4757
E: brian.egolf@nmlegis.gov

Clerk of the House

Ms. Denise Greenlaw Ramonas
Chief Clerk of the House
State Capitol, Room 100
Santa Fe, NM 87501
P: (505) 986-4751
F: (505) 986-4755
E: Denise.Ramonas@nmlegis.gov

Members of the House

Adkins, David Edward (R, 29)*
State Capitol Building, Room 203HCN
Santa Fe, NM 87501
P: (505) 986-4453
E: david.adkins@nmlegis.gov

New Mexico

Alcon, Eliseo Lee (D, 6)
State Capitol Building, Room 202B
Santa Fe, NM 87501
P: (505) 986-4220
E: eliseo.alcon@nmlegis.gov

Armstrong, Deborah (D, 17)*
State Capitol Building, Room 413A
Santa Fe, NM 87501
P: (505) 986-4435
E: deborah.armstrong@nmlegis.gov

Baldonado, Alonzo (R, 8)
State Capitol Building, Room 134
Santa Fe, NM 87501
P: (505) 986-4774
E: alonzo.baldonado@nmlegis.gov

Bandy, Paul C. (R, 3)
State Capitol Building, Room 203ECN
Santa Fe, NM 87501
P: (505) 986-4211
E: paul@paulbandy.org

Brown, Cathrynn N. (R, 55)
State Capitol Building, Room 314C
Santa Fe, NM 87501
P: (505) 986-4415
E: cath@cathrynnbrown.com

Chasey, Gail (D, 18)
State Capitol Building, Room 413E
Santa Fe, NM 87501
P: (505) 986-5325
E: gail@gailchasey.com

Clahchischilliage, Sharon (R, 4)
State Capitol Building, Room 203FCN
Santa Fe, NM 87501
P: (505) 986-4211
E: sharon.clahchischill@nmlegis.gov

Cook, Zachary (R, 56)
State Capitol Building, Room 308
Santa Fe, NM 87501
P: (505) 986-4411
E: zachary.cook@nmlegis.gov

Crowder, Randal S. (R, 64)*
State Capitol Building, Room 204B
Santa Fe, NM 87501
P: (505) 986-4210
E: randal.crowder@nmlegis.gov

Dines, James Mitchell (R, 20)*
State Capitol Building, Room 205B
Santa Fe, NM 87501
P: (505) 986-4242
E: jim.dines@nmlegis.gov

Dodge Jr., George (D, 63)
State Capitol Building, Room 203
Santa Fe, NM 87501
P: (505) 986-4227
E: george.dodgejr@nmlegis.gov

Egolf Jr., Brian F. (D, 47)
State Capitol Building, Room 125
Santa Fe, NM 87501
P: (505) 986-4757
E: brian.egolf@nmlegis.gov

Espinoza, Nora (R, 59)
State Capitol Building, Room 313
Santa Fe, NM 87501
P: (505) 986-4852
E: noralee@cableone.net

Ezzell, Candy Spence (R, 58)
State Capitol Building, Room 316B
Santa Fe, NM 87501
P: (505) 986-4420
E: csecows@aol.com

Fajardo, Kelly K. (R, 7)
State Capitol Building, Room 204A
Santa Fe, NM 87501
P: (505) 986-4237
E: kelly.fajardo@nmlegis.gov

Gallegos, David (R, 61)
State Capitol Building, Room 203ICN
Santa Fe, NM 87501
P: (505) 986-4454
E: david.rsi@hotmail.com

Gallegos, Doreen Y. (D, 52)
State Capitol Building, Room 203ACN
Santa Fe, NM 87501
P: (505) 986-4255
E: doreen.gallegos@nmlegis.gov

Garcia, Miguel P. (D, 14)
State Capitol Building, Room 413F
Santa Fe, NM 87501
P: (505) 986-4432
E: miguel.garcia@nmlegis.gov

Garcia Richard, Stephanie (D, 43)
State Capitol Building, Room 203BCN
Santa Fe, NM 87501
P: (505) 986-4464
E: stephanie.garciarichard@nmlegis.gov

Gentry, Nate (R, 30)
State Capitol Building, Room 134
Santa Fe, NM 87501
P: (505) 986-4776
E: natefornm@gmail.com

Gomez, Bill (D, 34)*
State Capitol Building, Room 202A
Santa Fe, NM 87501
P: (505) 986-4221
E: bealquin.gomez@nmlegis.gov

Gonzales, Roberto J. (D, 42)
State Capitol Building, Room 413B
Santa Fe, NM 87501
P: (505) 986-4438
E: roberto.gonzales@nmlegis.gov

Hall, Jimmie C. (R, 28)
State Capitol Building, Room 304C
Santa Fe, NM 87501
P: (505) 986-4320
E: jimmie.hall@nmlegis.gov

Hamilton, Dianne Miller (R, 38)
State Capitol Building, Room 202A
Santa Fe, NM 87501
P: (505) 986-4221
E: tavisha38@gmail.com

Harper, Jason (R, 57)
State Capitol Building, Room 316A
Santa Fe, NM 87501
P: (505) 986-4421
E: JasonHarperNM@gmail.com

Herrell, Yvette (R, 51)
State Capitol Building, Room 314A
Santa Fe, NM 87501
P: (505) 986-4416
E: yherrell@yahoo.com

Irwin, Dona G. (D, 32)
State Capitol Building, Room 201A
Santa Fe, NM 87501
P: (505) 986-4215
E: donagale@zianet.com

James, Conrad D. (R, 24)
State Capitol Building, Room 205A
Santa Fe, NM 87501
P: (505) 986-4243
E: conradjamesforhd24@gmail.com

Johnson, Doreen W. (D, 5)*
State Capitol Building, Room 413A
Santa Fe, NM 87501
P: (505) 986-4435
E: dwonda.johnson@nmlegis.gov

Larranaga, Larry A. (R, 27)
State Capitol Building, Room 304B
Santa Fe, NM 87501
P: (505) 986-4320
E: larry@larranaga.com

Lewis, Tim D. (R, 60)
State Capitol Building, Room 203HCN
Santa Fe, NM 87501
P: (505) 986-4453
E: lewisfornm@gmail.com

Little, Rick (R, 53)
State Capitol Building, Room 203HCN
Santa Fe, NM 87501
P: (505) 986-4453
E: rick.little@nmlegis.gov

Louis, Georgene (D, 26)
State Capitol Building, Room 413E
Santa Fe, NM 87501
P: (505) 986-5325
E: georgene.louis@nmlegis.gov

Lundstrom, Patricia A. (D, 9)
State Capitol Building, Room 413B
Santa Fe, NM 87501
P: (505) 986-4438
E: patricia.lundstrom@nmlegis.gov

Madalena, James Roger (D, 65)
State Capitol Building, Room 203A
Santa Fe, NM 87501
P: (505) 986-4227
E: james.madalena@nmlegis.gov

Maestas, Antonio (D, 16)
State Capitol Building, Room 201B
Santa Fe, NM 87501
P: (505) 986-4214
E: antonio.maestas@nmlegis.gov

Maestas Barnes, Sarah (R, 15)*
State Capitol Building, Room 205A
Santa Fe, NM 87501
P: (505) 986-4243
E: sarah.maestasbarnes@nmlegis.gov

Maez, Stephanie (D, 21)*
State Capitol Building, Room 203CCN
Santa Fe, NM 87501
P: (505) 986-4254
E: stephanie.maez@nmlegis.gov

Martinez, Javier I. (D, 11)*
State Capitol Building, Room 203BCN
Santa Fe, NM 87501
P: (505) 986-4464
E: javier.martinez@nmlegis.gov

Martinez, W. Ken (D, 69)
State Capitol Building, Room 203B
Santa Fe, NM 87501
P: (505) 986-4226
E: ken.martinez@nmlegis.gov

McCamley, Bill (D, 33)
State Capitol Building, Room 413C
Santa Fe, NM 87501
P: (505) 986-4436
E: bill.mccamley@nmlegis.gov

McMillan, Terry (R, 37)
State Capitol Building, Room 312A
Santa Fe, NM 87501
P: (505) 986-4327
E: docmcmillan@gmail.com

McQueen, Matthew (D, 50)*
State Capitol Building, Room 201B
Santa Fe, NM 87501
P: (505) 986-4214
E: matthew.mcqueen@nmlegis.gov

Montoya, Rodney D. (R, 1)*
State Capitol Building, Room 203ECN
Santa Fe, NM 87501
P: (505) 986-4211
E: roddmontoya@gmail.com

Nunez, Andrew (R, 36)
State Capitol Building, Room 204B
Santa Fe, NM 87501
P: (505) 986-4210
E: annunez@zianet.com

Pacheco, Paul (R, 23)
State Capitol Building, Room 204A
Santa Fe, NM 87501
P: (505) 986-4238
E: paul.pacheco@nmlegis.gov

Powdrell-Culbert, Jane E. (R, 44)
State Capitol Building, Room 306
Santa Fe, NM 87501
P: (505) 986-4329
E: jpandp@comcast.net

Rehm, Bill R. (R, 31)
State Capitol Building, Room 314B
Santa Fe, NM 87501
P: (505) 986-4425
E: bill.rehm@nmlegis.gov

Roch, Dennis J. (R, 67)
State Capitol Building, Room 313
Santa Fe, NM 87501
P: (505) 986-4341
E: denroch@hotmail.com

Rodella, Debbie A. (D, 41)
State Capitol Building, Room 202B
Santa Fe, NM 87501
P: (505) 986-4424
E: debbie.rodella@nmlegis.gov

Romero, G. Andres (D, 10)*
State Capitol Building, Room 203DCN
Santa Fe, NM 87501
P: (505) 986-4336
E: andres.romero@nmlegis.gov

Roybal Caballero, Patricia (D, 13)
State Capitol Building, Room 202A
Santa Fe, NM 87501
P: (505) 986-4221
E: pat.roybalcaballero@nmlegis.gov

Ruiloba, Patricio R. (D, 12)*
State Capitol Building, Room 203CCN
Santa Fe, NM 87501
P: (505) 986-4254
E: patricio.ruiloba@nmlegis.gov

Salazar, Nick L. (D, 40)
State Capitol Building, Room 413D
Santa Fe, NM 87501
P: (505) 986-4433

Salazar, Tomás (D, 70)
State Capitol Building, Room 413F
Santa Fe, NM 87501
P: (505) 986-4432
E: tomas.salazar@nmlegis.gov

Scott, Larry R. (R, 62)*
State Capitol Building, Room 203GCN
Santa Fe, NM 87501
P: (505) 986-4450
E: larry.scott@nmlegis.gov

Smith, James E. (R, 22)
State Capitol Building, Room 312B
Santa Fe, NM 87501
P: (505) 986-4454
E: jim@jimsmithnm.com

Stapleton, Sheryl Williams (D, 19)
State Capitol Building, Room 125
Santa Fe, NM 87501
P: (505) 986-4757
E: sheryl.stapleton@nmlegis.gov

Steinborn, Jeff (D, 35)
State Capitol Building, Room 413C
Santa Fe, NM 87501
P: (505) 986-4437
E: jeff.steinborn@nmlegis.gov

Strickler, James R.J. (R, 2)
State Capitol Building, Room 327
Santa Fe, NM 87501
P: (505) 986-4227
E: jamesstrickler@msn.com

Townsend, James G. (R, 54)*
State Capitol Building, Room 203GCN
Santa Fe, NM 87501
P: (505) 986-4450
E: james.townsend@nmlegis.gov

Tripp, Don L. (R, 49)
State Capitol Building, Room 100
Santa Fe, NM 87501
P: (505) 986-4782
E: trippsdon@netscape.net

Trujillo, Carl (D, 46)
State Capitol Building, Room 201A
Santa Fe, NM 87501
P: (505) 986-4215
E: carl.trujillo@nmlegis.gov

Trujillo, Christine (D, 25)
State Capitol Building, Room 203ACN
Santa Fe, NM 87501
P: (505) 986-4255
E: christine.trujillo@nmlegis.gov

Trujillo, Jim R. (D, 45)
State Capitol Building, Room 203DCN
Santa Fe, NM 87501
P: (505) 986-4336
E: jimtrujillo@msn.com

Varela, Luciano (D, 48)
State Capitol Building, Room 413D
Santa Fe, NM 87501
P: (505) 986-4320
E: lucky4st@msn.com

Wooley, Bob (R, 66)
State Capitol Building, Room 203ICN
Santa Fe, NM 87501
P: (505) 986-4454
E: bobwooley66@gmail.com

Youngblood, Monica (R, 68)
State Capitol Building, Room 205B
Santa Fe, NM 87501
P: (505) 986-4242
E: monica@MyNMStateRep.com

Zimmerman, John I. (R, 39)*
State Capitol Building, Room 206A
Santa Fe, NM 87501
P: (505) 986-4250
E: jzimmer_43@msn.com

New Mexico

Congress

Senate

Heinrich, Martin T. (D)
Udall, Tom (D)

House

Grisham, Michelle Lujan (D, 1)
Lujan, Ben R. (D, 3)
Pearce, Steve (R, 2)

New York

Executive

Governor

Hon. Andrew M. Cuomo (D)
Governor
State Capitol
Albany, NY 12224
P: (518) 474-7516

Lieutenant Governor

Hon. Kathy Hochul (D)
Lieutenant Governor
State Capitol
Albany, NY 12224
P: (518) 474-8390
F: (518) 474-7513

Attorney General

Hon. Eric T. Schneiderman (D)
Attorney General
Department of Law
The Capitol, 2nd Floor
Albany, NY 12224
P: (518) 474-7330

Comptroller

Hon. Thomas P. DiNapoli (D)
Comptroller
110 State Street
Albany, NY 12236
P: (518) 474-4040
F: (518) 474-3004
E: tdinapoli@osc.state.ny.us

Secretary of State

Hon. Cesar A. Perales (appointed)
Secretary of State
One Commerce Plaza
99 Washington Avenue, Suite 1100
Albany, NY 12231
P: (518) 486-9846
F: (518) 474-4797
E: info@dos.ny.gov

Treasurer

Honourable Eric Mostert (appointed)
Deputy Commissioner & Treasurer
P.O. Box 7002
Albany, NY 12225
P: (518) 474-4250
F: (518) 402-4118

Judiciary

Court of Appeals (GA)

Mr. Andrew W. Klein
Clerk of the Court
20 Eagle Street
Albany, NY 12207
P: (518) 455-7700
F: (518) 463-6869

Hon. Sheila Abdus-Salaam
Chief Judge
Hon. Eugene F. Pigott Jr.
Hon. Susan P. Read
Hon. Jenny Rivera
Hon. Robert S. Smith

Legislative Senate

Senate President

Hon. Kathy Hochul (D)
Lieutenant Governor
State Capitol
Albany, NY 12224
P: (518) 474-8390
F: (518) 474-7513

Senate Temporary President & Majority Leader

Sen. Dean G. Skelos (R)
Temporary President & Majority Leader
330 State Capitol Building
Albany, NY 12247
P: (518) 455-3171
E: skelos@nysenate.gov

Senate Coalition Co-Leader & Independent Democratic Conference Leader

Sen. Jeffrey D. Klein (D)
Temporary President & Independent Democratic Conference Leader
913 Legislative Office Building
Albany, NY 12247
P: (518) 455-3595
E: jdklein@nysenate.gov

Senate Democratic Conference Leader

Sen. Andrea Stewart-Cousins (D)
Democratic Conference Leader
907 Legislative Office Building
Albany, NY 12247
P: (518) 455-2585
F: (518) 426-6811
E: scousins@nysenate.gov

Secretary of the Senate

Mr. Frank Patience
Secretary of the Senate
State Capitol, Room 321
Albany, NY 12247
P: (518) 455-2051
F: (518) 455-3332

Members of the Senate

Addabbo, Joseph P. (D, 15)
613 Legislative Office Building
Albany, NY 12247
P: (518) 455-2322
F: (518) 426-6875
E: addabbo@nysenate.gov

Amedore Jr., George (R, 46)
802 Legislative Office Building
Albany, NY 12247
P: (518) 455-2350
F: (518) 426-6751
E: Amedore@nysenate.gov

Avella, Tony (D, 11)
902 Legislative Office Building
Albany, NY 12247
P: (518) 455-2210
F: (518) 426-6736
E: avella@nysenate.gov

Bonacic, John J. (R, 42)
509 Legislative Office Building
Albany, NY 12247
P: (518) 455-3181
E: bonacic@nysenate.gov

Boyle, Philip M. (R, 4)
814 Legislative Office Building
Albany, NY 12247
P: (518) 455-3411
E: pboyle@nysenate.gov

Breslin, Neil D. (D, 44)
414 State Capitol Building
Albany, NY 12247
P: (518) 455-2225
E: breslin@nysenate.gov

Carlucci, David (D, 38)
311 Legislative Office Building
Albany, NY 12247
P: (518) 455-2991
F: (518) 426-6737
E: carlucci@nysenate.gov

Comrie, Leroy (D, 14)*
617 Legislative Office Building
Albany, NY 12247
P: (518) 455-2701
E: Comrie@nysenate.gov

Croci, Tom (R, 3)*
306 Legislative Office Building
Albany, NY 12247
P: (518) 455-3570
E: Croci@nysenate.gov

DeFrancisco, John A. (R, 50)
416 State Capitol Building
Albany, NY 12247
P: (518) 455-3511
E: jdefranc@nysenate.gov

Diaz Sr., Ruben (D, 32)
606 Legislative Office Building
Albany, NY 12247
P: (518) 455-2511
F: (518) 426-6945
E: diaz@nysenate.gov

Dilan, Martin Malave (D, 18)
711B Legislative Office Building
Albany, NY 12247
P: (518) 455-2177
F: (518) 426-6947
E: dilan@nysenate.gov

Espaillat, Adriano (D, 31)
513 Legislative Office Building
Albany, NY 12247
P: (518) 455-2041
F: (518) 426-6847
E: espailla@nysenate.gov

Farley, Hugh T. (R, 49)
711 Legislative Office Building
Albany, NY 12247
P: (518) 455-2181
F: (518) 455-2271
E: Farley@nysenate.gov

Felder, Simcha (D, 17)
944 Legislative Office Building
Albany, NY 12247
P: (518) 455-2754
F: (518) 426-6931
E: felder@nysenate.gov

Flanagan, John J. (R, 2)
805 Legislative Office Building
Albany, NY 12247
P: (518) 455-2071
F: (518) 426-6904
E: flanagan@nysenate.gov

Funke, Rich (R, 55)*
905 Legislative Office Building
Albany, NY 12247
P: (518) 455-2215
F: (518) 426-6745
E: Funke@nysenate.gov

New York

Gallivan, Patrick M. (R, 59)
947 Legislative Office Building
Albany, NY 12247
P: (518) 455-3471
F: (518) 426-6949
E: gallivan@nysenate.gov

Gianaris, Michael N. (D, 12)
413 Legislative Office Building
Albany, NY 12247
P: (518) 455-3486
F: (518) 426-6929
E: gianaris@nysenate.gov

Golden, Martin J. (R, 22)
409 Legislative Office Building
Albany, NY 12247
P: (518) 455-2730
E: golden@nysenate.gov

Griffo, Joseph A. (R, 47)
612 Legislative Office Building
Albany, NY 12247
P: (518) 455-3334
F: (518) 426-6921
E: griffo@nysenate.gov

Hamilton, Jesse (D, 20)*
608 Legislative Office Building
Albany, NY 12247
P: (518) 455-2431
E: Hamilton@nysenate.gov

Hannon, Kemp (R, 6)
420 State Capitol Building
Albany, NY 12247
P: (518) 455-2200
E: hannon@nysenate.gov

Hassell-Thompson, Ruth (D, 36)
707 Legislative Office Building
Albany, NY 12247
P: (518) 455-2061
F: (518) 426-6998
E: hassellt@senate.state.ny.us

Hoylman, Brad (D, 27)
413 Legislative Office Building
Albany, NY 12247
P: (518) 455-2451
F: (518) 426-6846
E: hoylman@nysenate.gov

Kennedy, Timothy M. (D, 63)
506 Legislative Office Building
Albany, NY 12247
P: (518) 455-2426
F: (518) 426-6851
E: kennedy@nysenate.gov

Klein, Jeffrey D. (D, 34)
913 Legislative Office Building
Albany, NY 12247
P: (518) 455-3595
E: jdklein@nysenate.gov

Krueger, Liz (D, 28)
905 Legislative Office Building
Albany, NY 12247
P: (518) 455-2297
F: (518) 426-6874
E: lkrueger@nysenate.gov

Lanza, Andrew J. (R, 24)
708 Legislative Office Building
Albany, NY 12247
P: (518) 455-3215
F: (518) 426-6852
E: lanza@nysenate.gov

Larkin, William (R, 39)
502 Legislative Office Building
Albany, NY 12247
P: (518) 455-2770
E: larkin@nysenate.gov

Latimer, George S. (D, 37)
615 Legislative Office Building
Albany, NY 12247
P: (518) 455-2031
F: (518) 426-6860
E: latimer@nysenate.gov

LaValle, Kenneth P. (R, 1)
806 Legislative Office Building
Albany, NY 12247
P: (518) 455-3121
E: lavalle@nysenate.gov

Libous, Thomas W. (R, 52)
429 State Capitol Building
Albany, NY 12247
P: (518) 455-2677
E: Senator@Senatorlibous.com

Little, Elizabeth (R, 45)
310 Legislative Office Building
Albany, NY 12247
P: (518) 455-2811
E: little@nysenate.gov

Marcellino, Carl L. (R, 5)
811 Legislative Office Building
Albany, NY 12247
P: (518) 455-2390
F: (518) 426-6975
E: marcelli@nysenate.gov

Marchione, Kathleen A. (R, 43)
918 Legislative Office Building
Albany, NY 12247
P: (518) 455-2381
F: (518) 426-6985
E: marchione@nysenate.gov

Martins, Jack (R, 7)
915 Legislative Office Building
Albany, NY 12247
P: (518) 455-3265
F: (518) 426-6739
E: martins@nysenate.gov

Montgomery, Velmanette (D, 25)
903 Legislative Office Building
Albany, NY 12247
P: (518) 455-3451
F: (518) 426-6854
E: montgome@nysenate.gov

Murphy, Terrence P. (R, 40)*
817 Legislative Office Building
Albany, NY 12247
P: (518) 455-3111
E: murphy@nysenate.gov

Nozzolio, Michael F. (R, 54)
503 Legislative Office Building
Albany, NY 12247
P: (518) 455-2366
F: (518) 426-6953
E: nozzolio@nysenate.gov

O'Mara, Thomas F. (R, 58)
848 Legislative Office Building
Albany, NY 12247
P: (518) 455-2091
F: (518) 426-6976
E: omara@nysenate.gov

Ortt, Robert (R, 62)*
815 Legislative Office Building
Albany, NY 12247
P: (518) 455-2024
F: (518) 426-6987
E: Ortt@nysenate.gov

Panepinto, Marc (D, 60)*
302 Legislative Office Building
Albany, NY 12247
P: (518) 455-2760
E: Panepinto@nysenate.gov

Parker, Kevin S. (D, 21)
604 Legislative Office Building
Albany, NY 12247
P: (518) 455-2580
F: (518) 426-6843
E: parker@nysenate.gov

Peralta, Jose R. (D, 13)
415 Legislative Office Building
Albany, NY 12247
P: (518) 455-2529
F: (518) 426-6909
E: jperalta@nysenate.gov

Perkins, Bill (D, 30)
517 Legislative Office Building
Albany, NY 12247
P: (518) 455-2441
F: (518) 426-6809
E: perkins@nysenate.gov

Ranzenhofer, Michael H. (R, 61)
848 Legislative Office Building
Albany, NY 12247
P: (518) 455-3161
F: (518) 426-6963
E: ranz@nysenate.gov

Ritchie, Patricia A. (R, 48)
412 Legislative Office Building
Albany, NY 12247
P: (518) 455-3438
F: (518) 426-6740
E: ritchie@nysenate.gov

Rivera, J. Gustavo (D, 33)
408 Legislative Office Building
Albany, NY 12247
P: (518) 455-3395
F: (518) 426-6858
E: grivera@nysenate.gov

Robach, Joseph E. (R, 56)
803 Legislative Office Building
Albany, NY 12247
P: (518) 455-2909
E: robach@nysenate.gov

Sampson, John L. (D, 19)
808 Legislative Office Building
Albany, NY 12247
P: (518) 455-2788
F: (518) 426-6806
E: sampson@senate.state.ny.us

Sanders, James (D, 10)
508 Legislative Office Building
Albany, NY 12247
P: (518) 455-3531
F: (718) 523-3670
E: sanders@nysenate.gov

Savino, Diane J. (D, 23)
315 Legislative Office Building
Albany, NY 12247
P: (518) 455-2437
F: (518) 426-6943
E: savino@nysenate.gov

Serino, Sue (R, 41)*
812 Legislative Office Building
Albany, NY 12247
P: (518) 455-2945
F: (518) 426-6770
E: Serino@nysenate.gov

Serrano, Jose M. (D, 29)
406 Legislative Office Building
Albany, NY 12247
P: (518) 455-2795
F: (518) 426-6886
E: serrano@nysenate.gov

Seward, James L. (R, 51)
430 Legislative Office Building
Albany, NY 12247
P: (518) 455-3131
E: seward@nysenate.gov

Skelos, Dean G. (R, 9)
330 State Capitol Building
Albany, NY 12247
P: (518) 455-3171
E: skelos@nysenate.gov

Squadron, Daniel L. (D, 25)
515 Legislative Office Building
Albany, NY 12247
P: (518) 455-2625
F: (518) 426-6956
E: squadron@nysenate.gov

Stavisky, Toby Ann (D, 16)
706 Legislative Office Building
Albany, NY 12247
P: (518) 455-3461
F: (518) 426-6857
E: stavisky@nysenate.gov

Stewart-Cousins, Andrea (D, 35)
907 Legislative Office Building
Albany, NY 12247
P: (518) 455-2585
F: (518) 426-6811
E: scousins@nysenate.gov

Valesky, David J. (D, 53)
512 Legislative Office Building
Albany, NY 12247
P: (518) 455-2838
F: (518) 426-6885
E: valesky@nysenate.gov

Venditto, Michael (R, 8)*
946 Legislative Office Building
Albany, NY 12247
P: (518) 455-3341
F: (518) 426-6823
E: Venditto@nysenate.gov

Young, Catharine M. (R, 57)
307 Legislative Office Building
Albany, NY 12247
P: (518) 455-3563
F: (518) 426-6905
E: cyoung@nysenate.gov

Assembly

Speaker of the Assembly

Asmblymn. Carl E. Heastie (D)
Speaker of the Assembly
932 Legislative Office Building
Albany, NY 12248
P: (518) 455-4800
F: (518) 455-5459
E: HeastieC@assembly.state.ny.us

Speaker Pro Tempore of the Assembly

Asmblymn. Jeffrion L. Aubry (D)
Speaker Pro Tempore
646 Legislative Office Building
Albany, NY 12248
P: (518) 455-4561
F: (518) 455-4565
E: AubryJ@assembly.state.ny.us

Assembly Majority Leader

Asmblymn. Joseph D. Morelle (D)
Majority Leader
926 Legislative Office Building
Albany, NY 12248
P: (518) 455-5373
F: (518) 455-5647
E: morellej@assembly.state.ny.us

Assembly Minority Leader

Asmblymn. Brian M. Kolb (R)
Minority Leader
933 Legislative Office Building
Albany, NY 12248
P: (518) 455-3751
E: KolbB@assembly.state.ny.us

Clerk of the Assembly

Ms. Laurene R. Kretzler
Clerk of the Assembly
State Capitol, Room 437
Albany, NY 12248
P: (518) 455-4242

Members of the Assembly

Abbate Jr., Peter J. (D, 49)
839 Legislative Office Building
Albany, NY 12248
P: (518) 455-3053
E: abbatep@assembly.state.ny.us

Abinanti, Thomas J. (D, 92)
744 Legislative Office Building
Albany, NY 12248
P: (518) 455-5753
E: abinantit@assembly.state.ny.us

Arroyo, Carmen E. (D, 84)
734 Legislative Office Building
Albany, NY 12248
P: (518) 455-5402
E: ArroyoC@assembly.state.ny.us

Aubry, Jeffrion L. (D, 35)
646 Legislative Office Building
Albany, NY 12248
P: (518) 455-4561
F: (518) 455-4565
E: AubryJ@assembly.state.ny.us

Barclay, William A. (R, 120)
521 Legislative Office Building
Albany, NY 12248
P: (518) 455-5841
E: BarclaW@assembly.state.ny.us

Barrett, Didi (D, 106)
553 Legislative Office Building
Albany, NY 12248
P: (518) 455-5177
F: (518) 455-5418
E: BarrettD@assembly.state.ny.us

Barron, Charles (D, 60)*
532 Legislative Office Building
Albany, NY 12248
P: (518) 455-5912
E: barronc@assembly.state.ny.us

Benedetto, Michael (D, 82)
841 Legislative Office Building
Albany, NY 12248
P: (518) 455-5296
E: benedettom@assembly.state.ny.us

Bichotte, Rodneyse (D, 42)*
736 Legislative Office Building
Albany, NY 12248
P: (518) 455-5385
E: bichotter@assembly.state.ny.us

Blake, Michael (D, 79)*
Legislative Office Building
Albany, NY 12248
E: blakem@assembly.state.ny.us

Blankenbush, Ken (R, 117)
322 Legislative Office Building
Albany, NY 12248
P: (518) 455-5797
E: blankenbushk@assembly.state.ny.us

Borelli, Joseph (R, 62)
428 Legislative Office Building
Albany, NY 12248
P: (518) 455-4495
F: (518) 455-4501
E: BorelliJ@assembly.state.ny.us

Braunstein, Edward (D, 26)
557 Legislative Office Building
Albany, NY 12248
P: (518) 455-5425
F: (518) 455-4648
E: braunsteine@assembly.state.ny.us

Brennan, James F. (D, 44)
422 Legislative Office Building
Albany, NY 12248
P: (518) 455-5377
E: BrennaJ@assembly.state.ny.us

Brindisi, Anthony J. (D, 119)
538 Legislative Office Building
Albany, NY 12248
P: (518) 455-5454
F: (518) 455-5928
E: brindisia@assembly.state.ny.us

Bronson, Harry (D, 138)
502 Legislative Office Building
Albany, NY 12248
P: (518) 455-4527
E: bronsonh@assembly.state.ny.us

Brook-Krasny, Alec (D, 46)
639 Legislative Office Building
Albany, NY 12248
P: (518) 455-4811
E: BrookKrasnyA@assembly.state.ny.us

New York

Buchwald, David (D, 93)
326 Legislative Office Building
Albany, NY 12248
P: (518) 455-5397
E: BuchwaldD
@assembly.state.ny.us

Butler, Marc W. (R, 118)
525 Legislative Office Building
Albany, NY 12248
P: (518) 455-5393
E: ButlerM
@assembly.state.ny.us

Cahill, Kevin A. (D, 103)
716 Legislative Office Building
Albany, NY 12248
P: (518) 455-4436
E: CahillK
@assembly.state.ny.us

Camara, Karim (D, 43)
519 Legislative Office Building
Albany, NY 12248
P: (518) 455-5262
E: CamaraK
@assembly.state.ny.us

Ceretto, John D. (R, 145)
320 Legislative Office Building
Albany, NY 12248
P: (518) 455-5284
E: cerettoj
@assembly.state.ny.us

Clark, Barbara M. (D, 33)
547 Legislative Office Building
Albany, NY 12248
P: (518) 455-4711
E: ClarkB
@assembly.state.ny.us

Colton, William (D, 47)
733 Legislative Office Building
Albany, NY 12248
P: (518) 455-5828
E: ColtonW
@assembly.state.ny.us

Cook, Vivian E. (D, 32)
939 Legislative Office Building
Albany, NY 12248
P: (518) 455-4203
E: CookV
@assembly.state.ny.us

Corwin, Jane L. (R, 144)
446 Legislative Office Building
Albany, NY 12248
P: (518) 455-4601
E: CorwinJ
@assembly.state.ny.us

Crespo, Marcos A. (D, 85)
454 Legislative Office Building
Albany, NY 12248
P: (518) 455-5514
E: CrespoM
@assembly.state.ny.us

Crouch, Clifford W. (R, 122)
450 Legislative Office Building
Albany, NY 12248
P: (518) 455-5741
E: CrouchC
@assembly.state.ny.us

Curran, Brian (R, 21)
318 Legislative Office Building
Albany, NY 12248
P: (518) 455-4656
E: curranb
@assembly.state.ny.us

Cusick, Michael (D, 63)
724 Legislative Office Building
Albany, NY 12248
P: (518) 455-5526
E: CusickM
@assembly.state.ny.us

Cymbrowitz, Steven (D, 45)
627 Legislative Office Building
Albany, NY 12248
P: (518) 455-5214
E: CymbroS
@assembly.state.ny.us

Davila, Maritza (D, 53)
631 Legislative Office Building
Albany, NY 12248
P: (518) 455-5537
F: (518) 455-5789
E: DavilaM
@assembly.state.ny.us

DenDekker, Michael G. (D, 34)
331 Legislative Office Building
Albany, NY 12248
P: (518) 455-4545
E: DenDekkerM
@assembly.state.ny.us

Dilan, Erik (D, 54)*
Legislative Office Building
Albany, NY 12248
E: dilane
@assembly.state.ny.us

Dinowitz, Jeffrey (D, 81)
941 Legislative Office Building
Albany, NY 12248
P: (518) 455-5965
F: (518) 455-4437
E: DinowiJ
@assembly.state.ny.us

DiPietro, David (R, 147)
543 Legislative Office Building
Albany, NY 12248
P: (518) 455-5314
E: DiPietroD
@assembly.state.ny.us

Duprey, Janet (R, 115)
635 Legislative Office Building
Albany, NY 12248
P: (518) 455-5943
E: DupreyJ
@assembly.state.ny.us

Englebright, Steve (D, 4)
621 Legislative Office Building
Albany, NY 12248
P: (518) 455-4804
E: EngleS
@assembly.state.ny.us

Fahy, Patricia (D, 109)
452 Legislative Office Building
Albany, NY 12248
P: (518) 455-4178
E: FahyP
@assembly.state.ny.us

Farrell Jr., Herman D. (D, 71)
923 Legislative Office Building
Albany, NY 12248
P: (518) 455-5491
E: FarrelH
@assembly.state.ny.us

Finch, Gary D. (R, 126)
448 Legislative Office Building
Albany, NY 12248
P: (518) 455-5878
E: FinchG
@assembly.state.ny.us

Fitzpatrick, Michael J. (R, 8)
458 Legislative Office Building
Albany, NY 12248
P: (518) 455-5021
F: (518) 455-4394
E: FitzpatrickM
@assembly.state.ny.us

Friend, Christopher (R, 124)
938 Legislative Office Building
Albany, NY 12248
P: (518) 455-4538
E: friendc
@assembly.state.ny.us

Galef, Sandy (D, 95)
641 Legislative Office Building
Albany, NY 12248
P: (518) 455-5348
E: GalefS
@assembly.state.ny.us

Gantt, David F. (D, 137)
830 Legislative Office Building
Albany, NY 12248
P: (518) 455-5606
E: GanttD
@assembly.state.ny.us

Garbarino, Andrew R. (R, 7)
529 Legislative Office Building
Albany, NY 12248
P: (518) 455-4611
E: GarbarinoA
@assembly.state.ny.us

Giglio, Joe (R, 148)
439 Legislative Office Building
Albany, NY 12248
P: (518) 455-5241
E: GiglioJ
@assembly.state.ny.us

Gjonaj, Mark (D, 80)
633 Legislative Office Building
Albany, NY 12248
P: (518) 455-5844
E: GjonajM
@assembly.state.ny.us

Glick, Deborah J. (D, 66)
717 Legislative Office Building
Albany, NY 12248
P: (518) 455-4841
E: GlickD
@assembly.state.ny.us

Goldfeder III, Phillip (D, 23)
834 Legislative Office Building
Albany, NY 12248
P: (518) 455-4292
E: GoldfederP
@assembly.state.ny.us

Goodell, Andy (R, 150)
545 Legislative Office Building
Albany, NY 12248
P: (518) 455-4511
E: goodella
@assembly.state.ny.us

Gottfried, Richard N. (D, 75)
822 Legislative Office Building
Albany, NY 12248
P: (518) 455-4941
F: (518) 455-5939
E: GottfriedR
@assembly.state.ny.us

Graf, Al (R, 5)
433 Legislative Office Building
Albany, NY 12248
P: (517) 455-5937
E: grafa
@assembly.state.ny.us

Gunther, Aileen M. (D, 100)
826 Legislative Office Building
Albany, NY 12248
P: (518) 455-5355
E: GuntheA
@assembly.state.ny.us

Hawley, Stephen (R, 139)
329 Legislative Office Building
Albany, NY 12248
P: (518) 455-5811
E: HawleyS
@assembly.state.ny.us

Heastie, Carl E. (D, 83)
932 Legislative Office Building
Albany, NY 12248
P: (518) 455-4800
F: (518) 455-5459
E: HeastieC
@assembly.state.ny.us

Hevesi, Andrew (D, 28)
742 Legislative Office Building
Albany, NY 12248
P: (518) 455-4926
E: HevesiA
@assembly.state.ny.us

Hikind, Dov (D, 48)
551 Legislative Office Building
Albany, NY 12248
P: (518) 455-5721
F: (518) 455-5948
E: HikindD
@assembly.state.ny.us

Hooper, Earlene (D, 18)
739 Legislative Office Building
Albany, NY 12248
P: (518) 455-5861
E: hoopere
@assembly.statc.ny.us

Jaffee, Ellen (D, 97)
650 Legislative Office Building
Albany, NY 12248
P: (518) 455-5118
E: JaffeeE
@assembly.state.ny.us

Jean-Pierre, Kimberly (D, 11)*
625 Legislative Office Building
Albany, NY 12248
P: (518) 455-5787
E: jeanpierrek
@assembly.state.ny.us

Johns, Mark (R, 135)
549 Legislative Office Building
Albany, NY 12248
P: (518) 455-5784
E: johnsm
@assembly.state.ny.us

Joyner, Latoya (D, 77)*
427 Legislative Office Building
Albany, NY 12248
P: (518) 455-5671
F: (518) 455-5461
E: joynerl
@assembly.state.ny.us

Kaminsky, Todd (D, 20)*
331 Legislative Office Building
Albany, NY 12248
P: (518) 455-3028
E: kaminskyt
@assembly.state.ny.us

Katz, Steve (R, 94)
718 Legislative Office Building
Albany, NY 12248
P: (518) 455-5783
E: katzs
@assembly.state.ny.us

Kavanagh, Brian P. (D, 74)
419 Legislative Office Building
Albany, NY 12248
P: (518) 455-5506
E: KavanaghB
@assembly.state.ny.us

Kearns, Michael P. (D, 142)
431 Legislative Office Building
Albany, NY 12248
P: (518) 455-4691
E: kearnsm
@assembly.state.ny.us

Kim, Ron (D, 40)
429 Legislative Office Building
Albany, NY 12248
P: (518) 455-5411
E: KimR
@assembly.state.ny.us

Kolb, Brian M. (R, 131)
933 Legislative Office Building
Albany, NY 12248
P: (518) 455-3751
E: KolbB
@assembly.state.ny.us

Lalor, Kieran Michael (R, 105)
531 Legislative Office Building
Albany, NY 12248
P: (518) 455-5725
E: LalorK
@assembly.state.ny.us

Lavine, Charles D. (D, 13)
441 Legislative Office Building
Albany, NY 12248
P: (518) 455-5456
F: (518) 455-5467
E: LavineC
@assembly.state.ny.us

Lawrence, Peter (R, 134)*
722 Legislative Office Building
Albany, NY 12248
P: (518) 455-4664
E: lawrencep
@assembly.state.ny.us

Lentol, Joseph R. (D, 50)
632 Legislative Office Building
Albany, NY 12248
P: (518) 455-4477
E: LentolJ
@assembly.state.ny.us

Lifton, Barbara (D, 125)
555 Legislative Office Building
Albany, NY 12248
P: (518) 455-5444
E: LiftonB
@assembly.state.ny.us

Linares, Guillermo (D, 72)
534 Legislative Office Building
Albany, NY 12248
P: (518) 455-5807
E: linaresg
@assembly.state.ny.us

Lopez, Peter D. (R, 102)
402 Legislative Office Building
Albany, NY 12248
P: (518) 455-5363
E: LopezP
@assembly.state.ny.us

Lupardo, Donna (D, 123)
626 Legislative Office Building
Albany, NY 12248
P: (518) 455-5431
E: LupardoD
@assembly.state.ny.us

Lupinacci, Chad A. (R, 10)
937 Legislative Office Building
Albany, NY 12248
P: (518) 455-5732
E: lupinaccic
@assembly.state.ny.us

Magee, William (D, 121)
828 Legislative Office Building
Albany, NY 12248
P: (518) 455-4807
E: MageeW
@assembly.state.ny.us

Magnarelli, William B. (D, 129)
837 Legislative Office Building
Albany, NY 12248
P: (518) 455-4826
E: MagnarW
@assembly.state.ny.us

Malliotakis, Nicole (R, 64)
725 Legislative Office Building
Albany, NY 12248
P: (518) 455-5716
E: malliotakisn
@assembly.state.ny.us

Markey, Margaret M. (D, 30)
712 Legislative Office Building
Albany, NY 12248
P: (518) 455-4755
E: MarkeyM
@assembly.state.ny.us

Mayer, Shelley (D, 90)
327 Legislative Office Building
Albany, NY 12248
P: (518) 455-3662
F: (518) 455-5499
E: MayerS
@assembly.state.ny.us

McDonald III, John T. (D, 108)
417 Legislative Office Building
Albany, NY 12248
P: (518) 455-4474
E: McDonaldJ
@assembly.state.ny.us

McDonough, David G. (R, 14)
443 Legislative Office Building
Albany, NY 12248
P: (518) 455-4633
E: mcdonoughd
@assembly.state.ny.us

McKevitt, Tom (R, 17)
546 Legislative Office Building
Albany, NY 12248
P: (518) 455-5341
E: MckeviT
@assembly.state.ny.us

McLaughlin, Steven F. (R, 107)
533 Legislative Office Building
Albany, NY 12248
P: (518) 455-5777
E: mclaughlins
@assembly.state.ny.us

Miller, Michael (D, 38)
542 Legislative Office Building
Albany, NY 12248
P: (518) 455-4621
E: MillerMG
@assembly.state.ny.us

Montesano, Michael A. (R, 15)
437 Legislative Office Building
Albany, NY 12248
P: (518) 455-4684
E: MontesanoM
@assembly.state.ny.us

Morelle, Joseph D. (D, 136)
926 Legislative Office Building
Albany, NY 12248
P: (518) 455-5373
F: (518) 455-5647
E: morellej
@assembly.state.ny.us

New York

Mosley, Walter T. (D, 57)
528 Legislative Office Building
Albany, NY 12248
P: (518) 455-5325
E: MosleyW
@assembly.state.ny.us

Moya, Francisco P. (D, 39)
727 Legislative Office Building
Albany, NY 12248
P: (518) 455-4567
E: moyaf
@assembly.state.ny.us

Murray, Dean (R, 3)
430 Legislative Office Building
Albany, NY 12248
P: (518) 455-4901
E: MurrayD
@assembly.state.ny.us

Nojay, Bill (R, 133)
527 Legislative Office Building
Albany, NY 12248
P: (518) 455-5662
F: (518) 455-5918
E: NojayW
@assembly.state.ny.us

Nolan, Catherine (D, 37)
836 Legislative Office Building
Albany, NY 12248
P: (518) 455-4851
E: NolanC
@assembly.state.ny.us

Oaks, Bob (R, 130)
Capitol 444
Albany, NY 12248
P: (518) 455-5655
E: OaksR
@assembly.state.ny.us

O'Donnell, Daniel J. (D, 69)
526 Legislative Office Building
Albany, NY 12248
P: (518) 455-5603
E: OdonnellD
@assembly.state.ny.us

Ortiz, Felix (D, 51)
731 Legislative Office Building
Albany, NY 12248
P: (518) 455-3821
E: OrtizF
@assembly.state.ny.us

Otis, Steven (D, 91)
325 Legislative Office Building
Albany, NY 12248
P: (518) 455-4897
E: OtisS
@assembly.state.ny.us

Palmesano, Philip A. (R, 132)
723 Legislative Office Building
Albany, NY 12248
P: (518) 455-5791
F: (518) 455-4644
E: palmesanop
@assembly.state.ny.us

Palumbo, Anthony H. (R, 2)
719 Legislative Office Building
Albany, NY 12248
P: (518) 455-5294
E: palumboa
@assembly.state.ny.us

Paulin, Amy (D, 88)
713 Legislative Office Building
Albany, NY 12248
P: (518) 455-5585
E: PaulinA
@assembly.state.ny.us

Peoples-Stokes, Crystal D. (D, 141)
619 Legislative Office Building
Albany, NY 12248
P: (518) 455-5005
E: PeopleC
@assembly.state.ny.us

Perry, N. Nick (D, 58)
704 Legislative Office Building
Albany, NY 12248
P: (518) 455-4166
E: PerryN
@assembly.state.ny.us

Persaud, Roxanne (D, 59)*
Legislative Office Building
Albany, NY 12248
E: persaudr
@assembly.state.ny.us

Pichardo, Victor M. (D, 86)
920 Legislative Office Building
Albany, NY 12248
P: (518) 455-5511
E: PichardoV
@assembly.state.ny.us

Pretlow, J. Gary (D, 89)
845 Legislative Office Building
Albany, NY 12248
P: (518) 455-5291
E: PretloJ
@assembly.state.ny.us

Quart, Dan (D, 73)
530 Legislative Office Building
Albany, NY 12248
P: (518) 455-4794
E: quartd
@assembly.state.ny.us

Ra, Edward P. (R, 19)
544 Legislative Office Building
Albany, NY 12248
P: (518) 455-4627
E: rae@assembly.state.ny.us

Raia, Andrew P. (R, 12)
629 Legislative Office Building
Albany, NY 12248
P: (518) 455-5952
E: RaiaA
@assembly.state.ny.us

Ramos, Phil (D, 6)
648 Legislative Office Building
Albany, NY 12248
P: (518) 455-5185
E: RamosP
@assembly.state.ny.us

Rivera, Jose (D, 78)
536 Legislative Office Building
Albany, NY 12248
P: (518) 455-5414
E: RiveraJ
@assembly.state.ny.us

Roberts, Samuel D. (D, 128)
510 Legislative Office Building
Albany, NY 12248
P: (518) 455-5383
E: RobertsS
@assembly.state.ny.us

Robinson, Annette (D, 56)
424 Legislative Office Building
Albany, NY 12248
P: (518) 455-5474
E: RobinsonA
@assembly.state.ny.us

Rodriguez, Robert (D, 68)
729 Legislative Office Building
Albany, NY 12248
P: (518) 455-4781
E: rodriguezrj
@assembly.state.ny.us

Rosenthal, Linda B. (D, 67)
741 Legislative Office Building
Albany, NY 12248
P: (518) 455-5802
E: RosentL
@assembly.state.ny.us

Rozic, Nily (D, 25)
820 Legislative Office Building
Albany, NY 12248
P: (518) 455-5172
F: (518) 455-5479
E: RozicN
@assembly.state.ny.us

Russell, Addie Jenne (D, 116)
456 Legislative Office Building
Albany, NY 12248
P: (518) 455-5545
E: RussellA
@assembly.state.ny.us

Ryan, Sean (D, 149)
540 Legislative Office Building
Albany, NY 12248
P: (518) 455-4886
F: (518) 455-4890
E: ryans
@assembly.state.ny.us

Saladino, Joseph S. (R, 9)
720 Legislative Office Building
Albany, NY 12248
P: (518) 455-5305
E: SaladiJ
@assembly.state.ny.us

Santabarbara, Angelo (D, 111)
833 Legislative Office Building
Albany, NY 12248
P: (518) 455-5197
E: SantabarbaraA
@assembly.state.ny.us

Scarborough, William (D, 29)
622 Legislative Office Building
Albany, NY 12248
P: (518) 455-4451
E: ScarboW
@assembly.state.ny.us

Schimel, Michelle (D, 16)
702 Legislative Office Building
Albany, NY 12248
P: (518) 455-5192
E: SchimelM
@assembly.state.ny.us

Schimminger, Robin (D, 140)
847 Legislative Office Building
Albany, NY 12248
P: (518) 455-4767
E: SchimmR
@assembly.state.ny.us

Seawright, Rebecca (D, 76)*
654 Legislative Office Building
Albany, NY 12248
P: (518) 455-5676
E: seawrightr
@assembly.state.ny.us

Sepulveda, Luis R. (D, 87)
432 Legislative Office Building
Albany, NY 12248
P: (518) 455-5102
E: SepulvedaL
@assembly.state.ny.us

Silver, Sheldon (D, 65)
704 Legislative Office Building
Albany, NY 12248
P: (518) 455-3791
E: Speaker
@assembly.state.ny.us

Simanowitz, Michael (D, 27)
818 Legislative Office Building
Albany, NY 12248
P: (518) 455-4404
E: simanowitzm
@assembly.state.ny.us

Simon, Jo Anne (D, 52)*
824 Legislative Office Building
Albany, NY 12248
P: (518) 455-5426
E: simonj
@assembly.state.ny.us

Simotas, Aravella (D, 36)
652 Legislative Office Building
Albany, NY 12248
P: (518) 455-5014
E: simotasa
@assembly.state.ny.us

Skartados, Frank K. (D, 104)
435 Legislative Office Building
Albany, NY 12248
P: (518) 455-5762
F: (518) 455-5593
E: SkartadosF
@assembly.state.ny.us

Skoufis, James (D, 99)
821 Legislative Office Building
Albany, NY 12248
P: (518) 455-5441
E: SkoufisJ
@assembly.state.ny.us

Solages, Michaelle C. (D, 22)
827 Legislative Office Building
Albany, NY 12248
P: (518) 455-4465
F: (518) 455-5560
E: SolagesM
@assembly.state.ny.us

Stec, Dan (R, 114)
940 Legislative Office Building
Albany, NY 12248
P: (518) 455-5565
E: StecD
@assembly.state.ny.us

Steck, Phil (D, 110)
819 Legislative Office Building
Albany, NY 12248
P: (518) 455-5931
F: (518) 455-5840
E: SteckP
@assembly.state.ny.us

Stirpe Jr., Albert A. (D, 127)
656 Legislative Office Building
Albany, NY 12248
P: (518) 455-4505
E: StirpeA
@assembly.state.ny.us

Tedisco, James (R, 112)
404 Legislative Office Building
Albany, NY 12248
P: (518) 455-5772
E: TediscJ
@assembly.state.ny.us

Tenney, Claudia (R, 101)
426 Legislative Office Building
Albany, NY 12248
P: (515) 455-5334
E: tenneyc
@assembly.state.ny.us

Thiele Jr., Fred W. (I, 1)
746 Legislative Office Building
Albany, NY 12248
P: (518) 455-5997
E: ThieleF
@assembly.state.ny.us

Titone, Matthew (D, 61)
643 Legislative Office Building
Albany, NY 12248
P: (518) 455-4677
E: TitoneM
@assembly.state.ny.us

Titus, Michele R. (D, 31)
844 Legislative Office Building
Albany, NY 12248
P: (518) 455-5668
E: TitusM
@assembly.state.ny.us

Walker, Latrice (D, 55)*
628 Legislative Office Building
Albany, NY 12248
P: (518) 455-4466
E: walkerl
@assembly.state.ny.us

Walter, Raymond (R, 146)
550 Legislative Office Building
Albany, NY 12248
P: (518) 455-4618
F: (518) 455-5023
E: walterr
@assembly.state.ny.us

Weinstein, Helene E. (D, 41)
831 Legislative Office Building
Albany, NY 12248
P: (518) 455-5462
E: weinsth
@assembly.state.ny.us

Weprin, David I. (D, 24)
602 Legislative Office Building
Albany, NY 12248
P: (518) 455-5806
E: weprind
@assembly.state.ny.us

Woerner, Carrie (D, 113)*
323 Legislative Office Building
Albany, NY 12248
P: (518) 455-5404
E: woernerc
@assembly.state.ny.us

Wozniak, Angela (R, 143)*
721 Legislative Office Building
Albany, NY 12248
P: (518) 455-5921
E: wozniaka
@assembly.state.ny.us

Wright, Keith L.T. (D, 70)
943 Legislative Office Building
Albany, NY 12248
P: (518) 455-4793
E: WrightK
@assembly.state.ny.us

Zebrowski, Kenneth P. (D, 96)
637 Legislative Office Building
Albany, NY 12248
P: (518) 455-5735
E: ZebrowskiK
@assembly.state.ny.us

Congress

Senate

Gillibrand, Kirsten (D)
Schumer, Charles E. (D)

House

Bishop, Tim H. (D, 1)
Clarke, Yvette (D, 9)
Collins, Chris (R, 27)
Crowley, Joseph (D, 14)
Engel, Eliot L. (D, 16)
Gibson, Chris (R, 19)
Grimm, Michael (R, 11)
Hanna, Richard (R, 22)
Higgins, Brian M. (D, 26)
Israel, Steve (D, 3)
Jeffries, Hakeem (D, 8)
King, Peter T. (R, 2)
Lowey, Nita M. (D, 17)
Maffei, Dan (D, 24)
Maloney, Carolyn B. (D, 12)
Maloney, Sean Patrick (D, 18)
McCarthy, Carolyn (D, 4)
Meeks, Gregory (D, 5)
Meng, Grace (D, 6)
Nadler, Jerrold (D, 10)
Owens, Bill (D, 21)
Rangel, Charles B. (D, 13)
Reed, Tom (R, 23)
Serrano, Jose E. (D, 15)
Slaughter, Louise McIntosh (D, 25)
Tonko, Paul D. (D, 20)
Velazquez, Nydia M. (D, 7)

North Carolina

Executive

Governor
Hon. Pat McCrory (R)
Governor
20301 Mail Service Center
Raleigh, NC 27699
P: (919) 733-4240
F: (919) 733-2120

Lieutenant Governor
Hon. Dan Forest (R)
Lieutenant Governor
310 North Blount Street
Raleigh, NC 27601
P: (919) 733-7350
F: (919) 733-6595
E: lt.gov@nc.gov

Commissioner of Agriculture & Consumer Services
Mr. Steve Troxler (R)
Commissioner
1001 Mail Service Center
Raleigh, NC 27699
P: (919) 707-3000
F: (919) 733-1141

Attorney General
Hon. Roy A. Cooper III (D)
Attorney General
Department of Justice
P.O.Box 629
Raleigh, NC 27602
P: (919) 716-6400
F: (919) 716-6750
E: rcooper@ncdoj.gov

Auditor
Hon. Beth Wood (D)
State Auditor
2 South Salisbury Street
20601 Mail Service Center
Raleigh, NC 27699
P: (919) 807-7500
F: (919) 807-7647
E: Beth_Wood@ncauditor.net

Commissioner of Insurance
Hon. Wayne Goodwin (D)
Commissioner
430 North Salisbury Street
Dobbs Building, 1201 Mail Service Center
Raleigh, NC 27699
P: (919) 807-6000
F: (919) 733-6495
E: Commissioner@ncdoi.gov

Commissioner of Labor
Hon. Cherie K. Berry (R)
Commissioner
1101 Mail Service Center
Raleigh, NC 27699
P: (919) 807-2796
F: (919) 733-7640
E: cherie.berry@labor.nc.gov

Secretary of State
Hon. Elaine F. Marshall (D)
Secretary of State
P.O. Box 29622
Raleigh, NC 27626
P: (919) 807-2005
F: (919) 807-2010
E: emarshal@sosnc.com

Superintendent of Public Instruction
Dr. June Atkinson (D)
Superintendent of Public Instruction
6301 Mail Service Center
Raleigh, NC 27699
P: (919) 807-3300
F: (919) 807-3445
E: jatkinson@dpi.state.nc.us

Treasurer
Hon. Janet Cowell (D)
State Treasurer
325 North Salisbury Street
Raleigh, NC 27603
P: (919) 508-5176
F: (919) 508-5167
E: janet.cowell@nctreasurer.com

Judiciary

Supreme Court (PE)
Ms. Christie S. Cameron Roeder
Clerk
2 East Morgan Street
P.O. Box 2170
Raleigh, NC 27602
P: (919) 831-5700

Hon. Mark D. Martin
Chief Justice
Hon. Cheri Beasley
Hon. Robert H. Edmunds Jr.
Hon. Sam J. Ervin
Hon. Robin E. Hudson
Hon. Barbara Jackson
Hon. Paul Martin Newby

Legislative Senate

Senate President
Hon. Dan Forest (R)
Lieutenant Governor
310 North Blount Street
Raleigh, NC 27601
P: (919) 733-7350
F: (919) 733-6595
E: lt.gov@nc.gov

President Pro Tempore of the Senate
Sen. Phil Berger (R)
President Pro Tempore
2007 Legislative Building
16 West Jones Street
Raleigh, NC 27601
P: (919) 733-5708
F: (919) 733-2599
E: Phil.Berger@ncleg.net

Senate Majority Leader
Sen. Harry Brown (R)
Majority Leader
300-B Legislative Office Building
300 North Salisbury Street
Raleigh, NC 27603
P: (919) 715-3034
F: (919) 733-3113
E: Harry.Brown@ncleg.net

Senate Minority Leader
Sen. Dan Blue (D)
Democratic Leader
1129 Legislative Building
16 West Jones Street
Raleigh, NC 27601
P: (919) 733-5752
F: (919) 733-2599
E: Dan.Blue@ncleg.net

Secretary of the Senate
Ms. Sarah Lang
Principal Clerk of the Senate
2020 Legislative Building
16 West Jones Street
Raleigh, NC 27601
P: (919) 733-7761
E: sarahc@ncleg.net

Members of the Senate
Alexander Jr., John McKnitt (R, 15)*
2115 Legislative Building
16 West Jones Street
Raleigh, NC 27601
P: (919) 733-5850
F: (919) 733-2599
E: John.Alexander@ncleg.net

Apodaca, Tom (R, 48)
2010 Legislative Building
16 West Jones Street
Raleigh, NC 27601
P: (919) 733-5745
F: (919) 733-2599
E: Tom.Apodaca@ncleg.net

Barefoot, Chad (R, 18)
308 Legislative Office Building
300 North Salisbury Street
Raleigh, NC 27603
P: (919) 715-3036
F: (919) 733-3113
E: Chad.Barefoot@ncleg.net

Barringer, Tamara (R, 17)
620 Legislative Office Building
300 North Salisbury Street
Raleigh, NC 27603
P: (919) 733-5653
F: (919) 733-3113
E: Tamara.Barringer@ncleg.net

Berger, Phil (R, 26)
2007 Legislative Building
16 West Jones Street
Raleigh, NC 27601
P: (919) 733-5708
F: (919) 733-2599
E: Phil.Berger@ncleg.net

Bingham, Stan (R, 33)
625 Legislative Office Building
300 North Salisbury Street
Raleigh, NC 27603
P: (919) 733-5665
F: (919) 733-3113
E: Stan.Bingham@ncleg.net

Blue, Dan (D, 14)
1129 Legislative Building
16 West Jones Street
Raleigh, NC 27601
P: (919) 733-5752
F: (919) 733-2599
E: Dan.Blue@ncleg.net

Brock, Andrew C. (R, 34)
523 Legislative Office Building
300 North Salisbury Street
Raleigh, NC 27603
P: (919) 715-0690
F: (919) 733-3113
E: Andrew.Brock@ncleg.net

Brown, Harry (R, 6)
300-B Legislative Office Building
300 North Salisbury Street
Raleigh, NC 27603
P: (919) 715-3034
F: (919) 733-3113
E: Harry.Brown@ncleg.nct

Bryant, Angela R. (D, 4)
516 Legislative Office Building
300 North Salisbury Street
Raleigh, NC 27603
P: (919) 733-5878
F: (919) 733-3113
E: Angela.Bryant@ncleg.net

Clark, Ben (D, 21)
1117 Legislative Building
16 West Jones Street
Raleigh, NC 27601
P: (919) 733-9349
F: (919) 733-2599
E: Ben.Clark@ncleg.net

Cook, Bill (R, 1)
525 Legislative Office Building
300 North Salisbury Street
Raleigh, NC 27603
P: (919) 715-8293
F: (919) 733-3113
E: Bill.Cook@ncleg.net

Curtis, David L. (R, 44)
410 Legislative Office Building
300 North Salisbury Street
Raleigh, NC 27603
P: (919) 715-3038
F: (919) 733-2599
E: David.Curtis@ncleg.net

Daniel, Warren (R, 46)
623 Legislative Office Building
300 North Salisbury Street
Raleigh, NC 27603
P: (919) 715-7823
F: (919) 733-3113
E: Warren.Daniel@ncleg.net

Davis, Donald (D, 5)
519 Legislative Office Building
300 North Salisbury Street
Raleigh, NC 27603
P: (919) 715-8363
F: (919) 733-3113
E: Don.Davis@ncleg.net

Davis, Jim (R, 50)
408-B Legislative Office Building
300 North Salisbury Street
Raleigh, NC 27603
P: (919) 733-5875
F: (919) 733-3113
E: Jim.Davis@ncleg.net

Ford, Joel D.M. (D, 38)
1119 Legislative Building
16 West Jones Street
Raleigh, NC 27601
P: (919) 733-5955
F: (919) 733-2599
E: Joel.Ford@ncleg.net

Foushee, Valerie P. (D, 23)
517 Legislative Office Building
300 North Salisbury Strcct
Raleigh, NC 27601
P: (919) 733-5804
F: (919) 733-3113
E: Valerie.Foushee@ncleg.net

Gunn, Rick (R, 24)
312 Legislative Office Building
300 North Salisbury Street
Raleigh, NC 27603
P: (919) 301-1446
F: (919) 733-3113
E: Rick.Gunn@ncleg.net

Harrington, Kathy (R, 43)
300-C Legislative Office Building
300 North Salisbury Street
Raleigh, NC 27603
P: (919) 733-5734
F: (919) 733-3113
E: Kathy.Harrington@ncleg.net

Hartsell Jr., Fletcher L. (R, 36)
627 Legislative Office Building
300 North Salisbury Street
Raleigh, NC 27603
P: (919) 733-7223
F: (919) 733-3113
E: Fletcher.Hartsell@ncleg.net

Hise, Ralph (R, 47)
1026 Legislative Building
16 West Jones Street
Raleigh, NC 27601
P: (919) 733-3460
F: (919) 733-2599
E: Ralph.Hise@ncleg.net

Jackson, Brent (R, 10)
2022 Legislative Building
16 West Jones Street
Raleigh, NC 27601
P: (919) 733-5705
F: (919) 733-2599
E: Brent.Jackson@ncleg.net

Jackson, Jeff (D, 37)*
1104 Legislative Building
16 West Jones Street
Raleigh, NC 27601
P: (919) 715-8331
F: (919) 733-2599
E: Jeff.Jackson@ncleg.net

Krawiec, Joyce (R, 31)
2117 Legislative Building
16 West Jones Street
Raleigh, NC 27601
P: (919) 733-7850
F: (919) 733-2599
E: Joyce.Krawiec@ncleg.net

Lee, Michael V. (R, 9)*
2111 Legislative Building
16 West Jones Street
Raleigh, NC 27601
P: (919) 715-2525
F: (919) 733-2599
E: Michael.Lee@ncleg.net

Lowe Jr., Paul A. (D, 32)*
1121 Legislative Building
16 West Jones Street
Raleigh, NC 27601
P: (919) 733-5620
F: (919) 733-2599
E: Paul.Lowe@ncleg.net

McInnis, Thomas Moses (R, 25)*
2106 Legislative Building
16 West Jones Street
Raleigh, NC 27601
P: (919) 733-5953
F: (919) 733-2599
E: Tom.McInnis@ncleg.net

McKissick Jr., Floyd B. (D, 20)
629 Legislative Office Building
300 North Salisbury Street
Raleigh, NC 27603
P: (919) 733-4599
F: (919) 733-3113
E: Floyd.McKissick@ncleg.net

Meredith, Wesley (R, 19)
314 Legislative Office Building
300 North Salisbury Street
Raleigh, NC 27603
P: (919) 733-5776
F: (919) 733-3113
E: Wesley.Meredith@ncleg.net

Newton, E.S. (R, 11)
621 Legislative Office Building
300 North Salisbury Street
Raleigh, NC 27603
P: (919) 715-3030
F: (919) 733-3113
E: Buck.Newton@ncleg.net

Pate Jr., Louis M. (R, 5)
1028 Legislative Building
16 West Jones Street
Raleigh, NC 27601
P: (919) 733-5621
F: (919) 733-2599
E: Louis.Pate@ncleg.net

Rabin, Ronald J. (R, 12)
411 Legislative Office Building
300 North Salisbury Street
Raleigh, NC 27603
P: (919) 733-5748
F: (919) 733-3113
E: Ron.Rabin@ncleg.net

Rabon, Bill (R, 8)
311 Legislative Office Building
300 North Salisbury Street
Raleigh, NC 27603
P: (919) 733-5963
F: (919) 733-3113
E: Bill.Rabon@ncleg.net

Randleman, Shirley B. (R, 30)
628 Legislative Office Building
300 North Salisbury Street
Raleigh, NC 27603
P: (919) 733-5743
F: (919) 733-3113
E: Shirley.Randleman@ncleg.net

North Carolina

Robinson, Gladys A. (D, 28)
1120 Legislative Building
16 West Jones Street
Raleigh, NC 27601
P: (919) 715-3042
F: (919) 733-2599
E: Gladys.Robinson@ncleg.net

Rucho, Robert A. (R, 39)
300-A Legislative Office Building
300 North Salisbury Street
Raleigh, NC 27603
P: (919) 733-5655
F: (919) 733-3113
E: Bob.Rucho@ncleg.net

Sanderson, Norman W. (R, 2)
406 Legislative Office Building
300 North Salisbury Street
Raleigh, NC 27603
P: (919) 733-5706
F: (919) 733-3113
E: Norman.Sanderson@ncleg.net

Smith, Jane Waller (D, 13)*
520 Legislative Office Building
300 North Salisbury Street
Raleigh, NC 27603
P: (919) 733-5651
F: (919) 733-3113
E: Jane.Smith@ncleg.net

Smith-Ingram, Erica Danette (D, 3)*
1118 Legislative Building
16 West Jones Street
Raleigh, NC 27601
P: (919) 733-3040
F: (919) 733-3113
E: Erica.Smith-Ingram@ncleg.net

Soucek, Dan (R, 45)
310 Legislative Office Building
300 North Salisbury Street
Raleigh, NC 27603
P: (919) 733-5742
F: (919) 733-3113
E: Dan.Soucek@ncleg.net

Stein, Josh (D, 16)
1113 Legislative Building
16 West Jones Street
Raleigh, NC 27601
P: (919) 715-6400
F: (919) 733-2599
E: Josh.Stein@ncleg.net

Tarte, Jeff (R, 41)
2108 Legislative Building
16 West Jones Street
Raleigh, NC 27601
P: (919) 715-3050
F: (919) 733-2599
E: Jeff.Tarte@ncleg.net

Tillman, Jerry W. (R, 29)
309 Legislative Office Building
300 North Salisbury Street
Raleigh, NC 27603
P: (919) 733-5870
F: (919) 733-3113
E: Jerry.Tillman@ncleg.net

Tucker, Tommy (R, 35)
1127 Legislative Building
16 West Jones Street
Raleigh, NC 27601
P: (919) 733-7659
F: (919) 733-2599
E: Tommy.Tucker@ncleg.net

Van Duyn, Terry (D, 49)*
1025 Legislative Building
16 West Jones Street
Raleigh, NC 27601
P: (919) 715-3001
F: (919) 733-2599
E: Terry.VanDuyn@ncleg.net

Waddell, Joyce D. (D, 40)*
515 Legislative Office Building
300 North Salisbury Street
Raleigh, NC 27603
F: (919) 733-5650
E: Joyce.Waddell@ncleg.net

Wade, Trudy (R, 27)
521 Legislative Office Building
300 North Salisbury Street
Raleigh, NC 27603
P: (919) 733-5856
F: (919) 733-3113
E: Trudy.Wade@ncleg.net

Wells Jr., Andy (R, 42)
2113 Legislative Building
16 West Jones Street
Raleigh, NC 27601
P: (919) 733-5988
F: (919) 733-2599
E: Andy.Wells@ncleg.net

Woodard, Mike (D, 22)
518 Legislative Office Building
300 North Salisbury Street
Raleigh, NC 27603
P: (919) 733-4809
F: (919) 733-3113
E: Mike.Woodard@ncleg.net

House

Speaker of the House

Rep. Tim Moore (R)
Speaker of the House
2304 Legislative Building
16 West Jones Street
Raleigh, NC 27601
P: (919) 733-4838
F: (919) 733-2599
E: Tim.Moore@ncleg.net

Speaker Pro Tempore of the House

Rep. Paul Stam (R)
Speaker Pro Tempore
612 Legislative Office Building
300 North Salisbury Street
Raleigh, NC 27603
P: (919) 733-2962
F: (919) 733-3113
E: Paul.Stam@ncleg.net

House Majority Leader

Rep. Mike Hager (R)
Majority Leader
301F Legislative Office Building
300 North Salisbury Street
Raleigh, NC 27603
P: (919) 733-5749
F: (919) 733-3113
E: Mike.Hager@ncleg.net

House Minority Leader

Rep. Larry D. Hall (D)
Democratic Minority Leader
506 Legislative Office Building
300 North Salisbury Street
Raleigh, NC 27603
P: (919) 733-5872
F: (919) 733-3113
E: Larry.Hall@ncleg.net

Clerk of the House

Ms. Denise Weeks
Principal Clerk of the House
2319 Legislative Building
16 West Jones Street
Raleigh, NC 27601
P: (919) 733-7760
F: (919) 733-2599
E: denisew@ncleg.net

Members of the House

Adams Jr., James Cecil (R, 96)*
2215 Legislative Building
16 West Jones Street
Raleigh, NC 27601
P: (919) 733-5988
F: (919) 733-2599
E: Jay.Adams@ncleg.net

Adcock, Gale B. (D, 41)*
1211 Legislative Building
16 West Jones Street
Raleigh, NC 27601
P: (919) 733-5602
F: (919) 733-2599
E: Gale.Adcock@ncleg.net

Ager Jr., John Curtis (D, 115)*
1315 Legislative Building
16 West Jones Street
Raleigh, NC 27601
P: (919) 733-5746
F: (919) 733-2599
E: John.Ager@ncleg.net

Alexander Jr., Kelly M. (D, 107)
404 Legislative Office Building
300 North Salisbury Street
Raleigh, NC 27603
P: (919) 733-5778
F: (919) 733-3113
E: Kelly.Alexander@ncleg.net

Arp, Dean (R, 69)
531 Legislative Office Building
300 North Salisbury Street
Raleigh, NC 27603
P: (919) 715-3007
F: (919) 733-3113
E: Dean.Arp@ncleg.net

Avila, Marilyn (R, 40)
2217 Legislative Building
16 West Jones Street
Raleigh, NC 27601
P: (919) 733-5530
F: (919) 733-2599
E: Marilyn.Avila@ncleg.net

Baskerville, Nathan (D, 32)
1004 Legislative Building
16 West Jones Street
Raleigh, NC 27601
P: (919) 733-5824
F: (919) 733-2599
E: Nathan.Baskerville@ncleg.net

Bell IV, John R. (R, 10)
419B Legislative Office Building
300 North Salisbury Street
Raleigh, NC 27603
P: (919) 715-3017
F: (919) 733-3113
E: John.Bell@ncleg.net

Bell, Larry M. (D, 21)
510 Legislative Office Building
300 North Salisbury Street
Raleigh, NC 27603
P: (919) 733-5863
F: (919) 733-3113
E: Larry.Bell@ncleg.net

Bishop, James Daniel (R, 104)*
607 Legislative Office Building
300 North Salisbury Street
Raleigh, NC 27603
P: (919) 715-3009
F: (919) 733-3113
E: Dan.Bishop@ncleg.net

Blackwell, Hugh (R, 86)
541 Legislative Office Building
300 North Salisbury Street
Raleigh, NC 27603
P: (919) 733-5805
F: (919) 733-3113
E: Hugh.Blackwell@ncleg.net

Blust, John M. (R, 62)
2208 Legislative Building
16 West Jones Street
Raleigh, NC 27601
P: (919) 733-5781
F: (919) 733-2599
E: John.Blust@ncleg.net

Boles Jr., James L. (R, 52)
528 Legislative Office Building
300 North Salisbury Street
Raleigh, NC 27603
P: (919) 733-5903
F: (919) 733-3113
E: Jamie.Boles@ncleg.net

Bradford III, John Ray (R, 98)*
2123 Legislative Building
16 West Jones Street
Raleigh, NC 27601
P: (919) 733-5825
F: (919) 733-2599
E: John.Bradford@ncleg.net

Brawley, William (R, 103)
534 Legislative Office Building
300 North Salisbury Street
Raleigh, NC 27603
P: (919) 733-5800
F: (919) 733-3113
E: Bill.Brawley@ncleg.net

Brisson, William (D, 22)
405 Legislative Office Building
300 North Salisbury Street
Raleigh, NC 27603
P: (919) 733-5772
F: (919) 733-3113
E: William.Brisson@ncleg.net

Brockman, Cecil Antonio (D, 60)*
1311 Legislative Building
16 West Jones Street
Raleigh, NC 27601
P: (919) 733-5825
F: (919) 733-2599
E: Cecil.Brockman@ncleg.net

Brody, Mark (R, 55)
2219 Legislative Building
16 West Jones Street
Raleigh, NC 27601
P: (919) 715-3029
F: (919) 733-2599
E: Mark.Brody@ncleg.net

Brown, Brian (R, 9)
604 Legislative Office Building
300 North Salisbury Street
Raleigh, NC 27603
P: (919) 733-5757
F: (919) 733-3113
E: Brian.Brown@ncleg.net

Brown, Rayne (R, 81)
633 Legislative Office Building
300 North Salisbury Street
Raleigh, NC 27603
P: (919) 715-0873
F: (919) 733-3113
E: Rayne.Brown@ncleg.net

Bryan, Rob (R, 88)
536 Legislative Office Building
300 North Salisbury Street
Raleigh, NC 27603
P: (919) 733-5607
F: (919) 733-3113
E: Rob.Bryan@ncleg.net

Bumgardner, Dana (R, 109)
2119 Legislative Building
16 West Jones Street
Raleigh, NC 27601
P: (919) 733-5809
F: (919) 733-2599
E: Dana.Bumgardner@ncleg.net

Burr, Justin P. (R, 67)
307A Legislative Office Building
300 North Salisbury Street
Raleigh, NC 27603
P: (919) 733-5908
F: (919) 733-3113
E: Justin.Burr@ncleg.net

Carney, Becky (D, 102)
1221 Legislative Building
16 West Jones Street
Raleigh, NC 27601
P: (919) 733-5827
F: (919) 733-2599
E: Becky.Carney@ncleg.net

Catlin, Rick (R, 20)
638 Legislative Office Building
300 North Salisbury Street
Raleigh, NC 27603
P: (919) 733-5830
F: (919) 733-3113
E: Rick.Catlin@ncleg.net

Cleveland, George G. (R, 14)
417A Legislative Office Building
300 North Salisbury Street
Raleigh, NC 27603
P: (919) 715-6707
F: (919) 733-3113
E: George.Cleveland@ncleg.net

Collins, Jeff (R, 25)
1106 Legislative Building
16 West Jones Street
Raleigh, NC 27601
P: (919) 733-5802
F: (919) 733-2599
E: Jeff.Collins@ncleg.net

Conrad, Debra (R, 74)
606 Legislative Office Building
300 North Salisbury Street
Raleigh, NC 27603
P: (919) 733-5787
F: (919) 733-3113
E: Debra.Conrad@ncleg.net

Cotham, Tricia Ann (D, 100)
402 Legislative Office Building
300 North Salisbury Street
Raleigh, NC 27603
P: (919) 715-0706
F: (919) 733-3113
E: Tricia.Cotham@ncleg.net

Cunningham, Carla D. (D, 106)
1109 Legislative Building
16 West Jones Street
Raleigh, NC 27601
P: (919) 733-5807
F: (919) 733-2599
E: Carla.Cunningham@ncleg.net

Daughtry, N. Leo (R, 26)
2207 Legislative Building
16 West Jones Street
Raleigh, NC 27601
P: (919) 733-5605
F: (919) 733-2599
E: Leo.Daughtry@ncleg.net

Davis Jr., Ted (R, 19)
418B Legislative Office Building
300 North Salisbury Street
Raleigh, NC 27603
P: (919) 733-5786
F: (919) 733-3113
E: Ted.Davis@ncleg.net

Dixon, Jimmy (R, 4)
416B Legislative Office Building
300 North Salisbury Street
Raleigh, NC 27603
P: (919) 715-3021
F: (919) 733-3113
E: Jimmy.Dixon@ncleg.net

Dobson, Josh (R, 85)
301N Legislative Office Building
300 North Salisbury Street
Raleigh, NC 27603
P: (919) 733-5862
F: (919) 733-3113
E: Josh.Dobson@ncleg.net

Dollar, Nelson (R, 36)
307B Legislative Office Building
300 North Salisbury Street
Raleigh, NC 27603
P: (919) 715-0795
F: (919) 733-3113
E: Nelson.Dollar@ncleg.net

Earle, Beverly M. (D, 101)
514 Legislative Office Building
300 North Salisbury Street
Raleigh, NC 27603
P: (919) 715-2530
F: (919) 733-3113
E: Beverly.Earle@ncleg.net

Elmore, Jeffrey (R, 94)
306A3 Legislative Office Building
300 North Salisbury Street
Raleigh, NC 27603
P: (919) 733-5935
F: (919) 733-3113
E: Jeffrey.Elmore@ncleg.net

Faircloth, John (R, 61)
613 Legislative Office Building
300 North Salisbury Street
Raleigh, NC 27603
P: (919) 733-5877
F: (919) 733-3113
E: John.Faircloth@ncleg.net

Farmer-Butterfield, Jean (D, 24)
1220 Legislative Building
16 West Jones Street
Raleigh, NC 27601
P: (919) 733-5898
F: (919) 733-2599
E: Jean.Farmer-Butterfield@ncleg.net

North Carolina

Fisher, Susan C. (D, 114)
504 Legislative Office Building
300 North Salisbury Street
Raleigh, NC 27603
P: (919) 715-2013
F: (919) 733-3113
E: Susan.Fisher@ncleg.net

Floyd, Elmer (D, 43)
1325 Legislative Building
16 West Jones Street
Raleigh, NC 27601
P: (919) 733-5959
F: (919) 733-2599
E: Elmer.Floyd@ncleg.net

Ford, Carl (R, 76)
608 Legislative Office Building
300 North Salisbury Street
Raleigh, NC 27603
P: (919) 733-5881
F: (919) 733-3113
E: Carl.Ford@ncleg.net

Fraley, John A. (R, 95)*
637 Legislative Office Building
300 North Salisbury Street
Raleigh, NC 27603
P: (919) 733-5741
F: (919) 733-3113
E: John.Fraley@ncleg.net

Gill, Rosa U. (D, 33)
1303 Legislative Building
16 West Jones Street
Raleigh, NC 27601
P: (919) 733-5880
F: (919) 733-2599
E: Rosa.Gill@ncleg.net

Glazier, Rick (D, 44)
1021 Legislative Building
16 West Jones Street
Raleigh, NC 27601
P: (919) 733-5601
F: (919) 733-2599
E: Rick.Glazier@ncleg.net

Goodman, Ken (D, 66)
542 Legislative Office Building
300 North Salisbury Street
Raleigh, NC 27603
P: (919) 733-5823
F: (919) 733-3113
E: Ken.Goodman@ncleg.net

Graham, Charles (D, 47)
1309 Legislative Building
16 West Jones Street
Raleigh, NC 27601
P: (919) 715-0875
F: (919) 733-2599
E: Charles.Graham@ncleg.net

Graham, George (D, 12)
1321 Legislative Building
16 West Jones Street
Raleigh, NC 27601
P: (919) 733-5995
F: (919) 733-2599
E: George.Graham@ncleg.net

Hager, Mike (R, 112)
301F Legislative Office Building
300 North Salisbury Street
Raleigh, NC 27603
P: (919) 733-5749
F: (919) 733-3113
E: Mike.Hager@ncleg.net

Hall, Duane (D, 11)
1019 Legislative Building
16 West Jones Street
Raleigh, NC 27601
P: (919) 733-5755
F: (919) 733-2599
E: Duane.Hall@ncleg.net

Hall, Larry D. (D, 29)
506 Legislative Office Building
300 North Salisbury Street
Raleigh, NC 27603
P: (919) 733-5872
F: (919) 733-3113
E: Larry.Hall@ncleg.net

Hamilton, Susi H. (D, 18)
1313 Legislative Building
16 West Jones Street
Raleigh, NC 27601
P: (919) 733-5754
F: (919) 733-2599
E: Susi.Hamilton@ncleg.net

Hanes Jr., Edward (D, 72)
1006 Legislative Building
16 West Jones Street
Raleigh, NC 27601
P: (919) 733-5829
F: (919) 733-2599
E: Edward.Hanes@ncleg.net

Hardister, Jon (R, 59)
632 Legislative Office Building
300 North Salisbury Street
Raleigh, NC 27603
P: (919) 733-5191
F: (919) 733-3113
E: Jon.Hardister@ncleg.net

Harrison, Pricey (D, 57)
1218 Legislative Building
16 West Jones Street
Raleigh, NC 27601
P: (919) 733-5771
F: (919) 733-2599
E: Pricey.Harrison@ncleg.net

Hastings, Kelly E. (R, 110)
1206 Legislative Building
16 West Jones Street
Raleigh, NC 27601
P: (919) 715-2002
F: (919) 733-2599
E: Kelly.Hastings@ncleg.net

Holley, Yvonne Lewis (D, 38)
1213 Legislative Building
16 West Jones Street
Raleigh, NC 27601
P: (919) 733-5758
F: (919) 733-2599
E: Yvonne.Holley@ncleg.net

Holloway, Bryan R. (R, 91)
305 Legislative Office Building
300 North Salisbury Street
Raleigh, NC 27603
P: (919) 733-5609
F: (919) 733-3113
E: Bryan.Holloway@ncleg.net

Horn, D. Craig (R, 68)
419-A Legislative Office Building
300 North Salisbury Street
Raleigh, NC 27603
P: (919) 733-2406
F: (919) 733-3113
E: Craig.Horn@ncleg.net

Howard, Julia C. (R, 79)
302 Legislative Office Building
300 North Salisbury Street
Raleigh, NC 27603
P: (919) 733-5904
F: (919) 733-3113
E: Julia.Howard@ncleg.net

Hunter III, Howard Jacque (D, 5)*
1307 Legislative Building
16 West Jones Street
Raleigh, NC 27601
P: (919) 733-5780
F: (919) 733-2599
E: Howard.Hunter@ncleg.net

Hurley, Pat B. (R, 70)
532 Legislative Office Building
300 North Salisbury Street
Raleigh, NC 27603
P: (919) 733-5865
F: (919) 733-3113
E: Pat.Hurley@ncleg.net

Iler, Frank (R, 17)
639 Legislative Office Building
300 North Salisbury Street
Raleigh, NC 27603
P: (919) 301-1450
F: (919) 733-3113
E: Frank.Iler@ncleg.net

Insko, Verla (D, 56)
502 Legislative Office Building
300 North Salisbury Street
Raleigh, NC 27603
P: (919) 733-7208
F: (919) 733-3113
E: Verla.Insko@ncleg.net

Jackson, Darren G. (D, 39)
1013 Legislative Building
16 West Jones Street
Raleigh, NC 27601
P: (919) 733-5974
F: (919) 733-2599
E: Darren.Jackson@ncleg.net

Jeter, Charles (R, 92)
2226 Legislative Building
16 West Jones Street
Raleigh, NC 27601
P: (919) 733-5654
F: (919) 733-2599
E: Charles.Jeter@ncleg.net

Johnson, Linda P. (R, 83)
301-D Legislative Office Building
300 North Salisbury Street
Raleigh, NC 27603
P: (919) 733-5861
F: (919) 733-3113
E: Linda.Johnson2@ncleg.net

Johnson, Ralph Chuckie (D, 58)*
1317 Legislative Building
16 West Jones Street
Raleigh, NC 27601
P: (919) 733-5902
F: (919) 733-2599
E: Ralph.Johnson@ncleg.net

Jones, Bert (R, 65)
416-A Legislative Office Building
300 North Salisbury Street
Raleigh, NC 27603
P: (919) 733-5779
F: (919) 733-3113
E: Bert.Jones@ncleg.net

Jordan, Jonathan C. (R, 93)
420 Legislative Office Building
300 North Salisbury Street
Raleigh, NC 27603
P: (919) 733-7727
F: (919) 733-3113
E: Jonathan.Jordan@ncleg.net

Lambeth, Donny (R, 75)
303 Legislative Office Building
300 North Salisbury Street
Raleigh, NC 27603
P: (919) 733-5747
F: (919) 733-3113
E: Donny.Lambeth@ncleg.net

Langdon Jr., James H. (R, 28)
417-B Legislative Office Building
300 North Salisbury Street
Raleigh, NC 27603
P: (919) 733-5849
F: (919) 733-3113
E: James.Langdon@ncleg.net

Lewis, David R. (R, 53)
2301 Legislative Building
16 West Jones Street
Raleigh, NC 27601
P: (919) 715-3015
F: (919) 733-2599
E: David.Lewis@ncleg.net

Lucas, Marvin W. (D, 42)
509 Legislative Office Building
300 North Salisbury Street
Raleigh, NC 27603
P: (919) 733-5775
F: (919) 733-3113
E: Marvin.Lucas@ncleg.net

Luebke, Paul (D, 30)
513 Legislative Office Building
300 North Salisbury Street
Raleigh, NC 27603
P: (919) 733-7663
F: (919) 733-3113
E: Paul.Luebke@ncleg.net

Malone, Chris (R, 35)
603 Legislative Office Building
300 North Salisbury Street
Raleigh, NC 27603
P: (919) 715-3010
F: (919) 733-3113
E: Chris.Malone@ncleg.net

Martin, Grier (D, 34)
1023 Legislative Building
16 West Jones Street
Raleigh, NC 27601
P: (919) 733-5773
F: (919) 733-2599
E: Grier.Martin@ncleg.net

Martin, Susan (R, 8)
526 Legislative Office Building
300 North Salisbury Street
Raleigh, NC 27603
P: (919) 715-3023
F: (919) 733-3113
E: Susan.Martin@ncleg.net

McElraft, Pat (R, 13)
634 Legislative Office Building
300 North Salisbury Street
Raleigh, NC 27603
P: (919) 733-6275
F: (919) 733-3113
E: Pat.McElraft@ncleg.net

McGrady, Chuck (R, 117)
304 Legislative Office Building
300 North Salisbury Street
Raleigh, NC 27603
P: (919) 733-5956
F: (919) 733-3113
E: Chuck.McGrady@ncleg.net

McNeill, Allen (R, 78)
418C Legislative Office Building
300 North Salisbury Street
Raleigh, NC 27603
P: (919) 715-4946
F: (919) 733-3113
E: Allen.McNeill@ncleg.net

Meyer, Graig R. (D, 50)
1111 Legislative Building
16 West Jones Street
Raleigh, NC 27601
P: (919) 715-3019
F: (919) 733-2599
E: Graig.Meyer@ncleg.net

Michaux Jr., Henry M. (D, 31)
1227 Legislative Building
16 West Jones Street
Raleigh, NC 27601
P: (919) 715-2528
F: (919) 733-2599
E: Mickey.Michaux@ncleg.net

Millis, Chris (R, 16)
609 Legislative Office Building
300 North Salisbury Street
Raleigh, NC 27603
P: (919) 715-9664
F: (919) 733-3113
E: Chris.Millis@ncleg.net

Moore, Rodney W. (D, 99)
1219 Legislative Building
16 West Jones Street
Raleigh, NC 27601
P: (919) 733-5606
F: (919) 733-2599
E: Rodney.Moore@ncleg.net

Moore, Tim (R, 111)
2304 Legislative Building
16 West Jones Street
Raleigh, NC 27601
P: (919) 733-4838
F: (919) 733-2599
E: Tim.Moore@ncleg.net

Pendleton, Gary (R, 49)*
610 Legislative Office Building
300 North Salisbury Street
Raleigh, NC 27603
P: (919) 733-5860
F: (919) 733-3113
E: Gary.Pendleton@ncleg.net

Pierce, Garland E. (D, 48)
1204 Legislative Building
16 West Jones Street
Raleigh, NC 27601
P: (919) 733-5803
F: (919) 733-2599
E: Garland.Pierce@ncleg.net

Pittman, Larry G. (R, 82)
1010 Legislative Building
16 West Jones Street
Raleigh, NC 27601
P: (919) 715-2009
F: (919) 733-2599
E: Larry.Pittman@ncleg.net

Presnell, Michele D. (R, 118)
418A Legislative Office Building
300 North Salisbury Street
Raleigh, NC 27603
P: (919) 733-5732
F: (919) 733-3113
E: Michele.Presnell@ncleg.net

Queen, Joe Sam (D, 119)
1017 Legislative Building
16 West Jones Street
Raleigh, NC 27601
P: (919) 715-3005
F: (919) 733-2599
E: Joe.Queen@ncleg.net

Reives II, Robert T. (D, 54)
1323 Legislative Building
16 West Jones Street
Raleigh, NC 27601
P: (919) 733-0057
F: (919) 733-2599
E: Robert.Reives@ncleg.net

Richardson, Bobbie (D, 7)
1217 Legislative Building
16 West Jones Street
Raleigh, NC 27601
P: (919) 715-3032
F: (919) 733-2599
E: Bobbie.Richardson@ncleg.net

Riddell, Dennis (R, 64)
533 Legislative Office Building
300 North Salisbury Street
Raleigh, NC 27603
P: (919) 733-5905
F: (919) 733-3113
E: Dennis.Riddell@ncleg.net

Robinson, George S. (R, 87)
306C Legislative Office Building
300 North Salisbury Street
Raleigh, NC 27601
P: (919) 733-5931
E: George.Robinson@ncleg.net

Ross, Stephen M. (R, 63)
2221 Legislative Building
16 West Jones Street
Raleigh, NC 27601
P: (919) 733-5820
F: (919) 733-2599
E: Stephen.Ross@ncleg.net

Saine, Jason (R, 97)
1326 Legislative Building
16 West Jones Street
Raleigh, NC 27601
P: (919) 733-5782
F: (919) 733-2599
E: Jason.Saine@ncleg.net

Salmon, Brad Andrew (D, 51)*
1319 Legislative Building
16 West Jones Street
Raleigh, NC 27601
P: (919) 715-3026
F: (919) 733-2599
E: Brad.Salmon@ncleg.net

Schaffer, Jacqueline M. (R, 105)
2213 Legislative Building
16 West Jones Street
Raleigh, NC 27601
P: (919) 733-5886
F: (919) 733-2599
E: Jacqueline.Schaffer@ncleg.net

Setzer, Mitchell S. (R, 89)
2204 Legislative Building
16 West Jones Street
Raleigh, NC 27601
P: (919) 733-4948
F: (919) 733-2599
E: Mitchell.Setzer@ncleg.net

Shepard, Phil R. (R, 15)
530 Legislative Office Building
300 North Salisbury Street
Raleigh, NC 27603
P: (919) 715-9644
F: (919) 733-3113
E: Phil.Shepard@ncleg.net

North Carolina

Speciale, Michael (R, 3)
1008 Legislative Building
16 West Jones Street
Raleigh, NC 27601
P: (919) 733-5853
F: (919) 733-2599
E: Michael.Speciale@ncleg.net

Stam, Paul (R, 37)
612 Legislative Office Building
300 North Salisbury Street
Raleigh, NC 27603
P: (919) 733-2962
F: (919) 733-3113
E: Paul.Stam@ncleg.net

Steinburg, Bob (R, 1)
301B Legislative Office Building
300 North Salisbury Street
Raleigh, NC 27603
P: (919) 733-0010
F: (919) 733-3113
E: Bob.Steinburg@ncleg.net

Stevens, Sarah (R, 90)
635 Legislative Office Building
300 North Salisbury Street
Raleigh, NC 27603
P: (919) 715-1883
F: (919) 733-3113
E: Sarah.Stevens@ncleg.net

Szoka, John (R, 45)
2223 Legislative Building
16 West Jones Street
Raleigh, NC 27601
P: (919) 733-9892
F: (919) 733-2599
E: John.Szoka@ncleg.net

Terry, Evelyn (D, 71)
1015 Legislative Building
16 West Jones Street
Raleigh, NC 27601
P: (919) 733-5777
F: (919) 733-2599
E: Evelyn.Terry@ncleg.net

Tine, Paul (D, 6)
529 Legislative Office Building
300 North Salisbury Street
Raleigh, NC 27603
P: (919) 733-5906
F: (919) 733-3113
E: Paul.Tine@ncleg.net

Torbett, John A. (R, 108)
538 Legislative Office Building
300 North Salisbury Street
Raleigh, NC 27603
P: (919) 733-5868
F: (919) 733-3113
E: John.Torbett@ncleg.net

Turner, Brian Mills (D, 116)*
1209 Legislative Building
16 West Jones Street
Raleigh, NC 27601
P: (919) 715-3012
F: (919) 733-2599
E: Brian.Turner@ncleg.net

Turner, Rena W. (R, 84)
602 Legislative Office Building
300 North Salisbury Street
Raleigh, NC 27603
P: (919) 733-5661
F: (919) 733-3113
E: Rena.Turner@ncleg.net

Waddell, Ken (D, 46)
403 Legislative Office Building
300 North Salisbury Street
Raleigh, NC 27603
P: (919) 733-5821
F: (919) 733-3113
E: Ken.Waddell@ncleg.net

Warren, Harry (R, 77)
611 Legislative Office Building
300 North Salisbury Street
Raleigh, NC 27603
P: (919) 733-5784
F: (919) 733-3113
E: Harry.Warren@ncleg.net

Watford, Samuel Lee (R, 80)*
2121 Legislative Building
16 West Jones Street
Raleigh, NC 27601
P: (919) 715-2526
F: (919) 733-2599
E: Sam.Watford@ncleg.net

West, Roger (R, 120)
1229 Legislative Building
16 West Jones Street
Raleigh, NC 27601
P: (919) 733-5859
F: (919) 733-2599
E: Roger.West@ncleg.net

Whitmire, Chris (R, 113)
537 Legislative Office Building
300 North Salisbury Street
Raleigh, NC 27603
P: (919) 715-4466
F: (919) 733-3113
E: Chris.Whitmire@ncleg.net

Willingham, Shelly (D, 23)
501 Legislative Office Building
300 North Salisbury Street
Raleigh, NC 27603
P: (919) 715-3024
F: (919) 733-3113
E: Shelly.Willingham@ncleg.net

Wray, Michael H. (D, 27)
503 Legislative Office Building
300 North Salisbury Street
Raleigh, NC 27603
P: (919) 733-5662
F: (919) 733-3113
E: Michael.Wray@ncleg.net

Yarborough, Lawrence (R, 2)*
1301 Legislative Building
16 West Jones Street
Raleigh, NC 27601
P: (919) 715-0850
F: (919) 733-2599
E: Larry.Yarborough@ncleg.net

Zachary Jr., Walter Lee (R, 73)*
1002 Legislative Building
16 West Jones Street
Raleigh, NC 27601
P: (919) 715-8361
F: (919) 733-2599
E: Lee.Zachary@ncleg.net

Congress

Senate

Burr, Richard (R)
Tillis, Thom (R)

House

Adams, Alma (D, 12)
Butterfield, G.K. (D, 1)
Ellmers, Renee (R, 2)
Foxx, Virginia (R, 5)
Holding, George (R, 13)
Hudson, Richard (R, 8)
Jones Jr., Walter (R, 3)
McHenry, Patrick T. (R, 10)
Meadows, Mark (R, 11)
Pittenger, Robert (R, 9)
Price, David (D, 4)
Rouzer, David (R, 7)
Walker, Mark (R, 6)

North Dakota

Executive

Governor

Hon. Jack Dalrymple (R)
Governor
Department 101
600 East Boulevard Avenue
Bismarck, ND 58505
P: (701) 328-2200
F: (701) 328-2205

Lieutenant Governor

Hon. Drew Wrigley (R)
Lieutenant Governor
State Capitol
Bismarck, ND 58505
P: (701) 328-2200
F: (701) 328-2205

Commissioner of Agriculture

Mr. Doug Goehring (R)
Commissioner
600 East Boulevard Avenue
Department 602
Bismarck, ND 58505
P: (701) 328-2231
F: (701) 328-4567
E: ndda@nd.gov

Attorney General

Hon. Wayne Stenehjem (R)
Attorney General
State Capitol
600 East Boulevard Avenue
Bismarck, ND 58505
P: (701) 328-2210
F: (701) 328-2226
E: wstenehjem@nd.gov

Auditor

Hon. Robert R. Peterson (R)
State Auditor
600 East Boulevard Avenue, 3rd Floor
Bismarck, ND 58505
P: (701) 328-2241
F: (701) 328-1406
E: rpeterso@nd.gov

Commissioner of Insurance

Hon. Adam Hamm (R)
Commissioner
State Capitol, 5th Floor
600 East Boulevard Avenue
Bismarck, ND 58505
P: (701) 328-2440
F: (701) 328-4880
E: insurance@nd.gov

Public Service Commission

Hon. Randy Christmann (R)
Commissioner
600 East Boulevard Avenue
Department 408
Bismarck, ND 58505
P: (701) 328-2400
F: (701) 328-2410
E: rchristmann@nd.gov

Hon. Julie Fedorchak (R)
Commissioner
600 East Boulevard Avenue
Department 408
Bismarck, ND 58505
P: (701) 328-2400
F: (701) 328-2410
E: jfedorchak@nd.gov

Hon. Brian Kalk (R)
Chair
600 East Boulevard Avenue,
Department 408
Bismarck, ND 58505
P: (701) 328-4195
F: (701) 328-2410
E: bkalk@nd.gov

Secretary of State

Hon. Alvin A. Jaeger (R)
Secretary of State
600 East Boulevard
Department 108
Bismarck, ND 58505
P: (701) 328-2900
F: (701) 328-2992
E: sos@nd.gov

Superintendent of Public Instruction

Hon. Kirsten Baesler
Superintendent of Public Instruction
600 East Boulevard Avenue
Department 201
Bismarck, ND 58505
P: (701) 328-4570
F: (701) 328-2461
E: kbaesler@nd.gov

Tax Commissioner

Hon. Ryan Rauschenberger (R)
Commissioner
600 East Boulevard Avenue
Department 127
Bismarck, ND 58505
P: (701) 328-7088
F: (701) 328-3700
E: rrauschenberger@nd.gov

Treasurer

Hon. Kelly L. Schmidt (R)
State Treasurer
State Capitol, 3rd Floor
600 East Boulevard Avenue,
Dept. 120
Bismarck, ND 58505
P: (701) 328-2643
F: (701) 328-3002
E: treasurer@nd.gov

Judiciary

Supreme Court (NE)

Ms. Penny Miller
Clerk of Supreme Court
Judicial Wing, 1st Floor
600 East Boulevard Avenue
Bismarck, ND 58505
P: (701) 328-2221
F: (701) 328-4480
E: PMiller@ndcourts.gov

Hon. Gerald W. VandeWalle
Chief Justice
Hon. Daniel J. Crothers
Hon. Carol Ronning Kapsner
Hon. Lisa Fair McEvers
Hon. Dale V. Sandstrom

Legislative Senate

Senate President

Hon. Drew Wrigley (R)
Lieutenant Governor
State Capitol
Bismarck, ND 58505
P: (701) 328-2200
F: (701) 328-2205

President Pro Tempore of the Senate

Sen. Dick Dever (R)
Senate President Pro Tempore
State Capitol
600 East Boulevard Avenue
Bismarck, ND 58505
P: (701) 328-3373
E: ddever@nd.gov

Senate Majority Leader

Sen. Rich Wardner (R)
Senate Majority Leader
State Capitol
600 East Boulevard Avenue
Bismarck, ND 58505
P: (701) 328-3373
E: rwardner@nd.gov

Senate Minority Leader

Sen. Mac Schneider (D)
Senate Minority Leader
State Capitol
600 East Boulevard Avenue
Bismarck, ND 58505
P: (701) 328-3373
E: macschneider@nd.gov

Secretary of the Senate

Mr. William R. Horton
Secretary of the Senate
State Capitol
600 East Boulevard Avenue
Bismarck, ND 58505
P: (701) 328-2916
F: (701) 328-3615

Members of the Senate

Anderson Jr., Howard C. (R, 8)
State Capitol
600 East Boulevard Avenue
Bismarck, ND 58505
P: (701) 328-3373
E: hcanderson@nd.gov

Armstrong, Kelly M. (R, 36)
State Capitol
600 East Boulevard Avenue
Bismarck, ND 58505
P: (701) 328-3373
E: karmstrong@nd.gov

Axness, Tyler (D, 16)
State Capitol
600 East Boulevard Avenue
Bismarck, ND 58505
P: (701) 328-3373
E: taxness@nd.gov

Bekkedahl, Brad (R, 1)*
State Capitol
600 East Boulevard Avenue
Bismarck, ND 58505
P: (701) 328-3373
E: bbekkedahl@nd.gov

North Dakota

Bowman, Bill L. (R, 39)
State Capitol
600 East Boulevard Avenue
Bismarck, ND 58505
P: (701) 328-3373
E: bbowman@nd.gov

Burckhard, Randy (R, 5)
State Capitol
600 East Boulevard Avenue
Bismarck, ND 58505
P: (701) 328-3373
E: raburckhard@nd.gov

Campbell, Tom (R, 19)
State Capitol
600 East Boulevard Avenue
Bismarck, ND 58505
P: (701) 328-3373
E: tomcampbell@nd.gov

Carlisle, Ron (R, 30)
State Capitol
600 East Boulevard Avenue
Bismarck, ND 58505
P: (701) 328-3373
E: rcarlisle@nd.gov

Casper, Jon (R, 27)*
State Capitol
600 East Boulevard Avenue
Bismarck, ND 58505
P: (701) 328-3373
E: jcasper@nd.gov

Cook, Dwight (R, 34)
State Capitol
600 East Boulevard Avenue
Bismarck, ND 58505
P: (701) 328-3373
E: dcook@nd.gov

Davison, Kyle (R, 41)*
State Capitol
600 East Boulevard Avenue
Bismarck, ND 58505
P: (701) 328-3373
E: kdavison@nd.gov

Dever, Dick (R, 32)
State Capitol
600 East Boulevard Avenue
Bismarck, ND 58505
P: (701) 328-3373
E: ddever@nd.gov

Dotzenrod, Jim (D, 26)
State Capitol
600 East Boulevard Avenue
Bismarck, ND 58505
P: (701) 328-3373
E: jdotzenrod@nd.gov

Erbele, Robert S. (R, 28)
State Capitol
600 East Boulevard Avenue
Bismarck, ND 58505
P: (701) 328-3373
E: rerbele@nd.gov

Flakoll, Tim (R, 44)
State Capitol
600 East Boulevard Avenue
Bismarck, ND 58505
P: (701) 367-5954
E: tflakoll@nd.gov

Grabinger, John (D, 12)
State Capitol
600 East Boulevard Avenue
Bismarck, ND 58505
P: (701) 328-3373
E: jgrabinger@nd.gov

Heckaman, Joan (D, 23)
State Capitol
600 East Boulevard Avenue
Bismarck, ND 58505
P: (701) 328-3373
E: jheckaman@nd.gov

Hogue, David (R, 38)
State Capitol
600 East Boulevard Avenue
Bismarck, ND 58505
P: (701) 328-3373
E: dhogue@nd.gov

Holmberg, Ray (R, 17)
State Capitol
600 East Boulevard Avenue
Bismarck, ND 58505
P: (701) 328-3373
E: rholmberg@nd.gov

Kilzer, Ralph L. (R, 47)
State Capitol
600 East Boulevard Avenue
Bismarck, ND 58505
P: (701) 328-3373
E: rkilzer@nd.gov

Klein, Jerry (R, 14)
State Capitol
600 East Boulevard Avenue
Bismarck, ND 58505
P: (701) 328-3373
E: jklein@nd.gov

Krebsbach, Karen K. (R, 40)
State Capitol
600 East Boulevard Avenue
Bismarck, ND 58505
P: (701) 328-3373
E: kkrebsbach@nd.gov

Laffen, Lonnie (R, 43)
State Capitol
600 East Boulevard Avenue
Bismarck, ND 58505
P: (701) 328-3373
E: llaffen@nd.gov

Larsen, Oley (R, 3)
State Capitol
600 East Boulevard Avenue
Bismarck, ND 58505
P: (701) 328-3373
E: olarsen@nd.gov

Lee, Gary A. (R, 22)
State Capitol
600 East Boulevard Avenue
Bismarck, ND 58505
P: (701) 328-3373
E: galee@nd.gov

Lee, Judy (R, 13)
State Capitol
600 East Boulevard Avenue
Bismarck, ND 58505
P: (701) 328-3373
E: jlee@nd.gov

Luick, Larry (R, 25)
State Capitol
600 East Boulevard Avenue
Bismarck, ND 58505
P: (701) 328-3373
E: lluick@nd.gov

Marcellais, Richard (D, 9)
State Capitol
600 East Boulevard Avenue
Bismarck, ND 58505
P: (701) 328-3373
E: rmarcellais@nd.gov

Mathern, Tim (D, 11)
State Capitol
600 East Boulevard Avenue
Bismarck, ND 58505
P: (701) 328-3373
E: tmathern@nd.gov

Miller, Joe (R, 10)
State Capitol
600 East Boulevard Avenue
Bismarck, ND 58505
P: (701) 328-3373
E: joetmiller@nd.gov

Murphy, Philip M. (D, 20)
State Capitol
600 East Boulevard Avenue
Bismarck, ND 58505
P: (701) 328-3373
E: pmmurphy@nd.gov

Nelson, Carolyn C. (D, 21)
State Capitol
600 East Boulevard Avenue
Bismarck, ND 58505
P: (701) 328-3373
E: cnelson@nd.gov

Oban, Erin (D, 35)*
State Capitol
600 East Boulevard Avenue
Bismarck, ND 58505
P: (701) 328-3373
E: eoban@nd.gov

O'Connell, David (D, 6)
State Capitol
600 East Boulevard Avenue
Bismarck, ND 58505
P: (701) 328-3373
E: doconnell@nd.gov

Oehlke, Dave (R, 15)
State Capitol
600 East Boulevard Avenue
Bismarck, ND 58505
P: (701) 328-3373
E: doehlke@nd.gov

Poolman, Nicole (R, 7)
State Capitol
600 East Boulevard Avenue
Bismarck, ND 58505
P: (701) 328-3373
E: npoolman@nd.gov

Robinson, Larry J. (D, 24)
State Capitol
600 East Boulevard Avenue
Bismarck, ND 58505
P: (701) 328-3373
E: lrobinson@nd.gov

Schaible, Donald (R, 31)
State Capitol
600 East Boulevard Avenue
Bismarck, ND 58505
P: (701) 328-3373
E: dgschaible@nd.gov

Schneider, Mac (D, 42)
State Capitol
600 East Boulevard Avenue
Bismarck, ND 58505
P: (701) 328-3373
E: macschneider@nd.gov

Sinner, George B. (D, 46)
State Capitol
600 East Boulevard Avenue
Bismarck, ND 58505
P: (701) 328-3373
E: georgesinner@nd.gov

Sorvaag, Ronald (R, 45)
State Capitol
600 East Boulevard Avenue
Bismarck, ND 58505
P: (701) 328-3373
E: rsorvaag@nd.gov

Triplett, Connie (D, 18)
State Capitol
600 East Boulevard Avenue
Bismarck, ND 58505
P: (701) 328-3373
E: ctriplett@nd.gov

Unruh, Jessica K. (R, 33)
State Capitol
600 East Boulevard Avenue
Bismarck, ND 58505
P: (701) 328-3373
E: jkunruh@nd.gov

Wanzek, Terry M. (R, 29)
State Capitol
600 East Boulevard Avenue
Bismarck, ND 58505
P: (701) 328-3373
E: tmwanzek@nd.gov

Wardner, Rich (R, 37)
State Capitol
600 East Boulevard Avenue
Bismarck, ND 58505
P: (701) 328-3373
E: rwardner@nd.gov

Warner, John M. (D, 4)
State Capitol
600 East Boulevard Avenue
Bismarck, ND 58779
P: (701) 328-3373
E: jwarner@nd.gov

House

Speaker of the House

Rep. Wesley R. Belter (R)
Speaker of the House
State Capitol
600 East Boulevard Avenue
Bismarck, ND 58505
P: (701) 328-3373
E: wbelter@nd.gov

House Majority Leader

Rep. Al Carlson (R)
House Majority Leader
State Capitol
600 East Boulevard Avenue
Bismarck, ND 58505
P: (701) 328-3373
E: acarlson@nd.gov

House Minority Leader

Rep. Kenton Onstad (D)
House Minority Leader
State Capitol
600 East Boulevard Avenue
Bismarck, ND 58505
P: (701) 328-3373
E: konstad@nd.gov

Clerk of the House

Mr. Buell Reich
Chief Clerk of the House
State Capitol
600 East Boulevard Avenue
Bismarck, ND 58505
P: (701) 328-2916
F: (701) 328-3615

Members of the House

Amerman, Bill (D, 26)
State Capitol
600 East Boulevard Avenue
Bismarck, ND 58505
P: (701) 328-3373
E: bamerman@nd.gov

Anderson, Bert (R, 2)*
State Capitol
600 East Boulevard Avenue
Bismarck, ND 58505
P: (701) 328-3373
E: bertanderson@nd.gov

Anderson, Dick (R, 6)
State Capitol
600 East Boulevard Avenue
Bismarck, ND 58505
P: (701) 228-4782
E: dickanderson@nd.gov

Anderson, Pamela (D, 41)*
State Capitol
600 East Boulevard Avenue
Bismarck, ND 58505
P: (701) 328-3373
E: pkanderson@nd.gov

Beadle, Thomas (R, 27)
State Capitol
600 East Boulevard Avenue
Bismarck, ND 58505
P: (701) 328-3373
E: tbeadle@nd.gov

Becker, Rich (R, 43)*
State Capitol
600 East Boulevard Avenue
Bismarck, ND 58505
P: (701) 328-3373
E: rsbecker@nd.gov

Becker, Rick C. (R, 7)
State Capitol
600 East Boulevard Avenue
Bismarck, ND 58505
P: (701) 328-3373
E: rcbecker@nd.gov

Bellew, Larry (R, 38)
State Capitol
600 East Boulevard Avenue
Bismarck, ND 58505
P: (701) 328-3373
E: lbellew@nd.gov

Belter, Wesley R. (R, 22)
State Capitol
600 East Boulevard Avenue
Bismarck, ND 58505
P: (701) 328-3373
E: wbelter@nd.gov

Boe, Tracy (D, 9)
State Capitol
600 East Boulevard Avenue
Bismarck, ND 58505
P: (701) 328-3373
E: tboe@nd.gov

Boehning, Randy (R, 27)
State Capitol
600 East Boulevard Avenue
Bismarck, ND 58505
P: (701) 328-3373
E: rboehning@nd.gov

Boschee, Joshua A. (D, 44)
State Capitol
600 East Boulevard Avenue
Bismarck, ND 58505
P: (701) 328-3373
E: jboschee@nd.gov

Brabandt, Roger (R, 5)
State Capitol
600 East Boulevard Avenue
Bismarck, ND 58505
P: (701) 328-3373
E: rbrabandt@nd.gov

Brandenburg, Michael D. (R, 28)
State Capitol
600 East Boulevard Avenue
Bismarck, ND 58505
P: (701) 328-3373
E: mbrandenburg@nd.gov

Carlson, Al (R, 41)
State Capitol
600 East Boulevard Avenue
Bismarck, ND 58505
P: (701) 328-3373
E: acarlson@nd.gov

Damschen, Chuck (R, 10)
State Capitol
600 East Boulevard Avenue
Bismarck, ND 58505
P: (701) 868-3281
E: cdamschen@nd.gov

Delmore, Lois (D, 43)
State Capitol
600 East Boulevard Avenue
Bismarck, ND 58505
P: (701) 328-3373
E: ldelmore@nd.gov

Delzer, Jeff (R, 8)
State Capitol
600 East Boulevard Avenue
Bismarck, ND 58505
P: (701) 328-3373
E: jdelzer@nd.gov

Devlin, Bill (R, 23)
State Capitol
600 East Boulevard Avenue
Bismarck, ND 58505
P: (701) 328-3373
E: bdevlin@nd.gov

Dockter, Jason (R, 7)
State Capitol
600 East Boulevard Avenue
Bismarck, ND 58505
P: (701) 258-4378
E: jddockter@nd.gov

Dosch, Mark A. (R, 32)
State Capitol
600 East Boulevard Avenue
Bismarck, ND 58505
P: (701) 328-3373
E: mdosch@nd.gov

Fehr, Alan (R, 36)
State Capitol
600 East Boulevard Avenue
Bismarck, ND 58505
P: (701) 328-3373
E: afehr@nd.gov

Frantsvog, Bob (R, 40)
State Capitol
600 East Boulevard Avenue
Bismarck, ND 58505
P: (701) 328-3373
E: rfrantsvog@nd.gov

Froseth, Glen (R, 4)
State Capitol
600 East Boulevard Avenue
Bismarck, ND 58505
P: (701) 328-3373
E: gfroseth@nd.gov

Glassheim, Eliot (D, 18)
State Capitol
600 East Boulevard Avenue
Bismarck, ND 58505
P: (701) 328-3373
E: eglassheim@nd.gov

Guggisberg, Ron (D, 11)
State Capitol
600 East Boulevard Avenue
Bismarck, ND 58505
P: (701) 328-3373
E: rguggisberg@nd.gov

Haak, Jessica (D, 12)
State Capitol
600 East Boulevard Avenue
Bismarck, ND 58505
P: (701) 328-3373
E: jehaak@nd.gov

Hanson, Ben W. (D, 16)
State Capitol
600 East Boulevard Avenue
Bismarck, ND 58505
P: (701) 328-3373
E: bwhanson@nd.gov

North Dakota

Hatlestad, Patrick R. (R, 1)
State Capitol
600 East Boulevard Avenue
Bismarck, ND 58505
P: (701) 328-3373
E: phatlestad@nd.gov

Hawken, Kathy (R, 46)
State Capitol
600 East Boulevard Avenue
Bismarck, ND 58505
P: (701) 328-3373
E: khawken@nd.gov

Headland, Craig (R, 29)
State Capitol
600 East Boulevard Avenue
Bismarck, ND 58505
P: (701) 328-3373
E: cheadland@nd.gov

Hofstad, Curt (R, 15)
State Capitol
600 East Boulevard Avenue
Bismarck, ND 58505
P: (701) 328-3373
E: chofstad@nd.gov

Hogan, Kathy (D, 21)
State Capitol
600 East Boulevard Avenue
Bismarck, ND 58505
P: (701) 328-3373
E: khogan@nd.gov

Holman, Rick G. (D, 20)
State Capitol
600 East Boulevard Avenue
Bismarck, ND 58505
P: (701) 328-3373
E: rholman@nd.gov

Hunskor, Bob (D, 6)
State Capitol
600 East Boulevard Avenue
Bismarck, ND 58505
P: (701) 328-3373
E: bhunskor@nd.gov

Johnson, Dennis (R, 15)
State Capitol
600 East Boulevard Avenue
Bismarck, ND 58505
P: (701) 328-3373
E: djohnson@nd.gov

Johnson, Mary C. (R, 45)*
State Capitol
600 East Boulevard Avenue
Bismarck, ND 58505
P: (701) 328-3373
E: marycjohnson@nd.gov

Kading, Tom (R, 45)*
State Capitol
600 East Boulevard Avenue
Bismarck, ND 58505
P: (701) 328-3373
E: tkading@nd.gov

Karls, Karen (R, 35)
State Capitol
600 East Boulevard Avenue
Bismarck, ND 58505
P: (701) 328-3373
E: kkarls@nd.gov

Kasper, Jim (R, 46)
State Capitol
600 East Boulevard Avenue
Bismarck, ND 58505
P: (701) 328-3373
E: jkasper@nd.gov

Keiser, George J. (R, 47)
State Capitol
600 East Boulevard Avenue
Bismarck, ND 58505
P: (701) 258-0333
E: gkeiser@nd.gov

Kelsh, Jerome (D, 26)
State Capitol
600 East Boulevard Avenue
Bismarck, ND 58505
P: (701) 328-3373
E: jkelsh@nd.gov

Kempenich, Keith (R, 39)
State Capitol
600 East Boulevard Avenue
Bismarck, ND 58505
P: (701) 328-3373
E: kkempenich@nd.gov

Kiefert, Dwight (R, 24)
State Capitol
600 East Boulevard Avenue
Bismarck, ND 58505
P: (701) 328-3373
E: dhkiefert@nd.gov

Klein, Matthew M. (R, 40)
State Capitol
600 East Boulevard Avenue
Bismarck, ND 58505
P: (701) 328-3373
E: mklein@nd.gov

Klemin, Lawrence R. (R, 47)
State Capitol
600 East Boulevard Avenue
Bismarck, ND 58505
P: (701) 328-3373
E: lklemin@nd.gov

Koppelman, Ben (R, 16)
State Capitol
600 East Boulevard Avenue
Bismarck, ND 58505
P: (701) 328-3373
E: bkoppelman@nd.gov

Koppelman, Kim (R, 13)
State Capitol
600 East Boulevard Avenue
Bismarck, ND 58505
P: (701) 328-3373
E: kkoppelman@nd.gov

Kreidt, Gary (R, 33)
State Capitol
600 East Boulevard Avenue
Bismarck, ND 58505
P: (701) 328-3373
E: gkreidt@nd.gov

Kretschmar, William E. (R, 28)
State Capitol
600 East Boulevard Avenue
Bismarck, ND 58505
P: (701) 328-3373
E: wkretschmar@nd.gov

Laning, Vernon R. (R, 8)
State Capitol
600 East Boulevard Avenue
Bismarck, ND 58505
P: (701) 328-3373
E: vrlaning@nd.gov

Larson, Diane (R, 30)
State Capitol
600 East Boulevard Avenue
Bismarck, ND 58505
P: (701) 328-3373
E: dklarson@nd.gov

Lefor, Mike (R, 37)*
State Capitol
600 East Boulevard Avenue
Bismarck, ND 58505
P: (701) 328-3373
E: mlefor@nd.gov

Looysen, Alex (R, 12)
State Capitol
600 East Boulevard Avenue
Bismarck, ND 58505
P: (701) 328-3373
E: alooysen@nd.gov

Louser, Scott (R, 5)
State Capitol
600 East Boulevard Avenue
Bismarck, ND 58505
P: (701) 328-3373
E: sclouser@nd.gov

Maragos, Andrew G. (R, 3)
State Capitol
600 East Boulevard Avenue
Bismarck, ND 58505
P: (701) 328-3373
E: amaragos@nd.gov

Martinson, Bob (R, 35)
State Capitol
600 East Boulevard Avenue
Bismarck, ND 58505
P: (701) 328-3373
E: bmartinson@nd.gov

Meier, Lisa (R, 32)
State Capitol
600 East Boulevard Avenue
Bismarck, ND 58505
P: (701) 328-3373
E: lmeier@nd.gov

Mitskog, Alisa (D, 25)*
State Capitol
600 East Boulevard Avenue
Bismarck, ND 58505
P: (701) 328-3373
E: amitskog@nd.gov

Mock, Corey (D, 42)
State Capitol
600 East Boulevard Avenue
Bismarck, ND 58505
P: (701) 328-3373
E: crmock@nd.gov

Monson, David (R, 10)
State Capitol
600 East Boulevard Avenue
Bismarck, ND 58505
P: (701) 328-3373
E: dmonson@nd.gov

Mooney, Gail (D, 20)
State Capitol
600 East Boulevard Avenue
Bismarck, ND 58505
P: (701) 328-3373
E: gmooney@nd.gov

Muscha, Naomi (D, 24)
State Capitol
600 East Boulevard Avenue
Bismarck, ND 58505
P: (701) 328-3373
E: nmuscha@nd.gov

Nathe, Mike (R, 30)
State Capitol
600 East Boulevard Avenue
Bismarck, ND 58505
P: (701) 328-3373
E: mrnathe@nd.gov

Nelson, Jon O. (R, 14)
State Capitol
600 East Boulevard Avenue
Bismarck, ND 58505
P: (701) 328-3373
E: jonelson@nd.gov

Nelson, Marvin (D, 9)
State Capitol
600 East Boulevard Avenue
Bismarck, ND 58505
P: (701) 328-3373
E: menelson@nd.gov

Olson Esq., Christopher (D, 13)*
State Capitol
600 East Boulevard Avenue
Bismarck, ND 58505
P: (701) 328-3373
E: cdolson@nd.gov

Onstad, Kenton (D, 4)
State Capitol
600 East Boulevard Avenue
Bismarck, ND 58505
P: (701) 328-3373
E: konstad@nd.gov

Oversen, Kylie (D, 42)
State Capitol
600 East Boulevard Avenue
Bismarck, ND 58505
P: (701) 328-3373
E: koversen@nd.gov

Owens, Mark S. (R, 17)
State Capitol
600 East Boulevard Avenue
Bismarck, ND 58505
P: (701) 328-3373
E: mowens@nd.gov

Paur, Gary (R, 19)
State Capitol
600 East Boulevard Avenue
Bismarck, ND 58505
P: (701) 328-3373
E: gpaur@nd.gov

Pollert, Chet (R, 29)
State Capitol
600 East Boulevard Avenue
Bismarck, ND 58505
P: (701) 328-3373
E: cpollert@nd.gov

Porter, Todd (R, 34)
State Capitol
600 East Boulevard Avenue
Bismarck, ND 58505
P: (701) 328-3373
E: tkporter@nd.gov

Rohr, Karen (R, 31)
State Capitol
600 East Boulevard Avenue
Bismarck, ND 58505
P: (701) 328-3373
E: kmrohr@nd.gov

Ruby, Dan J. (R, 38)
State Capitol
600 East Boulevard Avenue
Bismarck, ND 58505
P: (701) 328-3373
E: druby@nd.gov

Rust, David S. (R, 2)
State Capitol
600 East Boulevard Avenue
Bismarck, ND 58505
P: (701) 328-3373
E: drust@nd.gov

Sanford, Mark (R, 17)
State Capitol
600 East Boulevard Avenue
Bismarck, ND 58505
P: (701) 328-3373
E: masanford@nd.gov

Schatz, Mike (R, 36)
State Capitol
600 East Boulevard Avenue
Bismarck, ND 58505
P: (701) 328-3373
E: mischatz@nd.gov

Schmidt, James E. (R, 31)
State Capitol
600 East Boulevard Avenue
Bismarck, ND 58505
P: (701) 328-3373
E: jeschmidt@nd.gov

Schneider, Mary (D, 21)*
State Capitol
600 East Boulevard Avenue
Bismarck, ND 58505
P: (701) 328-3373
E: mschneider@nd.gov

Schreiber Beck, Cindy (R, 25)*
State Capitol
600 East Boulevard Avenue
Bismarck, ND 58505
P: (701) 328-3373
E: cschreiberbeck@nd.gov

Seibel, Jay (R, 33)*
State Capitol
600 East Boulevard Avenue
Bismarck, ND 58505
P: (701) 328-3373
E: jayseibel@nd.gov

Silbernagel, Peter F. (R, 22)
State Capitol
600 East Boulevard Avenue
Bismarck, ND 58505
P: (701) 328-3373
E: psilbernagel@nd.gov

Skarphol, Bob (R, 2)
State Capitol
600 East Boulevard Avenue
Bismarck, ND 58505
P: (701) 328-3373
E: bskarphol@nd.gov

Steiner, Vicky (R, 37)
State Capitol
600 East Boulevard Avenue
Bismarck, ND 58505
P: (701) 328-3373
E: vsteiner@nd.gov

Streyle, Roscoe K. (R, 3)
State Capitol
600 East Boulevard Avenue
Bismarck, ND 58505
P: (701) 328-3373
E: rstreyle@nd.gov

Strinden, Marie (D, 18)
State Capitol
600 East Boulevard Avenue
Bismarck, ND 58505
P: (701) 328-3373
E: mjstrinden@nd.gov

Sukut, Gary (R, 1)
State Capitol
600 East Boulevard Avenue
Bismarck, ND 58505
P: (701) 328-3373
E: gsukut@nd.gov

Thoreson, Blair (R, 44)
State Capitol
600 East Boulevard Avenue
Bismarck, ND 58505
P: (701) 328-3373
E: bthoreson@nd.gov

Toman, Nathan (R, 34)
State Capitol
600 East Boulevard Avenue
Bismarck, ND 58505
P: (701) 328-3373
E: nptoman@nd.gov

Trottier, Wayne (R, 19)
State Capitol
600 East Boulevard Avenue
Bismarck, ND 58505
P: (701) 328-3373
E: wtrottier@nd.gov

Vigesaa, Don (R, 23)
State Capitol
600 East Boulevard Avenue
Bismarck, ND 58505
P: (701) 328-3373
E: dwvigesaa@nd.gov

Wallman, Kris (D, 11)*
State Capitol
600 East Boulevard Avenue
Bismarck, ND 58505
P: (701) 328-3373
E: kwallman@nd.gov

Weisz, Robin (R, 14)
State Capitol
600 East Boulevard Avenue
Bismarck, ND 58505
P: (701) 328-3373
E: rweisz@nd.gov

Zubke, Denton (R, 39)*
State Capitol
600 East Boulevard Avenue
Bismarck, ND 58505
P: (701) 328-3373
E: dzubke@nd.gov

Congress

Senate

Heitkamp, Heidi (D)
Hoeven, John (R)

House

Cramer, Kevin (R, At-Large)

Northern Mariana Islands

Executive

Governor

Hon. Eloy S. Inos (R)
Governor
Caller Box 10007
Saipan, MP 96950
P: (670) 664-2280
F: (670) 664-2211

Lieutenant Governor

Sen. Ralph Torres (R)
Lieutenant Governor
Caller Box 10007
Saipan, MP 96950
P: (670) 664-2300
F: (670) 664-2311

Secretary of State

Northern Mariana Islands does not have the office of secretary of state.

Attorney General

Hon. Joey Patrick San Nicolas
Attorney General
Administration Building
P.O. Box 10007
Saipan, MP 96950
P: (670) 664-2341

Treasurer

Hon. Antoinette S. Calvo
CMNI Treasurer
P.O. Box 5234, CHRB
Saipan, MP 96950
P: (670) 664-1000
F: (670) 322-4643

Judiciary

Commonwealth Supreme Court

Ms. Deanna Ogo
Clerk
P.O. Box 502165
Saipan, MP 96950
P: (670) 236-9800
F: (670) 236-9702
E: supreme.court@saipan.com

Hon. Alexandro C. Castro
Chief Justice

Hon. Perry Borja Inos
Hon. John A. Manglona

Commonwealth Legislature

Senate President

Sen. Victor B. Hocog (R)
President
P.O. Box 500129
Saipan, MP 96950
P: (670) 664-8807
F: (670) 664-8809
E: sen.hocogv
@cnmileg.gov.mp

Vice President of the Senate

Sen. Francisco M. Borja (I)
Vice President
P.O. Box 500129
Saipan, MP 96950
P: (670) 664-8874
F: (670) 664-8976
E: sen.borjaf
@cnmileg.gov.mp

Senate Majority Leader

Sen. Arnold I. Palacios (R)
Majority Floor Leader
P.O. Box 500129
Saipan, MP 96950
P: (670) 664-8803
F: (670) 664-8824
E: sen.palaciosa
@cnmileg.gov.mp

Secretary of the Senate

Ms. Dolores S. Bermudes
Senate Clerk
P.O. Box 500129
Saipan, MP 96950
P: (670) 664-8850
F: (670) 664-8849
E: bermudesd@cnmileg.gov.mp

Members of the Senate

Borja, Francisco M. (I, TINIAN-2)
P.O. Box 500129
Saipan, MP 96950
P: (670) 664-8874
F: (670) 664-8976
E: sen.borjaf
@cnmileg.gov.mp

Cruz, Francisco Q. (R, TINIAN-2)
P.O. Box 500129
Saipan, MP 96950
P: (670) 664-8922
F: (670) 664-8938
E: sen.cruzf@cnmileg.gov.mp

Hocog, Victor B. (R, ROTA-1)
P.O. Box 500129
Saipan, MP 96950
P: (670) 664-8807
F: (670) 664-8809
E: sen.hocogv
@cnmileg.gov.mp

Hofschneider, Jude U. (R, Rota-2)*
P.O. Box 500129
Saipan, MP 96950
P: (670) 664-8868
F: (670) 664-8908
E: sen.hofschneiderj
@cnmileg.gov.mp

Igisomar, Sixto K. (R, Saipan-3)*
P.O. Box 500129
Saipan, MP 96950
P: (670) 664-8812
F: (670) 664-8813
E: sen.igisomars
@cnmileg.gov.mp

Mesngon, Steven King (R, Rota-1)*
P.O. Box 500129
Saipan, MP 96950
P: (670) 664-8858
F: (670) 664-8860
E: sen.mesngons
@cnmileg.gov.mp

Palacios, Arnold I. (R, Rota-3)
P.O. Box 500129
Saipan, MP 96950
P: (670) 664-8803
F: (670) 664-8824
E: sen.palaciosa
@cnmileg.gov.mp

Quitugua, Justo S. (R, Rota-3)
P.O. Box 500129
Saipan, MP 96950
P: (670) 664-8967
F: (670) 664-8919
E: sen.quituguaj
@cnmileg.gov.mp

Santos, Teresita A. (R, ROTA-1)
P.O. Box 500129
Saipan, MP 96950
P: (670) 664-8814
F: (670) 664-8815
E: sen.santost
@cnmileg.gov.mp

House

Speaker of the House

Rep. Joseph P. Deleon Guerrero (I)
Speaker of the House
P.O. Box 500586
Saipan, MP 96950
P: (670) 664-8971
F: (670) 664-8900
E: rep.dlguerreroj
@cnmileg.gov.mp

Vice President of the House

Rep. Rafael S. Demapan (C)
Vice Speaker
P.O. Box 500586
Saipan, MP 96950
P: (670) 664-8974
F: (670) 664-8864
E: rep.demapanr
@cnmileg.gov.mp

House Majority Leader

Rep. George N. Camacho (R)
Majority Floor Leader
P.O. Box 500586
Saipan, MP 96950
P: (670) 664-8836
F: (670) 664-8985
E: rep.camachog
@cnmileg.gov.mp

Clerk of the House

Ms. Linda B. Muna
Clerk of the House
P.O. Box 500586
Saipan, MP 96950
P: (670) 664-8848
F: (670) 664-8849
E: munal@cnmileg.gov.mp

Members of the House

Aldan, Edwin P. (I, TINIAN-6)
P.O. Box 500586
Saipan, MP 96950
P: (670) 664-8806
F: (670) 664-8952
E: rep.aldan@gmail.com

Attao, Blass Jonathan (I, Saipan-3)*
P.O. Box 500586
Saipan, MP 96950
P: (670) 664-8925
F: (670) 664-8871
E: rep.attaob
@cnmileg.gov.mp

Benavente, Anthony T. (I, SAIPAN-3)
P.O. Box 500586
Saipan, MP 96950
P: (670) 664-8826
F: (670) 664-8822
E: rep.benaventea@cnmileg.gov.mp

Benavente, Roman C. (I, SAIPAN-1)
P.O. Box 500586
Saipan, MP 96950
P: (670) 664-8881
F: (670) 664-8895
E: rep.benaventer@cnmileg.gov.mp

Camacho, George N. (R, SAIPAN-4)
P.O. Box 500586
Saipan, MP 96950
P: (670) 664-8836
F: (670) 664-8985
E: rep.camachog@cnmileg.gov.mp

Deleon Guerrero, Joseph P. (I, SAIPAN-1)
P.O. Box 500586
Saipan, MP 96950
P: (670) 664-8971
F: (670) 664-8900
E: rep.dlguerreroj@cnmileg.gov.mp

Deleon Guerrero, Lorenzo I. (I, SAIPAN-5)
P.O. Box 500586
Saipan, MP 96950
P: (670) 664-8888
F: (670) 664-8889
E: rep.dlguerrerol@cnmileg.gov.mp

Demapan, Angel A. (R, Saipan-1)*
P.O. Box 500586
Saipan, MP 96950
P: (670) 664-8983
F: (670) 664-8985
E: rep.demapana@cnmileg.gov.mp

Demapan, Rafael S. (C, SAIPAN-2)
P.O. Box 500586
Saipan, MP 96950
P: (670) 664-8974
F: (670) 664-8864
E: rep.demapanr@cnmileg.gov.mp

Guerrero, Joseph L. (R, Saipan-1)*
P.O. Box 500586
Saipan, MP 96950
P: (670) 664-8899
F: (670) 664-8948
E: rep.guerreroj@cnmileg.gov.mp

Maratita, Glenn L. (R, Rota-7)*
P.O. Box 500586
Saipan, MP 96950
P: (670) 664-8890
F: (670) 664-8892
E: rep.maratitag@cnmileg.gov.mp

Ogumoro, Felicidad T. (R, SAIPAN-3)
P.O. Box 500586
Saipan, MP 96950
P: (670) 664-8841
F: (670) 664-8827
E: rep.ogumorof@cnmileg.gov.mp

Propst, Edward K. (I, Saipan-1)*
P.O. Box 500586
Saipan, MP 96950
P: (670) 664-8829
F: (670) 664-8816
E: propste@cnmileg.gov.mp

Sablan, Antonio P. (I, SAIPAN-1)
P.O. Box 500586
Saipan, MP 96950
P: (670) 664-8923
F: (670) 664-8926
E: rep.sablana@cnmileg.gov.mp

Sablan, John Paul (C, SAIPAN-2)
P.O. Box 500586
Saipan, MP 96950
P: (670) 664-8965
F: (670) 664-8966
E: rep.sablanj@cnmileg.gov.mp

Sablan, Vison E. (I, Saipan-4)*
P.O. Box 500586
Saipan, MP 96950
P: (670) 664-8928
F: (670) 664-8930
E: rep.sablanv@cnmileg.gov.mp

Taimano, Francis (I, Saipan-5)*
P.O. Box 500586
Saipan, MP 96950
P: (670) 664-8830
F: (670) 664-8831
E: rep.taimanof@cnmileg.gov.mp

Tebuteb, Ramon A. (I, SAIPAN-3)
P.O. Box 500586
Saipan, MP 96950
P: (670) 664-8903
F: (670) 664-8842
E: rep.tebutebr@cnmileg.gov.mp

Villagomez, Edmund S. (C, SAIPAN-3)
P.O. Box 500586
Saipan, MP 96950
P: (670) 664-8897
F: (670) 664-8902
E: rep.evillagomez@cnmileg.gov.mp

Yumul, Ralph N. (I, SAIPAN-3)
P.O. Box 500586
Saipan, MP 96950
P: (670) 664-8931
F: (670) 664-8880
E: rep.yumulr@cnmileg.gov.mp

Ohio

Executive

Governor

Hon. John Kasich (R)
Governor
77 South High Street, 30th Floor
Columbus, OH 43215
P: (614) 466-3555
F: (614) 466-9354

Lieutenant Governor

Hon. Mary Taylor (R)
Lieutenant Governor
77 High Street, 30th Floor
Columbus, OH 43215
P: (614) 644-0935
F: (614) 466-9354

Attorney General

Hon. Mike DeWine (R)
Attorney General
State Office Tower
30 East Broad Street
Columbus, OH 43266
P: (614) 466-4320

Auditor

Hon. David A. Yost (R)
Auditor of State
88 East Broad Street, 5th Floor
P.O. Box 1140
Columbus, OH 43216
P: (614) 466-4514
F: (614) 466-4490
E: contactus
@auditor.state.oh.us

Secretary of State

Hon. Jon Husted (R)
Secretary of State
180 East Broad Street
Columbus, OH 43215
P: (614) 466-2655
F: (614) 644-0649
E: jhusted
@ohiosecretaryofstate.gov

Treasurer

Hon. Josh Mandel (R)
Treasurer of State
30 East Broad Street
9th Floor
Columbus, OH 43215
P: (614) 466-2160
F: (614) 644-7313

Judiciary

Supreme Court (NE)

Ms. Sandra Huth Grosko
Clerk of Court
65 South Front Street, 8th Floor
Columbus, OH 43215
P: (614) 387-9530

Hon. Maureen O'Connor
Chief Justice
Hon. Judith L. French
Hon. Sharon L. Kennedy
Hon. Judith Ann Lanzinger
Hon. Terrence O'Donnell
Hon. William M. O'Neill
Hon. Paul E. Pfeifer

Legislative Senate

Senate President

Sen. Keith Faber (R)
Senate President
Statehouse
1 Capitol Square, 2nd Floor
Columbus, OH 43215
P: (614) 466-7584
E: Faber@ohiosenate.gov

President Pro Tempore of the Senate

Sen. Chris Widener (R)
Senate President Pro Tempore
Senate Building
1 Capitol Square, 1st Floor
Columbus, OH 43215
P: (614) 466-3780
E: Widener@ohiosenate.gov

Senate Majority Leader

Sen. Thomas F. Patton (R)
Senate Majority Floor Leader
Senate Building
1 Capitol Square, 1st Floor
Columbus, OH 43215
P: (614) 466-8056
E: Patton@ohiosenate.gov

Senate Minority Leader

Sen. Joe Schiavoni (D)
Senate Minority Leader
Senate Building
1 Capitol Square, 3rd Floor
Columbus, OH 43215
P: (614) 466-8285
E: Schiavoni@ohiosenate.gov

Secretary of the Senate

Mr. Vincent Keeran
Clerk of the Senate
Statehouse, Second Floor
Columbus, OH 43215
P: (614) 466-4900
F: (614) 466-8261

Members of the Senate

Bacon, Kevin (R, 3)
Senate Building
1 Capitol Square, Ground Floor
Columbus, OH 43215
P: (614) 466-8064
E: Bacon@ohiosenate.gov

Balderson, Troy (R, 20)
Senate Building
1 Capitol Square, Ground Floor
Columbus, OH 43215
P: (614) 466-8076
E: Balderson@ohiosenate.gov

Beagle, Bill (R, 5)
Senate Building
1 Capitol Square, 1st Floor
Columbus, OH 43215
P: (614) 466-6247
E: Beagle@ohiosenate.gov

Brown, Edna (D, 11)
Senate Building
1 Capitol Square, Ground Floor
Columbus, OH 43215
P: (614) 466-5204
E: Brown@ohiosenate.gov

Burke, David (R, 26)
Senate Building
1 Capitol Square, Ground Floor
Columbus, OH 43215
P: (614) 466-8049
E: Burke@ohiosenate.gov

Cafaro, Capri S. (D, 32)
Senate Building
1 Capitol Square, Ground Floor
Columbus, OH 43215
P: (614) 466-7182
E: Cafaro@ohiosenate.gov

Coley II, William P. (R, 4)
Senate Building
1 Capitol Square, 1st Floor
Columbus, OH 43215
P: (614) 466-8072
E: Coley@ohiosenate.gov

Eklund, John (R, 18)
Senate Building
1 Capitol Square, 1st Floor
Columbus, OH 43215
P: (614) 644-7718
E: Eklund@ohiosenate.gov

Faber, Keith (R, 12)
Statehouse
1 Capitol Square, 2nd Floor
Columbus, OH 43215
P: (614) 466-7584
E: Faber@ohiosenate.gov

Gardner, Randy (R, 2)
Senate Building
1 Capitol Square, 2nd Floor
Columbus, OH 43215
P: (614) 466-8060
E: Gardner@ohiosenate.gov

Gentile, Lou (D, 30)
Senate Building
1 Capitol Square, Ground Floor
Columbus, OH 43215
P: (614) 466-6508
E: Gentile@ohiosenate.gov

Hite, Cliff (R, 1)
Senate Building
1 Capitol Square, 1st Floor
Columbus, OH 43215
P: (614) 466-8150
E: Hite@ohiosenate.gov

Hottinger, Jay (R, 31)
Senate Building
1 Capitol Square, 2nd Floor
Columbus, OH 43215
P: (614) 466-5838
F: (614) 719-3971
E: hottinger@ohiosenate.gov

Hughes, Jim (R, 16)
Senate Building
1 Capitol Square, 1st Floor
Columbus, OH 43215
P: (614) 466-5981
E: Hughes@ohiosenate.gov

Jones, Shannon (R, 7)
Senate Building
1 Capitol Square, 1st Floor
Columbus, OH 43215
P: (614) 466-9737
E: Jones@ohiosenate.gov

Jordan, Kris (R, 19)
Senate Building
1 Capitol Square, Ground Floor
Columbus, OH 43215
P: (614) 466-8086
E: Jordan@ohiosenate.gov

LaRose, Frank (R, 27)
Senate Building
1 Capitol Square, 2nd Floor
Columbus, OH 43215
P: (614) 466-4823
E: LaRose@ohiosenate.gov

Lehner, Peggy (R, 6)
Senate Building
1 Capitol Square, Ground Floor
Columbus, OH 43215
P: (614) 466-4538
E: Lehner@ohiosenate.gov

Manning, Gayle (R, 13)
Senate Building
1 Capitol Square, Ground Floor
Columbus, OH 43215
P: (614) 644-7613
E: Manning@ohiosenate.gov

Obhof, Larry (R, 22)
Senate Building
1 Capitol Square, 2nd Floor
Columbus, OH 43215
P: (614) 466-7505
E: Obhof@ohiosenate.gov

Oelslager, W. Scott (R, 29)
Senate Building
1 Capitol Square, 1st Floor
Columbus, OH 43215
P: (614) 466-0626
E: Oelslager@ohiosenate.gov

Patton, Thomas F. (R, 24)
Senate Building
1 Capitol Square, 1st Floor
Columbus, OH 43215
P: (614) 466-8056
E: Patton@ohiosenate.gov

Peterson, Bob (R, 17)
Senate Building
1 Capitol Square, Ground Floor
Columbus, OH 43215
P: (614) 644-8156
E: Peterson@ohiosenate.gov

Sawyer, Tom (D, 28)
Senate Building
1 Capitol Square, Ground Floor
Columbus, OH 43215
P: (614) 466-7041
E: Sawyer@ohiosenate.gov

Schiavoni, Joe (D, 33)
Senate Building
1 Capitol Square, 3rd Floor
Columbus, OH 43215
P: (614) 466-8285
E: Schiavoni@ohiosenate.gov

Seitz, Bill (R, 8)
Senate Building
1 Capitol Square, 1st Floor
Columbus, OH 43215
P: (614) 466-8068
E: Seitz@ohiosenate.gov

Skindell, Michael J. (D, 23)
Senate Building
1 Capitol Square, Ground Floor
Columbus, OH 43215
P: (614) 466-5123
E: Skindell@ohiosenate.gov

Tavares, Charleta B. (D, 15)
Senate Building
1 Capitol Square, 2nd Floor
Columbus, OH 43215
P: (614) 466-5131
E: Tavares@ohiosenate.gov

Thomas, Cecil (D, 9)*
Senate Building
1 Capitol Square, 3rd Floor
Columbus, OH 43215
P: (614) 466-5980
E: thomas@ohiosenate.gov

Uecker, Joseph (R, 14)
Senate Building
1 Capitol Square, 1st Floor
Columbus, OH 43215
P: (614) 466-8082
E: Uecker@ohiosenate.gov

Widener, Chris (R, 10)
Senate Building
1 Capitol Square, 1st Floor
Columbus, OH 43215
P: (614) 466-3780
E: Widener@ohiosenate.gov

Williams, Sandra (D, 21)
Senate Building
1 Capitol Square, Ground Floor
Columbus, OH 43215
P: (614) 466-4857
E: williams@ohiosenate.gov

Yuko, Kenny (D, 25)
Senate Building
1 Capitol Square, 2nd Floor
Columbus, OH 43215
P: (614) 466-4583
E: yuko@ohiosenate.gov

House

Speaker of the House

Rep. Cliff Rosenberger (R)
Speaker of the House
77 South High Street
13th Floor
Columbus, OH 43215
P: (614) 466-3506
E: Rep91@ohiohouse.gov

Speaker Pro Tempore of the House

Rep. Ron Amstutz (R)
House Speaker Pro Tempore
77 South High Street
14th Floor
Columbus, OH 43215
P: (614) 466-1474
E: Rep01@ohiohouse.gov

House Majority Leader

Rep. Barbara Sears (R)
House Majority Floor Leader
77 South High Street
14th Floor
Columbus, OH 43215
P: (614) 466-1731
E: Rep47@ohiohouse.gov

House Minority Leader

Rep. Fred Strahorn (D)
House Minority Leader
77 South High Street
10th Floor
Columbus, OH 43215
P: (614) 466-1607
E: Rep39@ohiohouse.gov

Clerk of the House

Mr. Bradley J. Young
Legislative Clerk of the House
Statehouse
Columbus, OH 43215
P: (614) 466-3357

Members of the House

Amstutz, Ron (R, 1)
77 South High Street
14th Floor
Columbus, OH 43215
P: (614) 466-1474
E: Rep01@ohiohouse.gov

Anielski, Marlene (R, 6)
77 South High Street
12th Floor
Columbus, OH 43215
P: (614) 644-6041
E: Rep06@ohiohouse.gov

Antani, Niraj J. (R, 42)*
77 South High Street
11th Floor
Columbus, OH 43215
P: (614) 466-6504
E: rep42@ohiohouse.gov

Antonio, Nickie (D, 13)
77 South High Street
11th Floor
Columbus, OH 43215
P: (614) 466-5921
F: (614) 719-3913
E: Rep13@ohiohouse.gov

Ashford, Mike (D, 44)
77 South High Street
14th Floor
Columbus, OH 43215
P: (614) 466-1401
E: Rep44@ohiohouse.gov

Baker, Nan (R, 16)
77 South High Street
12th Floor
Columbus, OH 43215
P: (614) 466-0961
F: (614) 719-3998
E: Rep16@ohiohouse.gov

Barnes Jr., John E. (D, 12)
77 South High Street
11th Floor
Columbus, OH 43215
P: (614) 466-1408
F: (614) 719-3912
E: Rep12@ohiohouse.gov

Becker, John (R, 65)
77 South High Street
12th Floor
Columbus, OH 43215
P: (614) 466-8134
E: Rep65@ohiohouse.gov

Bishoff, Heather (D, 20)
77 South High Street
10th Floor
Columbus, OH 43215
P: (614) 644-6002
E: Rep20@ohiohouse.gov

Blessing III, Louis W. (R, 29)
77 South High Street
13th Floor
Columbus, OH 43215
P: (614) 644-9091
E: Rep29@ohiohouse.gov

Boose, Terry (R, 57)
77 South High Street
12th Floor
Columbus, OH 43215
P: (614) 466-9628
F: (614) 719-3958
E: Rep57@ohiohouse.gov

Boyce, Kevin L. (D, 25)
77 South High Street
10th Floor
Columbus, OH 43215
P: (614) 466-5343
E: Rep25@ohiohouse.gov

Boyd, Janine (D, 9)*
77 South High Street
10th Floor
Columbus, OH 43215
P: (614) 644-5079
E: rep09@ohiohouse.gov

Ohio

Brenner, Andrew (R, 67)
77 South High Street
13th Floor
Columbus, OH 43215
P: (614) 644-6711
F: (614) 719-0002
E: Rep67@ohiohouse.gov

Brinkman Jr., Tom (R, 27)
77 South High Street
11th Floor
Columbus, OH 43215
P: (614) 644-6886
E: rep27@ohiohouse.gov

Brown, Tim W. (R, 3)
77 South High Street
13th Floor
Columbus, OH 43215
P: (614) 644-8104
E: Rep03@ohiohouse.gov

Bryant Kuhns, Christie (D, 32)*
77 South High Street
10th Floor
Columbus, OH 43215
P: (614) 466-1645
E: rep32@ohiohouse.gov

Buchy, Jim (R, 84)
77 South High Street
14th Floor
Columbus, OH 43215
P: (614) 466-6344
E: Rep84@ohiohouse.gov

Burkley, Tony (R, 82)
77 South High Street
13th Floor
Columbus, OH 43215
P: (614) 644-5091
E: Rep82@ohiohouse.gov

Butler, James (R, 41)
77 South High Street
13th Floor
Columbus, OH 43215
P: (614) 644-6008
E: Rep41@ohiohouse.gov

Celebrezze, Nicholas J. (D, 15)
77 South High Street
11th Floor
Columbus, OH 43215
P: (614) 466-3485
F: (614) 719-3911
E: Rep15@ohiohouse.gov

Cera, Jack (D, 96)
77 South High Street
11th Floor
Columbus, OH 43215
P: (614) 466-3735
E: Rep96@ohiohouse.gov

Clyde, Kathleen (D, 75)
77 South High Street
11th Floor
Columbus, OH 43215
P: (614) 466-2004
E: Rep75@ohiohouse.gov

Conditt, Margaret (R, 52)
77 South High Street
11th Floor
Columbus, OH 43215
P: (614) 466-8550
E: Rep52@ohiohouse.gov

Craig, Hearcel F. (D, 26)*
77 South High Street
14th Floor
Columbus, OH 43215
P: (614) 466-8010
E: rep26@ohiohouse.gov

Cupp, Robert R. (R, 4)
77 South High Street
13th Floor
Columbus, OH 43215
P: (614) 466-4895
E: rep07@ohiohouse.gov

Curtin, Michael F. (D, 17)
77 South High Street
10th Floor
Columbus, OH 43215
P: (614) 644-6005
E: Rep17@ohiohouse.gov

Derickson, Timothy (R, 53)
77 South High Street
13th Floor
Columbus, OH 43215
P: (614) 644-5094
F: (614) 719-6953
E: Rep53@ohiohouse.gov

Dever, Jonathan (R, 28)*
77 South High Street
10th Floor
Columbus, OH 43215
P: (614) 466-8120
E: rep28@ohiohouse.gov

DeVitis, Anthony (R, 36)
77 South High Street
11th Floor
Columbus, OH 43215
P: (614) 466-1790
E: Rep36@ohiohouse.gov

Dovilla, Mike (R, 7)
77 South High Street
14th Floor
Columbus, OH 43215
P: (614) 466-4895
E: Rep07@ohiohouse.gov

Driehaus, Denise (D, 31)
77 South High Street
10th Floor
Columbus, OH 43215
P: (614) 466-5786
F: (614) 719-3585
E: Rep31@ohiohouse.gov

Duffey, Mike (R, 21)
77 South High Street
13th Floor
Columbus, OH 43215
P: (614) 644-6030
F: (614) 719-6960
E: Rep21@ohiohouse.gov

Fedor, Teresa (D, 45)
77 South High Street
10th Floor
Columbus, OH 43215
P: (614) 644-6017
E: Rep45@ohiohouse.gov

Gerberry, Ronald V. (D, 59)
77 South High Street
10th Floor
Columbus, OH 43215
P: (614) 466-6107
F: (614) 719-3959
E: Rep59@ohiohouse.gov

Ginter, Tim (R, 5)*
77 South High Street
13th FLoor
Columbus, OH 43215
P: (614) 466-8022
E: rep05@ohiohouse.gov

Gonzales, Anne (R, 19)
77 South High Street
13th Floor
Columbus, OH 43215
P: (614) 466-4847
F: (614) 719-6958
E: Rep19@ohiohouse.gov

Green, Doug (R, 66)
77 South High Street
11th Floor
Columbus, OH 43215
P: (614) 644-6034
E: Rep66@ohiohouse.gov

Grossman, Cheryl (R, 23)
77 South High Street
13th Floor
Columbus, OH 43215
P: (614) 466-9690
F: (614) 719-6962
E: Rep23@ohiohouse.gov

Hackett, Robert D. (R, 74)
77 South High Street
11th Floor
Columbus, OH 43215
P: (614) 466-1470
E: Rep74@ohiohouse.gov

Hagan, Christina (R, 50)
77 South High Street
13th Floor
Columbus, OH 43215
P: (614) 466-9078
F: (614) 719-6950
E: Rep50@ohiohouse.gov

Hall, David (R, 70)
77 South High Street
11th Floor
Columbus, OH 43215
P: (614) 466-2994
E: Rep70@ohiohouse.gov

Hambley, Stephen D. (R, 69)*
77 South High Street
14th Floor
Columbus, OH 43215
P: (614) 466-8140
E: rep69@ohiohouse.gov

Hayes, Bill (R, 72)
77 South High Street
12th Floor
Columbus, OH 43215
P: (614) 466 2500
E: Rep72@ohiohouse.gov

Henne, Michael (R, 40)
77 South High Street
13th Floor
Columbus, OH 43215
P: (614) 644-8051
F: (614) 719-3590
E: Rep40@ohiohouse.gov

Hill, Brian (R, 97)
77 South High Street
11th Floor
Columbus, OH 43215
P: (614) 644-6014
E: Rep97@ohiohouse.gov

Hood, Ron (R, 78)
77 South High Street
12th Floor
Columbus, OH 43215
P: (614) 466-1464
E: Rep78@ohiohouse.gov

Howse, Stephanie (D, 11)*
77 South High Street
10th Floor
Columbus, OH 43215
P: (614) 466-1414
E: rep11@ohiohouse.gov

Huffman, Stephen A. (R, 80)*
77 South High Street
11th Floor
Columbus, OH 43215
P: (614) 466-8114
E: rep80@ohiohouse.gov

Johnson, Greta (D, 35)*
77 South High Street
11th Floor
Columbus, OH 43215
P: (614) 644-6037
E: rep35@ohiohouse.gov

Johnson, Terry (R, 90)
77 South High Street
13th Floor
Columbus, OH 43215
P: (614) 466-2124
E: Rep90@ohiohouse.gov

Koehler, Kyle (R, 79)*
77 South High Street
11th Floor
Columbus, OH 43215
P: (614) 466-2038
E: rep79@ohiohouse.gov

Kraus, Steven W. (R, 89)*
77 South High Street
10th Floor
Columbus, OH 43215
P: (614) 644-6011
E: rep89@ohiohouse.gov

Kunze, Stephanie (R, 24)
77 South High Street
11th Floor
Columbus, OH 43215
P: (614) 466-8012
E: Rep24@ohiohouse.gov

Landis, Al (R, 98)
77 South High Street
11th Floor
Columbus, OH 43215
P: (614) 466-8035
E: Rep98@ohiohouse.gov

LaTourette, Sarah (R, 76)*
77 South High Street
13th Floor
Columbus, OH 43215
P: (614) 644-5088
E: rep76@ohiohouse.gov

Leland, David (D, 22)*
77 South High Street
10th Floor
Columbus, OH 43215
P: (614) 466-2473
E: rep22@ohiohouse.gov

Lepore-Hagan, Michele (D, 58)*
77 South High Street
10th Floor
Columbus, OH 43215
P: (614) 466-9435
E: rep58@ohiohouse.gov

Maag, Ron (R, 62)
77 South High Street
13th Floor
Columbus, OH 43215
P: (614) 644-6023
E: Rep62@ohiohouse.gov

Manning, Nathan H. (R, 55)*
77 South High Street
10th Floor
Columbus, OH 43215
P: (614) 644-5076
E: rep55@ohiohouse.gov

McClain, Jeffrey A. (R, 87)
77 South High Street
13th Floor
Columbus, OH 43215
P: (614) 644-6265
E: Rep87@ohiohouse.gov

McColley, Robert (R, 81)*
77 South High Street
13th Floor
Columbus, OH 43215
P: (614) 466-3760
E: rep81@ohiohouse.gov

O'Brien, Michael J. (D, 64)*
77 South High Street
11th Floor
Columbus, OH 43215
P: (614) 466-5358
E: rep64@ohiohouse.gov

O'Brien, Sean (D, 65)
77 South High Street
11th Floor
Columbus, OH 43215
P: (614) 466-3488
E: Rep63@ohiohouse.gov

Patmon, Bill (D, 10)
77 South High Street
11th Floor
Columbus, OH 43215
P: (614) 466-7954
F: (614) 719-0010
E: Rep10@ohiohouse.gov

Patterson, John (D, 99)
77 South High Street
10th Floor
Columbus, OH 43215
P: (614) 466-1405
E: Rep99@ohiohouse.gov

Pelanda, Dorothy (R, 86)
77 South High Street
12th Floor
Columbus, OH 43215
P: (614) 466-8147
E: Rep86@ohiohouse.gov

Perales, Rick (R, 73)
77 South High Street
13th Floor
Columbus, OH 43215
P: (614) 644-6020
E: Rep73@ohiohouse.gov

Phillips, Debbie (D, 94)
77 South High Street
14th Floor
Columbus, OH 43215
P: (614) 466-2158
E: Rep94@ohiohouse.gov

Ramos, Dan (D, 56)
77 South High Street
14th Floor
Columbus, OH 43215
P: (614) 466-5141
F: (614) 719-3956
E: Rep56@ohiohouse.gov

Reece, Alicia (D, 33)
77 South High Street
10th Floor
Columbus, OH 43215
P: (614) 466-1308
F: (614) 719-3587
E: Rep33@ohiohouse.gov

Reineke Jr., Bill (R, 88)*
77 South High Street
12th Floor
Columbus, OH 43215
P: (614) 466-1374
E: rep88@ohiohouse.gov

Retherford, Wes (R, 51)
77 South High Street
11th Floor
Columbus, OH 43215
P: (614) 644-6721
E: Rep51@ohiohouse.gov

Rezabek, Jeff (R, 43)*
77 South High Street
11th Floor
Columbus, OH 43215
P: (614) 466-2960
E: rep43@ohiohouse.gov

Roegner, Kristina (R, 37)
77 South High Street
11th Floor
Columbus, OH 43215
P: (614) 466-1177
E: Rep37@ohiohouse.gov

Rogers, John M. (D, 60)
77 South High Street
10th Floor
Columbus, OH 43215
P: (614) 466-7251
E: Rep60@ohiohouse.gov

Romanchuk, Mark J. (R, 2)
77 South High Street
11th Floor
Columbus, OH 43215
P: (614) 466-5802
E: Rep02@ohiohouse.gov

Rosenberger, Cliff (R, 91)
77 South High Street
13th Floor
Columbus, OH 43215
P: (614) 466-3506
E: Rep91@ohiohouse.gov

Ruhl, Margaret Ann (R, 68)
77 South High Street
11th Floor
Columbus, OH 43215
P: (614) 466-1431
E: Rep68@ohiohouse.gov

Ryan, Scott K. (R, 71)*
77 South High Street
13th Floor
Columbus, OH 43215
P: (614) 466-1482
E: rep71@ohiohouse.gov

Schaffer, Timothy (R, 77)
77 South High Street
13th Floor
Columbus, OH 43215
P: (614) 466-8100
E: rep77@ohiohouse.gov

Scherer, Gary (R, 92)
77 South High Street
13th Floor
Columbus, OH 43215
P: (614) 644-7928
E: Rep92@ohiohouse.gov

Schuring, Kirk (R, 48)
77 South High Street
11th Floor
Columbus, OH 43215
P: (614) 752-2438
E: Rep48@ohiohouse.gov

Sears, Barbara (R, 47)
77 South High Street
14th Floor
Columbus, OH 43215
P: (614) 466-1731
E: Rep47@ohiohouse.gov

Sheehy, Michael (D, 46)
77 South High Street
10th Floor
Columbus, OH 43215
P: (614) 466-1418
E: Rep46@ohiohouse.gov

Ohio

Slaby, Lynn (R, 38)
77 South High Street
11th Floor
Columbus, OH 43215
P: (614) 644-5085
F: (614) 719-6941
E: Rep38@ohiohouse.gov

Slesnick, Stephen (D, 49)
77 South High Street
10th Floor
Columbus, OH 43215
P: (614) 466-8030
E: Rep49@ohiohouse.gov

Smith, Kent (D, 8)*
77 South High Street
14th Floor
Columbus, OH 43215
P: (614) 466-5441
E: rep08@ohiohouse.gov

Smith, Ryan (R, 93)
77 South High Street
13th Floor
Columbus, OH 43215
P: (614) 466-1366
E: Rep93@ohiohouse.gov

Sprague, Robert (R, 83)
77 South High Street
13th Floor
Columbus, OH 43215
P: (614) 466-3819
E: Rep83@ohiohouse.gov

Stinziano, Michael (D, 18)
77 South High Street
11th Floor
Columbus, OH 43215
P: (614) 466-1896
F: (614) 719-6964
E: Rep18@ohiohouse.gov

Strahorn, Fred (D, 39)
77 South High Street
10th Floor
Columbus, OH 43215
P: (614) 466-1607
E: Rep39@ohiohouse.gov

Sweeney, Martin J. (D, 14)*
77 South High Street
10th Floor
Columbus, OH 43215
P: (614) 466-3350
E: rep14@ohiohouse.gov

Sykes, Emilia Strong (D, 34)*
77 South High Street
10th Floor
Columtus, OH 43215
P: (614) 466-3100
E: rep34@ohiohouse.gov

Terhar, Louis (R, 30)
77 South High Street
13th Floor
Columbus, OH 43215
P: (614) 466-8258
F: (614) 719-3584
E: Rep30@ohiohouse.gov

Thompson, Andy (R, 95)
77 South High Street
11th Floor
Columbus, OH 43215
P: (614) 644-8728
E: Rep95@ohiohouse.gov

Vitale, Nino (R, 85)*
77 South High Street
14th Floor
Columbus, OH 43215
P: (614) 466-1507
E: rep85@ohiohouse.gov

Young, Ron (R, 61)
77 South High Street
11th Floor
Columbus, OH 43215
P: (614) 644-6074
E: Rep61@ohiohouse.gov

Zeltwanger, Paul (R, 54)*
77 South High Street
13th Floor
Columbus, OH 43215
P: (614) 644-6027
E: rep54@ohiohouse.gov

Congress

Senate

Brown, Sherrod (D)
Portman, Rob (R)

House

Beatty, Joyce (D, 3)
Boehner, John A. (R, 8)
Chabot, Steve (R, 1)
Fudge, Marcia L. (D, 11)
Gibbs, Bob (R, 18)
Johnson, Bill (R, 6)
Jordan, Jim (R, 4)
Joyce, David (R, 14)
Kaptur, Marcy (D, 9)
Latta, Robert E. (R, 5)
Renacci, Jim (R, 16)
Ryan, Timothy J. (D, 13)
Stivers, Steve (R, 15)
Tiberi, Patrick (R, 12)
Turner, Michael (R, 10)
Wenstrup, Brad (R, 2)

Oklahoma

Executive

Governor
Hon. Mary Fallin (R)
Governor
Capitol Building
2300 Lincoln Boulevard, Room 212
Oklahoma City, OK 73105
P: (405) 521-2342
F: (405) 521-3353

Lieutenant Governor
Hon. Todd Lamb (R)
Lieutenant Governor
State Capitol, Room 211
Oklahoma City, OK 73105
P: (405) 521-2161
F: (405) 522-8694

Attorney General
Hon. Scott Pruitt (R)
Attorney General
313 Northeast 21st Street
Oklahoma City, OK 73105
P: (405) 521-3921

Auditor
Hon. Gary Jones (R)
State Auditor & Inspector
2300 North Lincoln Boulevard
State Capitol Building, Room 100
Oklahoma City, OK 73105
P: (405) 521-3495
F: (405) 521-3426
E: gjones@sai.ok.gov

Commissioner of Insurance
Hon. John D. Doak
Commissioner
Five Corporate Plaza
3625 Northwest 56th Street, Suite 100
Oklahoma City, OK 73112
P: (405) 521-2828
F: (405) 521-6635

Commissioner of Labor
Hon. Mark Costello (R)
Commissioner of Labor
3017 North Stiles, Suite 100
Oklahoma City, OK 73105
P: (405) 521-6100
F: (405) 521-6018

Corporation Commission
Hon. Bob Anthony (R)
Commissioner
Jim Thorpe Office Building
2101 North Lincoln Boulevard
Oklahoma City, OK 73105
P: (405) 521-2261
F: (405) 521-4532
E: b.anthony@occemail.com

Hon. Todd Hiett (R)
Commissioner
2101 North Lincoln Boulevard
P.O. Box 52000
Oklahoma City, OK 73152
P: (405) 521-2264
F: (405) 522-1623

Hon. Dana Murphy (R)
Commissioner
2101 North Lincoln Boulevard
P.O. Box 52000
Oklahoma City, OK 73152
P: (405) 521-2267
F: (405) 522-1623
E: d.murphy@occemail.com

Secretary of State
Hon. Chris Benge
(appointed)
Secretary of State
2300 North Lincoln Boulevard, Suite 101
Oklahoma City, OK 73105
P: (405) 521-6434
F: (405) 521-2031
E: webmaster@sos.ok.gov

Superintendent of Public Instruction
Hon. Joy Hofmeister (R)
Superintendent of Public Instruction
2500 North Lincoln Boulevard
Oklahoma City, OK 73105
P: (405) 521-3301
F: (405) 521-6938

Treasurer
Hon. Ken Miller (R)
State Treasurer
Room 217, State Capitol Building
2300 North Lincoln Boulevard
Oklahoma City, OK 73105
P: (405) 521-3191
F: (405) 521-4994

Judiciary

Supreme Court (MR)
Mr. Michael S. Richie
Supreme Court Clerk
P.O. Box 53126
Oklahoma City, OK 73152
P: (405) 521-2163

Hon. John F. Reif
Chief Justice
Hon. Tom Colbert
Hon. Doug Combs
Hon. James E. Edmondson
Hon. Noma Gurich
Hon. Yvonne Kauger
Hon. Steven W. Taylor
Hon. Joseph M. Watt
Hon. James R. Winchester

Legislative Senate

Senate President
Hon. Todd Lamb (R)
Lieutenant Governor
State Capitol, Room 211
Oklahoma City, OK 73105
P: (405) 521-2161
F: (405) 522-8694

President Pro Tempore of the Senate
Sen. Brian Bingman (R)
President Pro Tempore
Room 422
2300 North Lincoln Boulevard
Oklahoma City, OK 73105
P: (405) 521-5565
E: bingman@oksenate.gov

Senate Majority Leader
Sen. Mike Schulz (R)
Majority Floor Leader
Room 418
2300 North Lincoln Boulevard
Oklahoma City, OK 73105
P: (405) 521-5612
E: schulz@oksenate.gov

Senate Minority Leader
Sen. Randy Bass (D)
Democratic Floor Leader
Room 519
2300 North Lincoln Boulevard
Oklahoma City, OK 73105
P: (405) 521-5567
E: bass@oksenate.gov

Secretary of the Senate
Mr. Paul Ziriax
Secretary
Room 6, State Capitol
Oklahoma City, OK 73105
P: (405) 522-6615
F: (405) 521-6457
E: pziriax@elections.ok.gov

Members of the Senate
Allen, Mark (R, 4)
Room 415
2300 North Lincoln Boulevard
Oklahoma City, OK 73105
P: (405) 521-5576
E: allen@oksenate.gov

Anderson, Patrick (R, 19)
Room 233
2300 North Lincoln Boulevard
Oklahoma City, OK 73105
P: (405) 521-5630
E: anderson@oksenate.gov

Barrington, Don (R, 31)
Room 232
2300 North Lincoln Boulevard
Oklahoma City, OK 73105
P: (405) 521-5563
E: barrington@oksenate.gov

Bass, Randy (D, 32)
Room 519
2300 North Lincoln Boulevard
Oklahoma City, OK 73105
P: (405) 521-5567
E: bass@oksenate.gov

Bice, Stephanie (R, 22)*
Room 531
2300 North Lincoln Boulevard
Oklahoma City, OK 73105
P: (405) 521-5592
E: bice@oksenate.gov

Bingman, Brian (R, 12)
Room 422
2300 North Lincoln Boulevard
Oklahoma City, OK 73105
P: (405) 521-5565
E: bingman@oksenate.gov

Oklahoma

Boggs, Larry (R, 7)
Room 529A
2300 North Lincoln Boulevard
Oklahoma City, OK 73105
P: (405) 521-5604
E: boggs@oksenate.gov

Brecheen, Josh (R, 6)
Room 413
2300 North Lincoln Boulevard
Oklahoma City, OK 73105
P: (405) 521-5586
E: brecheen@oksenate.gov

Brinkley, Rick (R, 34)
Room 238
2300 North Lincoln Boulevard
Oklahoma City, OK 73105
P: (405) 521-5566
E: brinkley@oksenate.gov

Brooks, Corey (R, 43)
Room 529-B
2300 North Lincoln Boulevard
Oklahoma City, OK 73105
P: (405) 521-5522
E: brooks@oksenate.gov

Brown, Bill (R, 36)
Room 412
2300 North Lincoln Boulevard
Oklahoma City, OK 73105
P: (405) 521-5602
E: brownb@oksenate.gov

Crain, Brian (R, 39)
Room 417B
2300 North Lincoln Boulevard
Oklahoma City, OK 73105
P: (405) 521-5620
E: crain@oksenate.gov

Dahm, Nathan (R, 33)
Room 534
2300 North Lincoln Boulevard
Oklahoma City, OK 73105
P: (405) 521-5551
E: dahm@oksenate.gov

David, Kim (R, 18)
Room 417C
2300 North Lincoln Boulevard
Oklahoma City, OK 73105
P: (405) 521-5590
E: david@oksenate.gov

Fields, Eddie (R, 10)
Room 530
2300 North Lincoln Boulevard
Oklahoma City, OK 73105
P: (405) 521-5581
E: efields@oksenate.gov

Floyd, Kay (D, 46)
Room 522A
2300 North Lincoln Boulevard
Oklahoma City, OK 73105
P: (405) 521-5610
E: kay.floyd@okhouse.gov

Ford, John W. (R, 29)
Room 424A
2300 North Lincoln Boulevard
Oklahoma City, OK 73105
P: (405) 521-5634
E: fordj@oksenate.gov

Fry, Jack (R, 42)*
Room 413A
2300 North Lincoln Boulevard
Oklahoma City, OK 73105
P: (405) 521-5584
E: fry@oksenate.gov

Garrison, Earl (D, 9)
Room 520
2300 North Lincoln Boulevard
Oklahoma City, OK 73105
P: (405) 521-5533
E: whitep@oksenate.gov

Griffin, AJ (R, 20)
Room 428B
2300 North Lincoln Boulevard
Oklahoma City, OK 73105
P: (405) 521-5628
E: griffin@oksenate.gov

Halligan, Jim (R, 21)
Room 425
2300 North Lincoln Boulevard
Oklahoma City, OK 73105
P: (405) 521-5572
E: halligan@oksenate.gov

Holt, David (R, 30)
Room 423
2300 North Lincoln Boulevard
Oklahoma City, OK 73105
P: (405) 521-5636
E: holt@oksenate.gov

Jech, Darcy A. (R, 26)*
Room 528A
2300 North Lincoln Boulevard
Oklahoma City, OK 73105
P: (405) 521-5584
E: jech@oksenate.gov

Jolley, Clark (R, 41)
Room 537
2300 North Lincoln Boulevard
Oklahoma City, OK 73105
P: (405) 521-5622
E: jolley@oksenate.gov

Justice, Ron (R, 23)
Room 526
2300 North Lincoln Boulevard
Oklahoma City, OK 73105
P: (405) 521-5537
E: justice@oksenate.gov

Loveless, Kyle (R, 45)
Room 237
2300 North Lincoln Boulevard
Oklahoma City, OK 73105
P: (405) 521-5618
E: loveless@oksenate.gov

Marlatt, Bryce (R, 27)
Room 428
2300 North Lincoln Boulevard
Oklahoma City, OK 73105
P: (405) 521-5626
E: marlatt@oksenate.gov

Mazzei, Mike (R, 25)
Room 424
2300 North Lincoln Boulevard
Oklahoma City, OK 73105
P: (405) 521-5675
E: mazzei@oksenate.gov

Newberry, Dan (R, 37)
Room 234
2300 North Lincoln Boulevard
Oklahoma City, OK 73105
P: (405) 521-5600
E: newberry@oksenate.gov

Paddack, Susan (D, 13)
Room 522B
2300 North Lincoln Boulevard
Oklahoma City, OK 73105
P: (405) 521-5541
E: paddack@oksenate.gov

Pittman, Anastasia (D, 48)
Room 518
2300 North Lincoln Boulevard
Oklahoma City, OK 73105
P: (405) 521-5531
E: pittman@oksenate.gov

Quinn, Marty (R, 2)
Room 528B
2300 North Lincoln Boulevard
Oklahoma City, OK 73105
P: (405) 521-5555
E: quinn@oksenate.gov

Schulz, Mike (R, 38)
Room 418
2300 North Lincoln Boulevard
Oklahoma City, OK 73105
P: (405) 521-5612
E: schulz@oksenate.gov

Sharp, Ron (R, 17)
Room 429
2300 North Lincoln Boulevard
Oklahoma City, OK 73105
P: (405) 521-5539
E: sharp@oksenate.gov

Shaw, Wayne (R, 3)
Room 235
2300 North Lincoln Boulevard
Oklahoma City, OK 73105
P: (405) 521-5574
E: shaw@oksenate.gov

Shortey, Ralph (R, 44)
Room 527A
2300 North Lincoln Boulevard
Oklahoma City, OK 73105
P: (405) 521-5557
E: shortey@oksenate.gov

Silk, Joseph W. (R, 5)*
Room 536
2300 North Lincoln Boulevard
Oklahoma City, OK 73105
P: (405) 521-5614
E: silk@oksenate.gov

Simpson, Frank (R, 14)
Room 414
2300 North Lincoln Boulevard
Oklahoma City, OK 73105
P: (405) 521-5607
E: simpson@oksenate.gov

Smalley, Jason (R, 28)
Room 416
2300 North Lincoln Boulevard
Oklahoma City, OK 73105
P: (405) 521-5547
E: smalley@oksenate.gov

Sparks, John (D, 16)
Room 521B
2300 North Lincoln Boulevard
Oklahoma City, OK 73105
P: (405) 521-5553
E: sparks@oksenate.gov

Standridge, Rob (R, 15)
Room 417A
2300 North Lincoln Boulevard
Oklahoma City, OK 73105
P: (405) 521-5535
E: standridge@oksenate.gov

Stanislawski, Gary (R, 35)
Room 427A
2300 North Lincoln Boulevard
Oklahoma City, OK 73105
P: (405) 521-5624
E: stanislawski
@oksenate.gov

Sykes, Anthony (R, 24)
Room 426
2300 North Lincoln Boulevard
Oklahoma City, OK 73105
P: (405) 521-5569
E: lewis@oksenate.gov

Thompson, Roger (R, 8)*
Room 527B
2300 North Lincoln Boulevard
Oklahoma City, OK 73105
P: (405) 521-5588
E: thompson@oksenate.gov

Treat, Greg (R, 47)
Room 427
2300 North Lincoln Boulevard
Oklahoma City, OK 73105
P: (405) 521-5632
E: treat@oksenate.gov

Wyrick, Charles (D, 1)
Room 523
2300 North Lincoln Boulevard
Oklahoma City, OK 73105
P: (405) 521-5561
E: wyrick@oksenate.gov

Yen, Ervin (R, 40)*
Room 411A
2300 North Lincoln Boulevard
Oklahoma City, OK 73105
P: (405) 521-5543
E: yen@oksenate.gov

House

Speaker of the House

Rep. Jeffrey W. Hickman (R)
Speaker
Room 401
2300 North Lincoln Boulevard
Oklahoma City, OK 73105
P: (405) 557-7339
E: jwhickman@okhouse.gov

Speaker Pro Tempore of the House

Rep. Lee Denney (R)
Speaker Pro Tempore
Room 441
2300 North Lincoln Boulevard
Oklahoma City, OK 73105
P: (405) 557-7304
E: leedenney@okhouse.gov

House Majority Leader

Rep. Charles L. Ortega (R)
Majority Floor Leader
Room 442
2300 North Lincoln Boulevard
Oklahoma City, OK 73105
P: (405) 557-7369
E: charles.ortega
@okhouse.gov

House Minority Leader

Rep. Scott Inman (D)
Democrat Minority Leader
Room 548
2300 North Lincoln Boulevard
Oklahoma City, OK 73105
P: (405) 557-7370
E: scott.inman@okhouse.gov

Clerk of the House

Ms. Jan Harrison
Chief Clerk Of The House
2300 North Lincoln Boulevard
Oklahoma City, OK 73105
P: (405) 521-2711
E: harrisonja@okhouse.gov

Members of the House

Banz, Gary W. (R, 101)
Room 433
2300 North Lincoln Boulevard
Oklahoma City, OK 73105
P: (405) 557-7395
E: garybanz@okhouse.gov

Bennett, John (R, 2)
Room 300A
2300 North Lincoln Boulevard
Oklahoma City, OK 73105
P: (405) 557-7315
E: john.bennett@okhouse.gov

Biggs, Scott R. (R, 51)
Room 242
2300 North Lincoln Boulevard
Oklahoma City, OK 73105
P: (405) 557-7405
E: scott.biggs@okhouse.gov

Billy, Lisa J. (R, 42)
Room 440
2300 North Lincoln Boulevard
Oklahoma City, OK 73105
P: (405) 557-7365
E: lisajbilly@okhouse.gov

Brown, Mike (D, 4)
Room 545
2300 North Lincoln Boulevard
Oklahoma City, OK 73105
P: (405) 557-7408
E: mikebrown@okhouse.gov

Brumbaugh, David (R, 76)
Room 400B
2300 North Lincoln Boulevard
Oklahoma City, OK 73105
P: (405) 557-7347
E: david.brumbaugh
@okhouse.gov

Caldwell, Chad (R, 40)*
Room 329A
2300 North Lincoln Boulevard
Oklahoma City, OK 73105
P: (405) 557-7317
E: chad.caldwell
@okhouse.gov

Calvey, Kevin (R, 82)
Room 301A
2300 North Lincoln Boulevard
Oklahoma City, OK 73105
P: (405) 557-7357
E: kevincalvey@okhouse.gov

Cannaday, Ed (D, 15)
Room 546
2300 North Lincoln Boulevard
Oklahoma City, OK 73105
P: (405) 557-7375
E: ed.cannaday@okhouse.gov

Casey, Dennis (R, 35)
Room 337
2300 North Lincoln Boulevard
Oklahoma City, OK 73105
P: (405) 557-7344
E: dennis.casey@okhouse.gov

Christian, Mike (R, 93)
Room 303
2300 North Lincoln Boulevard
Oklahoma City, OK 73105
P: (405) 557-7371
E: mike.christian
@okhouse.gov

Cleveland, Bobby (R, 20)
Room 240
2300 North Lincoln Boulevard
Oklahoma City, OK 73105
P: (405) 557-7308
E: bob.cleveland
@okhouse.gov

Cockroft, Josh (R, 27)
Room 303A
2300 North Lincoln Boulevard
Oklahoma City, OK 73105
P: (405) 557-7349
E: josh.cockroft
@okhouse.gov

Condit, Donnie (D, 18)
Room 502
2300 North Lincoln Boulevard
Oklahoma City, OK 73105
P: (405) 557-7376
E: donnie.condit
@okhouse.gov

Coody, Ann (R, 64)
Room 439
2300 North Lincoln Boulevard
Oklahoma City, OK 73105
P: (405) 557-7398
E: anncoody@okhouse.gov

Coody, Jeff (R, 63)*
Room 338
2300 North Lincoln Boulevard
Oklahoma City, OK 73105
P: (405) 557-7307
E: jeff.coody@okhouse.gov

Cooksey, Marian (R, 39)
Room 409
2300 North Lincoln Boulevard
Oklahoma City, OK 73105
P: (405) 557-7342
E: mariancooksey
@okhouse.gov

Cox, Doug (R, 5)
Room 331
2300 North Lincoln Boulevard
Oklahoma City, OK 73105
P: (405) 557-7415
E: dougcox@okhouse.gov

Dank, David (R, 85)
Room 435
2300 North Lincoln Boulevard
Oklahoma City, OK 73105
P: (405) 557-7392
E: david.dank@okhouse.gov

Denney, Lee (R, 33)
Room 441
2300 North Lincoln Boulevard
Oklahoma City, OK 73105
P: (405) 557-7304
E: leedenney@okhouse.gov

Derby, David (R, 74)
Room 408
2300 North Lincoln Boulevard
Oklahoma City, OK 73105
P: (405) 557-7377
E: david.derby@okhouse.gov

Dunlap, Travis (R, 10)*
Room 250A
2300 North Lincoln Boulevard
Oklahoma City, OK 73105
P: (405) 557-7402
E: travis.dunlap
@okhouse.gov

Dunnington, Jason (D, 88)*
Room 500A
2300 North Lincoln Boulevard
Oklahoma City, OK 73105
P: (405) 557-7396
E: jason.dunnington
@okhouse.gov

Echols, Jon (R, 90)
Room 248
2300 North Lincoln Boulevard
Oklahoma City, OK 73105
P: (405) 557-7354
E: jon.echols@okhouse.gov

Enns, John (R, 41)
Room 434
2300 North Lincoln Boulevard
Oklahoma City, OK 73105
P: (405) 557-7321
E: john.enns@okhouse.gov

Oklahoma

Faught, George (R, 14)
Room 301B
2300 North Lincoln Boulevard
Oklahoma City, OK 73105
P: (405) 557-7310
E: george.faught
@okhouse.gov

Fisher, Dan (R, 60)
Room 202
2300 North Lincoln Boulevard
Oklahoma City, OK 73105
P: (405) 557-7311
E: dan.fisher@okhouse.gov

Fourkiller, William (D, 86)
Room 542
2300 North Lincoln Boulevard
Oklahoma City, OK 73105
P: (405) 557-7394
E: will.fourkiller
@okhouse.gov

Grau, Randy (R, 81)
Room 330
2300 North Lincoln Boulevard
Oklahoma City, OK 73105
P: (405) 557-7360
E: randy.grau@okhouse.gov

Griffith, Claudia (D, 45)*
Room 539
2300 North Lincoln Boulevard
Oklahoma City, OK 73105
P: (405) 557-7386
E: claudia.griffith
@okhouse.gov

Hall, Elise (R, 100)
Room 200A
2300 North Lincoln Boulevard
Oklahoma City, OK 73105
P: (405) 557-7403
E: elise.hall@okhouse.gov

Hardin, Tommy (R, 49)
Room 336
2300 North Lincoln Boulevard
Oklahoma City, OK 73105
P: (405) 557-7383
E: tommy.hardin@okhouse.gov

Henke, Katie (R, 71)
Room 244B
2300 North Lincoln Boulevard
Oklahoma City, OK 73105
P: (405) 557-7361
E: katie.henke@okhouse.gov

Hickman, Jeffrey W. (R, 58)
Room 401
2300 North Lincoln Boulevard
Oklahoma City, OK 73105
P: (405) 557-7339
E: jwhickman@okhouse.gov

Hoskin, Chuck (D, 6)
Room 509
2300 North Lincoln Boulevard
Oklahoma City, OK 73105
P: (405) 557-7319
E: chuck.hoskin@okhouse.gov

Inman, Scott (D, 94)
Room 548
2300 North Lincoln Boulevard
Oklahoma City, OK 73105
P: (405) 557-7370
E: scott.inman@okhouse.gov

Johnson, Dennis (R, 50)
Room 407
2300 North Lincoln Boulevard
Oklahoma City, OK 73105
P: (405) 557-7327
E: dennis.johnson
@okhouse.gov

Jordan, John Paul (R, 43)*
Room 328B
2300 North Lincoln Boulevard
Oklahoma City, OK 73105
P: (405) 557-7352
E: jp.jordan@okhouse.gov

Joyner, Charlie (R, 95)
Room 436
2300 North Lincoln Boulevard
Oklahoma City, OK 73105
P: (405) 557-7314
E: charlie.joyner
@okhouse.gov

Kannady, Chris (R, 91)*
Room 246A
2300 North Lincoln Boulevard
Oklahoma City, OK 73105
P: (405) 557-7337
E: chris.kannady
@okhouse.gov

Kern, Sally (R, 84)
Room 304
2300 North Lincoln Boulevard
Oklahoma City, OK 73105
P: (405) 557-7348
E: sallykern@okhouse.gov

Kirby, Dan (R, 75)
Room 302A
2300 North Lincoln Boulevard
Oklahoma City, OK 73105
P: (405) 557-7356
E: dan.kirby@okhouse.gov

Kouplen, Steve (D, 24)
Room 541
2300 North Lincoln Boulevard
Oklahoma City, OK 73105
P: (405) 557-7306
E: steve.kouplen
@okhouse.gov

Leewright, James (R, 29)*
Room 204B
2300 North Lincoln Boulevard
Oklahoma City, OK 73105
P: (405) 557-7353
E: james.leewright
@okhouse.gov

Lepak, Mark Paul (R, 9)*
Room 328A
2300 North Lincoln Boulevard
Oklahoma City, OK 73105
P: (405) 557-7380
E: mark.lepak@okhouse.gov

Lockhart, James (D, 3)
Room 505
2300 North Lincoln Boulevard
Oklahoma City, OK 73105
P: (405) 557-7413
E: james.lockhart
@okhouse.gov

Loring, Ben (D, 7)*
Room 539B
2300 North Lincoln Boulevard
Oklahoma City, OK 73105
P: (405) 557-7399
E: ben.loring@okhouse.gov

Martin, Scott (R, 46)
Room 441
2300 North Lincoln Boulevard
Oklahoma City, OK 73105
P: (405) 557-7329
E: scott.martin@okhouse.gov

Matthews, Kevin (D, 73)
Room 510
2300 North Lincoln Boulevard
Oklahoma City, OK 73105
P: (405) 557-7406
E: kevin.matthews
@okhouse.gov

McBride, Mark (R, 53)
Room 248
2300 North Lincoln Boulevard
Oklahoma City, OK 73105
P: (405) 557-7346
E: mark.mcbride@okhouse.gov

McCall, Charles A. (R, 22)
Room 244
2300 North Lincoln Boulevard
Oklahoma City, OK 73105
P: (405) 557-7412
E: charles.mccall
@okhouse.gov

McCullough, Mark (R, 30)
Room 435A
2300 North Lincoln Boulevard
Oklahoma City, OK 73105
P: (405) 557-7414
E: mark.mccullough
@okhouse.gov

McDaniel, Jeannie (D, 78)
Room 508
2300 North Lincoln Boulevard
Oklahoma City, OK 73105
P: (405) 557-7334
E: jeanniemcdaniel
@okhouse.gov

McDaniel, Randy (R, 83)
Room 438
2300 North Lincoln Boulevard
Oklahoma City, OK 73105
P: (405) 557-7409
E: randy.mcdaniel
@okhouse.gov

McPeak, Jerry (D, 13)
Room 503
2300 North Lincoln Boulevard
Oklahoma City, OK 73105
P: (405) 557-7302
E: jerrymcpeak@okhouse.gov

Montgomery, John Michael (R, 62)*
Room 329B
2300 North Lincoln Boulevard
Oklahoma City, OK 73105
P: (405) 557-7374
E: john.montgomery
@okhouse.gov

Moore, Lewis H. (R, 96)
Room 329
2300 North Lincoln Boulevard
Oklahoma City, OK 73105
P: (405) 557-7400
E: lewis.moore@okhouse.gov

Morrissette, Richard (D, 92)
Room 543
2300 North Lincoln Boulevard
Oklahoma City, OK 73105
P: (405) 557-7404
E: richardmorrissette
@okhouse.gov

Mulready, Glen (R, 68)
Room 200
2300 North Lincoln Boulevard
Oklahoma City, OK 73105
P: (405) 557-7340
E: glen.mulready
@okhouse.gov

Murdock, Casey (R, 61)*
Room 301
2300 North Lincoln Boulevard
Oklahoma City, OK 73105
P: (405) 557-7384
E: casey.murdock
@okhouse.gov

Murphey, Jason (R, 31)
Room 437
2300 North Lincoln Boulevard
Oklahoma City, OK 73105
P: (405) 557-7350
E: jason.murphey
@okhouse.gov

Nelson, Jason (R, 87)
Room 305A
2300 North Lincoln Boulevard
Oklahoma City, OK 73105
P: (405) 557-7335
E: jason.nelson@okhouse.gov

Newell, Tom (R, 28)
Room 302
2300 North Lincoln Boulevard
Oklahoma City, OK 73105
P: (405) 557-7372
E: tom.newell@okhouse.gov

Nollan, Jadine (R, 66)
Room 333
2300 North Lincoln Boulevard
Oklahoma City, OK 73105
P: (405) 557-7390
E: jadine.nollan
@okhouse.gov

O'Donnell, Terry (R, 23)
Room 242
2300 North Lincoln Boulevard
Oklahoma City, OK 73105
P: (405) 557-7379
E: terry.odonnell
@okhouse.gov

Ortega, Charles L. (R, 52)
Room 442
2300 North Lincoln Boulevard
Oklahoma City, OK 73105
P: (405) 557-7369
E: charles.ortega
@okhouse.gov

Osborn, Leslie (R, 47)
Room 303B
2300 North Lincoln Boulevard
Oklahoma City, OK 73105
P: (405) 557-7333
E: leslie.osborn
@okhouse.gov

Ownbey, Pat (R, 48)
Room 334
2300 North Lincoln Boulevard
Oklahoma City, OK 73105
P: (405) 557-7326
E: pat.ownbey@okhouse.gov

Park, Scooter (R, 65)*
Room 338
2300 North Lincoln Boulevard
Oklahoma City, OK 73105
P: (405) 557-7305
E: scooter.park@okhouse.gov

Perryman, David L. (D, 56)
Room 540
2300 North Lincoln Boulevard
Oklahoma City, OK 73105
P: (405) 557-7401
E: david.perryman
@okhouse.gov

Peterson, Pam (R, 67)
Room 405
2300 North Lincoln Boulevard
Oklahoma City, OK 73105
P: (405) 557-7341
E: pampeterson@okhouse.gov

Pfeiffer, John (R, 38)*
Room 301
2300 North Lincoln Boulevard
Oklahoma City, OK 73105
P: (405) 557-7332
E: john.pfeiffer
@okhouse.gov

Proctor, Eric (D, 77)
Room 540A
2300 North Lincoln Boulevard
Oklahoma City, OK 73105
P: (405) 557-7410
E: eric.proctor@okhouse.gov

Pruett, R.C. (D, 19)
Room 501
2300 North Lincoln Boulevard
Oklahoma City, OK 73105
P: (405) 557-7382
E: rcpruett@okhouse.gov

Renegar, Brian (D, 17)
Room 504
2300 North Lincoln Boulevard
Oklahoma City, OK 73105
P: (405) 557-7381
E: brian.renegar
@okhouse.gov

Ritze, Mike (R, 80)
Room 433B
2300 North Lincoln Boulevard
Oklahoma City, OK 73105
P: (405) 557-7338
E: mike.ritze@okhouse.gov

Roberts, Dustin (R, 21)
Room 302B
2300 North Lincoln Boulevard
Oklahoma City, OK 73105
P: (405) 557-7366
E: dustin.roberts
@okhouse.gov

Roberts, Sean (R, 36)
Room 250
2300 North Lincoln Boulevard
Oklahoma City, OK 73105
P: (405) 557-7322
E: sean.roberts@okhouse.gov

Rogers, Michael (R, 98)*
Room 300B
2300 North Lincoln Boulevard
Oklahoma City, OK 73105
P: (405) 557-7362
E: michael.rogers
@okhouse.gov

Rousselot, Wade (D, 12)
Room 507
2300 North Lincoln Boulevard
Oklahoma City, OK 73105
P: (405) 557-7388
E: waderousselot
@okhouse.gov

Russ, Todd (R, 55)
Room 300
2300 North Lincoln Boulevard
Oklahoma City, OK 73105
P: (405) 557-7312
E: todd.russ@okhouse.gov

Sanders, Mike (R, 59)
Room 205
2300 North Lincoln Boulevard
Oklahoma City, OK 73105
P: (405) 557-7407
E: mike.sanders@okhouse.gov

Scott, Seneca (D, 72)
Room 510
2300 North Lincoln Boulevard
Oklahoma City, OK 73105
P: (405) 557-7391
E: seneca.scott@okhouse.gov

Sears, Earl (R, 11)
Room 432D
2300 North Lincoln Boulevard
Oklahoma City, OK 73105
P: (405) 557-7358
E: earl.sears@okhouse.gov

Shelton, Mike (D, 97)
Room 539
2300 North Lincoln Boulevard
Oklahoma City, OK 73105
P: (405) 557-7367
E: mikeshelton@okhouse.gov

Sherrer, Ben (D, 8)
Room 500
2300 North Lincoln Boulevard
Oklahoma City, OK 73105
P: (405) 557-7364
E: bensherrer@okhouse.gov

Shoemake, Jerry (D, 16)
Room 506
2300 North Lincoln Boulevard
Oklahoma City, OK 73105
P: (405) 557-7373
E: jerryshoemake
@okhouse.gov

Stone, Shane (D, 89)*
Room 510A
2300 North Lincoln Boulevard
Oklahoma City, OK 73105
P: (405) 557-7397
E: shane.stone@okhouse.gov

Strohm, Chuck (R, 69)*
Room 300C
2300 North Lincoln Boulevard
Oklahoma City, OK 73105
P: (405) 557-7331
E: chuck.strohm@okhouse.gov

Tadlock, Johnny (D, 1)*
Room 539B
2300 North Lincoln Boulevard
Oklahoma City, OK 73105
P: (405) 557-7363
E: johnny.tadlock
@okhouse.gov

Thomsen, Todd (R, 25)
Room 410
2300 North Lincoln Boulevard
Oklahoma City, OK 73105
P: (405) 557-7336
E: todd.thomsen@okhouse.gov

Vaughan, Steve (R, 37)
Room 335
2300 North Lincoln Boulevard
Oklahoma City, OK 73105
P: (405) 557-7355
E: steve.vaughan
@okhouse.gov

Virgin, Emily (D, 44)
Room 500
2300 North Lincoln Boulevard
Oklahoma City, OK 73105
P: (405) 557-7323
E: emily.virgin@okhouse.gov

Walker, Ken (R, 70)
Room 204
2300 North Lincoln Boulevard
Oklahoma City, OK 73105
P: (405) 557-7359
E: ken.walker@okhouse.gov

Wallace, Kevin (R, 32)*
Room 246B
2300 North Lincoln Boulevard
Oklahoma City, OK 73105
P: (405) 557-7368
E: kevin.wallace
@okhouse.gov

Watson, Weldon (R, 79)
Room 406
2300 North Lincoln Boulevard
Oklahoma City, OK 73105
P: (405) 557-7330
E: weldon.watson
@okhouse.gov

Oklahoma

Wesselhoft, Paul (R, 54)
Room 328
2300 North Lincoln Boulevard
Oklahoma City, OK 73105
P: (405) 557-7343
E: paulwesselhoft
@okhouse.gov

Williams, Cory T. (D, 34)
Room 544
2300 North Lincoln Boulevard
Oklahoma City, OK 73105
P: (405) 557-7411
E: cory.williams
@okhouse.gov

Wood, Justin F. (R, 26)
Room 202
2300 North Lincoln Boulevard
Oklahoma City, OK 73105
P: (405) 557-7345
E: justin.wood@okhouse.gov

Wright, Harold (R, 57)
Room 332
2300 North Lincoln Boulevard
Oklahoma City, OK 73105
P: (405) 557-7325
E: harold.wright
@okhouse.gov

Young, George E. (D, 99)*
Room 510B
2300 North Lincoln Boulevard
Oklahoma City, OK 73105
P: (405) 557-7393
E: george.young@okhouse.gov

Congress

Senate
Inhofe, James M. (R)
Lankford, James (R)

House
Bridenstine, Jim (R, 1)
Cole, Tom (R, 4)
Lucas, Frank D. (R, 3)
Mullin, Markwayne (R, 2)
Russell, Steve (R, 5)

Oregon

Executive

Governor
Hon. Kate Brown (D)
Governor
State Capitol, Room 160
900 Court Street North
Salem, OR 97310
P: (503) 373-1027
F: (503) 373-8970

Lieutenant Governor
This state does not have the office of lieutenant governor. The secretary of state is next in line of succession to the governorship.

Attorney General
Hon. Ellen Rosenblum (D)
Attorney General
Justice Building
1162 Court Street, Northeast
Salem, OR 97301
P: (503) 378-6002
F: (503) 378-4017

Auditor
Mr. Gary Blackmer
(appointed)
Director
255 Capitol Street, Northeast
Suite 500
Salem, OR 97310
P: (503) 986-2255
F: (503) 378-6767
E: gary.blackmer
@state.or.us

Secretary of State
Mr. Robert Taylor
Acting Secretary of State
136 State Capitol
Salem, OR 97301
P: (503) 986-1523
F: (503) 986-1616
E: Robert.Taylor
@state.or.us

Treasurer
Hon. Ted Wheeler
State Treasurer
900 Court Street, Northeast
Room 159
Salem, OR 97301
P: (503) 378-4329
E: Oregon.Treasurer
@state.or.us

Judiciary

Supreme Court (NE)
Ms. Kingsley W. Click
State Court Administrator
Supreme Court Building
1163 State Street
Salem, OR 97301
P: (503) 986-5500
F: (503) 986-5503
E: kingsley.w.click
@state.or.us

Hon. Thomas A. Balmer
Chief Justice
Hon. Richard C. Baldwin
Hon. David V. Brewer
Hon. Rives Kistler
Hon. Jack L. Landau
Hon. Virginia L. Linder
Hon. Martha Lee Walters

Legislative Senate

Senate President
Sen. Peter Courtney (D)
Senate President
900 Court Street Northeast
S-201
Salem, OR 97301
P: (503) 986-1600
F: (503) 986-1004
E: sen.petercourtney
@state.or.us

President Pro Tempore of the Senate
Sen. Ginny Burdick (D)
President Pro Tempore
900 Court Street, Northeast
S-213
Salem, OR 97301
P: (503) 986-1718
E: sen.ginnyburdick
@state.or.us

Senate Majority Leader
Sen. Diane Rosenbaum (D)
Democratic Leader
900 Court Street, Northeast
S-223
Salem, OR 97301
P: (503) 986-1700
E: sen.dianerosenbaum
@state.or.us

Senate Minority Leader
Sen. Ted Ferrioli (R)
Republican Leader
900 Court Street, Northeast
S-323
Salem, OR 97301
P: (503) 986-1950
E: sen.tedferrioli
@state.or.us

Secretary of the Senate
Ms. Lori Brocker
Secretary of the Senate
900 Court Street, Northeast
Room 233
Salem, OR 97301
P: (503) 986-1851
E: lori.l.brocker
@state.or.us

Members of the Senate
Baertschiger, Herman (R, 2)
900 Court Street, Northeast
S-403
Salem, OR 97301
P: (503) 986-1702
E: Sen.HermanBaertschiger
@state.or.us

Bates, Alan C. (D, 3)
900 Court Street, Northeast
S-205
Salem, OR 97301
P: (503) 986-1703
E: sen.alanbates
@state.or.us

Beyer, Lee (D, 6)
900 Court Street, Northeast
S-419
Salem, OR 97301
P: (503) 986-1706
E: sen.leebeyer@state.or.us

Boquist, Brian (R, 12)
900 Court Street, Northeast
S-305
Salem, OR 97301
P: (503) 986-1712
E: sen.brianboquist
@state.or.us

Burdick, Ginny (D, 18)
900 Court Street, Northeast
S-213
Salem, OR 97301
P: (503) 986-1718
E: sen.ginnyburdick
@state.or.us

Courtney, Peter (D, 11)
900 Court Street Northeast
S-201
Salem, OR 97301
P: (503) 986-1600
F: (503) 986-1004
E: sen.petercourtney
@state.or.us

Dembrow, Michael E. (D, 23)
900 Court Street, Northeast
S-407
Salem, OR 97301
P: (503) 986-1723
E: Sen.MichaelDembrow
@state.or.us

Devlin, Richard (D, 19)
900 Court Street, Northeast
S-211
Salem, OR 97301
P: (503) 986-1719
E: sen.richarddevlin
@state.or.us

Edwards, Chris (D, 7)
900 Court Street, Northeast
S-411
Salem, OR 97301
P: (503) 986-1707
F: (541) 744-7110
E: sen.chrisedwards
@state.or.us

Ferrioli, Ted (R, 30)
900 Court Street, Northeast
S-323
Salem, OR 97301
P: (503) 986-1950
E: sen.tedferrioli
@state.or.us

Gelser, Sara (D, 8)
900 Court Street, Northeast
S-405
Salem, OR 97301
P: (503) 986-1708
E: Sen.SaraGelser
@state.or.us

Girod, Fred (R, 9)
900 Court Street, Northeast
S-401
Salem, OR 97301
P: (503) 986-1709
E: sen.fredgirod
@state.or.us

Oregon

Hansell, Bill (R, 29)
900 Court Street, Northeast
S-423
Salem, OR 97301
P: (503) 986-1729
E: Sen.BillHansell
@state.or.us

Hass, Mark (D, 14)
900 Court Street, Northeast
S-207
Salem, OR 97301
P: (503) 986-1714
E: sen.markhass@state.or.us

Johnson, Betsy (D, 16)
900 Court Street, Northeast
S-209
Salem, OR 97301
P: (503) 986-1716
E: sen.betsyjohnson
@state.or.us

Knopp, Tim (R, 27)
900 Court Street, Northeast
S-309
Salem, OR 97301
P: (503) 986-1727
E: sen.timknopp@state.or.us

Kruse, Jeff (R, 1)
900 Court Street, Northeast
S-315
Salem, OR 97301
P: (503) 986-1701
E: sen.jeffkruse
@state.or.us

Monnes Anderson, Laurie (D, 25)
900 Court Street, Northeast
S-413
Salem, OR 97301
P: (503) 986-1725
E: sen.
lauriemonnesanderson
@state.or.us

Monroe, Rod (D, 24)
900 Court Street, Northeast
S-409
Salem, OR 97301
P: (503) 986-1724
E: sen.rodmonroe
@state.or.us

Olsen, Alan (R, 20)
900 Court Street, Northeast
S-425
Salem, OR 97301
P: (503) 986-1720
E: sen.alanolsen
@state.or.us

Prozanski, Floyd (D, 4)
900 Court Street, Northeast
S-415
Salem, OR 97301
P: (503) 986-1704
E: sen.floydprozanski
@state.or.us

Riley, Chuck (D, 15)
900 Court Street, Northeast
S-303
Salem, OR 97301
P: (503) 986-1715
E: sen.chuckriley
@state.or.us

Roblan, Arnie (D, 5)
900 Court Street, Northeast
S-417
Salem, OR 97301
P: (503) 986-1705
E: sen.arnieroblan
@state.or.us

Rosenbaum, Diane (D, 21)
900 Court Street, Northeast
S-223
Salem, OR 97301
P: (503) 986-1700
E: sen.dianerosenbaum
@state.or.us

Shields, Chip (D, 22)
900 Court Street, Northeast
S-421
Salem, OR 97301
P: (503) 986-1722
E: sen.chipshields
@state.or.us

Steiner Hayward, Elizabeth (D, 17)
900 Court Street, Northeast
S-215
Salem, OR 97301
P: (503) 986-1717
E: Sen.
ElizabethSteinerHayward
@state.or.us

Thatcher, Kim (R, 13)
900 Court Street, Northeast
S-307
Salem, OR 97301
P: (503) 986-1713
E: Sen.KimThatcher
@state.or.us

Thomsen, Chuck (R, 26)
900 Court Street, Northeast
S-316
Salem, OR 97301
P: (503) 986-1726
E: sen.chuckthomsen
@state.or.us

Whitsett, Doug (R, 28)
900 Court Street, Northeast
S-311
Salem, OR 97301
P: (503) 986-1728
E: sen.dougwhitsett
@state.or.us

Winters, Jackie (R, 10)
900 Court Street, Northeast
S-301
Salem, OR 97301
P: (503) 986-1710
E: sen.jackiewinters
@state.or.us

House

Speaker of the House

Rep. Tina Kotek (D)
Speaker
900 Court Street, Northeast
H-269
Salem, OR 97301
P: (503) 986-1200
E: rep.tinakotek
@state.or.us

Speaker Pro Tempore of the House

Rep. Tobias Read (D)
Speaker Pro Tempore
900 Court Street, Northeast
H-286
Salem, OR 97301
P: (503) 986-1427
E: rep.tobiasread
@state.or.us

House Majority Leader

Rep. Val Hoyle (D)
Democratic Leader
900 Court Street, Northeast
H-295
Salem, OR 97301
P: (503) 986-1414
E: rep.valhoyle@state.or.us

House Minority Leader

Rep. Michael McLane (D)
Republican Leader
900 Court Street, Northeast
H-395
Salem, OR 97301
P: (503) 986-1400
E: rep.mikemclane
@state.or.us

Clerk of the House

Mr. Tim Sekerak
Chief Clerk of the House
900 Court Street, Northeast
H-271
Salem, OR 97301
P: (503) 986-1870
F: (503) 986-1876
E: tim.sekerak@state.or.us

Members of the House

Barker, Jeff (D, 28)
900 Court Street, Northeast
H-480
Salem, OR 97301
P: (503) 986-1428
E: rep.jeffbarker
@state.or.us

Barnhart, Phil (D, 11)
900 Court Street, Northeast
H-279
Salem, OR 97401
P: (503) 986-1411
E: rep.philbarnhart
@state.or.us

Barreto, Greg (R, 58)*
900 Court Street, Northeast
H-384
Salem, OR 97401
P: (503) 986-1458
E: rep.gregbarreto
@state.or.us

Barton, Brent (D, 40)
900 Court Street, Northeast
H-275
Salem, OR 97301
P: (503) 986-1440
E: rep.brentbarton
@state.or.us

Bentz, Cliff (R, 60)
900 Court Street, Northeast
H-475
Salem, OR 97301
P: (503) 986-1460
E: rep.cliffbentz
@state.or.us

Boone, Deborah (D, 32)
900 Court Street, Northeast
H-481
Salem, OR 97301
P: (503) 986-1432
E: rep.deborahboone
@state.or.us

Buckley, Peter (D, 5)
900 Court Street, Northeast
H-272
Salem, OR 97301
P: (503) 986-1405
E: rep.peterbuckley@state.or.us

Buehler, Knute C. (R, 54)*
900 Court Street, Northeast
H-389
Salem, OR 97401
P: (503) 986-1454
E: rep.knutebuehler@state.or.us

Clem, Brian (D, 21)
900 Court Street, Northeast
H-284
Salem, OR 97301
P: (503) 986-1421
E: rep.brianclem@state.or.us

Davis, John (R, 26)
900 Court Street, Northeast
H-483
Salem, OR 97301
P: (503) 986-1426
E: Rep.JohnDavis@state.or.us

Doherty, Margaret (D, 35)
900 Court Street, Northeast
H-282
Salem, OR 97301
P: (503) 986-1435
E: rep.margaretdoherty@state.or.us

Esquivel, Sal (R, 6)
900 Court Street, Northeast
H-382
Salem, OR 97301
P: (503) 986-1406
E: rep.salesquivel@state.or.us

Evans, Paul (D, 20)*
900 Court Street, Northeast
H-281
Salem, OR 97401
P: (503) 986-1420
E: rep.paulevans@state.or.us

Fagan, Shemia (D, 51)
900 Court Street, Northeast
H-274
Salem, OR 97301
P: (503) 986-1451
E: Rep.ShemiaFagan@state.or.us

Frederick, Lew (D, 43)
900 Court Street, Northeast
H-276
Salem, OR 97301
P: (503) 986-1443
E: rep.lewfrederick@state.or.us

Gallegos, Joe (D, 30)
900 Court Street, Northeast
H-492
Salem, OR 97301
P: (503) 986-1430
E: rep.joegallegos@state.or.us

Gilliam, Vic (R, 18)
900 Court Street, Northeast
H-479
Salem, OR 97301
P: (503) 986-1418
E: rep.vicgilliam@state.or.us

Gomberg, David (D, 10)
900 Court Street, Northeast
H-471
Salem, OR 97301
P: (503) 986-1410
E: rep.davidgomberg@state.or.us

Gorsek, Chris (D, 49)
900 Court Street, Northeast
H-486
Salem, OR 97301
P: (503) 986-1449
E: Rep.ChrisGorsek@state.or.us

Greenlick, Mitch (D, 33)
900 Court Street, Northeast
H-493
Salem, OR 97301
P: (503) 986-1433
E: rep.mitchgreenlick@state.or.us

Hack, Jodi L. (R, 19)*
900 Court Street, Northeast
H-385
Salem, OR 97401
P: (503) 986-1419
E: rep.jodihack@state.or.us

Hayden, Cedric (R, 7)
900 Court Street, Northeast
H-379
Salem, OR 97401
P: (503) 986-1407
E: rep.cedrichayden@state.or.us

Heard, Dallas (R, 2)*
900 Court Street, Northeast
H-386
Salem, OR 97401
P: (503) 986-1402
E: rep.dallasheard@state.or.us

Helm, Ken (D, 34)*
900 Court Street, Northeast
H-490
Salem, OR 97401
P: (503) 986-1434
E: rep.kenhelm@state.or.us

Holvey, Paul (D, 8)
900 Court Street, Northeast
H-277
Salem, OR 97301
P: (503) 986-1408
E: rep.paulholvey@state.or.us

Hoyle, Val (D, 14)
900 Court Street, Northeast
H-295
Salem, OR 97301
P: (503) 986-1414
E: rep.valhoyle@state.or.us

Huffman, John E. (R, 59)
900 Court Street, Northeast
H-477
Salem, OR 97301
P: (503) 986-1459
E: rep.johnhuffman@state.or.us

Johnson, Mark (R, 52)
900 Court Street, Northeast
H-489
Salem, OR 97301
P: (503) 986-1452
E: rep.markjohnson@state.or.us

Kennemer, Bill (R, 39)
900 Court Street, Northeast
H-380
Salem, OR 97301
P: (503) 986-1439
E: rep.billkennemer@state.or.us

Keny-Guyer, Alissa (D, 46)
900 Court Street, Northeast
H-484
Salem, OR 97301
P: (503) 986-1446
E: rep.alissakenyguyer@state.or.us

Komp, Betty (D, 22)
900 Court Street, Northeast
H-273
Salem, OR 97301
P: (503) 986-1422
E: rep.bettykomp@state.or.us

Kotek, Tina (D, 44)
900 Court Street, Northeast
H-269
Salem, OR 97301
P: (503) 986-1200
E: rep.tinakotek@state.or.us

Krieger, Wayne (R, 1)
900 Court Street, Northeast
H-381
Salem, OR 97301
P: (503) 986-1401
E: rep.waynekrieger@state.or.us

Lininger, Ann (D, 38)
900 Court Street Northeast,
H-485
Salem, OR 97301
P: (503) 986-1438
E: rep.annlininger@state.or.us

Lively, John (D, 12)
900 Court Street, Northeast
H-488
Salem, OR 97301
P: (503) 986-1412
E: rep.johnlively@state.or.us

McKeown, Caddy (D, 9)
900 Court Street, Northeast
H-476
Salem, OR 97301
P: (503) 986-1409
E: rep.caddymckeown@state.or.us

McLain, Susan (D, 29)*
900 Court Street, Northeast
H-376
Salem, OR 97401
P: (503) 986-1429
E: rep.susanmclain@state.or.us

McLane, Michael (D, 55)
900 Court Street, Northeast
H-395
Salem, OR 97301
P: (503) 986-1400
E: rep.mikemclane@state.or.us

Oregon

Nathanson, Nancy (D, 13)
900 Court Street, Northeast
H-280
Salem, OR 97301
P: (503) 986-1413
E: rep.nancynathanson
@state.or.us

Nearman, Mike (R, 23)*
900 Court Street, Northeast
H-378
Salem, OR 97401
P: (503) 986-1423
E: Rep.MikeNearman
@state.or.us

Nosse, Rob (D, 42)*
900 Court Street, Northeast
H-472
Salem, OR 97401
P: (503) 986-1442
E: Rep.RobNosse@state.or.us

Olson, Andy (R, 15)
900 Court Street, Northeast
H-478
Salem, OR 97301
P: (503) 986-1415
E: rep.andyolson
@state.or.us

Parrish, Julie (R, 37)
900 Court Street, Northeast
H-371
Salem, OR 97301
P: (503) 986-1437
E: rep.julieparrish
@state.or.us

Piluso, Carla C. (D, 50)*
900 Court Street, Northeast
H-491
Salem, OR 97401
P: (503) 986-1450
E: rep.carlapiluso
@state.or.us

Post, Bill (R, 25)*
900 Court Street, Northeast
H-373
Salem, OR 97401
P: (503) 986-1425
E: rep.billpost@state.or.us

Rayfield, Dan (D, 16)*
900 Court Street, Northeast
H-375
Salem, OR 97401
P: (503) 986-1416
E: rep.danrayfield
@state.or.us

Read, Tobias (D, 27)
900 Court Street, Northeast
H-286
Salem, OR 97301
P: (503) 986-1427
E: rep.tobiasread
@state.or.us

Reardon, Jeff (D, 48)
900 Court Street, Northeast
H-473
Salem, OR 97301
P: (503) 986-1448
E: rep.jeffreardon
@state.or.us

Smith, Greg (R, 57)
900 Court Street, Northeast
H-482
Salem, OR 97301
P: (503) 986-1457
E: rep.gregsmith
@state.or.us

Smith Warner, Barbara (D, 45)
900 Court Street, Northeast
H-487
Salem, OR 97301
P: (503) 986-1445
E: rep.barbarasmithwarner
@state.or.us

Sprenger, Sherrie (R, 17)
900 Court Street, Northeast
H-388
Salem, OR 97301
P: (503) 986-1417
E: rep.sherriesprenger
@state.or.us

Stark, Duane A. (R, 4)*
900 Court Street, Northeast
H-372
Salem, OR 97401
P: (503) 986-1404
E: rep.duanestark
@state.or.us

Taylor, Kathleen (D, 41)*
900 Court Street, Northeast
H-377
Salem, OR 97401
P: (503) 986-1441
E: rep.kathleentaylor
@state.or.us

Vega Pederson, Jessica (D, 47)
900 Court Street, Northeast
H-285
Salem, OR 97301
P: (503) 986-1447
E: rep.jessicavegapederson
@state.or.us

Weidner, Jim (R, 24)
900 Court Street, Northeast
H-387
Salem, OR 97301
P: (503) 986-1424
E: rep.jimweidner
@state.or.us

Whisnant, Gene (R, 53)
900 Court Street, Northeast
H-383
Salem, OR 97301
P: (503) 986-1453
E: rep.genewhisnant
@state.or.us

Whitsett, Gail (R, 56)
900 Court Street, Northeast
H-474
Salem, OR 97301
P: (503) 986-1456
E: rep.gailwhitsett
@state.or.us

Williamson, Jennifer (D, 36)
900 Court Street, Northeast
H-283
Salem, OR 97301
P: (503) 986-1436
E: rep.jenniferwilliamson
@state.or.us

Wilson, Carl (R, 3)
900 Court Street, Northeast
H-390
Salem, OR 97401
P: (503) 986-1403
E: rep.carlwilson
@state.or.us

Witt, Brad (D, 31)
900 Court Street, Northeast
H-374
Salem, OR 97301
P: (503) 986-1431
E: rep.bradwitt@state.or.us

Congress

Senate

Merkley, Jeff (D)
Wyden, Ron (D)

House

Blumenauer, Earl (D, 3)
Bonamici, Suzanne (D, 1)
DeFazio, Peter A. (D, 4)
Schrader, Kurt (D, 5)
Walden, Greg (R, 2)

Pennsylvania

Executive

Governor

Hon. Thomas W. Wolf (D)
Governor
225 Main Capitol Building
Harrisburg, PA 17120
P: (717) 787-2500
F: (717) 772-8284

Lieutenant Governor

Hon. Michael J. Stack (D)
Lieutenant Governor
200 Main Capitol Building
Harrisburg, PA 17120
P: (717) 787-3300
F: (717) 783-0150

Attorney General

Hon. Kathleen Kane (D)
Attorney General
1600 Strawberry Square
Harrisburg, PA 17120
P: (717) 787-3391
F: (717) 787-8242

Auditor

Hon. Eugene DePasquale (D)
Auditor General
229 Finance Building
Harrisburg, PA 17120
P: (717) 787-2543
F: (717) 783-4407
E: auditorgen
@auditorgen.state.pa.us

Secretary of State

Hon. Pedro A. Cortes
(appointed)
Acting Secretary of the Commonwealth
302 North Office Building
Harrisburg, PA 17120
P: (717) 787-6458
F: (717) 787-1734
E: pcortes@state.pa.us

Treasurer

Hon. Christopher Craig
Acting State Treasurer
Room 129, Finance Building
Harrisburg, PA 17120
P: (717) 787-2465
F: (717) 783-9760

Judiciary

Supreme Court (PE)

Ms. Patricia Johnson
Chief Clerk
468 City Hall
Philadelphia, PA 19107
P: (215) 560-6370

Ms. Patricia A. Nicola
Chief Clerk
801 City-County Building
Pittsburgh, PA 15219
P: (412) 565-2816

Ms. Elizabeth Zisk
Chief Clerk
601 Commonwealth Avenue, Suite 4500
P.O. Box 62575
Harrisburg, PA 17106
P: (717) 787-6181

Hon. Thomas G. Saylor
Chief Justice
Hon. Max Baer
Hon. J. Michael Eakin
Hon. Correale F. Stevens
Hon. Debra McCloskey Todd

Legislative Senate

Senate President

Hon. Michael J. Stack (D)
Lieutenant Governor
200 Main Capitol Building
Harrisburg, PA 17120
P: (717) 787-3300
F: (717) 783-0150

President Pro Tempore of the Senate

Sen. Joseph B. Scarnati III (R)
President Pro Tempore
292 Main Capitol
Senate Box 203025
Harrisburg, PA 17120
P: (717) 787-7084
F: (717) 772-2755
E: jscarnati@pasen.gov

Senate Majority Leader

Sen. Jake Corman (R)
Majority Leader
350 Main Capitol
Senate Box 203034
Harrisburg, PA 17120
P: (717) 787-1377
F: (717) 772-3146
E: jcorman@pasen.gov

Senate Minority Leader

Sen. Jay Costa (D)
Minority Floor Leader
535 Main Capitol
Senate Box 203043
Harrisburg, PA 17120
P: (717) 787-7683
F: (717) 783-5976
E: costa@pasenate.com

Secretary of the Senate

Ms. Megan Totino Consedine
Secretary-Parliamentarian of the Senate
462 Capitol Building
Senate Box 203053
Harrisburg, PA 17120
P: (717) 787-5920
E: mconsedine@os.pasen.gov

Members of the Senate

Alloway, Richard (R, 33)
172 Main Capitol
Senate Box 203033
Harrisburg, PA 17120
P: (717) 787-4651
F: (717) 772-2753
E: alloway@pasen.gov

Argall, David G. (R, 29)
171 Main Capitol
Senate Box 203029
Harrisburg, PA 17120
P: (717) 787-2637
F: (717) 783-8657
E: dargall@pasen.gov

Aument, Ryan P. (R, 36)
352 Main Capitol
Senate Box 203036
Harrisburg, PA 17120
P: (717) 787-4420
F: (717) 783-3156
E: raument@pasen.gov

Baker, Lisa (R, 20)
362 Main Capitol
Senate Box 203020
Harrisburg, PA 17120
P: (717) 787-7428
F: (717) 787-9242
E: lbaker@pasen.gov

Bartolotta, Camera (R, 46)*
460 Main Capitol
Senate Box 203046
Harrisburg, PA 17120
P: (717) 787-1463
F: (717) 772-2108
E: cbartolotta@pasen.gov

Blake, John P. (D, 22)
17 East Wing
Senate Box 203022
Harrisburg, PA 17120
P: (717) 787-6481
F: (717) 783-5198
E: senatorblake
@pasenate.com

Boscola, Lisa M. (D, 18)
458 Capitol Building
Senate Box 203018
Harrisburg, PA 17120
P: (717) 787-4236
F: (717) 783-1257
E: boscola@pasenate.com

Brewster, James R. (D, 45)
458 Main Capitol
Senate Box 203045
Harrisburg, PA 17120
P: (717) 787-5580
F: (717) 772-3588
E: brewster@pasenate.com

Brooks, Michele (R, 50)
459 Main Capitol
Senate Box 203050
Harrisburg, PA 17120
P: (717) 787-1322
F: (717) 772-0522

Browne, Patrick M. (R, 16)
281 Main Capitol
Senate Box 203016
Harrisburg, PA 17120
P: (717) 787-1349
F: (717) 772-3458
E: pbrowne@pasen.gov

Corman, Jake (R, 34)
350 Main Capitol
Senate Box 203034
Harrisburg, PA 17120
P: (717) 787-1377
F: (717) 772-3146
E: jcorman@pasen.gov

Costa, Jay (D, 43)
535 Main Capitol
Senate Box 203043
Harrisburg, PA 17120
P: (717) 787-7683
F: (717) 783-5976
E: costa@pasenate.com

Pennsylvania

Dinniman, Andrew E. (D, 19)
182 Main Capitol
Senate Box 203019
Harrisburg, PA 17120
P: (717) 787-5709
F: (717) 787-4384
E: andy@pasenate.com

Eichelberger, John H. (R, 30)
169 Main Capitol
Senate Box 203030
Harrisburg, PA 17120
P: (717) 787-5490
F: (717) 783-5192
E: jeichelberger@pasen.gov

Farnese Jr., Lawrence M. (D, 1)
543 Main Capitol
Senate Box 203001
Harrisburg, PA 17120
P: (717) 787-5662
F: (717) 787-4531
E: farnese@pasenate.com

Folmer, Mike (R, 48)
337 Main Capitol
Senate Box 203048
Harrisburg, PA 17120
P: (717) 787-5708
F: (717) 787-3455
E: mfolmer@pasen.gov

Fontana, Wayne D. (D, 42)
543 Main Capitol
Senate Box 203042
Harrisburg, PA 17120
P: (717) 787-5300
F: (717) 772-5484
E: fontana@pasenate.com

Gordner, John R. (R, 27)
177 Main Capitol
Senate Box 203027
Harrisburg, PA 17120
P: (717) 787-8928
F: (717) 787-9715
E: jgordner@pasen.gov

Greenleaf, Stewart J. (R, 12)
19 East Wing
Senate Box 203012
Harrisburg, PA 17120
P: (717) 787-6599
F: (717) 783-7328
E: sgreenleaf@pasen.gov

Haywood, Art (D, 4)*
457 Main Capitol
Senate Box 203004
Harrisburg, PA 17120
P: (717) 787-1427
F: (717) 772-0572
E: senatorhaywood@pasenate.com

Hughes, Vincent J. (D, 7)
545 Capitol Building
Senate Box 203007
Harrisburg, PA 17120
P: (717) 787-7112
F: (717) 772-0579
E: hughes@pasenate.com

Hutchinson, Scott E. (R, 21)
170 Main Capitol
Senate Box 203021
Harrisburg, PA 17120
P: (717) 787-9684
F: (717) 787-6088
E: shutchinson@pasen.gov

Kitchen, Shirley M. (D, 3)
463 Capitol Building
Senate Box 203003
Harrisburg, PA 17120
P: (717) 787-6735
F: (717) 772-0581
E: kitchen@pasenate.com

Leach, Daylin (D, 17)
184 Main Capitol
Senate Box 203017
Harrisburg, PA 17120
P: (717) 787-5544
F: (717) 705-7741
E: senatorleach@pasenate.com

McGarrigle, Thomas (R, 26)*
185 Main Capitol
Senate Box 203026
Harrisburg, PA 17120
P: (717) 787-1350
F: (717) 787-0196

McIlhinney Jr., Chuck T. (R, 10)
187 Main Capitol
Senate Box 203010
Harrisburg, PA 17120
P: (717) 787-7305
F: (717) 783-5962
E: cmcilhinney@pasen.gov

Mensch, Bob (R, 24)
16 East Wing
Senate Box 203024
Harrisburg, PA 17120
P: (717) 787-3110
F: (717) 787-8004
E: bmensch@pasen.gov

Pileggi, Dominic F. (R, 9)
9 East Wing
Senate Box 203009
Harrisburg, PA 17120
P: (717) 787-4712
F: (717) 783-7490
E: dpileggi@pasen.gov

Rafferty Jr., John C. (R, 44)
20 East Wing
Senate Box 203044
Harrisburg, PA 17120
P: (717) 787-1398
F: (717) 783-4587
E: jrafferty@pasen.gov

Scarnati III, Joseph B. (R, 25)
292 Main Capitol
Senate Box 203025
Harrisburg, PA 17120
P: (717) 787-7084
F: (717) 772-2755
E: jscarnati@pasen.gov

Scavello, Mario M. (R, 40)
168 Main Capitol
Senate Box 203040
Harrisburg, PA 17120
P: (717) 787-6123
F: (717) 772-3695

Schwank, Judith L. (D, 11)
457 Main Capitol
Senate Box 203011
Harrisburg, PA 17120
P: (717) 787-8925
F: (717) 772-0578
E: SenatorSchwank@pasenate.com

Smith, Matthew (D, 37)
366 Main Capitol
Senate Box 203037
Harrisburg, PA 17120
P: (717) 787-5839
F: (717) 772-4437
E: msmith@pasen.gov

Smucker, Lloyd (R, 13)
351 Main Capitol
Senate Box 203013
Harrisburg, PA 17120
P: (717) 787-6535
E: lsmucker@pasen.gov

Stefano, Pat (R, 32)*
183 Main Capitol
Senate Box 203032
Harrisburg, PA 17120
P: (717) 787-7175

Tartaglione, Christine M. (D, 2)
458 Main Capitol
Senate Box 203002
Harrisburg, PA 17120
P: (717) 787-1141
F: (717) 787-7439
E: tartaglione@pasenate.com

Teplitz, Rob (D, 15)
15 East Wing
Senate Box 203015
Harrisburg, PA 17120
P: (717) 787-6801
F: (717) 783-3722
E: senatorteplitz@pasenate.com

Tomlinson, Robert M. (R, 6)
281 Capitol Building
Senate Box 203006
Harrisburg, PA 17120
P: (717) 787-5072
F: (717) 772-2991
E: rtomlinson@pasen.gov

Vance, Patricia H. (R, 31)
173 Main Capitol
Senate Box 203031
Harrisburg, PA 17120
P: (717) 787-8524
F: (717) 772-0576
E: vance@pasen.gov

Vogel Jr., Elder A. (R, 47)
362 Main Capitol
Senate Box 203047
Harrisburg, PA 17120
P: (717) 787-3076
F: (717) 772-2756
E: evogel@pasen.gov

Vulakovich, Randy (R, 38)
168 Main Capitol
Senate Box 203038
Harrisburg, PA 17120
P: (717) 787-6538
F: (717) 787-8625
E: rvulakovich@pasen.gov

Wagner, Scott (R, 28)*
187 Main Capitol
Senate Box 203028
Harrisburg, PA 17120
P: (717) 787-3817
F: (717) 783-1900
E: swagner@pasen.gov

Ward, Kim L. (R, 39)
168 Main Capitol
Senate Box 203039
Harrisburg, PA 17120
P: (717) 787-6063
F: (717) 772-0580
E: kward@pasen.gov

White, Donald C. (R, 41)
286 Capitol Building
Senate Box 203041
Harrisburg, PA 17120
P: (717) 787-8724
F: (717) 772-1589
E: dwhite@pasen.gov

Wiley, Sean (D, 49)
535 Main Capitol
Senate Box 203049
Harrisburg, PA 17120
P: (717) 787-8927
F: (717) 772-1588
E: senatorwiley@pasenate.com

Williams, Anthony H. (D, 8)
11 East Wing
Senate Box 203008
Harrisburg, PA 17120
P: (717) 787-5970
F: (717) 772-0574
E: williams@pasenate.com

Wozniak, John N. (D, 35)
10 East Wing
Senate Box 203035
Harrisburg, PA 17120
P: (717) 787-5400
F: (717) 772-0573
E: wozniak@pasenate.com

Yaw, Gene (R, 23)
362 Main Capitol
Senate Box 203023
Harrisburg, PA 17120
P: (717) 787-3280
F: (717) 772-0575
E: gyaw@pasen.gov

Yudichak, John T. (D, 14)
458 Main Capitol
Senate Box 203014
Harrisburg, PA 17120
P: (717) 787-7105
F: (717) 783-4141
E: yudichak@pasenate.com

House

Speaker of the House

Rep. Mike Turzai (R)
Speaker of the House
139 Main Capitol
P.O. Box 202028
Harrisburg, PA 17120
P: (717) 772-9943
F: (717) 772-2470
E: mturzai@pahousegop.com

House Majority Leader

Rep. Dave Reed (R)
Majority Leader
110 Main Capitol Building
P.O. Box 202062
Harrisburg, PA 17120
P: (717) 705-7173
F: (717) 705-1947
E: dreed@pahousegop.com

House Minority Leader

Rep. Frank Dermody (D)
Democratic Leader
423 Main Capitol Building
P.O. Box 202033
Harrisburg, PA 17120
P: (717) 787-3566
F: (717) 787-8060
E: fdermody@pahouse.net

Clerk of the House

Mr. Anthony Frank Barbush
Chief Clerk of the House
129 Main Capitol Building
Harrisburg, PA 17120
P: (717) 787-2372

Members of the House

Acosta, Leslie (D, 197)*
111A East Wing
P.O. Box 202197
Harrisburg, PA 17120
P: (717) 772-2004
F: (717) 780-4784

Adolph Jr., William F. (R, 165)
245 Main Capitol Building
P.O. Box 202165
Harrisburg, PA 17120
P: (717) 787-1248
F: (717) 705-1851
E: Wadolph@pahousegop.com

Baker, Matthew E. (R, 68)
213 Ryan Office Building
P.O. Box 202068
Harrisburg, PA 17120
P: (717) 772-5371
F: (717) 705-1835
E: mbaker@pahousegop.com

Barbin, Bryan (D, 71)
4 East Wing
P.O. Box 202071
Harrisburg, PA 17120
P: (717) 783-1491
F: (717) 705-7001

Barrar, Stephen E. (R, 160)
18 East Wing
P.O. Box 202160
Harrisburg, PA 17120
P: (717) 783-3038
F: (717) 787-7604
E: parep160@aol.com

Benninghoff, Kerry A. (R, 171)
147 Main Capitol Building
P.O. Box 202171
Harrisburg, PA 17120
P: (717) 783-1918
F: (717) 260-6528
E: kbenning@pahousegop.com

Bishop, Louise Williams (D, 192)
326 Main Capitol Building
P.O. Box 202192
Harrisburg, PA 17120
P: (717) 783-2192
F: (717) 787-2960
E: lwbishop@pahouse.net

Bizzarro, Ryan A. (D, 3)
27B East Wing
P.O. Box 202003
Harrisburg, PA 17120
P: (717) 772-2297
F: (717) 780-4767

Bloom, Stephen (R, 199)
B16 Main Capitol Building
P.O. Box 202199
Harrisburg, PA 17120
P: (717) 772-2280

Boback, Karen (R, 117)
141B East Wing
P.O. Box 202117
Harrisburg, PA 17120
P: (717) 787-1117
F: (717) 705-1889
E: kboback@pahousegop.com

Boyle, Kevin J. (D, 172)
102 East Wing
P.O. Box 202172
Harrisburg, PA 17120
P: (717) 783-4944

Bradford, Matthew (D, 70)
109A East Wing
P.O. Box 202070
Harrisburg, PA 17120
P: (717) 772-2572
F: (717) 772-2360

Briggs, Tim (D, 149)
105B East Wing
P.O. Box 202149
Harrisburg, PA 17120
P: (717) 705-7011
F: (717) 772-9860

Brown, Rosemary M. (R, 189)
164A East Wing
P.O. Box 202189
Harrisburg, PA 17120
P: (717) 260-6171

Brown, Vanessa Lowery (D, 190)
328 Irvis Office Building
P.O. Box 202190
Harrisburg, PA 17120
P: (717) 783-3822
F: (717) 772-2384

Brownlee, Michelle F. (D, 195)
115A East Wing
P.O. Box 202195
Harrisburg, PA 17120
P: (717) 787-3480
F: (717) 772-9853

Burns, Frank (D, 72)
323 Main Capitol Building
P.O. Box 202072
Harrisburg, PA 17120
P: (717) 772-8056
F: (717) 772-9965

Caltagirone, Thomas R. (D, 127)
106 Irvis Office Building
P.O. Box 202127
Harrisburg, PA 17120
P: (717) 787-3525
F: (717) 772-5401
E: tcaltagi@pahouse.net

Carroll, Mike (D, 118)
300 Main Capitol Building
P.O. Box 202118
Harrisburg, PA 17120
P: (717) 787-3589
F: (717) 780-4763
E: mcarroll@pahouse.net

Causer, Martin T. (R, 67)
41B East Wing
P.O. Box 202067
Harrisburg, PA 17120
P: (717) 787-5075
F: (717) 705-7021
E: mcauser@pahousegop.com

Christiana, Jim (R, 15)
145B East Wing
P.O. Box 202015
Harrisburg, PA 17120
P: (717) 260-6144
F: (717) 260-6506
E: jchristi@pahousegop.com

Cohen, Mark B. (D, 202)
127 Irvis Office Building
P.O. Box 202202
Harrisburg, PA 17120
P: (717) 787-4117
F: (717) 783-4820
E: mcohen@pahouse.net

Pennsylvania

Conklin, H. Scott (D, 77)
325 Irvis Office Building
P.O. Box 202077
Harrisburg, PA 17120
P: (717) 787-9473
F: (717) 780-4764
E: sconklin@pahouse.net

Corbin, Becky (R, 155)
52A East Wing
P.O. Box 202155
Harrisburg, PA 17120
P: (717) 783-2520
F: (717) 782-2927

Costa, Dom (D, 21)
217 Irvis Office Building
P.O. Box 202021
Harrisburg, PA 17120
P: (717) 783-9114
F: (717) 780-4761

Costa, Paul (D, 34)
301 Irvis Office Building
P.O. Box 202034
Harrisburg, PA 17120
P: (717) 783-1914
F: (717) 705-2564
E: pcosta@pahouse.net

Cox, Jim (R, 129)
210 Ryan Office Building
P.O. Box 202129
Harrisburg, PA 17120
P: (717) 772-2435
F: (717) 705-1849
E: jcox@pahousegop.com

Cruz, Angel (D, 180)
528E Main Capitol Building
P.O. Box 202180
Harrisburg, PA 17120
P: (717) 787-1407
F: (717) 780-4769
E: acruz@pahouse.net

Cutler, Bryan (R, 100)
121 Main Capitol Building
P.O. Box 202100
Harrisburg, PA 17120
P: (717) 783-6424
F: (717) 772-9859

Daley, Mary Jo (D, 148)
103A East Wing
P.O. Box 202148
Harrisburg, PA 17120
P: (717) 787-9475
F: (717) 787-0861

Daley, Peter J. (D, 49)
202 Irvis Office Building
P.O. Box 202049
Harrisburg, PA 17120
P: (717) 783-9333
F: (717) 783-7558
E: pdaley@pahouse.net

Davidson, Margo L. (D, 164)
527E Main Capitol
P.O. Box 202164
Harrisburg, PA 17120
P: (717) 783-4907
F: (717) 780-4750

Davis, Tina M. (D, 141)
G14 Irvis Office Building
P.O. Box 202141
Harrisburg, PA 17120
P: (717) 783-4903

Dawkins, Jason (D, 179)*
26A East Wing
P.O. Box 202179
Harrisburg, PA 17120
P: (717) 797-1354

Day, Gary (R, 187)
163B East Wing
P.O. Box 202187
Harrisburg, PA 17120
P: (717) 787-3017
F: (717) 705-1951

Deasy, Daniel J. (D, 27)
323 Irvis Office Building
P.O. Box 202027
Harrisburg, PA 17120
P: (717) 772-8187

DeLissio, Pamela A. (D, 194)
109B East Wing
P.O. Box 202194
Harrisburg, PA 17120
P: (717) 783-4945

Delozier, Sheryl M. (R, 88)
159B East Wing
P.O. Box 202088
Harrisburg, PA 17120
P: (717) 783-5282
F: (717) 772-9994
E: sdelozie@pahousegop.com

DeLuca, Anthony M. (D, 32)
115 Irvis Office Building
P.O. Box 202032
Harrisburg, PA 17120
P: (717) 783-1011
F: (717) 772-9937
E: tdeluca@pahouse.net

Dermody, Frank (D, 33)
423 Main Capitol Building
P.O. Box 202033
Harrisburg, PA 17120
P: (717) 787-3566
F: (717) 787-8060
E: fdermody@pahouse.net

Diamond, Russ (R, 102)*
53B East Wing
P.O. Box 202102
Harrisburg, PA 17120
P: (717) 787-2686

DiGirolamo, Gene (R, 18)
49 East Wing
P.O. Box 202018
Harrisburg, PA 17120
P: (717) 783-7319
F: (717) 772-2414
E: gdigirol@pahousegop.com

Donatucci, Maria P. (D, 185)
G07 Irvis Office Building
P.O. Box 202185
Harrisburg, PA 17120
P: (717) 783-8634
F: (717) 772-9888

Driscoll, Mike (D, 173)*
27A East Wing
P.O. Box 202173
Harrisburg, PA 17120
P: (717) 787-4331
F: (717) 772-9962

Dunbar, George (R, 56)
147A East Wing
P.O. Box 202056
Harrisburg, PA 17120
P: (717) 260-6132
F: (717) 782-2880

Dush, Cris (R, 66)*
161A East Wing
P.O. Box 202066
Harrisburg, PA 17120
P: (717) 787-3845
F: (717) 782-2946

Ellis, Brian (R, 11)
128 Main Capitol Building
P.O. Box 202011
Harrisburg, PA 17120
P: (717) 787-7686
F: (717) 782-2907
E: bellis@pahousegop.com

Emrick, Joe (R, 137)
160B East Wing
P.O. Box 202137
Harrisburg, PA 17120
P: (717) 260-6159

English, Harold A. (R, 30)
111 Ryan Office Building
P.O. Box 202030
Harrisburg, PA 17120
P: (717) 260-6407
F: (717) 783-5740

Evankovich, Eli (R, 54)
3 East Wing
P.O. Box 202054
Harrisburg, PA 17120
P: (717) 260-6129

Evans, Dwight (D, 203)
38 East Wing
P.O. Box 202203
Harrisburg, PA 17120
P: (717) 783-4111
F: (717) 772-9996
E: devans@hacd.net

Everett, Garth D. (R, 84)
430 Irvis Office Building
P.O. Box 202084
Harrisburg, PA 17120
P: (717) 787-5270
F: (717) 772-9958

Fabrizio, Florindo J. (D, 2)
200 Irvis Office Building
P.O. Box 202002
Harrisburg, PA 17120
P: (717) 787-4358
F: (717) 780-4774
E: ffabrizi@pahouse.net

Farina, Frank (D, 112)
28B East Wing
P.O. Box 202112
Harrisburg, PA 17120
P: (717) 783-5043
F: (717) 787-1231

Farry, Frank (R, 142)
52B East Wing
P.O. Box 202142
Harrisburg, PA 17120
P: (717) 260-6140
F: (717) 782-2916
E: Ffarry@pahousegop.com

Fee, Mindy (R, 37)
164B East Wing
P.O. Box 202037
Harrisburg, PA 17120
P: (717) 772-5290
F: (717) 783-1904

Flynn, Marty (D, 113)
28A East Wing
P.O. Box 202113
Harrisburg, PA 17120
P: (717) 787-8981
F: (717) 705-1958

Frankel, Dan B. (D, 23)
417 Main Capitol Building
P.O. Box 202023
Harrisburg, PA 17120
P: (717) 705-1875
F: (717) 705-2034
E: dfrankel@pahouse.net

Freeman, Robert L. (D, 136)
207 Irvis Office Building
P.O. Box 202136
Harrisburg, PA 17120
P: (717) 783-3815
F: (717) 783-2152
E: rfreeman@pahouse.net

Gabler, Matt (R, 75)
150B East Wing
P.O. Box 202075
Harrisburg, PA 17120
P: (717) 260-6142

Gainey, Ed (D, 24)
116B East Wing
P.O. Box 202024
Harrisburg, PA 17120
P: (717) 783-1017

Galloway, John T. (D, 140)
104 Irvis Office Building
P.O. Box 202140
Harrisburg, PA 17120
P: (717) 787-1292
F: (717) 780-4780

Gergely, Marc J. (D, 35)
325 Main Capitol Building
P.O. Box 202035
Harrisburg, PA 17120
P: (717) 783-1018
F: (717) 780-4779
E: mgergely@pahouse.net

Gibbons, Jaret (D, 10)
302 Main Capitol Building
P.O. Box 202010
Harrisburg, PA 17120
P: (717) 705-2060
F: (717) 780-4766
E: jgibbons@pahouse.net

Gillen, Mark M. (R, 128)
408 Irvis Office Building
P.O. Box 202128
Harrisburg, PA 17020
P: (717) 787-8550

Gillespie, Keith J. (R, 47)
45 East Wing
P.O. Box 202047
Harrisburg, PA 17120
P: (717) 705-7167
F: (717) 782-2914
E: kgillesp@pahousegop.com

Gingrich, Mauree A. (R, 101)
106 Ryan Office Building
P.O. Box 202101
Harrisburg, PA 17120
P: (717) 783-1815
F: (717) 705-2569
E: mgingric@pahousegop.com

Godshall, Robert W. (R, 53)
150 Main Capitol Building
P.O. Box 202053
Harrisburg, PA 17120
P: (717) 783-6428
F: (717) 787-7424
E: rgodshal@pahousegop.com

Goodman, Neal P. (D, 123)
512-E Main Capitol Building
P.O. Box 202123
Harrisburg, PA 17120
P: (717) 787-2798
F: (717) 772-9948
E: ngoodman@pahouse.net

Greiner, Keith J. (R, 43)
54B East Wing
P.O. Box 202043
Harrisburg, PA 17120
P: (717) 783-6422
F: (717) 782-2926

Grell, Glen R. (R, 87)
314C Main Capitol Building
P.O. Box 202087
Harrisburg, PA 17120
P: (717) 783-2063
F: (717) 705-7012
E: ggrell@pahousegop.com

Grove, Seth (R, 196)
B8 Main Capitol Building
P.O. Box 202196
Harrisburg, PA 17120
P: (717) 783-2655
F: (717) 260-6482

Hackett, Joseph T. (R, 161)
406 Irvis Office Building
P.O. Box 202161
Harrisburg, PA 17120
P: (717) 260-6168
F: (717) 782-2891

Hahn, Marcia M. (R, 138)
402 A Irvis Office Building
P.O. Box 202138
Harrisburg, PA 17120
P: (717) 783-8573
F: (717) 783-3899

Hanna, Michael K. (D, 76)
428 Main Capitol Building
P.O. Box 202076
Harrisburg, PA 17120
P: (717) 772-2283
F: (717) 787-4137
E: mhanna@pahouse.net

Harhai, R. Ted (D, 58)
32 East Wing
P.O. Box 202058
Harrisburg, PA 17120
P: (717) 772-2820
F: (717) 772-0745
E: tharhai@pahouse.net

Harhart, Julie (R, 183)
313 Main Capitol Building
P.O. Box 202183
Harrisburg, PA 17120
P: (717) 772-5398
F: (717) 783-7667
E: jharhart@pahousegop.com

Harkins, Patrick J. (D, 1)
111 Irvis Office Building
P.O. Box 202001
Harrisburg, PA 17120
P: (717) 787-7406
F: (717) 780-4775

Harper, Kate (R, 61)
209 Ryan Office Building
P.O. Box 202061
Harrisburg, PA 17120
P: (717) 787-2801
F: (717) 787-2022
E: kharper@pahousegop.com

Harris, C. Adam (R, 82)
115 Ryan Office Building
P.O. Box 202082
Harrisburg, PA 17120
P: (717) 783-7830
F: (717) 772-9869
E: aharris@pahousegop.com

Harris, Jordan A. (D, 186)
104A East Wing
P.O. Box 202186
Harrisburg, PA 17120
P: (717) 783-1792
F: (717) 787-7172

Heffley, Doyle (R, 122)
403 Irvis Office Building
P.O. Box 202122
Harrisburg, PA 17120
P: (717) 260-6139
F: (717) 782-2885

Helm, Susan C. (R, 104)
141A East Wing
P.O. Box 202104
Harrisburg, PA 17120
P: (717) 787-1230
F: (717) 787-7375
E: shelm@pahousegop.com

Hennessey, Tim (R, 26)
312 Main Capitol Building
P.O. Box 202026
Harrisburg, PA 17120
P: (717) 787-3431
F: (717) 705-1849
E: thenness@pahousegop.com

Hickernell, David S. (R, 98)
43A East Wing
P.O. Box 202098
Harrisburg, PA 17120
P: (717) 783-2076
F: (717) 787-9175
E: dhickern@pahousegop.com

Hill, Kristin (R, 93)*
123B East Wing
P.O. Box 202093
Harrisburg, PA 17120
P: (717) 783-8389

Irvin, Rich (R, 81)*
5 East Wing
P.O. Box 202081
Harrisburg, PA 17120
P: (717) 787-3335
F: (717) 782-2884

James, R. Lee (R, 64)
53A East Wing
P.O. Box 202064
Harrisburg, PA 17120
P: (717) 783-8188

Jozwiak, Barry (R, 5)*
402A Irvis Office Building
P.O. Box 202005
Harrisburg, PA 17120
P: (787) 772-9940
F: (787) 782-2925

Kampf, Warren (R, 157)
153B East Wing
P.O. Box 202157
Harrisburg, PA 17120
P: (717) 260-6166
F: (717) 782-2888

Kaufer, Aaron (R, 120)*
B15 Main Capitol Building
P.O. Box 202120
Harrisburg, PA 17120
P: (717) 787-3798
F: (717) 782-2950

Kauffman, Rob W. (R, 89)
7 East Wing
P.O. Box 202089
Harrisburg, PA 17120
P: (717) 705-2004
F: (717) 787-9840
E: rkauffma@pahousegop.com

Kavulich, Sid Michaels (D, 114)
G05 Irvis Office Building
P.O. Box 202114
Harrisburg, PA 17120
P: (717) 783-4874

Keller, Fred (R, 85)
428 Irvis Office Building
P.O. Box 202085
Harrisburg, PA 17120
P: (717) 787-3443
F: (717) 782-2887

Keller, Mark K. (R, 86)
108 Ryan Office Building
P.O. Box 202086
Harrisburg, PA 17120
P: (717) 783-1593
F: (717) 782-2894
E: mkeller@pahousegop.com

Pennsylvania

Keller, William F. (D, 184)
333 Main Capitol Building
P.O. Box 202184
Harrisburg, PA 17120
P: (717) 787-5774
F: (717) 705-2088
E: wkeller@pahouse.net

Killion, Thomas H. (R, 168)
110 Ryan Office Building
P.O. Box 202168
Harrisburg, PA 17120
P: (717) 772-0855
F: (717) 772-9856
E: tkillion@pahousegop.com

Kim, Patty (D, 103)
G01 Irvis Office Building
P.O. Box 202103
Harrisburg, PA 17120
P: (717) 783-9342
F: (717) 787-8957

Kinsey, Stephen (D, 201)
106B East Wing
P.O. Box 202201
Harrisburg, PA 17120
P: (717) 787-3181
F: (717) 772-4038

Kirkland, Thaddeus (D, 159)
320 Irvis Office Building
P.O. Box 202159
Harrisburg, PA 17120
P: (717) 787-5881
F: (717) 787-9074
E: tkirklan@pahouse.net

Klunk, Kate (R, 169)*
123A East Wing
P.O. Box 202169
Harrisburg, PA 17120
P: (717) 787-4790

Knowles, Jerry (R, 124)
155A East Wing
P.O. Box 202124
Harrisburg, PA 17120
P: (717) 787-9029
F: (717) 783-3899

Kortz, William C. (D, 38)
114 Irvis Office Building
P.O. Box 202038
Harrisburg, PA 17120
P: (717) 787-8175
F: (717) 780-4783

Kotik, Nick (D, 45)
226 Irvis Office Building
P.O. Box 202045
Harrisburg, PA 17120
P: (717) 783-3780
F: (717) 780-4773
E: nkotik@pahouse.net

Krieger, Tim (R, 57)
B11 Main Capitol Building
P.O. Box 202057
Harrisburg, PA 17120
P: (717) 260-6146
F: (717) 782-2882

Lawrence, John A. (R, 13)
211 Ryan Office Building
P.O. Box 202013
Harrisburg, PA 17120
P: (717) 260-6117

Lewis, Harry (R, 74)*
153A East Wing
P.O. Box 202074
Harrisburg, PA 17120
P: (717) 787-1806
F: (717) 782-2947

Longietti, Mark (D, 7)
103 Irvis Office Building
P.O. Box 202007
Harrisburg, PA 17120
P: (717) 772-4035
F: (717) 780-4785

Mackenzie, Ryan E. (R, 134)
160A East Wing
P.O. Box 202134
Harrisburg, PA 17120
P: (717) 787-1000
F: (717) 782-2893

Maher, John A. (R, 40)
113 Ryan Office Building
P.O. Box 202040
Harrisburg, PA 17120
P: (717) 783-1522
F: (717) 783-8332
E: jmaher@pahousegop.com

Mahoney, Tim (D, 51)
324 Main Capitol
P.O. Box 202051
Harrisburg, PA 17120
P: (717) 772-2174
F: (717) 780-4786

Major, Sandra J. (R, 111)
120 Main Capitol Building
P.O. Box 202111
Harrisburg, PA 17120
P: (717) 783-2910
F: (717) 783-2010
E: smajor@pahousegop.com

Maloney Sr., David M. (R, 130)
6A East Wing
P.O. Box 202130
Harrisburg, PA 17120
P: (717) 260-6161
F: (717) 782-2883

Markosek, Joseph F. (D, 25)
512E Main Capitol Building
P.O. Box 202025
Harrisburg, PA 17120
P: (717) 783-1540
F: (717) 787-2334
E: jmarkose@pahouse.net

Marshall, Jim (R, 14)
145A East Wing
P.O. Box 202014
Harrisburg, PA 17120
P: (717) 260-6432
F: (717) 782-2918
E: jmarshal@pahousegop.com

Marsico, Ron S. (R, 105)
315J Main Capitol Building
P.O. Box 202105
Harrisburg, PA 17120
P: (717) 783-2014
F: (717) 705-2010
E: rmarsico@pahousegop.com

Masser, Kurt A. (R, 107)
415 Irvis Office Building
P.O. Box 202107
Harrisburg, PA 17120
P: (717) 260-6134
F: (717) 787-9463

Matzie, Robert (D, 16)
121 Irvis Office Building
P.O. Box 202016
Harrisburg, PA 17120
P: (717) 787-4444
F: (717) 780-4772

McCarter, Stephen (D, 154)
26B East Wing
P.O. Box 202154
Harrisburg, PA 17120
P: (717) 783-1079
F: (717) 787-2713

McGinnis, John D. (R, 79)
429 Irvis Office Building
P.O. Box 202079
Harrisburg, PA 17120
P: (717) 787-6419
F: (717) 782-2923

McNeill, Daniel (D, 133)
25A East Wing
P.O. Box 202133
Harrisburg, PA 17120
P: (717) 772-9902

Mentzer, Steven C. (R, 97)
51A East Wing
P.O. Box 202097
Harrisburg, PA 17120
P: (717) 787-1776
F: (717) 705-2031

Metcalfe, Daryl (R, 12)
144 Main Capitol Building
P.O. Box 202012
Harrisburg, PA 17120
P: (717) 783-1707
F: (717) 787-4771
E: dmetcalf@pahousegop.com

Metzgar, Carl (R, 69)
149A East Wing
P.O. Box 202069
Harrisburg, PA 17120
P: (717) 783-8756
F: (717) 782-2911

Miccarelli, Nick (R, 162)
432 Irvis Office Building
P.O. Box 202162
Harrisburg, PA 17120
P: (717) 787-3472
F: (717) 787-8215
E: NickMicc@pahousegop.com

Millard, David (R, 109)
316 Main Capitol Building
P.O. Box 202109
Harrisburg, PA 17120
P: (717) 783-1102
F: (717) 772-0094
E: dmillard@pahousegop.com

Miller, Brett (R, 41)*
54A East Wing
P.O. Box 202041
Harrisburg, PA 17120
P: (717) 705-7161

Miller, Daniel L. (D, 42)
116A East Wing
P.O. Box 202042
Harrisburg, PA 17120
P: (717) 783-1850
F: (717) 780-4756

Milne, Duane (R, 167)
150A East Wing
P.O. Box 202167
Harrisburg, PA 17120
P: (717) 787-8579
F: (717) 787-1295
E: dmilne@pahousegop.com

Moul, Dan (R, 91)
G32 Irvis Office Building
P.O. Box 202091
Harrisburg, PA 17120
P: (717) 783-5217
F: (717) 772-5499
E: dmoul@pahousegop.com

Mullery, Gerald J. (D, 119)
120 Irvis Office Building
P.O. Box 202119
Harrisburg, PA 17120
P: (717) 783-4893

Murt, Thomas P. (R, 152)
410 Irvis Office Building
P.O. Box 202152
Harrisburg, PA 17120
P: (717) 787-6886
F: (717) 782-2886
E: tmurt@pahousegop.com

Mustio, T. Mark (R, 44)
420 Irvis Office Building
P.O. Box 202044
Harrisburg, PA 17120
P: (717) 787-6651
F: (717) 782-2889
E: mmustio@pahousegop.com

Nesbit, Tedd (R, 8)*
121A East Wing
P.O. Box 202008
Harrisburg, PA 17120
P: (717) 783-6438
F: (717) 782-2943

Neuman, Brandon P. (D, 48)
225 Irvis Office Building
P.O. Box 202048
Harrisburg, PA 17020
P: (717) 783-4834
F: (717) 705-1887

Oberlander, Donna (R, 63)
152 Main Capitol Building
P.O. Box 202063
Harrisburg, PA 17120
P: (717) 772-9908
F: (717) 782-2912
E: Doberlan@pahousegop.com

O'Brien, Michael H. (D, 175)
107 East Wing
P.O. Box 202175
Harrisburg, PA 17120
P: (717) 783-8098
F: (717) 780-4787
E: mobrien@pahouse.net

O'Neill, Bernie T. (R, 29)
47 East Wing
P.O. Box 202029
Harrisburg, PA 17120
P: (717) 705-7170
F: (717) 783-3278
E: boneill@pahousegop.com

Ortitay, Jason (R, 46)*
125B East Wing
P.O. Box 202046
Harrisburg, PA 17120
P: (717) 787-1281

Parker, Cherelle L. (D, 200)
101 Irvis Office Building
P.O. Box 202200
Harrisburg, PA 17120
P: (717) 783-2178
F: (717) 783-7548
E: cparker@pahouse.net

Parker, David (R, 115)*
422 Irvis Office Building
P.O. Box 202115
Harrisburg, PA 17120
P: (717) 787-3364

Pashinski, Eddie Day (D, 121)
203 Irvis Office Building
P.O. Box 202121
Harrisburg, PA 17120
P: (717) 783-0686
F: (717) 772-2284

Payne, John D. (R, 106)
416 Irvis Office Building
P.O. Box 202106
Harrisburg, PA 17120
P: (717) 787-2684
F: (717) 787-7557
E: jpayne@pahousegop.com

Peifer, Michael (R, 139)
157 East Wing
P.O. Box 202139
Harrisburg, PA 17120
P: (717) 783-2037
F: (717) 782-2910
E: mpeifer@pahousegop.com

Petrarca, Joseph A. (D, 55)
220 Irvis Office Building
P.O. Box 202055
Harrisburg, PA 17120
P: (717) 787-5142
F: (717) 705-2014
E: jpetrarc@pahouse.net

Petri, Scott A. (R, 178)
107 Ryan Office Building
P.O. Box 202178
Harrisburg, PA 17120
P: (717) 787-9033
F: (717) 705-1802
E: spetri@pahousegop.com

Pickett, Tina (R, 110)
315-A Main Capitol Building
P.O. Box 202110
Harrisburg, PA 17120
P: (717) 783-8238
F: (717) 782-2881
E: tpickett@pahousegop.com

Pyle, Jeffrey P. (R, 60)
218 Ryan Office Building
P.O. Box 202060
Harrisburg, PA 17120
P: (717) 783-5327
F: (717) 782-2904
E: jpyle@pahousegop.com

Quigley, Thomas (R, 146)
Room 51A, East Wing
P.O. Box 202146
Harrisburg, PA 17120
P: (717) 772-9963
F: (717) 772-2434
E: tquigley@pahousegop.com

Quinn, Marguerite (R, 143)
159A East Wing
P.O. Box 202143
Harrisburg, PA 17120
P: (717) 772-1413
F: (717) 783-3793
E: mquinn@pahousegop.com

Rader Jr., Jack (R, 176)*
423 Irvis Office Building
P.O. Box 202176
Harrisburg, PA 17120
P: (717) 787-7732

Rapp, Kathy L. (R, 65)
143 East Wing
P.O. Box 202065
Harrisburg, PA 17120
P: (717) 787-1367
F: (717) 787-5854
E: klrapp@pahousegop.com

Ravenstahl, Adam (D, 20)
322 Irvis Office Building
P.O. Box 202020
Harrisburg, PA 17120
P: (717) 787-5470
F: (717) 783-0407

Readshaw, Harry A. (D, 36)
221 Irvis Office Building
P.O. Box 202036
Harrisburg, PA 17120
P: (717) 783-0411
F: (717) 705-2007
E: hreadsha@pahouse.net

Reed, Dave (R, 62)
110 Main Capitol Building
P.O. Box 202062
Harrisburg, PA 17120
P: (717) 705-7173
F: (717) 705-1947
E: dreed@pahousegop.com

Reese, Mike (R, 59)
147B East Wing
P.O. Box 202059
Harrisburg, PA 17120
P: (717) 783-9311
F: (717) 782-2900
E: Mreese@pahousegop.com

Regan, Mike (R, 92)
5 East Wing
P.O. Box 202092
Harrisburg, PA 17120
P: (717) 783-8783
F: (717) 782-2920

Roae, Brad (R, 6)
162B East Wing
P.O. Box 202006
Harrisburg, PA 17120
P: (717) 787-2353
F: (717) 260-6505
E: broae@pahousegop.com

Roebuck, Jim (D, 188)
208 Irvis Office Building
P.O. Box 202188
Harrisburg, PA 17120
P: (717) 783-1000
F: (717) 783-1665
E: jroebuck@pahouse.net

Ross, Chris (R, 158)
216 Ryan Office Building
P.O. Box 202158
Harrisburg, PA 17120
P: (717) 783-1574
F: (717) 705-2095
E: cross@pahousegop.com

Rozzi, Mark (D, 126)
103B East Wing
P.O. Box 202126
Harrisburg, PA 17120
P: (717) 783-3290
F: (717) 787-7517

Sabatina Jr., John P. (D, 174)
331 Irvis Office Building
P.O. Box 202174
Harrisburg, PA 17120
P: (717) 772-4032
F: (717) 783-1579

Saccone, Rick (R, 39)
6B East Wing
P.O. Box 202039
Harrisburg, PA 17120
P: (717) 260-6122

Sainato, Chris (D, 9)
30 East Wing
P.O. Box 202009
Harrisburg, PA 17120
P: (717) 772-2436
F: (717) 783-8536
E: csainato@pahouse.net

Samuelson, Steve (D, 135)
34 East Wing
P.O. Box 202135
Harrisburg, PA 17120
P: (717) 705-1881
F: (717) 772-2469
E: ssamuels@pahouse.net

Pennsylvania

Sankey, Tommy (R, 73)
149B East Wing
P.O. Box 202074
Harrisburg, PA 17120
P: (717) 787-7099
F: (717) 782-2922

Santarsiero, Steve (D, 31)
105A East Wing
P.O. Box 202031
Harrisburg, PA 17120
P: (717) 787-5475
F: (717) 787-6929
E: RepSantarsiero@pahouse.net

Santora, James (R, 163)*
432 Irvis Office Building
P.O. Box 202163
Harrisburg, PA 17120
P: (717) 783-8808
F: (717) 782-2955

Saylor, Stan (R, 94)
105 Ryan Office Building
P.O. Box 202094
Harrisburg, PA 17120
P: (717) 783-6426
F: (717) 783-7655
E: ssaylor@pahousegop.com

Schemel, Paul (R, 90)*
121B East Wing
P.O. Box 202090
Harrisburg, PA 17120
P: (717) 783-5118
F: (717) 782-2903

Schlegel Culver, Lynda (R, 108)
402 Irvis Office Building
P.O. Box 202108
Harrisburg, PA 17120
P: (717) 787-3485
F: (717) 782-2892

Schlossberg, Michael H. (D, 132)
25B East Wing
P.O. Box 202132
Harrisburg, PA 17120
P: (717) 705-1869

Schreiber, Kevin J. (D, 95)
106A East Wing
P.O. Box 202095
Harrisburg, PA 17120
P: (717) 787-7514
F: (717) 780-4765

Schweyer, Peter (D, 22)*
402 Irvis Office Building
P.O. Box 202022
Harrisburg, PA 17120
P: (717) 787-2909
F: (717) 787-2176

Simmons, Justin J. (R, 131)
5 East Wing
P.O. Box 202131
Harrisburg, PA 17120
P: (717) 783-1673
F: (717) 705-7012

Sims, Brian (D, 182)
104B East Wing
P.O. Box 202182
Harrisburg, PA 17120
P: (717) 783-4072
F: (717) 787-5066

Snyder, Pam (D, 50)
112 Irvis Office Building
P.O. Box 202050
Harrisburg, PA 17120
P: (717) 783-3797
F: (717) 772-3605

Sonney, Curtis G. (R, 4)
161B East Wing
P.O. Box 202004
Harrisburg, PA 17120
P: (717) 783-9087
F: (717) 787-2005
E: csonney@pahousegop.com

Staats, Craig (R, 145)*
412 Irvis Office Building
P.O. Box 202145
Harrisburg, PA 17120
P: (717) 783-3154
F: (717) 260-6521

Stephens, Todd (R, 151)
4A East Wing
P.O. Box 202151
Harrisburg, PA 17120
P: (717) 260-6163

Sturla, P. Michael (D, 96)
414 Main Capitol Building
P.O. Box 202096
Harrisburg, PA 17120
P: (717) 787-3555
F: (717) 705-1923
E: msturla@pahouse.net

Tallman, Will (R, 193)
427 Irvis Office Building
P.O. Box 202193
Harrisburg, PA 17120
P: (717) 783-8875
F: (717) 787-7588
E: Wtallman@pahousegop.com

Taylor, John J. (R, 177)
214 Ryan Office Building
P.O. Box 202177
Harrisburg, PA 17120
P: (717) 787-3179
F: (717) 260-6519
E: jtaylor@pahousegop.com

Thomas, W. Curtis (D, 181)
214 Irvis Office Building
P.O. Box 202181
Harrisburg, PA 17120
P: (717) 787-9471
F: (717) 787-7297
E: cthomas@pahouse.net

Tobash, Mike (R, 125)
4B East Wing
P.O. Box 202125
Harrisburg, PA 17120
P: (717) 260-6148

Toepel, Marcy (R, 147)
405 Irvis Office Building
P.O. Box 202147
Harrisburg, PA 17120
P: (717) 787-9501
F: (717) 787-8215

Toohil, Tarah (R, 116)
B14 Main Capitol Building
P.O. Box 202116
Harrisburg, PA 17120
P: (717) 260-6136

Topper, Jesse (R, 78)*
409 Irvis Office Building
P.O. Box 202078
Harrisburg, PA 17120
P: (717) 787-7076
F: (717) 782-2933

Truitt, Dan (R, 156)
155-B East Wing
P.O. Box 202156
Harrisburg, PA 17120
P: (717) 260-6164

Turzai, Mike (R, 28)
139 Main Capitol
P.O. Box 202028
Harrisburg, PA 17120
P: (717) 772-9943
F: (717) 772-2470
E: mturzai@pahousegop.com

Vereb, Mike (R, 150)
400 Irvis Office Building
P.O. Box 202150
Harrisburg, PA 17120
P: (717) 705-7164
F: (717) 260-6522
E: mvereb@pahousegop.com

Vitali, Greg (D, 166)
38B East Wing
P.O. Box 202166
Harrisburg, PA 17120
P: (717) 787-7647
F: (717) 705-2089
E: gvitali@pahouse.net

Ward, Judy (R, 80)*
413 Irvis Office Building
P.O. Box 202080
Harrisburg, PA 17120
P: (717) 787-9020
F: (717) 260-6521

Warner, Ryan (R, 52)*
B12 Main Capitol Building
P.O. Box 202052
Harrisburg, PA 17120
P: (717) 787-1540
F: (717) 782-2882

Waters, Ronald G. (D, 191)
117 East Wing
P.O. Box 202191
Harrisburg, PA 17120
P: (717) 772-9850
F: (717) 783-1516
E: rwaters@pahouse.net

Watson, Katharine M. (R, 144)
41A East Wing
P.O. Box 202144
Harrisburg, PA 17120
P: (717) 787-5452
F: (717) 783-8934
E: kwatson@pahousegop.com

Wentling, Parke (R, 17)*
162A East Wing
P.O. Box 202017
Harrisburg, PA 17120
P: (717) 783-5008
F: (717) 705-1948

Wheatley, Jake (D, 19)
317 Irvis Office Building
P.O. Box 202019
Harrisburg, PA 17120
P: (717) 783-3783
F: (717) 780-4753
E: jwheatley@pahouse.net

Wheeland, Jeff (R, 83)*
414 Irvis Office Building
P.O. Box 202083
Harrisburg, PA 17120
P: (717) 787-2885
F: (717) 782-2948

Youngblood, Rosita C. (D, 198)
331 Main Capitol Building
P.O. Box 202198
Harrisburg, PA 17120
P: (717) 787-7727
F: (717) 772-1313
E: ryoungbl@pahouse.net

Zimmerman, David (R, 99)*
51B East Wing
P.O. Box 202099
Harrisburg, PA 17120
P: (717) 787-3531
F: (717) 705-1986

Congress

Senate

Casey Jr., Robert P. (D)
Toomey, Patrick J. (R)

House

Barletta, Lou (R, 11)
Boyle, Brendan (D, 13)
Brady, Robert A. (D, 1)
Cartwright, Matthew (D, 17)
Costello, Ryan (R, 6)
Dent, Charles W. (R, 15)
Doyle, Michael F. (D, 14)
Fattah, Chaka (D, 2)
Fitzpatrick, Michael G. (R, 8)
Kelly, Mike (R, 3)
Marino, Tom (R, 10)
Meehan, Patrick (R, 7)
Murphy, Timothy F. (R, 18)
Perry, Scott (R, 4)
Pitts, Joseph R. (R, 16)
Rothfus, Keith (R, 12)
Shuster, Bill (R, 9)
Thompson, Glen (R, 5)

Puerto Rico

Executive

Governor

Hon. Alejandro García-Padilla (PDP)
Governor
La Fortaleza
P.O. Box 9020082
San Juan, PR 00902
P: (787) 721-7000
F: (787) 721-5072

Lieutenant Governor

Puerto Rico does not have the office of the lieutenant governor. The secretary of state is appointed by the governor and is next in line of succession to the governorship.

Attorney General

Hon. Cesar R. Miranda-Rodriguez
Attorney General
G.P.O. Box 902192
San Juan, PR 00902
P: (787) 721-2900

Auditor

Yesmin Valdivieso-Galib (appointed)
Comptroller
P.O. Box 366069
San Juan, PR 00963
P: (787) 250-3300
F: (787) 751-6768
E: ocpr@ocpr.gov.pr

Secretary of State

Hon. David Bernier (appointed)
Secretary of State
Department of State
Box 9023271
San Juan, PR 00902
P: (787) 722-2121
F: (787) 722-2684

Treasurer

Hon. Juan Zaragoza Gomez
Secretary of Treasury
P.O. Box 9024140
San Juan, PR 00902
P: (787) 721-2020
F: (787) 723-6213

Judiciary

Supreme Court (GA)

Ms. Patricia Oton Oliveri
Secretary of Supreme Court
P.O. Box 9022392
San Juan, PR 00902
P: (787) 723-6033
F: (787) 723-9199

Hon. Liana Fiol-Matta
Chief Justice
Hon. Roberto Cintron Feliberti
Hon. Luis Estrella Martinez
Hon. Erick V. Kolthoff Caraballo
Hon. Rafael L. Martinez Torres
Hon. Mildred G. Pabon Charneco
Hon. Edgardo Rivera Garcia
Hon. Anabelle Rodriguez Rodriguez
Hon. Maite Oronoz Rodriguez

Legislative Senate

Senate President

Sen. Eduardo Bhatia (PDP)
Senate President
The Capitol
P.O. Box 9023431
San Juan, PR 00902
P: (787) 724-2030 Ext. 3031
E: ebhatia@senado.pr.gov

President Pro Tempore of the Senate

Sen. Jose L. Dalmau Santiago (PDP)
Vice President
The Capitol
P.O. Box 9023431
San Juan, PR 00902
P: (787) 724-2030 Ext. 2357
E: jldalmau@senado.pr.gov

Senate Majority Leader

Sen. Anibal J. Torres Torres (PDP)
Majority Leader
The Capitol
P.O. Box 9023431
San Juan, PR 00902
P: (787) 724-2030 Ext. 2100
E: ajtorres@senado.pr.gov

Senate Minority Leader

Sen. Lawrence Seilhamer Rodriguez (NPP)
Minority Leader
The Capitol
P.O. Box 9023431
San Juan, PR 00902
P: (787) 724-2030 Ext. 1623
E: lseilhamer@senado.pr.gov

Secretary of the Senate

Ms. Tania Barbarossa
Secretary of the Senate
The Capitol
P.O. Box 9023431
San Juan, PR 00902
P: (787) 724-2030 ext. 2266

Members of the Senate

Bhatia, Eduardo (PDP, At-Large)
The Capitol
P.O. Box 9023431
San Juan, PR 00902
P: (787) 724-2030 Ext. 3031
E: ebhatia@senado.pr.gov

Dalmau Santiago, Jose L. (PDP, 7)
The Capitol
P.O. Box 9023431
San Juan, PR 00902
P: (787) 724-2030 Ext. 2357
E: jldalmau@senado.pr.gov

Fas Alzamora, Antonio J. (PDP, At-Large)
The Capitol
P.O. Box 9023431
San Juan, PR 00902
P: (787) 724-2030 Ext. 2022
E: afas@senadopr.us

Gonzalez Lopez, Maria T. (PDP, 4)
The Capitol
P.O. Box 9023431
San Juan, PR 00902
P: (787) 724-2030 Ext. 2682
E: mgonzalez@senado.pr.gov

Lopez Leon, Rossana (PDP, At-Large)
The Capitol
P.O. Box 9023431
San Juan, PR 00902
P: (787) 724-2030 Ext. 1020
E: rolopez@senado.pr.gov

Martinez Santiago, Angel (NPP, 3)
The Capitol
P.O. Box 9023431
San Juan, PR 00902
P: (787) 724-2030 Ext. 2762
E: anmartinez@senado.pr.gov

Nadal Power, Jose R. (PDP, 1)
The Capitol
P.O. Box 9023431
San Juan, PR 00902
P: (787) 724-2030 Ext. 2000
E: jnadal@senado.pr.gov

Nieves Perez, Ramon L. (PDP, 1)
The Capitol
P.O. Box 9023431
San Juan, PR 00902
P: (787) 724-2030 Ext. 2207
E: rnieves@senado.pr.gov

Nolasco Santiago, Margarita (NPP, At-Large)
The Capitol
P.O. Box 9023431
San Juan, PR 00902
P: (787) 724-2030 Ext. 2909
E: mnolasco@senado.pr.gov

Padilla Alvelo, Migdalia (NPP, 2)
The Capitol
P.O. Box 9023431
San Juan, PR 00902
P: (787) 724-2030 Ext. 2221
E: mpadilla@senado.pr.gov

Peña Ramirez, Itzamar (NPP, At-Large)
The Capitol
P.O. Box 9023431
San Juan, PR 00902
P: (787) 723-2030 Ext. 2383
E: ipena@senado.pr.gov

Pereira Castillo, Miguel A. (PDP, 6)
The Capitol
P.O. Box 9023431
San Juan, PR 00902
P: (787) 724-2030 Ext. 2504
E: mpereira@senado.pr.gov

Perez Rosa, Jose O. (NPP, 3)
The Capitol
P.O. Box 9023431
San Juan, PR 00902
P: (787) 724-2030 Ext. 2337
E: josperez@senado.pr.gov

Rios, Carmelo J. (NPP, 2)
The Capitol
P.O. Box 9023431
San Juan, PR 00902
P: (787) 724-2030 Ext. 2668
E: crios@senado.pr.gov

Rivera Filomeno, Luis D. (PDP, 8)
The Capitol
P.O. Box 9023431
San Juan, PR 00902
P: (787) 724-2030 Ext. 2928
E: ldrivera@senado.pr.gov

Rivera Schatz, Thomas (NPP, At-Large)
The Capitol
P.O. Box 9023431
San Juan, PR 00902
P: (787) 724-2030 Ext. 3008
E: trivera@senado.pr.gov

Rodriguez Gonzalez, Pedro A. (PDP, 8)
The Capitol
P.O. Box 9023431
San Juan, PR 00902
P: (787) 724-2030 Ext. 2352
E: prodriguez@senado.pr.gov

Rodriguez Otero, Angel M. (PDP, 6)
The Capitol
P.O. Box 9023431
San Juan, PR 00902
P: (787) 724-2030 Ext. 2752
E: anrodriguez @senado.pr.gov

Rodriguez Valle, Gilberto (PDP, 4)
The Capitol
P.O. Box 9023431
San Juan, PR 00902
P: (787) 724-2030 Ext. 2390
E: girodriguez @senado.pr.gov

Rosa Rodriguez, Angel R. (PDP, At-Large)
The Capitol
P.O. Box 9023431
San Juan, PR 00902
P: (787) 724-2030 Ext. 2006
E: arosa@senado.pr.gov

Ruiz Nieves, Ramon (PDP, 5)
The Capitol
P.O. Box 9023431
San Juan, PR 00902
P: (787) 724-2030 Ext. 2336
E: rruiz@senado.pr.gov

Santiago Negron, Maria De Lourdes (PIP, At-Large)
The Capitol
P.O. Box 9023431
San Juan, PR 00902
P: (787) 724-2030 Ext. 2704
E: masantiago@senado.pr.gov

Seilhamer Rodriguez, Lawrence (NPP, 5)
The Capitol
P.O. Box 9023431
San Juan, PR 00902
P: (787) 724-2030 Ext. 1623
E: lseilhamer@senado.pr.gov

Suarez, Jorge I. (PDP, 7)
The Capitol
P.O. Box 9023431
San Juan, PR 00902
P: (787) 724-2030 Ext. 2240
E: jsuarez@senado.pr.gov

Tirado Rivera Jr., Cirilo (PDP, At-Large)
The Capitol
P.O. Box 9023431
San Juan, PR 00902
P: (787) 724-2030 Ext. 2226
E: ctirado@senado.pr.gov

Torres Torres, Anibal J. (PDP, At-Large)
The Capitol
P.O. Box 9023431
San Juan, PR 00902
P: (787) 724-2030 Ext. 2100
E: ajtorres@senado.pr.gov

Vargas Morales, Martin (PDP, 5)
The Capitol
P.O. Box 9023431
San Juan, PR 00902
P: (787) 724-2030 Ext. 2120
E: mvargas@senado.pr.gov

House

Speaker of the House

Rep. Jaime R. Perelló (PDP)
Speaker
The Capitol
P.O. Box 9022228
San Juan, PR 00902
P: (787) 622-4953
F: (787) 722-6441
E: jperrello @camaraderepresentantes.org

Speaker Pro Tempore of the House

Rep. Roberto Rivera Ruiz De Porras (PDP)
Speaker Pro Tempore
The Capitol
P.O. Box 9022228
San Juan, PR 00902
P: (787) 622-4893
F: (787) 721-8253
E: rrivera @camaraderepresentantes.org

House Majority Leader

Rep. Carlos M. Hernandez Lopez (PDP)
Majority Leader
The Capitol
P.O. Box 9022228
San Juan, PR 00902
P: (787) 622-4896
F: (787) 622-4886
E: chernandez @camaraderepresentantes.org

House Minority Leader

Rep. Jenniffer Gonzalez-Colón (NPP)
Minority Leader
The Capitol
P.O. Box 9022228
San Juan, PR 00902
P: (787) 722-0458
F: (787) 724-0459
E: jgo @camaraderepresentantes.org

Clerk of the House

Ms. Brunilda Ortiz-Rodriguez
Clerk of the House
P.O. Box 9022228
San Juan, PR 00902
P: (787) 722-0830
F: (787) 723-4342

Members of the House

Aponte, Javier (PDP, 38)
The Capitol
P.O. Box 9022228
San Juan, PR 00902
P: (787) 722-7780
F: (787) 622-4963
E: apontedalmau @camaraderepresentantes.org

Aponte Hernández, José F. (NPP, At-Large)
The Capitol
P.O. Box 9022228
San Juan, PR 00902
P: (787) 723-1090
F: (787) 722-5106
E: japonte @camaraderepresentantes.org

Baez Rivera, Jose L. (PDP, 4)
The Capitol
P.O. Box 9022228
San Juan, PR 00902
P: (787) 622-4960
F: (787) 721-6620
E: jbaez @camaraderepresentantes.org

Bulerín Ramos, Angel L. (NPP, 37)
The Capitol
P.O. Box 9022228
San Juan, PR 00902
P: (787) 722-2508
F: (787) 721-6608
E: abulerin @camaraderepresentantes.org

Charbonier Laureano, Maria M. (NPP, At-Large)
The Capitol
P.O. Box 9022228
San Juan, PR 00902
P: (787) 721-6040
F: (787) 622-4882
E: mcharbonier @camaraderepresentantes.org

Cruz Burgos, Ramon Luis (PDP, 34)
The Capitol
P.O. Box 9022228
San Juan, PR 00902
P: (787) 622-3802
F: (787) 725-0437
E: rcruz @camaraderepresentantes.org

De Jesus Rodriguez, Efrain (PDP, 19)
The Capitol
P.O. Box 9022228
San Juan, PR 00902
P: (787) 722-4296
F: (787) 724-7423
E: edejesus @camaraderepresentantes.org

Puerto Rico

Espinosa, Narden Jaime (PDP, 35)
The Capitol
P.O. Box 9022228
San Juan, PR 00902
P: (787) 724-6262
F: (787) 721-6783
E: njaime @camaraderepresentantes.org

Franco Gonzalez, Armando (PDP, 17)
The Capitol
P.O. Box 9022228
San Juan, PR 00902
P: (787) 729-9005
F: (787) 622-4385
E: afranco @camaraderepresentantes.org

Gandara Menendez, Luisa (PDP, At-Large)
The Capitol
P.O. Box 9022228
San Juan, PR 09002
P: (787) 622-4979
F: (787) 725-0951
E: lgandara @camaraderepresentantes.org

Gonzalez-Colón, Jenniffer (NPP, At-Large)
The Capitol
P.O. Box 9022228
San Juan, PR 00902
P: (787) 722-0458
F: (787) 724-0459
E: jgo @camaraderepresentantes.org

Hernandez Alfonso, Cesar (PDP, 15)
The Capitol
P.O. Box 9022228
San Juan, PR 00902
P: (787) 725-5115
F: (787) 725-0630
E: cehernandez @camaraderepresentantes.org

Hernandez Alvarado, Urayoan (NPP, 26)
The Capitol
P.O. Box 9022228
San Juan, PR 00902
P: (787) 725-4431
F: (787) 723-2746
E: uhernandez @camaraderepresentantes.org

Hernandez Lopez, Carlos M. (PDP, At-Large)
The Capitol
P.O. Box 9022228
San Juan, PR 00902
P: (787) 622-4896
F: (787) 622-4886
E: chernandez @camaraderepresentantes.org

Hernández Montañez, Rafael (PDP, 11)
The Capitol
P.O. Box 9022228
San Juan, PR 00902
P: (787) 622-4997
F: (787) 723-1732
E: rahernandez @camaraderepresentantes.org

Lebrón Rodríguez, Yashira (NPP, 8)*
The Capitol
P.O. Box 9022228
San Juan, PR 00902
P: (787) 721-6040
F: (787) 622-4710

León, Luis (NPP, 24)
The Capitol
P.O. Box 9022228
San Juan, PR 00902
P: (787) 622-4965
F: (787) 721-8481
E: lleon @camaraderepresentantes.org

Llerandi Cruz, Ricardo J. (NPP, 14)
The Capitol
P.O. Box 9022228
San Juan, PR 00902
P: (787) 680-7835
F: (787) 725-9150
E: rllerandi @camaraderepresentantes.org

López De Arrarás, Brenda (PDP, At-Large)
The Capitol
P.O. Box 9022228
San Juan, PR 00902
P: (787) 725-2771
F: (787) 622-4970
E: blopez @camaraderepresentantes.org

Lopez Munoz, Jose (NPP, 1)
The Capitol
P.O. Box 9022228
San Juan, PR 00902
P: (787) 723-2212
F: (787) 725-8805
E: nunolopez @camaraderepresentantes.org

Matos Garcia, Angel (PDP, 40)
The Capitol
P.O. Box 9022228
San Juan, PR 00902
P: (787) 721-4039
F: (787) 722-5483
E: amatos @camaraderepresentantes.org

Melendez Ortiz, Jose E. (NPP, At-Large)
The Capitol
P.O. Box 9022228
San Juan, PR 00902
P: (787) 725-9189
F: (787) 721-6062
E: jem @camaraderepresentantes.org

Mendez Nuñez, Carlos (NPP, 36)
The Capitol
P.O. Box 9022228
San Juan, PR 00902
P: (787) 721-8011
F: (787) 721-3644
E: cmendez @camaraderepresentantes.org

Méndez Silva, Lydia (PDP, 21)
The Capitol
P.O. Box 9022228
San Juan, PR 00902
P: (787) 722-0801
F: (787) 721-0483
E: lmendez @camaraderepresentantes.org

Munoz Suarez, Angel (NPP, 18)
The Capitol
P.O. Box 9022228
San Juan, PR 00902
P: (787) 622-4992
F: (787) 724-7025
E: amunoz @camaraderepresentantes.org

Natal Albelo, Manuel (PDP, At-Large)
The Capitol
P.O. Box 9022228
San Juan, PR 00902
P: (787) 721-8011
F: (787) 722-8059
E: mnatal @camaraderepresentantes.org

Navarro Suárez, Jorge (NPP, 5)
The Capitol
P.O. Box 9022228
San Juan, PR 00902
P: (787) 724-4465
F: (787) 723-4711
E: jnavarro @camaraderepresentantes.org

Ortiz Lugo, Luis R. (PDP, 30)
The Capitol
P.O. Box 9022228
San Juan, PR 00902
P: (787) 721-5545
F: (787) 725-6669
E: lortiz @camaraderepresentantes.org

Pacheco Irigoyen, Sonia (PDP, 3)
The Capitol
P.O. Box 9022228
San Juan, PR 00902
P: (787) 622-4975
F: (787) 622-4880
E: spacheco @camaraderepresentantes.org

Peña Ramírez, Angel (NPP, 33)
The Capitol
P.O. Box 9022228
San Juan, PR 00902
P: (787) 622-4961
F: (787) 622-4995
E: anpena @camaraderepresentantes.org

Perelló, Jaime R. (PDP, At-Large)
The Capitol
P.O. Box 9022228
San Juan, PR 00902
P: (787) 622-4953
F: (787) 722-6441
E: jperrello @camaraderepresentantes.org

Pérez Ortiz, Luis (NPP, 7)
The Capitol
P.O. Box 9022228
San Juan, PR 00902
P: (787) 724-6262
F: (787) 723-9551
E: lperez @camaraderepresentantes.org

Quiles Rodríguez, Waldemar (NPP, 22)
The Capitol
P.O. Box 9022228
San Juan, PR 00902
P: (787) 725-9925
F: (787) 721-8116
E: wquiles@camaraderepresentantes.org

Ramos, María (NPP, At-Large)
The Capitol
P.O. Box 9022228
San Juan, PR 00902
P: (787) 721-1190
F: (787) 723-2139
E: lramos@camaraderepresentantes.org

Rivera Ortega, Rafael (NPP, 28)
The Capitol
P.O. Box 9022228
San Juan, PR 00902
P: (787) 977-2417
F: (787) 725-4290
E: rarivera@camaraderepresentantes.org

Rivera Ruiz De Porras, Roberto (PDP, 39)
The Capitol
P.O. Box 9022228
San Juan, PR 00902
P: (787) 622-4893
F: (787) 721-8253
E: rrivera@camaraderepresentantes.org

Rodríguez Aguiló, Gabriel (NPP, 13)
The Capitol
P.O. Box 9022228
San Juan, PR 00902
P: (787) 723-0109
F: (787) 622-4387
E: gfrodriguez@camaraderepresentantes.org

Rodríguez Miranda, Angel (NPP, 9)
The Capitol
P.O. Box 9022228
San Juan, PR 00902
P: (787) 725-6807
F: (787) 622-4375
E: angrodriguez@camaraderepresentantes.org

Rodriguez Quiles, Jose A. (PDP, 16)
The Capitol
P.O. Box 9022228
San Juan, PR 00902
P: (787) 622-4877
F: (787) 721-8019
E: joserodriguez@camaraderepresentantes.org

Santa Rodriguez, Jesus (PDP, 31)
The Capitol
P.O. Box 9022228
San Juan, PR 00902
P: (787) 725-5595
F: (787) 725-3411
E: jsanta@camaraderepresentantes.org

Santiago Guzman, Pedro J. (NPP, 10)
The Capitol
P.O. Box 9022228
San Juan, PR 00902
P: (787) 725-3350
F: (787) 721-6608
E: psantiago@camaraderepresentantes.org

Soto Torres, Antonio L. (NPP, 6)
The Capitol
P.O. Box 9022228
San Juan, PR 00902
P: (787) 725-2698
F: (787) 977-2477
E: ansoto@camaraderepresentantes.org

Torres, Nelson (PDP, 23)
The Capitol
P.O. Box 9022228
San Juan, PR 00902
P: (787) 721-5007
F: (787) 622-4899
E: njtorres@camaraderepresentantes.org

Torres Calderón, Héctor A. (NPP, 12)
The Capitol
P.O. Box 9022228
San Juan, PR 00902
P: (787) 725-1216
F: (787) 627-4892
E: hetorres@camaraderepresentantes.org

Torres Cruz, Luis R. (PDP, 2)
The Capitol
P.O. Box 9022228
San Juan, PR 00902
P: (787) 723-1816
F: (787) 722-3573
E: ltorres@camaraderepresentantes.org

Torres Ramírez, José (PDP, 27)
The Capitol
P.O. Box 9022228
San Juan, PR 00902
P: (787) 622-3822
F: (787) 723-8584
E: jrtorres@camaraderepresentantes.org

Varela Fernández, José M. (PDP, 32)
The Capitol
P.O. Box 9022228
San Juan, PR 00902
P: (787) 725-3928
F: (787) 723-4711
E: jvarela@camaraderepresentantes.org

Vargas Ferrer, Carlos J. (PDP, 29)
The Capitol
P.O. Box 9022228
San Juan, PR 00902
P: (787) 622-4885
F: (787) 725-3908
E: cjvargas@camaraderepresentantes.org

Vassallo Anadón, Victor (PDP, 25)
The Capitol
P.O. Box 9022228
San Juan, PR 00902
P: (787) 622-4290
F: (787) 622-4382
E: vvasallo@camaraderepresentantes.org

Vega Ramos, Luis R. (PDP, At-Large)
The Capitol
P.O. Box 9022228
San Juan, PR 00902
P: (787) 725-3898
F: (787) 622-4875
E: lvega@camaraderepresentantes.org

Congress

House Resident Commissioner

Pierluisi, Pedro (D, At-Large)

Rhode Island

Executive

Governor

Hon. Gina M. Raimondo (D)
Governor
82 Smith Street, Suite 128
Providence, RI 02903
P: (401) 222-2080
F: (401) 273-5729
E: governor@governor.ri.gov

Lieutenant Governor

Hon. Daniel McKee (D)
Lieutenant Governor
116 State House
Providence, RI 02903
P: (401) 222-2371

Attorney General

Hon. Peter F. Kilmartin (D)
Attorney General
150 South Main Street
Providence, RI 02903
P: (401) 274-4400

Auditor

Mr. Dennis E. Hoyle
(appointed by the Legislature)
Auditor General
86 Weybosset Street
Providence, RI 02903
P: (401) 222-2435
F: (401) 222-2111
E: ag@oag.ri.gov

Secretary of State

Hon. Nellie Gorbea
Secretary of State
82 Smith Street
217 State House
Providence, RI 02903
P: (401) 222-2357
F: (401) 222-1356
E: nelliegorbea@sos.ri.gov

Treasurer

Hon. Seth Magaziner (D)
General Treasurer
State House, Room 102
Providence, RI 02903
P: (401) 222-2397
F: (401) 222-6140
E: generaltreasurer
@treasury.ri.gov

Judiciary

Supreme Court (LA)

Ms. Debra A. Saunders
Supreme Court Clerk
Frank Licht Judicial Complex
250 Benefit Street
Providence, RI 02903
P: (401) 222-3272
E: dsaunders@courts.ri.gov

Hon. Paul A. Suttell
Chief Justice
Hon. Francis X. Flaherty
Hon. Maureen McKenna Goldberg
Hon. Gilbert V. Indeglia
Hon. William P. Robinson III

Legislative Senate

Senate President

Sen. M. Teresa Paiva-Weed (D)
Senate President
318 State House
Providence, RI 02903
P: (401) 222-6655
E: sen-paivaweed
@rilin.state.ri.us

President Pro Tempore of the Senate

Sen. William A. Walaska (D)
President Pro Tempore
140 Aldrich Avenue
Warwick, RI 02889
P: (401) 737-1065
E: sen-walaska
@rilin.state.ri.us

Senate Majority Leader

Sen. Dominick J. Ruggerio (D)
Majority Leader
42 Countryside Drive
North Providence, RI 02904
P: (401) 222-3310
E: sen-ruggerio
@rilin.state.ri.us

Senate Minority Leader

Sen. Dennis L. Algiere (R)
Minority Leader
6 Elm Street
Westerly, RI 02891
P: (401) 222-2708
E: sen-algiere
@rilin.state.ri.us

Secretary of the Senate

Mr. Joseph Brady
Secretary of the Senate
82 Smith Street
Providence, RI 02903
P: (401) 276-5558
E: jbrady@rilin.state.ri.us

Members of the Senate

Algiere, Dennis L. (R, 38)
6 Elm Street
Westerly, RI 02891
P: (401) 222-2708
E: sen-algiere
@rilin.state.ri.us

Archambault, Stephen R. (D, 22)
195 Whipple Road
Smithfield, RI 02917
P: (401) 276-5599
E: sen-archambault
@rilin.state.ri.us

Ciccone III, Frank A. (D, 7)
15 Mercy Street
Providence, RI 02909
P: (401) 275-0949
E: sen-ciccone
@rilin.state.ri.us

Conley Jr., William J. (D, 18)
3 Bridgham Court
Rumford, RI 02916
P: (401) 438-1924
E: sen-conley
@rilin.state.ri.us

Cote, Marc A. (D, 24)
144 Woodland Road
Woonsocket, RI 02895
P: (401) 765-3360
E: sen-cote
@rilin.state.ri.us

Coyne, Cynthia (D, 32)*
8 Newbrook Drive
Barrington, RI 02806
P: (401) 222-6655
E: sen-coyne
@rilin.state.ri.us

Crowley, Elizabeth A. (D, 16)
135 Perry Street
Central Falls, RI 02863
P: (401) 725-8526
E: sen-crowley
@rilin.state.ri.us

DaPonte, Daniel (D, 14)
52 Vine Street, #1
East Providence, RI 02914
P: (401) 222-3438
E: sen-daponte
@rilin.state.ri.us

DiPalma, Louis P. (D, 12)
24 Sail Court
Middletown, RI 02842
P: (401) 847-8540
E: sen-dipalma
@rilin.state.ri.us

Doyle II, James E. (D, 8)
8 Massasoit Avenue
Pawtucket, RI 02861
P: (401) 729-9988
E: sen-doyle
@rilin.state.ri.us

Felag Jr., Walter S. (D, 10)
51 Overhill Road
Warren, RI 02885
P: (401) 245-7521
E: sen-felag
@rilin.state.ri.us

Fogarty, Paul W. (D, 23)
P.O. Box 37
Harmony, RI 02829
P: (401) 949-0895
E: sen-fogarty
@rilin.state.ri.us

Gallo, Hanna M. (D, 27)
285 Meshanticut Valley Parkway
Cranston, RI 02920
P: (401) 942-8566
E: sen-gallo
@rilin.state.ri.us

Gee, Mark (R, 35)*
99 Middle Road
East Greenwich, RI 02818
P: (401) 222-6655
E: sen-gee
@rilin.state.ri.us

Goldin, Gayle L. (D, 3)
P.O. Box 2722
Providence, RI 02906
P: (401) 340-5050
E: sen-goldin
@rilin.state.ri.us

Goodwin, Maryellen (D, 1)
325 Smith Street
Providence, RI 02908
P: (401) 272-3102
E: sen-goodwin
@rilin.state.ri.us

Jabour, Paul V. (D, 5)
529 Broadway, 2nd Floor
Providence, RI 02909
P: (401) 751-3300
E: sen-jabour
@rilin.state.ri.us

Kettle, Nicholas D. (R, 21)
5 Autumn Ridge Road
Coventry, RI 02816
P: (401) 473-7784
E: sen-kettle
@rilin.state.ri.us

Lombardi, Frank S. (D, 26)
25 Briarbrooke Lane
Cranston, RI 02921
P: (401) 453-3900
E: sen-lombardi
@rilin.state.ri.us

Lombardo III, Frank (D, 25)
68 Rollingwood Drive
Johnston, RI 02919
P: (401) 270-1379
E: sen-lombardo
@rilin.state.ri.us

Lynch, Erin P. (D, 31)
28 Goodwin Street
Warwick, RI 02818
P: (401) 739-8500
E: sen-lynch
@rilin.state.ri.us

McCaffrey, Michael J. (D, 29)
115 Twin Oak Drive
Warwick, RI 02889
P: (401) 739-7576
E: sen-mccaffrey
@rilin.state.ri.us

Metts, Harold M. (D, 6)
31 Tanner Street
Providence, RI 02907
P: (401) 272-0112
E: sen-metts
@rilin.state.ri.us

Miller, Joshua B. (D, 28)
41 Talbot Manor
Cranston, RI 02905
P: (401) 276-5582
E: sen-miller
@rilin.state.ri.us

Morgan, Elaine (R, 34)*
P.O. Box 841
Ashaway, RI 02804
P: (401) 222-6655
E: sen-morgan
@rilin.state.ri.us

Nesselbush, Donna (D, 15)
181 Raleigh Avenue
Pawtucket, RI 02860
P: (401) 728-3244
E: sen-nesselbush
@rilin.state.ri.us

O'Neill, Edward J. (I, 17)
2 Lladnar Drive
Lincoln, RI 02865
P: (401) 728-3295
E: sen-oneill
@rilin.state.ri.us

Ottiano, Christopher Scott (R, 11)
10 Kaitlin Place
Portsmouth, RI 02871
P: (401) 222-2708
E: sen-ottiano
@rilin.state.ri.us

Paiva-Weed, M. Teresa (D, 13)
318 State House
Providence, RI 02903
P: (401) 222-6655
E: sen-paivaweed
@rilin.state.ri.us

Pearson, Ryan (D, 19)
1427 Diamond Hill Road
Cumberland, RI 02864
P: (401) 276-5594
E: sen-pearson
@rilin.state.ri.us

Picard, Roger A. (D, 20)
764 Mendon Road
Woonsocket, RI 02895
P: (401) 769-4902
E: sen-picard
@rilin.state.ri.us

Pichardo, Juan M. (D, 2)
229 Atlantic Avenue
Providence, RI 02907
P: (401) 461-2389
E: sen-pichardo
@rilin.state.ri.us

Raptakis, Leonidas P. (D, 33)
2080 Nooseneck Hill Road
Coventry, RI 02816
P: (401) 397-2720
E: sen-raptakis
@rilin.state.ri.us

Ruggerio, Dominick J. (D, 4)
42 Countryside Drive
North Providence, RI 02904
P: (401) 222-3310
E: sen-ruggerio
@rilin.state.ri.us

Satchell, Adam J. (D, 9)
18 Wyman Street
West Warwick, RI 02893
P: (401) 615-5170
E: sen-satchell
@rilin.state.ri.us

Sheehan, James C. (D, 36)
40 Blueberry Lane
North Kingstown, RI 02852
P: (401) 885-1988
E: sen-sheehan
@rilin.state.ri,us

Sosnowski, V. Susan (D, 37)
680 Glen Rock Road
West Kingston, RI 02892
P: (401) 783-7704
E: sen-sosnowski
@rilin.state.ri.us

Walaska, William A. (D, 30)
140 Aldrich Avenue
Warwick, RI 02889
P: (401) 737-1065
E: sen-walaska
@rilin.state.ri.us

House

Speaker of the House

Rep. Nicholas A. Mattiello (D)
House Speaker
323 State House
Providence, RI 02903
P: (401) 222-2466
E: rep-mattiello
@rilin.state.ri.us

House Majority Leader

Rep. John J. DeSimone (D)
House Majority Leader
18 Ralston Street
Providence, RI 02904
P: (401) 351-7373
E: rep-desimone
@rilin.state.ri.us

House Minority Leader

Rep. Brian C. Newberry (R)
Minority Leader
53 Follett Street
North Smithfield, RI 02896
P: (401) 222-2259
E: rep-newberry
@rilin.state.ri.us

Clerk of the House

Mr. Frank McCabe
Clerk of the House
82 Smith Street
Providence, RI 02903
P: (401) 222-3580

Members of the House

Abney, Marvin L. (D, 73)
12 Summer Street
Newport, RI 02840
P: (401) 487-1380
E: rep-abney
@rilin.state.ri.us

Ackerman, Mia A. (D, 45)
6 Shelter Lane
Cumberland, RI 02864
P: (401) 658-0981
E: rep-ackerman
@rilin.state.ri.us

Ajello, Edith H. (D, 1)
29 Benefit Street
Providence, RI 02904
P: (401) 274-7078
E: rep-ajello
@rilin.state.ri.us

Almeida, Joseph S. (D, 12)
299 California Avenue
Providence, RI 02905
P: (401) 467-7033
E: rep-almeida
@rilin.state.ri.us

Amore, Gregg (D, 65)
73 Plymouth Drive
East Providence, RI 02914
P: (401) 339-9378
E: rep-amore
@rilin.state.ri.us

Azzinaro, Samuel A. (D, 37)
20 Piezzo Drive
Westerly, RI 02891
P: (401) 596-1434
E: rep-azzinaro
@rilin.state.ri.us

Rhode Island

Barros, Jean (D, 59)*
1 William Street
Pawtucket, RI 02860
P: (401) 222-2466
E: rep-barros
@rilin.state.ri.us

Bennett, David A. (D, 20)
27 Shippee Avenue
Warwick, RI 02886
P: (401) 648-1171
E: rep-bennett
@rilin.state.ri.us

Blazejewski, Christopher R. (D, 2)
1 Thayer Street
Providence, RI 02906
P: (401) 484-8814
E: rep-blazejewski
@rilin.state.ri.us

Canario, Dennis M. (D, 71)
64 Birchwood Drive
Portsmouth, RI 02871
P: (401) 683-4926
E: rep-canario
@rilin.state.ri.us

Carnevale, John M. (D, 13)
150 Barbara Street
Providence, RI 02909
P: (401) 274-1353
E: rep-carnevale
@rilin.state.ri.us

Carson, Lauren (D, 75)*
11 Willow Street, #5
Newport, RI 02840
P: (401) 222-2466
E: rep-carson
@rilin.state.ri.us

Casey, Stephen (D, 50)
625 Park Avenue 2F
Woonsocket, RI 02895
P: (508) 942-0484
E: rep-casey
@rilin.state.ri.us

Chippendale, Michael W. (R, 40)
124 A Johnson Road
Foster, RI 02825
P: (401) 497-4495
E: rep-chippendale
@rilin.state.ri.us

Corvese, Arthur J. (D, 55)
234 Lexington Avenue
North Providence, RI 02904
P: (401) 353-8695
E: rep-corvese
@rilin.state.ri.us

Costa, Doreen Marie (R, 31)
39 Dyer Avenue
North Kingstown, RI 02852
P: (401) 206-6891
E: rep-costa
@rilin.state.ri.us

Costantino, Gregory J. (D, 44)
21 Greenwood Lane
Lincoln, RI 02865
P: (401) 426-0284
E: rep-costantino
@rilin.state.ri.us

Coughlin, David (D, 60)*
9 Armistice Boulevard
Pawtucket, RI 02860
P: (401) 222-2466
E: rep-coughlin
@rilin.state.ri.us

Craven Sr., Robert E. (D, 32)
24 Highland Road
Saunderstown, RI 02874
P: (401) 294-2222
E: rep-craven
@rilin.state.ri.us

DeSimone, John J. (D, 5)
18 Ralston Street
Providence, RI 02904
P: (401) 351-7373
E: rep-desimone
@rilin.state.ri.us

Diaz, Grace (D, 11)
45 Adelaide Avenue
Providence, RI 02907
P: (401) 467-8413
E: rep-diaz
@rilin.state.ri.us

Edwards, John G. (D, 70)
69 South Avenue
Tiverton, RI 02878
P: (401) 624-8879
E: rep-edwards
@rilin.state.ri.us

Fellela, Deborah A. (D, 43)
3 Diaz Street
Johnston, RI 02919
P: (401) 231-2014
E: rep-fellela
@rilin.state.ri.us

Filippi, Blake A. (I, 36)*
P.O. Box 298
New Shoreham, RI 02807
P: (401) 222-2466
E: rep-filippi
@rilin.state.ri.us

Fogarty, Kathleen (D, 35)*
50 Woodmark Way
Wakefield, RI 02879
P: (401) 222-2466
E: rep-fogarty
@rilin.state.ri.us

Gallison Jr., Raymond E. (D, 69)
50 King Philip Avenue
Bristol, RI 02809
P: (508) 677-4235
E: rep-gallison
@rilin.state.ri.us

Giarrusso, Antonio (R, 30)
5 Lenighan Lane
East Greenwich, RI 02818
P: (401) 415-5390
E: rep-giarrusso
@rilin.state.ri.us

Handy, Arthur (D, 18)
26 Welfare Avenue
Cranston, RI 02910
P: (401) 785-8996
E: rep-handy
@rilin.state.ri.us

Hearn, Joy (D, 66)
23 Brentonwood Avenue
Barrington, RI 02906
P: (401) 247-9867
E: rep-hearn
@rilin.state.ri.us

Hull, Raymond (D, 6)
616 Mount Pleasant Avenue
Providence, RI 02908
P: (401) 272-4026
E: rep-hull
@rilin.state.ri.us

Jacquard, Robert B. (D, 17)
34 Sagamore Road
Cranston, RI 02920
P: (401) 943-7799
E: rep-jacquard
@rilin.state.ri.us

Johnston Jr., Raymond H. (D, 61)
102 Archer Street
Pawtucket, RI 02861
P: (401) 288-7248
E: rep-johnston
@rilin.state.ri.us

Kazarian, Katherine S. (D, 63)
380 Pleasant Street
East Providence, RI 02916
P: (401) 438-1718
E: rep-kazarian
@rilin.state.ri.us

Keable, Cale (D, 47)
650 Camp Dixie Road
Pascoag, RI 02859
P: (401) 222-2258
E: rep-keable
@rilin.state.ri.us

Kennedy, Brian Patrick (D, 38)
P.O. Box 1001
Ashaway, RI 02804
P: (401) 377-8818
E: rep-kennedy
@rilin.state.ri.us

Lally Jr., Donald J. (D, 33)
887 Boston Neck Road
Suite One
Narragansett, RI 02882
P: (401) 792-9090
E: rep-lally
@rilin.state.ri.us

Lancia, Robert (R, 16)*
25 Church Hill Drive
Cranston, RI 02920
P: (401) 222-2259
E: rep-lancia
@rilin.state.ri.us

Lima, Charlene M. (D, 14)
455 Laurel Hill Avenue
Cranston, RI 02920
P: (401) 222-2258
E: rep-lima
@rilin.state.ri.us

Lombardi, John J. (D, 8)
48 Grove Street
Providence, RI 02909
P: (401) 453-3900
E: rep-lombardi
@rilin.state.ri.us

MacBeth, Karen L. (D, 52)
75 Newell Drive
Cumberland, RI 02864
P: (401) 333-5398
E: rep-macbeth
@rilin.state.ri.us

Maldonado, Shelby (D, 56)*
6 Washington Street
Central Falls, RI 02863
P: (401) 222-2466
E: rep-maldonado
@rilin.state.ri.us

Malik, Jan P. (D, 67)
23 Hezekiah Drive
Warren, RI 02885
P: (401) 247-1271
E: rep-malik
@rilin.state.ri.us

Marcello, Michael J. (D, 41)
874 Chopmist Hill Road
P.O. Box 114
Scituate, RI 02857
P: (401) 647-5905
E: rep-marcello@rilin.state.ri.us

Marshall, Kenneth A. (D, 68)
26 Harborview Avenue
Bristol, RI 02809
P: (401) 254-1377
E: rep-marshall@rilin.state.ri.us

Mattiello, Nicholas A. (D, 15)
323 State House
Providence, RI 02903
P: (401) 222-2466
E: rep-mattiello@rilin.state.ri.us

McKiernan, Daniel (D, 7)*
122 Whitford Avenue
Providence, RI 02908
P: (401) 222-2466
E: rep-mckiernan@rilin.state.ri.us

McLaughlin, James N. (D, 57)
15 Garden Street
Cumberland, RI 02864
P: (401) 333-4946
E: rep-mclaughlin@rilin.state.ri.us

McNamara, Joseph M. (D, 19)
23 Howie Avenue
Warwick, RI 02888
P: (401) 941-8319
E: rep-mcnamara@rilin.state.ri.us

Melo, Helio (D, 64)
1187 South Broadway
East Providence, RI 02914
P: (401) 222-8028
E: rep-melo@rilin.state.ri.us

Messier, Mary Duffy (D, 62)
25 Olympia Avenue
Pawtucket, RI 02861
P: (401) 728-1682
E: rep-messier@rilin.state.ri.us

Morgan, Patricia L. (R, 26)
411 Wakefield Street
West Warwick, RI 02893
P: (401) 222-2259
E: rep-morgan@rilin.state.ri.us

Morin, Michael A. (D, 49)*
180 Allen Street, Unit 202
Woonsocket, RI 02895
P: (401) 265-0910
E: rep-morin@rilin.state.ri.us

Nardolillo, Robert (R, 28)*
960 Maple Valley Road
Greene, RI 02827
P: (401) 222-2259
E: rep-nardolillo@rilin.state.ri.us

Naughton, Eileen S. (D, 21)
100 Old Homestead Road
Warwick, RI 02889
P: (401) 738-7928
E: rep-naughton@rilin.state.ri.us

Newberry, Brian C. (R, 48)
53 Follett Street
North Smithfield, RI 02896
P: (401) 222-2259
E: rep-newberry@rilin.state.ri.us

Nunes, Jared R. (D, 25)
52 Phillip Street
Coventry, RI 02816
P: (401) 821-8693
E: rep-nunes@rilin.state.ri.us

O'Brien, William W. (D, 54)
626 Smithfield Road #806
North Providence, RI 02904
P: (401) 440-4063
E: rep-obrien@rilin.state.ri.us

O'Grady, Jeremiah T. (D, 46)
24 Parker Street
Lincoln, RI 02865
P: (401) 725-7163
E: rep-ogrady@rilin.state.ri.us

Palangio, Thomas A. (D, 3)
60 Columbus Street
Providence, RI 02908
P: (401) 248-8877
E: rep-palangio@rilin.state.ri.us

Phillips, Robert (D, 51)
325 Dunlap Street
Woonsocket, RI 02895
P: (401) 762-2010
E: rep-phillips@rilin.state.ri.us

Price, Justin (R, 39)*
214 Shannock Village Road
Shannock, RI 02875
P: (401) 222-2259
E: rep-Price@rilin.state.ri.us

Regunberg, J. Aaron (D, 4)*
62 Camp Street
Providence, RI 02906
P: (401) 222-2466
E: rep-regunberg@rilin.state.ri.us

Reilly, Daniel Patrick (R, 72)
14 William Street
Portsmouth, RI 02871
P: (401) 222-2259
E: rep-reilly@rilin.state.ri.us

Roberts, Sherry (R, 29)*
22 Seminole Trail
West Greenwich, RI 02817
P: (401) 222-2259
E: rep-roberts@rilin.state.ri.us

Ruggiero, Deborah L. (D, 74)
78 Columbia Avenue
Jamestown, RI 02835
P: (401) 423-0444
E: rep-ruggiero@rilin.statc.ri.us

Serpa, Patricia A. (D, 27)
194 Kimberly Lane
West Warwick, RI 02893
P: (401) 828-5687
E: rep-serpa@rilin.state.ri.us

Shekarchi, K. Joseph (D, 23)
96 Haswill Street
Warwick, RI 02889
P: (401) 827-0100
E: rep-shekarchi@rilin.state.ri.us

Slater, Scott (D, 10)
74 Sawyer Street
Providence, RI 02907
P: (401) 741-7641
E: rep-slater@rilin.state.ri.us

Solomon, Joseph (D, 22)*
703 West Shore Road
Warwick, RI 02889
P: (401) 308-3904
E: rep-solomon@rilin.state.ri.us

Tanzi, Teresa Ann (D, 34)
57 Hillcrest Road
Wakefield, RI 02879
P: (401) 527-9468
E: rep-tanzi@rilin.state.ri.us

Tobon, Carlos (D, 58)*
30 Bloomingdale Avenue
Pawtucket, RI 02860
P: (401) 222-2466
E: rep-tobon@rilin.state.ri.us

Trillo, Joseph A. (R, 24)
643 East Avenue
Warwick, RI 02886
P: (401) 826-9100
E: rep-trillo@rilin.state.ri.us

Ucci, Stephen R. (D, 42)
12 East Scenic View Drive
Johnston, RI 02919
P: (401) 934-2121
E: rep-ucci@rilin.state.ri.us

Williams, Anastasia P. (D, 9)
32 Hammond Street
Providence, RI 02909
P: (401) 272-8135
E: rep-williams@rilin.state.ri.us

Winfield, Thomas (D, 53)
4 Church Street
Smithfield, RI 02828
P: (401) 949-3356
E: rep-winfield@rilin.state.ri.us

Rhode Island

Congress

Senate

Reed, Jack (D)
Whitehouse, Sheldon (D)

House

Cicilline, David N. (D, 1)
Langevin, James R. (D, 2)

South Carolina

Executive

Governor

Hon. Nikki Haley (R)
Governor
1205 Pendleton Street
Columbia, SC 29201
P: (803) 734-2100
F: (803) 734-5167

Lieutenant Governor

Hon. Henry D. McMaster (R)
Lieutenant Governor
P.O. Box 142
Columbia, SC 29202
P: (803) 734-2080
F: (803) 734-2082
E: HenryMcMaster@scsenate.gov

Adjutant General

Maj. Gen. Robert E. Livingston Jr.
Adjutant General
1 National Guard Road
Columbia, SC 29201
P: (803) 299-2500
F: (803) 806-4468
E: bob.livingston@us.army.mil

Commissioner of Agriculture

Mr. Hugh E. Weathers (R)
Commissioner
Wade Hampton Office Building
P.O. Box 11280
Columbia, SC 29211
P: (803) 734-2190
F: (803) 734-2192

Attorney General

Hon. Alan Wilson (R)
Attorney General
Rembert C. Dennis Office Building
P.O. Box 11549
Columbia, SC 29211
P: (803) 734-3970

Auditor

Hon. Richard H. Gilbert Jr. (appointed)
Interim State Auditor
1401 Main Street, Suite 1200
Columbia, SC 29201
P: (803) 253-4160
F: (803) 343-0723
E: rgilbert@osa.state.sc.us

Comptroller

Hon. Richard Eckstrom (R)
Comptroller General
305 Wade Hampton Office Building
1200 Senate Street
Columbia, SC 29201
P: (803) 734-2121
F: (803) 734-2064
E: reckstrom@cg.sc.gov

Secretary of State

Hon. Mark Hammond (R)
Secretary of State
1205 Pendleton Street, Suite 525
Columbia, SC 29201
P: (803) 734-2170
F: (803) 734-1661
E: rdaggerhart@sos.sc.gov

Superintendent of Education

Hon. Molly Mitchell Spearman (R)
Superintendent of Education
1429 Senate Street
Columbia, SC 29201
P: (803) 734-8500
F: (803) 734-3389

Treasurer

Hon. Curtis Loftis (R)
State Treasurer
1200 Senate Street
P.O. Box 11778
Columbia, SC 29211
P: (803) 734-2016
F: (803) 734-2690
E: treasurer@sto.sc.gov

Judiciary

Supreme Court (LA)

Mr. Daniel E. Shearouse
Clerk of Court
1231 Gervais Street
P.O. Box 11330
Columbia, SC 29211
P: (803) 734-1080
F: (803) 734-1499

Hon. Jean Hoefer Toal
Chief Justice
Hon. Donald W. Beatty
Hon. Kaye G. Hearn
Hon. John W. Kittredge
Hon. Costa M. Pleicones

Legislative Senate

Senate President

Hon. Henry D. McMaster (R)
Lieutenant Governor
P.O. Box 142
Columbia, SC 29202
P: (803) 734-2080
F: (803) 734-2082
E: HenryMcMaster@scsenate.gov

President Pro Tempore of the Senate

Sen. Hugh K. Leatherman Sr. (R)
President Pro Tempore
111 Gressette Building
P.O. Box 142
Columbia, SC 29202
P: (803) 212-6640
E: HughLeatherman@scsenate.gov

Senate Majority Leader

Sen. Harvey S. Peeler Jr. (R)
Majority Leader
213 Gressette Building
P.O. Box 142
Columbia, SC 29202
P: (803) 212-6430
E: HarveyPeeler@scsenate.gov

Senate Minority Leader

Sen. Nikki G. Setzler (D)
Minority Leader
510 Gressette Building
P.O. Box 142
Columbia, SC 29202
P: (803) 212-6140
E: NikkiSetzler@scsenate.gov

Secretary of the Senate

Mr. Jeffrey S. Gossett
Clerk of the Senate
P.O. Box 142
Columbia, SC 29202
P: (803) 212-6200
E: JeffreyGossett@scsenate.gov

Members of the Senate

Alexander, Thomas C. (R, 1)
313 Gressette Building
P.O. Box 142
Columbia, SC 29202
P: (803) 212-6220
E: ThomasAlexander@scsenate.gov

Allen, Karl B. (D, 7)
610 Gressette Building
P.O. Box 142
Columbia, SC 29202
P: (803) 212-6040
E: KarlAllen@scsenate.gov

Bennett, Sean (R, 38)
601 Gressette Building
P.O. Box 142
Columbia, SC 29202
P: (803) 212-6116
E: SeanBennett@scsenate.gov

Bright, Lee (R, 12)
602 Gressette Building
P.O. Box 142
Columbia, SC 29202
P: (803) 212-6008
E: LeeBright@scsenate.gov

Bryant, Kevin L. (R, 3)
402 Gressette Building
P.O. Box 142
Columbia, SC 29202
P: (803) 212-6320
E: KevinBryant@scsenate.gov

Campbell Jr., Paul G. (R, 44)
604 Gressette Building
P.O. Box 142
Columbia, SC 29202
P: (803) 212-6016
E: PaulCampbell@scsenate.gov

Campsen III, George E. (R, 43)
305 Gressette Building
P.O. Box 142
Columbia, SC 29202
P: (803) 212-6340
E: GeorgeCampsen@scsenate.gov

Cleary III, Raymond E. (R, 34)
610 Gressette Building
P.O. Box 142
Columbia, SC 29202
P: (803) 212-6040
E: RaymondCleary@scsenate.gov

South Carolina

Coleman, Creighton B. (D, 17)
508 Gressette Building
P.O. Box 142
Columbia, SC 29202
P: (803) 212-6132
E: CreightonColeman@scsenate.gov

Corbin, Thomas D. (R, 5)
501 Gressette Building
P.O. Box 142
Columbia, SC 29202
P: (803) 212-6100
E: TomCorbin@scsenate.gov

Courson, John E. (R, 20)
412 Gressette Building
P.O. Box 142
Columbia, SC 29202
P: (803) 212-6250
E: JohnCourson@scsenate.gov

Cromer, Ronnie W. (R, 18)
311 Gressette Building
P.O. Box 142
Columbia, SC 29202
P: (803) 212-6330
E: RonnieCromer@scsenate.gov

Davis, Tom (R, 46)
602 Gressette Building
P.O. Box 142
Columbia, SC 29202
P: (803) 212-6008
E: TomDavis@scsenate.gov

Fair, Michael L. (R, 6)
211 Gressette Building
P.O. Box 142
Columbia, SC 29202
P: (803) 212-6420
E: MichaelFair@scsenate.gov

Gregory, Chauncey K. (R, 16)
606 Gressette Building
P.O. Box 142
Columbia, SC 29202
P: (803) 212-6024
E: ChaunceyGregory@scsenate.gov

Grooms, Lawrence K. (R, 37)
203 Gressette Building
P.O. Box 142
Columbia, SC 29202
P: (803) 212-6400
E: LawrenceGrooms@scsenate.gov

Hayes Jr., Robert W. (R, 15)
410 Gressette Building
P.O. Box 142
Columbia, SC 29202
P: (803) 212-6240
E: RobertHayes@scsenate.gov

Hembree, Greg (R, 28)
604 Gressette Building
P.O. Box 142
Columbia, SC 29202
P: (803) 212-6016
E: GregHembree@scsenate.gov

Hutto, C. Bradley (D, 40)
510 Gressette Building
P.O. Box 142
Columbia, SC 29202
P: (803) 212-6140
E: BradHutto@scsenate.gov

Jackson, Darrell (D, 21)
612 Gressette Building
P.O. Box 142
Columbia, SC 29202
P: (803) 212-6048
E: DarrellJackson@scsenate.gov

Johnson, Kevin L. (D, 36)
612 Gressette Building
P.O. Box 142
Columbia, SC 29202
P: (803) 212-6048
E: KevinJohnson@scsenate.gov

Kimpson, Marlon E. (D, 42)
613 Gressette Building
P.O. Box 142
Columbia, SC 29201
P: (803) 212-6056
E: MarlonKimpson@scsenate.gov

Leatherman Sr., Hugh K. (R, 31)
111 Gressette Building
P.O. Box 142
Columbia, SC 29202
P: (803) 212-6640
E: HughLeatherman@scsenate.gov

Lourie, Joel (D, 22)
601 Gressette Building
P.O. Box 142
Columbia, SC 29202
P: (803) 212-6116
E: JoelLourie@scsenate.gov

Malloy, Gerald (D, 29)
513 Gressette Building
P.O. Box 142
Columbia, SC 29202
P: (803) 212-6172
E: GeraldMalloy@scsenate.gov

Martin, Larry A. (R, 2)
101 Gressette Building
P.O. Box 142
Columbia, SC 29202
P: (803) 212-6610
E: LarryMartin@scsenate.gov

Martin, Shane R. (R, 13)
501 Gressette Building
P.O. Box 142
Columbia, SC 29202
P: (803) 212-6100
E: ShaneMartin@scsenate.gov

Massey, A. Shane (R, 25)
606 Gressette Building
P.O. Box 142
Columbia, SC 29202
P: (803) 212-6024
E: ShaneMassey@scsenate.gov

Matthews Jr., John W. (D, 39)
613 Gressette Building
P.O. Box 142
Columbia, SC 29202
P: (803) 212-6056
E: JohnMatthews@scsenate.gov

McElveen III, J. Thomas (D, 35)
508 Gressette Building
P.O. Box 142
Columbia, SC 29556
P: (803) 212-6132

Nicholson, Floyd (D, 10)
608 Gressette Building
P.O. Box 142
Columbia, SC 29202
P: (803) 212-6000
E: FloydNicholson@scsenate.gov

O'Dell, William H. (R, 4)
303 Gressette Building
P.O. Box 142
Columbia, SC 29202
P: (803) 212-6350
E: WilliamO'Dell@scsenate.gov

Peeler Jr., Harvey S. (R, 14)
213 Gressette Building
P.O. Box 142
Columbia, SC 29202
P: (803) 212-6430
E: HarveyPeeler@scsenate.gov

Pinckney, Clementa C. (D, 45)
512 Gressette Building
P.O. Box 142
Columbia, SC 29202
P: (803) 212-6148
E: ClementaPinckney@scsenate.gov

Rankin Sr., Luke A. (R, 33)
205 Gressette Building
P.O. Box 142
Columbia, SC 29202
P: (803) 212-6410
E: LukeRankin@scsenate.gov

Reese, Glenn G. (D, 11)
502 Gressette Building
P.O. Box 142
Columbia, SC 29202
P: (803) 212-6108
E: GlennReese@scsenate.gov

Sabb, Ronnie A. (D, 32)
504 Gressette Building
P.O. Box 142
Columbia, SC 29202
P: (803) 212-6032
E: RonnieSabb@scsenate.gov

Scott Jr., John L. (D, 19)
506 Gressette Building
P.O. Box 142
Columbia, SC 29202
P: (803) 212-6124
E: JohnScott@scsenate.gov

Setzler, Nikki G. (D, 26)
510 Gressette Building
P.O. Box 142
Columbia, SC 29202
P: (803) 212-6140
E: NikkiSetzler@scsenate.gov

Shealy, Katrina Frye (R, 23)
502 Gressette Building
P.O. Box 142
Columbia, SC 29202
P: (803) 212-6108
E: KatrinaShealy@scsenate.gov

Sheheen, Vincent A. (D, 27)
504 Gressette Building
P.O. Box 142
Columbia, SC 29202
P: (803) 212-6032
E: VincentSheheen@scsenate.gov

Thurmond, Paul (R, 41)
513 Gressette Building
P.O. Box 142
Columbia, SC 29202
P: (803) 212-6172
E: PaulThurmond@scsenate.gov

Turner, Ross (R, 8)
512 Gressette Building
P.O. Box 142
Columbia, SC 29202
P: (803) 212-6148
E: RossTurner@scsenate.gov

Verdin III, Daniel B. (R, 9)
404 Gressette Building
P.O. Box 142
Columbia, SC 29202
P: (803) 212-6230
E: DanielVerdin@scsenate.gov

Williams, Kent M. (D, 30)
608 Gressette Building
P.O. Box 142
Columbia, SC 29202
P: (803) 212-6000
E: KentWilliams@scsenate.gov

Young Jr., Thomas R. (R, 24)
506 Gressette Building
P.O. Box 142
Columbia, SC 29202
P: (803) 212-6124
E: TomYoung@schouse.gov

House

Speaker of the House

Rep. James H. Lucas (R)
Speaker of the House
506 Blatt Building
P.O. Box 11867
Columbia, SC 29211
P: (803) 734-3125
E: JayLucas@schouse.gov

Speaker Pro Tempore of the House

Rep. Thomas E. Pope (R)
Speaker Pro Tempore
505 Blatt Building
P.O. Box 11867
Columbia, SC 29211
P: (803) 734-2701
E: TommyPope@schouse.gov

House Majority Leader

Rep. Bruce W. Bannister (R)
Majority Leader
518B Blatt Building
P.O. Box 11867
Columbia, SC 29211
P: (803) 734-3138
E: BruceBannister@schouse.gov

House Minority Leader

Rep. J. Todd Rutherford (D)
Minority Leader
335B Blatt Building
P.O. Box 11867
Columbia, SC 29211
P: (803) 734-9441
E: ToddRutherford@schouse.gov

Clerk of the House

Mr. Charles F. Reid
Clerk
P.O. Box 11867
Columbia, SC 29211
P: (803) 734-2403
F: (803) 734-0201

Members of the House

Alexander, Terry (D, 59)
314C Blatt Building
P.O. Box 11867
Columbia, SC 29211
P: (803) 734-3004
E: TerryAlexander@schouse.gov

Allison, Rita (R, 36)
429 Blatt Building
P.O. Box 11867
Columbia, SC 29211
P: (803) 734-3053
E: RitaAllison@schouse.gov

Anderson, Carl L. (D, 103)
304C Blatt Building
P.O. Box 11867
Columbia, SC 29211
P: (803) 734-2933
E: CarlAnderson@schouse.gov

Anthony, Michael A. (D, 42)
432C Blatt Building
P.O. Box 11867
Columbia, SC 29211
P: (803) 734-3060
E: MichaelAnthony@schouse.gov

Atwater, Todd K. (R, 87)
320D Blatt Building
P.O. Box 11867
Columbia, SC 29211
P: (803) 212-6924
E: ToddAtwater@schouse.gov

Bales, Jimmy C. (D, 80)
503A Blatt Building
P.O. Box 11867
Columbia, SC 29211
P: (803) 734-3107
E: JimmyBales@schouse.gov

Ballentine, Nathan (R, 71)
320B Blatt Building
P.O. Box 11867
Columbia, SC 29211
P: (803) 734-2969
E: NathanBallentine@schouse.gov

Bamberg, Justin (D, 90)*
404D Blatt Building
P.O. Box 11867
Columbia, SC 29211
P: (803) 212-6907
E: JustinBamberg@schouse.gov

Bannister, Bruce W. (R, 24)
518B Blatt Building
P.O. Box 11867
Columbia, SC 29211
P: (803) 734-3138
E: BruceBannister@schouse.gov

Bedingfield, Eric M. (R, 28)
312B Blatt Building
P.O. Box 11867
Columbia, SC 29211
P: (803) 734-2962
E: EricBedingfield@schouse.gov

Bernstein, Beth E. (D, 78)
434C Blatt Building
P.O. Box 11867
Columbia, SC 29211
P: (803) 212-6940
E: BethBernstein@schouse.gov

Bingham, Kenneth A. (R, 89)
519B Blatt Building
P.O. Box 11867
Columbia, SC 29211
P: (803) 734-3114
E: KennethBingham@schouse.gov

Bowers, William K. (D, 122)
310C Blatt Building
P.O. Box 11867
Columbia, SC 29211
P: (803) 734-2959
E: BillBowers@schouse.gov

Bradley, Jeff (R, 123)*
320A Blatt Building
P.O. Box 11867
Columbia, SC 29211
P: (803) 212-6928
E: JeffBradley@schouse.gov

Brannon, Norman D. (R, 38)
530C Blatt Building
P.O. Box 11867
Columbia, SC 29211
P: (803) 212-6876
E: DougBrannon@schouse.gov

Brown, Grady A. (D, 50)
304B Blatt Building
P.O. Box 11867
Columbia, SC 29211
P: (803) 734-2934
E: GradyBrown@schouse.gov

Brown, Robert L. (D, 116)
330D Blatt Building
P.O. Box 11867
Columbia, SC 29211
P: (803) 734-3170
E: RobertBrown@schouse.gov

Burns, James (R, 17)
326A Blatt Building
P.O. Box 11867
Columbia, SC 29211
P: (803) 212-6891

Chumley, William M. (R, 35)
304A Blatt Building
P.O. Box 11867
Columbia, SC 29211
P: (803) 212-6894
E: BillChumley@schouse.gov

South Carolina

Clary, Gary (R, 3)*
418A Blatt Building
P.O. Box 11867
Columbia, SC 29211
P: (803) 212-6908
E: GaryClary@schouse.gov

Clemmons, Alan D. (R, 107)
519C Blatt Building
P.O. Box 11867
Columbia, SC 29211
P: (803) 734-3113
E: AlanClemmons@schouse.gov

Clyburn, William (D, 82)
416C Blatt Building
P.O. Box 11867
Columbia, SC 29211
P: (803) 734-3033
E: BillClyburn@schouse.gov

Cobb-Hunter, Gilda (D, 66)
309C Blatt Building
P.O. Box 11867
Columbia, SC 29211
P: (803) 734-2809
E: GildaCobbHunter@schouse.gov

Cole Jr., J. Derham (R, 32)
402B Blatt Building
P.O. Box 11867
Columbia, SC 29211
P: (803) 212-6790
E: DerhamCole@schouse.gov

Collins, Neal (R, 5)*
418D Blatt Building
P.O. Box 11867
Columbia, SC 29211
P: (803) 212-6913
E: NealCollins@schouse.gov

Corley, Chris (R, 84)*
420A Blatt Building
P.O. Box 11867
Columbia, SC 29211
P: (803) 212-6917
E: ChrisCorley@schouse.gov

Crawford, Heather Ammons (R, 68)
522A Blatt Building
P.O. Box 11867
Columbia, SC 29211
P: (803) 212-6933
E: HeatherCrawford@schouse.gov

Crosby, William E. (R, 117)
310D Blatt Building
P.O. Box 11867
Columbia, SC 29211
P: (803) 212-6879
E: BillCrosby@schouse.gov

Daning, Joseph S. (R, 92)
310B Blatt Building
P.O. Box 11867
Columbia, SC 29211
P: (803) 734-2951
E: JoeDaning@schouse.gov

Delleney Jr., F. Gregory (R, 43)
512 Blatt Building
P.O. Box 11867
Columbia, SC 29211
P: (803) 734-3120
E: GregDelleney@schouse.gov

Dillard, Chandra (D, 23)
414B Blatt Building
P.O. Box 11867
Columbia, SC 29211
P: (803) 212-6791
E: ChandraDillard@schouse.gov

Douglas, MaryGail (D, 41)
314B Blatt Building
Columbia, SC 29201
P: (803) 212-6789
E: MaryGailDouglas@schouse.gov

Duckworth, Greg (R, 104)*
432D Blatt Building
P.O. Box 11867
Columbia, SC 29211
P: (803) 212-6918
E: GregDuckworth@schouse.gov

Erickson, Shannon S. (R, 124)
320C Blatt Building
P.O. Box 11867
Columbia, SC 29211
P: (803) 734-3261
E: shannonerickson@schouse.gov

Felder, Raye (R, 26)
414D Blatt Building
P.O. Box 11867
Columbia, SC 29211
P: (803) 212-6892
E: RayeFelder@schouse.gov

Finlay III, Kirkman (R, 75)
532A Blatt Building
P.O. Box 11867
Columbia, SC 29211
P: (803) 212-6943
E: KirkmanFinlay@schouse.gov

Forrester, P. Michael (R, 34)
402C Blatt Building
P.O. Box 11867
Columbia, SC 29211
P: (803) 212-6792
E: MikeForrester@schouse.gov

Funderburk, Laurie Slade (D, 52)
422C Blatt Building
P.O. Box 11867
Columbia, SC 29211
P: (803) 734-3044
E: LaurieFunderburk@schouse.gov

Gagnon, Craig A. (R, 11)
436A Blatt Building
P.O. Box 11867
Columbia, SC 29211
P: (803) 212-6934
E: CraigGagnon@schouse.gov

Gambrell, Michael W. (R, 7)
436B Blatt Building
P.O. Box 11867
Columbia, SC 29211
P: (803) 734-2947
E: MikeGambrell@schouse.gov

George, J. Wayne (D, 57)
333B Blatt Building
P.O. Box 11867
Columbia, SC 29211
P: (803) 212-6936
E: WayneGeorge@schouse.gov

Gilliard, Wendell G. (D, 111)
328A Blatt Building
P.O. Box 11867
Columbia, SC 29211
P: (803) 212-6793
E: WendellGilliard@schouse.gov

Goldfinch, Stephen (R, 108)
306A Blatt Building
P.O. Box 11867
Columbia, SC 29211
P: (803) 212-6927
E: StephenGoldfinch@schouse.gov

Govan Jr., Jerry N. (D, 95)
530B Blatt Building
P.O. Box 11867
Columbia, SC 29211
P: (803) 734-3012
E: JerryGovan@schouse.gov

Hamilton, Dan (R, 20)
312C Blatt Building
P.O. Box 11867
Columbia, SC 29211
P: (803) 212-6795
E: DanHamilton@schouse.gov

Hardee, Kevin (R, 105)
306C Blatt Building
P.O. Box 11867
Columbia, SC 29211
P: (803) 212-6796
E: KevinHardee@schouse.gov

Hardwick, Nelson L. (R, 106)
522B Blatt Building
P.O. Box 11867
Columbia, SC 29211
P: (803) 734-2967
E: NelsonHardwick@schouse.gov

Hart, Christopher R. (D, 73)
432B Blatt Building
P.O. Box 11867
Columbia, SC 29211
P: (803) 734-3061
E: ChristopherHart@schouse.gov

Hayes, Jackie E. (D, 55)
333C Blatt Building
P.O. Box 11867
Columbia, SC 29211
P: (803) 734-3099
E: JackieHayes@schouse.gov

Henderson, Phyllis (R, 21)
522D Blatt Building
P.O. Box 11867
Columbia, SC 29211
P: (803) 212-6883
E: PhyllisHenderson@schouse.gov

Henegan, Pat (D, 54)*
333A Blatt Building
P.O. Box 11867
Columbia, SC 29211
P: (803) 212-6986
E: PatHenegan@schouse.gov

Herbkersman, William G. (R, 118)
308B Blatt Building
P.O. Box 11867
Columbia, SC 29211
P: (803) 734-3063
E: BillHerbkersman@schouse.gov

Hicks, Donna C. (R, 37)
402D Blatt Building
P.O. Box 11867
Columbia, SC 29211
P: (803) 212-6878
E: DonnaWood@schouse.gov

Hill, Jonathan (R, 8)*
434A Blatt Building
P.O. Box 11867
Columbia, SC 29211
P: (803) 212-6919
E: JonathanHill@schouse.gov

Hiott, David R. (R, 4)
418B Blatt Building
P.O. Box 11867
Columbia, SC 29211
P: (803) 734-3022
E: DavidHiott@schouse.gov

Hixon, William M. (R, 83)
416A Blatt Building
P.O. Box 11867
Columbia, SC 29211
P: (803) 212-6898
E: BillHixon@schouse.gov

Hodges, Kenneth F. (D, 121)
434B Blatt Building
P.O. Box 11867
Columbia, SC 29211
P: (803) 734-3062
E: KennethHodges@schouse.gov

Horne, Jenny Anderson (R, 94)
308D Blatt Building
P.O. Box 11867
Columbia, SC 29211
P: (803) 212-6871
E: JennyHorne@schouse.gov

Hosey, Lonnie (D, 91)
404B Blatt Building
P.O. Box 11867
Columbia, SC 29211
P: (803) 734-2829
E: LonnieHosey@schouse.gov

Howard, Leon (D, 76)
425 Blatt Building
P.O. Box 11867
Columbia, SC 29211
P: (803) 734-3046
E: LeonHoward@schouse.gov

Huggins, Chip (R, 85)
323B Blatt Building
P.O. Box 11867
Columbia, SC 29211
P: (803) 734-2971
E: ChipHuggins@schouse.gov

Jefferson Jr., Joseph H. (D, 102)
304D Blatt Building
P.O. Box 11867
Columbia, SC 29211
P: (803) 734-2936
E: JosephJefferson@schouse.gov

Johnson, Jeff (R, 58)*
432A Blatt Building
P.O. Box 11867
Columbia, SC 29211
P: (803) 212-6946
E: Jeff.Johnson@schouse.gov

Kennedy Jr., Ralph Shealy (R, 39)
323A Blatt Building
P.O. Box 11867
Columbia, SC 29211
P: (803) 212-6938
E: RalphKennedy@schouse.gov

King, John Richard C. (D, 49)
309D Blatt Building
P.O. Box 11867
Columbia, SC 29211
P: (803) 212-6873
E: JohnKing@schouse.gov

Kirby, Roger (D, 61)*
314D Blatt Building
P.O. Box 11867
Columbia, SC 29211
P: (803) 212-6947
E: RogerKirby@schouse.gov

Knight, Patsy G. (D, 97)
306B Blatt Building
P.O. Box 11867
Columbia, SC 29211
P: (803) 734-2960
E: PatsyKnight@schouse.gov

Limehouse III, Harry B. (R, 110)
326C Blatt Building
P.O. Box 11867
Columbia, SC 29211
P: (803) 734-2977
E: HarryLimehouse@schouse.gov

Loftis, Dwight A. (R, 19)
522C Blatt Building
P.O. Box 11867
Columbia, SC 29211
P: (803) 734-3101
E: DwightLoftis@schouse.gov

Long, Deborah (R, 45)
414A Blatt Building
P.O. Box 11867
Columbia, SC 29211
P: (803) 212-6874
E: DeborahLong@schouse.gov

Lowe, Phillip D. (R, 60)
327B Blatt Building
P.O. Box 11867
Columbia, SC 29211
P: (803) 734-2975
E: PhillipLowe@schouse.gov

Lucas, James H. (R, 65)
506 Blatt Building
P.O. Box 11867
Columbia, SC 29211
P: (803) 734-3125
E: JayLucas@schouse.gov

Mack III, David J. (D, 109)
328D Blatt Building
P.O. Box 11867
Columbia, SC 29211
P: (803) 734-3192
E: DavidMack@schouse.gov

McCoy Jr., Peter M. (R, 115)
420D Blatt Building
P.O. Box 11867
Columbia, SC 29211
P: (803) 212-6872
E: PeterMcCoy@schouse.gov

McEachern, Joseph A. (D, 77)
330B Blatt Building
P.O. Box 11867
Columbia, SC 29211
P: (803) 212-6875
E: JoeMcEachern@schouse.gov

McKnight, Cezar (D, 101)*
314A Blatt Building
P.O. Box 11867
Columbia, SC 29211
P: (803) 212-6926
E: CezarMcKnight@schouse.gov

McLeod, Mia (D, 79)
335D Blatt Building
P.O. Box 11867
Columbia, SC 29211
P: (803) 212-6794
E: MiaMcLeod@schouse.gov

McLeod, Walton J. (D, 40)
422B Blatt Building
P.O. Box 11867
Columbia, SC 29211
P: (803) 734-3276
E: WaltonMcLeod@schouse.gov

Merrill, James H. (R, 99)
308C Blatt Building
P.O. Box 11867
Columbia, SC 29211
P: (803) 734-3072
E: JamesMerrill@schouse.gov

Mitchell Jr., Harold (D, 31)
414C Blatt Building
P.O. Box 11867
Columbia, SC 29211
P: (803) 734-6638
E: HaroldMitchell@schouse.gov

Moss, Dennis C. (R, 29)
503B Blatt Building
P.O. Box 11867
Columbia, SC 29211
P: (803) 734-3073
E: DennisMoss@schouse.gov

Moss, V. Stephen (R, 30)
418B Blatt Building
P.O. Box 11867
Columbia, SC 29211
P: (803) 212-6885
E: StephenMoss@schouse.gov

Murphy, Christopher J. (R, 98)
308A Blatt Building
P.O. Box 11867
Columbia, SC 29211
P: (803) 212-6925
E: ChrisMurphy@schouse.gov

Nanney, Wendy (R, 22)
312D Blatt Building
P.O. Box 11867
Columbia, SC 29211
P: (803) 212-6877
E: WendyNanney@schouse.gov

Neal, Joseph H. (D, 70)
309B Blatt Building
P.O. Box 11867
Columbia, SC 29211
P: (803) 734-2804
E: JoeNeal@schouse.gov

Newton, Weston J. (R, 120)
228 Blatt Building
P.O. Box 11867
Columbia, SC 29211
P: (803) 212-6810
E: WestonNewton@schouse.gov

Norman, Ralph W. (R, 48)
404C Blatt Building
P.O. Box 11867
Columbia, SC 29211
P: (803) 212-6888
E: RalphNorman@schouse.gov

Norrell, Mandy Powers (D, 44)
422D Blatt Building
P.O. Box 11867
Columbia, SC 29211
P: (803) 212-6937
E: MandyNorrell@schouse.gov

South Carolina

Ott, Russell L. (D, 93)
306D Blatt Building
P.O. Box 11867
Columbia, SC 29211
P: (803) 212-6945
E: RussellOtt@schouse.gov

Parks, J. Anne (D, 12)
434D Blatt Building
P.O. Box 11867
Columbia, SC 29211
P: (803) 734-3069
E: AnneParks@schouse.gov

Pitts, Michael A. (R, 14)
327C Blatt Building
P.O. Box 11867
Columbia, SC 29211
P: (803) 734-2830
E: MichaelPitts@schouse.gov

Pope, Thomas E. (R, 47)
505 Blatt Building
P.O. Box 11867
Columbia, SC 29211
P: (803) 734-2701
E: TommyPope@schouse.gov

Putnam, Joshua A. (R, 10)
418C Blatt Office Building
P.O. Box 11867
Columbia, SC 29211
P: (803) 212-6931
E: JoshuaPutnam@schouse.gov

Quinn, Rick (R, 69)
532C Blatt Building
P.O. Box 11867
Columbia, SC 29211
P: (803) 212-6897
E: RickQuinn@schouse.gov

Ridgeway III, Robert L. (D, 64)
422A Blatt Building
P.O. Box 11867
Columbia, SC 29211
P: (803) 212-6929
E: RobertRidgeway@schouse.gov

Riley, Robert Shannon (R, 13)
327A Blatt Building
P.O. Box 11867
Columbia, SC 29211
P: (803) 212-6939
E: RobertRiley@schouse.gov

Rivers Jr., Samuel (R, 15)
323D Blatt Building
P.O. Box 11867
Columbia, SC 29211
P: (803) 212-6890
E: SamuelRivers@schouse.gov

Robinson-Simpson, Leola C. (D, 25)
330A Blatt Building
P.O. Box 11867
Columbia, SC 29211
P: (803) 212-6941
E: LeolaRobinson-Simpson@schouse.gov

Rutherford, J. Todd (D, 74)
335B Blatt Building
P.O. Box 11867
Columbia, SC 29211
P: (803) 734-9441
E: ToddRutherford@schouse.gov

Ryhal, Mike (R, 56)
404A Blatt Building
P.O. Box 11867
Columbia, SC 29211
P: (803) 212-6935
E: MikeRyhal@schouse.gov

Sandifer III, William E. (R, 2)
407 Blatt Building
P.O. Box 11867
Columbia, SC 29211
P: (803) 734-3015
E: BillSandifer@schouse.gov

Simrill, J. Gary (R, 46)
518C Blatt Building
P.O. Box 11867
Columbia, SC 29211
P: (803) 734-3040
E: GarySimrill@schouse.gov

Smith Jr., G. Murrell (R, 67)
420B Blatt Building
P.O. Box 11867
Columbia, SC 29211
P: (803) 734-3042
E: MurrellSmith@schouse.gov

Smith, Garry R. (R, 27)
534 Blatt Building
P.O. Box 11867
Columbia, SC 29211
P: (803) 734-3141
E: GarrySmith@schouse.gov

Smith Jr., James E. (D, 72)
335C Blatt Building
P.O. Box 11867
Columbia, SC 29211
P: (803) 734-2997
E: JamesSmith@schouse.gov

Sottile, F. Michael (R, 112)
310A Blatt Building
P.O. Box 11867
Columbia, SC 29211
P: (803) 212-6880
E: MikeSottile@schouse.gov

Southard, Edward L. (R, 100)
530D Blatt Office Building
P.O. Box 11867
Columbia, SC 29211
P: (803) 212-6930
E: EdwardSouthard@schouse.gov

Spires, L. Kit (R, 96)
326D Blatt Building
P.O. Box 11867
Columbia, SC 29211
P: (803) 734-3010
E: KitSpires@schouse.gov

Stavrinakis, Leonidas E. (D, 119)
420C Blatt Building
P.O. Box 11867
Columbia, SC 29211
P: (803) 734-3039
E: LeonStavrinakis@schouse.gov

Stringer, Tommy (R, 18)
312A Blatt Building
P.O. Box 11867
Columbia, SC 29211
P: (803) 212-6881
E: TommyStringer@schouse.gov

Tallon Sr., Edward R. (R, 33)
402A Blatt Building
P.O. Box 11867
Columbia, SC 29211
P: (803) 212-6893
E: EddieTallon@schouse.gov

Taylor, Bill (R, 86)
416B Blatt Building
P.O. Box 11867
Columbia, SC 29211
P: (803) 212-6923
E: BillTaylor@schouse.gov

Thayer, Anne J. (R, 9)
436D Blatt Building
P.O. Box 11867
Columbia, SC 29211
P: (803) 212-6889
E: AnneThayer@schouse.gov

Tinkler, Mary (D, 114)*
333D Blatt Building
P.O. Box 11867
Columbia, SC 29211
P: (803) 212-6948
E: MaryTinkler@schouse.gov

Toole, McLain R. (R, 88)
323C Blatt Building
P.O. Box 11867
Columbia, SC 29211
P: (803) 734-2973
E: MacToole@schouse.gov

Weeks, J. David (D, 51)
330C Blatt Building
P.O. Box 11867
Columbia, SC 29211
P: (803) 734-3102
E: DavidWeeks@schouse.gov

Wells, Don L. (R, 81)
416D Blatt Building
P.O. Box 11867
Columbia, SC 29211
P: (803) 212-6884
E: DonWells@schouse.gov

Whipper, J. Seth (D, 113)
328C Blatt Building
P.O. Box 11867
Columbia, SC 29211
P: (803) 734-3191
E: SethWhipper@schouse.gov

White, W. Brian (R, 6)
525 Blatt Building
P.O. Box 11867
Columbia, SC 29211
P: (803) 734-3144
E: BrianWhite@schouse.gov

Whitmire, William R. (R, 1)
436C Blatt Building
P.O. Box 11867
Columbia, SC 29211
P: (803) 734-3068
E: BillWhitmire@schouse.gov

Williams, Robert Q. (D, 62)
328B Blatt Building
P.O. Box 11867
Columbia, SC 29211
P: (803) 734-3142
E: RobertWilliams@schouse.gov

Willis, Mark N. (R, 16)
326B Blatt Building
P.O. Box 11867
Columbia, SC 29211
P: (803) 212-6882
E: MarkWillis@schouse.gov

Yow, Richie (R, 53)*
327D Blatt Building
P.O. Box 11867
Columbia, SC 29211
P: (803) 212-6949

Congress

Senate

Graham, Lindsey O. (R)
Scott, Tim (R)

House

Clyburn, James E. (D, 6)
Duncan, Jeffrey D. (R, 3)
Gowdy, Trey (R, 4)
Mulvaney, J. Michael (R, 5)
Rice, Tom (R, 7)
Sanford, Mark (R, 1)
Wilson, Joe (R, 2)

South Dakota

Executive

Governor

Hon. Dennis Daugaard (R)
Governor
500 East Capitol Avenue
Pierre, SD 57501
P: (605) 773-3212
F: (605) 773-4711

Lieutenant Governor

Hon. Matthew Michels (R)
Lieutenant Governor
500 East Capitol Street
Pierre, SD 57501
P: (605) 773-3661
F: (605) 773-4711

Attorney General

Hon. Marty J. Jackley (R)
Attorney General
1302 East Highway 14, Suite 1
Pierre, SD 57501
P: (605) 773-3215
F: (605) 773-4106
E: atghelp@state.sd.us

Auditor

Hon. Steve Barnett (R)
State Auditor
500 East Capitol Avenue
Pierre, SD 57501
P: (605) 773-3341
F: (605) 773-5929
E: steve.barnett@state.sd.us

Commissioner of School & Public Lands

Hon. Ryan Brunner (R)
Commissioner
500 East Capitol Avenue
Pierre, SD 57501
P: (605) 773-3303
F: (605) 773-5520
E: ryan.brunner@state.sd.us

Public Utilities Commission

Hon. Kristie Fiegen (R)
Commissioner
State Capitol
500 East Capitol Avenue
Pierre, SD 57501
P: (605) 773-3201
F: (866) 757-6031
E: kristie.fiegen@state.sd.us

Hon. Gary W. Hanson (R)
Chair
State Capitol, 500 East Capitol Avenue
Pierre, SD 57501
P: (605) 773-3201
F: (866) 757-6031
E: gary.hanson@state.sd.us

Hon. Chris Nelson (R)
Chair
State Capitol
500 East Capitol Avenue
Pierre, SD 57501
P: (605) 773-3201
F: (866) 757-6031
E: Chris.Nelson@state.sd.us

Secretary of State

Hon. Shantel Krebs (R)
Secretary of State
500 East Capitol Avenue, Suite 204
Pierre, SD 57501
P: (605) 773-3537
F: (605) 773-6580

Treasurer

Hon. Rich L. Sattgast (R)
State Treasurer
State Capitol Building, Suite 212
500 East Capitol Avenue
Pierre, SD 57501
P: (605) 773-3378
F: (605) 773-3115
E: rich.sattgast@state.sd.us

Judiciary

Supreme Court (MR)

Ms. Shirley A. Jameson-Fergel
Clerk
500 East Capitol Avenue
Pierre, SD 57501
P: (605) 773-3511
F: (605) 773-6128

Hon. David Gilbertson
Chief Justice
Hon. Janine M. Kern
Hon. Glen Severson
Hon. Lori S. Wilbur
Hon. Steven L. Zinter

Legislative Senate

Senate President

Hon. Matthew Michels (R)
Lieutenant Governor
500 East Capitol Street
Pierre, SD 57501
P: (605) 773-3661
F: (605) 773-4711

President Pro Tempore of the Senate

Sen. Corey Brown (R)
Senate President Pro Tempore
State Capitol
500 East Capitol Avenue
Pierre, SD 57501
E: sen.brown@state.sd.us

Senate Majority Leader

Sen. Timothy A. Rave (R)
Senate Majority Leader
State Capitol
500 East Capitol Avenue
Pierre, SD 57501
E: sen.rave@state.sd.us

Senate Minority Leader

Sen. Billie H. Sutton (D)
Senate Minority Leader
State Capitol
500 East Capitol Avenue
Pierre, SD 57501
E: sen.sutton@state.sd.us

Secretary of the Senate

Ms. Jeanette Schipper
Secretary of the Senate
State Capitol, Room 330
500 East Capitol Avenue
Pierre, SD 57501
P: (605) 773-3825
F: (605) 773-6806

Members of the Senate

Bradford, Jim (D, 27)
State Capitol
500 East Capitol Avenue
Pierre, SD 57501
E: sen.bradford@state.sd.us

Brown, Corey (R, 23)
State Capitol
500 East Capitol Avenue
Pierre, SD 57501
E: sen.brown@state.sd.us

Buhl O'Donnell, Angie (D, 15)
State Capitol
500 East Capitol Avenue
Pierre, SD 57501
E: sen.buhl@state.sd.us

Cammack, Gary L. (R, 29)
State Capitol
500 East Capitol Avenue
Pierre, SD 57501
E: rep.cammack@state.sd.us

Curd, Blake (R, 12)
State Capitol
500 East Capitol Avenue
Pierre, SD 57501
E: sen.curd@state.sd.us

Ewing, Bob (R, 31)
State Capitol
500 East Capitol Avenue
Pierre, SD 57501
E: rep.ewing@state.sd.us

Frerichs, Jason (D, 1)
State Capitol
500 East Capitol Avenue
Pierre, SD 57501
E: sen.frerichs@state.sd.us

Greenfield, Brock L. (R, 2)
State Capitol
500 East Capitol Avenue
Pierre, SD 57501
E: rep.greenfield@state.sd.us

Haggar, Jenna (R, 10)
State Capitol
500 East Capitol Avenue
Pierre, SD 57501
E: rep.haggar@state.sd.us

Haverly, Terri (R, 35)*
State Capitol
500 East Capitol Avenue
Pierre, SD 57501
E: sen.haverly@state.sd.us

Heineman, Phyllis M. (R, 13)
State Capitol
500 East Capitol Avenue
Pierre, SD 57501
E: sen.heineman@state.sd.us

Heinert, Troy (D, 26)
State Capitol
500 East Capitol Avenue
Pierre, SD 57501
E: rep.heinert@state.sd.us

Holien, Ried S. (R, 5)
State Capitol
500 East Capitol Avenue
Pierre, SD 57501
E: sen.holien@state.sd.us

Hunhoff, Bernie (D, 18)
State Capitol
500 East Capitol Avenue
Pierre, SD 57501
E: rep.hunhoff@state.sd.us

Jensen, Phil (R, 33)
State Capitol
500 East Capitol Avenue
Pierre, SD 57501
E: sen.jensen@state.sd.us

Lederman, Dan (R, 16)
State Capitol
500 East Capitol Avenue
Pierre, SD 57501
E: sen.lederman@state.sd.us

Monroe, Jeff (R, 24)
State Capitol
500 East Capitol Avenue
Pierre, SD 57501
E: JDJJMKmonroe@aol.com

Novstrup, David (R, 3)
State Capitol
500 East Capitol Avenue
Pierre, SD 57501
E: rep.novstrup@state.sd.us

Olson, Betty (R, 28)
State Capitol
500 East Capitol Avenue
Pierre, SD 57501
E: rep.olson@state.sd.us

Omdahl, David M. (R, 11)
State Capitol
500 East Capitol Avenue
Pierre, SD 57501
E: sen.omdahl@state.sd.us

Otten, Ernie (R, 6)
State Capitol
500 East Capitol Avenue
Pierre, SD 57501
E: sen.otten@state.sd.us

Parsley, Scott (D, 8)
State Capitol
500 East Capitol Avenue
Pierre, SD 57501
E: rep.parsley@state.sd.us

Peters, Deb (R, 9)
State Capitol
500 East Capitol Avenue
Pierre, SD 57501
E: sen.peters@state.sd.us

Peterson, Jim (D, 4)
State Capitol
500 East Capitol Avenue
Pierre, SD 57501
E: rep.peterson@state.sd.us

Rampelberg, Bruce E. (R, 30)
State Capitol
500 East Capitol Avenue
Pierre, SD 57501
E: sen.rampelberg@state.sd.us

Rave, Timothy A. (R, 25)
State Capitol
500 East Capitol Avenue
Pierre, SD 57501
E: sen.rave@state.sd.us

Rusch, Arthur (R, 17)*
State Capitol
500 East Capitol Avenue
Pierre, SD 57501
E: sen.rusch@state.sd.us

Soholt, Deb (R, 14)
State Capitol
500 East Capitol Avenue
Pierre, SD 57501
E: sen.soholt@state.sd.us

Solano, Alan D. (R, 32)
State Capitol
500 East Capitol Avenue
Pierre, SD 57501
E: sen.solano@state.sd.us

Sutton, Billie H. (D, 21)
State Capitol
500 East Capitol Avenue
Pierre, SD 57501
E: sen.sutton@state.sd.us

Tidemann, Larry (R, 7)
State Capitol
500 East Capitol Avenue
Pierre, SD 57501
E: sen.tidemann@state.sd.us

Tieszen, Craig (R, 34)
State Capitol
500 East Capitol Avenue
Pierre, SD 57501
E: sen.tieszen@state.sd.us

Van Gerpen, Bill L. (R, 19)
State Capitol
500 East Capitol Avenue
Pierre, SD 57501
E: sen.vangerpen@state.sd.us

Vehle, Mike (R, 20)
State Capitol
500 East Capitol Avenue
Pierre, SD 57501
E: sen.vehle@state.sd.us

White, Jim (R, 22)
State Capitol
500 East Capitol Avenue
Pierre, SD 57501
E: sen.white@state.sd.us

House

Speaker of the House

Rep. Dean Wink (R)
Speaker of the House
State Capitol
500 East Capitol Avenue
Pierre, SD 57501
E: rep.wink@state.sd.us

Speaker Pro Tempore of the House

Rep. G. Mark Mickelson (R)
House Speaker Pro Tempore
State Capitol
500 East Capitol Avenue
Pierre, SD 57501
E: rep.mickelson@state.sd.us

House Majority Leader

Rep. Brian G. Gosch (R)
House Majority Leader
State Capitol
500 East Capitol Avenue
Pierre, SD 57501
E: rep.gosch@state.sd.us

House Minority Leader

Rep. Spencer Hawley (D)
House Minority Leader
State Capitol
500 East Capitol Avenue
Pierre, SD 57501
E: rep.hawley@state.sd.us

Clerk of the House

Ms. Arlene Kvislen
Chief Clerk of the House
State Capitol, Room 362
500 East Capitol Avenue
Pierre, SD 57501
P: (605) 773-3842
F: (605) 773-6806

Members of the House

Anderson, David (R, 16)
State Capitol
500 East Capitol Avenue
Pierre, SD 57501
P: (605) 764-5781
E: rep.anderson@state.sd.us

Bartling, Julie (D, 21)
State Capitol
500 East Capitol Avenue
Pierre, SD 57501
E: rep.bartling@state.sd.us

Beal, Arch (R, 12)*
State Capitol
500 East Capitol Avenue
Pierre, SD 57501
E: rep.beal@state.sd.us

Bolin, Jim (R, 16)
State Capitol
500 East Capitol Avenue
Pierre, SD 57501
E: rep.bolin@state.sd.us

Bordeaux, Shawn (D, 26A)*
State Capitol
500 East Capitol Avenue
Pierre, SD 57501
E: rep.bordeaux@state.sd.us

Brunner, Thomas J. (R, 29)
State Capitol
500 East Capitol Avenue
Pierre, SD 57501
P: (605) 257-2336
F: (605) 257-2336
E: rep.brunner@state.sd.us

Campbell, Blaine (R, 35)
State Capitol
500 East Capitol Avenue
Pierre, SD 57501
E: rep.campbell@state.sd.us

Conzet, Kristin A. (R, 32)
State Capitol
500 East Capitol Avenue
Pierre, SD 57501
E: rep.conzet@state.sd.us

Craig, Scott W. (R, 33)
State Capitol
500 East Capitol Avenue
Pierre, SD 57501
E: rep.craig@state.sd.us

Cronin, Justin R. (R, 23)
State Capitol
500 East Capitol Avenue
Pierre, SD 57501
E: rep.cronin@state.sd.us

South Dakota

Deutsch, Fred (R, 4)*
State Capitol
500 East Capitol Avenue
Pierre, SD 57501
E: rep.deutsch@state.sd.us

DiSanto, Lynne (R, 35)*
State Capitol
500 East Capitol Avenue
Pierre, SD 57501
E: rep.disanto@state.sd.us

Dryden, Dan (R, 34)
State Capitol
500 East Capitol Avenue
Pierre, SD 57501
E: rep.dryden@state.sd.us

Duvall, Mary (R, 24)
State Capitol
500 East Capitol Avenue
Pierre, SD 57501
E: rep.duvall@state.sd.us

Feickert, Dennis (D, 1)
State Capitol
500 East Capitol Avenue
Pierre, SD 57501
E: rep.feickert@state.sd.us

Gibson, Peggy (D, 22)
State Capitol
500 East Capitol Avenue
Pierre, SD 57501
E: rep.gibson@state.sd.us

Gosch, Brian G. (R, 32)
State Capitol
500 East Capitol Avenue
Pierre, SD 57501
E: rep.gosch@state.sd.us

Greenfield, Lana (R, 2)*
State Capitol
500 East Capitol Avenue
Pierre, SD 57501
E: rep.greenfield
@state.sd.us

Haggar, Don (R, 10)
State Capitol
500 East Capitol Avenue
Pierre, SD 57501
E: rep.donhaggar
@state.sd.us

Harrison, Michele (R, 23)*
State Capitol
500 East Capitol Avenue
Pierre, SD 57501
E: rep.harrison@state.sd.us

Haugaard, Steven (R, 10)*
State Capitol
500 East Capitol Avenue
Pierre, SD 57501
E: rep.haugaard@state.sd.us

Hawks, Paula (D, 9)
State Capitol
500 East Capitol Avenue
Pierre, SD 57501
E: rep.hawks@state.sd.us

Hawley, Spencer (D, 7)
State Capitol
500 East Capitol Avenue
Pierre, SD 57501
E: rep.hawley@state.sd.us

Heinemann, Leslie J. (R, 8)
State Capitol
500 East Capitol Avenue
Pierre, SD 57501
E: rep.heinemann
@state.sd.us

Hickey, Steve (R, 9)
State Capitol
500 East Capitol Avenue
Pierre, SD 57501
E: rep.hickey@state.sd.us

Holmes, Tom (R, 14)*
State Capitol
500 East Capitol Avenue
Pierre, SD 57501
E: rep.holmes@state.sd.us

Hunhoff, Jean M. (R, 18)
State Capitol
500 East Capitol Avenue
Pierre, SD 57501
E: rep.jeanhunhoff
@state.sd.us

Hunt, Roger (R, 25)
State Capitol
500 East Capitol Avenue
Pierre, SD 57501
P: (605) 582-3865
F: (605) 582-2481
E: rep.hunt@state.sd.us

Jensen, Alex (R, 12)*
State Capitol
500 East Capitol Avenue
Pierre, SD 57501
E: rep.jensen@state.sd.us

Johns, Timothy R. (R, 31)
State Capitol
500 East Capitol Avenue
Pierre, SD 57501
E: rep.johns@state.sd.us

Kaiser, Dan (R, 3)
State Capitol
500 East Capitol Avenue
Pierre, SD 57501
P: (605) 228-4988
E: rep.kaiser@state.sd.us

Killer, Kevin (D, 27)
State Capitol
500 East Capitol Avenue
Pierre, SD 57501
E: rep.killer@state.sd.us

Kirschman, Patrick A. (D, 15)
State Capitol
500 East Capitol Avenue
Pierre, SD 57501
E: rep.kirschman
@state.sd.us

Klumb, Joshua (R, 20)*
State Capitol
500 East Capitol Avenue
Pierre, SD 57501
E: rep.klumb@state.sd.us

Langer, Kris (R, 25)
State Capitol
500 East Capitol Avenue
Pierre, SD 57501
E: rep.langer@state.sd.us

Latterell, Isaac (R, 6)
State Capitol
500 East Capitol Avenue
Pierre, SD 57501
E: rep.latterell
@state.sd.us

Marty, J. Sam (R, 28B)*
State Capitol
500 East Capitol Avenue
Pierre, SD 57501
E: rep.marty@state.sd.us

May, Elizabeth (R, 27)
State Capitol
500 East Capitol Avenue
Pierre, SD 57501
E: rep.may@state.sd.us

McCleerey, Steven (D, 1)*
State Capitol
500 East Capitol Avenue
Pierre, SD 57501
E: rep.mccleerey
@state.sd.us

Mickelson, G. Mark (R, 13)
State Capitol
500 East Capitol Avenue
Pierre, SD 57501
E: rep.mickelson
@state.sd.us

Munsterman, Scott (R, 7)
State Capitol
500 East Capitol Avenue
Pierre, SD 57501
E: rep.munsterman
@state.sd.us

Novstrup, Al (R, 3)
State Capitol
500 East Capitol Avenue
Pierre, SD 57501
E: sen.novstrup@state.sd.us

Otten, Herman (R, 6)
State Capitol
500 East Capitol Avenue
Pierre, SD 57501
E: rep.otten@state.sd.us

Partridge, Jeff (R, 34)*
State Capitol
500 East Capitol Avenue
Pierre, SD 57501
E: rep.partridge
@state.sd.us

Peterson, Kent (R, 19)*
State Capitol
500 East Capitol Avenue
Pierre, SD 57501
E: rep.peterson@state.sd.us

Qualm, Lee (R, 21)
State Capitol
500 East Capitol Avenue
Pierre, SD 57501
E: rep.qualm@state.sd.us

Rasmussen, Nancy (R, 17)
State Capitol
500 East Capitol Avenue
Pierre, SD 57501
E: rep.hurley@state.sd.us

Ring, Ray (D, 17)
State Capitol
500 East Capitol Avenue
Pierre, SD 57501
E: rep.ring@state.sd.us

Romkema, Fred W. (R, 31)
State Capitol
500 East Capitol Avenue
Pierre, SD 57501
E: rep.romkema@state.sd.us

Rounds, Tim (R, 24)
State Capitol
500 East Capitol Avenue
Pierre, SD 57501
E: rep.rounds@state.sd.us

Rozum, Tona (R, 20)
State Capitol
500 East Capitol Avenue
Pierre, SD 57501
E: rep.rozum@state.sd.us

Russell, Lance S. (R, 30)
State Capitol
500 East Capitol Avenue
Pierre, SD 57501
E: rep.russell@state.sd.us

Schaefer, James G. (R, 26B)
State Capitol
500 East Capitol Avenue
Pierre, SD 57501
E: rep.schaefer@state.sd.us

Schoenbeck, Lee (R, 5)
State Capitol
500 East Capitol Avenue
Pierre, SD 57501
E: rep.schoenbeck
@state.sd.us

Schoenfish, Kyle (R, 19)
State Capitol
500 East Capitol Avenue
Pierre, SD 57501
E: rep.schoenfish
@state.sd.us

Schrempp, Dean (D, 28A)
State Capitol
500 East Capitol Avenue
Pierre, SD 57501
E: rep.schrempp@state.sd.us

Sly, Jacqueline (R, 33)
State Capitol
500 EAst Capitol Avenue
Pierre, SD 57501
E: rep.sly@state.sd.us

Soli, Karen L. (D, 15)
State Capitol
500 East Capitol Avenue
Pierre, SD 57501
E: rep.soli@state.sd.us

Solum, Roger (R, 5)
State Capitol
500 East Capitol Avenue
Pierre, SD 57501
E: rep.solum@state.sd.us

Stalzer, Jim (R, 11)
State Capitol
500 East Capitol Avenue
Pierre, SD 57501
E: rep.stalzer@state.sd.us

Stevens, Mike (R, 18)
State Capitol
500 East Capitol Avenue
Pierre, SD 57501
E: rep.stevens@state.sd.us

Tulson, Burt E. (R, 2)
State Capitol
500 East Capitol Avenue
Pierre, SD 57501
E: rep.tulson@state.sd.us

Verchio, Mike (R, 30)
State Capitol
500 East Capitol Avenue
Pierre, SD 57501
E: rep.verchio@state.sd.us

Werner, Dick (R, 22)
State Capitol
500 East Capitol Avenue
Pierre, SD 57501
E: rep.werner@state.sd.us

Westra, Steven (R, 13)
State Capitol
500 East Capitol Avenue
Pierre, SD 57501
E: rep.westra@state.sd.us

Wiik, John (R, 4)*
State Capitol
500 East Capitol Avenue
Pierre, SD 57501
E: rep.wiik@state.sd.us

Willadsen, Mark K. (R, 11)
State Capitol
500 East Capitol Avenue
Pierre, SD 57501
P: (605) 773-3851
E: rep.willadsen
@state.sd.us

Wink, Dean (R, 29)
State Capitol
500 East Capitol Avenue
Pierre, SD 57501
E: rep.wink@state.sd.us

Wollmann, Mathew (R, 8)*
State Capitol
500 East Capitol Avenue
Pierre, SD 57501
E: rep.wollmann@state.sd.us

Zikmund, Larry (R, 14)*
State Capitol
500 East Capitol Avenue
Pierre, SD 57501
E: rep.zikmund@state.sd.us

Congress

Senate
Rounds, Mike (R)
Thune, John R. (R)

House
Noem, Kristi (R, At-Large)

Tennessee

Executive

Governor

Hon. Bill Haslam (R)
Governor
State Capitol
Nashville, TN 37243
P: (615) 741-2001
F: (615) 532-9711
E: bill.haslam@tn.gov

Lieutenant Governor

Hon. Ron Ramsey
(elected by the Senate)
Lieutenant Governor/Speaker of the Senate
Suite 1, Legislative Plaza
301 6th Avenue North
Nashville, TN 37243
P: (615) 741-4524
F: (615) 253-0197
E: lt.gov.ron.ramsey@capitol.tn.gov

Attorney General

Hon. Herbert Slatery III
(appointed)
Attorney General
425 5th Avenue North
Nashville, TN 37243
P: (615) 741-3491
F: (615) 741-2009

Auditor

Mr. Justin P. Wilson
Comptroller of the Treasury
First Floor, State Capitol
Nashville, TN 37243
P: (615) 741-2775
F: (615) 741-7328
E: justin.wilson@tn.gov

Secretary of State

Hon. Tre Hargett
(elected by the Legislature)
Secretary of State
First Floor, State Capitol
Nashville, TN 37243
P: (615) 741-2819
F: (615) 741-5962
E: tre.hargett@tn.gov

Treasurer

Hon. David H. Lillard Jr.
(elected by the Legislature)
State Treasurer
State Capitol, First Floor
600 Charlotte Avenue
Nashville, TN 37243
P: (615) 741-2956
F: (615) 253-1591
E: david.lillard@tn.gov

Judiciary

Supreme Court (PE)

Mr. James Hivner
Appellate Court Clerk
Supreme Court Building
401 7th Avenue, North
Nashville, TN 37219
P: (615) 741-2681
F: (615) 532-8757

Hon. Sharon G. Lee
Chief Justice
Hon. Jeffrey Bivins
Hon. Cornelia Clark
Hon. Holly Kirby
Hon. Gary R. Wade

Legislative Senate

Speaker of the Senate

Hon. Ron Ramsey (R)
Lieutenant Governor/Speaker of the Senate
Suite 1, Legislative Plaza
301 6th Avenue North
Nashville, TN 37243
P: (615) 741-4524
F: (615) 253-0197
E: lt.gov.ron.ramsey@capitol.tn.gov

Speaker Pro Tempore of the Senate

Sen. Bo Watson (R)
Speaker Pro Tempore
Suite 13, Legislative Plaza
301 6th Avenue North
Nashville, TN 37243
P: (615) 741-3227
F: (615) 253-0280
E: sen.bo.watson@capitol.tn.gov

Senate Majority Leader

Sen. Mark Norris (R)
Majority Leader
Suite 9A, Legislative Plaza
301 6th Avenue North
Nashville, TN 37243
P: (615) 741-1967
F: (615) 253-0194
E: sen.mark.norris@capitol.tn.gov

Senate Minority Leader

Sen. Lee Harris (D)
Minority Leader
Suite 318, War Memorial Building
301 6th Avenue North
Nashville, TN 37243
P: (615) 741-1767
E: sen.lee.harris@capitol.tn.gov

Secretary of the Senate

Mr. Russell Humphrey
Chief Clerk of the Senate
State Capitol, 2nd Floor
Nashville, TN 37243
P: (615) 741-2730
E: russell.humphrey@capitol.tn.gov

Members of the Senate

Bailey, Paul (R, 15)
Suite 304, War Memorial Building
301 6th Avenue North
Nashville, TN 37243
P: (615) 741-3978
F: (615) 253-0207
E: sen.paul.bailey@capitol.tn.gov

Beavers, Mae (R, 17)
Suite 6, Legislative Plaza
301 6th Avenue North
Nashville, TN 37243
P: (615) 741-2421
E: sen.mae.beavers@capitol.tn.gov

Bell, Mike (R, 9)
Suite 309, War Memorial Building
301 6th Avenue North
Nashville, TN 37243
P: (615) 741-1946
F: (615) 253-0374
E: sen.mike.bell@capitol.tn.gov

Bowling, Janice (R, 16)
Suite 310A, War Memorial Building
301 6th Avenue North
Nashville, TN 37243
P: (615) 741-6694
E: sen.janice.bowling@capitol.tn.gov

Briggs, Richard (R, 7)*
Suite 317, War Memorial Building
301 6th Avenue North
Nashville, TN 37243
P: (615) 741-1766
E: sen.richard.briggs@capitol.tn.gov

Crowe, Rusty (R, 3)
Suite 8, Legislative Plaza
301 6th Avenue North
Nashville, TN 37243
P: (615) 741-2468
E: sen.rusty.crowe@capitol.tn.gov

Dickerson, Steven (R, 20)
Suite 310, War Memorial Building
301 6th Avenue North
Nashville, TN 37243
P: (615) 741-6679
E: sen.steven.dickerson@capitol.tn.gov

Gardenhire, Todd (R, 10)
Suite 11A, Legislative Plaza
301 6th Avenue North
Nashville, TN 37243
P: (615) 741-6682
F: (615) 253-0209
E: sen.todd.gardenhire@capitol.tn.gov

Green, Mark (R, 22)
Suite 4, Legislative Plaza
301 6th Avenue North
Nashville, TN 37243
P: (615) 741-2374
F: (615) 253-0193
E: sen.mark.green@capitol.tn.gov

Gresham, Dolores (R, 26)
Suite 308, War Memorial Building
301 6th Avenue North
Nashville, TN 37243
P: (615) 741-2368
E: sen.dolores.gresham@capitol.tn.gov

Haile, Ferrell (R, 18)
Suite 10A, Legislative Plaza
301 6th Avenue North
Nashville, TN 37243
P: (615) 741-1999
E: sen.ferrell.haile@capitol.tn.gov

Harper, Thelma (D, 19)
Suite 303, War Memorial Building
301 6th Avenue North
Nashville, TN 37243
P: (615) 741-2453
E: sen.thelma.harper@capitol.tn.gov

Harris, Lee (D, 21)*
Suite 318, War Memorial Building
301 6th Avenue North
Nashville, TN 37243
P: (615) 741-1767
E: sen.lee.harris@capitol.tn.gov

Hensley, Joey (R, 28)
Suite 309, War Memorial Building
301 6th Avenue North
Nashville, TN 37243
P: (615) 741-3100
F: (615) 253-0231
E: sen.joey.hensley@capitol.tn.gov

Jackson, Ed (R, 27)*
Suite 3, Legislative Plaza
301 6th Avenue North
Nashville, TN 37243
P: (615) 741-1810
F: (615) 253-0179
E: sen.ed.jackson@capitol.tn.gov

Johnson, Jack (R, 23)
Suite 11, Legislative Plaza
301 6th Avenue North
Nashville, TN 37243
P: (615) 741-2495
F: (615) 253-0321
E: sen.jack.johnson@capitol.tn.gov

Kelsey, Brian K. (R, 31)
Suite 7, Legislative Plaza
301 6th Avenue North
Nashville, TN 37243
P: (615) 741-3036
E: sen.brian.kelsey@capitol.tn.gov

Ketron, Bill (R, 13)
Suite 5, Legislative Plaza
301 6th Avenue North
Nashville, TN 37243
P: (615) 741-6853
F: (615) 741-7200
E: sen.bill.ketron@capitol.tn.gov

Kyle, Sara (D, 30)*
Suite 305, War Memorial Building
301 6th Avenue North
Nashville, TN 37243
P: (615) 741-4167
F: (615) 253-0221
E: sen.sara.kyle@capitol.tn.gov

Massey, Becky Duncan (R, 6)
Suite 6A, Legislative Plaza
301 6th Avenue North
Nashville, TN 37243
P: (615) 741-1648
E: sen.becky.massey@capitol.tn.gov

McNally, Randy (R, 5)
Suite 307, War Memorial Building
301 6th Avenue North
Nashville, TN 37243
P: (615) 741-6806
E: sen.randy.mcnally@capitol.tn.gov

Niceley, Frank S. (R, 8)
Suite 9, Legislative Plaza
301 6th Avenue North
Nashville, TN 37243
P: (615) 741-2061
E: sen.frank.niceley@capitol.tn.gov

Norris, Mark (R, 32)
Suite 9A, Legislative Plaza
301 6th Avenue North
Nashville, TN 37243
P: (615) 741-1967
F: (615) 253-0194
E: sen.mark.norris@capitol.tn.gov

Overbey, Doug (R, 2)
Suite 306, War Memorial Building
301 6th Avenue North
Nashville, TN 37243
P: (615) 741-0981
E: sen.doug.overbey@capitol.tn.gov

Ramsey, Ron (R, 4)
Suite 1, Legislative Plaza
301 6th Avenue North
Nashville, TN 37243
P: (615) 741-4524
F: (615) 253-0197
E: lt.gov.ron.ramsey@capitol.tn.gov

Roberts, Kerry (R, 25)
Suite 321, War Memorial Building
301 6th Avenue North
Nashville, TN 37243
P: (615) 741-4499
F: (615) 253-0207
E: sen.kerry.roberts@capitol.tn.gov

Southerland, Steve (R, 1)
Suite 10, Legislative Plaza
301 6th Avenue North
Nashville, TN 37243
P: (615) 741-3851
F: (615) 253-0330
E: sen.steve.southerland@capitol.tn.gov

Stevens, John (R, 24)
Suite 302, War Memorial Building
301 6th Avenue North
Nashville, TN 37243
P: (615) 741-4576
F: (615) 253-0161
E: sen.john.stevens@capitol.tn.gov

Tate, Reginald (D, 33)
Suite 320, War Memorial Building
301 6th Avenue North
Nashville, TN 37243
P: (615) 741-2509
F: (615) 253-0167
E: sen.reginald.tate@capitol.tn.gov

Tracy, Jim (R, 14)
Suite 2, Legislative Plaza
301 6th Avenue North
Nashville, TN 37243
P: (615) 741-1066
F: (615) 741-2255
E: sen.jim.tracy@capitol.tn.gov

Watson, Bo (R, 11)
Suite 13, Legislative Plaza
301 6th Avenue North
Nashville, TN 37243
P: (615) 741-3227
F: (615) 253-0280
E: sen.bo.watson@capitol.tn.gov

Yager, Ken (R, 12)
Suite G-19, War Memorial Building
301 6th Avenue North
Nashville, TN 37243
P: (615) 741-1449
F: (615) 253-0237
E: sen.ken.yager@capitol.tn.gov

Yarbro, Jeff (D, 21)*
Suite 312, War Memorial Building
301 6th Avenue North
Nashville, TN 37243
P: (615) 741-3291
E: sen.jeff.yarbro@capitol.tn.gov

House

Speaker of the House

Rep. Beth Harwell (R)
Speaker
Suite 19, Legislative Plaza
301 6th Avenue North
Nashville, TN 37243
P: (615) 741-0709
F: (615) 741-4917
E: speaker.beth.harwell@capitol.tn.gov

Speaker Pro Tempore of the House

Rep. Curtis G. Johnson (R)
Speaker Pro Tempore
Suite 15, Legislative Plaza
301 6th Avenue North
Nashville, TN 37243
P: (615) 741-4341
F: (615) 253-0269
E: rep.curtis.johnson@capitol.tn.gov

House Majority Leader

Rep. Gerald McCormick (R)
Republican Leader
Suite 18A, Legislative Plaza
301 6th Avenue North
Nashville, TN 37243
P: (615) 741-2548
F: (615) 253-0305
E: rep.gerald.mccormick@capitol.tn.gov

House Minority Leader

Rep. Craig Fitzhugh (D)
Democratic Leader
Suite 33, Legislative Plaza
301 6th Avenue North
Nashville, TN 37243
P: (615) 741-2134
F: (615) 741-1446
E: rep.craig.fitzhugh@capitol.tn.gov

Tennessee

Clerk of the House

Mr. Joe McCord
Chief Clerk of the House
State Capitol, 2nd Floor
Nashville, TN 37243
P: (615) 741-2901
E: joe.mccord
@capitol.tn.gov

Members of the House

Akbari, Raumesh (D, 91)
Suite 35, Legislative Plaza
301 6th Avenue North
Nashville, TN 37243
P: (615) 741-3830
F: (615) 253-0335
E: rep.raumesh.akbari
@capitol.tn.gov

Alexander, David (R, 39)
Suite 107, War Memorial Building
301 6th Avenue North
Nashville, TN 37243
P: (615) 741-8695
F: (615) 253-0314
E: rep.david.alexander
@capitol.tn.gov

Armstrong, Joe (D, 15)
Suite 33, Legislative Plaza
301 6th Avenue North
Nashville, TN 37243
P: (615) 741-0768
F: (615) 253-0316
E: rep.joe.armstrong
@capitol.tn.gov

Beck, Bill (D, 51)*
Suite 24, Legislative Plaza
301 6th Avenue North
Nashville, TN 37243
P: (615) 741-3229
F: (615) 253-0233
E: rep.bill.beck
@capitol.tn.gov

Brooks, Harry (R, 19)
Suite 117, War Memorial Building
301 6th Avenue North
Nashville, TN 37243
P: (615) 741-6879
F: (615) 253-0212
E: rep.harry.brooks
@capitol.tn.gov

Brooks, Kevin (R, 24)
Suite 103, War Memorial Building
301 6th Avenue North
Nashville, TN 37243
P: (615) 741-1350
F: (615) 253-0346
E: rep.kevin.brooks
@capitol.tn.gov

Butt, Sheila (R, 64)
Suite 106, War Memorial Building
301 6th Avenue North
Nashville, TN 37243
P: (615) 741-3005
F: (615) 253-0365
E: rep.sheila.butt
@capitol.tn.gov

Byrd, David (R, 71)*
Suite 110 War Memorial Building
301 6th Avenue North
Nashville, TN 37243
P: (615) 741-2190
F: (615) 253-0377
E: rep.david.byrd
@capitol.tn.gov

Calfee, Kent (R, 32)
Suite 219, War Memorial Building
301 6th Avenue North
Nashville, TN 37243
P: (615) 741-7658
F: (615) 253-0163
E: rep.kent.calfee
@capitol.tn.gov

Camper, Karen D. (D, 87)
Suite 32, Legislative Plaza
301 6th Avenue North
Nashville, TN 37243
P: (615) 741-1898
F: (615) 253-0211
E: rep.karen.camper
@capitol.tn.gov

Carr, Dale (R, 12)
Suite 107, War Memorial Building
301 6th Avenue North
Nashville, TN 37243
P: (615) 741-5981
F: (615) 253-0303
E: rep.dale.carr
@capitol.tn.gov

Carter, Mike (R, 29)
Suite G-3, War Memorial Building
301 6th Avenue North
Nashville, TN 37243
P: (615) 741-3025
F: (615) 253-0241
E: rep.mike.carter
@capitol.tn.gov

Casada, Glen (R, 63)
Suite 25, Legislative Plaza
301 6th Avenue North
Nashville, TN 37243
P: (615) 741-4389
F: (615) 253-0229
E: rep.glen.casada
@capitol.tn.gov

Clemmons, John (D, 55)*
Suite 38, Legislative Plaza
301 6th Avenue North
Nashville, TN 37243
P: (615) 741-4410
F: (615) 253-0202
E: rep.john.ray.clemmons
@capitol.tn.gov

Coley, Jim (R, 97)
Suite 207, War Memorial Building
301 6th Avenue North
Nashville, TN 37243
P: (651) 741-8201
F: (615) 253-0267
E: rep.jim.coley
@capitol.tn.gov

Cooper, Barbara Ward (D, 86)
Suite 38, Legislative Plaza
301 6th Avenue North
Nashville, TN 37243
P: (615) 741-4295
F: (615) 253-0327
E: rep.barbara.cooper
@capitol.tn.gov

Daniel, Martin (R, 18)*
Suite 109, War Memorial Building
301 6th Avenue North
Nashville, TN 37243
P: (615) 741-2287
F: (615) 253-0348
E: rep.martin.daniel
@capitol.tn.gov

DeBerry Jr., John J. (D, 90)
Suite 26, Legislative Plaza
301 6th Avenue North
Nashville, TN 37243
P: (615) 741-2239
F: (615) 253-0292
E: rep.john.deberry
@capitol.tn.gov

Doss, Barry (R, 70)
Suite 106, War Memorial Building
301 6th Avenue North
Nashville, TN 37243
P: (615) 741-7476
F: (615) 253-0258
E: rep.barry.doss
@capitol.tn.gov

Dunlap, Kevin (D, 43)*
Suite 32, Legislative Plaza
301 6th Avenue North
Nashville, TN 37243
P: (615) 741-1963
F: (615) 253-0207
E: rep.kevin.dunlap
@capitol.tn.gov

Dunn, Bill (R, 16)
Suite 115, War Memorial Building
301 6th Avenue North
Nashville, TN 37243
P: (615) 741-1721
F: (615) 253-0276
E: rep.bill.dunn
@capitol.tn.gov

Durham, Jeremy (R, 65)
Suite 102, War Memorial Building
301 6th Avenue North
Nashville, TN 37243
P: (615) 741-1864
F: (615) 253-0228
E: rep.jeremy.durham
@capitol.tn.gov

Eldridge, Jimmy A. (R, 73)
Suite 208, War Memorial Building
301 6th Avenue North
Nashville, TN 37243
P: (615) 741-7475
F: (615) 253-0373
E: rep.jimmy.eldridge
@capitol.tn.gov

Faison, Jeremy (R, 11)
Suite 202, War Memorial Building
301 6th Avenue North
Nashville, TN 37243
P: (615) 741-6871
F: (615) 253-0225
E: rep.jeremy.faison
@capitol.tn.gov

Farmer, Andrew (R, 17)
Suite 109, War Memorial Building
301 6th Avenue North
Nashville, TN 37243
P: (615) 741-4419
F: (615) 253-0203
E: rep.andrew.farmer@capitol.tn.gov

Favors, JoAnne (D, 28)
Suite 35, Legislative Plaza
301 6th Avenue North
Nashville, TN 37243
P: (615) 741-2702
F: (615) 253-0351
E: rep.joanne.favors@capitol.tn.gov

Fitzhugh, Craig (D, 82)
Suite 33, Legislative Plaza
301 6th Avenue North
Nashville, TN 37243
P: (615) 741-2134
F: (615) 741-1446
E: rep.craig.fitzhugh@capitol.tn.gov

Forgety, John (R, 23)
Suite 109, War Memorial Building
301 6th Avenue North
Nashville, TN 37243
P: (615) 741-1725
F: (615) 253-0309
E: rep.john.forgety@capitol.tn.gov

Gilmore, Brenda (D, 54)
Suite 26, Legislative Plaza
301 6th Avenue North
Nashville, TN 37243
P: (615) 741-1997
F: (615) 253-0361
E: rep.brenda.gilmore@capitol.tn.gov

Goins, Tilman (R, 10)
Suite 207, War Memorial Building
301 6th Avenue North
Nashville, TN 37243
P: (615) 741-6877
F: (615) 253-0182
E: rep.tilman.goins@capitol.tn.gov

Gravitt, Marc (R, 30)*
Suite 107, War Memorial Building
301 6th Avenue North
Nashville, TN 37243
P: (615) 741-1934
F: (615) 253-0271
E: rep.marc.gravitt@capitol.tn.gov

Halford, Curtis (R, 79)
Suite 108, War Memorial Building
301 6th Avenue North
Nashville, TN 37243
P: (615) 741-7478
F: (615) 253-0218
E: rep.curtis.halford@capitol.tn.gov

Hardaway, G. A. (D, 93)
Suite 37, Legislative Plaza
301 6th Avenue North
Nashville, TN 37243
P: (615) 741-5625
F: (615) 253-0185
E: rep.ga.hardaway@capitol.tn.gov

Harrison, Mike (R, 9)
Suite 206A, War Memorial Building
301 6th Avenue North
Nashville, TN 37243
P: (615) 741-7480
F: (615) 253-0307
E: rep.mike.harrison@capitol.tn.gov

Harwell, Beth (R, 56)
Suite 19, Legislative Plaza
301 6th Avenue North
Nashville, TN 37243
P: (615) 741-0709
F: (615) 741-4917
E: speaker.beth.harwell@capitol.tn.gov

Hawk, David (R, 5)
Suite 201, War Memorial Building
301 6th Avenue North
Nashville, TN 37243
P: (615) 741-7482
F: (615) 253-0210
E: rep.david.hawk@capitol.tn.gov

Haynes, Ryan A. (R, 14)
Suite 214, War Memorial Building
301 6th Avenue North
Nashville, TN 37243
P: (615) 741-2264
F: (615) 253-0317
E: rep.ryan.haynes@capitol.tn.gov

Hazlewood, Patsy (R, 27)*
Suite 20, Legislative Plaza
301 6th Avenue North
Nashville, TN 37243
P: (615) 741-2746
F: (615) 253-0304
E: rep.patsy.hazlewood@capitol.tn.gov

Hill, Matthew (R, 7)
Suite 23, Legislative Plaza
301 6th Avenue North
Nashville, TN 37243
P: (615) 741-2251
F: (615) 253-0299
E: rep.matthew.hill@capitol.tn.gov

Hill, Timothy (R, 3)
Suite 23, Legislative Plaza
301 6th Avenue North
Nashville, TN 37243
P: (615) 741-2050
F: (615) 253-0298
E: rep.timothy.hill@capitol.tn.gov

Holsclaw Jr., John (R, 4)*
Suite G-24, War Memorial Building
301 6th Avenue North
Nashville, TN 37243
P: (615) 741-7450
F: (615) 253-0310
E: rep.john.holsclaw@capitol.tn.gov

Holt, Andy (R, 76)
Suite 205, War Memorial Building
301 6th Avenue North
Nashville, TN 37243
P: (615) 741-7847
F: (615) 253-0293
E: rep.andy.holt@capitol.tn.gov

Howell, Dan (R, 22)*
Suite 110, War Memorial Building
301 6th Avenue North
Nashville, TN 37243
P: (615) 741-7799
F: (615) 253-0252
E: rep.dan.howell@capitol.tn.gov

Hulsey, Bud (R, 2)*
Suite 204, War Memorial Building
301 6th Avenue North
Nashville, TN 37243
P: (615) 741-2886
F: (615) 253-0247
E: rep.bud.hulsey@capitol.tn.gov

Jernigan, Darren (D, 60)
Suite 24, Legislative Plaza
301 6th Avenue North
Nashville, TN 37243
P: (615)741-6959
E: rep.darren.jernigan@capitol.tn.gov

Johnson, Curtis G. (R, 68)
Suite 15, Legislative Plaza
301 6th Avenue North
Nashville, TN 37243
P: (615) 741-4341
F: (615) 253-0269
E: rep.curtis.johnson@capitol.tn.gov

Jones, Sherry (D, 59)
Suite 26, Legislative Plaza
301 6th Avenue North
Nashville, TN 37243
P: (615) 741-2035
F: (615) 253-0290
E: rep.sherry.jones@capitol.tn.gov

Kane, Roger (R, 89)
Suite 202A, War Memorial Building
301 6th Avenue North
Nashville, TN 37243
P: (615) 741-4110
E: rep.roger.kane@capitol.tn.gov

Keisling, Kelly (R, 38)
Suite 108, War Memorial Building
301 6th Avenue North
Nashville, TN 37243
P: (615) 741-6852
F: (615) 253-0234
E: rep.kelly.keisling@capitol.tn.gov

Kumar, Sabi (R, 66)*
Suite G-28, War Memorial Building
301 6th Avenue North
Nashville, TN 37243
P: (615) 741-2860
F: (615) 253-0283
E: rep.sabi.kumar@capitol.tn.gov

Lamberth, William (R, 44)
Suite 22, Legislative Plaza
301 6th Avenue North
Nashville, TN 37243
P: (615) 741-1980
F: (615) 253-0336
E: rep.william.lamberth@capitol.tn.gov

Littleton, Mary (R, 78)
Suite 104, War Memorial Building
301 6th Avenue North
Nashville, TN 37243
P: (615) 741-7477
E: rep.mary.littleton@capitol.tn.gov

Tennessee

Lollar, Ron (R, 99)
Suite 214, War Memorial Building
301 6th Avenue North
Nashville, TN 37243
P: (615) 741-7084
F: (615) 253-0294
E: rep.ron.lollar@capitol.tn.gov

Love Jr., Harold M. (D, 58)
Suite 35, Legislative Plaza
301 6th Avenue North
Nashville, TN 37243
P: (615) 741-3831
F: (615) 253-0323
E: rep.harold.love@capitol.tn.gov

Lundberg, Jon (R, 1)
Suite 20, Legislative Plaza
301 6th Avenue North
Nashville, TN 37243
P: (615) 741-7623
F: (615) 253-0272
E: rep.jon.lundberg@capitol.tn.gov

Lynn, Susan M. (R, 57)
Suite 104, War Memorial Building
301 6th Avenue North
Nashville, TN 37243
P: (615) 741-7462
F: (615) 253-0353
E: rep.susan.lynn@capitol.tn.gov

Marsh, Pat (R, 62)
Suite G19-A, War Memorial Building
301 6th Avenue North
Nashville, TN 37243
P: (615) 741-6824
F: (615) 253-0344
E: rep.pat.marsh@capitol.tn.gov

Matheny, Judd (R, 47)
Suite 215, War Memorial Building
301 6th Avenue North
Nashville, TN 37243
P: (615) 741-7448
F: (615) 253-0226
E: rep.judd.matheny@capitol.tn.gov

Matlock, Jimmy (R, 21)
Suite 219, War Memorial Building
301 6th Avenue North
Nashville, TN 37243
P: (615) 741-3736
F: (615) 253-0312
E: rep.jimmy.matlock@capitol.tn.gov

McCormick, Gerald (R, 26)
Suite 18A, Legislative Plaza
301 6th Avenue North
Nashville, TN 37243
P: (615) 741-2548
F: (615) 253-0305
E: rep.gerald.mccormick@capitol.tn.gov

McDaniel, Steve (R, 72)
Suite 18, Legislative Plaza
301 6th Avenue North
Nashville, TN 37243
P: (615) 741-0750
F: (615) 253-0213
E: rep.steve.mcdaniel@capitol.tn.gov

McManus, Steve (R, 96)
Suite 20, Legislative Plaza
301 6th Avenue North
Nashville, TN 37243
P: (615) 741-1920
F: (615) 253-0232
E: rep.steve.mcmanus@capitol.tn.gov

Miller, Larry J. (D, 88)
Suite 36, Legislative Plaza
301 6th Avenue North
Nashville, TN 37243
P: (615) 741-4453
F: (615) 253-0329
E: rep.larry.miller@capitol.tn.gov

Mitchell, Bo (D, 50)
Suite 37, Legislative Plaza
301 6th Avenue North
Nashville, TN 37243
P: (615) 741-4317
E: rep.bo.mitchell@capitol.tn.gov

Moody, Debra (R, 81)
Suite 205, War Memorial Building
301 6th Avenue North
Nashville, TN 37243
P: (615) 741-3774
E: rep.debra.moody@capitol.tn.gov

Parkinson, Antonio (D, 98)
Suite 36B, Legislative Plaza
301 6th Avenue North
Nashville, TN 37243
P: (615) 741-4575
F: (615) 253-0347
E: rep.antonio.parkinson@capitol.tn.gov

Pitts, Joe (D, 67)
Suite 32, Legislative Plaza
301 6th Avenue North
Nashville, TN 37243
P: (615) 741-2043
F: (615) 253-0200
E: rep.joe.pitts@capitol.tn.gov

Pody, Mark (R, 46)
Suite 203, War Memorial Building
301 6th Avenue North
Nashville, TN 37243
P: (615) 741-7086
F: (615) 253-0206
E: rep.mark.pody@capitol.tn.gov

Powell, Jason (D, 53)
Suite 34, Legislative Plaza
301 6th Avenue North
Nashville, TN 37243
P: (615) 741-6861
E: rep.jason.powell@capitol.tn.gov

Powers, Dennis (R, 36)
Suite G-27, War Memorial Building
301 6th Avenue North
Nashville, TN 37243
P: (615) 741-3335
F: (615) 253-0296
E: rep.dennis.powers@capitol.tn.gov

Ragan, John (R, 33)
Suite G-24, War Memorial Building
301 6th Avenue North
Nashville, TN 37243
P: (615) 741-4400
F: (615) 253-0297
E: rep.john.ragan@capitol.tn.gov

Ramsey, Bob (R, 20)
Suite 212, War Memorial Building
301 6th Avenue North
Nashville, TN 37243
P: (615) 741-3560
F: (615) 253-0376
E: rep.bob.ramsey@capitol.tn.gov

Reedy, Jay (R, 74)*
Suite 22, Legislative Plaza
301 6th Avenue North
Nashville, TN 37243
P: (615) 741-7098
F: (615) 253-0315
E: rep.jay.reedy@capitol.tn.gov

Rogers, Courtney (R, 45)
Suite 110A, War Memorial Building
301 6th Avenue North
Nashville, TN 37243
P: (615) 741-3893
F: (615) 253-0350
E: rep.courtney.rogers@capitol.tn.gov

Sanderson, Bill (R, 77)
Suite 204, War Memorial Building
301 6th Avenue North
Nashville, TN 37243
P: (615) 741-0718
F: (615) 253-0214
E: rep.bill.sanderson@capitol.tn.gov

Sargent, Charles Michael (R, 61)
Suite 206, War Memorial Building
301 6th Avenue North
Nashville, TN 37243
P: (615) 741-6808
F: (615) 253-0217
E: rep.charles.sargent@capitol.tn.gov

Sexton, Cameron (R, 25)
Suite 114, War Memorial Building
301 6th Avenue North
Nashville, TN 37243
P: (615) 741-2343
F: (615) 253-0230
E: rep.cameron.sexton@capitol.tn.gov

Sexton, Jerry (R, 35)*
Suite 113, War Memorial Building
301 6th Avenue North
Nashville, TN 37243
P: (615) 741-2534
F: (615) 253-0273
E: rep.jerry.sexton@capitol.tn.gov

Shaw, Johnny (D, 80)
Suite 36C, Legislative Plaza
301 6th Avenue North
Nashville, TN 37243
P: (615) 741-4538
F: (615) 253-0356
E: rep.johnny.shaw@capitol.tn.gov

Shepard, David (D, 69)
Suite 34, Legislative Plaza
301 6th Avenue North
Nashville, TN 37243
P: (615) 741-3513
F: (615) 253-0244
E: rep.david.shepard
@capitol.tn.gov

Smith, Eddie (R, 13)*
Suite 207, War Memorial Building
301 6th Avenue North
Nashville, TN 37243
P: (615) 741-2031
E: rep.eddie.smith
@capitol.tn.gov

Sparks, Mike (R, 49)
Suite 113, War Memorial Building
301 6th Avenue North
Nashville, TN 37243
P: (615) 741-6829
F: (615) 253-0332
E: rep.mike.sparks
@capitol.tn.gov

Spivey, Billy (R, 92)
Suite 205, War Memorial Building
301 6th Avenue North
Nashville, TN 37243
P: (615) 741-4170
E: rep.billy.spivey
@capitol.tn.gov

Stewart, Mike (D, 52)
Suite 17, Legislative Plaza
301 6th Avenue North
Nashville, TN 37243
P: (615) 741-2184
F: (615) 253-0181
E: rep.mike.stewart
@capitol.tn.gov

Swann, Art (R, 8)
Suite G-19A, War Memorial Building
301 6th Avenue North
Nashville, TN 37243
P: (615) 741-5481
F: (615) 253-0220
E: rep.art.swann
@capitol.tn.gov

Terry, Bryan (R, 48)*
Suite 105, War Memorial Building
301 6th Avenue North
Nashville, TN 37243
P: (615) 741-2180
F: (615) 253-0372
E: rep.bryan.terry
@capitol.tn.gov

Todd, Curry (R, 95)
Suite 209, War Memorial Building
301 6th Avenue North
Nashville, TN 37243
P: (615) 741-1866
F: (615) 253-0208
E: rep.curry.todd
@capitol.tn.gov

Towns Jr., Joe (D, 84)
Suite 37, Legislative Plaza
301 6th Avenue North
Nashville, TN 37243
P: (615) 741-2189
F: (615) 253-0201
E: rep.joe.towns
@capitol.tn.gov

Travis, Ron (R, 31)
Suite G-3, War Memorial Building
301 6th Avenue North
Nashville, TN 37243
P: (615) 741-1450
F: (615) 253-0262
E: rep.ron.travis
@capitol.tn.gov

Turner, Johnnie (D, 85)
Suite 38, Legislative Plaza
301 6th Avenue North
Nashville, TN 37243
P: (615) 741-6954
F: (615) 253-0339
E: rep.johnnie.turner
@capitol.tn.gov

Van Huss, James (R, 6)
Suite 23, Legislative Plaza
301 6th Avenue North
Nashville, TN 37243
P: (615) 741-1717
F: (615) 253-0301
E: rep.james.vanhuss
@capitol.tn.gov

Weaver, Terri Lynn (R, 40)
Suite 105, War Memorial
301 6th Avenue North
Nashville, TN 37243
P: (615) 741-2192
F: (615) 253-0378
E: rep.terri.lynn.weaver
@capitol.tn.gov

White, Dawn (R, 37)
Suite 209A, War Memorial Building
301 6th Avenue North
Nashville, TN 37243
P: (615) 741-6849
F: (615) 253-0264
E: rep.dawn.white
@capitol.tn.gov

White, Mark (R, 83)
Suite 217, War Memorial Building
301 6th Avenue North
Nashville, TN 37243
P: (615) 741-4415
F: (615) 253-0349
E: mark.white
@capitol.tn.gov

Wilburn, Leigh (R, 94)*
Suite 212, War Memorial Building
301 6th Avenue North
Nashville, TN 37243
P: (615) 741-6890
F: (615) 253-0380
E: rep.leigh.wilburn
@capitol.tn.gov

Williams, Ryan (R, 42)
Suite 114, War Memorial Building
301 6th Avenue North
Nashville, TN 37243
P: (615) 741-1875
F: (615) 253-0160
E: rep.ryan.williams
@capitol.tn.gov

Windle, John Mark (D, 41)
Suite 24, Legislative Plaza
301 6th Avenue North
Nashville, TN 37243
P: (615) 741-1260
F: (615) 253-0328
E: rep.john.windle
@capitol.tn.gov

Wirgau, Tim (R, 75)
Suite G-2, War Memorial Building
301 6th Avenue North
Nashville, TN 37243
P: (615) 741-6804
F: (615) 253-0239
E: rep.tim.wirgau
@capitol.tn.gov

Womick, Rick (R, 34)
Suite G-29, War Memorial Building
301 6th Avenue North
Nashville, TN 37243
P: (615) 741-2804
F: (615) 253-0322
E: rep.rick.womick
@capitol.tn.gov

Congress

Senate
Alexander, Lamar (R)
Corker, Bob (R)

House
Black, Diane (R, 6)
Blackburn, Marsha (R, 7)
Cohen, Steve I. (D, 9)
Cooper, Jim (D, 5)
DesJarlais, Scott (R, 4)
Duncan Jr., John J. (R, 2)
Fincher, Stephen (R, 8)
Fleischmann, Chuck (R, 3)
Roe, Phil (R, 1)

Texas

Executive

Governor

Hon. Greg Abbott (R)
Governor
P.O. Box 12428
Austin, TX 78711
P: (512) 463-2000
F: (512) 463-5571

Lieutenant Governor

Hon. Dan Patrick (R)
Lieutenant Governor
Capitol Station
P.O. Box 12068
Austin, TX 78711
P: (512) 463-0001
F: (512) 463-0677

Commissioner of Agriculture

Hon. Sid Miller (R)
Commissioner
P.O. Box 12847
Austin, TX 78711
P: (512) 463-7476
F: (512) 463-1104

Attorney General

Hon. Ken Paxton (R)
Attorney General
P.O. Box 12548
Austin, TX 78711
P: (512) 463-2100
F: (512) 475-2994
E: ken.paxton
@texasattorneygeneral.gov

Auditor

Hon. John Keel
(appointed by the Legislature)
State Auditor
1501 North Congress
P.O. Box 12067
Austin, TX 78711
P: (512) 936-9500
F: (512) 936-9400
E: eguzman@sao.state.tx.us

Commissioner of the General Land Office

Hon. George P. Bush (R)
Commissioner
1700 North Congress Avenue, Suite 935
Austin, TX 78701
P: (512) 463-5001

Railroad Commission

Hon. Christi Craddick
Commissioner
P.O. Box 12967
Austin, TX 78711
P: (512) 463-7140
F: (512) 463-7161
E: christi.craddick
@rrc.state.tx.us

Hon. David Porter
Commissioner
P.O. Box 12967
Austin, TX 78711
P: (512) 463-7131
F: (512) 463-7161
E: David.Porter
@rrc.state.tx.us

Hon. Ryan Sitton (R)
Commissioner
1701 North Congress Avenue
P.O. Box 12967
Austin, TX 78711
P: (512) 463-7144
F: (512) 462-7161
E: ryan.sitton
@rrc.state.tx.us

Secretary of State

Hon. Carlos Cascos
(appointed)
Secretary of State
1100 Congress Avenue
Austin, TX 78701
P: (512) 463-5770
F: (512) 475-2761
E: secretary@sos.texas.gov

Treasurer

Hon. Glenn Hegar (R)
Comptroller of Public Accounts
LBJ Building, 111 East 17th Street
P.O. Box 13528
Austin, TX 78711
P: (512) 463-4444
F: (512) 475-0352
E: glenn.hegar
@cpa.state.tx.us

Judiciary

Supreme Court (PE)

Mr. Blake A. Hawthorne
Clerk of the Court
201 West 14th Street, Room 104
P.O. Box 12248
Austin, TX 78711
P: (512) 463-1312
F: (512) 463-1365

Hon. Nathan L. Hecht
Chief Justice
Hon. Jeffrey S. Boyd
Hon. Jeff Brown
Hon. Phillip Devine
Hon. Paul Green
Hon. Eva Guzman
Hon. Phil Johnson
Hon. Debra Lehrmann
Hon. Don R. Willett

Legislative Senate

Senate President

Hon. Dan Patrick (R)
Lieutenant Governor
Capitol Station
P.O. Box 12068
Austin, TX 78711
P: (512) 463-0001
F: (512) 463-0677

President Pro Tempore of the Senate

Sen. Juan Hinojosa (D)
President Pro Tempore
Capitol Office Room 3E.10
P.O. Box 12068
Austin, TX 78711
P: (512) 463-0120
F: (512) 463-0229
E: Juan.Hinojosa
@senate.state.tx.us

Secretary of the Senate

Ms. Patsy Spaw
Secretary of the Senate
P.O. Box 12068
Austin, TX 78711
P: (512) 463-0100
F: (512) 463-6034
E: patsy.spaw
@senate.state.tx.us

Members of the Senate

Bettencourt, Paul (R, 7)*
Capitol Office Room E1.712
P.O. Box 12068
Austin, TX 78711
P: (512) 463-0107
E: Paul.Bettencourt
@senate.state.tx.us

Birdwell, Brian (R, 22)
Capitol Office Room E1.706
P.O. Box 12068
Austin, TX 78711
P: (512) 463-0122
F: (512) 475-3729
E: Brian.Birdwell
@senate.state.tx.us

Burton, Konni (R, 10)*
Capitol Office Room GE.7
P.O. Box 12068
Austin, TX 78711
P: (512) 463-0110
E: Konni.Burton
@senate.state.tx.us

Campbell, Donna (R, 25)
Capitol Office Room 3E.8
P.O. Box 12068
Austin, TX 78711
P: (512) 463-0125
F: (512) 463-7794
E: Donna.Campbell
@senate.state.tx.us

Creighton, Brandon (R, 4)
Capitol Office Room E1.606
P.O. Box 12068
Austin, TX 78711
P: (512) 463-0104
E: Brandon.Creighton
@senate.state.tx.us

Ellis, Rodney (D, 13)
Capitol Office Room 3E.6
P.O. Box 12068
Austin, TX 78711
P: (512) 463-0113
F: (512) 463-0006
E: Rodney.Ellis
@senate.state.tx.us

Eltife, Kevin (R, 1)
Capitol Office Room 3E.16
P.O. Box 12068
Austin, TX 78711
P: (512) 463-0101
F: (512) 475-3751
E: Kevin.Eltife
@senate.state.tx.us

Estes, Craig (R, 30)
Capitol Office Room 3E.18
P.O. Box 12068
Austin, TX 78711
P: (512) 463-0130
F: (512) 463-8874
E: Craig.Estes
@senate.state.tx.us

Fraser, Troy (R, 24)
Capitol Office Room 1E.12
P.O. Box 12068
Austin, TX 78711
P: (512) 463-0124
E: Troy.Fraser
@senate.state.tx.us

Garcia, Sylvia (D, 6)
Capitol Office Room 3E.12
P.O. Box 12068
Austin, TX 78711
P: (512) 463-0106
E: Sylvia.Garcia
@senate.state.tx.us

Hall, Bob (R, 2)*
Capitol Office Room E1.808
P.O. Box 12068
Austin, TX 78711
P: (512) 463-0102
E: Bob.Hall
@senate.state.tx.us

Hancock, Kelly (R, 9)
Capitol Office Room 1E.9
P.O. Box 12068
Austin, TX 78711
P: (512) 463-0109
E: Kelly.Hancock
@senate.state.tx.us

Hinojosa, Juan (D, 20)
Capitol Office Room 3E.10
P.O. Box 12068
Austin, TX 78711
P: (512) 463-0120
F: (512) 463-0229
E: Juan.Hinojosa
@senate.state.tx.us

Huffines, Don (R, 16)*
Capitol Office Room E1.608
P.O. Box 12068
Austin, TX 78711
P: (512) 463-0116
E: Don.Huffines
@senate.state.tx.us

Huffman, Joan (R, 17)
Capitol Office Room 1E.15
P.O. Box 12068
Austin, TX 78711
P: (512) 463-0117
E: Joan.Huffman
@senate.state.tx.us

Kolkhorst, Lois W. (R, 18)
Capitol Office Room 3E.2
P.O. Box 12068
Austin, TX 78768
P: (512) 463-0118
E: Lois.Kolkhorst
@senate.state.tx.us

Lucio Jr., Eddie (D, 27)
Capitol Office Room 3S.5
P.O. Box 12068
Austin, TX 78711
P: (512) 463-0127
F: (512) 463-0061
E: Eddie.Lucio
@senate.state.tx.us

Menendez, Jose (D, 26)
Capitol Office Room GW.5
P.O. Box 2910
Austin, TX 78768
P: (512) 463-0126
E: Jose.Menendez
@house.state.tx.us

Nelson, Jane (R, 12)
Capitol Office Room 1E.5
P.O. Box 12068
Austin, TX 78711
P: (512) 463-0112
F: (512) 463-0923
E: Jane.Nelson
@senate.state.tx.us

Nichols, Robert (R, 3)
Capitol Office Room E1.704
P.O. Box 12068
Austin, TX 78711
P: (512) 463-0103
E: Robert.Nichols
@senate.state.tx.us

Perry, Charles Lee (R, 28)
Capitol Office Room E1.810
P.O. Box 12068
Austin, TX 78768
P: (512) 463-0128
E: Charles.Perry
@senate.state.tx.us

Rodriguez, Jose (D, 29)
Capitol Office Room E1.610
P.O. Box 12068
Austin, TX 78711
P: (512) 463-0129
E: Jose.Rodriguez
@senate.state.tx.us

Schwertner, Charles (R, 5)
Capitol Office Room E1.806
P.O. Box 12068
Austin, TX 78711
P: (512) 463-0105
F: (512) 463-5713

Seliger, Kel (R, 31)
Capitol Office Room GE.4
P.O. Box 12068
Austin, TX 78711
P: (512) 463-0131
F: (512) 475-3733
E: Kel.Seliger
@senate.state.tx.us

Taylor, Larry (R, 11)
Capitol Office Room GE.5
P.O. Box 12068
Austin, TX 78711
P: (512) 463-0111
E: Larry.Taylor
@senate.state.tx.us

Taylor, Van (R, 8)
Capitol Office, Room E1.708
P.O. Box 2910
Austin, TX 78768
P: (512) 463-0108
F: (512) 463-1021
E: Van.Taylor
@house.state.tx.us

Uresti, Carlos (D, 19)
Capitol Office Room 4E.2
P.O. Box 12068
Austin, TX 78711
P: (512) 463-0119
F: (512) 463-1017
E: Carlos.Uresti
@senate.state.tx.us

Watson, Kirk (D, 14)
Capitol Office Room E1.804
P.O. Box 12068
Austin, TX 78711
P: (512) 463-0114
F: (512) 463-5949
E: Kirk.Watson
@senate.state.tx.us

West, Royce (D, 23)
Capitol Office Room 1E.3
P.O. Box 12068
Austin, TX 78711
P: (512) 463-0123
F: (512) 463-0299
E: Royce.West
@senate.state.tx.us

Whitmire, John (D, 15)
Capitol Office Room 1E.13
P.O. Box 12068
Austin, TX 78711
P: (512) 463-0115
E: John.Whitmire
@senate.state.tx.us

Zaffirini, Judith (D, 21)
Capitol Office Room 1E.14
P.O. Box 12068
Austin, TX 78711
P: (512) 463-0121
E: Judith.Zaffirini
@senate.state.tx.us

House

Speaker of the House

Rep. Joe Straus (R)
Speaker
Capitol Office Room CAP 2W.13
P.O. Box 2910
Austin, TX 78768
P: (512) 463-1000
F: (512) 463-0675
E: Joe.Straus
@house.state.tx.us

Speaker Pro Tempore of the House

Rep. Dennis Bonnen (R)
Speaker Pro Tempore
Capitol Office Room 1W.6
P.O. Box 2910
Austin, TX 78768
P: (512) 463-0564
F: (512) 463-8414
E: Dennis.Bonnen
@house.state.tx.us

Clerk of the House

Mr. Robert Haney
Chief Clerk of the House
Capitol Room 2W.29
P.O. Box 2910
Austin, TX 78768
P: (512) 463-0845
F: (512) 463-5896
E: robert.haney
@house.state.tx.us

Members of the House

Allen, Alma A. (D, 131)
Capitol Office Room E1.506
P.O. Box 2910
Austin, TX 78768
P: (512) 463-0744
F: (512) 463-0761
E: Alma.Allen
@house.state.tx.us

Texas

Alonzo, Roberto R. (D, 104)
Capitol Office Room CAP 1N.12
P.O. Box 2910
Austin, TX 78768
P: (512) 463-0408
F: (512) 463-1817
E: Roberto.Alonzo@house.state.tx.us

Alvarado, Carol (D, 145)
Capitol Office Room E2.808
P.O. Box 2910
Austin, TX 78768
P: (512) 463-0732
F: (512) 463-4781
E: Carol.Alvarado@house.state.tx.us

Anchia, Rafael (D, 103)
Capitol Office Room 4N.6
P.O. Box 2910
Austin, TX 78768
P: (512) 463-0746
F: (512) 463-0044
E: Rafael.Anchia@house.state.tx.us

Anderson, Charles (R, 56)
Capitol Office Room GW.8
P.O. Box 2910
Austin, TX 78768
P: (512) 463-0135
F: (512) 463-0642
E: Charles.Anderson@house.state.tx.us

Anderson, Rodney (R, 105)
Capitol Office Room E1.424
P.O. Box 2910
Austin, TX 78768
P: (512) 463-0641
F: (512) 463-1130
E: Rodney.Anderson@house.state.tx.us

Ashby, Trent (R, 57)
Capitol Office Room E2.414
P.O. Box 2910
Austin, TX 78768
P: (512) 463-0508
F: (512) 463-5896
E: Trent.Ashby@house.state.tx.us

Aycock, Jimmie Don (R, 54)
Capitol Office Room GW.18
P.O. Box 2910
Austin, TX 78768
P: (512) 463-0684
F: (512) 463-8987
E: JimmieDon.Aycock@house.state.tx.us

Bell, Cecil (R, 3)
Capitol Office Room E2.710
P.O. Box 2910
Austin, TX 78768
P: (512) 463-0650
F: (512) 463-0575
E: Cecil.Bell@house.state.tx.us

Bernal, Diego (D, 123)*
Capitol Office, Room E2.806
P.O. Box 2910
Austin, TX 78768
P: (512) 463-0532
E: Diego.Bernal@house.state.tx.us

Blanco, Cesar (D, 76)*
Capitol Office Room E1.218
P.O. Box 2910
Austin, TX 78768
P: (512) 463-0622
F: (512) 463-0931
E: Cesar.Blanco@house.state.tx.us

Bohac, Dwayne (R, 138)
Capitol Office Room GS.6
P.O. Box 2910
Austin, TX 78768
P: (512) 463-0727
F: (512) 463-0681
E: Dwayne.Bohac@house.state.tx.us

Bonnen, Dennis (R, 25)
Capitol Office Room 1W.6
P.O. Box 2910
Austin, TX 78768
P: (512) 463-0564
F: (512) 463-8414
E: Dennis.Bonnen@house.state.tx.us

Bonnen, Greg (R, 24)
Capitol Office Room E2.504
P.O. Box 2910
Austin, TX 78768
P: (512) 463-0729
E: Greg.Bonnen@house.state.tx.us

Burkett, Cindy (R, 113)
Capitol Office Room E2.322
P.O. Box 2910
Austin, TX 78768
P: (512) 463-0464
F: (512) 463-9295
E: Cindy.Burkett@house.state.tx.us

Burns, DeWayne (R, 58)*
Capitol Office Room E2.804
P.O. Box 2910
Austin, TX 78768
P: (512) 463-0538
F: (512) 463-0897
E: DeWayne.Burns@house.state.tx.us

Burrows, Dustin (R, 83)*
Capitol Office Room E2.820
P.O. Box 2910
Austin, TX 78768
P: (512) 463-0542
F: (512) 463-0671
E: Dustin.Burrows@house.state.tx.us

Button, Angie Chen (R, 112)
Capitol Office, Room E2.910
P.O. Box 2910
Austin, TX 78768
P: (512) 463-0486
E: AngieChen.Button@house.state.tx.us

Canales, Terry (D, 40)
Capitol Office Room E2.816
P.O. Box 2910
Austin, TX 78768
P: (512) 463-0426
F: (512) 463-0043
E: Terry.Canales@house.state.tx.us

Capriglione, Giovanni (R, 98)
Capitol Office Room E2.714
P.O. Box 2910
Austin, TX 78768
P: (512) 463-0690
F: (512) 463-1004
E: Giovanni.Capriglione@house.state.tx.us

Clardy, Travis (R, 11)
Capitol Office Room E2.314
P.O. Box 2910
Austin, TX 78768
P: (512) 463-0592
F: (512) 463-8792
E: Travis.Clardy@house.state.tx.us

Coleman, Garnet F. (D, 147)
Capitol Office Room 4N.10
P.O. Box 2910
Austin, TX 78768
P: (512) 463-0524
F: (512) 463-1260
E: Garnet.Coleman@house.state.tx.us

Collier, Nicole (D, 95)
Capitol Office Room E2.508
P.O. Box 2910
Austin, TX 78768
P: (512) 463-0716
F: (512) 463-1516
E: Nicole.Collier@house.state.tx.us

Cook, Byron (R, 8)
Capitol Office Room GN.11
P.O. Box 2910
Austin, TX 78768
P: (512) 463-0730
F: (512) 463-2506
E: Byron.Cook@house.state.tx.us

Craddick, Tom R. (R, 82)
Capitol Office Room 1W.09
P.O. Box 2910
Austin, TX 78768
P: (512) 463-0500
F: (512) 463-7722
E: Tom.Craddick@house.state.tx.us

Crownover, Myra (R, 64)
Capitol Office Room 1N.10
P.O. Box 2910
Austin, TX 78768
P: (512) 463-0582
F: (512) 463-0471
E: Myra.Crownover@house.state.tx.us

Cyrier, John (R, 17)*
Capitol Office, Room E2.802
P.O. Box 2910
Austin, TX 78768
P: (512) 463-0682
F: (512) 463-9955
E: John.Cyrier@house.state.tx.us

Dale, Tony (R, 136)
Capitol Office Room E2.904
P.O. Box 2910
Austin, TX 78768
P: (512) 463-0696
F: (512) 463-9333
E: Tony.Dale@house.state.tx.us

Darby, Drew (R, 72)
Capitol Office Room E1.308
P.O. Box 2910
Austin, TX 78768
P: (512) 463-0331
F: (512) 463-0517
E: Drew.Darby@house.state.tx.us

Davis, Sarah (R, 134)
Capitol Office Room E2.310
P.O. Box 2910
Austin, TX 78768
P: (512) 463-0389
F: (512) 463-1374
E: Sarah.Davis
@house.state.tx.us

Davis, Yvonne (D, 111)
Capitol Office Room 4N.9
P.O. Box 2910
Austin, TX 78768
P: (512) 463-0598
F: (512) 463-2297
E: Yvonne.Davis
@house.state.tx.us

Deshotel, Joe D. (D, 22)
Capitol Office Room GW.12
P.O. Box 2910
Austin, TX 78768
P: (512) 463-0662
F: (512) 463-8381
E: Joe.Deshotel
@house.state.tx.us

Dukes, Dawnna (D, 46)
Capitol Office Room 1W.2
P.O. Box 2910
Austin, TX 78768
P: (512) 463-0506
F: (512) 463-7864
E: Dawnna.Dukes
@house.state.tx.us

Dutton Jr., Harold V. (D, 142)
Capitol Office Room 3N.5
P.O. Box 2910
Austin, TX 78768
P: (512) 463-0510
F: (512) 463-8333
E: Harold.Dutton
@house.state.tx.us

Elkins, Gary (R, 135)
Capitol Office Room 4N.03
P.O. Box 2910
Austin, TX 78768
P: (512) 463-0722
F: (512) 463-2331
E: Gary.Elkins
@house.state.tx.us

Faircloth, Wayne (R, 23)*
Capitol Office Room E2.812
P.O. Box 2910
Austin, TX 78768
P: (512) 463-0502
F: (512) 936-4260
E: Wayne.Faircloth
@house.state.tx.us

Fallon, Pat (R, 106)
Capitol Office Room E2.604
P.O. Box 2910
Austin, TX 78768
P: (512) 463-0694
F: (512) 463-1130
E: Pat.Fallon
@house.state.tx.us

Farias, Joe (D, 118)
Capitol Office Room 4S.4
P.O. Box 2910
Austin, TX 78768
P: (512) 463-0714
F: (512) 463-1458
E: Joe.Farias
@house.state.tx.us

Farney, Marsha (R, 20)
Capitol Office Room E2.606
P.O. Box 2910
Austin, TX 78768
P: (512) 463-0309
F: (512) 463-0049
E: Marsha.Farney
@house.state.tx.us

Farrar, Jessica C. (D, 148)
Capitol Office Room 1N.8
P.O. Box 2910
Austin, TX 78768
P: (512) 463-0620
F: (512) 463-0894
E: Jessica.Farrar
@house.state.tx.us

Fletcher, Allen (R, 130)
Capitol Office Room GW.4
P.O. Box 2910
Austin, TX 78768
P: (512) 463-0661
F: (512) 463-4130
E: Allen.Fletcher
@house.state.tx.us

Flynn, Dan (R, 2)
Capitol Office Room GN.7
P.O. Box 2910
Austin, TX 78768
P: (512) 463-0880
F: (512) 463-2188
E: Dan.Flynn
@house.state.tx.us

Frank, James (R, 69)
Capitol Office Room E2.304
P.O. Box 2910
Austin, TX 78768
P: (512) 463-0534
F: (512) 463-8161
E: James.Frank
@house.state.tx.us

Frullo, John (R, 84)
Capitol Office Room E2.608
P.O. Box 2910
Austin, TX 78768
P: (512) 463-0676
F: (512) 463-0072
E: John.Frullo
@house.state.tx.us

Galindo, Rick (R, 117)*
Capitol Office Room E1.410
P.O. Box 2910
Austin, TX 78768
P: (512) 463-0269
F: (512) 463-1096
E: Rick.Galindo
@house.state.tx.us

Geren, Charlie (R, 99)
Capitol Office Room GW.17
P.O. Box 2910
Austin, TX 78768
P: (512) 463-0610
F: (512) 463-8310
E: Charlie.Geren
@house.state.tx.us

Giddings, Helen (D, 109)
Capitol Office Room GW.11
P.O. Box 2910
Austin, TX 78768
P: (512) 463-0953
F: (512) 463-5887
E: Helen.Giddings
@house.state.tx.us

Goldman, Craig (R, 97)
Capitol Office Room E2.720
P.O. Box 2910
Austin, TX 78768
P: (512) 463-0608
F: (512) 463-8342
E: Craig.Goldman
@house.state.tx.us

Gonzales, Larry (R, 52)
Capitol Office Room E2.418
P.O. Box 2910
Austin, TX 78768
P: (512) 463-0670
F: (512) 463-1469
E: Larry.Gonzales
@house.state.tx.us

Gonzalez, Mary (D, 75)
Capitol Office Room E1.302
P.O. Box 2910
Austin, TX 78768
P: (512) 463-0613
F: (512) 463-1237
E: Mary.Gonzalez
@house.state.tx.us

Guerra, Bobby (D, 41)
Capitol Office Room E2.818
P.O. Box 2910
Austin, TX 78768
P: (512) 463-0578
F: (512) 463-1482
E: Bobby.Guerra
@house.state.tx.us

Guillen, Ryan (D, 31)
Capitol Office Room 4S.3
P.O. Box 2910
Austin, TX 78768
P: (512) 463-0416
F: (512) 463-1012
E: Ryan.Guillen
@house.state.tx.us

Gutierrez, Roland (D, 119)
Capitol Office Room GN.9
P.O. Box 2910
Austin, TX 78768
P: (512) 463-0452
F: (512) 463-1447
E: Roland.Gutierrez
@house.state.tx.us

Harless, Patricia (R, 126)
Capitol Office Room E2.408
P.O. Box 2910
Austin, TX 78768
P: (512) 463-0496
F: (512) 463-1507
E: Patricia.Harless
@house.state.tx.us

Hernandez, Ana E. (D, 143)
Capitol Office Room 4S.2
P.O. Box 2910
Austin, TX 78768
P: (512) 463-0614
F: (512) 463-0612
E: Ana.Hernandez
@house.state.tx.us

Herrero, Abel (D, 34)
Capitol Office Room GW.6
P.O. Box 2910
Austin, TX 78768
P: (512) 463-0462
F: (512) 463-1705
E: Abel.Herrero
@house.state.tx.us

Howard, Donna (D, 48)
Capitol Office Room E1.420
P.O. Box 2910
Austin, TX 78768
P: (512) 463-0631
F: (512) 463-0901
E: Donna.Howard
@house.state.tx.us

Texas

Huberty, Daniel G. (R, 127)
Capitol Office, Room E2.722
P.O. Box 2910
Austin, TX 78768
P: (512) 463-0520
F: (512) 463-1606
E: Daniel.Huberty
@house.state.tx.us

Hughes, Bryan (R, 5)
Capitol Office Room 4S.5
P.O. Box 2910
Austin, TX 78768
P: (512) 463-0271
F: (512) 463-1515
E: Bryan.Hughes
@house.state.tx.us

Hunter, Todd A. (R, 32)
Capitol Office Room GW.5
P.O. Box 2910
Austin, TX 78768
P: (512) 463-0672
E: Todd.Hunter
@house.state.tx.us

Isaac, Jason (R, 45)
Capitol Office Room E1.414
P.O. Box 2910
Austin, TX 78768
P: (512) 463-0647
F: (512) 463-3573
E: Jason.Isaac
@house.state.tx.us

Israel, Celia (D, 50)*
Capitol Office Room E1.406
P.O. Box 2910
Austin, TX 78768
P: (512) 463-0821
E: Celia.Israel
@house.state.tx.us

Johnson, Eric (D, 100)
Capitol Office Room E1.204
P.O. Box 2910
Austin, TX 78768
P: (512) 463-0586
F: (512) 463-8147
E: Eric.Johnson
@house.state.tx.us

Kacal, Kyle (R, 12)
Capitol Office Room E2.420
P.O. Box 2910
Austin, TX 78768
P: (512) 463-0412
F: (512) 463-9059
E: Kyle.Kacal
@house.state.tx.us

Keffer, James L. (R, 60)
Capitol Office Room 1W.11
P.O. Box 2910
Austin, TX 78768
P: (512) 463-0656
F: (512) 478-8805
E: James.Keffer
@house.state.tx.us

Keough, Mark (R, 15)*
Capitol Office Room E2.402
P.O. Box 2910
Austin, TX 78768
P: (512) 463-0797
F: (512) 463-0898
E: Mark.Keough
@house.state.tx.us

King, Ken (R, 88)
Capitol Office Room E2.416
P.O. Box 2910
Austin, TX 78768
P: (512) 463-0736
F: (512) 463-0211
E: Ken.King
@house.state.tx.us

King, Phil (R, 61)
Capitol Office Room 1N.5
P.O. Box 2910
Austin, TX 78768
P: (512) 463-0738
F: (512) 463-1957
E: Phil.King
@house.state.tx.us

King, Susan (R, 71)
Capitol Office Room GN.12
P.O. Box 2910
Austin, TX 78768
P: (512) 463-0718
F: (512) 463-0994
E: Susan.King
@house.state.tx.us

King, Tracy O. (D, 80)
Capitol Office Room GW.07
P.O. Box 2910
Austin, TX 78768
P: (512) 463-0194
F: (512) 463-1220
E: Tracy.King
@house.state.tx.us

Klick, Stephanie (R, 91)
Capitol Office Room E2.716
P.O. Box 2910
Austin, TX 78768
P: (512) 463-0599
F: (512) 463-0751
E: Stephanie.Klick
@house.state.tx.us

Koop, Linda (R, 102)*
Capitol Office Room E1.512
P.O. Box 2910
Austin, TX 78768
P: (512) 463-0454
F: (512) 463-1121
E: Linda.Koop
@house.state.tx.us

Krause, Matt (R, 93)
Capitol Office Room E2.212
P.O. Box 2910
Austin, TX 78768
P: (512) 463-0562
F: (512) 463-2053
E: Matt.Krause
@house.state.tx.us

Kuempel, John (R, 44)
Capitol Office Room E2.422
P.O. Box 2910
Austin, TX 78768
P: (512) 463-0602
F: (512) 480-0391
E: John.Kuempel
@house.state.tx.us

Landgraf, Brooks (R, 81)*
Capitol Office Room E1.312
P.O. Box 2910
Austin, TX 78768
P: (512) 463-0546
F: (512) 463-8067
E: Brooks.Landgraf
@house.state.tx.us

Larson, Lyle T. (R, 122)
Capitol Office Room E2.406
P.O. Box 2910
Austin, TX 78768
P: (512) 463-0646
F: (512) 463-0893
E: Lyle.Larson
@house.state.tx.us

Laubenberg, Jodie (R, 89)
Capitol Office Room 1N.7
P.O. Box 2910
Austin, TX 78768
P: (512) 463-0186
F: (512) 463-5896
E: Jodie.Laubenberg
@house.state.tx.us

Leach, Jeff (R, 67)
Capitol Office Room E1.314
P.O. Box 2910
Austin, TX 78768
P: (512) 463-0544
F: (512) 463-9974
E: Jeff.Leach
@house.state.tx.us

Longoria, Oscar (D, 35)
Capitol Office Room EXT
E1.510
P.O. Box 2910
Austin, TX 78768
P: (512) 463-0645
F: (512) 463-0559
E: Oscar.Longoria
@house.state.tx.us

Lozano, Jose Manuel (D, 43)
Capitol Office Room E2.908
P.O. Box 2910
Austin, TX 78768
P: (512) 463-0463
F: (512) 463-1765
E: JoseManuel.Lozano
@house.state.tx.us

Lucio III, Eddie (D, 38)
Capitol Office Room E1.320
P.O. Box 2910
Austin, TX 78768
P: (512) 463-0606
F: (512) 463-0660
E: Eddie.Lucio
@house.state.tx.us

Marquez, Marisa (D, 77)
Capitol Office Room E2.822
P.O. Box 2910
Austin, TX 78768
P: (512) 463-0638
F: (512) 463-8908
E: Marisa.Marquez
@house.state.tx.us

Martinez, Armando (D, 39)
Capitol Office Room 4N.4
P.O. Box 2910
Austin, TX 78768
P: (512) 463-0530
F: (512) 463-0849
E: Armando.Martinez
@house.state.tx.us

Martinez Fischer, Trey (D, 116)
Capitol Office Room 1W.3
P.O. Box 2910
Austin, TX 78768
P: (512) 463-0616
F: (512) 463-4873
E: TreyMartinez.Fischer
@house.state.tx.us

McClendon, Ruth Jones (D, 120)
Capitol Office Room CAP 3S.02
P.O. Box 2910
Austin, TX 78768
P: (512) 463-0708
F: (512) 463-7071
E: RuthJones.McClendon
@house.state.tx.us

Metcalf, Will (R, 16)*
Capitol Office Room E2.704
P.O. Box 2910
Austin, TX 78768
P: (512) 463-0726
F: (512) 463-8428
E: Will.Metcalf
@house.state.tx.us

Meyer, Morgan (R, 108)*
Capitol Office Room E1.418
P.O. Box 2910
Austin, TX 78768
P: (512) 463-0367
F: (512) 463-0078

Miles, Borris L. (D, 146)
Capitol Office Room E2.718
P.O. Box 2910
Austin, TX 78768
P: (512) 463-0518
F: (512) 463-0941
E: Borris.Miles
@house.state.tx.us

Miller, Doug (R, 73)
Capitol Office Room GN.10
P.O. Box 2910
Austin, TX 78768
P: (512) 463-0325
E: Doug.Miller
@house.state.tx.us

Miller, Rick (R, 26)
Capitol Office Room E2.312
P.O. Box 2910
Austin, TX 78768
P: (512) 463-0710
F: (512) 463-0711
E: Rick.Miller
@house.state.tx.us

Moody, Joseph (D, 78)
Capitol Office Room E2.214
P.O. Box 2910
Austin, TX 78768
P: (512) 463-0728
F: (512) 463-0397
E: Joseph.Moody
@house.state.tx.us

Morrison, Geanie (R, 30)
Capitol Office Room 1N.9
P.O. Box 2910
Austin, TX 78768
P: (512) 463-0456
F: (512) 463-0158
E: Geanie.Morrison
@house.state.tx.us

Munoz Jr., Sergio (D, 36)
Capitol Office Room E1.508
P.O. Box 2910
Austin, TX 78768
P: (512) 463-0704
F: (512) 463-5364
E: Sergio.Munoz
@house.state.tx.us

Murphy, Jim (R, 133)
Capitol Office Room E1.408
P.O. Box 2910
Austin, TX 78768
P: (512) 463-0514
F: (512) 463-8715
E: Jim.Murphy
@house.state.tx.us

Murr, Andrew S. (R, 53)*
Capitol Office Room E1.412
P.O. Box 2910
Austin, TX 78768
P: (512) 463-0536
F: (512) 463-1449
E: Andrew.Murr
@house.state.tx.us

Naishtat, Elliott (D, 49)
Capitol Office Room GW.16
P.O. Box 2910
Austin, TX 78768
P: (512) 463-0668
F: (512) 463-8022
E: Elliott.Naishtat
@house.state.tx.us

Nevarez, Poncho (D, 74)
Capitol Office Room E1.306
P.O. Box 2910
Austin, TX 78768
P: (512) 463-0566
F: (512) 236-9408
E: Poncho.Nevarez
@house.state.tx.us

Oliveira, Rene O. (D, 37)
Capitol Office Room 3N.06
P.O. Box 2910
Austin, TX 78768
P: (512) 463-0640
F: (512) 463-8186
E: Rene.Oliveira
@house.state.tx.us

Otto, John C. (R, 18)
Capitol Office Room E1.504
P.O. Box 2910
Austin, TX 78768
P: (512) 463-0570
F: (512) 463-0315
E: John.Otto
@house.state.tx.us

Paddie, Chris (R, 9)
Capitol Office Room E2.412
P.O. Box 2910
Austin, TX 78768
P: (512) 463-0556
F: (512) 463-5896
E: Chris.Paddie
@house.state.tx.us

Parker, Tan (R, 63)
Capitol Office Room E2.602
P.O. Box 2910
Austin, TX 78768
P: (512) 463-0688
F: (512) 480-0694
E: Tan.Parker
@house.state.tx.us

Paul, Dennis (R, 129)*
Capitol Office Room E2.814
P.O. Box 2910
Austin, TX 78768
P: (512) 463-0734
F: (512) 479-6955
E: Dennis.Paul
@house.state.tx.us

Pena, Gilbert (R, 144)*
Capitol Office Room E1.416
P.O. Box 2910
Austin, TX 78768
P: (512) 463-0460
F: (512) 463-0763
E: Gilbert.Pena
@house.state.tx.us

Phelan, Dade (R, 21)*
Capitol Office Room E1.324
P.O. Box 2910
Austin, TX 78768
P: (512) 463-0706
F: (512) 463-1861
E: Dade.Phelan
@house.state.tx.us

Phillips, Larry (R, 62)
Capitol Office Room 4N.5
P.O. Box 2910
Austin, TX 78768
P: (512) 463-0297
F: (512) 463-1561
E: Larry.Phillips
@house.state.tx.us

Pickett, Joe C. (D, 79)
Capitol Office Room 1W.05
P.O. Box 2910
Austin, TX 78768
P: (512) 463-0596
F: (512) 463-6504
E: Joe.Pickett
@house.state.tx.us

Price, Walter (R, 87)
Capitol Office Room E2.610
P.O. Box 2910
Austin, TX 78768
P: (512) 463-0470
E: Walter.Price
@house.state.tx.us

Raney, John (R, 14)
Capitol Office, Room E2.706
P.O. Box 2910
Austin, TX 78768
P: (512) 463-0698
F: (512) 463-5109
E: John.Raney
@house.state.tx.us

Raymond, Richard Pena (D, 42)
Capitol Office Room 1W.4
P.O. Box 2910
Austin, TX 78768
P: (512) 463-0558
F: (512) 463-6296
E: Richard.Raymond
@house.state.tx.us

Reynolds, Ron (D, 27)
Capitol Office Room E2.306
P.O. Box 2910
Austin, TX 78768
P: (512) 463-0494
F: (512) 463-1403
E: Ron.Reynolds
@house.state.tx.us

Riddle, Debbie (R, 150)
Capitol Office Room 4N.7
P.O. Box 2910
Austin, TX 78768
P: (512) 463-0572
F: (512) 463-1908
E: Debbie.Riddle
@house.state.tx.us

Rinaldi, Matt (R, 115)*
Capitol Office Room E1.422
P.O. Box 2910
Austin, TX 78768
P: (512) 463-0468
F: (512) 463-1044
E: Matt.Rinaldi
@house.state.tx.us

Rodriguez, Eddie (D, 51)
Capitol Office Room 4S.6
P.O. Box 2910
Austin, TX 78768
P: (512) 463-0674
F: (512) 463-0314
E: Eddie.Rodriguez
@house.state.tx.us

Rodriguez, Justin (D, 125)
Capitol Office Room E1.212
P.O. Box 2910
Austin, TX 78768
P: (512) 463-0669
F: (512) 463-5074
E: Justin.Rodriguez
@house.state.tx.us

Texas

Romero Jr., Ramon (D, 90)*
Capitol Office Room E1.208
P.O. Box 2910
Austin, TX 78768
P: (512) 463-0740
F: (512) 463-1075
E: Ramon.Romero
@house.state.tx.us

Rose, Toni (D, 110)
Capitol Office Room E2.302
P.O. Box 2910
Austin, TX 78768
P: (512) 463-0664
F: (512) 463-0476
E: Toni.Rose
@house.state.tx.us

Sanford, Scott (R, 70)
Capitol Office Room E2.210
P.O. Box 2910
Austin, TX 78768
P: (512) 463-0356
F: (512) 463-0701
E: Scott.Sanford
@house.state.tx.us

Schaefer, Matt (R, 6)
Capitol Office Room E2.510
P.O. Box 2910
Austin, TX 78768
P: (512) 463-0584
E: Matt.Schaefer
@house.state.tx.us

Schofield, Mike (R, 132)*
Capitol Office Room E2.316
P.O. Box 2910
Austin, TX 78768
P: (512) 463-0528
F: (512) 463-7820
E: Mike.Schofield
@house.state.tx.us

Schubert, Leighton (R, 13)*
Captiol Office, Room E2.208
P.O. Box 2910
Austin, TX 78768
P: (512) 463-0600
F: (512) 463-5240
E: Leighton.Schubert
@house.state.tx.us

Shaheen, Matt (R, 66)*
Capitol Office Room E1.322
P.O. Box 2910
Austin, TX 78768
P: (512) 463-0594
F: (512) 463-1021
E: Matt.Shaheen
@house.state.tx.us

Sheets, Kenneth (R, 107)
Capitol Office Room E1.404
P.O. Box 2910
Austin, TX 78768
P: (512) 463-0244
F: (512) 463-9967
E: Kenneth.Sheets
@house.state.tx.us

Sheffield, J.D. (R, 59)
Capitol Office Room E2.320
P.O. Box 2910
Austin, TX 78768
P: (512) 463-0628
F: (512) 463-3644
E: JD.Sheffield
@house.state.tx.us

Simmons, Ron (R, 65)
Capitol Office Room E2.712
P.O. Box 2910
Austin, TX 78768
P: (512) 463-0478
F: (512) 463-2089
E: Ron.Simmons
@house.state.tx.us

Simpson, David P. (R, 7)
Capitol Office Room E2.502
P.O. Box 2910
Austin, TX 78768
P: (512) 463-0750
F: (512) 463-9085
E: David.Simpson
@house.state.tx.us

Smith, Wayne (R, 128)
Capitol Office Room GN.8
P.O. Box 2910
Austin, TX 78768
P: (512) 463-0733
F: (512) 463-1323
E: Wayne.Smith
@house.state.tx.us

Smithee, John T. (R, 86)
Capitol Ofice Room 1W.10
P.O. Box 2910
Austin, TX 78768
P: (512) 463-0702
F: (512) 476-7016
E: John.Smithee
@house.state.tx.us

Spitzer, Stuart (R, 4)*
Capitol Office Room E1.316
P.O. Box 2910
Austin, TX 78768
P: (512) 463-0458
F: (512) 463-2040
E: Stuart.Spitzer
@house.state.tx.us

Springer, Drew (R, 68)
Capitol Office Room E2.410
P.O. Box 2910
Austin, TX 78768
P: (512) 463-0526
F: (512) 463-1011
E: Drew.Springer
@house.state.tx.us

Stephenson, Phil (R, 85)
Capitol Office Room E2.906
P.O. Box 2910
Austin, TX 78768
P: (512) 463-0604
F: (512) 463-5244
E: Phil.Stephenson
@house.state.tx.us

Stickland, Jonathan (R, 92)
Capitol Office Room E1.402
P.O. Box 2910
Austin, TX 78768
P: (512) 463-0522
F: (512) 463-9529
E: Jonathan.Stickland
@house.state.tx.us

Straus, Joe (R, 121)
Capitol Office Room CAP
2W.13
P.O. Box 2910
Austin, TX 78768
P: (512) 463-1000
F: (512) 463-0675
E: Joe.Straus
@house.state.tx.us

Thompson, Ed (R, 29)
Capitol Office Room E2.506
P.O. Box 2910
Austin, TX 78768
P: (512) 463-0707
F: (512) 463-8717
E: Ed.Thompson
@house.state.tx.us

Thompson, Senfronia (D, 141)
Capitol Office Room 3S.6
P.O. Box 2910
Austin, TX 78768
P: (512) 463-0720
F: (512) 463-6306
E: Senfronia.Thompson
@house.state.tx.us

Tinderholt, Tony (R, 94)*
Capitol Office Room E1.216
P.O. Box 2910
Austin, TX 78768
P: (512) 463-0624
F: (512) 463-8386
E: Tony.Tinderholt
@house.state.tx.us

Turner, Chris (D, 101)
Capitol Office Room E2.318
P.O. Box 2910
Austin, TX 78768
P: (512) 463-0574
F: (512) 463-1481
E: Chris.Turner
@house.state.tx.us

Turner, Scott (R, 33)
Capitol Office Room E1.318
P.O. Box 2910
Austin, TX 78768
P: (512) 463-0484
F: (512) 463-7834
E: Scott.Turner
@house.state.tx.us

Turner, Sylvester (D, 139)
Capitol Office Room GW.15
P.O. Box 2910
Austin, TX 78768
P: (512) 463-0554
F: (512) 463-8380
E: Sylvester.Turner
@house.state.tx.us

VanDeaver, Gary (R, 1)*
Capitol Office Room E1.310
P.O. Box 2910
Austin, TX 78768
P: (512) 463-0692
F: (512) 463-0902
E: Gary.VanDeaver
@house.state.tx.us

Villalba, Jason (R, 114)
Capitol Office Room E2.404
P.O. Box 2910
Austin, TX 78768
P: (512) 463-0576
F: (512) 463-7827
E: Jason.Villalba
@house.state.tx.us

Vo, Hubert (D, 149)
Capitol Office Room 4N.8
P.O. Box 2910
Austin, TX 78768
P: (512) 463-0568
F: (512) 463-0548
E: Hubert.Vo
@house.state.tx.us

Walle, Armando Lucio (D, 140)
Capitol Office Room E1.304
P.O. Box 2910
Austin, TX 78768
P: (512) 463-0924
F: (512) 463-1510
E: ArmandoLucio.Walle
@house.state.tx.us

White, James E. (R, 19)
Capitol Office Room E2.204
P.O. Box 2910
Austin, TX 78768
P: (512) 463-0490
F: (512) 463-9059
E: James.White
@house.state.tx.us

White, Molly S. (R, 55)*
Capitol Office Room E2.702
P.O. Box 2910
Austin, TX 78768
P: (512) 463-0630
F: (512) 463-0937
E: Molly.White
@house.state.tx.us

Workman, Paul Daniel (R, 47)
Capitol Office Room E2.902
P.O. Box 2910
Austin, TX 78768
P: (512) 463-0652
F: (512) 463-0565
E: PaulDaniel.Workman
@house.state.tx.us

Wray, John (R, 10)*
Capitol Office Room E1.220
P.O. Box 2910
Austin, TX 78768
P: (512) 463-0516
F: (512) 463-1051
E: John.Wray
@house.state.tx.us

Wu, Gene (D, 137)
Capitol Office Room E2.810
P.O. Box 2910
Austin, TX 78768
P: (512) 463-0492
F: (512) 463-1182
E: Gene.Wu
@house.state.tx.us

Zedler, Bill (R, 96)
Capitol Office Room GS.2
P.O. Box 2910
Austin, TX 78768
P: (512) 463-0374
F: (512) 463-0364
E: Bill.Zedler
@house.state.tx.us

Zerwas, John (R, 28)
Capitol Office Room E2.308
P.O. Box 2910
Austin, TX 78768
P: (512) 463-0657
F: (512) 236-0713
E: John.Zerwas
@house.state.tx.us

Congress

Senate
Cornyn, John (R)
Cruz, Ted (R)

House
Babin, Brian (R, 36)
Barton, Joseph (R, 6)
Brady, Kevin (R, 8)
Burgess, Michael C. (R, 26)
Carter, John R. (R, 31)
Castro, Joaquin (D, 20)
Conaway, Mike (R, 11)
Cuellar, Henry (D, 28)
Culberson, John (R, 7)
Doggett, Lloyd (D, 35)
Farenthold, Blake (R, 27)
Flores, Bill (R, 17)
Gohmert, Louie B. (R, 1)
Granger, Kay (R, 12)
Green, Al (D, 9)
Green, Gene (D, 29)
Hensarling, Jeb (R, 5)
Hinojosa, Ruben (D, 15)
Hurd, Will (R, 23)
Jackson-Lee, Sheila (D, 18)
Johnson, Eddie Bernice (D, 30)
Johnson, Sam (R, 3)
Marchant, Kenny (R, 24)
McCaul, Michael (R, 10)
Neugebauer, Randy (R, 19)
Olson, Pete (R, 22)
O'Rourke, Beto (D, 16)
Poe, Ted (R, 2)
Ratcliffe, John (R, 4)
Sessions, Pete (R, 32)
Smith, Lamar S. (R, 21)
Thornberry, William M. (R, 13)
Veasey, Marc (D, 33)
Vela, Filemon (D, 34)
Weber, Randy (R, 14)
Williams, Roger (R, 25)

U.S. Virgin Islands

Executive

Governor

Hon. Kenneth Mapp (I)
Governor
Government House 21-22
Kongens Gade
St. Thomas, VI 00802
P: (340) 774-0001
F: (340) 693-4374

Lieutenant Governor

Hon. Osbert Potter (I)
Lieutenant Governor
1331 Kings Street, Suite101
Christiansted
St. Croix, VI 00802
P: (340) 773-6449
F: (340) 773-0330

Secretary of State

The U.S. Virgin Islands do not have the office of secretary of state. Some of the duties of the secretary of state are performed by the office of lieutenant governor.

Attorney General

Hon. Terri Griffiths (appointed)
Acting Attorney General
Department of Justice, G.E.R.S. Complex
34-38 Kronprinsdens Gade
St. Thomas, VI 00802
P: (340) 774-5666
F: (340) 774-9710

Treasurer

Hon. Laurel Payne (appointed)
Director of Treasury
2314 Kronprindsens Gade
Charlotte Amalie, VI 00802
P: (340) 774-4750
F: (340) 776-4028

Judiciary

Supreme Court (GA)

Ms. Veronica J. Handy
Clerk of the Court
P.O. Box 590
St. Thomas, VI 00804
P: (340) 774-2237
F: (340) 774-2258

Hon. Rhys S. Hodge
Chief Justice
Hon. Maria M. Cabret
Hon. Ive Arlington Swan

Legislative Senate

Senate President

Sen. Neville A. James (D)
Senate President
#1 Lagoon Street Complex
Frederiksted
St. Croix, VI 00804
P: (340) 712-2279
F: (340) 712-2384
E: njames@legvi.org

Vice President of the Senate

Sen. Janette Millin Young (D)
Vice President
Capitol Building, Charlotte Amalie
P.O. Box 1690
St. Thomas, VI 00804
P: (340) 693-3515
F: (340) 693-3633
E: jyoung@legvi.org

Secretary of the Senate

Sen. Janette Millin Young
Vice President
Capitol Building, Charlotte Amalie
P.O. Box 1690
St. Thomas, VI 00804
P: (340) 693-3515
F: (340) 693-3633
E: jyoung@legvi.org

Members of the Senate

Blyden, Marvin A. (D)*
Capitol Building, Charlotte Amalie
P.O. Box 1690
St. Thomas, VI 00804
P: (340) 774-0880
E: mblyden@legvi.org

Forde, Jean (D)*
Capitol Building, Charlotte Amalie
P.O. Box 1690
St. Thomas, VI 00804
P: (340) 774-0880
E: jforde@legvi.org

Francis Jr., Novelle E. (D,)*
#1 Lagoon Street Complex
Frederiksted
St. Croix, VI 00840
P: (340) 773-2424
E: nfrancis@legvi.org

Gittens, Kenneth (D)
#1 Lagoon Street Complex
Frederiksted
St. Croix, VI 00840
P: (340) 693-3573
E: kgittens@legvi.org

Graham, Clifford (D)
Capitol Building, Charlotte Amalie
P.O. Box 1690
St. Thomas, VI 00804
P: (340) 693-3631
F: (340) 693-3631
E: cgraham@legvi.org

Harrigan Sr., Justin (D)*
Capitol Building, Charlotte Amalie
P.O. Box 1690
St. Thomas, VI 00804
P: (340) 773-6663
F: (340) 692-9563
E: jharrington@legvi.org

Jackson, Myron D. (D)
Capitol Building, Charlotte Amalie
P.O. Box 1690
St. Thomas, VI 00804
P: (340) 693-3519
E: mjackson@legvi.org

James, Neville A. (D)
#1 Lagoon Street Complex
Frederiksted
St. Croix, VI 00804
P: (340) 712-2279
F: (340) 712-2384
E: njames@legvi.org

Liburd, Almando (I, At-Large)
#1 Lagoon Street Complex
Frederiksted
St. Croix, VI 00840
P: (340) 693-3546
F: (340) 712-2382
E: aliburd@legvi.org

Nelson, Terrence "Positive" (ICM,)
#1 Lagoon Street Complex
Frederiksted
St. Croix, VI 00850
P: (340) 712-2210
F: (340) 712-2374
E: tnelson@legvi.org

Rivera-O'Reilly, Nellie (I)
#1 Lagoon Street Complex
St. Croix, VI 00840
P: (340) 712-2222
F: (340) 712-2378
E: noreilly@legvi.org

Roach, Tregenza (I)
Capitol Building, Charlotte Amalie
P.O. Box 1690
St. Thomas, VI 00804
P: (340) 693-3706
F: (340) 693-3660
E: troach@legvi.org

Sanes, Sammuel (D)
#1 Lagoon Street Complex
St. Croix, VI 00840
P: (340) 712-2278
F: (340) 712-2380
E: ssanes@legvi.org

Vialet, Kurt (D)*
#1 Lagoon Street Complex
Frederiksted
St. Croix, VI 00840
P: (340) 773-2424
E: kvialet@legvi.org

Young, Janette Millin (D)
Capitol Building, Charlotte Amalie
P.O. Box 1690
St. Thomas, VI 00804
P: (340) 693-3515
F: (340) 693-3633
E: jyoung@legvi.org

Congress

House Delegate

Plaskett, Stacey (D, At-Large)

Utah

Executive

Governor

Hon. Gary R. Herbert (R)
Governor
State Capitol, Suite 200
Salt Lake City, UT 84114
P: (801) 538-1000
F: (801) 538-1557

Lieutenant Governor

Hon. Spencer J. Cox (R)
Lieutenant Governor
P.O. Box 142325
Salt Lake City, UT 84114
P: (801) 538-1041
F: (801) 538-1133

Secretary of State

Utah does not have the office of secretary of state. Some of the duties of the secretary of state are performed by the office of the lieutenant governor.

Attorney General

Hon. Sean D. Reyes (R)
Attorney General
State Capitol, Room 236
Salt Lake City, UT 84114
P: (801) 538-9600
F: (801) 538-1121
E: uag@utah.gov

Auditor

Hon. John Dougall (R)
State Auditor
East Office Building, Suite E310
P.O. Box 142310
Salt Lake City, UT 84114
P: (801) 538-1025
F: (801) 538-1383
E: jdougall@utah.gov

Treasurer

Hon. Richard K. Ellis (R)
State Treasurer
350 North State Street, Suite 180
P.O. Box 142315
Salt Lake City, UT 84114
P: (801) 538-1042
F: (801) 538-1465
E: sto@utah.gov

Judiciary

Supreme Court (MR)

Ms. Andrea Martinez
Clerk of the Supreme Court
450 South State Street, 5th Floor
P.O. Box 140210
Salt Lake City, UT 84114
P: (801) 238-7974
F: (801) 578-3999
E: andrearm@utcourts.gov

Hon. Matthew B. Durrant
Chief Justice
Hon. Christine M. Durham
Hon. Thomas R. Lee
Hon. Ronald E. Nehring
Hon. Jill N. Parrish

Legislative Senate

Senate President

Sen. Wayne Niederhauser (R)
Senate President
320 State Capitol
P.O. Box 145115
Salt Lake City, UT 84114
P: (801) 538-1035
F: (801) 326-1475
E: wniederhauser@le.utah.gov

Senate Majority Leader

Sen. Ralph Okerlund (R)
Majority Leader
320 State Capitol
P.O. Box 145115
Salt Lake City, UT 84114
P: (801) 538-1035
F: (801) 326-1475
E: rokerlund@le.utah.gov

Senate Minority Leader

Sen. Gene Davis (D)
Minority Leader
320 State Capitol
P.O. Box 145115
Salt Lake City, UT 84114
P: (801) 538-1035
F: (801) 326-1475
E: gdavis@le.utah.gov

Secretary of the Senate

Ms. Leslie D. McLean
Secretary of the Senate
320 State Capitol
P.O. Box 145115
Salt Lake City, UT 84114
P: (801) 538-1458
F: (801) 326-1475
E: lmclean@utahsenate.org

Members of the Senate

Adams, Stuart (R, 22)
320 State Capitol
P.O. Box 145115
Salt Lake City, UT 84114
P: (801) 538-1035
F: (801) 326-1475
E: jsadams@le.utah.gov

Bramble, Curtis S. (R, 16)
320 State Capitol
P.O. Box 145115
Salt Lake City, UT 84114
P: (801) 538-1035
F: (801) 326-1475
E: curt@cbramble.com

Christensen, Allen M. (R, 19)
320 State Capitol
P.O. Box 145115
Salt Lake City, UT 84114
P: (801) 538-1035
F: (801) 326-1475
E: achristensen@le.utah.gov

Dabakis, Jim (D, 2)
320 State Capitol
P.O. Box 145115
Salt Lake City, UT 84114
P: (801) 538-1035
F: (801) 326-1475
E: jdabakis@le.utah.gov

Davis, Gene (D, 3)
320 State Capitol
P.O. Box 145115
Salt Lake City, UT 84114
P: (801) 538-1035
F: (801) 326-1475
E: gdavis@le.utah.gov

Dayton, Margaret (R, 15)
320 State Capitol
P.O. Box 145115
Salt Lake City, UT 84114
P: (801) 538-1035
F: (801) 326-1475
E: mdayton@le.utah.gov

Escamilla, Luz (D, 1)
320 State Capitol
P.O. Box 145115
Salt Lake City, UT 84114
P: (801) 538-1035
F: (801) 326-1475
E: lescamilla@le.utah.gov

Harper, Wayne A. (R, 6)
320 State Capitol
P.O. Box 145115
Salt Lake City, UT 84114
P: (801) 538-1035
F: (801) 326-1475
E: wharper@le.utah.gov

Henderson, Deidre M. (R, 7)
320 State Capitol
P.O. Box 145115
Salt Lake City, UT 84114
P: (801) 538-1035
F: (801) 326-1475
E: dhenderson@le.utah.gov

Hillyard, Lyle W. (R, 25)
320 State Capitol
P.O. Box 145115
Salt Lake City, UT 84114
P: (801) 538-1035
F: (801) 326-1475
E: lhillyard@le.utah.gov

Hinkins, David P. (R, 27)
320 State Capitol
P.O. Box 145115
Salt Lake City, UT 84114
P: (801) 538-1035
F: (801) 326-1475
E: dhinkins@le.utah.gov

Iwamoto, Jani (D, 4)*
320 State Capitol
P.O. Box 145115
Salt Lake City, UT 84114
P: (801) 538-1035
F: (801) 326-1475
E: jiwamoto@le.utah.gov

Jackson, Alvin (R, 14)*
320 State Capitol
P.O. Box 145115
Salt Lake City, UT 84114
P: (801) 538-1035
F: (801) 326-1475
E: abjackson@le.utah.gov

Jenkins, Scott K. (R, 20)
320 State Capitol
P.O. Box 145115
Salt Lake City, UT 84114
P: (801) 538-1035
F: (801) 326-1475
E: sjenkins@le.utah.gov

Knudson, Peter C. (R, 17)
320 State Capitol
P.O. Box 145115
Salt Lake City, UT 84114
P: (801) 538-1035
F: (801) 326-1475
E: pknudson@le.utah.gov

Madsen, Mark B. (R, 13)
320 State Capitol
P.O. Box 145115
Salt Lake City, UT 84114
P: (801) 538-1035
F: (801) 326-1475
E: mmadsen@le.utah.gov

Mayne, Karen (D, 5)
320 State Capitol
P.O. Box 145115
Salt Lake City, UT 84114
P: (801) 538-1035
F: (801) 326-1475
E: kmayne@le.utah.gov

Millner, Ann (R, 18)*
320 State Capitol
P.O. Box 145115
Salt Lake City, UT 84114
P: (801) 538-1035
F: (801) 326-1475
E: amillner@le.utah.gov

Niederhauser, Wayne (R, 9)
320 State Capitol
P.O. Box 145115
Salt Lake City, UT 84114
P: (801) 538 1035
F: (801) 326-1475
E: wniederhauser@le.utah.gov

Okerlund, Ralph (R, 24)
320 State Capitol
P.O. Box 145115
Salt Lake City, UT 84114
P: (801) 538-1035
F: (801) 326-1475
E: rokerlund@le.utah.gov

Osmond, Aaron (R, 10)
320 State Capitol
P.O. Box 145115
Salt Lake City, UT 84114
P: (801) 538-1035
F: (801) 326-1475
E: aosmond@le.utah.gov

Shiozawa, Brian E. (R, 8)
320 State Capitol
P.O. Box 145115
Salt Lake City, UT 84114
P: (801) 538-1035
F: (801) 326-1475
E: bshiozawa@le.utah.gov

Stephenson, Howard A. (R, 11)
320 State Capitol
P.O. Box 145115
Salt Lake City, UT 84114
P: (801) 538-1035
F: (801) 326-1475
E: hstephenson@le.utah.gov

Stevenson, Jerry W. (R, 21)
320 State Capitol
P.O. Box 145115
Salt Lake City, UT 84114
P: (801) 538-1035
F: (801) 326-1475
E: jwstevenson@le.utah.gov

Thatcher, Daniel W. (R, 12)
320 State Capitol
P.O. Box 145115
Salt Lake City, UT 84114
P: (801) 538-1035
F: (801) 326-1475
E: dthatcher@le.utah.gov

Urquhart, Stephen H. (R, 29)
320 State Capitol
P.O. Box 145115
Salt Lake City, UT 84114
P: (801) 538-1035
F: (801) 326-1475
E: surquhart@le.utah.gov

Van Tassell, Kevin (R, 26)
320 State Capitol
P.O. Box 145115
Salt Lake City, UT 84114
P: (801) 538-1035
F: (801) 326-1475
E: kvantassell@le.utah.gov

Vickers, Evan J. (R, 28)
320 State Capitol
P.O. Box 145115
Salt Lake City, UT 84114
P: (801) 538-1035
F: (801) 326-1475
E: evickers@le.utah.gov

Weiler, Todd (R, 23)
320 State Capitol
P.O. Box 145115
Salt Lake City, UT 84114
P: (801) 538-1035
F: (801) 326-1475
E: tweiler@le.utah.gov

House

Speaker of the House

Rep. Gregory H. Hughes (R)
Speaker
350 North State, Suite 350
P.O. Box 145030
Salt Lake City, UT 84114
P: (801) 538-1029
F: (801) 326-1544
E: greghughes@le.utah.gov

House Majority Leader

Rep. James A. Dunnigan (R)
Majority Leader
350 North State, Suite 350
P.O. Box 145030
Salt Lake City, UT 84114
P: (801) 538-1029
F: (801) 326-1544
E: jdunnigan@le.utah.gov

House Minority Leader

Rep. Brian S. King (D)
Minority Leader
350 North State, Suite 350
P.O. Box 145030
Salt Lake City, UT 84114
P: (801) 538-1029
F: (801) 326-1544
E: briansking@le.utah.gov

Clerk of the House

Ms. Sandy D. Tenney
Chief Clerk of the House
350 North State, Suite 350
P.O. Box 145030
Salt Lake City, UT 84114
P: (801) 538-1029
F: (801) 326-1544
E: stenney@le.utah.gov

Members of the House

Anderegg, Jacob L. (R, 6)
350 North State, Suite 350
P.O. Box 145030
Salt Lake City, UT 84114
P: (801) 538-1029
F: (801) 326-1544
E: janderegg@le.utah.gov

Anderson, Johnny (R, 34)
350 North State, Suite 350
P.O. Box 145030
Salt Lake City, UT 84114
P: (801) 538-1029
F: (801) 326-1544
E: janderson34@le.utah.gov

Arent, Patrice (D, 36)
350 North State, Suite 350
P.O. Box 145030
Salt Lake City, UT 84114
P: (801) 538-1029
F: (801) 326-1544
E: parent@le.utah.gov

Barlow, Stewart (R, 17)
350 North State, Suite 350
P.O. Box 145030
Salt Lake City, UT 84114
P: (801) 538-1029
F: (801) 326-1544
E: sbarlow@le.utah.gov

Briscoe, Joel K. (D, 25)
350 North State, Suite 350
P.O. Box 145030
Salt Lake City, UT 84114
P: (801) 538-1029
F: (801) 326-1544
E: jbriscoe@le.utah.gov

Brown, Melvin R. (R, 53)
350 North State, Suite 350
P.O. Box 145030
Salt Lake City, UT 84114
P: (801) 538-1029
F: (801) 326-1544
E: melbrown@le.utah.gov

Chavez-Houck, Rebecca (D, 24)
350 North State, Suite 350
P.O. Box 145030
Salt Lake City, UT 84114
P: (801) 538-1029
F: (801) 326-1544
E: rchouck@le.utah.gov

Chew, Scott H. (R, 55)*
350 North State, Suite 350
P.O. Box 145030
Salt Lake City, UT 84114
P: (801) 538-1029
F: (801) 326-1544
E: scottchew@le.utah.gov

Christensen, LaVar (R, 32)
350 North State, Suite 350
P.O. Box 145030
Salt Lake City, UT 84114
P: (801) 538-1029
F: (801) 326-1544
E: lavarchristensen@le.utah.gov

Christofferson, Kay J. (R, 56)
350 North State, Suite 350
P.O. Box 145030
Salt Lake City, UT 84114
P: (801) 538-1029
F: (801) 326-1544
E: kchristofferson@le.utah.gov

Coleman, Kim (R, 42)*
350 North State, Suite 350
P.O. Box 145030
Salt Lake City, UT 84114
P: (801) 538-1029
F: (801) 326-1544
E: kimcoleman@le.utah.gov

Utah

Cox, Fred C. (R, 30)
350 North State, Suite 350
P.O. Box 145030
Salt Lake City, UT 84114
P: (801) 538-1029
F: (801) 326-1544
E: fredcox@le.utah.gov

Cox, Jon (R, 58)
350 North State, Suite 350
P.O. Box 145030
Salt Lake City, UT 84114
P: (801) 538-1029
F: (801) 326-1544
E: jcox@le.utah.gov

Cunningham, Rich (R, 50)
350 North State, Suite 350
P.O. Box 145030
Salt Lake City, UT 84114
P: (801) 538-1029
F: (801) 326-1544
E: rcunningham@le.utah.gov

Cutler, Bruce R. (R, 44)*
350 North State, Suite 350
P.O. Box 145030
Salt Lake City, UT 84114
P: (801) 538-1029
F: (801) 326-1544
E: brucecutler@le.utah.gov

Daw, Bradley M. (R, 60)
350 North State, Suite 350
P.O. Box 145030
Salt Lake City, UT 84114
P: (801) 538-1029
F: (801) 326-1544
E: bdaw@le.utah.gov

Dee, Brad L. (R, 11)
350 North State, Suite 350
P.O. Box 145030
Salt Lake City, UT 84114
P: (801) 538-1029
F: (801) 326-1544
E: bdee@le.utah.gov

DiCaro, Sophia M. (R, 31)*
350 North State, Suite 350
P.O. Box 145030
Salt Lake City, UT 84114
P: (801) 538-1029
F: (801) 326-1544
E: sdicaro@le.utah.gov

Draxler, Jack R. (R, 3)
350 North State, Suite 350
P.O. Box 145030
Salt Lake City, UT 84114
P: (801) 538-1029
F: (801) 326-1544
E: jdraxler@le.utah.gov

Duckworth, Susan (D, 22)
350 North State, Suite 350
P.O. Box 145030
Salt Lake City, UT 84114
P: (801) 538-1029
F: (801) 326-1544
E: sduckworth@le.utah.gov

Dunnigan, James A. (R, 39)
350 North State, Suite 350
P.O. Box 145030
Salt Lake City, UT 84114
P: (801) 538-1029
F: (801) 326-1544
E: jdunnigan@le.utah.gov

Edwards, Becky (R, 20)
350 North State, Suite 350
P.O. Box 145030
Salt Lake City, UT 84114
P: (801) 538-1029
F: (801) 326-1544
E: beckyedwards@le.utah.gov

Eliason, Steve (R, 45)
350 North State, Suite 350
P.O. Box 145030
Salt Lake City, UT 84114
P: (801) 538-1029
F: (801) 326-1544
E: seliason@le.utah.gov

Fawson, Justin L. (R, 7)
350 North State, Suite 350
P.O. Box 145030
Salt Lake City, UT 84114
P: (801) 538-1029
F: (801) 326-1544
E: justinfawson@le.utah.gov

Froerer, Gage (R, 8)
350 North State, Suite 350
P.O. Box 145030
Salt Lake City, UT 84114
P: (801) 538-1029
F: (801) 326-1544
E: gfroerer@le.utah.gov

Gibson, Francis D. (R, 65)
350 North State, Suite 350
P.O. Box 145030
Salt Lake City, UT 84114
P: (801) 538-1029
F: (801) 326-1544
E: fgibson@le.utah.gov

Greene, Brian M. (R, 57)
350 North State, Suite 350
P.O. Box 145030
Salt Lake City, UT 84114
P: (801) 538-1029
F: (801) 326-1544
E: bgreene@le.utah.gov

Grover, Keith (R, 61)
350 North State, Suite 350
P.O. Box 145030
Salt Lake City, UT 84114
P: (801) 538-1029
F: (801) 326-1544
E: keithgrover@le.utah.gov

Hall, Craig (R, 33)
350 North State, Suite 350
P.O. Box 145030
Salt Lake City, UT 84114
P: (801) 538-1029
F: (801) 326-1544
E: chall@le.utah.gov

Handy, Stephen G. (R, 16)
350 North State, Suite 350
P.O. Box 145030
Salt Lake City, UT 84114
P: (801) 538-1029
F: (801) 326-1544
E: stevehandy@le.utah.gov

Hawkes, Timothy D. (R, 18)*
350 North State, Suite 350
P.O. Box 145030
Salt Lake City, UT 84114
P: (801) 538-1029
F: (801) 326-1544
E: thawkes@le.utah.gov

Hollins, Sandra (D, 23)*
350 North State, Suite 350
P.O. Box 145030
Salt Lake City, UT 84114
P: (801) 538-1029
F: (801) 326-1544
E: shollins@le.utah.gov

Hughes, Gregory H. (R, 51)
350 North State, Suite 350
P.O. Box 145030
Salt Lake City, UT 84114
P: (801) 538-1029
F: (801) 326-1544
E: greghughes@le.utah.gov

Hutchings, Eric K. (R, 38)
350 North State, Suite 350
P.O. Box 145030
Salt Lake City, UT 84114
P: (801) 538-1029
F: (801) 326-1544
E: ehutchings@le.utah.gov

Ipson, Don L. (R, 75)
350 North State, Suite 350
P.O. Box 145030
Salt Lake City, UT 84114
P: (801) 538-1029
F: (801) 326-1544
E: dipson@le.utah.gov

Ivory, Ken (R, 47)
350 North State, Suite 350
P.O. Box 145030
Salt Lake City, UT 84114
P: (801) 538-1029
F: (801) 326-1544
E: kivory@le.utah.gov

Kennedy, Michael S. (R, 27)
350 North State, Suite 350
P.O. Box 145030
Salt Lake City, UT 84114
P: (801) 538-1029
F: (801) 326-1544
E: mikekennedy@le.utah.gov

King, Brad (D, 69)
350 North State, Suite 350
P.O. Box 145030
Salt Lake City, UT 84114
P: (801) 538-1029
F: (801) 326-1544
E: bking@le.utah.gov

King, Brian S. (D, 28)
350 North State, Suite 350
P.O. Box 145030
Salt Lake City, UT 84114
P: (801) 538-1029
F: (801) 326-1544
E: briansking@le.utah.gov

Knotwell, John (R, 52)
350 North State, Suite 350
P.O. Box 145030
Salt Lake City, UT 84114
P: (801) 538-1029
F: (801) 326-1544
E: jknotwell@le.utah.gov

Last, Bradley G. (R, 71)
350 North State, Suite 350
P.O. Box 145030
Salt Lake City, UT 84114
P: (801) 538-1029
F: (801) 326-1544
E: blast@le.utah.gov

Lifferth, David E. (R, 2)
350 North State, Suite 350
P.O. Box 145030
Salt Lake City, UT 84114
P: (801) 538-1029
F: (801) 326-1544
E: dlifferth@le.utah.gov

McCay, Daniel (R, 41)
350 North State, Suite 350
P.O. Box 145030
Salt Lake City, UT 84114
P: (801) 538-1029
F: (801) 326-1544
E: dmccay@le.utah.gov

McIff, Kay L. (R, 70)
350 North State, Suite 350
P.O. Box 145030
Salt Lake City, UT 84114
P: (801) 538-1029
F: (801) 326-1544
E: kaymciff@le.utah.gov

McKell, Mike K. (R, 66)
350 North State, Suite 350
P.O. Box 145030
Salt Lake City, UT 84114
P: (801) 538-1029
F: (801) 326-1544
E: mmckell@le.utah.gov

Miller, Justin J. (D, 40)*
350 North State, Suite 350
P.O. Box 145030
Salt Lake City, UT 84114
P: (801) 538-1029
F: (801) 326-1544
E: jjmiller@le.utah.gov

Moss, Carol Spackman (D, 37)
350 North State, Suite 350
P.O. Box 145030
Salt Lake City, UT 84114
P: (801) 538-1029
F: (801) 326-1544
E: csmoss@le.utah.gov

Nelson, Merrill F. (R, 68)
350 North State, Suite 350
P.O. Box 145030
Salt Lake City, UT 84114
P: (801) 538-1029
F: (801) 326-1544
E: mnelson@le.utah.gov

Noel, Michael E. (R, 73)
350 North State, Suite 350
P.O. Box 145030
Salt Lake City, UT 84114
P: (801) 538-1029
F: (801) 326-1544
E: mnoel@kanab.net

Oda, Curtis (R, 14)
350 North State, Suite 350
P.O. Box 145030
Salt Lake City, UT 84114
P: (801) 538-1029
F: (801) 326-1544
E: coda@le.utah.gov

Perry, Lee B. (R, 29)
350 North State, Suite 350
P.O. Box 145030
Salt Lake City, UT 84114
P: (801) 538-1029
F: (801) 326-1544
E: leeperry@le.utah.gov

Peterson, Jeremy A. (R, 9)
350 North State, Suite 350
P.O. Box 145030
Salt Lake City, UT 84114
P: (801) 538-1029
F: (801) 326-1544
E: jeremyapeterson@le.utah.gov

Peterson, Val (R, 59)
350 North State, Suite 350
P.O. Box 145030
Salt Lake City, UT 84114
P: (801) 538-1029
F: (801) 326-1544
E: vpeterson@le.utah.gov

Pitcher, Dixon M. (R, 10)
350 North State, Suite 350
P.O. Box 145030
Salt Lake City, UT 84114
P: (801) 538-1029
F: (801) 326-1475
E: dpitcher@le.utah.gov

Poulson, Marie H. (D, 46)
350 North State, Suite 350
P.O. Box 145030
Salt Lake City, UT 84114
P: (801) 538-1029
F: (801) 326-1544
E: mariepoulson@le.utah.gov

Powell, Kraig (R, 54)
350 North State, Suite 350
P.O. Box 145030
Salt Lake City, UT 84114
P: (801) 538-1029
F: (801) 326-1544
E: kraigpowell@le.utah.gov

Ray, Paul (R, 13)
350 North State, Suite 350
P.O. Box 145030
Salt Lake City, UT 84114
P: (801) 538-1029
F: (801) 326-1544
E: pray@le.utah.gov

Redd, Edward H. (R, 4)
350 North State, Suite 350
P.O. Box 145030
Salt Lake City, UT 84114
P: (801) 538-1029
F: (801) 326-1544
E: eredd@le.utah.gov

Roberts, Marc K. (R, 67)
350 North State, Suite 350
P.O. Box 145030
Salt Lake City, UT 84114
P: (801) 538-1029
F: (801) 326-1544
E: mroberts@le.utah.gov

Romero, Angela (D, 26)
350 North State, Suite 350
P.O. Box 145030
Salt Lake City, UT 84114
P: (801) 538-1029
F: (801) 326-1544
E: angelaromero@le.utah.gov

Sagers, Doug (R, 21)
350 North State, Suite 350
P.O. Box 145030
Salt Lake City, UT 84114
P: (801) 538-1029
F: (801) 326-1544
E: dougsagers@le.utah.gov

Sandall, Scott (R, 1)*
350 North State, Suite 350
P.O. Box 145030
Salt Lake City, UT 84114
P: (801) 538-1029
F: (801) 326-1544
E: ssandall@le.utah.gov

Sanpei, Dean (R, 63)
350 North State, Suite 350
P.O. Box 145030
Salt Lake City, UT 84114
P: (801) 538-1029
F: (801) 326-1544
E: dsanpei@le.utah.gov

Schultz, Mike (R, 12)*
350 North State, Suite 350
P.O. Box 145030
Salt Lake City, UT 84114
P: (801) 538-1029
F: (801) 326-1544
E: mikeschultz@le.utah.gov

Snow, V. Lowry (R, 74)
350 North State, Suite 350
P.O. Box 145030
Salt Lake City, UT 84114
P: (801) 538-1029
F: (801) 326-1544
E: vlsnow@le.utah.gov

Spendlove, Robert (R, 49)
350 North State, Suite 350
P.O. Box 145030
Salt Lake City, UT 84114
P: (801) 538-1029
F: (801) 326-1544
E: rspendlove@le.utah.gov

Stanard, Jon E. (R, 62)
350 North State, Suite 350
P.O. Box 145030
Salt Lake City, UT 84114
P: (801) 538-1029
F: (801) 326-1544
E: jstanard@le.utah.gov

Stratton, Keven J. (R, 48)
350 North State, Suite 350
P.O. Box 145030
Salt Lake City, UT 84114
P: (801) 538-1029
F: (801) 326-1544
E: kstratton@le.utah.gov

Tanner, Earl D. (R, 43)
350 North State, Suite 350
P.O. Box 145030
Salt Lake City, UT 84114
P: (801) 538-1029
F: (801) 326-1544
E: earltanner@le.utah.gov

Thurston, Norman (R, 64)*
350 North State, Suite 350
P.O. Box 145030
Salt Lake City, UT 84114
P: (801) 538-1029
F: (801) 326-1544
E: normthurston@le.utah.gov

Ward, Raymond (R, 19)*
350 North State, Suite 350
P.O. Box 145030
Salt Lake City, UT 84114
P: (801) 538-1029
F: (801) 326-1544
E: rayward@le.utah.gov

Webb, R. Curt (R, 5)
350 North State, Suite 350
P.O. Box 145030
Salt Lake City, UT 84114
P: (801) 538-1029
F: (801) 326-1544
E: curtwebb@le.utah.gov

Westwood, John R. (R, 72)
350 North State, Suite 350
P.O. Box 145030
Salt Lake City, UT 84114
P: (801) 538-1029
F: (801) 326-1544
E: jwestwood@le.utah.gov

Wheatley, Mark A. (D, 35)
350 North State, Suite 350
P.O. Box 145030
Salt Lake City, UT 84114
P: (801) 538-1029
F: (801) 326-1544
E: markwheatley@le.utah.gov

Wilson, Brad R. (R, 15)
350 North State, Suite 350
P.O. Box 145030
Salt Lake City, UT 84114
P: (801) 538-1029
F: (801) 326-1544
E: bradwilson@le.utah.gov

Utah

Congress

Senate

Hatch, Orrin G. (R)
Lee, Mike (R)

House

Bishop, Rob (R, 1)
Chaffetz, Jason E. (R, 3)
Love, Mia (R, 4)
Stewart, Chris (R, 2)

Vermont

Executive

Governor

Hon. Peter E. Shumlin (D)
Governor
109 State Street
Pavilion Office Building
Montpelier, VT 05609
P: (802) 828-3333
F: (802) 828-3339

Lieutenant Governor

Hon. Phil Scott (R)
Lieutenant Governor
115 State Street
Montpelier, VT 05633
P: (802) 828-2226
F: (802) 828-3198
E: pscott14@aol.com

Attorney General

Hon. William H. Sorrell (D)
Attorney General
109 State Street
Montpelier, VT 05609
P: (802) 828-3171
F: (802) 828-3187

Auditor

Hon. Douglas R. Hoffer (D)
State Auditor
132 State Street
Montpelier, VT 05633
P: (802) 828-1094
F: (802) 828-2198
E: doug.hoffer@state.vt.us

Secretary of State

Hon. Jim Condos (D)
Secretary of State
128 State Street
Montpelier, VT 05633
P: (802) 828-2148
F: (802) 828-2496
E: jim.condos@sec.state.vt.us

Treasurer

Hon. Elizabeth Pearce
State Treasurer
109 State Street
Montpelier, VT 05609
P: (802) 828-2301
F: (802) 828-2772
E: Beth.Pearce@state.vt.us

Judiciary

Supreme Court (MC)

Ms. Patricia Gabel
Court Administrator & Clerk
109 State Street
Montpelier, VT 05609
P: (802) 828-3278
F: (802) 828-4750

Hon. Paul L. Reiber
Chief Justice
Hon. John A. Dooley III
Hon. Harold Eaton
Hon. Beth Robinson
Hon. Marilyn S. Skoglund

Legislative Senate

Senate President

Hon. Phil Scott (R)
Lieutenant Governor
115 State Street
Montpelier, VT 05633
P: (802) 828-2226
F: (802) 828-3198
E: pscott14@aol.com

President Pro Tempore of the Senate

Sen. John F. Campbell (D)
President Pro Tempore
P.O. Box 1306
Quechee, VT 05059
P: (802) 295-6238
F: (802) 295-6344
E: jcampbell@leg.state.vt.us

Senate Majority Leader

Sen. Philip Baruth (D)
Majority Leader
87 Curtis Avenue
Burlington, VT 05408
P: (802) 503-5266
E: pbaruth@leg.state.vt.us

Senate Minority Leader

Sen. William T. Doyle (R)
Minority Leader
186 Murray Road
Montpelier, VT 05602
P: (802) 223-2851
E: wdoyle@leg.state.vt.us

Secretary of the Senate

Mr. John H. Bloomer Jr.
Secretary of the Senate
115 State Street
Montpelier, VT 05633
P: (802) 828-2241
F: (802) 828-1272
E: jbloomer@leg.state.vt.us

Members of the Senate

Ashe, Tim (D, SP4)
45 Lakeview Terrace
Burlington, VT 05401
P: (802) 318-0903
E: tashe@leg.state.vt.us

Ayer, Claire D. (D, SP1)
1020 Tritown Road
Addison, VT 05491
P: (802) 759-2748
E: cayer@leg.state.vt.us

Balint, Becca (D, SP12)*
271 South Main Street
Brattleboro, VT 05301
P: (802) 257-4162
E: bbalint@leg.state.vt.us

Baruth, Philip (D, SP4)
87 Curtis Avenue
Burlington, VT 05408
P: (802) 503-5266
E: pbaruth@leg.state.vt.us

Benning, Joe (R, SP3)
291 Happy Hill Road
P.O. Box 142
Lyndonville, VT 05851
P: (802) 626-3600
E: jbenning@leg.state.vt.us

Bray, Christopher A. (D, SP1)
829 South Street
New Haven, VT 05472
P: (802) 453-3444
F: (802) 329-2256
E: cbray@leg.state.vt.us

Campbell, John F. (D, SP13)
P.O. Box 1306
Quechee, VT 05059
P: (802) 295-6238
F: (802) 295-6344
E: jcampbell@leg.state.vt.us

Campion, Brian (D, SP2)
1292 West Road
Bennington, VT 05201
P: (802) 753-7705
E: bcampion@leg.state.vt.us

Collamore, Brian P. (R, SP10)*
124 Patricia Lane
Rutland, VT 05701
P: (802) 773-1365
E: bcollamore@leg.state.vt.us

Cummings, Ann E. (D, SP11)
24 Colonial Drive
Montpelier, VT 05602
P: (802) 223-6043
E: acummings@leg.state.vt.us

Degree, Dustin Allard (R, SP6)
31 Bank Street
St. Albans, VT 05478
P: (802) 782-4507
E: ddegree@leg.state.vt.us

Doyle, William T. (R, SP11)
186 Murray Road
Montpelier, VT 05602
P: (802) 223-2851
E: wdoyle@leg.state.vt.us

Flory, Peg (D, SP10)
3011 U.S. Route 7
Pittsford, VT 05763
P: (802) 483-6854
E: pflory@leg.state.vt.us

Kitchel, M. Jane (D, SP3)
81 Walden Hill Road
P.O. Box 82
Danville, VT 05828
P: (802) 684-3482
E: jkitchel@leg.state.vt.us

Lyons, Virginia (D, SP4)
241 White Birch Lane
Williston, VT 05495
P: (802) 863-6129
E: vlyons@leg.state.vt.us

MacDonald, Mark A. (D, SP9)
404 MacDonald Road
Williamstown, VT 05679
P: (802) 433-5867
F: (802) 433-1035
E: mmacdonald@leg.state.vt.us

Mazza, Richard T. (D, SP7)
777 West Lakeshore Drive
Colchester, VT 05446
P: (802) 863-1067
F: (802) 859-9215

McAllister, Norman H. (R, SP6)
712 Hanna Road
Franklin, VT 05457
P: (802) 285-6363
F: (802) 285-6363
E: nmcallister@leg.state.vt.us

Vermont

McCormack, Richard J. (D, SP13)
127 Cleveland Brook Road
Bethel, VT 05032
P: (802) 234-5497
E: rmccormack@leg.state.vt.us

Mullin, Kevin J. (R, SP10)
118 Oxyoke Drive
Rutland, VT 05701
P: (802) 353-6770
E: kjmbjm@aol.com

Nitka, Alice W. (D, SP13)
P.O. Box 136
Ludlow, VT 05149
P: (802) 228-8432
E: anitka@leg.state.vt.us

Pollina, Anthony (P, SP11)
93 Story Road
North Middlesex, VT 05682
P: (802) 229-5809
E: apollina@leg.state.vt.us

Rodgers, John S. (D, SP5)
P.O. Box 217
Glover, VT 05839
P: (802) 525-4182
E: jrodgers@leg.state.vt.us

Sears Jr., Richard W. (D, SP2)
343 Matteson Road
North Bennington, VT 05257
P: (802) 442-9139
E: rsears@leg.state.vt.us

Sirotkin, Michael (D, SP4)*
80 Bartlett Bay Road
South Burlington, VT 05403
P: (802) 999-4360
E: msirotkin@leg.state.vt.us

Snelling, Diane (R, SP4)
304 Piette Road
Hinesburg, VT 05461
P: (802) 482-4382
E: dsnelling@leg.state.vt.us

Starr Jr., Robert A. (D, SP5)
958 Route 105W
North Troy, VT 05859
P: (802) 988-2877
E: rstarr@leg.state.vt.us

Westman, Richard A. (R, SP8)
2439 Iron Gate Road
Cambridge, VT 05444
P: (802) 644-2297
F: (802) 644-2297
E: rawestman@gmail.com

White, Jeanette K. (D, SP12)
35A Old Depot Road
Putney, VT 05346
P: (802) 387-4379
E: jwhite@leg.state.vt.us

Zuckerman, David (P, SP4)
2083 Gilman Road
Hinesburg, VT 05461
P: (802) 482-2199
E: dzuckerman@leg.state.vt.us

House

Speaker of the House

Rep. Shap Smith (D)
Speaker
Office of the Speaker of the House
115 State Street
Montpelier, VT 05633
P: (802) 828-2245
E: speaker@leg.state.vt.us

House Majority Leader

Rep. Willem Jewett (D)
Majority Leader
P.O. Box 129
Ripton, VT 05766
P: (802) 388-0320
E: wjewett@leg.state.vt.us

House Minority Leader

Rep. Donald H. Turner (R)
Minority Leader
P.O. Box 487
Milton, VT 05468
P: (802) 893-1419
F: (802) 893-3467
E: dturner@leg.state.vt.us

Clerk of the House

Mr. Donald G. Milne
Clerk of the House
State House
115 State Street
Montpelier, VT 05633
P: (802) 828-2247
F: (802) 828-0724
E: don@leg.state.vt.us

Members of the House

Ancel, Janet (D, SP95)
P.O. Box 123
Calais, VT 05648
P: (802) 223-5350
E: janetancel@earthlink.net

Bancroft, Robert L. (R, SP51)*
405 Brookside Road
Westford, VT 05494
P: (802) 879-7386
E: rbancroft@leg.state.vt.us

Bartholomew, John (D, SP108)
23 Linden Road
Hartland, VT 05048
P: (802) 436-2151
E: jbartholomew@leg.state.vt.us

Baser, Fred K. (R, SP17)*
35 Mountain Street
Bristol, VT 05443
P: (802) 453-4391
E: fbaser@leg.state.vt.us

Batchelor, Lynn (R, SP74)
165 Beach Street
Derby Line, VT 05830
P: (802) 873-3006
E: lbatchelor@leg.state.vt.us

Beck, Scott (R, SP28)*
93 Overlook Drive
St. Johnsbury, VT 05819
P: (802) 748-4228
E: sbeck@leg.state.vt.us

Berry, Steve (D, SP24)*
P.O. Box 858
Manchester, VT 05254
P: (802) 362-5738
E: sberry@leg.state.vt.us

Beyor, Steve (R, SP62)
P.O. Box 287
Highgate Springs, VT 05460
P: (802) 868-3456
E: sbeyor@leg.state.vt.us

Bissonnette, Clem (D, SP44)
11 Dufresne Drive
Winooski, VT 05404
P: (802) 655-9527
E: cbissonnette@leg.state.vt.us

Botzow, Bill (D, SP20)
1225 South Stream Road
Bennington, VT 05201
P: (802) 447-7717
E: bbotzow@leg.state.vt.us

Branagan, Carolyn Whitney (R, SP57)
1295 Ballard Road
Georgia, VT 05478
P: (802) 527-7694
F: (802) 524-9533
E: cbranagan@leg.state.vt.us

Brennan, Patrick M. (R, SP53)
P.O. Box 796
Colchester, VT 05446
P: (802) 863-3773
E: pbrennan@leg.state.vt.us

Briglin, Tim (D, SP116)*
459 Tucker Hill Road
Thetford Center, VT 05075
P: (802) 785-2414
E: tbriglin@leg.state.vt.us

Browning, Cynthia (D, SP24)
P.O. Box 389
Arlington, VT 05250
P: (802) 375-9019
E: cbrowning@leg.state.vt.us

Burditt, Tom (R, SP79)
1118 Clarendon Avenue
West Rutland, VT 05777
P: (802) 438-0031
E: tburditt@leg.state.vt.us

Burke, Mollie S. (P, SP100)
62 West Street
Brattleboro, VT 05301
P: (802) 257-4844
E: mburke@leg.state.vt.us

Buxton, Sarah E. (D, SP115)
318 Vermont Route 110
Tunbridge, VT 05077
P: (802) 223-0274
E: sbuxton@leg.state.vt.us

Canfield, William (R, SP80)
12 Pine Street
Fair Haven, VT 05743
P: (802) 265-4428
E: wcanfield@leg.state.vt.us

Carr, Steve (D, SP86)
P.O. Box 206
Brandon, VT 05733
P: (802) 247-3921
E: scarr@leg.state.vt.us

Chesnut-Tangerman, Robin (D, SP87)*
72 Sundog Lane
Middletown Springs, VT 05757
P: (802) 235-2050
E: rchesnut-tangerman@leg.state.vt.us

Christie, Kevin (D, SP113)
682 Christian Street
White River Junction, VT 05001
P: (802) 295-1066
E: kchristie@leg.state.vt.us

Clarkson, Alison H. (D, SP114)
18 Golf Avenue
Woodstock, VT 05091
P: (802) 457-4627
F: (802) 457-4627
E: aclarkson@leg.state.vt.us

Cole, Joanna (D, SP38)
108 Rivers Edge Drive
Burlington, VT 05408
P: (802) 660-7175
E: jcole@leg.state.vt.us

Condon, Jim (D, SP52)
500A Dalton Drive
Colchester, VT 05446
P: (802) 655-5764
E: jimcondon@lycos.com

Connor, Dan (D, SP63)
4367 Route 36
Fairfield, VT 05455
P: (802) 827-4436
E: dconnor@leg.state.vt.us

Conquest, Chip (D, SP73)
409 Bible Hill Road
Wells River, VT 05081
P: (802) 757-3803
E: cconquest@leg.state.vt.us

Copeland-Hanzas, Sarah (D, SP71)
P.O. Box 43
Bradford, VT 05033
P: (802) 222-3536
E: scopelandhanzas@leg.state.vt.us

Corcoran, Timothy R. (D, SP21)
8 Corey Lane
Bennington, VT 05201
P: (802) 447-0929
E: tcorcoran@leg.state.vt.us

Cupoli, Larry (R, SP83)
57 Piedmont Pond Road
Rutland, VT 05701
P: (802) 747-4399
F: (802) 775-3179
E: lcupoli@leg.state.vt.us

Dakin, Leigh (D, SP110)
P.O. Box 467
Chester, VT 05143
P: (802) 875-3456
E: ldakin@leg.state.vt.us

Dakin, Maureen P. (D, SP53)*
60 Woodlins Circle, #4
Colchester, VT 05446
P: (802) 777-8507
E: mdakin@leg.state.vt.us

Dame, Paul (R, SP50)*
P.O. Box 8852
Essex Junction, VT 05453
P: (802) 318-7544
E: pdame@leg.state.vt.us

Davis, Susan (P, SP70)
75 Notchend Road
West Topsham, VT 05086
P: (802) 439-5103
E: sdavis@leg.state.vt.us

Deen, David L. (D, SP103)
5607 Westminster West Road
Putney, VT 05346
P: (802) 869-3116
F: (802) 869-1103
E: ddeen@leg.state.vt.us

Devereux, Dennis J. (R, SP89)
P.O. Box 1
Route 155
Belmont, VT 05730
P: (802) 259-2460
E: ddevereux@leg.state.vt.us

Dickinson, Eileen (D, SP60)
69 Button Road
St. Albans, VT 05478
P: (802) 524-3404
F: (802) 527-3767
E: edickinson@leg.state.vt.us

Donahue, Anne B. (R, SP90)
148 Donahue Drive
Northfield, VT 05663
P: (802) 485-6431
E: adonahue@leg.state.vt.us

Donovan, Johannah Leddy (D, SP42)
38 Bayview Street
Burlington, VT 05401
P: (802) 863-4634
E: jdonovan@leg.state.vt.us

Eastman, Alyson (I, SP19)*
375 Mount Independence Road
Orwell, VT 05760
P: (802) 989-1088
E: aeastman@leg.state.vt.us

Ellis, Rebecca (D, SP97)
1531 Ripley Road
Waterbury Center, VT 05677
P: (802) 244-5687
E: rellis@leg.state.vt.us

Emmons, Alice M. (D, SP111)
318 Summer Street
Springfield, VT 05156
P: (802) 885-5893
E: aemmons@leg.state.vt.us

Evans, Debbie (D, SP49)
53 Greenfield Road
Essex Junction, VT 05452
P: (802) 878-4317
E: devans@leg.state.vt.us

Fagan, Peter J. (R, SP82)
17 Clinton Avenue
Rutland, VT 05701
P: (802) 342-1214
E: pfagan@leg.state.vt.us

Feltus, Marty (R, SP29)
P.O. Box 963
Lyndonville, VT 05851
P: (802) 626-9516
E: martyfeltus@gmail.com

Fields, Rachael (D, SP21)*
802 Overlea Road
Bennington, VT 05201
P: (518) 368-8631
E: rfields@leg.state.vt.us

Fiske, Larry G. (R, SP64)*
50 St. Albans Street
Enosburg Falls, VT 05450
P: (802) 933-8410
E: lfiske@leg.state.vt.us

Forguites, Robert (D, SP111)*
P.O. Box 303
North Springfield, VT 05150
P: (802) 886-2654
E: rforguites@leg.state.vt.us

Frank, William R. (D, SP33)
19 Poker Hill Road
Underhill, VT 05489
P: (802) 899-3136
E: bill@repbillfrank.com

French, Patsy (D, SP72)
886 Harlow Hill
Randolph, VT 05060
P: (802) 728-9421
E: pfrench@leg.state.vt.us

Gage, Doug (R, SP85)
41 Hazel Street
Rutland, VT 05701
P: (802) 773-0616
E: dgage@leg.state.vt.us

Gamache, Marianna (R, SP61)*
P.O. Box 435
Swanton, VT 05488
P: (802) 393-1169
E: mgamache@leg.state.vt.us

Gonzalez, Diana (D, SP44)*
27 LeClair Street
Winooski, VT 05404
P: (802) 661-4053
E: dgonzalez@leg.state.vt.us

Grad, Maxine Jo (D, SP96)
301 Paddy Hill Road
Moretown, VT 05660
P: (802) 496-7667
F: (802) 496-6104
E: mgrad@leg.state.vt.us

Graham, Rodney (R, SP70)*
859 Graham Road
Williamstown, VT 05679
P: (802) 433-6127
E: rgraham@leg.state.vt.us

Greshin, Adam (I, SP96)
611 Eurich Pond Road
Warren, VT 05674
P: (802) 583-3223
E: agreshin@leg.state.vt.us

Haas, Sandy (P, SP117)
360 South Main Street
Rochester, VT 05767
P: (802) 767-4751
E: shaas@leg.state.vt.us

Head, Helen (D, SP47)
65 East Terrace
South Burlington, VT 05403
P: (802) 862-2267
E: helen@helenhead.com

Hebert, Michael (R, SP98)
P.O. Box 120
Vernon, VT 05354
P: (802) 451-9088
F: (802) 254-3660
E: mhebert@leg.state.vt.us

Helm, Robert (R, SP80)
647 Route 4A, East
Fair Haven, VT 05743
P: (802) 265-2145
E: rhelm@leg.state.vt.us

Higley, Mark A. (R, SP77)
P.O. Box 10
Lowell, VT 05847
P: (802) 744-6379
E: mhigley@leg.state.vt.us

Hooper, Mary (D, SP93)
882 North Street
Montpelier, VT 05602
P: (802) 223-2892
E: mhooper@leg.state.vt.us

Vermont

Hubert, Ronald E. (R, SP54)
68 Woodcrest Circle
Milton, VT 05468
P: (802) 893-1368
F: (802) 893-3814
E: rhubert@leg.state.vt.us

Huntley, Mark (D, SP109)
535 Center Road
Cavendish, VT 05142
P: (802) 236-6722
E: mhuntley@leg.state.vt.us

Jerman, Tim (D, SP50)
5 Sycamore Lane
Essex Junction, VT 05452
P: (802) 878-2972
E: tjerman@leg.state.vt.us

Jewett, Willem (D, SP15)
P.O. Box 129
Ripton, VT 05766
P: (802) 388-0320
E: wjewett@leg.state.vt.us

Johnson, Mitzi (D, SP65)
P.O. Box 144
South Hero, VT 05486
P: (802) 363-4448
E: mjohnson@leg.state.vt.us

Juskiewicz, Bernie (R, SP68)
P.O. Box 93
Cambridge, VT 05444
P: (802) 644-5606
E: bjuskiewicz@leg.state.vt.us

Keenan, Kathleen C. (D, SP59)
8 Thorpe Avenue
Saint Albans, VT 05478
P: (802) 524-5013
E: kkeenan@leg.state.vt.us

Kitzmiller, Warren F. (D, SP93)
138 North Street
Montpelier, VT 05602
P: (802) 229-0878
E: wkitzmiller@leg.state.vt.us

Klein, Tony (D, SP94)
95 Powder Horn Glen
Montpelier, VT 05602
P: (802) 223-8926
F: (802) 224-9096
E: tklein@leg.state.vt.us

Komline, Patti (R, SP25)
P.O. Box 513
Dorset, VT 05251
P: (802) 867-4232
E: pkomline@leg.state.vt.us

Krebs, Bob (D, SP65)
134 East Shore Road
South Hero, VT 05486
P: (802) 372-4567
E: rkrebs@leg.state.vt.us

Krowinski, Jill (D, SP40)
27 Spring Street
Burlington, VT 05401
P: (802) 363-3907
E: jkrowinskiz@leg.state.vt.us

Laclair, Rob (R, SP91)*
146 Airport Road
Barre, VT 05641
P: (802) 476-9668
E: rlaclair@leg.state.vt.us

Lalonde, Martin (D, SP45)*
304 Four Sisters Road
South Burlington, VT 05403
P: (802) 863-3086
E: mlalonde@leg.state.vt.us

Lanpher, Diane (D, SP16)
194 South Maple Street
P.O. Box 165
Vergennes, VT 05491
P: (802) 877-2230
E: dlanpher@leg.state.vt.us

Lawrence, Richard (R, SP29)
194 Bean Pond Road
Lyndonville, VT 05851
P: (802) 626-5917
F: (802) 626-8081
E: rlawrence@leg.state.vt.us

Lefebvre, Paul D. (R, SP56)*
P.O. Box 397
Island Pond, VT 05846
P: (802) 467-8338
E: plefebvre@leg.state.vt.us

Lenes, Joan G. (D, SP37)
197 Governor's Lane
Shelburne, VT 05482
P: (802) 985-8515
F: (802) 399-2671
E: jlenes@leg.state.vt.us

Lewis, Patti J. (R, SP90)
449 East Road
Berlin, VT 05641
P: (802) 223-6319
E: plewis@leg.state.vt.us

Lippert Jr., William J. (D, SP35)
2751 Baldwin Road
Hinesburg, VT 05461
P: (802) 482-3528
F: (802) 482-3528
E: wlippert@leg.state.vt.us

Long, Emily (D, SP104)*
239 Wiswall Hill Road
Newfane, VT 05345
P: (802) 365-7360
E: elong@leg.state.vt.us

Lucke, Gabrielle (D, SP113)*
554 Campbell Street
White River Junction, VT 05001
P: (802) 296-2690
E: glucke@leg.state.vt.us

Macaig, Terence (D, SP32)
82 Pamela Court
Williston, VT 05495
P: (802) 878-3872
E: tmacaig@leg.state.vt.us

Manwaring, Ann (D, SP105)
P.O. Box 1089
Wilmington, VT 05363
P: (802) 464-2150
E: amanwaring@leg.state.vt.us

Marcotte, Michael J. (R, SP75)
106 Private Pond Road
Newport, VT 05855
P: (802) 334-6302
E: mmarcotte@leg.state.vt.us

Martel, Marcia Robinson (R, SP26)*
1087 Slate Ledge Road
Waterford, VT 05819
P: (802) 748-9134
E: mmartel@leg.state.vt.us

Martin, Linda J. (D, SP67)
P.O. Box 94
Wolcott, VT 05680
P: (802) 888-5654
E: lmartin@leg.state.vt.us

Masland, Jim (D, SP116)
714 Pero Hill Road
Thetford Center, VT 05075
P: (802) 785-4146
E: jmasland@leg.state.vt.us

McCormack, Curt (D, SP40)
221 North Winooski Avenue
Burlington, VT 05401
P: (802) 318-2585
E: cmccormack@leg.state.vt.us

McCoy, Patricia A. (R, SP78)*
1392 High Road
Poultney, VT 05764
P: (802) 287-9625
E: pmccoy@leg.state.vt.us

McCullough, Jim (D, SP32)
592 Governor Chittenden Road
Williston, VT 05495
P: (802) 878-2180
E: jim_mccullough@myfairpoint.net

McFaun, Francis (R, SP91)
97 Sunset Road
Barre Town, VT 05641
P: (802) 479-9843
E: fmcfaun@leg.state.vt.us

Miller, Alice (D, SP23)
88 Horton Hill Road
Shaftsbury, VT 05262
P: (802) 442-9825
F: (802) 442-9825
E: amiller@leg.state.vt.us

Morris, Kiah (D, SP22)*
P.O. Box 4705
Bennington, VT 05201
P: (802) 688-3300
E: kmorris@leg.state.vt.us

Morrissey, Mary A. (R, SP22)
228 Dewey Street
Bennington, VT 05201
P: (802) 442-2092
E: mmorrissey@leg.state.vt.us

Mrowicki, Mike (D, SP103)
299 South Pine Banks Road
Putney, VT 05346
P: (802) 387-8787
E: mmrowicki@leg.state.vt.us

Murphy, Barbara S. (I, SP58)*
7 Lily Road
Fairfax, VT 05454
P: (802) 849-6545
E: bmurphy@leg.state.vt.us

Myers, Linda K. (R, SP49)
51 Forest Road
Essex Junction, VT 05452
P: (802) 878-3514
E: lmyers@leg.state.vt.us

Nuovo, Betty A. (D, SP14)
70 Maple Street, Unit 308
Middlebury, VT 05753
P: (802) 388-2024
E: bnuovo@leg.state.vt.us

O'Brien, Anne Theresa (D, SP31)
2406 Hinesburg Road
Richmond, VT 05477
P: (802) 434-4250
E: aobrien@leg.state.vt.us

Olsen, Oliver K. (R, SP107)
1320 Middletown Road
Londonderry, VT 05155
P: (802) 444-9004
E: oolsen@leg.state.vt.us

O'Sullivan, Jean (D, SP39)
37 Village Green
Burlington, VT 05408
P: (802) 658-0492
F: (802) 658-0492
E: josullivan
@leg.state.vt.us

Parent, Corey (R, SP59)*
160 North Main Street, Unit 3
St. Albans, VT 05478
P: (802) 370-0494
E: cparent@leg.state.vt.us

Partridge, Carolyn W. (D, SP102)
1612 Old Cheney Road
Windham, VT 05359
P: (802) 874-4182
F: (802) 874-4182
E: cpartridge
@leg.state.vt.us

Patt, Avram (D, SP69)*
139 West Hill Road
Worcester, VT 05682
P: (802) 223-1014
E: apatt@leg.state.vt.us

Pearce, Albert (D, SP62)
84 Magoon Road
Richford, VT 05476
P: (802) 848-7813
E: apearce@leg.state.vt.us

Pearson, Christopher A. (P, SP41)
12 Brookes Avenue
Burlington, VT 05401
P: (802) 860-3933
E: cpearson@leg.state.vt.us

Poirier, Paul N. (D, SP92)
33 Abbott Avenue
Barre, VT 05641
P: (802) 476-7870
E: ppoirier@leg.state.vt.us

Potter, Dave (D, SP79)
P.O. Box 426
North Clarendon, VT 05759
P: (802) 438-5385
E: dpotter@leg.state.vt.us

Pugh, Ann D. (D, SP46)
67 Bayberry Lane
South Burlington, VT 05403
P: (802) 863-6705
E: apugh@leg.state.vt.us

Purvis, Joey A. (R, SP52)
364 HIdden Oaks Drive
Colchester, VT 05446
P: (802) 879-6110
E: jpurvis@leg.state.vt.us

Quimby, Connie (R, SP55)
P.O. Box 373
Concord, VT 05824
P: (802) 695-2575
E: cquimby@leg.state.vt.us

Rachelson, Barbara (D, SP43)
205 Summit Street
Burlington, VT 05401
P: (802) 862-1290
E: brachelson
@leg.state.vt.us

Ram, Kesha (D, SP41)
31 North Prospect Street
Burlington, VT 05401
P: (802) 881-4433
E: kram@leg.state.vt.us

Russell, Herb (D, SP84)
188 State Street
Rutland, VT 05701
P: (802) 779-7370
E: hrussell@leg.state.vt.us

Ryerson, Marjorie Q. (D, SP72)
36 Randolph Avenue
Randolph, VT 05060
P: (802) 728-4127
E: mryerson@leg.state.vt.us

Savage, Brian K. (R, SP61)
17 Linda Avenue
Swanton, VT 05488
P: (802) 868-3566
E: bsavage@leg.state.vt.us

Scheuermann, Heidi E. (R, SP66)
P.O. Box 908
Stowe, VT 05672
P: (802) 253-2275
F: (802) 253-2275
E: heidi
@heidischeuermann.com

Sharpe, David (D, SP17)
1209 Meehan Road
Bristol, VT 05443
P: (802) 453-2754
E: dsharpe@leg.state.vt.us

Shaw, Butch (R, SP86)
910 Markowski Road
Florence, VT 05744
P: (802) 483-2398
E: bshaw@leg.state.vt.us

Shaw, Loren T. (R, SP74)
320 Foxwood Lane
Derby, VT 05829
P: (802) 766-5022
E: lshaw@leg.state.vt.us

Sheldon, Amy (D, SP14)*
P.O. Box 311
East Middlebury, VT 05740
E: asheldon@leg.state.vt.us

Sibilia, Laura (I, SP106)*
P.O. Box 2052
West Dover, VT 05356
P: (802) 348-7131
E: lsibilia@leg.state.vt.us

Smith, Harvey T. (R, SP18)
2516 Lime Kiln Road
New Haven, VT 05472
P: (802) 877-2712
E: hsmith@leg.state.vt.us

Smith, Shap (D, SP69)
Office of the Speaker of the House
115 State Street
Montpelier, VT 05633
P: (802) 828-2245
E: speaker@leg.state.vt.us

Stevens, Tom (D, SP97)
12 Winooski Street
Waterbury, VT 05676
P: (802) 244-4164
E: tstevens@leg.state.vt.us

Strong, Vicki (R, SP73)
1367 Creek Road
Irasburg, VT 05845
P: (802) 754-2790
E: vstrong@leg.state.vt.us

Stuart, Valerie A. (D, SP99)
520 Meadowbrook Road
Brattleboro, VT 05301
P: (802) 257-0249
E: vstuart@leg.state.vt.us

Sullivan, Mary M. (D, SP42)*
84 Caroline Street
Burlington, VT 05401
P: (802) 862-6632
E: msullivan
@leg.state.vt.us

Sweaney, Donna G. (D, SP108)
2 Runnemede Lane
Windsor, VT 05089
P: (802) 674-5175
E: dsweaney@leg.state.vt.us

Tate, Job (R, SP88)*
111 Birchwood Drive, #6
Mendon, VT 05701
P: (802) 558-5153
E: jtate@leg.state.vt.us

Terenzini, Thomas (R, SP81)
34B Chasanna Drive
Rutland, VT 05701
P: (802) 855-1945
E: tterenzini
@leg.state.vt.us

Till, George (D, SP33)
74 Foothills Drive
Jericho, VT 05465
P: (802) 899-2984
F: (802) 878-6131
E: gtill@leg.state.vt.us

Toleno, Tristan (D, SP101)
33 Highlawn Road
Brattleboro, VT 05301
P: (802) 579-5511
E: toleno@leg.state.vt.us

Toll, Kitty Beattie (D, SP30)
P.O. Box 192
Danville, VT 05828
P: (802) 684-3671
E: ktoll@leg.state.vt.us

Townsend, Maida (D, SP48)
232 Patchen Road
South Burlington, VT 05403
P: (802) 862-7404
E: mtownsend
@leg.state.vt.us

Trieber, Matthew (D, SP102)
82 Atkinson Street
Bellows Falls, VT 05101
P: (802) 376-1134
E: matrieber@gmail.com

Troiano, Chip (D, SP27)*
261 Hutchins Farm Road
East Hardwick, VT 05839
P: (802) 533-7712
E: Chiptroiano@gmail.com

Turner, Donald H. (R, SP54)
P.O. Box 487
Milton, VT 05468
P: (802) 893-1419
F: (802) 893-3467
E: dturner@leg.state.vt.us

Van Wyck, Warren (R, SP16)
3502 Middlebrook Road
Ferrisburgh, VT 05456
P: (802) 877-2169
E: wvanwyck@leg.state.vt.us

Vermont

Viens, Gary (R, SP75)*
50 Mountain View Drive
Newport, VT 05855
P: (802) 323-2183
E: gviens@leg.state.vt.us

Walz, Tommy (D, SP92)*
157 Camp Street
Barre, VT 05641
P: (802) 476-7819
E: twalz@leg.state.vt.us

Webb, Kate (D, SP36)
1611 Harbor Road
Shelburne, VT 05482
P: (802) 985-2789
E: kwebb@leg.state.vt.us

Willhoit, Janssen (R, SP28)*
46 Hastings Hill
St. Johnsbury, VT 05819
P: (802) 431-5118
E: jwillhoit@leg.state.vt.us

Woodward, Mark (D, SP67)
110 Woodward Road
Johnson, VT 05656
P: (802) 635-7166
E: mwoodward@leg.state.vt.us

Wright, Kurt (R, SP38)
31 Vine Street
Burlington, VT 05401
P: (802) 658-1410
E: kwright@leg.state.vt.us

Yantachka, Mike (D, SP34)
393 Natures Way
Charlotte, VT 05445
P: (802) 425-3960
E: myantachka@leg.state.vt.us

Young, Sam (D, SP76)
P.O. Box 10
Glover, VT 05875
P: (802) 321-0365
E: syoung@leg.state.vt.us

Zagar, Teo (D, SP112)
P.O. Box 875
Barnard, VT 05031
P: (802) 558-3966
E: tzagar@leg.state.vt.us

Congress

Senate

Leahy, Patrick J. (D)
Sanders, Bernard (I)

House

Welch, Peter F. (D, At-Large)

Virginia

Executive

Governor

Hon. Terry McAuliffe (D)
Governor
P.O. Box 1475
Richmond, VA 23218
P: (804) 786-2211

Lieutenant Governor

Hon. Ralph S. Northam (D)
Lieutenant Governor
102 Governor Street
Richmond, VA 23219
P: (804) 786-2078
F: (804) 786-7514
E: ltgov@ltgov.virginia.gov

Attorney General

Hon. Mark R. Herring (D)
Attorney General
900 East Main Street
Richmond, VA 23219
P: (804) 786-2071

Auditor

Ms. Martha Mavredes
(appointed by the Legislature)
Auditor of Public Accounts
P.O. Box 1295
Richmond, VA 23218
P: (804) 225-3350
F: (804) 225-3357
E: martha.mavredes
@apa.virginia.gov

Secretary of the Commonwealth

Hon. Levar Stoney
(appointed)
Secretary of the Commonwealth
P.O. Box 2454
Richmond, VA 23218
P: (804) 786-2441
F: (804) 371-0017
E: socmail
@governor.virginia.gov

Treasurer

Hon. Manju Ganeriwala
(appointed)
State Treasurer
101 North 14th Street, 3rd Floor
James Monroe Building, P.O. Box 1879
Richmond, VA 23218
P: (804) 225-2142
F: (804) 225-3187
E: Manju.Ganeriwala
@trs.virginia.gov

Judiciary

Supreme Court (LA)

Ms. Patricia L. Harrington
Clerk
100 North 9th Street, 5th Floor
P.O. Box 1315
Richmond, VA 23219
P: (804) 786-2251

Hon. Donald W. Lemons
Chief Justice
Hon. S. Bernard Goodwyn
Hon. D. Arthur Kelsey
Hon. Elizabeth A. McClanahan
Hon. LeRoy F. Millette Jr.
Hon. William C. Mims
Hon. Cleo E. Powell

Legislative Senate

Senate President

Hon. Ralph S. Northam (D)
Lieutenant Governor
102 Governor Street
Richmond, VA 23219
P: (804) 786-2078
F: (804) 786-7514
E: ltgov@ltgov.virginia.gov

President Pro Tempore of the Senate

Sen. Walter A. Stosch (R)
President Pro Tempore
General Assembly Building, Room 626
P.O. Box 396
Richmond, VA 23218
P: (804) 698-7512
F: (804) 698-7651
E: district12
@senate.virginia.gov

Senate Majority Leader

Sen. Thomas K. Norment Jr. (R)
Majority Leader
General Assembly Building, Room 621
P.O. Box 396
Richmond, VA 23218
P: (804) 698-7503
F: 804) 698-7651
E: district03
@senate.virginia.gov

Senate Minority Leader

Sen. Richard L. Saslaw (D)
Minority Leader
General Assembly Building, Room 613
P.O. Box 396
Richmond, VA 23218
P: (804) 698-7535
F: (804) 698-7651
E: district35
@senate.virginia.gov

Secretary of the Senate

Ms. Susan Clarke Schaar
Clerk of the Senate
P.O. Box 396
Richmond, VA 23218
P: (804) 698-7400
F: (804) 698-7670
E: sschaar
@senate.virginia.gov

Members of the Senate

Alexander, Kenneth C. (D, 5)
General Assembly Building, Room 305
P.O. Box 396
Richmond, VA 23218
P: (804) 698-7505
F: (804) 698-7651
E: district05
@senate.virginia.gov

Barker, George L. (D, 39)
General Assembly Building, Room 315
P.O. Box 396
Richmond, VA 23218
P: (804) 698-7539
F: (804) 698-7651
E: district39
@senate.virginia.gov

Black, Richard H. (R, 13)
General Assembly Building, Room 308
P.O. Box 396
Richmond, VA 23218
P: (804) 698-7513
F: (804) 698-7651
E: district13
@senate.virginia.gov

Carrico Sr., Charles W. (R, 40)
General Assembly Building, Room 330
P.O. Box 396
Richmond, VA 23218
P: (804) 698-7540
F: (804) 698-7651
E: district40
@senate.virginia.gov

Chafin Jr., A. Benton (R, 38)
General Assembly Building, Room 307
P.O. Box 396
Richmond, VA 23218
P: (804) 698-7538
F: (804) 698-7651
E: district38
@senate.virginia.gov

Colgan, Charles J. (D, 29)
General Assembly Building, Room 326
P.O. Box 396
Richmond, VA 23218
P: (804) 698-7529
F: (804) 698-7651
E: district29
@senate.virginia.gov

Cosgrove Jr., John A. (R, 14)
General Assembly Building, Room 323
P.O. Box 396
Richmond, VA 23218
P: (804) 698-7514
F: (804) 698-7651
E: district14
@senate.virginia.gov

Dance, Rosalyn R. (D, 16)
General Assembly Building, Room 322
P.O. Box 396
Richmond, VA 23218
P: (804) 698-7516
F: (804) 698-7651
E: district16
@senate.virginia.gov

Virginia

Deeds, R. Creigh (D, 25)
General Assembly Building,
Room 430
P.O. Box 396
Richmond, VA 23218
P: (804) 698-7525
F: (804) 698-7651
E: district25
@senate.virginia.gov

Ebbin, Adam P. (D, 30)
General Assembly Building,
Room 328
P.O. Box 396
Richmond, VA 23218
P: (804) 698-7530
F: (804) 698-7651
E: district30
@senate.virginia.gov

Edwards, John S. (D, 21)
General Assembly Building,
Room 301
P.O. Box 396
Richmond, VA 23218
P: (804) 698-7521
F: (804) 698-7651
E: district21
@senate.virginia.gov

Favola, Barbara A. (D, 31)
General Assembly Building,
Room 316
P.O. Box 396
Richmond, VA 23218
P: (804) 698-7531
F: (804) 698-7651
E: district31
@senate.virginia.gov

Garrett Jr., Thomas A. (R, 22)
General Assembly Building,
Room 317
P.O. Box 396
Richmond, VA 23218
P: (804) 698-7522
F: (804) 698-7651
E: district22
@senate.virginia.gov

Hanger Jr., Emmett W. (R, 24)
General Assembly Building,
Room 431
P.O. Box 396
Richmond, VA 23218
P: (804) 698-7524
F: (804) 698-7651
E: district24
@senate.virginia.gov

Howell, Janet D. (D, 32)
General Assembly Building,
Room 321
P.O. Box 396
Richmond, VA 23218
P: (804) 698-7532
F: (804) 698-7651
E: district32
@senate.virginia.gov

Lewis Jr., Lynwood W. (D, 6)
General Assembly Building,
Room 318
P.O. Box 406
Richmond, VA 23218
P: (804) 698-7506
F: (804) 698-7651
E: district06
@senate.virginia.gov

Locke, Mamie E. (D, 2)
General Assembly Building,
Room 427
P.O. Box 396
Richmond, VA 23218
P: (804) 698-7502
F: (804) 698-7651
E: district02
@senate.virginia.gov

Lucas, Louise (D, 18)
General Assembly Building,
Room 426
P.O. Box 396
Richmond, VA 23218
P: (804) 698-7518
F: (804) 698-7651
E: district18
@senate.virginia.gov

Marsden, David W. (D, 37)
General Assembly Building,
Room 429
P.O. Box 396
Richmond, VA 23218
P: (804) 698-7537
F: (804) 698-7651
E: district37
@senate.virginia.gov

Martin, Stephen H. (R, 11)
General Assembly Building,
Room 432
P.O. Box 396
Richmond, VA 23218
P: (804) 698-7511
F: (804) 698-7651
E: district11
@senate.virginia.gov

McDougle, Ryan T. (R, 4)
General Assembly Building,
Room 314
P.O. Box 396
Richmond, VA 23218
P: (804) 698-7504
F: (804) 698-7943
E: district04
@senate.virginia.gov

McEachin, A. Donald (D, 9)
General Assembly Building,
Room 428
P.O. Box 396
Richmond, VA 23218
P: (804) 698-7509
F: (804) 698-7651
E: district09
@senate.virginia.gov

McWaters, Jeffrey L. (R, 8)
General Assembly Building,
Room 310
P.O. Box 396
Richmond, VA 23218
P: (804) 698-7508
F: (804) 698-7651
E: district08@senate.va.gov

Miller, John C. (D, 1)
General Assembly Building,
Room 306
P.O. Box 396
Richmond, VA 23218
P: (804) 698-7501
F: (804) 698-7651
E: district01
@senate.virginia.gov

Newman, Stephen D. (R, 23)
General Assembly Building,
Room 304
P.O. Box 396
Richmond, VA 23218
P: (804) 698-7523
F: (804) 698-7651
E: district23
@senate.virginia.gov

Norment Jr., Thomas K. (R, 3)
General Assembly Building,
Room 621
P.O. Box 396
Richmond, VA 23218
P: (804) 698-7503
F: 804) 698-7651
E: district03
@senate.virginia.gov

Obenshain, Mark D. (R, 26)
General Assembly Building,
Room 327
P.O. Box 396
Richmond, VA 23218
P: (804) 698-7526
F: (804) 698-7651
E: district26
@senate.virginia.gov

Petersen, Chap (D, 34)
General Assembly Building,
Room 329
P.O. Box 396
Richmond, VA 23218
P: (804) 698-7534
F: (804) 698-7651
E: district34
@senate.virginia.gov

Puller, Toddy (D, 36)
General Assembly Building,
Room 332
P.O. Box 396
Richmond, VA 23218
P: (804) 698-7536
F: (804) 698-7651
E: district36
@senate.virginia.gov

Reeves, Bryce (R, 17)
General Assembly Building,
Room 312
P.O. Box 396
Richmond, VA 23218
P: (804) 698-7517
F: (804) 698-7651
E: district17
@senate.virginia.gov

Ruff Jr., Frank M. (R, 15)
General Assembly Building,
Room 311
P.O. Box 396
Richmond, VA 23218
P: (804) 698-7515
F: (804) 698-7651
E: district15
@senate.virginia.gov

Saslaw, Richard L. (D, 35)
General Assembly Building,
Room 613
P.O. Box 396
Richmond, VA 23218
P: (804) 698-7535
F: (804) 698-7651
E: district35
@senate.virginia.gov

Smith, Ralph K. (R, 19)
General Assembly Building,
Room 319
P.O. Box 396
Richmond, VA 23218
P: (804) 698-7519
F: (804) 698-7651
E: district19
@senate.virginia.gov

Stanley Jr., William M. (R, 20)
General Assembly Building,
Room 313
P.O. Box 396
Richmond, VA 23218
P: (804) 698-7520
F: (804) 698-7651
E: district20
@senate.virginia.gov

Stosch, Walter A. (R, 12)
General Assembly Building,
Room 626
P.O. Box 396
Richmond, VA 23218
P: (804) 698-7512
F: (804) 698-7651
E: district12
@senate.virginia.gov

Stuart, Richard H. (R, 28)
General Assembly Building,
Room 302
P.O. Box 396
Richmond, VA 23218
P: (804) 698-7528
F: (804) 698-7651
E: district28
@senate.virginia.gov

Vogel, Jill Holtzman (R, 27)
General Assembly Building,
Room 309
P.O. Box 396
Richmond, VA 23218
P: (804) 698-7527
F: (804) 698-7651
E: district27
@senate.virginia.gov

Wagner, Frank W. (R, 7)
General Assembly Building,
Room 303
P.O. Box 396
Richmond, VA 23218
P: (804) 698-7507
F: (804) 698-7651
E: district07
@senate.virginia.gov

Watkins, John C. (R, 10)
General Assembly Building,
Room 331
P.O. Box 396
Richmond, VA 23218
P: (804) 698-7510
F: (804) 698-7651
E: district10
@senate.virginia.gov

Wexton, Jennifer T. (D, 33)
General Assembly Building,
Room 320
P.O. Box 396
Richmond, VA 23218
P: (804) 698-7533
F: (804) 698-7651
E: district33
@senate.virginia.gov

House

Speaker of the House

Delegate William J. Howell (R)
Speaker
General Assembly Building,
Room 635
P.O. Box 406
Richmond, VA 23218
P: (804) 698-1028
F: (804) 698-6728
E: delwhowell
@house.virginia.gov

House Majority Leader

Delegate M. Kirkland Cox (R)
House Majority Leader
General Assembly Building,
Room 607
P.O. Box 406
Richmond, VA 23218
P: (804) 698-1066
F: (804) 698-6766
E: DelKCox
@house.virginia.gov

House Minority Leader

Delegate David J. Toscano (D)
Democratic Leader
General Assembly Building,
Room 614
P.O. Box 406
Richmond, VA 23218
P: (804) 698-1057
F: (804) 698-6757
E: DelDToscano
@house.virginia.gov

Clerk of the House

Mr. G. Paul Nardo
Clerk of the House
General Assembly Building,
Third Floor
P.O. Box 406
Richmond, VA 23218
P: (804) 698-1619
F: (804) 698-1800
E: GPNardo
@house.virginia.gov

Members of the House

Adams, Leslie R. (R, 16)
General Assembly Building,
Room 719
P.O. Box 406
Richmond, VA 23218
P: (804) 698-1016
F: (804) 698-6716
E: DelLAdams
@house.virginia.gov

Albo, David B. (R, 42)
General Assembly Building,
Room 529
P.O. Box 406
Richmond, VA 23218
P: (804) 698-1042
F: (804) 698-6742
E: DelDAlbo
@house.virginia.gov

Anderson, Richard L. (R, 51)
General Assembly Building,
Room 406
P.O. Box 406
Richmond, VA 23218
P: (804) 698-1051
F: (804) 698-6751
E: DelRAnderson
@house.virginia.gov

Austin, Terry L. (R, 19)
General Assembly Building,
Room 412
P.O. Box 406
Richmond, VA 23218
P: (804) 698-1019
F: (804) 698-6719
E: DelTAustin
@house.virginia.gov

BaCote, Mayme E. (D, 95)
General Assembly Building,
Room 507
P.O. Box 406
Richmond, VA 23218
P: (804) 698-1095
F: (804) 698-6795
E: DelMBaCote
@house.virginia.gov

Bell, Richard P. (R, 20)
General Assembly Building,
Room 517
P.O. Box 406
Richmond, VA 23218
P: (804) 698-1020
F: (804) 698-6720
E: DelDBell
@house.virginia.gov

Bell, Robert B. (R, 58)
General Assembly Building,
Room 801
P.O. Box 406
Richmond, VA 23218
P: (804) 698-1058
F: (804) 698-6758
E: DelRBell
@house.virginia.gov

Berg, Mark J. (R, 29)
General Assembly Building,
Room 512
P.O. Box 406
Richmond, VA 23218
P: (804) 698-1029
F: (804) 698-6729
E: DelMBerg
@house.virginia.gov

Bloxom Jr., Robert S. (R, 100)
General Assembly Building,
Room 405
P.O. Box 406
Richmond, VA 23218
P: (804) 698-1000
E: DelRBloxom
@house.virginia.gov

Bulova, David L. (D, 37)
General Assembly Building,
Room 402
P.O. Box 406
Richmond, VA 23218
P: (804) 698-1037
F: (804) 698-6737
E: DelDBulova
@house.virginia.gov

Byron, Kathy J. (R, 22)
General Assembly Building,
Room 411
P.O. Box 406
Richmond, VA 23218
P: (804) 698-1022
F: (804) 698-6722
E: DelKByron
@house.virginia.gov

Virginia

Campbell, Jeffrey L. (R, 6)
General Assembly Building,
Room 817
P.O. Box 406
Richmond, VA 23218
P: (804) 698-1006
F: (804) 698-6706
E: DelJCampbell
@house.virginia.gov

Carr, Betsy B. (D, 69)
General Assembly Building,
Room 414
P.O. Box 406
Richmond, VA 23218
P: (804) 698-1069
F: (804) 698-6769
E: DelBCarr
@house.virginia.gov

Cline, Benjamin L. (R, 24)
General Assembly Building,
Room 722
P.O. Box 406
Richmond, VA 23218
P: (804) 698-1024
F: (804) 698-6724
E: DelBCline
@house.virginia.gov

Cole, Mark L. (R, 88)
General Assembly Building,
Room 822
P.O. Box 406
Richmond, VA 23218
P: (804) 698-1088
F: (804) 698-6788
E: DelMCole
@house.virginia.gov

Cox, M. Kirkland (R, 66)
General Assembly Building,
Room 607
P.O. Box 406
Richmond, VA 23218
P: (804) 698-1066
F: (804) 698-6766
E: DelKCox
@house.virginia.gov

Davis Jr., Glenn R. (R, 84)
General Assembly Building,
Room 416
P.O. Box 406
Richmond, VA 23218
P: (804) 698-1084
E: DelGDavis
@house.virginia.gov

DeSteph Jr., William R. (R, 82)
General Assembly Building,
Room 420
P.O. Box 406
Richmond, VA 23218
P: (804) 698-1082
F: (804) 698-6782
E: DelBDeSteph
@house.virginia.gov

Edmunds II, James E. (R, 60)
General Assembly Building,
Room 805
P.O. Box 406
Richmond, VA 23218
P: (804) 698-1060
F: (804) 698-6760
E: DelJEdmunds
@house.virginia.gov

Fariss, C. Matt (R, 59)
General Assembly Building,
Room 808
P.O. Box 406
Richmond, VA 23218
P: (804) 698-1059
F: (804) 698-6759
E: DelMFariss
@house.virginia.gov

Farrell, Peter F. (R, 56)
General Assembly Building,
Room 528
P.O. Box 406
Richmond, VA 23218
P: (804) 698-1056
F: (804) 698-6756
E: DelPFarrell
@house.virginia.gov

Filler-Corn, Eileen (D, 41)
General Assembly Building,
Room 705
P.O. Box 406
Richmond, VA 23218
P: (804) 698-1041
F: (804) 698-6741
E: DelEFiller-Corn
@house.virginia.gov

Fowler Jr., Hyland F. (R, 55)
General Assembly Building,
Room 810
P.O. Box 406
Richmond, VA 23218
P: (804) 698-1055
F: (804) 698-6755
E: DelBFowler
@house.virginia.gov

Futrell, Michael T. (D, 2)
General Assembly Building,
Room 509
P.O. Box 406
Richmond, VA 23218
P: (804) 698-1002
F: (804) 698-6702
E: DelMFutrell
@house.virginia.gov

Garrett, T. Scott (R, 23)
General Assembly Building,
Room 524
P.O. Box 406
Richmond, VA 23218
P: (804) 698-1023
F: (804) 698-6723
E: DelSGarrett
@house.virginia.gov

Gilbert, C. Todd (R, 15)
General Assembly Building,
Room 511
P.O. Box 406
Richmond, VA 23218
P: (804) 698-1015
F: (804) 698-6715
E: DelTGilbert
@house.virginia.gov

Greason, Thomas A. (R, 32)
General Assembly Building,
Room 703
P.O. Box 406
Richmond, VA 23218
P: (804) 698-1032
F: (804) 698-6732
E: DelTGreason
@house.virginia.gov

Habeeb, Gregory D. (R, 8)
General Assembly Building,
Room 713
P.O. Box 406
Richmond, VA 23218
P: (804) 698-1008
F: (804) 698-6708
E: DelGHabeeb
@house.virginia.gov

Head, Chris T. (R, 17)
General Assembly Building,
Room 408
P.O. Box 406
Richmond, VA 23218
P: (804) 698-1017
F: (804) 698-6717
E: DelCHead
@house.virginia.gov

Helsel, Gordon C. (R, 91)
General Assembly Building,
Room 812
P.O. Box 406
Richmond, VA 23218
P: (804) 698-1091
E: DelGHelsel
@house.virginia.gov

Herring, Charniele L. (D, 46)
General Assembly Building,
Room 816
P.O. Box 406
Richmond, VA 23218
P: (804) 698-1046
F: (804) 698-6746
E: DelCHerring
@house.virginia.gov

Hester, Daun Sessoms (D, 89)
General Assembly Building,
Room 813
P.O. Box 406
Richmond, VA 23218
P: (804) 698-1089
F: (804) 698-6789
E: DelDHester
@house.virginia.gov

Hodges, M. Keith (R, 98)
General Assembly Building,
Room 821
P.O. Box 406
Richmond, VA 23218
P: (804) 698-1098
F: (804) 698-6798
E: DelKHodges
@house.virginia.gov

Hope, Patrick A. (D, 47)
General Assembly Building,
Room 712
P.O. Box 406
Richmond, VA 23218
P: (804) 698-1047
F: (804) 698-6747
E: DelPHope
@house.virginia.gov

Howell, William J. (R, 28)
General Assembly Building,
Room 635
P.O. Box 406
Richmond, VA 23218
P: (804) 698-1028
F: (804) 698-6728
E: delwhowell
@house.virginia.gov

Hugo, Timothy D. (R, 40)
General Assembly Building,
Room 523
P.O. Box 406
Richmond, VA 23218
P: (804) 698-1040
F: (804) 698-6740
E: DelTHugo
@house.virginia.gov

Ingram, Riley E. (R, 62)
General Assembly Building,
Room 404
P.O. Box 406
Richmond, VA 23218
P: (804) 698-1062
F: (804) 698-6762
E: DelRIngram
@house.virginia.gov

James, Matthew (D, 80)
General Assembly Building,
Room 803
P.O. Box 406
Richmond, VA 23218
P: (804) 698-1080
F: (804) 698-6780
E: DelMJames
@house.virginia.gov

Joannou, Johnny S. (D, 79)
General Assembly Building,
Room 423
P.O. Box 406
Richmond, VA 23218
P: (804) 698-1079
F: (804) 698-6779
E: DelJJoannou
@house.virginia.gov

Jones, S. Chris (R, 76)
General Assembly Building,
Room 948
P.O. Box 406
Richmond, VA 23218
P: (804) 698-1076
F: (804) 698-6776
E: DelCJones
@house.virginia.gov

Keam, Mark L. (D, 35)
General Assembly Building,
Room 706
P.O. Box 406
Richmond, VA 23218
P: (804) 698-1035
F: (804) 698-6735
E: DelMKeam
@house.virginia.gov

Kilgore, Terry G. (R, 1)
General Assembly Building,
Room 704
P.O. Box 406
Richmond, VA 23218
P: (804) 698-1001
F: (804) 698-6701
E: DelTKilgore
@house.virginia.gov

Knight, Barry D. (R, 81)
General Assembly Building,
Room 415
P.O. Box 406
Richmond, VA 23218
P: (804) 698-1081
F: (804) 698-6781
E: DelBKnight
@house.virginia.gov

Kory, Kaye (D, 38)
General Assembly Building,
Room 709
P.O. Box 406
Richmond, VA 23218
P: (804) 698-1038
F: (804) 698-6738
E: DelKKory
@house.virginia.gov

Krupicka Jr., K. Robert (D, 45)
General Assembly Building,
Room 707
P.O. Box 406
Richmond, VA 23218
P: (804) 698-1045
F: (804) 698-6745
E: DelRKrupicka
@house.virginia.gov

Landes, R. Steven (R, 25)
General Assembly Building,
Room 947
P.O. Box 406
Richmond, VA 23218
P: (804) 698-1025
F: (804) 698-6725
E: DelSLandes
@house.virginia.gov

LaRock, David A. (R, 33)
General Assembly Building,
Room 721
P.O. Box 406
Richmond, VA 23218
P: (804) 698-1033
F: (804) 698-6733
E: DelDLaRock
@house.virginia.gov

Leftwich Jr., James A. (R, 78)
General Assembly Building,
Room 417
P.O. Box 406
Richmond, VA 23218
P: (804) 698-1078
F: (804) 698-6778
E: DelJLeftwich
@house.virginia.gov

LeMunyon, James M. (R, 67)
General Assembly Building,
Room 419
P.O. Box 406
Richmond, VA 23218
P: (804) 698-1067
F: (804) 698-6767
E: DelJLeMunyon
@house.virginia.gov

Lindsey, Joseph C. (D, 90)*
General Assembly Building,
Room 505
P.O. Box 406
Richmond, VA 23218
P: (804) 698-1090
F: (804) 698-6790
E: DelJLindsey
@house.virginia.gov

Lingamfelter, L. Scott (R, 31)
General Assembly Building,
Room 504
P.O. Box 406
Richmond, VA 23218
P: (804) 698-1031
F: (804) 698-6731
E: DelSLingamfelter
@house.virginia.gov

Lopez, Alfonso (D, 49)
General Assembly Building,
Room 716
P.O. Box 406
Richmond, VA 23218
P: (804) 698-1049
F: (804) 698-6749
E: DelALopez
@House.virginia.gov

Loupassi, G. Manuel (R, 68)
General Assembly Building,
Room 520
P.O. Box 406
Richmond, VA 23218
P: (804) 698-1068
F: (804) 698-6768
E: DelMLoupassi
@house.virginia.gov

Marshall III, Daniel W. (R, 14)
General Assembly Building,
Room 702
P.O. Box 406
Richmond, VA 23218
P: (804) 698-1014
F: (804) 698-6714
E: DelDMarshall
@house.virginia.gov

Marshall, Robert G. (R, 13)
General Assembly Building,
Room 501
P.O. Box 406
Richmond, VA 23218
P: (804) 698-1013
F: (804) 698-6713
E: DelBMarshall
@house.virginia.gov

Mason, T. Montgomery (D, 93)
General Assembly Building,
Room 806
P.O. Box 806
Richmond, VA 23218
P: (804) 698-1093
F: (804) 698-6793
E: DelMMason
@house.virginia.gov

Massie III, James P. (R, 72)
General Assembly Building,
Room 516
P.O. Box 406
Richmond, VA 23218
P: (804) 698-1072
F: (804) 698-6772
E: DelJMassie
@house.virginia.gov

McClellan, Jennifer L. (D, 71)
General Assembly Building,
Room 515
P.O. Box 406
Richmond, VA 23218
P: (804) 698-1071
F: (804) 698-6771
E: DelJMcClellan
@house.virginia.gov

McQuinn, Delores L. (D, 70)
General Assembly Building,
Room 522
P.O. Box 406
Richmond, VA 23218
P: (804) 698-1070
F: (804) 698-6770
E: DelDMcQuinn
@house.virginia.gov

Virginia

Miller, Jackson H. (R, 50)
General Assembly Building,
Room 720
P.O. Box 406
Richmond, VA 23218
P: (804) 698-1050
F: (804) 698-6750
E: DelJMiller
@house.virginia.gov

Minchew, J. Randy (R, 10)
General Assembly Building,
Room 513
P.O. Box 406
Richmond, VA 23218
P: (804) 698-1010
F: (804) 698-6710
E: DelRMinchew
@house.virginia.gov

Morefield, James W. (R, 3)
General Assembly Building,
Room 714
P.O. Box 406
Richmond, VA 23218
P: (804) 698-1003
F: (804) 698-6703
E: DelJMorefield
@house.virginia.gov

Morris, Richard L. (R, 64)
General Assembly Building,
Room 807
P.O. Box 406
Richmond, VA 23218
P: (804) 698-1064
F: (804) 698-6764
E: DelRMorris
@house.virginia.gov

Morrissey, Joseph D. (I, 74)
General Assembly Building,
Room 715
P.O. Box 406
Richmond, VA 23218
P: (804) 698-1074
F: (804) 698-6774
E: DelJMorrissey
@house.virginia.gov

Murphy, Kathleen J. (D, 34)*
General Assembly Building,
Room 413
P.O. Box 406
Richmond, VA 23218
P: (804) 698-1034
F: (804) 698-6734
E: DelKMurphy
@house.virginia.gov

O'Bannon III, John M. (R, 73)
General Assembly Building,
Room 521
P.O. Box 406
Richmond, VA 23218
P: (804) 698-1073
F: (804) 698-6773
E: DelJOBannon
@house.virginia.gov

O'Quinn, Israel D. (R, 5)
General Assembly Building,
Room 818
P.O. Box 406
Richmond, VA 23218
P: (804) 698-1005
F: (804) 698-6705
E: DelIOQuinn
@house.virginia.gov

Orrock Sr., Robert D. (R, 54)
General Assembly Building,
Room 701
P.O. Box 406
Richmond, VA 23218
P: (804) 698-1054
F: (804) 698-6754
E: DelBOrrock
@house.virginia.gov

Peace, Christopher Kilian (R, 97)
General Assembly Building,
Room 527
P.O. Box 406
Richmond, VA 23218
P: (804) 698-1097
F: (804) 698-6797
E: DelCPeace
@house.virginia.gov

Pillion, Todd E. (R, 4)*
General Assembly Building,
Room 410
P.O. Box 406
Richmond, VA 23218
P: (804) 698-1004
F: (804) 698-6704
E: DelTPillion
@house.virginia.gov

Plum, Kenneth R. (D, 36)
General Assembly Building,
Room 401
P.O. Box 406
Richmond, VA 23218
P: (804) 698-1036
F: (804) 698-6736
E: DelKPlum
@house.virginia.gov

Pogge, Brenda L. (R, 96)
General Assembly Building,
Room 403
P.O. Box 406
Richmond, VA 23218
P: (804) 698-1096
F: (804) 698-1196
E: DelBPogge
@house.virginia.gov

Poindexter, Charles D. (R, 9)
General Assembly Building,
Room 802
P.O. Box 406
Richmond, VA 23218
P: (804) 698-1009
F: (804) 698-6709
E: DelCPoindexter
@house.virginia.gov

Preston, Joseph E. (D, 63)*
General Assembly Building,
Room 407
P.O. Box 406
Richmond, VA 23218
P: (804) 698-1060
F: (804) 698-6763
E: DelJPreston
@house.virginia.gov

Ramadan, David I. (R, 87)
General Assembly Building,
Room 718
P.O. Box 406
Richmond, VA 23218
P: (804) 698-1087
F: (804) 698-6787
E: DelDRamadan
@house.virginia.gov

Ransone, Margaret Bevans (R, 99)
General Assembly Building,
Room 809
P.O. Box 406
Richmond, VA 23218
P: (804) 698-1099
F: (804) 786-6310
E: DelMRansone
@house.virginia.gov

Rasoul, Sam (D, 11)
General Assembly Building,
Room 814
P.O. Box 406
Richmond, VA 23218
P: (804) 698-1011
F: (804) 698-6711
E: DelSRasoul
@house.virginia.gov

Robinson, Roxann L. (R, 27)
General Assembly Building,
Room 409
P.O. Box 406
Richmond, VA 23218
P: (804) 698-1027
F: (804) 698-6727
E: DelRRobinson
@house.virginia.gov

Rush, L. Nick (R, 7)
General Assembly Building,
Room 519
P.O. Box 406
Richmond, VA 23218
P: (804) 698-1007
F: (804) 698-6707
E: DelNRush
@house.virginia.gov

Rust, Thomas Davis (R, 86)
General Assembly Building,
Room 820
P.O. Box 406
Richmond, VA 23218
P: (804) 698-1086
F: (804) 698-6786
E: DelTRust
@house.virginia.gov

Scott, Edward T. (R, 30)
General Assembly Building,
Room 525
P.O. Box 406
Richmond, VA 23218
P: (804) 698-1030
F: (804) 698-6730
E: DelEScott
@house.virginia.gov

Sickles, Mark D. (D, 43)
General Assembly Building,
Room 711
P.O. Box 406
Richmond, VA 23218
P: (804) 698-1043
F: (804) 698-6743
E: DelMSickles
@house.virginia.gov

Simon, Marcus B. (D, 53)
General Assembly Building,
Room 710
P.O. Box 406
Richmond, VA 23218
P: (804) 698-1053
F: (804) 698-6753
E: DelMSimon
@house.virginia.gov

Spruill Sr., Lionell (D, 77)
General Assembly Building, Room 804
P.O. Box 406
Richmond, VA 23218
P: (804) 698-1077
F: (804) 698-6777
E: DelLSpruill@house.virginia.gov

Stolle, Christopher P. (R, 83)
General Assembly Building, Room 422
P.O. Box 406
Richmond, VA 23218
P: (804) 698-1083
F: (804) 698-6783
E: DelCStolle@house.virginia.gov

Sullivan Jr., Richard C. (D, 48)*
General Assembly Building, Room 819
P.O. Box 406
Richmond, VA 23218
P: (804) 698-1048
F: (804) 698-6748
E: DelRSullivan@house.virginia.gov

Surovell, Scott A. (D, 44)
General Assembly Building, Room 708
P.O. Box 406
Richmond, VA 23218
P: (804) 698-1044
F: (804) 698-6744
E: DelSSurovell@house.virginia.gov

Taylor, Scott W. (R, 85)
General Assembly Building, Room 418
P.O. Box 406
Richmond, VA 23218
P: (804) 698-1085
F: (804) 698-6785
E: DelSTaylor@house.virginia.gov

Torian, Luke E. (D, 52)
General Assembly Building, Room 508
P.O. Box 406
Richmond, VA 23218
P: (804) 698-1052
F: (804) 698-6752
E: DelLTorian@house.virginia.gov

Toscano, David J. (D, 57)
General Assembly Building, Room 614
P.O. Box 406
Richmond, VA 23218
P: (804) 698-1057
F: (804) 698-6757
E: DelDToscano@house.virginia.gov

Tyler, Roslyn C. (D, 75)
General Assembly Building, Room 506
P.O. Box 406
Richmond, VA 23218
P: (804) 698-1075
F: (804) 698-6775
E: DelRTyler@house.virginia.gov

Villanueva, Ronald A. (R, 21)
General Assembly Building, Room 503
P.O. Box 406
Richmond, VA 23218
P: (804) 698-1021
F: (804) 698-6721
E: DelRVillanueva@house.virginia.gov

Ward, Jeion A. (D, 92)
General Assembly Building, Room 502
P.O. Box 406
Richmond, VA 23218
P: (804) 698-1092
F: (804) 698-6792
E: DelJWard@house.virginia.gov

Ware Jr., R. Lee (R, 65)
General Assembly Building, Room 421
P.O. Box 406
Richmond, VA 23218
P: (804) 698-1065
F: (804) 698-6765
E: DelLWare@house.virginia.gov

Watts, Vivian E. (D, 39)
General Assembly Building, Room 514
P.O. Box 406
Richmond, VA 23218
P: (804) 698-1039
F: (804) 698-6739
E: DelVWatts@house.virginia.gov

Webert, Michael J. (R, 18)
General Assembly Building, Room 510
P.O. Box 406
Richmond, VA 23218
P: (804) 698-1018
F: (804) 698-6718
E: DelMWebert@house.virginia.gov

Wilt, Tony O. (R, 26)
General Assembly Building, Room 526
P.O. Box 406
Richmond, VA 23218
P: (804) 698-1026
F: (804) 698-6726
E: DelTWilt@house.virginia.gov

Wright Jr., Thomas C. (R, 61)
General Assembly Building, Room 811
P.O. Box 406
Richmond, VA 23218
P: (804) 698-1061
F: (804) 698-6761
E: DelTWright@house.virginia.gov

Yancey, David E. (R, 94)
General Assembly Building, Room 717
P.O. Box 406
Richmond, VA 23218
P: (804) 698-1094
F: (804) 698-6794
E: DelDYancey@house.virginia.gov

Yost, Joseph R. (R, 12)
General Assembly Building, Room 518
P.O. Box 406
Richmond, VA 23218
P: (804) 698-1012
F: (804) 698-6712
E: DelJYost@House.virginia.gov

Congress

Senate

Kaine, Timothy M. (D)
Warner, Mark (D)

House

Beyer, Don (D, 8)
Brat, Dave (R, 7)
Comstock, Barbara J. (R, 10)
Connolly, Gerald (D, 11)
Forbes, J. Randy (R, 4)
Goodlatte, Bob W. (R, 6)
Griffith, H. Morgan (R, 9)
Hurt, Robert (R, 5)
Rigell, Scott (R, 2)
Scott, Robert C. (D, 3)
Wittman, Robert J. (R, 1)

Washington

Executive

Governor
Hon. Jay Inslee (D)
Governor
P.O. Box 40002
Olympia, WA 98504
P: (360) 902-4111
F: (360) 753-4110

Lieutenant Governor
Hon. Brad Owen (D)
Lieutenant Governor
416 14th Avenue, Southwest
P.O. Box 40400
Olympia, WA 98504
P: (360) 786-7700
F: (360) 786-7749
E: ltgov@leg.wa.gov

Attorney General
Hon. Bob Ferguson (D)
Attorney General
1125 Washington Street, Southeast
P.O. Box 40100
Olympia, WA 98504
P: (360) 753-6200
F: (360) 664-0228
E: bob.ferguson@atg.wa.gov

Auditor
Hon. Troy Kelley (D)
State Auditor
Capitol Campus
302 Sid Snyder Avenue, Southwest
Olympia, WA 98504
P: (360) 902-0370
F: (360) 753-0646
E: auditor@sao.wa.gov

Commissioner of Insurance
Hon. Mike Kreidler (D)
Commissioner
P.O. Box 40256
Olympia, WA 98504
P: (360) 725-7000
F: (360) 586-3535
E: askMike@oic.wa.gov

Commissioner of Public Lands
Hon. Peter J. Goldmark (D)
Commissioner of Public Lands
1111 Washington Street, Southeast
P.O. Box 47000
Olympia, WA 98504
P: (360) 902-1000
F: (360) 902-1775
E: cpl@dnr.wa.gov

Secretary of State
Hon. Kim Wyman (R)
Secretary of State
P.O. Box 40220
Olympia, WA 98504
P: (360) 902-4151
F: (360) 586-5629
E: mail@sos.wa.gov

Superintendent of Public Instruction
Hon. Randy Dorn
Superintendent of Public Instruction
Old Capitol Building
Olympia, WA 98504
P: (360) 725-6000
F: (360) 753-6712
E: randy.dorn@k12.wa.us

Treasurer
Hon. James L. McIntire (D)
State Treasurer
Legislative Building
P.O. Box 40200
Olympia, WA 98504
P: (360) 902-9000
F: (360) 902-9037
E: watreas@tre.wa.gov

Judiciary

Supreme Court (NE)
Mr. Ronald R. Carpenter
Clerk
415 12th Avenue, Southwest
P.O. Box 40929
Olympia, WA 98504
P: (360) 357-2077
F: (360) 357-2102
E: supreme@courts.wa.gov

Hon. Barbara A. Madsen
Chief Justice
Hon. Mary E. Fairhurst
Hon. Steven C. Gonzalez
Hon. Charles W. Johnson
Hon. Sheryl Gordon McCloud
Hon. Susan J. Owens
Hon. Debra L. Stephens
Hon. Charlie Wiggins
Hon. Mary Yu

Legislative Senate

Senate President
Hon. Brad Owen (D)
Lieutenant Governor
416 14th Avenue, Southwest
P.O. Box 40400
Olympia, WA 98504
P: (360) 786-7700
F: (360) 786-7749
E: ltgov@leg.wa.gov

President Pro Tempore of the Senate
Sen. Pam Roach (R)
President Pro Tempore
112 Irv Newhouse Building
P.O. Box 40431
Olympia, WA 98504
P: (360) 786-7660
F: (360) 786-7173
E: pam.roach@leg.wa.gov

Senate Majority Leader
Sen. Mark Schoesler (R)
Majority Leader
307 Legislative Building
P.O. Box 40409
Olympia, WA 98504
P: (360) 786-7620
F: (360) 786-1999
E: mark.schoesler@leg.wa.gov

Senate Minority Leader
Sen. Sharon Nelson (D)
Democratic Leader
316 Legislative Building
P.O. Box 40434
Olympia, WA 98504
P: (360) 786-7667
E: sharon.nelson@leg.wa.gov

Secretary of the Senate
Mr. Hunter G. Goodman
Secretary of the Senate
418 Legislative Building
P.O. Box 40482
Olympia, WA 98504
P: (360) 786-7550
E: hunter.goodman@leg.wa.gov

Members of the Senate
Angel, Jan (R, 26)
203A Irv Newhouse Building
P.O. Box 40426
Olympia, WA 98504
P: (360) 786-7650
E: jan.angel@leg.wa.gov

Bailey, Barbara (R, 10)
109B Irv Newhouse Building
P.O. Box 40410
Olympia, WA 98504
P: (360) 786-7618
E: barbara.bailey@leg.wa.gov

Baumgartner, Michael (R, 6)
404 Legislative Building
P.O. Box 40406
Olympia, WA 98504
P: (360) 786-7610
E: michael.baumgartner@leg.wa.gov

Becker, Randi (R, 2)
110 Irv Newhouse Building
P.O. Box 40402
Olympia, WA 98504
P: (360) 786-7602
E: randi.becker@leg.wa.gov

Benton, Don (R, 17)
409 Legislative Building
P.O. Box 40417
Olympia, WA 98504
P: (360) 786-7632
F: (360) 786-7819
E: don.benton@leg.wa.gov

Billig, Andy (D, 3)
412 Legislative Building
P.O. Box 40403
Olympia, WA 98504
P: (360) 786-7604
E: andy.billig@leg.wa.gov

Braun, John (R, 20)
407 Legislative Building
P.O. Box 40420
Olympia, WA 98504
P: (360) 786-7638
E: john.braun@leg.wa.gov

Brown, Sharon (R, 8)
202 Irv Newhouse Building
P.O. Box 40408
Olympia, WA 98504
P: (360) 786-7614
E: sharon.brown@leg.wa.gov

Chase, Maralyn (D, 32)
218 John A. Cherberg Building
P.O. Box 40432
Olympia, WA 98504
P: (360) 786-7662
E: maralyn.chase@leg.wa.gov

Cleveland, Annette (D, 49)
220 John A. Cherberg Building
P.O. Box 40449
Olympia, WA 98504
P: (360) 786-7696
E: Annette.Cleveland
@leg.wa.gov

Conway, Steve (D, 29)
212 John A. Cherberg Building
P.O. Box 40429
Olympia, WA 98504
P: (360) 786-7656
E: steve.conway@leg.wa.gov

Dammeier, Bruce (R, 25)
205 Irv Newhouse Building
P.O. Box 40425
Olympia, WA 98504
P: (360) 786-7648
E: bruce.dammeier
@leg.wa.gov

Dansel, Brian (R, 7)
115B Irv Newhouse Building
P.O. Box 40407
Olympia, WA 98504
P: (360) 786-7612
E: brian.dansel@leg.wa.gov

Darneille, Jeannie (D, 27)
227 John A. Cherberg Building
P.O. Box 40427
Olympia, WA 98504
P: (360) 786-7652
E: jeannie.darneille
@leg.wa.gov

Ericksen, Doug (R, 42)
414 Legislative Building
P.O. Box 40442
Olympia, WA 98504
P: (360) 786-7682
E: doug.ericksen@leg.wa.gov

Fain, Joe (R, 47)
309 Legislative Building
P.O. Box 40447
Olympia, WA 98504
P: (360) 786-7692
E: joe.fain@leg.wa.gov

Fraser, Karen (D, 22)
314 Legislative Building
P.O. Box 40422
Olympia, WA 98504
P: (360) 786-7642
F: (360) 786-1999
E: karen.fraser@leg.wa.gov

Frockt, David (D, 46)
402 Legislative Building
P.O. Box 40446
Olympia, WA 98504
P: (360) 786-7690
E: david.frockt@leg.wa.gov

Habib, Cyrus (D, 48)
230 John A. Cherberg Building
P.O. Box 40448
Olympia, WA 98504
P: (360) 786-7694
E: cyrus.habib@leg.wa.gov

Hargrove, James (D, 24)
411 Legislative Building
P.O. Box 40424
Olympia, WA 98504
P: (360) 786-7646
F: (360) 786-1323
E: jim.hargrove@leg.wa.gov

Hasegawa, Bob (D, 11)
223 John A. Cherberg Building
P.O. Box 40411
Olympia, WA 98504
P: (360) 786-7616
E: bob.hasegawa@leg.wa.gov

Hatfield, Brian (D, 19)
237 John A. Cherberg Building
P.O. Box 40419
Olympia, WA 98504
P: (360) 786-7636
E: brian.hatfield
@leg.wa.gov

Hewitt, Mike (R, 16)
204 Irv Newhouse Building
P.O. Box 40416
Olympia, WA 98504
P: (360) 786-7630
F: (369) 786-1266
E: mike.hewitt@leg.wa.gov

Hill, Andy (R, 45)
303 John A. Cherberg Building
P.O. Box 40445
Olympia, WA 98504
P: (360) 786-7672
E: andy.hill@leg.wa.gov

Hobbs, Steve (D, 44)
239 John A. Cherberg Building
P.O. Box 40444
Olympia, WA 98504
P: (360) 786-7686
E: steve.hobbs@leg.wa.gov

Honeyford, Jim (R, 15)
107 Irv Newhouse Building
P.O. Box 40415
Olympia, WA 98504
P: (360) 786-7684
F: (360) 786-1999
E: jim.honeyford@leg.wa.gov

Jayapal, Pramila (D, 37)*
213 John A. Cherberg Building
P.O. Box 40437
Olympia, WA 98504
P: (360) 786-7688
E: pramila.jayapal
@leg.wa.gov

Keiser, Karen (D, 33)
224A John A. Cherberg
Building
P.O. Box 40433
Olympia, WA 98504
P: (360) 786-7664
F: (360) 786-1999
E: karen.keiser@leg.wa.gov

King, Curtis (R, 14)
305 John A. Cherberg Building
P.O. Box 40414
Olympia, WA 98504
P: (360) 786-7626
F: (360) 786-1999
E: curtis.king@leg.wa.gov

Kohl-Welles, Jeanne (D, 36)
219 John A. Cherberg Building
P.O. Box 40436
Olympia, WA 98504
P: (360) 786-7670
F: (360) 786-1999
E: jeanne.kohl-welles
@leg.wa.gov

Liias, Marko (D, 21)
226 John A. Cherberg Building
P.O. Box 40421
Olympia, WA 98504
P: (360) 786-7640
E: marko.liias@leg.wa.gov

Litzow, Steve (R, 41)
416 Legislative Building
P.O. Box 40441
Olympia, WA 98504
P: (360) 786-7641
E: steve.litzow@leg.wa.gov

McAuliffe, Rosemary (D, 1)
403 Legislative Building
P.O. Box 40401
Olympia, WA 98504
P: (360) 786-7600
F: (360) 786-1999
E: rosemary.mcauliffe
@leg.wa.gov

McCoy, John (D, 38)
241 John A. Cherberg Building
P.O. Box 40438
Olympia, WA 98504
P: (360) 786-7674
E: john.mccoy@leg.wa.gov

Miloscia, Mark (D, 30)
105 Irv Newhouse Building
P.O. Box 40430
Olympia, WA 98504
P: (360) 786-7658
E: mark.miloscia@leg.wa.gov

Mullet, Mark (D, 5)
415 Legislative Building
PO Box 40405
Olympia, WA 98504
P: (360) 786-7608
E: mark.mullet@leg.wa.gov

Nelson, Sharon (D, 34)
316 Legislative Building
P.O. Box 40434
Olympia, WA 98504
P: (360) 786-7667
E: sharon.nelson@leg.wa.gov

O'Ban, Steve (R, 28)
102 Irv Newhouse Building
P.O. Box 40428
Olympia, WA 98504
P: (360) 786-7654
E: steve.oban@leg.wa.gov

Padden, Mike (R, 4)
106 Irv Newhouse Building
P.O. Box 40404
Olympia, WA 98504
P: (360) 786-7606
E: mike.padden@leg.wa.gov

Parlette, Linda Evans (R, 12)
305 Legislative Building
P.O. Box 40412
Olympia, WA 98504
P: (360) 786-7622
F: (360) 786-1266
E: linda.parlette
@leg.wa.gov

Pearson, Kirk (R, 39)
115D Irv Newhouse Building
P.O. Box 40439
Olympia, WA 98504
P: (360) 786-7676
E: kirk.pearson@leg.wa.gov

Pedersen, Jamie (D, 43)
235 John A. Cherberg Building
P.O. Box 40443
Olympia, WA 98504
P: (360) 786-7628
E: jamie.pedersen
@leg.wa.gov

Ranker, Kevin (D, 40)
215 John A. Cherberg Building
P.O. Box 40440
Olympia, WA 98504
P: (360) 786-7678
E: kevin.ranker@leg.wa.gov

Rivers, Ann (R, 18)
405 Legislative Building
P.O. Box 40418
Olympia, WA 98504
P: (360) 786-7634
E: ann.rivers@leg.wa.gov

Washington

Roach, Pam (R, 31)
112 Irv Newhouse Building
P.O. Box 40431
Olympia, WA 98504
P: (360) 786-7660
F: (360) 786-7173
E: pam.roach@leg.wa.gov

Rolfes, Christine (D, 23)
233 John A. Cherberg Building
P.O. Box 40423
Olympia, WA 98504
P: (360) 786-7644
E: christine.rolfes@leg.wa.gov

Schoesler, Mark (R, 9)
307 Legislative Building
P.O. Box 40409
Olympia, WA 98504
P: (360) 786-7620
F: (360) 786-1999
E: mark.schoesler@leg.wa.gov

Sheldon, Tim (D, 35)
312 Legislative Building
P.O. Box 40435
Olympia, WA 98504
P: (360) 786-7668
F: (360) 786-1999
E: timothy.sheldon@leg.wa.gov

Warnick, Judy (R, 13)
103 Irv Newhouse Building
P.O. Box 40413
Olympia, WA 98504
P: (360) 786-7624
E: judy.warnick@leg.wa.gov

House

Speaker of the House

Rep. Frank Chopp (D)
Speaker
339C Legislative Building
P.O. Box 40600
Olympia, WA 98504
P: (360) 786-7920
E: frank.chopp@leg.wa.gov

Speaker Pro Tempore of the House

Rep. Jim Moeller (D)
Speaker Pro Tem
429B Legislative Building
P.O. Box 40600
Olympia, WA 98504
P: (360) 786-7872
E: jim.moeller@leg.wa.gov

House Majority Leader

Rep. Pat Sullivan (D)
Majority Leader
339A Legislative Building
P.O. Box 40600
Olympia, WA 98504
P: (360) 786-7858
E: pat.sullivan@leg.wa.gov

House Minority Leader

Rep. Dan Kristiansen (R)
Minority Leader
335C Legislative Building
P.O. Box 40600
Olympia, WA 98504
P: (360) 786-7967
E: dan.kristiansen@leg.wa.gov

Clerk of the House

Ms. Barbara Baker
Chief Clerk
338B Legislative Building
P.O. Box 40600
Olympia, WA 98504
P: (360) 786-7750
F: (360) 786-1999
E: barbara.baker@leg.wa.gov

Members of the House

Appleton, Sherry (D, 23)
132F Legislative Building
P.O. Box 40600
Olympia, WA 98504
P: (360) 786-7934
E: sherry.appleton@leg.wa.gov

Bergquist, Steve (D, 11)
322 John L. O'Brien Building
P.O. Box 40600
Olympia, WA 98504
P: (360) 786-7862
E: steve.bergquist@leg.wa.gov

Blake, Brian (D, 19)
437A Legislative Building
P.O. Box 40600
Olympia, WA 98504
P: (360) 786-7870
E: brian.blake@leg.wa.gov

Buys, Vincent (R, 42)
465 John L. O'Brien Building
P.O. Box 40600
Olympia, WA 98504
P: (360) 786-7854
E: vincent.buys@leg.wa.gov

Caldier, Michelle (R, 26)*
417 John L. O'Brien Building
P.O. Box 40600
Olympia, WA 98504
P: (360) 786-7802
E: michelle.caldier@leg.wa.gov

Carlyle, Reuven (D, 36)
325 John L. O'Brien Building
P.O. Box 40600
Olympia, WA 98504
P: (360) 786-7814
E: reuven.carlyle@leg.wa.gov

Chandler, Bruce (R, 15)
427B Legislative Building
P.O. Box 40600
Olympia, WA 98504
P: (360) 786-7960
E: bruce.chandler@leg.wa.gov

Chopp, Frank (D, 43)
339C Legislative Building
P.O. Box 40600
Olympia, WA 98504
P: (360) 786-7920
E: frank.chopp@leg.wa.gov

Clibborn, Judy (D, 41)
415 John L. O'Brien Building
P.O. Box 40600
Olympia, WA 98504
P: (360) 786-7926
E: judy.clibborn@leg.wa.gov

Cody, Eileen (D, 34)
303 John L. O'Brien Building
P.O. Box 40600
Olympia, WA 98504
P: (360) 786-7978
E: eileen.cody@leg.wa.gov

Condotta, Cary (R, 12)
425B Legislative Building
P.O. Box 40600
Olympia, WA 98504
P: (360) 786-7954
E: cary.condotta@leg.wa.gov

DeBolt, Richard (R, 20)
425A Legislative Building
P.O. Box 40600
Olympia, WA 98504
P: (360) 786-7896
E: richard.debolt@leg.wa.gov

Dent, Tom (R, 13)*
411 John L. O'Brien Building
P.O. Box 40600
Olympia, WA 98504
P: (360) 786-7932
E: tom.dent@leg.wa.gov

Dunshee, Hans (D, 44)
314 John L. O'Brien Building
P.O. Box 40600
Olympia, WA 98504
P: (360) 786-7804
E: hans.dunshee@leg.wa.gov

Fagan, Susan (R, 9)
432 John L. O'Brien Building
P.O. Box 40600
Olympia, WA 98504
P: (360) 786-7942
E: susan.fagan@leg.wa.gov

Farrell, Jessyn (D, 46)
370 John L. O'Brien Building
P.O. Box 40600
Olympia, WA 98504
P: (360) 786-7818
E: jessyn.farrell@leg.wa.gov

Fey, Jake (D, 27)
414 John L. O'Brien Building
P.O. Box 40600
Olympia, WA 98504
P: (360) 786-7974
E: jake.fey@leg.wa.gov

Fitzgibbon, Joe (D, 34)
305 John L. O'Brien Building
P.O. Box 40600
Olympia, WA 98504
P: (360) 786-7952
E: joe.fitzgibbon@leg.wa.gov

Goodman, Roger (D, 45)
436B Legislative Building
P.O. Box 40600
Olympia, WA 98504
P: (360) 786-7878
E: roger.goodman@leg.wa.gov

Gregerson, Mia (D, 33)
318 John L. O'Brien Building
P.O. Box 40600
Olympia, WA 98504
P: (360) 786-7868
E: mia.gregerson@leg.wa.gov

Gregory, Carol (D, 30)*
317 John L. O'Brien Building
P.O. Box 40600
Olympia, WA 98504
P: (360) 786-7830
E: carol.gregory@leg.wa.gov

Griffey, Daniel (R, 35)*
410 John L. O'Brien Building
P.O. Box 40600
Olympia, WA 98504
P: (360) 786-7966
E: daniel.griffey@leg.wa.gov

Haler, Larry (R, 8)
122D Legislative Building
P.O. Box 40600
Olympia, WA 98504
P: (360) 786-7986
E: larry.haler@leg.wa.gov

Hansen, Drew (D, 23)
369 John L. O'Brien Building
P.O. Box 40600
Olympia, WA 98504
P: (360) 786-7842
E: drew.hansen@leg.wa.gov

Hargrove, Mark (R, 47)
409 John L. O'Brien Building
P.O. Box 40600
Olympia, WA 98504
P: (360) 786-7918
E: mark.hargrove@leg.wa.gov

Harmsworth, Mark (R, 44)*
466 John L. O'Brien Building
P.O. Box 40600
Olympia, WA 98504
P: (360) 786-7892
E: mark.harmsworth
@leg.wa.gov

Harris, Paul (R, 17)
403 John L. O'Brien Building
P.O. Box 40600
Olympia, WA 98504
P: (360) 786-7976
E: paul.harris@leg.wa.gov

Hawkins, Brad (R, 12)
122G Legislative Building
P.O. Box 40600
Olympia, WA 98504
P: (360) 786-7832
E: brad.hawkins@leg.wa.gov

Hayes, Dave (R, 10)
467 John L. O'Brien Building
P.O. Box 40600
Olympia, WA 98504
P: (360) 786-7914
E: dave.hayes@leg.wa.gov

Holy, Jeff (R, 6)
405 John L. O'Brien Building
P.O. Box 40600
Olympia, WA 98504
P: (360) 786-7962
E: jeff.holy@leg.wa.gov

Hudgins, Zack (D, 11)
438A Legislative Building
P.O. Box 40600
Olympia, WA 98504
P: (360) 786-7956
E: zack.hudgins@leg.wa.gov

Hunt, Graham (R, 2)
406 John L. O'Brien Building
P.O. Box 40600
Olympia, WA 98504
P: (360) 786-7824
E: graham.hunt@leg.wa.gov

Hunt, Sam (D, 22)
438B Legislative Building
P.O. Box 40600
Olympia, WA 98504
P: (360) 786-7992
E: sam.hunt@leg.wa.gov

Hunter, Ross (D, 48)
315 John L. O'Brien Building
P.O. Box 40600
Olympia, WA 98504
P: (360) 786-7936
E: ross.hunter@leg.wa.gov

Hurst, Christopher (D, 31)
320 John L. O'Brien Building
P.O. Box 40600
Olympia, WA 98504
P: (360) 786-7866
E: christopher.hurst
@leg.wa.gov

Jinkins, Laurie A. (D, 27)
311 John L. O'Brien Building
P.O. Box 40600
Olympia, WA 98504
P: (360) 786-7930
E: laurie.jinkins
@leg.wa.gov

Johnson, Norm (R, 14)
122C Legislative Building
P.O. Box 40600
Olympia, WA 98504
P: (360) 786-7810
E: norm.johnson@leg.wa.gov

Kagi, Ruth (D, 32)
308 John L. O'Brien Building
P.O. Box 40600
Olympia, WA 98504
P: (360) 786-7910
E: ruth.kagi@leg.wa.gov

Kilduff, Christine (D, 28)*
331 John L. O'Brien Building
P.O. Box 40600
Olympia, WA 98504
P: (360) 786-7958
E: christine.kilduff
@leg.wa.gov

Kirby, Steve (D, 29)
437B Legislative Building
P.O. Box 40600
Olympia, WA 98504
P: (360) 786-7996
E: steve.kirby@leg.wa.gov

Klippert, Brad (R, 8)
122A Legislative Building
P.O. Box 40600
Olympia, WA 98504
P: (360) 786-7882
E: brad.klippert@leg.wa.gov

Kochmar, Linda (R, 30)
122F Legislative Building
P.O. Box 40600
Olympia, WA 98504
P: (360) 786-7898
E: linda.kochmar@leg.wa.gov

Kretz, Joel (R, 7)
335A Legislative Building
P.O. Box 40600
Olympia, WA 98504
P: (360) 786-7988
E: joel.kretz@leg.wa.gov

Kristiansen, Dan (R, 39)
335C Legislative Building
P.O. Box 40600
Olympia, WA 98504
P: (360) 786-7967
E: dan.kristiansen
@leg.wa.gov

Lytton, Kristine (D, 40)
429A Legislative Building
P.O. Box 40600
Olympia, WA 98504
P: (360) 786-7800
E: kristine.lytton
@leg.wa.gov

MacEwen, Drew (R, 35)
434 John L. O'Brien Building
P.O. Box 40600
Olympia, WA 98504
P: (360) 786-7902
E: drew.macewen@leg.wa.gov

Magendanz, Chad (R, 5)
427 John L. O'Brien Building
P.O. Box 40600
Olympia, WA 98504
P: (360) 786-7876
E: chad.magendanz
@leg.wa.gov

Manweller, Matt (R, 13)
470 John L. O'Brien Building
P.O. Box 40600
Olympia, WA 98504
P: (360) 786-7808
E: matt.manweller
@leg.wa.gov

McBride, Joan (D, 48)*
335 John L. O'Brien Building
P.O. Box 40600
Olympia, WA 98504
P: (360) 786-7848
E: joan.mcbride@leg.wa.gov

McCabe, Gina (R, 14)*
431 John L. O'Brien Building
P.O. Box 40600
Olympia, WA 98504
P: (360) 786-7856
E: gina.mccabe@leg.wa.gov

McCaslin, Bob (R, 4)
425 John L. O'Brien Building
P.O. Box 40600
Olympia, WA 98504
P: (360) 786-7820
F: (360) 786-1999
E: mccaslin.bob@leg.wa.gov

Moeller, Jim (D, 49)
429B Legislative Building
P.O. Box 40600
Olympia, WA 98504
P: (360) 786-7872
E: jim.moeller@leg.wa.gov

Morris, Jeff (D, 40)
436A Legislative Building
P.O. Box 40600
Olympia, WA 98504
P: (360) 786-7970
E: jeff.morris@leg.wa.gov

Moscoso, Luis (D, 1)
132A Legislative Building
P.O. Box 40600
Olympia, WA 98504
P: (360) 786-7900
E: luis.moscoso@leg.wa.gov

Muri, Dick (R, 28)
424 John L. O'Brien Building
P.O. Box 40600
Olympia, WA 98504
P: (360) 786-7890
E: dick.muri@leg.wa.gov

Nealey, Terry (R, 16)
404 John L. O'Brien Building
P.O. Box 40600
Olympia, WA 98504
P: (360) 786-7828
E: terry.nealey@leg.wa.gov

Orcutt, Ed (R, 20)
408 John L. O'Brien Building
P.O. Box 40600
Olympia, WA 98504
P: (360) 786-7990
E: ed.orcutt@leg.wa.gov

Ormsby, Timm (D, 3)
122H Legislative Building
P.O. Box 40600
Olympia, WA 98504
P: (360) 786-7946
E: timm.ormsby@leg.wa.gov

Washington

Ortiz-Self, Lillian (D, 21)
330 John L. O'Brien Buidling
P.O. Box 40600
Olympia, WA 98504
P: (360) 786-7972
E: lillian.ortiz-self
@leg.wa.gov

Orwall, Tina L. (D, 33)
326 John L. O'Brien Building
P.O. Box 40600
Olympia, WA 98504
P: (360) 786-7834
E: tina.orwall@leg.wa.gov

Parker, Kevin (R, 6)
421 John L. O'Brien Building
P.O. Box 40600
Olympia, WA 98504
P: (340) 786-7922
E: kevin.parker@leg.wa.gov

Peterson, Strom (D, 21)*
324 John L. O'Brien Building
P.O. Box 40600
Olympia, WA 98504
P: (360) 786-7950

Pettigrew, Eric (D, 37)
434B Legislative Building
P.O. Box 40600
Olympia, WA 98504
P: (360) 786-7838
E: eric.pettigrew
@leg.wa.gov

Pike, Liz (R, 18)
122B Legislative Building
P.O. Box 40600
Olympia, WA 98504
P: (360) 786-7812
E: liz.pike@leg.wa.gov

Pollet, Gerry (D, 46)
132C Legislative Building
P.O. Box 40600
Olympia, WA 98504
P: (360) 786-7886
E: gerry.pollet@leg.wa.gov

Reykdal, Chris (D, 22)
319 John L. O'Brien Building
P.O. Box 40600
Olympia, WA 98504
P: (360) 786-7940
E: chris.reykdal@leg.wa.gov

Riccelli, Marcus (D, 3)
327 John L. O'Brien Building
P.O. Box 40600
Olympia, WA 98504
P: (360) 786-7888
E: marcus.riccelli
@leg.wa.gov

Robinson, June (D, 38)
332 John L. O'Brien Building
P.O. Box 40600
Olympia, WA 98504
P: (360) 786-7864
E: june.robinson@leg.wa.gov

Rodne, Jay (R, 5)
430 John L. O'Brien Building
P.O. Box 40600
Olympia, WA 98504
P: (360) 786-7852
E: jay.rodne@leg.wa.gov

Ryu, Cindy (D, 32)
132D Legislative Building
P.O. Box 40600
Olympia, WA 98504
P: (360) 786-7880
E: cindy.ryu@leg.wa.gov

Santos, Sharon Tomiko (D, 37)
321 John L. O'Brien Building
P.O. Box 40600
Olympia, WA 98504
P: (360) 786-7944
E: sharontomiko.santos
@leg.wa.gov

Sawyer, David (D, 29)
306 John L. O'Brien Building
P.O. Box 40600
Olympia, WA 98504
P: (360) 786-7906
E: david.sawyer@leg.wa.gov

Schmick, Joe (R, 9)
426B Legislative Building
P.O. Box 40600
Olympia, WA 98504
P: (360) 786-7844
E: joe.schmick@leg.wa.gov

Scott, Elizabeth (R, 39)
436 John L. O'Brien Building
P.O. Box 40600
Olympia, WA 98504
P: (360) 786-7816
E: elizabeth.scott
@leg.wa.gov

Sells, Mike (D, 38)
132B Legislative Building
P.O. Box 40600
Olympia, WA 98504
P: (360) 786-7840
E: mike.sells@leg.wa.gov

Senn, Tana (D, 41)
309 John L. O'Brien Building
P.O. Box 40600
Olympia, WA 98504
P: (360) 786-7894
E: tana.senn@leg.wa.gov

Shea, Matthew (R, 4)
437 John L. O'Brien Building
P.O. Box 40600
Olympia, WA 98504
P: (340) 786-7984
E: matt.shea@leg.wa.gov

Short, Shelly (R, 7)
427A Legislative Building
P.O. Box 40600
Olympia, WA 98504
P: (340) 786-7908
E: shelly.short@leg.wa.gov

Smith, Norma (R, 10)
435 John L. O'Brien Building
P.O. Box 40600
Olympia, WA 98504
P: (360) 786-7884
E: norma.smith@leg.wa.gov

Springer, Larry (D, 45)
132E Legislative Building
P.O. Box 40600
Olympia, WA 98504
P: (360) 786-7822
E: larry.springer
@leg.wa.gov

Stambaugh, Melanie (R, 25)*
122E Legislative Building
P.O. Box 40600
Olympia, WA 98504
P: (360) 786-7948
E: melanie.stambaugh
@leg.wa.gov

Stanford, Derek (D, 1)
304 John L. O'Brien Building
P.O. Box 40600
Olympia, WA 98504
P: (360) 786-7928
E: derek.stanford
@leg.wa.gov

Stokesbary, Drew (R, 31)*
426 John L. O'Brien Building
P.O. Box 40600
Olympia, WA 98504
P: (360) 786-7846
E: drew.stokesbary
@leg.wa.gov

Sullivan, Pat (D, 47)
339A Legislative Building
P.O. Box 40600
Olympia, WA 98504
P: (360) 786-7858
E: pat.sullivan@leg.wa.gov

Takko, Dean (D, 19)
336 John L. O'Brien Building
P.O. Box 40600
Olympia, WA 98504
P: (360) 786-7806
E: dean.takko@leg.wa.gov

Tarleton, Gael (D, 36)
334 John L. O'Brien Building
P.O. Box 40600
Olympia, WA 98504
P: (360) 786-7860
E: gael.tarleton@leg.wa.gov

Taylor, David (R, 15)
428 John L. O'Brien Building
P.O. Box 40600
Olympia, WA 98504
P: (360) 786-7874
E: david.taylor@leg.wa.gov

Tharinger, Steve (D, 24)
368 John L. O'Brien Building
P.O. Box 40600
Olympia, WA 98504
P: (360) 786-7904
E: steve.tharinger
@leg.wa.gov

Van De Wege, Kevin (D, 24)
434A Legislative Building
P.O. Box 40600
Olympia, WA 98504
P: (360) 786-7916
E: kevin.vandewege
@leg.wa.gov

VanWerven, Luanna (R, 42)*
419 John L. O'Brien Building
P.O. Box 40600
Olympia, WA 98504
P: (360) 786-7980
E: luanna.vanwerven
@leg.wa.gov

Vick, Brandon (R, 18)
469 John L. O'Brien Building
P.O. Box 40600
Olympia, WA 98504
P: (360) 786-7850
E: Brandon.Vick@leg.wa.gov

Walkinshaw, Brady (D, 43)
328 John L. O'Brien Building
P.O. Box 40600
Olympia, WA 98504
P: (360) 786-7826
E: brady.walkinshaw
@leg.wa.gov

Walsh, Maureen (R, 16)
420 John L. O'Brien Building
P.O. Box 40600
Olympia, WA 98504
P: (360) 786-7836
E: maureen.walsh@leg.wa.gov

Wilcox, J.T. (R, 2)
426A Legislative Building
P.O. Box 40600
Olympia, WA 98504
P: (360) 786-7912
E: jt.wilcox@leg.wa.gov

Wilson, Lynda (R, 17)*
418 John L. O'Brien Building
P.O. Box 40600
Olympia, WA 98504
P: (360) 786-7994
E: lynda.wilson@leg.wa.gov

Wylie, Sharon (D, 49)
310 John L. O'Brien Building
P.O. Box 40600
Olympia, WA 98504
P: (360) 786-7924
E: sharon.wylie@leg.wa.gov

Young, Jesse (R, 26)
422 John L. O'Brien Building
P.O. Box 40600
Olympia, WA 98504
P: (360) 786-7964
E: jesse.young@leg.wa.gov

Zeiger, Hans (R, 25)
468 John L. O'Brien Building
P.O. Box 40600
Olympia, WA 98504
P: (360) 786-7968
E: hans.zeiger@leg.wa.gov

Congress

Senate

Cantwell, Maria (D)
Murray, Patty (D)

House

Beutler, Jaime Herrera (R, 3)
DelBene, Suzan (D, 1)
Heck, Denny (D, 10)
Kilmer, Derek (D, 6)
Larsen, Rick (D, 2)
McDermott, Jim (D, 7)
Reichert, Dave G. (R, 8)
Rodgers, Cathy McMorris (R, 5)
Smith, Adam (D, 9)

West Virginia

Executive

Governor

Hon. Earl Ray Tomblin (D)
Governor
1900 Kanawha Boulevard, East
Charleston, WV 25305
P: (304) 558-2000

Lieutenant Governor

Sen. Bill Cole (R)
(elected by the Legislature)
Senate President/Lieutenant Governor
Room 229M, Building 1
State Capitol Complex
Charleston, WV 25305
P: (304) 357-7801
E: bill.cole@wvsenate.gov

Commissioner of Agriculture

Mr. Walt Helmick
Commissioner
1900 Kanawha Boulevard, East
Room E-28
Charleston, WV 25305
P: (304) 558-3550
F: (304) 558-2203
E: whelmick@wvda.us

Attorney General

Hon. Patrick Morrisey (R)
Attorney General
Capitol Complex Building 1, Room E-26
1900 Kanawha Boulevard, East
Charleston, WV 25305
P: (304) 558-2021
F: (304) 558-0140

Auditor

Hon. Glen B. Gainer III
State Auditor
1900 Kanawha Boulevard, East
Building 1, Room W-100
Charleston, WV 25305
P: (304) 558-2261
F: (304) 558-5200

Secretary of State

Hon. Natalie Tennant (D)
Secretary of State
Building 1, Suite-157K
1900 Kanawha Boulevard, East
Charleston, WV 25305
P: (304) 558-6000
F: (304) 558-0900
E: wvsos@wvsos.com

Treasurer

Hon. John D. Perdue (D)
State Treasurer
1900 Kanawha Boulevard, East
Capitol Complex Building 1, Room E-145
Charleston, WV 25305
P: (304) 558-5000

Judiciary

Supreme Court of Appeals (PE)

Mr. Rory L. Perry II
Clerk of Court
State Capitol, Room E-317
1900 Kanawha Boulevard, East
Charleston, WV 25305
P: (304) 558-2601
F: (304) 558-3815

Hon. Margaret L. Workman
Chief Justice
Hon. Brent D. Benjamin
Hon. Robin Jean Davis
Hon. Menis Ketchum II
Hon. Allen H. Loughry II

Legislative Senate

Senate President

Sen. Bill Cole (R)
Senate President/Lieutenant Governor
Room 229M, Building 1
State Capitol Complex
Charleston, WV 25305
P: (304) 357-7801
E: bill.cole@wvsenate.gov

President Pro Tempore of the Senate

Sen. Donna J. Boley (R)
President Pro Tempore
Room 206W, Building 1
State Capitol Complex
Charleston, WV 25305
P: (304) 357-7905
E: donnaboley@suddenlink.net

Senate Majority Leader

Sen. Mitch Carmichael (R)
Majority Leader
Room 227M, Building 1
State Capitol Complex
Charleston, WV 25305
P: (304) 357-7855
E: mitch.carmichael@wvsenate.gov

Senate Minority Leader

Sen. Jeffrey V. Kessler (D)
Minority Leader
Room 257M, Building 1
State Capitol Complex
Charleston, WV 25305
P: (304) 357-7902
E: jeff.kessler@wvsenate.gov

Clerk of the Senate

Mr. Clark S. Barnes
Clerk of the Senate
Room 211M, Building 1
State Capitol Complex
Charleston, WV 25305
P: (304) 357-7800
E: senate.clerk@wvsenate.gov

Members of the Senate

Beach, Robert D. (D, 13)
Room 204W, Building 1
State Capitol Complex
Charleston, WV 25305
P: (304) 357-7919
E: bob.beach@wvsenate.gov

Blair, Craig (R, 15)
Room 217W, Building 1
State Capitol Complex
Charleston, WV 25305
P: (304) 357-7867
E: craig@craigblair.com

Boley, Donna J. (R, 3)
Room 206W, Building 1
State Capitol Complex
Charleston, WV 25305
P: (304) 357-7905
E: donnaboley@suddenlink.net

Boso, Greg (R, 11)*
Room 210W, Building 1
State Capitol Complex
Charleston, WV 25305
P: (304) 357-7973
E: greg.boso@wvsenate.gov

Carmichael, Mitch (R, 4)
Room 227M, Building 1
State Capitol Complex
Charleston, WV 25305
P: (304) 357-7855
E: mitch.carmichael@wvsenate.gov

Cole, Bill (R, 6)
Room 229M, Building 1
State Capitol Complex
Charleston, WV 25305
P: (304) 357-7801
E: bill.cole@wvsenate.gov

Facemire, Douglas E. (D, 12)
Room 213W, Building 1
State Capitol Complex
Charleston, WV 25305
P: (304) 357-7845
E: douglas.facemire@wvsenate.gov

Ferns, Ryan (R, 1)
Room 439M, Building 1
State Capitol Complex
Charleston, WV 25305
P: (304) 357-7918
E: ryan.ferns@wvsenate.gov

Gaunch, Ed (R, 8)*
Room 216W, Building 1
State Capitol Complex
Charleston, WV 25305
P: (304) 357-7841
E: ed.gaunch@wvsenate.gov

Hall, Daniel J. (D, 9)
Room 216W, Building 1
State Capitol Complex
Charleston, WV 25305
P: (304) 357-7807
E: daniel.hall@wvsenate.gov

Hall, Mike (R, 4)
Room 465M, Building 1
State Capitol Complex
Charleston, WV 25305
P: (304) 357-7901
E: mike.hall@wvsenate.gov

Karnes, Robert L. (R, 11)*
Room 200W, Building 1
State Capitol Complex
Charleston, WV 25305
P: (304) 357-7906
E: robert.karnes@wvsenate.gov

Kessler, Jeffrey V. (D, 2)
Room 257M, Building 1
State Capitol Complex
Charleston, WV 25305
P: (304) 357-7902
E: jeff.kessler@wvsenate.gov

Kirkendoll, Art (D, 7)
Room 218W, Building 1
State Capitol Complex
Charleston, WV 25305
P: (304) 357-7857
E: art.kirkendoll@wvsenate.gov

Laird IV, William R. (D, 10)
Room 229W, Building 1
State Capitol Complex
Charleston, WV 25305
P: (304) 357-7849
E: william.laird@wvsenate.gov

Leonhardt, Kent (R, 2)*
Room 200W, Building 1
State Capitol Complex
Charleston, WV 25305
P: (304) 357-7827
E: Kent.Leonhardt@wvsenate.gov

Maynard, Mark R. (R, 6)*
Room 206W, Building 1
State Capitol Complex
Charleston, WV 25305
P: (304) 357-7808
E: Mark.Maynard@wvsenate.gov

Miller, Ronald F. (D, 10)
Room 229W, Building 1
State Capitol Complex
Charleston, WV 25305
P: (304) 357-7959
E: ronald.miller@wvsenate.gov

Mullins, Jeff (R, 9)*
Room 203W, Building 1
State Capitol Complex
Charleston, WV 25305
P: (304) 357-7831
E: jeff.mullins@wvsenate.gov

Nohe, David (R, 3)
Room 214W, Building 1
State Capitol Complex
Charleston, WV 25305
P: (304) 357-7970
E: david.nohe@wvsenate.gov

Palumbo, Corey L. (D, 17)
Room 209W, Building 1
State Capitol Complex
Charleston, WV 25305
P: (304) 357-7854
E: corey.palumbo@wvsenate.gov

Plymale, Robert H. (D, 5)
Room 204W, Building 1
State Capitol Complex
Charleston, WV 25305
P: (304) 357-7937
E: robert.plymale@wvsenate.gov

Prezioso, Roman (D, 13)
Room 223W, Building 1
State Capitol Complex
Charleston, WV 25305
P: (304) 357-7961
E: roman.prezioso@wvsenate.gov

Romano, Mike (D, 12)*
Room 441M, Building 1
State Capitol Complex
Charleston, WV 25305
P: (304) 357-7904
E: mike.romano@wvsenate.gov

Snyder, Herb (D, 16)
Room 213W, Building 1
State Capitol Complex
Charleston, WV 25305
P: (304) 357-7957
E: herb.snyder@wvsenate.gov

Stollings, Ron (D, 7)
Room 209W, Building 1
State Capitol Complex
Charleston, WV 25305
P: (304) 357-7939
E: ron.stollings@frontier.com

Sypolt, Dave (R, 14)
Room 417M, Building 1
State Capitol Complex
Charleston, WV 25305
P: (304) 357-7914
E: davesypolt@wvsenate.com

Takubo, Tom (R, 17)*
Room 417M, Building 1
State Capitol Complex
Charleston, WV 25305
P: (304) 357-7990
E: drtomtakubo@gmail.com

Trump IV, Charles S. (R, 15)
Room 210W, Building 1
State Capitol Complex
Charleston, WV 25305
P: (304) 357-7980
F: (304) 340-3315
E: charles.trump@wvsenate.gov

Unger II, John (D, 16)
Room 245M, Building 1
State Capitol Complex
Charleston, WV 25305
P: (304) 357-7933
E: john.unger@wvsenate.gov

Walters, Chris (R, 8)
Room 217W, Building 1
State Capitol Complex
Charleston, WV 25305
P: (304) 357-7866
E: chris.walters@wvsenate.gov

Williams, Bob (D, 14)
Room 223W, Building 1
State Capitol Complex
Charleston, WV 25305
P: (304) 357-7995
E: bob.williams@wvsenate.gov

Woelfel, Mike (D, 5)*
Room 441M, Building 1
State Capitol Complex
Charleston, WV 25305
P: (304) 357-7956
E: mike.woelfel@wvsenate.gov

Yost, Jack (D, 1)
Room 218W, Building 1
State Capitol Complex
Charleston, WV 25305
P: (304) 357-7984
E: jack.yost@wvsenate.gov

House

Speaker of the House

Delegate Tim Armstead (R)
Speaker of the House
Room 228M, Building 1
State Capitol Complex
Charleston, WV 25305
P: (304) 340-3210
E: tim.armstead@wvhouse.gov

Speaker Pro Tempore of the House

Delegate Bill Anderson (R)
Speaker Pro Tempore
Room 242M, Building 1
State Capitol Complex
Charleston, WV 25305
P: (304) 340-3168
E: bill.anderson@wvhouse.gov

House Majority Leader

Delegate Daryl E. Cowles (R)
Majority Leader
Room 228M, Building 1
State Capitol Complex
Charleston, WV 25305
P: (304) 340-3220
E: daryl.cowles@wvhouse.gov

House Minority Leader

Delegate Tim Miley (D)
Room 264M, Building 1
State Capitol Complex
Charleston, WV 25305
P: (304) 340-3240
E: tim.miley@wvhouse.gov

Clerk of the House

Mr. Steve Harrison
Clerk of the House
Room 212M, Building 1
1900 Kanawha Boulevard, East
Charleston, WV 25305
P: (304) 340-3200
E: house.clerk@wvhouse.gov

Members of the House

Ambler, George (R, 42)
Room 203E, Building 1
State Capitol Complex
Charleston, WV 25305
P: (304) 340-3129
E: george.ambler@wvhouse.gov

Anderson, Bill (R, 8)
Room 242M, Building 1
State Capitol Complex
Charleston, WV 25305
P: (304) 340-3168
E: bill.anderson@wvhouse.gov

Armstead, Tim (R, 40)
Room 228M, Building 1
State Capitol Complex
Charleston, WV 25305
P: (304) 340-3210
E: tim.armstead@wvhouse.gov

Arvon, Karen (R, 31)
Room 211E, Building 1
State Capitol Complex
Charleston, WV 25305
P: (304) 340-3384
E: karen.arvon@wvhouse.gov

West Virginia

Ashley, Bob (R, 11)
Room 472M, Building 1
State Capitol Complex
Charleston, WV 25305
P: (304) 340-3185
E: bob.ashley@wvhouse.gov

Azinger, Mike (R, 10)*
Room 221E, Building 1
State Capitol Complex
Charleston, WV 25305
P: (304) 340-3202
E: mike.azinger@wvhouse.gov

Bates, Mick (D, 30)*
Room 150R, Building 1
State Capitol Complex
Charleston, WV 25305
P: (304) 340-3180
E: mick.bates@wvhouse.gov

Blair, Saira (R, 59)*
Room 218E, Building 1
State Capitol Complex
Charleston, WV 25305
P: (304) 340-3122
E: saira.blair@wvhouse.gov

Boggs, Brent (D, 34)
Room 230E, Building 1
State Capitol Complex
Charleston, WV 25305
P: (304) 340-3142
E: brent.boggs@wvhouse.gov

Border-Sheppard, Anna (R, 9)
Room 227E, Building 1
State Capitol Complex
Charleston, WV 25305
P: (304) 340-3136
E: anna.border@wvhouse.gov

Butler, Jim (R, 14)
Room 222E, Building 1
State Capitol Complex
Charleston, WV 25305
P: (304) 340-3199
E: jim.butler@wvhouse.gov

Byrd, Andrew D. (D, 35)*
Room 151R, Building 1
State Capitol Complex
Charleston, WV 25305
P: (304) 340-3362
E: andrew.byrd@wvhouse.gov

Cadle, Scott (R, 13)
Room 223E, Building 1
State Capitol Complex
Charleston, WV 25305
P: (304) 340-3118
E: scott.cadle@wvhouse.gov

Campbell, Denise L. (D, 43)
Room 151R, Building 1
State Capitol Complex
Charleston, WV 25305
P: (304) 340-3145
E: denise.campbell@wvhouse.gov

Canterbury, Ray (R, 42)
Room 212E, Building 1
State Capitol Complex
Charleston, WV 25305
P: (304) 340-3131
E: ray.canterbury@wvhouse.gov

Caputo, Mike (D, 50)
Room 258M, Building 1
State Capitol Complex
Charleston, WV 25305
P: (304) 340-3249
E: mike.caputo@wvhouse.gov

Cooper, Roy (R, 28)
Room 203E, Building 1
State Capitol Complex
Charleston, WV 25305
P: (304) 340-3119
E: roy.cooper@wvhouse.gov

Cowles, Daryl E. (R, 58)
Room 228M, Building 1
State Capitol Complex
Charleston, WV 25305
P: (304) 340-3220
E: daryl.cowles@wvhouse.gov

Deem, Frank (R, 10)
Room 276M, Building 1
State Capitol Complex
Charleston, WV 25305
P: (304) 340-3137
F: (304) 357-7829
E: frank.deem@wvhouse.gov

Duke, Walter E. (R, 61)
Room 442M, Building 1
State Capitol Complex
Charleston, WV 25305
P: (304) 340-3188
F: (304) 340-3315
E: walter.duke@wvhouse.gov

Eldridge, Jeff (D, 22)
Room 151R, Building 1
State Capitol Complex
Charleston, WV 25305
P: (304) 340-3113
E: jeff.eldridge@wvhouse.gov

Ellington, Joe (R, 27)
Room 215E, Building 1
State Capitol Complex
Charleston, WV 25305
P: (304) 340-3269
E: joe.ellington@wvhouse.gov

Espinosa, Paul (R, 66)
Room 219E, Building 1
State Capitol Complex
Charleston, WV 25305
P: (304) 340-3130
E: paul.espinosa@wvhouse.gov

Evans, Allen V. (R, 54)
Room 216E, Building 1
State Capitol Complex
Charleston, WV 25305
P: (304) 340-3399
E: allen.evans@wvhouse.gov

Evans, David (R, 4)
Room 225E, Building 1
State Capitol Complex
Charleston, WV 25305
P: (304) 340-3151
E: david.evans@wvhouse.gov

Faircloth, Larry V. (R, 60)
Room 225E, Building 1
State Capitol Complex
Charleston, WV 25305
P: (304) 340-3147
E: larry.faircloth@wvhouse.gov

Fast, Tom (R, 32)*
Room 228E, Building 1
State Capitol Complex
Charleston, WV 25305
P: (304) 340-3170
E: tom.fast@wvhouse.gov

Ferro, Michael T. (D, 4)
Room 230E, Building 1
State Capitol Complex
Charleston, WV 25305
P: (304) 340-3111
E: mike.ferro@wvhouse.gov

Fleischauer, Barbara Evans (D, 51)
Room 231E, Building 1
State Capitol Complex
Charleston, WV 25305
P: (304) 340-3127
E: barbaraf@wvhouse.gov

Fluharty, Shawn (D, 3)*
Room 150R, Building 1
State Capitol Complex
Charleston, WV 25305
P: (304) 340-3270
E: shawn.fluharty@wvhouse.gov

Folk, Michael (R, 63)
Room 229E, Building 1
State Capitol Complex
Charleston, WV 25305
P: (304) 340-3350
E: michael.folk@wvhouse.gov

Foster, Geoff (R, 15)*
Room 223E, Building 1
State Capitol Complex
Charleston, WV 25305
P: (304) 340-3121
E: geoff.foster@wvhouse.gov

Frich, Cindy (R, 51)
Room 205E, Building 1
State Capitol Complex
Charleston, WV 25305
P: (304) 340-3125
E: cindy.frich@wvhouse.gov

Gearheart, Marty (R, 27)
Room 200E-A, Building 1
State Capitol Complex
Charleston, WV 25305
P: (304) 340-3179
E: marty.gearheart@wvhouse.gov

Guthrie, Nancy Peoples (D, 36)
Room 4R, Building 1
State Capitol Complex
Charleston, WV 25305
P: (304) 340-3156
E: nancy.guthrie@wvhouse.gov

Hamilton, Bill (R, 45)
Room 216E, Building 1
State Capitol Complex
Charleston, WV 25305
P: (304) 340-3167
E: bill.hamilton@wvhouse.gov

Hamrick, Danny (R, 48)
Room 208E, Building 1
State Capitol Complex
Charleston, WV 25305
P: (304) 340-3141
E: danny.hamrick@wvhouse.gov

Hanshaw, Roger (R, 33)*
Room 229E, Building 1
State Capitol Complex
Charleston, WV 25305
P: (304) 340-3135
E: roger.hanshaw@wvhouse.gov

Hartman, William G. (D, 43)
Room 231E, Building 1
State Capitol Complex
Charleston, WV 25305
P: (304) 340-3178
E: billhartman@suddenlink.net

Hicks, Ken (D, 19)*
Room 151R, Building 1
State Capitol Complex
Charleston, WV 25305
P: (304) 340-3155
E: ken.hicks@wvhouse.gov

Hill, Jordan (R, 41)*
Room 228E, Building 1
State Capitol Complex
Charleston, WV 25305
P: (304) 340-3352
E: jordan.hill@wvhouse.gov

Hornbuckle, Sean (D, 16)*
Room 151R, Building 1
State Capitol Complex
Charleston, WV 25305
P: (304) 340-3395
E: sean.hornbuckle
@wvhouse.gov

Householder, Eric L. (R, 64)
Room 217E, Building 1
State Capitol Complex
Charleston, WV 25305
P: (304) 340-3274
E: eric.householder
@wvhouse.gov

Howell, Gary G. (R, 56)
Room 213E, Building 1
State Capitol Complex
Charleston, WV 25305
P: (304) 340-3192
E: gary.howell@wvhouse.gov

Ihle, Michael (R, 13)*
Room 222E, Building 1
State Capitol Complex
Charleston, WV 25305
P: (304) 340-3146
E: michael.ihle@wvhouse.gov

Ireland, Lynwood (R, 7)
Room 200E-C, Building 1
State Capitol Complex
Charleston, WV 25305
P: (304) 340-3195
E: woody.ireland
@wvhouse.gov

Kelly, John R. (R, 10)*
Room 221E, Building 1
State Capitol Complex
Charleston, WV 25305
P: (304) 340-3394
E: john.kelly@wvhouse.gov

Kessinger, Kayla (R, 32)*
Room 227E, Building 1
State Capitol Complex
Charleston, WV 25305
P: (304) 340-3197
E: kayla.kessinger
@wvhouse.gov

Kurcaba, Brian (R, 49)*
Room 220E, Building 1
State Capitol Complex
Charleston, WV 25305
P: (304) 340-3173
E: brian.kurcaba
@wvhouse.gov

Lane, Patrick (R, 38)
Room 400M, Building 1
State Capitol Complex
Charleston, WV 25305
P: (304) 340-3252
E: patrick.lane@wvhouse.gov

Longstreth, Linda (D, 50)
Room 6U-A, Building 1
State Capitol Complex
Charleston, WV 25305
P: (304) 340-3124
E: linda.longstreth
@wvhouse.gov

Lynch, Dana (D, 44)
Room 150R, Building 1
State Capitol Complex
Charleston, WV 25305
P: (304) 340-3916
E: dana.lynch@wvhouse.gov

Manchin, Tim (D, 50)
Room 151R, Building 1
State Capitol Complex
Charleston, WV 25305
P: (304) 340-3331
E: tmanchin
@manchininjurylaw.com

Marcum, Justin (D, 20)
Room 150R, Building 1
State Capitol Complex
Charleston, WV 25305
P: (304) 340-3126
E: justin.marcum
@wvhouse.gov

McCuskey, John (R, 35)
Room 476M, Building 1
State Capitol Complex
Charleston, WV 25305
P: (304) 340-3183
E: john.mccuskey
@wvhouse.gov

McGeehan, Pat (R, 1)
Room 226E, Building 1
State Capitol Complex
Charleston, WV 25305
P: (304) 340-3397
F: (304) 340-3315
E: pat.mcgeehan@wvhouse.gov

Miley, Tim (D, 48)
Room 264M, Building 1
State Capitol Complex
Charleston, WV 25305
P: (304) 340-3240
E: tim.miley@wvhouse.gov

Miller, Carol (R, 16)
Room 240M, Building 1
State Capitol Complex
Charleston, WV 25305
P: (304) 340-3176
E: carol.miller@wvhouse.gov

Moffatt, Michel G. (R, 22)*
Room 206E, Building 1
State Capitol Complex
Charleston, WV 25305
P: (304) 340-3152
E: michel.moffatt
@wvhouse.gov

Moore, Clif (D, 26)
Room 231E, Building 1
State Capitol Complex
Charleston, WV 25305
P: (304) 340-3165
E: clif.moore@wvhouse.gov

Morgan, Jim (D, 16)
Room 231E, Building 1
State Capitol Complex
Charleston, WV 25305
P: (304) 340-3277
E: delegatejim@aol.com

Moye, Ricky (D, 29)
Room 2R, Building 1
State Capitol Complex
Charleston, WV 25305
P: (304) 340-3162
E: rmoyewvhouse@yahoo.com

Nelson, Eric (R, 35)
Room 462M, Building 1
State Capitol Complex
Charleston, WV 25305
P: (304) 340-3230
E: nelson@wvhouse.gov

Nelson, Joshua (R, 23)
Room 206E, Building 1
State Capitol Complex
Charleston, WV 25305
P: (304) 340-3184
E: joshua.nelson
@wvhouse.gov

O'Neal IV, John D. (R, 28)
Room 246M, Building 1
State Capitol Complex
Charleston, WV 25305
P: (304) 340-3164
E: john.oneal@wvhouse.gov

Overington, John (R, 62)
Room 214E, Building 1
State Capitol Complex
Charleston, WV 25305
P: (304) 340-3148
E: john@overington.com

Pasdon, Amanda (R, 51)
Room 434M, Building 1
State Capitol Complex
Charleston, WV 25305
P: (304) 340-3265
E: amanda@amandapasdon.com

Perdue, Don (D, 19)
Room 6R-A, Building 1
State Capitol Complex
Charleston, WV 25305
P: (304) 340-3355
E: don.perdue@wvhouse.gov

Perry, David G. (D, 32)
Room 233E, Building 1
State Capitol Complex
Charleston, WV 25305
P: (304) 340-3337
E: d.perry@wvhouse.gov

Pethtel, Dave (D, 5)
Room 230E, Building 1
State Capitol Complex
Charleston, WV 25305
P: (304) 340-3158
E: dave.pethtel@wvhouse.gov

Phillips, Linda Goode (D, 25)
Room 4R, Building 1
State Capitol Complex
Charleston, WV 25305
P: (304) 340-3163
E: linda.phillips
@wvhouse.gov

Phillips Jr., Rupert (D, 24)
Room 150R, Building 1
State Capitol Complex
Charleston, WV 25305
P: (304) 340-3174
E: rupert.phillips
@wvhouse.gov

Pushkin, Mike (D, 37)*
Room 150R, Building 1
State Capitol Complex
Charleston, WV 25305
P: (304) 340-3106
E: mike.pushkin@wvhouse.gov

Reynolds, Doug (D, 17)
Room 150R, Building 1
State Capitol Complex
Charleston, WV 25305
P: (304) 340-3280
F: (304) 340-3315
E: delegatedoug@yahoo.com

West Virginia

Rodighiero, Ralph (D, 24)
Room 2R, Building 1
State Capitol Complex
Charleston, WV 25305
P: (304) 340-3297
F: (304) 340-3315
E: ralph.rodighiero@wvhouse.gov

Rohrbach, Matthew (R, 17)*
Room 209E, Building 1
State Capitol Complex
Charleston, WV 25305
P: (304) 340-3221
E: matthew.rohrbach@wvhouse.gov

Romine, William R. (R, 6)
Room 210E, Building 1
State Capitol Complex
Charleston, WV 25305
P: (304) 340-3226
E: roger.romine@wvhouse.gov

Rowan, Ruth (R, 57)
Room 210E, Building 1
State Capitol Complex
Charleston, WV 25305
P: (304) 340-3157
E: ruth.rowan@wvhouse.gov

Rowe, Larry L. (D, 36)
Room 230E, Building 1
State Capitol Complex
Charleston, WV 25305
P: (304) 340-3287
F: (304) 357-7829
E: larry.rowe@wvhouse.gov

Shott, John (R, 27)
Room 418M, Building 1
State Capitol Complex
Charleston, WV 25305
P: (304) 340-3252
E: john.shott@wvhouse.gov

Skinner, Stephen (D, 67)
Room 150R, Building 1
State Capitol Complex
Charleston, WV 25305
P: (304) 340-3248
E: stephen.skinner@wvhouse.gov

Smith, Margaret Donaldson (D, 46)
Room 6R, Building 1
State Capitol Complex
Charleston, WV 25305
P: (304) 340-3123
E: delegatepeggysmith@msn.com

Smith, Randy (R, 53)
Room 201E, Building 1
State Capitol Complex
Charleston, WV 25305
P: (304) 340-3396
E: randy.smith@wvhouse.gov

Sobonya, Kelli (R, 18)
Room 207E, Building 1
State Capitol Complex
Charleston, WV 25305
P: (304) 340-3175
E: kelli.sobonya@wvhouse.gov

Sponaugle, Isaac (D, 55)
Room 6R-A, Building 1
State Capitol Complex
Charleston, WV 25305
P: (304) 340-3154
E: isaac.sponaugle@wvhouse.gov

Stansbury, Chris (R, 35)*
Room 209E, Building 1
State Capitol Complex
Charleston, WV 25305
P: (304) 340-3340
E: chris.stansbury@wvhouse.gov

Statler, Joe (R, 51)*
Room 220E, Building 1
State Capitol Complex
Charleston, WV 25305
P: (304) 340-3900
E: joe.statler@wvhouse.gov

Storch, Erikka (R, 3)
Room 202E, Building 1
State Capitol Complex
Charleston, WV 25305
P: (304) 340-3378
E: erikka.storch@wvhouse.gov

Summers, Amy (R, 49)*
Room 218E, Building 1
State Capitol Complex
Charleston, WV 25305
P: (304) 340-3139
E: amy.summers@wvhouse.gov

Trecost II, Patsy Samuel (D, 48)*
Room 150R, Building 1
State Capitol Complex
Charleston, WV 25305
P: (304) 340-3102
E: patsy.trecost@wvhouse.gov

Upson, Jill (R, 65)*
Room 219E, Building 1
State Capitol Complex
Charleston, WV 25305
P: (304) 340-3366
E: jill.upson@wvhouse.gov

Wagner, Danny (R, 47)*
Room 226E, Building 1
State Capitol Complex
Charleston, WV 25305
P: (304) 340-3398
E: danny.wagner@wvhouse.gov

Walters, Ron (R, 39)
Room 212E, Building 1
State Capitol Complex
Charleston, WV 25305
P: (304) 340-3194
E: ron.walters@wvhouse.gov

Waxman, Theresa (R, 48)*
Room 208E, Building 1
State Capitol Complex
Charleston, WV 25305
P: (304) 340-3171
E: terry.waxman@wvhouse.gov

Weld, Ryan W. (R, 2)*
Room 224E, Building 1
State Capitol Complex
Charleston, WV 25305
P: (304) 340-3367
E: ryan.weld@wvhouse.gov

Westfall, Steve (R, 12)
Room 204E, Building 1
State Capitol Complex
Charleston, WV 25305
P: (304) 340-3140
E: steve.westfall@wvhouse.gov

White, Brad (R, 36)*
Room 204E, Building 1
State Capitol Complex
Charleston, WV 25305
P: (304) 340-3138
E: brad.white@wvhouse.gov

White, Harry Keith (D, 21)
Room 258M, Building 1
State Capitol Complex
Charleston, WV 25305
P: (304) 340-3304
E: hkwhite@wvhouse.gov

Williams, Larry A. (D, 52)
Room 258M, Building 1
State Capitol Complex
Charleston, WV 25305
P: (304) 340-3160
E: lawii@frontier.com

Zatezalo, Mark (R, 1)*
Room 224E, Building 1
State Capitol Complex
Charleston, WV 25305
P: (304) 340-3120
E: mark.zatezalo@wvhouse.gov

Congress

Senate

Capito, Shelley M. (R)
Manchin III, Joe (D)

House

Jenkins, Evan H. (R, 3)
McKinley, David (R, 1)
Mooney, Alex X. (R, 2)

Wisconsin

Executive

Governor

Hon. Scott K. Walker (R)
Governor
115 East State Capitol
Madison, WI 53707
P: (608) 266-1212
F: (608) 267-8983

Lieutenant Governor

Hon. Rebecca Kleefisch (R)
Lieutenant Governor
Room 19, East State Capitol
P.O. Box 2043
Madison, WI 53702
P: (608) 266-3516
F: (608) 267-3571

Attorney General

Hon. Brad Schimel (R)
Attorney General
State Capitol, Suite 114 East
P.O. Box 7857
Madison, WI 53707
P: (608) 266-1221

Auditor

Mr. Joe Chrisman
(appointed by the Legislature)
State Auditor
22 East Mifflin Street, Suite 500
Madison, WI 53703
P: (608) 266-2818
F: (608) 267-0410
E: joe.chrisman
@legis.wisconsin.gov

Secretary of State

Hon. Douglas J. La Follette (D)
Secretary of State
P.O. Box 7848
Madison, WI 53707
P: (608) 266-8888
F: (608) 266-3159
E: doug.lafollette
@sos.state.wi.us

Superintendent of Public Instruction

Hon. Anthony Evers
Superintendent of Public Instruction
125 South Webster Street
Madison, WI 53707
P: (608) 266-1771
E: anthony.evers@dpi.wi.gov

Treasurer

Hon. Matt Adamczyk (R)
State Treasurer
P.O. Box 2114
Madison, WI 53707
P: (608) 266-1714
F: (608) 266-2647
E: Matt.Adamczyk
@wisconsin.gov

Judiciary

Supreme Court (NE)

Ms. Diane M. Fremgen
Clerk of the Supreme Court
100 East Main Street, Suite 215
P.O. Box 1688
Madison, WI 53701
P: (608) 261-4300
F: (608) 267-0640
E: Diane.Fremgen
@courts.state.wi.us

Hon. Shirley S. Abrahamson
Chief Justice
Hon. Ann Walsh Bradley
Hon. N. Patrick Crooks
Hon. Michael J. Gableman
Hon. David T. Prosser Jr.
Hon. Patience D. Roggensack
Hon. Annette Kingsland Ziegler

Legislative Senate

Senate President

Sen. Mary Lazich (R)
Senate President
219-S, State Capitol
P.O. Box 7882
Madison, WI 53707
P: (608) 266-5400
F: (608) 267-6790
E: Sen.Lazich
@legis.wisconsin.gov

President Pro Tempore of the Senate

Sen. Richard Gudex (R)
Senate President Pro Tempore
415-S, State Capitol
P.O. Box 7882
Madison, WI 53707
P: (608) 266-5300
E: Sen.Gudex
@legis.wisconsin.gov

Senate Majority Leader

Sen. Scott L. Fitzgerald (R)
Senate Majority Leader
211-S, State Capitol
P.O. Box 7882
Madison, WI 53707
P: (608) 266-5660
F: (608) 267-6795
E: Sen.Fitzgerald
@legis.wisconsin.gov

Senate Minority Leader

Sen. Jennifer Shilling (D)
Senate Minority Leader
206-S, State Capitol
P.O. Box 7882
Madison, WI 53708
P: (608) 266-5490
F: (608) 282-3572
E: Sen.Shilling
@legis.wisconsin.gov

Chief Clerk of the Senate

Mr. Jeffery Renk
Senate Chief Clerk & Director of Operations
Room B205 South, State Capitol
P.O. Box 7882
Madison, WI 53707
P: (608) 266-2517
F: (608) 266-0643
E: jeff.renk
@legis.wisconsin.gov

Members of the Senate

Bewley, Janet (D, 25)
Room 126-S, State Capitol
P.O. Box 7882
Madison, WI 53708
P: (608) 266-3510
E: sen.Bewley@legis.wi.gov

Carpenter, Tim (D, 3)
109-S, State Capitol
P.O. Box 7882
Madison, WI 53707
P: (608) 266-8535
F: (608) 282-3543
E: Sen.Carpenter
@legis.wisconsin.gov

Cowles, Robert L. (R, 2)
118-S, State Capitol
P.O. Box 7882
Madison, WI 53707
P: (608) 266-0484
F: (608) 267-0304
E: Sen.Cowles
@legis.wisconsin.gov

Darling, Alberta (R, 8)
317-E, State Capitol
P.O. Box 7882
Madison, WI 53707
P: (608) 266-5830
F: (608) 267-0588
E: Sen.Darling
@legis.wisconsin.gov

Erpenbach, Jon B. (D, 27)
104-S, State Capitol
P.O. Box 7882
Madison, WI 53707
P: (608) 266-6670
F: (608) 266-2508
E: Sen.Erpenbach
@legis.wisconsin.gov

Farrow, Paul (R, 33)
323-S State Capitol
P.O. Box 7882
Madison, WI 53707
P: (608) 266-9174
E: Sen.Farrow
@legis.wisconsin.gov

Fitzgerald, Scott L. (R, 13)
211-S, State Capitol
P.O. Box 7882
Madison, WI 53707
P: (608) 266-5660
F: (608) 267-6795
E: Sen.Fitzgerald
@legis.wisconsin.gov

Gudex, Richard (R, 18)
415-S, State Capitol
P.O. Box 7882
Madison, WI 53707
P: (608) 266-5300
E: Sen.Gudex
@legis.wisconsin.gov

Hansen, Dave (D, 30)
106-S, State Capitol
P.O. Box 7882
Madison, WI 53707
P: (608) 266-5670
F: (608) 267-6791
E: Sen.Hansen
@legis.wisconsin.gov

Wisconsin

Harris Dodd, Nikiya (D, 6)
3-S, State Capitol
P.O. Box 7882
Madison, WI 53707
P: (608) 266-2500
E: Sen.Harris
@legis.wisconsin.gov

Harsdorf, Sheila (R, 10)
122-S, State Capitol
P.O. Box 7882
Madison, WI 53707
P: (608) 266-7745
F: (608) 267-0369
E: Sen.Harsdorf
@legis.wisconsin.gov

Larson, Chris (D, 7)
5-S, State Capitol
P.O. Box 7882
Madison, WI 53707
P: (608) 266-7505
F: (608) 282-3547
E: Sen.Larson
@legis.wisconsin.gov

Lasee, Frank G. (R, 1)
316-S, State Capitol
P.O. Box 7882
Madison, WI 53707
P: (608) 266-3512
F: (608) 267-6792
E: Sen.Lasee
@legis.wisconsin.gov

Lassa, Julie M. (D, 24)
20-S, State Capitol
P.O. Box 7882
Madison, WI 53707
P: (608) 266-3123
F: (608) 267-6797
E: Sen.Lassa
@legis.wisconsin.gov

Lazich, Mary (R, 28)
219-S, State Capitol
P.O. Box 7882
Madison, WI 53707
P: (608) 266-5400
F: (608) 267-6790
E: Sen.Lazich
@legis.wisconsin.gov

LeMahieu, Devin (R, 9)*
15-S, State Capitol
P.O. Box 7882
Madison, WI 53707
P: (608) 266-2056
E: sen.lemahieu
@llegis.wisconsin.gov

Marklein, Howard (R, 17)
8-S, State Capitol
P.O. Box 7882
Madison, WI 53707
P: (608) 266-0703
E: sen.Marklein
@legis.wisconsin.gov

Miller, Mark (D, 16)
7-S, State Capitol
P.O. Box 7882
Madison, WI 53707
P: (608) 266-9170
F: (608) 282-3556
E: Sen.Miller
@legis.wisconsin.gov

Moulton, Terry A. (R, 23)
310-S, State Capitol
P.O. Box 7882
Madison, WI 53707
P: (608) 266-7511
F: (608) 282-3563
E: Sen.Moulton
@legis.wisconsin.gov

Nass, Stephen L. (R, 11)
10-S, State Capitol
P.O. Box 7882
Madison, WI 53708
P: (608) 266-2635
F: (608) 282-3631
E: sen.Nass
@legis.wisconsin.gov

Olsen, Luther S. (R, 14)
313-S, State Capitol
P.O. Box 7882
Madison, WI 53707
P: (608) 266-0751
F: (608) 267-4350
E: Sen.Olsen
@legis.wisconsin.gov

Petrowski, Jerry (R, 29)
123-S, State Capitol
P.O. Box 7882
Madison, WI 53707
P: (608) 266-2502
E: Sen.Petrowski
@legis.wisconsin.gov

Ringhand, Janis (D, 15)
22-S, State Capitol
P.O. Box 8952
Madison, WI 53707
P: (608) 266-2253
E: sen.Ringhand
@legis.wisconsin.gov

Risser, Fred A. (D, 26)
130-S, State Capitol
P.O. Box 7882
Madison, WI 53707
P: (608) 266-1627
F: (608) 266-1629
E: Sen.Risser
@legis.wisconsin.gov

Roth Jr., Roger J. (R, 19)
306-S, State Capitol
P.O. Box 7882
Madison, WI 53707
P: (608) 266-0718
E: sen.Roth
@legis.wisconsin.gov

Shilling, Jennifer (D, 32)
206-S, State Capitol
P.O. Box 7882
Madison, WI 53708
P: (608) 266-5490
F: (608) 282-3572
E: Sen.Shilling
@legis.wisconsin.gov

Taylor, Lena C. (D, 4)
19-S, State Capitol
P.O. Box 7882
Madison, WI 53707
P: (608) 266-5810
F: (608) 282-3544
E: Sen.Taylor
@legis.wisconsin.gov

Tiffany, Thomas (R, 12)
Room 409 South, State Capitol
P.O. Box 7882
Madison, WI 53707
P: (608) 266-2509
E: Sen.Tiffany@legis.wi.gov

Vinehout, Kathleen (D, 31)
108-S, State Capitol
P.O. Box 7882
Madison, WI 53707
P: (608) 266-8546
F: (608) 267-2871
E: Sen.Vinehout
@legis.wisconsin.gov

Vukmir, Leah (R, 5)
131-S, State Capitol
P.O. Box 7882
Madison, WI 53707
P: (608) 266-2512
F: (608) 267-0367
E: Sen.Vukmir
@legis.wisconsin.gov

Wanggaard, Van (R, 21)
319-S, State Capitol
P.O. Box 7882
Madison, WI 53707
P: (608) 266-1832
F: (608) 282-3561
E: Sen.Wanggaard
@legis.wisconsin.gov

Wirch, Robert W. (D, 22)
127-S, State Capitol
P.O. Box 7882
Madison, WI 53707
P: (608) 267-8979
F: (608) 267-0984
E: Sen.Wirch
@legis.wisconsin.gov

Assembly

Speaker of the Assembly

Rep. Robin J. Vos (R)
Speaker of the Assembly
Room 211 West, State Capitol
P.O. Box 8953
Madison, WI 53708
P: (608) 266-3387
F: (608) 282-3663
E: Rep.Vos
@legis.wisconsin.gov

Speaker Pro Tempore of the Assembly

Rep. Tyler August (R)
Speaker Pro Tempore
Room 119 West, State Capitol
P.O. Box 8952
Madison, WI 53708
P: (608) 266-1190
F: (608) 282-3632
E: Rep.August
@legis.wisconsin.gov

Assembly Majority Leader

Rep. Jim Steineke (R)
Assembly Majority Leader
Room 115 West, State Capitol
P.O. Box 8953
Madison, WI 53708
P: (608) 266-2418
F: (608) 282-3605
E: Rep.Steineke
@legis.wisconsin.gov

Assembly Minority Leader

Rep. Peter W. Barca (D)
Assembly Minority Leader
Room 201 West, State Capitol
P.O. Box 8952
Madison, WI 53708
P: (608) 266-5504
F: (608) 282-3664
E: Rep.Barca
@legis.wisconsin.gov

Clerk of the Assembly

Mr. Patrick Fuller
Chief Clerk of the Assembly
17 West Main Street, Room 401
P.O. Box 8952
Madison, WI 53708
P: (608) 266-1501
F: (608) 266-5617
E: patrick.fuller
@legis.wisconsin.gov

Members of the Assembly

Allen, Scott (R, 97)*
Room 8 West, State Capitol
P.O. Box 8952
Madison, WI 53708
P: (608) 266-8580
E: rep.allen
@legis.wisconsin.gov

August, Tyler (R, 32)
Room 119 West, State Capitol
P.O. Box 8952
Madison, WI 53708
P: (608) 266-1190
F: (608) 282-3632
E: Rep.August
@legis.wisconsin.gov

Ballweg, Joan A. (R, 41)
Room 210 North, State Capitol
P.O. Box 8952
Madison, WI 53708
P: (608) 266-8077
F: (608) 282-3641
E: Rep.Ballweg
@legis.wisconsin.gov

Barca, Peter W. (D, 64)
Room 201 West, State Capitol
P.O. Box 8952
Madison, WI 53708
P: (608) 266-5504
F: (608) 282-3664
E: Rep.Barca
@legis.wisconsin.gov

Barnes, Mandela (D, 11)
Room 5 North, State Capitol
P.O. Box 8952
Madison, WI 53708
P: (608) 266-3756
E: Rep.Barnes
@legis.wisconsin.gov

Berceau, Terese (D, 77)
Room 104 North, State Capitol
P.O. Box 8952
Madison, WI 53708
P: (608) 266-3784
F: (608) 282-3676
E: Rep.Berceau
@legis.wisconsin.gov

Bernier, Kathleen (R, 68)
Room 314 North, State Capitol
P.O. Box 8953
Madison, WI 53708
P: (608) 266-9172
F: (608) 282-3668
E: Rep.Bernier
@legis.wisconsin.gov

Billings, Jill (D, 95)
Room 307 West, State Capitol
P.O. Box 8952
Madison, WI 53708
P: (608) 266-5780
E: Rep.Billings
@legis.wisconsin.gov

Born, Mark (R, 39)
Room 312 North, State Capitol
P.O. Box 8952
Madison, WI 53708
P: (608) 266-2540
F: (608) 282-3639
E: Rep.Born
@legis.wisconsin.gov

Bowen, David (D, 10)*
Room 3 North, State Capitol
P.O. Box 8952
Madison, WI 53708
P: (608) 266-7671
E: rep.bowen
@legis.wisconsin.gov

Brandtjen, Janel (R, 22)*
Room 121 West, State Capitol
P.O. Box 8952
Madison, WI 53708
P: (608) 266-2367
E: rep.brandtjen
@legis.wisconsin.gov

Brooks, Edward (R, 50)
Room 20 North, State Capitol
P.O. Box 8952
Madison, WI 53708
P: (608) 266-8531
F: (608) 282-3650
E: Rep.Brooks
@legis.wisconsin.gov

Brooks, Robert (R, 60)*
Room 107 West, State Capitol
P.O. Box 8953
Madison, WI 53708
P: (608) 267-2369
E: rep.brooks
@legis.wisconsin.gov

Brostoff, Jonathan (D, 19)*
Room 3 North, State Capitol
P.O. Box 8952
Madison, WI 53708
P: (608) 266-0650
E: jbrostoff
@legis.wisconsin.gov

Considine, Dave (D, 81)*
Room 412 North, State Capitol
P.O. Box 8952
Madison, WI 53708
P: (608) 266-7746
E: rep.considine
@legis.wisconsin.gov

Craig, David (R, 83)
Room 127 West, State Capitol
P.O. Box 8952
Madison, WI 53708
P: (608) 266-3363
F: (608) 282-3683
E: Rep.Craig
@legis.wisconsin.gov

Czaja, Mary (R, 35)
Room 321 East, State Capitol
P.O. Box 8953
Madison, WI 53708
P: (608) 266-7694
F: (608) 282-3635
E: Rep.Czaja
@legis.wisconsin.gov

Danou, Chris (D, 92)
Room 107 North, State Capitol
P.O. Box 8952
Madison, WI 53708
P: (608) 266-7015
F: (608) 282-3691
E: Rep.Danou
@legis.wisconsin.gov

Doyle, Steve (D, 94)
Room 124 North, State Capitol
P.O. Box 8952
Madison, WI 53708
P: (608) 266-0631
F: (608) 282-3694
E: Rep.Doyle
@legis.wisconsin.gov

Edming, James W. (R, 87)*
Room 109 West, State Capitol
P.O. Box 8952
Madison, WI 53708
P: (608) 266-7506
E: rep.edming
@legis.wisconsin.gov

Gannon, Bob (R, 58)*
Room 12 West, State Capitol
P.O. Box 8952
Madison, WI 53708
P: (608) 264-8486
E: rep.gannon
@legis.wisconsin.gov

Genrich, Eric (D, 90)
Room 304 West, State Capitol
P.O. Box 8952
Madison, WI 53708
P: (608) 266-0616
F: (608) 282-3690
E: Rep.Genrich
@legis.wisconsin.gov

Goyke, Evan (D, 18)
Room 303 West, State Capitol
P.O. Box 8952
Madison, WI 53708
P: (608) 266-0645
F: (608) 282-3618
E: Rep.Goyke
@legis.wisconsin.gov

Heaton, Dave (R, 85)*
Room 9 West, State Capitol
P.O. Box 8952
Madison, WI 53708
P: (608) 266-0654
E: rep.heaton
@legis.wisconsin.gov

Hebl, Gary A. (D, 46)
Room 120 North, State Capitol
P.O. Box 8952
Madison, WI 53708
P: (608) 266-7678
F: (608) 282-3646
E: Rep.Hebl
@legis.wisconsin.gov

Hesselbein, Dianne (D, 79)
Room 9 North, State Capitol
P.O. Box 8952
Madison, WI 53708
P: (608) 266-5340
F: (608) 282-3679
E: Rep.Hesselbein
@legis.wisconsin.gov

Hintz, Gordon (D, 54)
Room 109 North, State Capitol
P.O. Box 8952
Madison, WI 53708
P: (608) 266-2254
E: Rep.Hintz
@legis.wisconsin.gov

Horlacher, Cody (R, 33)*
Room 17 North, State Capitol
P.O. Box 8952
Madison, WI 53708
P: (608) 266-5715
E: rep.horlacher
@legis.wisconsin.gov

Wisconsin

Hutton, Rob (R, 13)
Room 220 North, State Capitol
P.O. Box 8952
Madison, WI 53708
P: (608) 267-9836
F: (608) 282-3613
E: Rep.Hutton
@legis.wisconsin.gov

Jacque, Andre (R, 2)
Room 212 North, State Capitol
P.O. Box 8953
Madison, WI 53708
P: (608) 266-9870
F: (608) 282-3602
E: Rep.Jacque
@legis.wisconsin.gov

Jagler, John (R, 37)
Room 316 North, State Capitol
P.O. Box 8952
Madison, WI 53708
P: (608) 266-9650
F: (608) 282-3637
E: Rep.Jagler
@legis.wisconsin.gov

Jarchow, Adam (R, 28)*
Room 19 North, State Capitol
P.O. Box 8952
Madison, WI 53708
P: (608) 267-2365
E: rep.jarchow
@legis.wisconsin.gov

Johnson, LaTonya (D, 17)
Room 320 West, State Capitol
P.O. Box 8952
Madison, WI 53708
P: (608) 266-5580
F: (608) 282-3617
E: Rep.Johnson
@legis.wisconsin.gov

Jorgensen, Andy (D, 43)
Room 113 North, State Capitol
P.O. Box 8952
Madison, WI 53708
P: (608) 266-3790
E: Rep.Jorgensen
@legis.wisconsin.gov

Kahl, Robb (D, 47)
Room 322 West, State Capitol
P.O. Box 8952
Madison, WI 53708
P: (608) 266-8570
F: (608) 282-3647
E: Rep.Kahl
@legis.wisconsin.gov

Kapenga, Chris (R, 99)
Room 221 North, State Capitol
P.O. Box 8953
Madison, WI 53708
P: (608) 266-3007
F: (608) 282-3633
E: Rep.Kapenga
@legis.wisconsin.gov

Katsma, Terry (R, 26)*
Room 18 North, State Capitol
P.O. Box 8952
Madison, WI 53708
P: (608) 266-0656
E: rep.katsma
@legis.wisconsin.gov

Kerkman, Samantha (R, 61)
Room 315 North, State Capitol
P.O. Box 8952
Madison, WI 53708
P: (608) 266-2530
F: (608) 282-3666
E: Rep.Kerkman
@legis.wisconsin.gov

Kessler, Frederick P. (D, 12)
Room 111 North, State Capitol
P.O. Box 8952
Madison, WI 53708
P: (608) 266-5813
F: (608) 282-3612
E: Rep.Kessler
@legis.wisconsin.gov

Kitchens, Joel C. (R, 1)*
Room 10 West, State Capitol
P.O. Box 8952
Madison, WI 53708
P: (608) 266-5350
E: rep.kitchens
@legis.wisconsin.gov

Kleefisch, Joel M. (R, 38)
Room 216 North, State Capitol
P.O. Box 8952
Madison, WI 53708
P: (608) 266-8551
F: (608) 282-3638
E: Rep.Kleefisch
@legis.wisconsin.gov

Knodl, Dan (R, 24)
Room 218 North, State Capitol
P.O. Box 8952
Madison, WI 53708
P: (608) 266-3796
F: (608) 282-3624
E: Rep.Knodl
@legis.wisconsin.gov

Knudson, Dean (R, 30)
Room 304 East, State Capitol
P.O. Box 8953
Madison, WI 53708
P: (608) 266-1526
F: (608) 282-3630
E: Rep.Knudson
@legis.wisconsin.gov

Kolste, Debra (D, 44)
Room 8 North, State Capitol
P.O. Box 8952
Madison, WI 53708
P: (608) 266-7503
F: (608) 282-3644
E: Rep.Kolste
@legis.wisconsin.gov

Kooyenga, Dale (R, 14)
Room 324 East, State Capitol
P.O. Box 8952
Madison, WI 53708
P: (608) 266-9180
F: (608) 282-3614
E: Rep.Kooyenga
@legis.wisconsin.gov

Kremer, Jesse (R, 59)*
Room 17 West, State Capitol
P.O. Box 8952
Madison, WI 53708
P: (608) 266-9175
E: rep.kremer
@legis.wisconsin.gov

Krug, Scott (R, 72)
Room 207 North, State Capitol
P.O. Box 8952
Madison, WI 53708
P: (608) 266-0215
F: (608) 282-3672
E: Rep.Krug
@legis.wisconsin.gov

Kuglitsch, Mike (R, 84)
Room 129 West, State Capitol
P.O. Box 8952
Madison, WI 53708
P: (608) 267-5158
F: (608) 282-3684
E: Rep.Kuglitsch
@legis.wisconsin.gov

Kulp, Bob (R, 69)
Room 15 West, State Capitol
P.O. Box 8952
Madison, WI 53708
P: (608) 267-0280
F: (608) 282-3669
E: Rep.Kulp
@legis.wisconsin.gov

Larson, Thomas (R, 67)
Room 214 North, State Capitol
P.O. Box 8952
Madison, WI 53708
P: (608) 266-1194
F: (608) 282-3667
E: Rep.Larson
@legis.wisconsin.gov

Loudenbeck, Amy (R, 31)
Room 306 East, State Capitol
P.O. Box 8952
Madison, WI 53708
P: (608) 266-9967
F: (608) 282-3645
E: Rep.Loudenbeck
@legis.wisconsin.gov

Macco, John (R, 88)*
Room 22 West, State Capitol
P.O. Box 8952
Madison, WI 53708
P: (608) 266-0485
E: rep.macco
@legis.wisconsin.gov

Mason, Cory (D, 66)
Room 6 North, State Capitol
P.O. Box 8953
Madison, WI 53708
P: (608) 266-0634
F: (608) 282-3662
E: Rep.Mason
@legis.wisconsin.gov

Meyers, Beth (D, 74)*
Room 409 North, State Capitol
P.O. Box 8952
Madison, WI 53708
P: (608) 266-7690
E: rep.meyers
@legis.wisconsin.gov

Milroy, Nick (D, 73)
Room 126 West, State Capitol
P.O. Box 8953
Madison, WI 53708
P: (608) 266-0640
F: (608) 282-3673
E: Rep.Milroy
@legis.wisconsin.gov

Murphy, David (R, 56)
Room 318 North, State Capitol
P.O. Box 8953
Madison, WI 53708
P: (608) 266-7500
F: (608) 282-3656
E: Rep.Murphy
@legis.wisconsin.gov

Mursau, Jeffrey L. (R, 36)
Room 113 West, State Capitol
P.O. Box 8953
Madison, WI 53708
P: (608) 266-3780
F: (608) 282-3636
E: Rep.Mursau
@legis.wisconsin.gov

Murtha, John (R, 29)
Room 309 North, State Capitol
P.O. Box 8953
Madison, WI 53708
P: (608) 266-7683
E: Rep.Murtha
@legis.wisconsin.gov

Nerison, Lee (R, 96)
Room 310 North, State Capitol
P.O. Box 8953
Madison, WI 53708
P: (608) 266-3534
F: (608) 282-3696
E: Rep.Nerison
@legis.wisconsin.gov

Neylon, Adam (R, 98)
Room 125 West, State Capitol
P.O. Box 8953
Madison, WI 53708
P: (608) 266-5120
E: Rep.Neylon@legis.wi.gov

Novak, Todd (R, 51)*
Room 304 North, State Capitol
P.O. Box 8953
Madison, WI 53708
P: (608) 266-7502
E: rep.novak
@legis.wisconsin.gov

Nygren, John (R, 89)
Room 309 East, State Capitol
P.O. Box 8953
Madison, WI 53708
P: (608) 266-2343
E: Rep.Nygren
@legis.wisconsin.gov

Ohnstad, Tod (D, 65)
Room 128 North, State Capitol
P.O. Box 8953
Madison, WI 53708
P: (608) 266-0455
F: (608) 282-3665
E: Rep.Ohnstad
@legis.wisconsin.gov

Ott, Alvin R. (R, 3)
Room 323 North, State Capitol
P.O. Box 8953
Madison, WI 53708
P: (608) 266-5831
F: (608) 282-3603
E: Rep.Ott
@legis.wisconsin.gov

Ott, Jim (R, 23)
Room 317 North, State Capitol
P.O. Box 8953
Madison, WI 53708
P: (608) 266-0486
E: Rep.OttJ
@legis.wisconsin.gov

Petersen, Kevin David (R, 40)
Room 105 West, State Capitol
P.O. Box 8953
Madison, WI 53708
P: (608) 266-3794
E: Rep.Petersen
@legis.wisconsin.gov

Petryk, Warren (R, 93)
Room 103 North, State Capitol
P.O. Box 8953
Madison, WI 53708
P: (608) 266-0660
F: (608) 282-3693
E: Rep.Petryk
@legis.wisconsin.gov

Pope, Sondy (D, 80)
Room 118 North, State Capitol
P.O. Box 8953
Madison, WI 53708
P: (608) 266-3520
F: (608) 282-3679
E: Rep.Pope
@legis.wisconsin.gov

Quinn, Romaine Robert (R, 75)*
Room 7 West, State Capitol
P.O. Box 8953
Madison, WI 53708
P: (608) 266-2519
E: rep.quinn
@legis.wisconsin.gov

Riemer, Daniel (D, 7)
Room 122 North, State Capitol
P.O. Box 8953
Madison, WI 53708
P: (608) 266-1733
F: (608) 282-3607
E: Rep.Riemer
@legis.wisconsin.gov

Ripp, Keith (R, 42)
Room 223 North, State Capitol
P.O. Box 8953
Madison, WI 53708
P: (608) 266-3404
F: (608) 282-3647
E: Rep.Ripp
@legis.wisconsin.gov

Rodriguez, Jessie (R, 21)
Room 204 North, State Capitol
P.O. Box 8953
Madison, WI 53708
P: (608) 266-0610
F: (608) 282-3621
E: Rep.Rodriguez
@legis.wisconsin.gov

Rohrkaste, Mike (R, 55)*
Room 208 North, State Capitol
P.O. Box 8953
Madison, WI 53708
P: (608) 266-5719
E: rep.rohrkaste
@legis.wisconsin.gov

Sanfelippo, Joe (R, 15)
Room 306 North, State Capitol
P.O. Box 8953
Madison, WI 53708
P: (608) 266-0620
F: (608) 282-3615
E: Rep.Sanfelippo
@legis.wisconsin.gov

Sargent, Melissa (D, 48)
Room 321 West, State Capitol
P.O. Box 8953
Madison, WI 53708
P: (608) 266-0960
F: (608) 282-3648
E: Rep.Sargent
@legis.wisconsin.gov

Schraa, Michael (R, 53)
Room 320 East, State Capitol
P.O. Box 8953
Madison, WI 53708
P: (608) 267-7990
F: (608) 282-3653
E: Rep.Schraa
@legis.wisconsin.gov

Shankland, Katrina (D, 71)
Room 119 North, State Capitol
P.O. Box 8953
Madison, WI 53708
P: (608) 267-9649
F: (608) 282-3671
E: Rep.Shankland
@legis.wisconsin.gov

Sinicki, Christine (D, 20)
Room 114 North, State Capitol
P.O. Box 8953
Madison, WI 53708
P: (608) 266-8588
F: (608) 282-3620
E: Rep.Sinicki
@legis.wisconsin.gov

Skowronski, Ken (R, 82)
Room 209 North, State Capitol
P.O. Box 8953
Madison, WI 53708
P: (608) 266-8590
F: (608) 282-3682
E: Rep.Skowronski
@legis.wisconsin.gov

Spiros, John (R, 86)
Room 15 North, State Capitol
P.O. Box 8953
Madison, WI 53708
P: (608) 266-1182
F: (608) 282-3686
E: Rep.Spiros
@legis.wisconsin.gov

Spreitzer, Mark (D, 33)*
Room 420 North, State Capitol
P.O. Box 8953
Madison, WI 53708
P: (608) 266-1192
E: rep.spreitzer
@legis.wisconsin.gov

Steffen, David (R, 4)*
Room 21 North, State Capitol
P.O. Box 8953
Madison, WI 53708
P: (608) 266-5840
E: rep.steffen
@legis.wisconsin.gov

Steineke, Jim (R, 5)
Room 115 West, State Capitol
P.O. Box 8953
Madison, WI 53708
P: (608) 266-2418
F: (608) 282-3605
E: Rep.Steineke
@legis.wisconsin.gov

Stuck, Amanda
Room 4 West, State Capitol
P.O. Box 8953
Madison, WI 53708
P: (608) 266-3070
E: rep.stuck
@legis.wisconsin.gov

Subeck, Lisa (D, 78)*
Room 418 North, State Capitol
P.O. Box 8953
Madison, WI 53708
P: (608) 266-7521
E: rep.subeck
@legis.wisconsin.gov

Swearingen, Rob (R, 34)
Room 123 West, State Capitol
P.O. Box 8953
Madison, WI 53708
P: (608) 266-7141
F: (608) 282-3634
E: Rep.Swearingen
@legis.wisconsin.gov

Wisconsin

Tauchen, Gary (R, 6)
Room 13 West, State Capitol
P.O. Box 8953
Madison, WI 53708
P: (608) 266-3097
E: Rep.Tauchen
@legis.wisconsin.gov

Taylor, Chris (D, 76)
Room 306 West, State Capitol
P.O. Box 8953
Madison, WI 53708
P: (608) 266-5342
F: (608) 282-3648
E: Rep.Taylor
@legis.wisconsin.gov

Thiesfeldt, Jeremy (R, 52)
Room 16 West, State Capitol
P.O. Box 8953
Madison, WI 53708
P: (608) 266-3156
F: (608) 282-3652
E: Rep.Thiesfeldt
@legis.wisconsin.gov

Tittl, Paul (R, 25)
Room 219 North, State Capitol
P.O. Box 8953
Madison, WI 53708
P: (608) 266-0315
F: (608) 282-3625
E: Rep.Tittl
@legis.wisconsin.gov

Tranel, Travis (R, 49)
Room 308 North, State Capitol
P.O. Box 8952
Madison, WI 53708
P: (608) 266-1170
E: Rep.Tranel
@legis.wisconsin.gov

VanderMeer, Nancy Lynn (R, 70)*
Room 11 West, State Capitol
P.O. Box 8953
Madison, WI 53708
P: (608) 266-8366
E: rep.vandermeer
@legis.wisconsin.gov

Vorpagel, Tyler (R, 27)*
Room 18 West, State Capitol
P.O. Box 8953
Madison, WI 53708
P: (608) 266-8530
E: rep.vorpagel
@legis.wisconsin.gov

Vos, Robin J. (R, 63)
Room 211 West, State Capitol
P.O. Box 8953
Madison, WI 53708
P: (608) 266-3387
F: (608) 282-3663
E: Rep.Vos
@legis.wisconsin.gov

Wachs, Dana (D, 91)
Room 302 North, State Capitol
P.O. Box 8953
Madison, WI 53708
P: (608) 266-7461
F: (608) 282-3691
E: Rep.Wachs
@legis.wisconsin.gov

Weatherston, Thomas (R, 62)
Room 307 North, State Capitol
P.O. Box 8953
Madison, WI 53708
P: (608) 266-0731
F: (608) 282-3691
E: Rep.Weatherson
@legis.wisconsin.gov

Young, Leon D. (D, 16)
Room 11 North, State Capitol
P.O. Box 8953
Madison, WI 53708
P: (608) 266-3786
F: (608) 282-3616
E: Rep.Young
@legis.wisconsin.gov

Zamarripa, JoCasta (D, 8)
Room 112 North, State Capitol
P.O. Box 8952
Madison, WI 53708
P: (608) 267-7669
F: (608) 282-3608
E: Rep.Zamarripa
@legis.wisconsin.gov

Zepnick, Josh (D, 9)
Room 7 North, State Capitol
P.O. Box 8953
Madison, WI 53708
P: (608) 266-1707
F: (608) 282-3609
E: Rep.Zepnick
@legis.wisconsin.gov

Congress

Senate

Baldwin, Tammy (D)
Johnson, Ron (R)

House

Duffy, Sean (R, 7)
Grothman, Glenn (R, 6)
Kind, Ron (D, 3)
Moore, Gwendolynne S. (D, 4)
Pocan, Mark (D, 2)
Ribble, Reid (R, 8)
Ryan, Paul D. (R, 1)
Sensenbrenner Jr., F. James (R, 5)

Wyoming

Executive

Governor

Hon. Matthew Mead (R)
Governor
State Capitol Building, Room 124
Cheyenne, WY 82002
P: (307) 777-7434
F: (307) 632-3909

Lieutenant Governor

This state does not have the office of lieutenant governor. The secretary of state is next in line of succession to the governorship.

Attorney General

Hon. Peter K. Michael (appointed)
Attorney General
State Capitol Building, Room 123
Cheyenne, WY 82002
P: (307) 777-7841
F: (307) 777-6869

Auditor

Hon. Cynthia I. Cloud (R)
State Auditor
State Capitol, Suite 114
200 West 24th Street
Cheyenne, WY 82002
P: (307) 777-7831
F: (307) 777-6983
E: SAOAdmin@wyo.gov

Secretary of State

Hon. Ed Murray (R)
Secretary of State
State Capitol Building, Room 106
200 West 24th Street
Cheyenne, WY 82002
P: (307) 777-7378
F: (307) 777-6217
E: secofstate@wyo.gov

Superintendent of Public Instruction

Hon. Jillian Balow (R)
Superintendent of Public Instruction
Barrett Building, Suite 260
2301 Central Avenue
Cheyenne, WY 82002
P: (307) 777-2053
F: (307) 777-6234

Treasurer

Hon. Mark Gordon
State Treasurer
200 West 24th Street
Cheyenne, WY 82002
P: (307) 777-7408
F: (307) 777-5411
E: treasurer@wyo.gov

Judiciary

Supreme Court (MR)

Ms. Carol Thompson
Clerk of Court
2301 Capitol Avenue
Cheyenne, WY 82002
P: (307) 777-7316
F: (307) 777-6129
E: cthompson@courts.state.wy.us

Hon. E. James Burke
Chief Justice
Hon. Michael K. Davis
Hon. Kate Fox
Hon. William U. Hill
Hon. Marilyn S. Kite

Legislative Senate

Senate President

Sen. Phil A. Nicholas (R)
Senate President
213 State Capitol Building
Cheyenne, WY 82002
P: (307) 777-7881
F: (307) 777-5466
E: Phil.Nicholas@wyoleg.gov

Vice President of the Senate

Sen. Drew A. Perkins (R)
Senate Vice President
213 State Capitol Building
Cheyenne, WY 82002
P: (307) 777-7881
F: (307) 777-5466
E: Drew.Perkins@wyoleg.gov

Senate Majority Leader

Sen. Eli D. Bebout (R)
Majority Floor Leader
213 State Capitol Building
Cheyenne, WY 82002
P: (307) 777-7881
F: (307) 777-5466
E: Eli.Bebout@wyoleg.gov

Senate Minority Leader

Sen. Chris Rothfuss (D)
Minority Floor Leader
213 State Capitol Building
Cheyenne, WY 82002
P: (307) 777-7881
F: (307) 777-5466
E: Chris.Rothfuss@wyoleg.gov

Secretary of the Senate

Ms. Diana Williamson
2202 Park Avenue
Cheyenne, WY
P: (307) 777-7725
F: (307) 777-5466

Members of the Senate

Anderson, James Lee (R, 28)
213 State Capitol Building
Cheyenne, WY 82002
P: (307) 777-7881
F: (307) 777-5466
E: Jameslee.Anderson@wyoleg.gov

Barnard, Paul (R, 15)
213 State Capitol Building
Cheyenne, WY 82002
P: (307) 777-7881
F: (307) 777-5466
E: Paul.Barnard@wyoleg.gov

Bebout, Eli D. (R, 26)
213 State Capitol Building
Cheyenne, WY 82002
P: (307) 777-7881
F: (307) 777-5466
E: Eli.Bebout@wyoleg.gov

Burns, Bruce (R, 21)
213 State Capitol Building
Cheyenne, WY 82002
P: (307) 777-7881
F: (307) 777-5466
E: Bruce.Burns@wyoleg.gov

Case, Cale (R, 25)
213 State Capitol Building
Cheyenne, WY 82002
P: (307) 777-7881
F: (307) 777-5466
E: Cale.Case@wyoleg.gov

Christensen, Leland G. (R, 17)
213 State Capitol Building
Cheyenne, WY 82002
P: (307) 777-7881
F: (307) 777-5466
E: Leland.Christensen@wyoleg.gov

Coe, Hank (R, 18)
213 State Capitol Building
Cheyenne, WY 82002
P: (307) 777-7881
F: (307) 777-5466
E: Hank.Coe@wyoleg.gov

Cooper, Stan (R, 14)
213 State Capitol Building
Cheyenne, WY 82002
P: (307) 777-7881
F: (307) 777-5466
E: Stan.Cooper@wyoleg.gov

Craft, Bernadine (D, 12)
213 State Capitol Building
Cheyenne, WY 82002
P: (307) 777-7881
F: (307) 777-5466
E: Bernadine.Craft@wyoleg.gov

Dockstader, Dan (R, 16)
213 State Capitol Building
Cheyenne, WY 82002
P: (307) 777-7881
F: (307) 777-5466
E: Dan.Dockstader@wyoleg.gov

Driskill, Ogden (R, 1)
213 State Capitol Building
Cheyenne, WY 82002
P: (307) 777-7881
F: (307) 777-5466
E: Ogden.Driskill@wyoleg.gov

Emerich, Fred (R, 5)
213 State Capitol Building
Cheyenne, WY 82002
P: (307) 777-7881
F: (307) 777-5466
E: Fred.Emerich@wyoleg.gov

Esquibel, Floyd A. (D, 8)
213 State Capitol Building
Cheyenne, WY 82002
P: (307) 777-7881
F: (307) 777-5466
E: Floyd.Esquibel@wyoleg.gov

Wyoming

Geis, Gerald E. (R, 20)
213 State Capitol Building
Cheyenne, WY 82002
P: (307) 777-7881
F: (307) 777-5466
E: Gerald.Geis@wyoleg.gov

Hastert, John M. (D, 13)
213 State Capitol Building
Cheyenne, WY 82002
P: (307) 777-7881
F: (307) 777-5466
E: John.Hastert@wyoleg.gov

Hicks, Larry (R, 11)
213 State Capitol Building
Cheyenne, WY 82002
P: (307) 777-7881
F: (307) 777-5466
E: Larry.Hicks@wyoleg.gov

Johnson, Wayne H. (R, 6)
213 State Capitol Building
Cheyenne, WY 82002
P: (307) 777-7881
F: (307) 777-5466
E: Wayne.Johnson@wyoleg.gov

Kinskey, Dave (R, 22)*
213 State Capitol Building
Cheyenne, WY 82002
P: (307) 777-7881
F: (307) 777-5466
E: Dave.Kinskey@wyoleg.gov

Landen, Bill (R, 27)
213 State Capitol Building
Cheyenne, WY 82002
P: (307) 777-7881
F: (307) 777-5466
E: Bill.Landen@wyoleg.gov

Meier, Curt (R, 3)
213 State Capitol Building
Cheyenne, WY 82002
P: (307) 777-7881
F: (307) 777-5466
E: Curt.Meier@wyoleg.gov

Nicholas, Phil A. (R, 10)
213 State Capitol Building
Cheyenne, WY 82002
P: (307) 777-7881
F: (307) 777-5466
E: Phil.Nicholas@wyoleg.gov

Pappas, Stephan (R, 7)*
213 State Capitol Building
Cheyenne, WY 82002
P: (307) 777-7881
F: (307) 777-5466
E: Stephan.Pappas
@wyoleg.gov

Perkins, Drew A. (R, 29)
213 State Capitol Building
Cheyenne, WY 82002
P: (307) 777-7881
F: (307) 777-5466
E: Drew.Perkins@wyoleg.gov

Peterson, R. Ray (R, 19)
213 State Capitol Building
Cheyenne, WY 82002
P: (307) 777-7881
F: (307) 777-5466
E: Ray.Peterson@wyoleg.gov

Ross, Tony (R, 4)
213 State Capitol Building
Cheyenne, WY 82002
P: (307) 777-7881
F: (307) 777-5466
E: Tony.Ross@wyoleg.gov

Rothfuss, Chris (D, 9)
213 State Capitol Building
Cheyenne, WY 82002
P: (307) 777-7881
F: (307) 777-5466
E: Chris.Rothfuss
@wyoleg.gov

Scott, Charles K. (R, 30)
213 State Capitol Building
Cheyenne, WY 82002
P: (307) 777-7881
F: (307) 777-5466
E: Charles.Scott@wyoleg.gov

Von Flatern, Michael (R, 24)
213 State Capitol Building
Cheyenne, WY 82002
P: (307) 777-7881
F: (307) 777-5466
E: Michael.VonFlatern
@wyoleg.gov

Wasserburger, Jeff (R, 23)
213 State Capitol Building
Cheyenne, WY 82002
P: (307) 777-7881
F: (307) 777-5466
E: Jeff.Wasserburger
@wyoleg.gov

House

Speaker of the House

Rep. Kermit C. Brown (R)
Speaker of the House
213 State Capitol Building
Cheyenne, WY 82002
P: (307) 777-7881
F: (307) 777-5466
E: Kermit.Brown@wyoleg.gov

Speaker Pro Tempore of the House

Rep. Tim Stubson (R)
Speaker Pro Tempore
213 State Capitol Building
Cheyenne, WY 82002
P: (307) 777-7881
F: (307) 777-5466
E: Tim.Stubson@wyoleg.gov

House Majority Leader

Rep. Rosie Berger (R)
Majority Floor Leader
213 State Capitol Building
Cheyenne, WY 82002
P: (307) 777-7881
F: (307) 777-5466
E: rosie.berger@wyoleg.gov

House Minority Leader

Rep. Mary Throne (D)
Minority Floor Leader
213 State Capitol Building
Cheyenne, WY 82002
P: (307) 777-7881
F: (307) 777-5466
E: Mary.Throne@wyoleg.gov

Clerk of the House

Ms. Patricia Benskin
Chief Clerk of the House
P.O. Box 2831
Cheyenne, WY 82003
P: (307) 777-7852

Members of the House

Allen, Jim (R, 33)
213 State Capitol Building
Cheyenne, WY 82002
P: (307) 777-7881
F: (307) 777-5466
E: Jim.Allen@wyoleg.gov

Baker, Mark (R, 48)
213 State Capitol Building
Cheyenne, WY 82002
P: (307) 777-7881
F: (307) 777-5466
E: Mark.Baker@wyoleg.gov

Baldwin, Fred A. (R, 18)*
213 State Capitol Building
Cheyenne, WY 82002
P: (307) 777-7881
F: (307) 777-5466
E: Fred.Baldwin@wyoleg.gov

Barlow, Eric (R, 3)
213 State Capitol Building
Cheyenne, WY 82002
P: (307) 777-7881
F: (307) 777-5466
E: Eric.Barlow@wyoleg.gov

Berger, Rosie (R, 51)
213 State Capitol Building
Cheyenne, WY 82002
P: (307) 777-7881
F: (307) 777-5466
E: rosie.berger@wyoleg.gov

Blackburn, Jim (R, 42)*
213 State Capitol Building
Cheyenne, WY 82002
P: (307) 777-7881
F: (307) 777-5466
E: Jim.Blackburn@wyoleg.gov

Blake, Stan (D, 39)
213 State Capitol Building
Cheyenne, WY 82002
P: (307) 777-7881
F: (307) 777-5466
E: Stan.Blake@wyoleg.gov

Brown, Kermit C. (R, 14)
213 State Capitol Building
Cheyenne, WY 82002
P: (307) 777-7881
F: (307) 777-5466
E: Kermit.Brown@wyoleg.gov

Burkhart Jr., Donald E. (R, 15)
213 State Capitol Building
Cheyenne, WY 82002
P: (307) 777-7881
F: (307) 777-5466
E: Donald.Burkhart
@wyoleg.gov

Byrd, Jim W. (D, 44)
213 State Capitol Building
Cheyenne, WY 82002
P: (307) 777-7881
F: (307) 777-5466
E: James.Byrd@wyoleg.gov

Campbell, Rita (R, 34)
213 State Capitol Building
Cheyenne, WY 82002
P: (307) 777-7881
F: (307) 777-5466
E: Rita.Campbell@wyoleg.gov

Cannady, Richard L. (R, 6)
213 State Capitol Building
Cheyenne, WY 82002
P: (307) 777-7881
F: (307) 777-5466
E: Richard.Cannady
@wyoleg.gov

Clem, Scott (R, 31)*
213 State Capitol Building
Cheyenne, WY 82002
P: (307) 777-7881
F: (307) 777-5466
E: Scott.Clem@wyoleg.gov

Connolly, Cathy (D, 13)
213 State Capitol Building
Cheyenne, WY 82002
P: (307) 777-7881
F: (307) 777-5466
E: Cathy.Connolly@wyoleg.go

Dayton, JoAnn (D, 17)*
213 State Capitol Building
Cheyenne, WY 82002
P: (307) 777-7881
F: (307) 777-5466
E: JoAnn.Dayton@wyoleg.gov

Edmonds, Harlan (R, 12)*
213 State Capitol Building
Cheyenne, WY 82002
P: (307) 777-7881
F: (307) 777-5466
E: Harlan.Edmonds
@wyoleg.gov

Edwards, Roy (R, 53)*
213 State Capitol Building
Cheyenne, WY 82002
P: (307) 777-7881
F: (307) 777-5466
E: Roy.Edwards@wyoleg.gov

Eklund, John (R, 10)
213 State Capitol Building
Cheyenne, WY 82002
P: (307) 777-7881
F: (307) 777-5466
E: John.Eklund@wyoleg.gov

Esquibel, Ken A. (D, 41)
213 State Capitol Building
Cheyenne, WY 82002
P: (307) 777-7881
F: (307) 777-5466
E: Ken.Esquibel@wyoleg.gov

Freeman, John (D, 60)
213 State Capitol Building
Cheyenne, WY 82002
P: (307) 777-7881
F: (307) 777-5466
E: John.Freeman@wyoleg.gov

Gay, Gerald (R, 36)
213 State Capitol Building
Cheyenne, WY 82002
P: (307) 777-7881
F: (307) 777-5466
E: Gerald.Gay@wyoleg.gov

Greear, Mike (R, 27)
213 State Capitol Building
Cheyenne, WY 82002
P: (307) 777-7881
F: (307) 777-5466
E: Mike.Greear@wyoleg.gov

Halverson, Marti (R, 22)
213 State Capitol Building
Cheyenne, WY 82002
P: (307) 777-7881
F: (307) 777-5466
E: Marti.Halverson
@wyoleg.gov

Harshman, Steve (R, 37)
213 State Capitol Building
Cheyenne, WY 82002
P: (307) 777-7881
F: (307) 777-5466
E: Steve.Harshman
@wyoleg.gov

Harvey, Elaine (R, 26)
213 State Capitol Building
Cheyenne, WY 82002
P: (307) 777-7881
F: (307) 777-5466
E: Elaine.Harvey@wyoleg.gov

Hunt, Hans (R, 2)
213 State Capitol Building
Cheyenne, WY 82002
P: (307) 777-7881
F: (307) 777-5466
E: Hans.Hunt@wyoleg.gov

Jaggi, Allen M. (R, 19)
213 State Capitol Building
Cheyenne, WY 82002
P: (307) 777-7881
F: (307) 777-5466
E: Allen.Jaggi@wyoleg.gov

Jennings, Mark (R, 30)*
213 State Capitol Building
Cheyenne, WY 82002
P: (307) 777-7881
F: (307) 777-5466
E: Mark.Jennings@wyoleg.gov

Kasperik, Norine (R, 32)
213 State Capitol Building
Cheyenne, WY 82002
P: (307) 777-7881
F: (307) 777-5466
E: Norine.Kasperik
@wyoleg.gov

Kirkbride, Dan R. (R, 4)
213 State Capitol Building
Cheyenne, WY 82002
P: (307) 777-7881
F: (307) 777-5466
E: Dan.Kirkbride@wyoleg.gov

Kroeker, Kendell (R, 35)
213 State Capitol Building
Cheyenne, WY 82002
P: (307) 777-7881
F: (307) 777-5466
E: Kendell.Kroeker
@wyoleg.gov

Krone, Samuel P. (R, 24)
213 State Capitol Building
Cheyenne, WY 82002
P: (307) 777-7881
F: (307) 777-5466
E: Samuel.Krone@wyoleg.gov

Larsen, Lloyd Charles (R, 54)
213 State Capitol Building
Cheyenne, WY 82002
P: (307) 777-7881
F: (307) 777-5466
E: Lloyd.Larsen@wyoleg.gov

Laursen, Dan (R, 25)*
213 State Capitol Building
Cheyenne, WY 82002
P: (307) 777-7881
F: (307) 777-5466
E: Dan.Laursen@wyoleg.gov

Lindholm, Tyler (R, 1)*
213 State Capitol Building
Cheyenne, WY 82002
P: (307) 777-7881
F: (307) 777-5466
E: Tyler.Lindholm
@wyoleg.gov

Lockhart, Thomas A. (R, 57)
213 State Capitol Building
Cheyenne, WY 82002
P: (307) 777-7881
F: (307) 777-5466
E: Tom.Lockhart@wyoleg.gov

Loucks, Bunky (R, 59)
213 State Capitol Building
Cheyenne, WY 82002
P: (307) 777-7881
F: (307) 777-5466
E: Bunky.Loucks@wyoleg.gov

Madden, Michael K. (R, 40)
213 State Capitol Building
Cheyenne, WY 82002
P: (307) 777-7881
F: (307) 777-5466
E: Mike.Madden@wyoleg.gov

McKim, Robert M. (R, 21)
213 State Capitol Building
Cheyenne, WY 82002
P: (307) 777-7881
F: (307) 777-5466
E: Robert.McKim@wyoleg.gov

Miller, David R. (R, 55)
213 State Capitol Building
Cheyenne, WY 82002
P: (307) 777-7881
F: (307) 777-5466
E: David.Miller@wyoleg.gov

Moniz, Glenn (R, 46)
213 State Capitol Building
Cheyenne, WY 82002
P: (307) 777-7881
F: (307) 777-5466
E: Glenn.Moniz@wyoleg.gov

Nicholas, Bob (R, 8)
213 State Capitol Building
Cheyenne, WY 82002
P: (307) 777-7881
F: (307) 777-5466
E: Bob.Nicholas@wyoleg.gov

Northrup, David (R, 50)
213 State Capitol Building
Cheyenne, WY 82002
P: (307) 777-7881
F: (307) 777-5466
E: David.Northrup
@wyoleg.gov

Patton, John W. (R, 29)
213 State Capitol Building
Cheyenne, WY 82002
P: (307) 777-7881
F: (307) 777-5466
E: John.Patton@wyoleg.gov

Paxton, Jerry D. (R, 47)
213 State Capitol Building
Cheyenne, WY 82002
P: (307) 777-7881
F: (307) 777-5466
E: Jerry.Paxton@wyoleg.gov

Pelkey, Charles F. (D, 45)*
213 State Capitol Building
Cheyenne, WY 82002
P: (307) 777-7881
F: (307) 777-5466
E: Charles.Pelkey
@wyoleg.gov

Petroff, Ruth A. (R, 16)
213 State Capitol Building
Cheyenne, WY 82002
P: (307) 777-7881
F: (307) 777-5466
E: Ruth.Petroff@wyoleg.gov

Piiparinen, Garry C. (R, 49)
213 State Capitol Building
Cheyenne, WY 82002
P: (307) 777-7881
F: (307) 777-5466
E: Garry.Piiparinen
@wyoleg.gov

Wyoming

Pownall, William (R, 52)*
213 State Capitol Building
Cheyenne, WY 82002
P: (307) 777-7881
F: (307) 777-5466
E: Bill.Pownall@wyoleg.gov

Reeder, Tom (R, 58)
213 State Capitol Building
Cheyenne, WY 82002
P: (307) 777-7881
F: (307) 777-5466
E: Tom.Reeder@wyoleg.gov

Schwartz, Andy (D, 23)*
213 State Capitol Building
Cheyenne, WY 82002
P: (307) 777-7881
F: (307) 777-5466
E: Andy.Schwartz@wyoleg.gov

Sommers, Albert (R, 20)
213 State Capitol Building
Cheyenne, WY 82002
P: (307) 777-7881
F: (307) 777-5466
E: Albert.Sommers
@wyoleg.gov

Steinmetz, Cheri (R, 5)*
213 State Capitol Building
Cheyenne, WY 82002
P: (307) 777-7881
F: (307) 777-5466
E: Cheri.Steinmetz
@wyoleg.gov

Stubson, Tim (R, 56)
213 State Capitol Building
Cheyenne, WY 82002
P: (307) 777-7881
F: (307) 777-5466
E: Tim.Stubson@wyoleg.gov

Throne, Mary (D, 11)
213 State Capitol Building
Cheyenne, WY 82002
P: (307) 777-7881
F: (307) 777-5466
E: Mary.Throne@wyoleg.gov

Walters, Tom (R, 38)
213 State Capitol Building
Cheyenne, WY 82002
P: (307) 777-7881
F: (307) 777-5466
E: Tom.Walters@wyoleg.gov

Wilson, Sue (R, 7)
213 State Capitol Building
Cheyenne, WY 82002
P: (307) 777-7881
F: (307) 777-5466
E: Sue.Wilson@wyoleg.gov

Winters, Nathan (R, 28)
213 State Capitol Building
Cheyenne, WY 82002
P: (307) 777-7881
F: (307) 777-5466
E: Nathan.Winters
@wyoleg.gov

Zwonitzer, Dan (R, 43)
213 State Capitol Building
Cheyenne, WY 82002
P: (307) 777-7881
F: (307) 777-5466
E: Dan.Zwonitzer@wyoleg.gov

Zwonitzer, David L. (R, 9)
213 State Capitol Building
Cheyenne, WY 82002
P: (307) 777-7881
F: (307) 777-5466
E: David.Zwonitzer
@wyoleg.gov

Congress

Senate

Barrasso, John A. (R)
Enzi, Michael B. (R)

House

Lummis, Cynthia M.
(R, At-Large)

Massachusetts District Table

This table lists the full name of the district. To find the legislator's district name, please refer to the "SP" code in parenthesis next to each name.

Code	District Name
SP1	= First Barnstable
SP2	= Second Barnstable
SP3	= Third Barnstable
SP4	= Fourth Barnstable
SP5	= Fifth Barnstable
SP6	= Barnstable, Dukes, Nantucket
SP7	= First Berkshire
SP8	= Second Berkshire
SP9	= Third Berkshire
SP10	= Fourth Berkshire
SP11	= First Bristol
SP12	= Second Bristol
SP13	= Third Bristol
SP14	= Fourth Bristol
SP15	= Fifth Bristol
SP16	= Sixth Bristol
SP17	= Seventh Bristol
SP18	= Eighth Bristol
SP19	= Ninth Bristol
SP20	= Tenth Bristol
SP21	= Eleventh Bristol
SP22	= Twelfth Bristol
SP23	= Thirteenth Bristol
SP24	= Fourteenth Bristol
SP25	= First Essex
SP26	= Second Essex
SP27	= Third Essex
SP28	= Fourth Essex
SP29	= Fifth Essex
SP30	= Sixth Essex
SP31	= Seventh Essex
SP32	= Eighth Essex
SP33	= Ninth Essex
SP34	= Tenth Essex
SP35	= Eleventh Essex
SP36	= Twelfth Essex
SP37	= Thirteenth Essex
SP38	= Fourteenth Essex
SP39	= Fifteenth Essex
SP40	= Sixteenth Essex
SP41	= Seventeenth Essex
SP42	= Eighteenth Essex
SP43	= First Franklin
SP44	= Second Franklin
SP45	= First Hampden
SP46	= Second Hampden
SP47	= Third Hampden
SP48	= Fourth Hampden
SP49	= Fifth Hampden
SP50	= Sixth Hampden
SP51	= Seventh Hampden
SP52	= Eighth Hampden
SP53	= Ninth Hampden
SP54	= Tenth Hampden
SP55	= Eleventh Hampden
SP56	= Twelfth Hampden
SP57	= First Hampshire
SP58	= Second Hampshire
SP59	= Third Hampshire
SP60	= First Middlesex
SP61	= Second Middlesex
SP62	= Third Middlesex
SP63	= Fourth Middlesex
SP64	= Fifth Middlesex
SP65	= Sixth Middlesex
SP66	= Seventh Middlesex
SP67	= Eighth Middlesex
SP68	= Ninth Middlesex
SP69	= Tenth Middlesex
SP70	= Eleventh Middlesex
SP71	= Twelfth Middlesex
SP72	= Thirteenth Middlesex
SP73	= Fourteenth Middlesex
SP74	= Fifteenth Middlesex
SP75	= Sixteenth Middlesex
SP76	= Seventeenth Middlesex
SP77	= Eighteenth Middlesex
SP78	= Nineteenth Middlesex
SP79	= Twentieth Middlesex
SP80	= Twenty-first Middlesex
SP81	= Twenty-second Middlesex
SP82	= Twenty-third Middlesex
SP83	= Twenty-fourth Middlesex
SP84	= Twenty-fifth Middlesex
SP85	= Twenty-sixth Middlesex
SP86	= Twenty-seventh Middlesex
SP87	= Twenty-eighth Middlesex
SP88	= Twenty-ninth Middlesex
SP89	= Thirtieth Middlesex
SP90	= Thirty-first Middlesex
SP91	= Thirty-second Middlesex
SP92	= Thirty-third Middlesex
SP93	= Thirty-fourth Middlesex
SP94	= Thirty-fifth Middlesex
SP95	= Thirty-sixth Middlesex
SP96	= Thirty-seventh Middlesex
SP97	= First Norfolk
SP98	= Second Norfolk
SP99	= Third Norfolk
SP100	= Fourth Norfolk
SP101	= Fifth Norfolk
SP102	= Sixth Norfolk
SP103	= Seventh Norfolk
SP104	= Eighth Norfolk
SP105	= Ninth Norfolk
SP106	= Tenth Norfolk
SP107	= Eleventh Norfolk
SP108	= Twelfth Norfolk
SP109	= Thirteenth Norfolk
SP110	= Fourteenth Norfolk
SP111	= Fifteenth Norfolk
SP112	= First Plymouth
SP113	= Second Plymouth
SP114	= Third Plymouth
SP115	= Fourth Plymouth
SP116	= Fifth Plymouth
SP117	= Sixth Plymouth
SP118	= Seventh Plymouth
SP119	= Eighth Plymouth
SP120	= Ninth Plymouth
SP121	= Tenth Plymouth
SP122	= Eleventh Plymouth
SP123	= Twelfth Plymouth
SP124	= First Suffolk
SP125	= Second Suffolk
SP126	= Third Suffolk
SP127	= Fourth Suffolk
SP128	= Fifth Suffolk
SP129	= Sixth Suffolk
SP130	= Seventh Suffolk
SP131	= Eighth Suffolk
SP132	= Ninth Suffolk
SP133	= Tenth Suffolk
SP134	= Eleventh Suffolk
SP135	= Twelfth Suffolk
SP136	= Thirteenth Suffolk
SP137	= Fourteenth Suffolk
SP138	= Fifteenth Suffolk
SP139	= Sixteenth Suffolk
SP140	= Seventeenth Suffolk
SP141	= Eighteenth Suffolk
SP142	= Nineteenth Suffolk
SP143	= First Worcester
SP144	= Second Worcester
SP145	= Third Worcester
SP146	= Fourth Worcester
SP147	= Fifth Worcester
SP148	= Sixth Worcester
SP149	= Seventh Worcester
SP150	= Eighth Worcester
SP151	= Ninth Worcester
SP152	= Tenth Worcester
SP153	= Eleventh Worcester
SP154	= Twelfth Worcester
SP155	= Thirteenth Worcester
SP156	= Fourteenth Worcester
SP157	= Fifteenth Worcester
SP158	= Sixteenth Worcester
SP159	= Seventeenth Worcester
SP160	= Eighteenth Worcester
SP161	= Berkshire, Hampshire, Franklin, Hampden
SP162	= Bristol, Norfolk
SP163	= First Bristol, Plymouth
SP164	= Second Bristol, Plymouth
SP165	= Cape, Islands
SP166	= First Essex, Middlesex
SP167	= Second Essex, Middlesex
SP168	= Third Essex, Middlesex
SP169	= Hampden
SP170	= First Hampden, Hampshire
SP171	= Second Hampden, Hampshire
SP172	= Hampshire, Franklin, Worcester
SP173	= Middlesex, Essex
SP174	= First Middlesex, Norfolk
SP175	= Second Middlesex, Norfolk
SP176	= Middlesex, Suffolk
SP177	= Middlesex, Worcester
SP178	= Norfolk, Bristol, Plymouth
SP179	= Norfolk, Bristol, Middlesex
SP180	= Norfolk, Plymouth
SP181	= Plymouth, Barnstable
SP182	= First Plymouth, Bristol
SP183	= Second Plymouth, Bristol
SP184	= Plymouth, Norfolk
SP185	= First Suffolk, Middlesex
SP186	= Second Suffolk, Middlesex
SP187	= Suffolk, Norfolk
SP188	= Worcester, Hampden, Hampshire, Middlesex
SP189	= Worcester, Middlesex
SP190	= Worcester, Norfolk

New Hampshire District Table

This table lists the full name of the district. To find the legislator's district name, please refer to the "SP" code in parenthesis next to each name.

Code	District Name
SP1	Belknap 1
SP2	Belknap 2
SP3	Belknap 3
SP4	Belknap 4
SP5	Belknap 5
SP6	Belknap 6
SP7	Belknap 7
SP8	Belknap 8
SP9	Belknap 9
SP10	Carroll 1
SP11	Carroll 2
SP12	Carroll 3
SP13	Carroll 4
SP14	Carroll 5
SP15	Carroll 6
SP16	Carroll 7
SP17	Carroll 8
SP18	Cheshire 1
SP19	Cheshire 2
SP20	Cheshire 3
SP21	Cheshire 4
SP22	Cheshire 5
SP23	Cheshire 6
SP24	Cheshire 7
SP25	Cheshire 8
SP26	Cheshire 9
SP27	Cheshire 10
SP28	Cheshire 11
SP29	Cheshire 12
SP30	Cheshire 13
SP31	Cheshire 14
SP32	Cheshire 15
SP33	Cheshire 16
SP34	Coos 1
SP35	Coos 2
SP36	Coos 3
SP37	Coos 4
SP38	Coos 5
SP39	Coos 6
SP40	Coos 7
SP41	Grafton 1
SP42	Grafton 2
SP43	Grafton 3
SP44	Grafton 4
SP45	Grafton 5
SP46	Grafton 6
SP47	Grafton 7
SP48	Grafton 8
SP49	Grafton 9
SP50	Grafton 10
SP51	Grafton 11
SP52	Grafton 12
SP53	Grafton 13
SP54	Grafton 14
SP55	Grafton 15
SP56	Grafton 16
SP57	Grafton 17
SP58	Hillsborough 1
SP59	Hillsborough 2
SP60	Hillsborough 3
SP61	Hillsborough 4
SP62	Hillsborough 5
SP63	Hillsborough 6
SP64	Hillsborough 7
SP65	Hillsborough 8
SP66	Hillsborough 9
SP67	Hillsborough 10
SP68	Hillsborough 11
SP69	Hillsborough 12
SP70	Hillsborough 13
SP71	Hillsborough 14
SP72	Hillsborough 15
SP73	Hillsborough 16
SP74	Hillsborough 17
SP75	Hillsborough 18
SP76	Hillsborough 19
SP77	Hillsborough 20
SP78	Hillsborough 21
SP79	Hillsborough 22
SP80	Hillsborough 23
SP81	Hillsborough 24
SP82	Hillsborough 25
SP83	Hillsborough 26
SP84	Hillsborough 27
SP85	Hillsborough 28
SP86	Hillsborough 29
SP87	Hillsborough 30
SP88	Hillsborough 31
SP89	Hillsborough 32
SP90	Hillsborough 33
SP91	Hillsborough 34
SP92	Hillsborough 35
SP93	Hillsborough 36
SP94	Hillsborough 37
SP95	Hillsborough 38
SP96	Hillsborough 39
SP97	Hillsborough 40
SP98	Hillsborough 41
SP99	Hillsborough 42
SP100	Hillsborough 43
SP101	Hillsborough 44
SP102	Hillsborough 45
SP103	Merrimack 1
SP104	Merrimack 2
SP105	Merrimack 3
SP106	Merrimack 4
SP107	Merrimack 5
SP108	Merrimack 6
SP109	Merrimack 7
SP110	Merrimack 8
SP111	Merrimack 9
SP112	Merrimack 10
SP113	Merrimack 11
SP114	Merrimack 12
SP115	Merrimack 13
SP116	Merrimack 14
SP117	Merrimack 15
SP118	Merrimack 16
SP119	Merrimack 17
SP120	Merrimack 18
SP121	Merrimack 19
SP122	Merrimack 20
SP123	Merrimack 21
SP124	Merrimack 22
SP125	Merrimack 23
SP126	Merrimack 24
SP127	Merrimack 25
SP128	Merrimack 26
SP129	Merrimack 27
SP130	Merrimack 28
SP131	Merrimack 29
SP132	Rockingham 1
SP133	Rockingham 2
SP134	Rockingham 3
SP135	Rockingham 4
SP136	Rockingham 5
SP137	Rockingham 6
SP138	Rockingham 7
SP139	Rockingham 8
SP140	Rockingham 9
SP141	Rockingham 10
SP142	Rockingham 11
SP143	Rockingham 12
SP144	Rockingham 13
SP145	Rockingham 14
SP146	Rockingham 15
SP147	Rockingham 16
SP148	Rockingham 17
SP149	Rockingham 18
SP150	Rockingham 19
SP151	Rockingham 20
SP152	Rockingham 21
SP153	Rockingham 22
SP154	Rockingham 23
SP155	Rockingham 24
SP156	Rockingham 25
SP157	Rockingham 26
SP158	Rockingham 27
SP159	Rockingham 28
SP160	Rockingham 29
SP161	Rockingham 30
SP162	Rockingham 31
SP163	Rockingham 32
SP164	Rockingham 33
SP165	Rockingham 34
SP166	Rockingham 35
SP167	Rockingham 36
SP168	Rockingham 37
SP169	Strafford 1
SP170	Strafford 2
SP171	Strafford 3
SP172	Strafford 4
SP173	Strafford 5
SP174	Strafford 6
SP175	Strafford 7
SP176	Strafford 8
SP177	Strafford 9
SP178	Strafford 10
SP179	Strafford 11
SP180	Strafford 12
SP181	Strafford 13
SP182	Strafford 14
SP183	Strafford 15
SP184	Strafford 16
SP185	Strafford 17
SP186	Strafford 18
SP187	Strafford 19
SP188	Strafford 20
SP189	Strafford 21
SP190	Strafford 22
SP191	Strafford 23
SP192	Strafford 24
SP193	Strafford 25
SP194	Sullivan 1
SP195	Sullivan 2
SP196	Sullivan 3
SP197	Sullivan 4
SP198	Sullivan 5
SP199	Sullivan 6
SP200	Sullivan 7
SP201	Sullivan 8
SP202	Sullivan 9
SP203	Sullivan 10
SP204	Sullivan 11

Vermont District Table

This table lists the full name of the district. To find the legislator's district name, please refer to the "SP" code in parenthesis next to each name.

Code		District Name
SP1	=	Addison
SP2	=	Bennington
SP3	=	Caledonia
SP4	=	Chittenden
SP5	=	Essex, Orleans
SP6	=	Franklin
SP7	=	Chittenden, Grand Isle
SP8	=	Lamoille
SP9	=	Orange
SP10	=	Rutland
SP11	=	Washington
SP12	=	Windham
SP13	=	Windsor
SP14	=	Addison-1
SP15	=	Addison-2
SP16	=	Addison-3
SP17	=	Addison-4
SP18	=	Addison-5
SP19	=	Addison, Rutland
SP20	=	Bennington-1
SP21	=	Bennington-2-1
SP22	=	Bennington-2-2
SP23	=	Bennington-3
SP24	=	Bennington-4
SP25	=	Bennington, Rutland
SP26	=	Caledonia-1
SP27	=	Caledonia-2
SP28	=	Caledonia-3
SP29	=	Caledonia-4
SP30	=	Caledonia, Washington
SP31	=	Chittenden-1
SP32	=	Chittenden-2
SP33	=	Chittenden-3
SP34	=	Chittenden-4-1
SP35	=	Chittenden 4-2
SP36	=	Chittenden-5-1
SP37	=	Chittenden-5-2
SP38	=	Chittenden-6-1
SP39	=	Chittenden-6-2
SP40	=	Chittenden-6-3
SP41	=	Chittenden-6-4
SP42	=	Chittenden-6-5
SP43	=	Chittenden-6-6
SP44	=	Chittenden-6-7
SP45	=	Chittenden-7-1
SP46	=	Chittenden-7-2
SP47	=	Chittenden-7-3
SP48	=	Chittenden-7-4
SP49	=	Chittenden-8-1
SP50	=	Chittenden-8-2
SP51	=	Chittenden-8-3
SP52	=	Chittenden-9-1
SP53	=	Chittenden-9-2
SP54	=	Chittenden-10
SP55	=	Essex, Caledonia
SP56	=	Essex, Caledonia, Orleans
SP57	=	Franklin-1
SP58	=	Franklin-2
SP59	=	Franklin-3-1
SP60	=	Franklin-3-2
SP61	=	Franklin-4
SP62	=	Franklin-5
SP63	=	Franklin-6
SP64	=	Franklin-7
SP65	=	Grand Isle, Chittenden
SP66	=	Lamoille-1
SP67	=	Lamoille-2
SP68	=	Lamoille-3
SP69	=	Lamoille, Washington
SP70	=	Orange-1
SP71	=	Orange-2
SP72	=	Orange, Washington, Addison
SP73	=	Orange, Caledonia
SP74	=	Orleans-1
SP75	=	Orleans-2
SP76	=	Orleans, Caledonia
SP77	=	Orleans, Lamoille
SP78	=	Rutland-1
SP79	=	Rutland-2
SP80	=	Rutland-3
SP81	=	Rutland-4
SP82	=	Rutland-5-1
SP83	=	Rutland-5-2
SP84	=	Rutland-5-3
SP85	=	Rutland-5-4
SP86	=	Rutland-6
SP87	=	Rutland, Bennington
SP88	=	Rutland, Windsor-1
SP89	=	Rutland, Windsor-2
SP90	=	Washington-1
SP91	=	Washington-2
SP92	=	Washington-3
SP93	=	Washington-4
SP94	=	Washington-5
SP95	=	Washington-6
SP96	=	Washington-7
SP97	=	Washington, Chittenden
SP98	=	Windham-1
SP99	=	Windham-2-1
SP100	=	Windham-2-2
SP101	=	Windham-2-3
SP102	=	Windham-3
SP103	=	Windham-4
SP104	=	Windham-5
SP105	=	Windham-6
SP106	=	Windham, Bennington
SP107	=	Windham, Bennington, Windsor
SP108	=	Windsor-1
SP109	=	Windsor-2
SP110	=	Windsor-3-1
SP111	=	Windsor-3-2
SP112	=	Windsor-4-1
SP113	=	Windsor-4-2
SP114	=	Windsor-5
SP115	=	Windsor, Orange-1
SP116	=	Windsor, Orange-2
SP117	=	Windsor, Rutland